and their meaning

Symbol	Meaning	Example

The following notation is peculiar to sets:

{ }	A set of elements listed between the braces	
$\in$	Is an element of	$2 \in \{2, 4, 6, 8\}$
$\notin$	Is not an element of	$3 \notin \{2, 4, 6, 8\}$
$\subset$	Is a subset of	$\{2, 4\} \subset \{2, 4, 6, 8\}$
$\varnothing$	The null, or empty, set	$\varnothing = \{\ \}$
x	Any element	$\{x\|x > 2\}$ is read "the set of all
|	Such that	numbers x such that the number x is greater than 2"

Capital letters are usually used for the names of sets. For example,

$$B = \{x\|x \in U \text{ and } x \text{ is even}\} \quad \text{where } U = \{1, 2, 3, \ldots, 10\}$$

This example is read "Set B consists of all elements of U that are even integers." In this case, set B is composed of the elements 2, 4, 6, 8, and 10.

```
Dennis D. Dingley
258 South Ste. Clair St.
Painesville, OH 44077
```

introductory mathematics for technicians

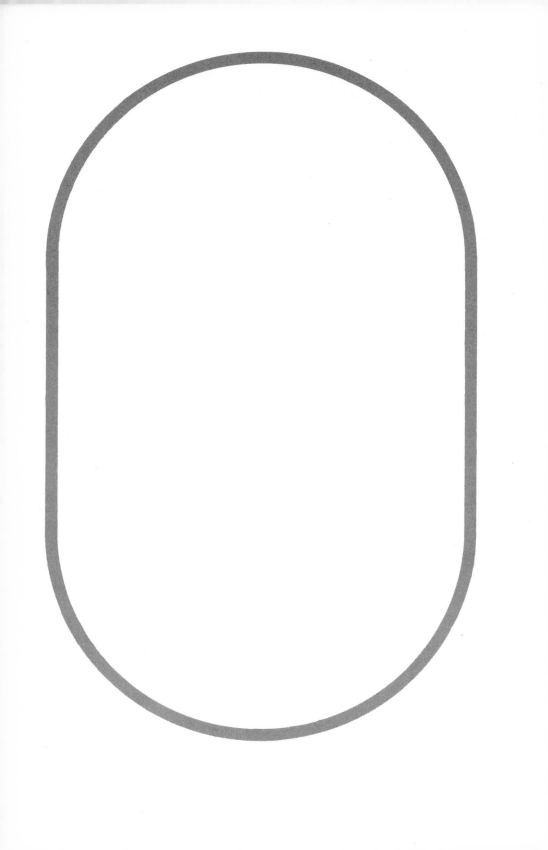

Alvin B. Auerbach
Vivian Shaw Groza

Sacramento City College

introductory mathematics for technicians

The Macmillan Company
New York
Collier-Macmillan Limited
London

THE MACMILLAN COMPANY
866 Third Avenue, New York, New York 10022
Collier-Macmillan Canada, Ltd., Toronto, Ontario

Library of Congress catalog card number: 74-146939
First Printing

Preface

This book is designed for a foundation technical mathematics course as offered in colleges and technical institutes. It presents contemporary coverage of the basic mathematics essential for the technician in engineering and scientific fields. The recommendations of engineering educators and studies, such as the Michigan Study, on the present and future needs of technicians were used as a basis for the content, organization, and development of the subject matter.

Assuming that the student has a certain degree of competency in elementary arithmetic, *Introductory Mathematics for Technicians* presents the techniques and applications of computational methods, elementary algebra, geometric concepts, and the trigonometry of the right triangle. Mastery of these topics will give the student proficiency in performing directed calculations of some complexity, by the use of the slide rule, tables of functions of numbers, logarithmic tables, or trigonometric tables. Also the student will be adequately prepared for training in elementary programming of electronic desk calculators or computers.

Besides calculations, the student will have developed the ability to use formulas and perform algebraic manipulations pertaining to problems met in industrial practice, and he will have the ability to solve problems by applications of algebra, geometry, and trigonometry of the right triangle.

Upon completion of this course, the student becomes immediately employable in some technologies; second, he is prepared for certain mathematically based technical courses such as surveying, physics, and hydraulics; and third, he is prepared for an advanced course in technical mathematics required by other engineering or scientific fields.

This book, then, develops the basic skills that are needed by technicians in all classifications. Salient features that distinguish this text from others currently available are:

(1) The *broadest possible up-to-date coverage* of material likely to be encountered by a technician in modern industry.
(2) *Ample and adequate problem sets* following each topic and designed to provide at least one homework assignment and one classroom assignment on each topic. For important subjects, additional problems are provided for two periods or more. Problems are graded in difficulty and matched so that the series with answers parallel those without answers.
(3) *Verbal problems* are provided for most topics, to the maximum extent possible, and are based generally upon actual industrial relationships. Sketches are used when the real situation would indicate that the engineer or scientist in charge would give a sketch to his technician assistant.

(4) *Computational methods* are introduced early in the text. The slide rule and, when accuracy requires, a modern desk calculator or logarithms are used to expedite problems that would otherwise be too time consuming. This permits the free use of nonintegral constants, the numbers actually met in industrial practice. The ready availability of the slide rule makes it the most useful tool; the need to make engineering calculations in remote localities far from office machines requires that logarithms be understood. In all cases, suggestions are offered that reduce computational time by choice of method or systems in problem solving. Where multiple methods of solving the same type of problem are shown, the advantages and disadvantages of the several methods are cited.

It has been the intent of the authors to provide a comprehensive coverage of the basic mathematics needed by all types of technicians. It follows that every topic in the text would not necessarily be used in every college or institute. However, this wider, all-inclusive scope permits an individual instructor to select those topics pertinent to his college's curriculum and also permits a student to study new topics by himself according to his interests or job requirements after graduation.

A logical order of topics has been presented but the development is such that other orders are possible. The requirements of any college can be met by selecting topics in the order deemed best by the instructor.

Because much of the material included in this work was compiled from many sources, we believe this will help to make the book serve as both a permanent reference book and a classroom text. If, at the end of the course, the margins and covers have short, neat notes on them and the student feels that this is *his* book, to be used for many more years and not quickly discarded, the authors will feel that the book is a success.

In appreciation for permission to use various source materials, the authors would like to express their gratitude to

(1) The American Society of Heating, Refrigerating and Air Conditioning Engineers, Inc., for material from their *Heating, Ventilating, Air Conditioning Guide*, from which problems were adapted.
(2) The American Society for Testing and Materials for material in their publications.
(3) The Acu-Rule Manufacturing Company, Division of Sterling Plastics Company, for the use of Acu-Math slide-rule descriptions.
(4) The Keuffel & Esser Company for the use of GP-12 slide-rule descriptions.

A. B. A.
V. S. G.

Contents

The world of numbers

1.01 / Introduction

An English dictionary from 1791 states: "Mathematicks is that Science which contemplates whatever is capable of being numbered or measured." This book will try to make the contemplation easier, the results more meaningful, and the methods as direct and as painless as possible. The final goal is to produce a technician capable of working in the closely knit fields of science and engineering, whose professional competency is so high as to make him a fully responsible member of the engineer–technician team now so vital in industry and the scientific laboratory.

The large number of new computational devices now on the market have relieved some of the dull work of routine calculations and vastly decreased the time required for them. But even the more complicated and expensive machines require that the user understand the fundamentals of mathematics so that he can direct the machine to execute the proper operations and, of more importance, to analyze the output. The emphasis of this book is toward problem solving; the trained technician must select the best method, obtain the desired answer to the degree of precision warranted, and know that his results are reasonable.

In this first chapter, the world of numbers will be reviewed to emphasize the properties of various sets of numbers. Some arithmetic operations will also be reviewed, but from a mature, adult viewpoint.

1.02 / Sets

A set is a well-defined collection of objects. An example is a set of socket wrenches. **Well-defined** means that it is always possible to decide whether an object belongs to the set. A collection of fasteners would be a poorly defined collection and thus not a set. To a dressmaker, fasteners would mean snaps, hooks and eyes, buttons, and so on; she would not recognize a speed nut as a fastener.

A set of numbers is a collection of some kind of numbers that must be well-defined. The individual numbers collected are called the **elements** of the set. A capital letter is usually used as the name of a particular set. The symbol $\in$ is used to indicate that a certain object is an element of a set. For example, if D is the set of digits $\{0, 1, 2, 3, 4, 5, 6, 7, 8, 9\}$, then $3 \in D$ means that 3 is an element of set D; that is, 3 belongs to the set of digits.

The symbol $\notin$ is used to indicate that a certain object is not an element of a set. For example, let C be the set of counting numbers; that is, $C = \{1, 2, 3, 4, 5, \ldots\}$, where the three dots mean that the pattern continues indefinitely. Then $\frac{1}{2} \notin C$ means that $\frac{1}{2}$ is not a counting number.

There are three different ways to define particular sets: the listing method, the informal description method, and the formal description method. In the listing method, the names of the elements are written separated by commas and enclosed by braces. In the informal description method, a property is stated which each element must have to belong to the set. In the formal description method, the letter x is written after a brace and is followed by a vertical line which is followed by a statement, usually in symbols, that determines membership in the set.

As an example, suppose a carpenter has a set of auger bits ranging in size from $\frac{1}{16}$ inch to 1 inch by sixteenths of an inch. Then the set of the sizes of these auger bits could be defined by the three different methods as follows.

Listing method:

$$S = \{\tfrac{1}{16}, \tfrac{1}{8}, \tfrac{3}{16}, \tfrac{1}{4}, \tfrac{5}{16}, \tfrac{3}{8}, \tfrac{7}{16}, \tfrac{1}{2}, \tfrac{9}{16}, \tfrac{5}{8}, \tfrac{11}{16}, \tfrac{3}{4}, \tfrac{13}{16}, \tfrac{7}{8}, \tfrac{15}{16}, 1\}$$

or $\qquad S = \{\tfrac{1}{16}, \tfrac{1}{8}, \tfrac{3}{16}, \ldots, \tfrac{15}{16}, 1\}$

where the three dots (. . .) mean that the pattern continues.

Informal description method:

$\qquad S = $ the sizes of auger bits ranging in size from $\frac{1}{16}$ inch to 1 inch by sixteenths of an inch

Formal description method:

$$S = \left\{ x \mid x = \frac{n}{16} \text{ and } n \text{ is a counting number from 1 to 16} \right\}$$

A **finite** set is a set for which there is a counting number that tells how many elements are in the set. For example, the set of digits {0, 1, 2, 3, 4, 5, 6, 7, 8, 9} is a finite set that has 10 elements. Numbers arranged in this order, separated by a difference of 1, are called **consecutive numbers.**

Some sets have a never-ending list of elements; these sets are called **infinite** sets. The difficulty or impossibility of actually counting the elements does not make a set infinite. The set of particles of matter in the atmosphere of the earth is, at any instant of time, a finite set. The fact that new particles are being added and that others drop to earth does not change the concept that some number exists, even if it cannot be found, that would represent the number of elements in this set. Many sets of numbers are infinite. Consider the set of numbers obtained by starting with 1 and repeatedly dividing by 2. The elements of this set may be listed as $\{1, \frac{1}{2}, \frac{1}{4}, \frac{1}{8}, \ldots\}$; because the three dots (read "and so on") indicate that the elements continue in this manner without ending, the set is infinite. After 99 divisions there is an element $1/633825300114114700748351602688$, but this certainly is not the last element, for there is no end to the operation of dividing by 2, even though the numbers are getting fantastically small.

The **null,** or **empty,** set is the set that has no elements. The word "null" is Latin for "none." There are experiments in physics that seek a null point, where nothing is registered on the recording meter. The set of auger bits smaller than 0.01 inch (in.) is an example of the null set, since an auger bit cannot be made that small. The null set is obtained when there is no solution to the problem to be solved. Zero is a number, and a set containing just zero is not the null set but a set of one element, 0.

The **universe,** or the **universal** set, is the set containing all elements being considered in a particular discussion. Some elements in this universe may not be usable in a specific problem and are called **inadmissible values.** If a set of counting numbers is being written, an element such as $\frac{2}{3}$ is not admissible even though it belongs to the universe of numbers.

There are sets called **subsets** of other sets. There is a subset of even digits {0, 2, 4, 6, 8} of the set of digits.

A **subset** of a set S is a set whose elements belong to S.

All sets of a particular discussion are subsets of the universal set for that discussion. The symbol $\subset$ is used to indicate that one set is a subset of another set. For example,

$$\{0, 2, 4, 6, 8\} \subset \{0, 1, 2, 3, 4, 5, 6, 7, 8, 9\}$$

means that the set of even digits is a subset of the set of digits.

These set concepts will prove useful not only for the following discussion on sets of numbers but also for the understanding of some geometric concepts and algebraic operations that will be considered later. Many mathematical statements about numbers depend on the set or sets to which the numbers belong. For example, "from three subtract four" is not possible in the set of counting numbers but is quite meaningful in a larger set of numbers that includes negative numbers. The mathematical names that are to be developed will become familiar words in one's mathematical vocabulary.

1.03 / Numbers and numerals

If three stones are placed in a pile, a North American says there are "three" and he would write 3. A Mexican would say "tres" and would also write 3. A German would say "drei" and would write the symbol slightly differently: 3. A Chinese would say "san" and would write ≡. All these people have the same number in mind but are calling it by a different-sounding word which is the name of the number. They are also using different symbols, called **numerals,** to name the same number.

Besides words and numerals, letters may also be used as the names of numbers. It is often convenient to use a letter such as n or x (or any letter of the alphabet) when the meaning is a number not specified at the time. In technical fields, the first letter of a descriptive word is often used, such as v for velocity. Table 1.1 shows the symbols used for the common arithmetic operations.

Although it is necessary to use the names of numbers (words, numerals, or letters) in a discussion about numbers, the important idea is the basic mathematical concept of number together with the properties of numbers. These are truly universal among all peoples, and, if understood, permit easy acquisition of new mathematical skills.

1.04 / Symbols

The symbols listed in Table 1.2 will be used throughout this book. The table also appears on the front inside cover for easy reference.

Table 1.1

NUMBER NAMES	OPERATION			
	Addition	*Subtraction*	*Multiplication*	*Division*
Numerals	$5 + 2$	$5 - 2$	5×2 or $5 \cdot 2$	$5 \div 2$ or $\dfrac{5}{2}$
Numeral and letter	$x + 2$	$x - 2$	$5x$ or $5(x)$	$x \div 2$ or $\dfrac{x}{2}$
Letters	$x + n$	$x - n$	nx or $(n)(x)$	$x \div n$ or $\dfrac{x}{n}$

4 □ *1 / The world of numbers*

Table 1.2

Symbol	Meaning	Example
$+$	Positive	$+5$
$+$	Add (plus)	$2 + 3 = 5$
$-$	Negative	-5 or (-5)
$-$	Subtract (minus)	$5 - 2 = 3$
$\times$ or $\cdot$	Multiply	$3 \times 2 = 6,\ 3 \cdot 2 = 6$
$\div$ or ——	Divide	$6 \div 3 = 2,\ \dfrac{6}{3} = 2$
$(\ )$	Parentheses ⎫	⎧ $2(3 + 1) = 8$
$[\ ]$	Brackets ⎬ Grouping	⎨ $2[1 + (2 + 1)] = 8$
$\{\ \}$	Braces ⎭	⎩ $2\{1 + [1 + (1 + 1)]\} = 8$
$=$	Equals	$6 = 3 + 3$
$\neq$	Does not equal	$5 \neq 3 + 3$
$\equiv$	Is identical to	$2 \equiv 2$
$>$	Is greater than	$3 > 2$
$\geq$	Is greater than or equal to	$x \geq n$
$\ngtr$	Is not greater than	$2 \ngtr 3$
$<$	Is less than	$2 < 3$
$\leq$	Is less than or equal to	$x \leq n$
$\nless$	Is not less than	$3 \nless 2$
$\pm$	Plus or minus	$x = \pm 2;\ x = +2$ or $x = -2$
$\mp$	Minus or plus	$3 \mp 2;\ 3 - 2 = 1$ or $3 + 2 = 5$
$:$	A point whose coordinates are	$P:(3, 2)$
$\sqrt{}$	Positive square root	$\sqrt{9} = 3$
$\sqrt[n]{}$	Real nth root	$\sqrt[3]{8} = 2$ and $\sqrt[3]{-8} = -2$
$\lvert x \rvert$	Absolute value	$\lvert -2 \rvert$ means without sign, or 2
$\sim$	Varies as	$C \sim r$ (circumference varies as the radius)
$\approx$	Approximately equals	$\sqrt{5} \approx 2.4$
$\rightarrow$	Implies	$7462 \rightarrow 7500$ if rounded off to two significant digits
∞	Infinity, infinite	As x gets close to 0, $\dfrac{1}{x}$ tends to ∞
	Numerically larger than any fixed value	
1, 2, 3, . . .	An infinite set of numbers; the three dots mean "and so on"	
1, 2, . . . , 7	A finite set of numbers 1 through 7	

The following notation is peculiar to sets:

$\{\ \}$	A set of elements listed between the braces	
$\in$	Is an element of	$2 \in \{2, 4, 6, 8\}$
$\notin$	Is not an element of	$3 \notin \{2, 4, 6, 8\}$
$\subset$	Is a subset of	$\{2, 4\} \subset \{2, 4, 6, 8\}$
$\varnothing$	The null, or empty, set	$\varnothing = \{\ \}$

Table 1.2 (continued)

Symbol	Meaning	Example

x   Any element ⎫ $\{x|x > 2\}$ is read "the set of all numbers

| Such that ⎭   *x* such that the number *x* is greater than 2

Capital letters are usually used for the names of sets. For example,

$$B = \{x|x \in U \text{ and } x \text{ is even}\} \qquad \text{where } U = \{1, 2, 3, \ldots, 10\}$$

This example is read "Set *B* consists of all elements of *U* that are even integers." In this case, set *B* is composed of the elements 2, 4, 6, 8, and 10.

Problem Set 1.1

1–10

List all the elements of the following sets, which are defined by description. (Enclose the elements in braces and use commas to separate the elements.)

1. All months in the year with 31 days. (Use abbreviations.)
2. All months in the year with exactly 30 days. (Use abbreviations.)
3. All months in the year with less than 30 days.
4. All months in the year with more than 31 days.
5. All leap years between 1960 and 1980, both dates included.
6. All leap years between 1890 and 1910, both dates included.
7. All digits such that any digit in the set added to 5 is a digit.
8. All digits such that any digit in the set added to 3 is a digit.
9. All digits such that any one multiplied by itself has a product less than 60.
10. All sets of consecutive digits whose product is 30 or less. (Consider all possible sets of two or more digits, and list each suitable set as an element enclosed in braces. Order does not count; $\{5, 6\}$ and $\{6, 5\}$ are the same element. For this problem only, do not use the digit 0.)

11–14

Given the set $B = \{0, 2, 4, 6, 8, 10, 12\}$, *list the elements of the following subsets.*

11. $G = \{x|x \in B \text{ and } x = 6\}$
12. $H = \{x|x \in B \text{ and } 2 \leq x < 10\}$ $(2 \leq x < 10 \text{ means } 2 \leq x \text{ and } x < 10)$
13. $J = \{x|x \in B \text{ and } x \not> 8\}$
14. $K = \{x|x \in B \text{ and } x \not< 8\}$

15–24

Given the set $C = \{1, 2, 3, \ldots, 12\}$. List all the elements, x, of set M so that $M \subset C$ and

15. $x = 5$

16. $x \neq 5$

17. $3x \in C$

18. $2x \in C$

19. $2x = x + x$

20. $3x = x + x + x$

21. $x + 5 = 8$

22. $x - 5 = 8$

23. x is even

24. $\dfrac{x}{2}$ is a digit

25–30

Given the universal set U consisting of all counting numbers from 1 to 100 inclusive. Using the formal description method, write a statement that defines just the listed elements.

Sample
12, 24, 36, . . . , 96.

SOLUTION
$S = \{x | x \in U \text{ and } x = \text{a multiple of } 12\}$.

25. 10, 20, 30, . . . , 100

26. 16, 25, 36, 49, 64, 81, 100

27. 1, 8, 27, 64

28. 26, 39, 52, 65, 78

29. 95, 96, 97, 98, 99, 100

30. 1, 2, 3, 4, 5, 6, 7

1.05 / The set of natural numbers; the set of integers

Early man soon found that the set of numbers from 1 to 10 was much too small to use in counting the physical things he saw in his daily life. Strangely enough, the matching of things to fingers, which is common to most primitive tribes, did not result in the early use of our present-day decimal numeral system. The 12-inches-in-a-foot system of measurement is a leftover from the Roman measuring system based upon twelves. The 60 seconds in a minute and 60 minutes in an hour represent an even more ancient system used by the Babylonians. The Maya people of Mexico used 20 as their primary base.

Our decimal numeral system, or Hindu–Arabic numeral system, is a contribution of the Hindus (400–800 A.D.) and was later transmitted to Europe by the Arabs. Using the ten symbols from zero through nine, all numbers needed to count things can be expressed by the position of these digit symbols. Zeros are used as placeholders; that is, they fill in vacant places so that the actual counting symbol can be placed in the proper column. For example, 1000 is one unit of a thousand, with the three zeros giving the value of that unit. The **set of natural numbers,** which is the same set as the set of counting numbers, can be written as follows:

$$N = \{1, 2, 3, \ldots\}$$

The set of natural numbers is an infinite set. To whatever "largest" number that can be imagined, 1 can be added and another number obtained.

Early man found that a pile of things could be separated into two piles by moving these things two at a time and placing one in each pile. If, at the final step, there were two left, each pile had the same number of things in it, and therefore the original number was an even number. If there was only one thing left at the final step, then one pile had one more than the other pile and the original number was odd. Of the two piles, if the pile with the smaller number of things (or either pile if they are the same size) has "n" number of things in it, then the number of the original pile can be written as "$2n$" if the number is *even* and as "$2n + 1$" if the number is *odd*.

Many natural numbers can be exactly divided by some other natural number. (Some piles of objects can be separated into a certain number of equal piles.) A natural number that is an exact divisor of another natural number is called a **factor** of that number. For example, 1, 2, 3, 4, 6, and 12 are factors of 12. A natural number, different from 1, that has no factors except itself and 1 is called a **prime number** or a **prime.** Some examples of prime numbers are 2, 3, 5, 7, 11, 13, 17, and 1847. A natural number different from 1 and not a prime number is called **factorable** or **composite.**

The physical world soon required that man develop a concept of **negative numbers.** If he built a storage platform on stilts, he was above the surface of the earth. If he dug a well, he was below it. If a merchant had a profitable year, he could record on his ledger a positive gain in his wealth. But what of misfortune? Thus, to the original concept of positive natural numbers was added the logical concept of opposite negative numbers, sometimes called minus numbers, since they are written with a minus sign in front of the numeral symbol for a natural number. Today there are many everyday uses of negative numbers. A normal winter day at Fairbanks, Alaska, might be $-50°F$, meaning 50 degrees below $0°F$. The Dead Sea is at elevation -1286 feet (ft), meaning 1286 ft below sea level. The annual financial report of a large corporation may show a loss in some one operation and the loss is indicated as a negative number.

Between the smallest positive natural number (1) and its negative (-1) there is a number called **zero** (0). Zero itself is neither positive nor negative. The term "integer," a Latin word meaning "whole," is used to indicate a natural number, zero, or the negative of a natural number. The set of natural numbers is also called the **set of positive integers.** The set of natural numbers and zero is called the **set of nonnegative integers,** of the **set of whole**

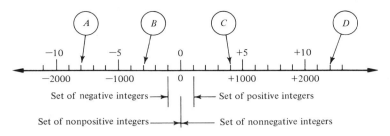

Figure 1.1
The number line

numbers. The **set of integers,** I, can be written as follows:

$$I = \{\ldots, -3, -2, -1, 0, 1, 2, 3, \ldots\}$$

The **number line** is a very convenient way to visualize numbers and their relationships. A decimally graduated ruler is an example of a part of a number line. In Figure 1.1 the number line is a horizontal line infinitely long, as indicated by the arrowheads at each end. At some convenient point a zero point is selected, and, with a desired scale, unit intervals are laid off. For ease in reading, selected marks, called **major values,** are numbered. Experience shows that major values chosen at intervals of 1, 2, or 5 are the best to mark.

For any integer whatever, positive or negative, large or small, there is exactly one point on the number line that represents that number. The point assigned to a number is called the **graph** of the number. The number assigned to a point on the number line is called the **coordinate** of the point.

Although the scale selected may change the number of inches a *given number* is plotted from the zero point, the number of units left or right of zero is always the same for this number.

On the other hand, although the scale selected does not change the number of inches a *given point* is from the zero point, the number of units left or right of zero corresponding to the given point does change with the scale. For example, if the scale selected for Figure 1.1 is 1 inch equals 5 units, the coordinates of the four points shown are easily read as

$$A = -8 \qquad B = -3 \qquad C = +4 \qquad D = +12$$

If the scale were 1 inch equals 1000 units, then $A = -1600$ and $D = +2400$.

The conventional horizontal number line illustrates the concept of **order.** Any value to the left of another value is the smaller of the two. Since C is to the left of D, 4 is smaller than 12. In symbols, $4 < 12$. Since A is to the left of B, -8 is smaller than -3. In symbols, $-8 < -3$. As an example, $-8°$ is colder than $-3°$.

The **absolute value** of a number is either 0 or a positive number. In symbols, $|n|$ designates the absolute value of the number n. If n is positive or 0, $|n| = n$. If $-n$ is negative, $|-n| = n$. For example, $|5| = 5$, $|0| = 0$, and $|-5| = 5$.

Distances, which are never negative, can be designated by using this concept of absolute value.

If two points are on *opposite* sides of the zero point, the distance between them is the *sum* of the absolute values of their coordinates.

If two points are on the *same* side of the zero point, the distance between them is the *difference* of the absolute values of their coordinates (the smaller absolute value being subtracted from the larger).

For example, in Figure 1.1, the distance from B to C is the same as the distance from C to B and is $|-3| + |+4| = 7$ units. The distance from A to B is $|-8| - |-3| = 5$ units.

Problem Set 1.2

1. List all prime numbers from 1 through 30.
2. List all prime numbers from 31 through 60.
3. List all prime numbers from 100 through 120.
4. List all prime numbers from 121 through 140.

5–16
Plot each given set of numbers on a number line. Use quadrille-ruled paper five squares to the inch, or draw a graphical scale with a ruler. Label appropriate major values, and graph the given coordinates using a black dot and the letter symbol. Then find the distance from the smallest value graphed to the largest.

Sample
$A = -4, B = -2, C = 1, D = 5$.

SOLUTION

Distance A to D is 9 units.

	A	B	C	D			A	B	C	D
5.	−4	2	4	5		**11.**	−5	5	10	20
6.	−6	−3	−1	4		**12.**	−30	10	25	45
7.	−1	1	7	12		**13.**	12	−12	−8	8
8.	−3	−1	8	13		**14.**	10	−15	−25	15
9.	−21	−18	−7	−1		**15.**	−300	400	−100	500
10.	−31	−27	−17	−11		**16.**	600	−400	200	−100

17–20

Plot each given set of numbers on a number line as in problems 5–16. After plotting, find the three distances A to B, A to C, and A to D.

	A	B	C	D
17.	50	60	−10	−30
18.	50	−60	10	40
19.	−50	0	−30	−10
20.	−50	−40	0	20

21. On the Celsius[1] thermometer, the freezing point of water is 0°C, the boiling point is 100°C, and the coldest possible temperature, absolute zero, is −273°C. How many degrees are there from the boiling point of water to absolute zero?

22. On the Fahrenheit thermometer, the freezing point of water is 32°F, the boiling point is 212°F, and the value of absolute zero is −460°F. How many degrees are there from boiling point to absolute zero?

23. In Africa, the highest mountain is Kilimanjaro in Tanzania at 19,340 ft above sea level, and the lowest spot is the Egyptian Qattara Depression, which is 436 ft below sea level. How many feet above the Qattara Depression is the mountain peak?

24. On the North American continent, the highest mountain is Mt. McKinley in Alaska at 20,320 ft above sea level, and the lowest spot is Death Valley in California, which is 282 ft below sea level. How many feet below the peak of Mt. McKinley is the floor of Death Valley?

1.06 / The set of real numbers

The need to divide a given amount of things into a given number of portions was a problem met by early man. If seven animals were slain by three hunters, each hunter took two animals and a part of one. This part was his fractional share, and the concept of fractions dates back over 4000 years. For centuries fractions have had the form $\frac{2}{3}$ or $\frac{4}{5}$. Any number that can be expressed as a division of two integers is called a *rational number* (since the quotient forms a ratio). Since the bottom number can be 1, the set of rational numbers includes the set of integers. For example, $3 = \frac{3}{1}$ and $-5 = \frac{-5}{1}$.

Any rational number can be accurately located upon the number line by using a proper scale. The distance between unit marks is made equal to the lower number (denominator) of the ratio. The location of the upper

[1] Formerly called centigrade.

Figure 1.2
The graph of a fraction

number is obtained by counting from the integer part of the number. For example, the graph of $2\frac{3}{8}(=\frac{19}{8})$ is shown in Figure 1.2.

If a decimal with a finite number of digits, such as 0.2473, is to be graphed, it is written in the fractional form indicated by its name, 2473 ten thousandths, or $\frac{2473}{10,000}$, and the method shown in Figure 1.2 is used. Chapter 11 will include a problem in changing repeating decimals, which are always rational numbers, to fractional form. At this time, some common fractions that are repeating decimals are shown below. The decimal notation may be obtained by the long-division process used in arithmetic.

$$\frac{1}{3} = 0.33333\ldots$$

$$\frac{1}{7} = 0.142857142857\ldots$$

$$\frac{1}{11} = 0.090909\ldots$$

Recall that the three dots, . . . , used here at the end of the decimal representation, mean that the pattern continues indefinitely. In general, any quotient of integers (rational number) can be written as a terminating decimal or as a nonterminating, repeating decimal.

The nonterminating, nonrepeating decimals are called **irrational numbers.** These numbers cannot be expressed as the ratio of two integers and thus they are not rational.

In elementary arithmetic, **a square root** of a positive number is defined as that positive number which when multiplied by itself (or *squared*) produces the number whose square root is desired. For example,

the square root of 9 is 3 since 3 squared is 9

In symbols, $\sqrt{9} = 3$ since $3^2 = 3 \times 3 = 9$

Similarly, $\sqrt{\dfrac{25}{16}} = \dfrac{5}{4}$ since $\left(\dfrac{5}{4}\right)^2 = \left(\dfrac{5}{4}\right)\left(\dfrac{5}{4}\right) = \dfrac{25}{16}$

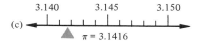

Figure 1.3
The effect of scale

There are some positive rational numbers that do not have a rational square root. For example, the square root of 2 (written $\sqrt{2}$) is an irrational number since it cannot be written as the ratio of two integers. However, there is an exact graphical construction for $\sqrt{2}$ as the diagonal of a unit square. The Greeks, during the time of Pythagoras (ca. 600 B.C.), showed that the square root of every prime number is irrational.

Another example of an irrational number, known to the Greeks, is π, the ratio of the circumference of any circle to its diameter. Although π is defined as a ratio (π is the initial letter of the Greek word for ratio), π is *not* a ratio of two integers; that is, either the circumference or the diameter or both must be an irrational number. Expressed in decimal form,

$$\sqrt{2} = 1.4142135\ldots$$

$$\pi = 3.1415926535\ldots \qquad (\pi \approx 3\tfrac{1}{7})$$

The three dots here mean that the digits continue without end but there are no blocks of digits that repeat.

For any practical purpose, an irrational number may be graphed as follows. Depending upon the precision desired, the irrational number is located between two adjacent rational numbers, one just larger and one just smaller by the specified degree of precision. In Figure 1.3, π is graphed to four different degrees of precision.

The set of **real numbers** is the set consisting of all the rational numbers and all the irrational numbers. This is the set used in most engineering calculations and the set given the maximum coverage in this book. The sets previously mentioned are subsets of the set of real numbers. These subsets will be used when it is desired to limit solutions of problems to a particular type of answer, such as just integers or just digits.

Problem Set 1.3

1–4
Given the following sets of real numbers, rearrange the elements of each set so that the elements are in increasing order. Use Table 1 of the Appendix

if desired, but record the roots to two decimal places only.

1. $A = \{\sqrt{3}, -\sqrt{3}, 2, 5, 0, -1\}$
2. $B = \{-5, \frac{3}{4}, -\frac{2}{3}, \pi, \sqrt{8}, -\sqrt{7}\}$
3. $C = \{|-3|, -2, \sqrt{4}, -\frac{7}{4}, -\frac{5}{3}\}$
4. $D = \{0, -\frac{1}{2}, -|-2|, -1, \frac{2}{1}, \frac{1}{2}\}$

5–10

Graph on a number line the listed elements of each set. Choose and state a scale for each set so that the values are not too crowded and are correctly spaced. Try to use about a 6-in. horizontal line for each set. Use a black dot for each element.

5. $E = \{-1, -3, -4, 0, 2, 1\}$
6. $F = \{4, -2, 0, -1, 3, -1\}$
7. $G = \{\frac{1}{6}, \frac{1}{4}, \frac{1}{3}, 1, 2\}$
8. $H = \{\frac{2}{3}, \frac{2}{9}, -\frac{5}{6}, -1\frac{1}{3}\}$
9. $J = \{|-2|, |-3|, 4, |3|, 0, -1\}$
10. $K = \{-2, |-3|, \pi, -|\pi|, |0|, -|-1|\}$

11–16

Express each of the following numbers in decimal notation.

11. $\frac{3}{8}$
12. $\frac{5}{6}$
13. $\frac{8}{9}$

14. $\frac{7}{25}$
15. $\frac{41}{12}$
16. $\frac{91}{18}$

17–30

Look at the following numbers. If they are rational, write them in fractional form: if irrational, so state. Any unfamiliar repeating decimal has been chosen so that the equivalent fraction has a numerator of 1.

17. $0.66666\ldots$
18. $0.22222\ldots$
19. $\sqrt{144}$
20. $\sqrt{169}$
21. $\sqrt{82}$

22. $\sqrt{47}$
23. $\frac{3}{4}\pi$
24. $\dfrac{1}{\pi}$
25. 0.125

26. 0.625
27. $0.142857142857\ldots$
28. $0.076923076923\ldots$
29. $0.0454545\ldots$
30. $0.0370370\ldots$

31–40

(a) *State whether the set of positive integers, the set of all integers, the set of positive reals, or the set of all reals best describes quantities of the same type as the number given in each problem.*
(b) *If it has meaning, write the negative of each given number and state its meaning in words.*
(c) *State the meaning of the number 0 for each problem, if it has meaning.*

Sample

A temperature of 20 degrees Fahrenheit.

SOLUTION

(a) All reals.

(b) -20; twenty degrees below zero.

(c) Zero degrees Fahrenheit, a cold temperature 32° below the freezing point of water.

31. An elevation of 410 ft above sea level.

32. 2500 miles per hour (mph) upward, the velocity of a missile moving directly upward.

33. The year 1980 A.D.

34. 2 pounds (lb), a certain weekly gain in the weight of a person.

35. 64 in., the height of a person.

36. A bank transaction depositing 5635 cents.

37. $\frac{7}{8}$, a certain daily increase in the price of a certain stock, as quoted in a newspaper.

38. 1239 bolts, made by a certain machine on a given day.

39. 7, the score of one side in a baseball game.

40. A sprint of 100 yards (yd).

1.07 / Imaginary numbers and the set of complex numbers

Just as the square root of a rational number is not always rational, the square root of a real number is not always real. For example, what meaning can be given to the square root of (-9)? Since no real number multiplied by itself gives a negative product, the number denoted by $\sqrt{-9}$ is not a real number but is called an **imaginary number**. Imaginary numbers were first considered as useless, meaningless numbers. Later mathematicians recognized their importance as solutions of equations and as numbers needed to complete the development of the properties of numbers. After 1750 applications were found in hydrodynamics, aerodynamics, map making, and electrical engineering. However, imaginary numbers have little application to problem solving outside the area of electrical and electronic calculations, so this book will treat them very briefly. Imaginary numbers may occur in the steps of solving a problem, but for most practical problems, answers will be limited to the set of real numbers.

If the set of real numbers is united with the set of imaginary numbers, the resulting set is called the set of **complex numbers.** Instead of writing $\sqrt{-9}$, it is convenient to use the symbol j for $\sqrt{-1}$, so $\sqrt{-9}$ becomes $\sqrt{9(-1)}$ or $\sqrt{9}j$, which can now be written as $3j$; that is, $\sqrt{-9} = 3j$.

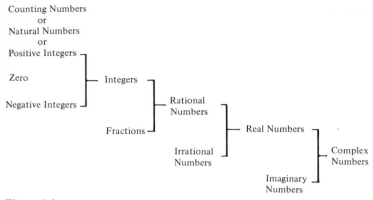

Figure 1.4
The world of numbers

In most engineering texts j is used; i is used in most mathematics texts. However, there is no difference in meaning. $3j$ is read "three jay." The letter j by itself is called the jay operator so that it will not be confused with a letter name of an unspecified number. Just as n has been used to stand for a number, complex numbers are written in the **general form** $a + bj$, where a and b each represent some real number. If a is 0, $a + bj = 0 + bj = bj$ and bj represents an element of the set of **pure imaginary numbers.** If $b = 0$, $a + bj = a + 0j = a$ represents any element of the set of real numbers. If b is not 0, $a + bj$ is an imaginary number. The set of complex numbers is the set consisting of all the real numbers and all the imaginary numbers. The set of imaginary numbers has as a subset the set of pure imaginary numbers. The world of numbers can now be shown as related sets, as illustrated in Figure 1.4.

Every set of numbers that has been discussed is seen as a subset of the set of complex numbers. However, only the set of real numbers and its subsets can be graphed on the number line. It can be shown that there is exactly one point on the number line for each real number and exactly one real number for each point on the number line. In other words, there is a one-to-one correspondence between the set of real numbers and the set of points on the number line.

Problem Set 1.4

For each of the following numbers,
(a) *Perform any indicated arithmetic operation, if possible, and change any decimal to an equivalent fraction reduced to lowest terms.*

(b) *Using Figure 1.4, select the leftmost set of numbers to which the given number belongs.*

(c) *If the number is a positive integer, state if it is odd or even and if it is a prime number or factorable.*

Sample

0.0125.

SOLUTION

(a) $0.0125 = \dfrac{125}{10,000} = \dfrac{1}{80}$ (reduced to lowest terms).

(b) Rational (since a ratio of integers).

(c) N/A (not applicable since not a positive integer).

1. -2 **6.** 90   **11.** $\sqrt{-4}$ **16.** $\sqrt{-91}$

2. π **7.** 900   **12.** $2j$ **17.** $|-4|$

3. $\pi + j$ **8.** $\frac{1}{90}$ **13.** $\frac{2}{4}$ **18.** $2 + 0j$

4. -9 **9.** $\sqrt{9}$ **14.** $2 + 2j$ **19.** $\sqrt{3}$

5. 0.9   **10.** $\sqrt{90}$ **15.** 0.75   **20.** 0.44444 . . .

1.08 / Properties of real numbers

Closure law   Just as a social club is called closed when membership is restricted, mathematical operations are called closed when the result belongs to the same set as the numbers on which the operation is performed. If any elements of the set of real numbers are added, subtracted, multiplied, or divided (the divisor must not be zero), the answer is always a real number. Stated in mathematical language, **the set of real numbers is closed with respect to addition, subtraction, multiplication, and division.**

The set of real numbers is *not* closed with respect to the operation of root extraction. For example, -3 is a real number but $\sqrt{-3}$ is not a real number.

Commutative law   A commuter is a person who travels or changes his position. The commutative law for real numbers tells what happens if the positions of real numbers being added or multiplied are changed. The commutative law states that for real numbers the *order* in which the real numbers are arranged for addition or multiplication does not affect the result.

For example, $2 + 3 = 3 + 2 = 5$

and $2 \cdot 3 = 3 \cdot 2 = 6$

In general, $a + b = b + a$

and $a \cdot b = b \cdot a$

Associative law An association is a group of people. The associative law for real numbers states that the way in which real numbers are *grouped* for addition or multiplication does not affect the result. For example, for addition

$$(2 + 3) + 4 = 2 + (3 + 4) = 9$$

$$5 + 4 = 2 + 7 = 9$$

and for multiplication

$$(2 \cdot 3) \cdot 4 = 2 \cdot (3 \cdot 4) = 24$$

$$6 \cdot 4 = 2 \cdot 12 = 24$$

In general, $$(a + b) + c = a + (b + c)$$

and $$(ab)c = a(bc)$$

By combining the commutative and associative laws, the terms of a sum or the factors of a product may be rearranged in any order or grouping without affecting the result. For example,

$$(2 + 3) + 4 = (2 + 4) + 3 = 3 + (2 + 4) = 9$$

and $$(2 \cdot 3) \cdot 4 = (2 \cdot 4) \cdot 3 = 3 \cdot (2 \cdot 4) = 24$$

Distributive law There is a law for real numbers that applies to combined addition and multiplication. It covers the multiplication of a sum such as $2(3 + 4)$ and states that this multiplication gives the same result as multiplying each part of the sum and adding the partial products. Thus $2(3 + 4)$ can be written as $2 \cdot 3$ added to $2 \cdot 4$. Evaluating this,

$$2(3 + 4) = (2 \cdot 3) + (2 \cdot 4)$$

$$2 \cdot 7 = 6 + 8$$

$$14 \equiv 14$$

In general, $$a(b + c) = ab + ac$$

This statement is called the **distributive law.** There can be any quantity of numbers in the sum portion. For example,

$$2(3 + 4 + 5 + 6) = 2 \cdot 3 + 2 \cdot 4 + 2 \cdot 5 + 2 \cdot 6$$

$$2 \cdot 18 = 6 + 8 + 10 + 12$$

$$36 \equiv 36$$

Since this is a law for real numbers, it holds for fractions, decimals, and even irrational numbers. For example,

$$\tfrac{1}{2}(\tfrac{1}{2} + 4 + 0.5) = \tfrac{1}{2} \cdot \tfrac{1}{2} + \tfrac{1}{2} \cdot 4 + \tfrac{1}{2} \cdot 0.5$$

$$\tfrac{1}{2}(5) = \tfrac{1}{4} + 2 + 0.25$$

$$2.5 \equiv 2.5$$

The distributive law is symmetrical; that is, it works in either direction. The examples so far are called **expansions,** because one product was expanded into a sum of products. The reversal of this process is called **factoring,** because the final result is a product equal to the original sum. For example,

$$3 + 6 + 9 + 12 = 3 \cdot 1 + 3 \cdot 2 + 3 \cdot 3 + 3 \cdot 4$$
$$= 3(1 + 2 + 3 + 4)$$
$$= 3(10)$$
$$30 \equiv 30$$

Usually, factoring is restricted to factors that are integers.

1.09 / Additional properties of real numbers

Identity property, 0 and 1   In the set of real numbers, two particular numbers have special properties unlike any other numbers, and are given special names to emphasize these qualities. The number 0 is called the **additive identity** because adding 0 to a number does not change the original number. For example, $2 + 0 = 2$ and $0 + 5 = 5$. There are cases in later sections where adding 0 to a number permits a solution, although the 0 might be in the form $(3 - 3)$.

The other special number is 1, called the **multiplicative identity,** for any number multiplied by 1 is unchanged. For example, $2 \cdot 1 = 2$ and $1 \cdot 5 = 5$. This property is widely used when dealing with fractions. If 3 were to be expressed in fourths, the fact that $1 = \frac{4}{4}$ is used to obtain

$$3 = 3 \cdot 1 = 3 \cdot \frac{4}{4} = \frac{12}{4}$$

Inverse property, opposites and reciprocals   Every real number has an **additive inverse,** or **opposite,** and every nonzero real number has a **multiplicative inverse,** or **reciprocal.**

The **additive inverse,** or **opposite,** of a number is that number which, if added to the original number, gives a sum of 0. The opposite of 4 is -4 since $4 + (-4) = 0$. The opposite of a negative number is a positive number. The opposite of -4 is $+4$ since $-4 + (+4) = 0$.

The **multiplicative inverse,** or **reciprocal,** of any nonzero real number is that number by which the original number is multiplied to give a product of 1. In other words, the reciprocal is found by dividing 1 by the original number. The reciprocal of 4 is 0.25 since $\frac{1}{4} = 0.25$ and $4(0.25) = 1$. This idea is used when saying that there are four quarters in a dollar. Similarly, the reciprocal of 10 is $\frac{1}{10}$ or 0.10, since $10(0.10) = 10(\frac{1}{10}) = 1$. This idea is used when saying that there are ten dimes in one dollar.

Order Real numbers possess **order**. Exactly one of these three conditions must be true: one number is smaller than, equal to, or larger than another number. This was seen in Problem Set 1.3, when a set of integers, rational numbers, and irrational numbers were all graphed on the same number line. Any number *a* to the left of another *b* was always the smaller number. In symbols, $a < b$. Also any number *b* to the right of another *a* is the larger of the two, or $b > a$.

Equality laws There are four equality laws that apply to operations on real numbers. They are called *equality* laws because they apply to statements about *equal* real numbers. These laws state that for any two equal real numbers, regardless of the form in which they are written, the results obtained are equal if

(1) The same number is added to each, or
(2) The same number is subtracted from each, or
(3) Each is multiplied by the same number, or
(4) Each is divided by the same number (not 0).

Visualize a platform balance such as those used in a laboratory. Figure 1.5 is a simplified sketch of such a scale, which has four 1-lb weights on the right side and one 4-lb weight on the left.

To check the first law, a 3-lb weight is added to the right side and three 1-lb weights added to the left. The net result is then

$$7 = 4 + 1 + 1 + 1 = 1 + 1 + 1 + 1 + 3 = 7$$

The scale remains balanced and the pointer does not move.

To check the second law, remove a 1-lb weight from each side, giving this situation:

$$6 = 4 + 1 + 1 = 1 + 1 + 1 + 3 = 6$$

Figure 1.5
A balance scale

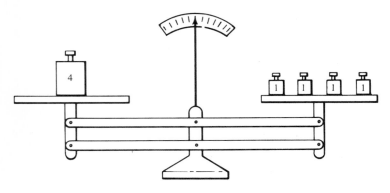

For checking the third law, the multiplier chosen is 2, so every weight on each side will be matched with one just like itself, giving

$$12 = (4+4)+(1+1)+(1+1) = (1+1)+(1+1)+(1+1)+(3+3) = 12$$

Again the balance has been kept.

Finally, for the fourth law, 3 is the chosen divisor. Before dividing, each platform is rearranged to give groups of three like things so that the two platforms look as follows:

$$4 + 4 + 4 = (1 + 1 + 1) + (3 + 3 + 3)$$

Using the distributive law, this arrangement can also be written

$$3(4) = 3(1 + 3) = 12$$

Now, dividing by 3, $4 = 1 + 3$.

Problem Set 1.5

1–20

Determine whether each statement is true or false.

1. $2 + 5 + 7 = 5 + 2 + 7$
2. $(12 + 6) - 7 = (12 - 7) + 6$
3. $(4 - 2) - 1 = 4 - (2 - 1)$
4. $(3 - \frac{1}{3}) + 1 = (1 + 3) - \frac{1}{3}$
5. $5(8 - 2) = (5 \cdot 8) - (5 \cdot 2)$
6. $11 - 7 = 7 - 11$
7. $3(2 + 4) = (4 + 2)3$
8. $4(5 + 3) = (3 + 5)4$
9. $2 \cdot 7 \cdot \frac{1}{2} = \frac{1}{2} \cdot 2 \cdot 7$
10. $\frac{1}{3}(4 + 3)6 = 7(6 \cdot \frac{1}{3})$
11. $(24 \div 6) \div 2 = 24 \div (6 \div 2)$
12. $60 \div (20 + 30) = \frac{60}{20} + \frac{60}{30}$
13. $(20 + 30) \div 60 = \frac{20}{60} + \frac{30}{60}$
14. $60 \div 5 = 5 \div 60$
15. $32 - 2(6 - 3) = (32 - 12) - 3$
16. $10 + 3(8 - 2) = (10 + 24) - 2$
17. $40 - 5(2 + 3) = (40 - 10) + 3$
18. $40 - 5(2 + 3) = (40 - 10) - 15$
19. $4(5 - 5) = 0$
20. $0.125(8 \cdot \sqrt{2}) = \sqrt{2}$

21–26

Write in expanded form and then total.

21. $5(8 + 6)$
22. $3(20 + 7)$
23. $\frac{1}{4}(36 + 28)$
24. $\frac{1}{9}(81 + 72)$
25. $(600 + 40 + 3)2$
26. $(13 + 5 + 7)4$

27–30

Write in factored form.

27. $28 + 35$
28. $49 + 63$
29. $77 + 22 + 121$
30. $65 + 52 + 39$

By using one or more of the commutative, associative, and distributive laws, rearrange the numbers in each of the following so that the calculation can be performed mentally as easily as possible. Write the result of this mental calculation.

Sample
$(\frac{1}{4} + \frac{1}{3}) + \frac{3}{4}$.

SOLUTION

$$(\frac{1}{4} + \frac{1}{3}) + \frac{3}{4} = (\frac{1}{4} + \frac{3}{4}) + \frac{1}{3} = 1 + \frac{1}{3} \qquad \text{(done mentally)}$$

$$= 1\frac{1}{3} \qquad \text{(written)}$$

31. $(45 + 79) + 55$
32. $\frac{1}{8}(243 \cdot 16)$
33. $(4 \cdot 786)25$
34. $6\frac{2}{5} + (4\frac{5}{7} + 3\frac{3}{5})$
35. $\frac{1}{6}(18 + 24)$

36. $(\frac{5}{12} \cdot 391) + (\frac{7}{12} \cdot 391)$
37. $(\frac{4}{9} \cdot 35) + (\frac{4}{9} \cdot 55)$
38. $36(\frac{5}{12} + \frac{7}{18})$
39. $0.2 \, (9\frac{2}{3} + \frac{4}{5} + 10\frac{1}{3})$
40. $0.625 \, (3.25) + 0.625 \, (6.00) + 0.625 \, (6.75)$

41–50

Given the following equalities, do the operation directed and write the final form, showing every step used. Do not combine the numbers within parentheses.

Sample
$(4 + 6) = (12 - 2)$.   Divide both sides by 2.

SOLUTION

$$\frac{4}{2} + \frac{6}{2} = \frac{12}{2} - \frac{2}{2}$$

$$2 + 3 = 6 - 1$$

$$5 = 5$$

41. $(2\frac{3}{4} + 3\frac{5}{6}) = (11\frac{3}{4} - 5\frac{1}{6})$ Add $5\frac{1}{6}$ to each side.
42. $(13\frac{2}{9} - 1\frac{8}{15}) = (8\frac{2}{9} + 3\frac{7}{15})$ Subtract $3\frac{7}{15}$ from each side.
43. $(1 + \frac{1}{2}) = (2 - \frac{1}{2})$ Multiply both sides by 2.
44. $(\frac{1}{2} + \frac{1}{4}) = (1 - \frac{1}{4})$ Multiply both sides by 4.
45. $(2 + 1) = (6 - 3)$ Divide both sides by 2.
46. $(9 - 6) = (7 - 4)$ Divide both sides by 3.
47. $(\frac{5}{3} + \frac{1}{2}) = (\frac{17}{6} - \frac{2}{3})$ Multiply both sides by 6.
48. $(\frac{23}{12} - \frac{11}{18}) = (\frac{19}{36} + \frac{7}{9})$ Multiply both sides by 36.
49. $(625 - 125) = (375 + 125)$ Multiply both sides by $\frac{1}{25}$.
50. $(400 + 500) = (1200 - 300)$ Multiply both sides by 0.01.

1.10 / Measurements

Accuracy and precision

If the bolts in a connection are counted, the result is recorded as a number without a decimal point because only an integral number can be the answer. The perimeter of a square can be written as 4 times the length of a side, $4S$. Again there is no decimal point placed after the 4. In both these examples the two numbers are called *exact numbers* and a decimal point is not necessary. $26.35 is also an exact number because it means exactly 2635 pennies, although a decimal point is required in this case.

Almost all engineering and scientific observations involve some sort of measurement. When the observation is written as some number, the immediate questions are: How good is this number? Does it really describe what has been measured? Accuracy and precision are two words that are used for an answer to this question.

Accuracy is a measure of how close an observation is to the true value. In most cases the true value is not known. In scientific experiments a highly reliable standard may be used to calibrate the measuring device used in a test. In this case the accuracy of the testing instrument may be determined.

The **precision** of a measurement is a statement of how reliable the measurement is. The precision is expressed either in parts or in the smallest physical unit of measurement believed correct. For example, a land survey can be directed to obtain a precision of 1 part in 5000. Then, if 1 mile, 5280 ft, is measured, the allowable error can be 1 ft. As another example, a steel bolt may be measured with micrometer calipers (see Figure 1.6) and found to have a 1-in. diameter measured to the nearest thousandth of an inch. This would be written 1.000 in. $\pm$ 0.001 in., where ± 0.001 in. states the degree

Figure 1.6
A micrometer caliper

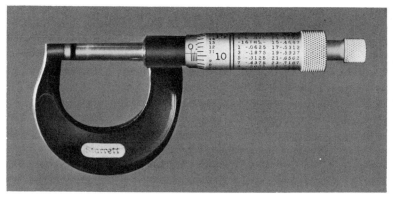

of precision. Expressed as a part, the bolt has been measured to 1 part in 1000. In both these examples, the accuracy cannot be computed, because neither the *true* distance nor the *true* diameter of the bolt is known.

To further illustrate the difference between accuracy and precision, consider the following example. Suppose the true value of something is 1.2634 and the measured value is 1.25 measured to the nearest 0.01 unit. Then

$$\text{the error} = 1.2634 - 1.25 = 0.0134$$

$$\text{the percentage error} = \frac{0.0134}{1.2634} \cdot 100 = 1.06 = 1.06\%$$

$$\text{the accuracy} = 100\% - 1.06\% = 98.94\%$$

$$\text{the precision} = \frac{0.01}{1.25} = 0.8\%, \text{ or 1 part in 125}$$

Upon comparing the measurement of the land survey with the measurement of the steel bolt in the previous examples, it may seem strange that an error of as small an amount as one thousandth of an inch is less precise than an error of 1 ft in 1 mile. However, the survey is actually 5 times more precise. An error of 1 part in 5000 is 5 times more precise than an error of 1 part in 1000. This is an important concept in the application of mathematics to engineering problems. It is necessary to study a result and find the true meaning and not make instant guesses based upon a hunch.

A thousandth of an inch may seem like a very small number and thus may imply falsely a high degree of precision. Johansson gauge blocks, used in the finest machine shops, are accurate and precise to the nearest millionth of an inch. If the two devices, the Johansson gauge blocks and the micrometer calipers, are compared for the measurement of the same object, the ratio of their degrees of precision can be written as

$$\frac{\dfrac{1}{1000}}{\dfrac{1}{1,000,000}} = \frac{0.001}{0.000\,001} = \frac{1}{0.001} = \frac{1000}{1}$$

Therefore, the Johansson gauge blocks measured this object with a precision 1000 times that obtained by using the micrometer calipers.

On the other hand, the size of the object does affect the precision measure. The 1-in. bolt measured with the micrometer calipers has a precision measurement of $\frac{1}{1000}$, while a No. 40 wire (0.0031 in.) measured with Johansson gauge blocks would be

$$\frac{0.000\,001}{0.003\,100} = \frac{1}{3100}$$

In the above example, the zeros in front of the digit 1 indicate only the size of the unit being measured and, for this reason, are called placeholders. This same concept applies to large numbers. For example, in a newspaper, a Congressional appropriation may be written $2.3 billion rather than $2,300,000,000. The zeros here are again placeholders.

Significant figures

Significant figures are the digits that reflect the precision of a measurement, observation, or calculation.

If a number is *exact*, all its digits are significant.

If a number is *inexact*, the significant figures of this number when written in positional notation are determined as follows.

(1) All digits that are not 0.

(2) The digit 0 if
    (a) it is between nonzero digits, or
    (b) it is to the right of a decimal point when there is a nonzero digit to the left of the zero, or
    (c) it is to the left of a decimal point actually printed and to the right of nonzero digits.

Example 1.1

Given number	Significant figures	Reason
18	2	Case 1
1,834	4	Case 1
18,000	2	Case 1
18,001	5	Case 2(a)
18.0	3	Case 2(b)
0.0180	3	Case 2(b)
0.000018	2	Case 1
18,000.	5	Case 2(c)
18,000 pennies	5	Exact

The conditions of the problem will indicate if the number is exact.

1.11 / Applications to arithmetic

Rounding off: addition and subtraction

The drum on the micrometer caliper shown in Figure 1.6 has appreciable space between the graduations on the drum which give the number of thousandths of an inch. Sometimes the reading falls exactly halfway between two lines. It could be read and written 0.7605, but, if results are being recorded to the nearest thousandth, then a decision is needed as to whether 0.760 or 0.761 is the best result. Since so many engineering formulas have a $\frac{1}{2}$ factor in them, the rule is to select the result ending in an even digit. The process of reducing a given number to another number with fewer digits is called *rounding off*.

Rules for Rounding Off
If the excess digits represent
(1) *more than a half unit, the round off is upward,*
(2) *less than a half unit, the round off is downward,*
(3) *exactly one half unit, the round off is to the nearest even digit.*

Example 1.2

Given number	Rounded off to the nearest integer
24.37	24
24.41412767	24
24.50000001	25
24.49999999	24
24.5	24
23.5	24
23.49999999	23

In doing arithmetic operations, a great deal of time can be saved by using the smallest number of significant figures that give the proper answer. For example, suppose that the following numbers, representing observed data and recorded in the same unit of measurement, are to be added:

$$24.5414$$
$$267.1$$
$$0.00010$$
$$1764.040$$

Looking at the accuracy of these numbers (that is, to what subunit of measurement is each recorded), the second number is the least accurate, since any value from 267.051 to 267.149 would be recorded as 267.1. (Note that 267.15 would be rounded off to an even final digit, 267.2.) This means that there is an uncertainty of 9 units in the hundredths column, and no digits in the hundredths (or smaller) column should be used. Consequently, the problem is now written as follows:

$$24.5$$
$$267.1$$
$$\underline{1764.0}$$
$$2055.6 = \text{sum}$$

Sometimes the digits 3 or 4 appear in the next column to the right of the least accurate column for several observations. These digits are rejected in rounding off and, if too many are dropped, the answer may be affected appreciably. It can be assumed that there are as many numbers rounded up as rounded down, but this may not always be true. To avoid this difficulty, one more column than the data indicate is kept for the actual addition and the final sum is rounded off. So now the same problem looks as follows.

$$24.54$$
$$267.1$$
$$\underline{1764.04}$$
$$2055.68 \rightarrow 2055.7 = \text{sum}$$

In summary, for problems of addition, subtraction, or both combined, round off each number to one more column to the right than the column containing the rightmost digit of the least accurate number. Round off the result one column.

Example 1.3
Add:

$$24,000$$
$$1,120$$
$$42,780$$
$$670$$

SOLUTION

$$24,000 \rightarrow 24,000 \text{ (the 4 is the controlling digit)}$$
$$1,120 \rightarrow 1,100$$
$$42,780 \rightarrow 42,800$$
$$670 \rightarrow \underline{700}$$
$$68,600 \rightarrow 69,000 \text{ (rounded off to the column with the ``4'')}$$

The above example illustrates the addition of inexact values. Suppose the problem had been stated: The following deposits were made in a bank. How much money is in the account? In that case there is no question of significant figures. Each number represents an exact number of dollars and the answer would be $68,570.

Rounding off: multiplication and division   For multiplication and division, percentage precision is used and the answer is rounded off to the largest percentage error of any factor. It is assumed that the probable error is $\frac{1}{2}$ unit of the last column of each factor. For example,

$$24.5 \qquad \times \qquad 16.02 \qquad = \qquad 392.49$$
$$\tfrac{1}{2} \text{ part in 245 is } 0.2\% \qquad \tfrac{1}{2} \text{ part in 1600 is } 0.03\% \qquad 0.2\% \text{ of 392 is } 0.8$$

Since the answer can be in error by 1 unit, it should be recorded as 392. To see that this is realistic, use the upper and lower limits of the least precise factor as follows:

the smallest value: 24.46 × 16.02 = 391.85

the largest value: 24.54 × 16.02 = 393.13

The answer 392 falls between these limiting values, which differ in the units column. Thus, the roundoff to the nearest unit is a realistic result for this case.

Rounding off: multiplication and subtraction There is one special exception to the basic rules stated above. This is the case of the difference of two numbers very nearly alike being multiplied by a very large number. For example,

$$4000(40.0 \times 40.0 - 51.6 \times 31.0) = 4000(1600 - 1599.6)$$
$$= 4000 \times 0.4$$
$$= 1600$$

If the numbers in this problem are observed values, the least precise is 31.0, which could be in error by 0.05, or 5 parts in 3100, which is approximately 1 part in 600. Since $\frac{1}{600}$ of 1600 is about 2.7, there is no justification for retaining tenths, such as 0.4. However, calculations of this type, which occur in problems such as checking the loading of aircraft, indicate that a 1600-unit result should not be ignored. Experience in the special area of application will indicate if an exception to the basic rules is to be made.

1.12 / Significant figures: angles and distances

Although many engineering calculations use angles subdivided into decimal parts such as 30.267°, surveyors, astronomers, and others still use the older system of degrees, minutes, and seconds. Again assuming that the error of observation is one half of the unit read, Table 1.3 can be constructed. The last column is somewhat arbitrary, for the precision measure depends upon the size of the angle. However, it does indicate that if the angles are

Table 1.3

Angle measured to nearest:	Decimal parts of a degree	Approximate decimal	Significant figures warranted for calculations
10′	0.167°	0.1°	2
1′	0.0167°	0.01°	3
10″	0.00278°	0.001°	4
1″	0.00028°	0.0001°	5

not measured with real precision, there is no point in calculating distances to six or seven significant figures just because a machine will deliver that many digits. If angles are measured only to the nearest 10' or the nearest minute, slide-rule calculations (giving a precision of three significant figures) are adequate for calculating distances. The converse is equally true. The precision of the lengths measured indicates how precisely the angle should be calculated.

The "approximate decimal" column is used for calculations where angles are given in degrees and decimal parts. For example, if a distance was measured as 23.5 ft (three significant figures), the angle that would be used for calculations would be selected as 37°21' (correct to the nearest minute), or as 37.35° (correct to the nearest 0.01°).

Problem Set 1.6

For Problems 1–10, assume that the possible error is one-half of the smallest recorded subunit of measurement.

Sample 1
Find the possible error, the error in parts, and the percentage error for a measurement of 2.0002 in.

SOLUTION
Possible error is $\frac{1}{2}(0.0001)$ in. $= 0.000\ 05$ in. Error in parts is $\dfrac{0.000\ 05}{2.000\ 2} = 1:40,000$. Percentage error is $100(1/40,000)\% = 0.0025\%$.

Sample 2
Find the possible error, the error in parts, and the percentage error for a measurement of $2\frac{5}{16}$ in.

SOLUTION
Possible error is $\frac{1}{2}(\frac{1}{16})$ in. $= \frac{1}{32}$ in. Error in parts is $(\frac{1}{32})/(\frac{37}{16}) = 1:74$. Percentage error is $100(\frac{1}{74})\% = 1.35\%$.

1–10
Copy and complete the table, recording results to two or three significant figures, as appropriate.

Problem	Measurement	Possible error	Error in parts	% Error
Sample 1	2.0002 in.	0.000 05 in.	1 : 40,000	0.0025
Sample 2	$2\frac{5}{16}$ in.	$\frac{1}{32}$ in.	1 : 74	1.35
1.	17.54 ft			
2.	86.32 ft			

Problem	Measurement	Possible error	Error in parts	% Error
3.	0.0012 in.			
4.	0.012 in			
5.	$5\frac{3}{4}$ in.			
6.	$6\frac{7}{8}$ in.			
7.	$3'\text{-}0\frac{1}{2}''$ (read 3 ft, $\frac{1}{2}$ in. or $36\frac{1}{2}$ in.)			
8.	$4'\text{-}2\frac{1}{4}''$			
9.	$5°\ \ 2'\ \ 12''$			
10.	$7°\ \ 33'\ \ 24''$			

11–16
Find the indicated sums, observing the rules for rounding off.

11.	**12.**	**13.**	**14.**	**15.**	**16.**
3.004	640.24	0.002 4	12.0	1.7624	3.69
0.0027	739.19	0.000 24	120.0	0.0917	7.278
14.087	2002.0	0.000 24	1200.0	3.9878	0.1768
127.93	26.676	0.000 024	12000.0	4	4.0

17–24
Find the indicated products, observing the rules for rounding off.

17. 24.0×0.113

18. 4.16×2.02

19. 0.010×1728.92

20. 0.002×1728.98

21. 3.060×123

22. 1.24×50500

23. $2000(7.95 \times 6.04 - 0.0120 \times 4000.0)$

24. $3000(4390 \times 24.0 - 15.05 \times 6985)$

25. A screw-making machine during a 5-day work week broke down Friday morning. The daily output was 15,216; 18,314; 17,872; 19,021; and 270. What was the output for the week?

26. A surveying party mapped a rugged area and had good weather except on Wednesday, when it rained most of the day. Their daily output, in square miles mapped, was 1.02; 0.86; 0.04; 1.11; and 1.18. How much terrain was mapped that week?

27–30

Find the distance D in each figure.

27.

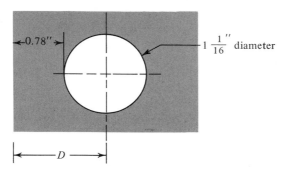

28.

Two 2 × 4 blocks which are $1\frac{5}{8}''$ wide after planing in mill.

#26 gauge sheet metal on each side. This metal is 0.0188″ thick.

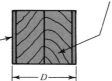

29.

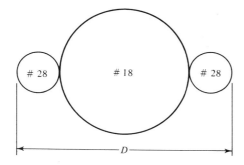

Wire size	Diameter (inches)
# 10	0.102
# 18	0.040
# 22	0.0253
# 28	0.0126
# 32	0.0080

30.

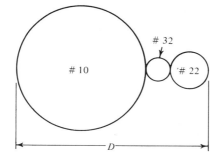

Wire size	Diameter (inches)
# 10	0.102
# 18	0.040
# 22	0.0253
# 28	0.0126
# 32	0.0080

31. In a laboratory test, the following data were recorded.

Observation	Angle	Distance, cm
A	7.2°	16.154
B	37.2°	17.117
C	25.54°	9.082
D	31.76°	6.112
E	14.081°	12.0234
F	11.987°	19.1000

Write the appropriate distance to use in calculations for each of the angles listed.

32. In some surveying observations, the following baselines were measured and adjusted to the recorded lengths. The angles were observed but should be adjusted to be compatible with the baselines. Write the proper angle to use in calculations for each length listed.

Baseline	Length, ft	Angle
A—B	980.	36°54'10"
B—C	980.2	37° 1' 4"
C—D	980.24	63°12'10"
D—E	980.241	72°56' 9"
E—F	79.01	3° 0'30"
F—G	84.49	5°59'45"

1.13 / Powers

Early mathematicians soon grew bored with writing $6 \times 6 \times 6 \times 6$ to indicate that the factor 6 was to be used 4 times to form a product. A notation was developed as a shorthand writing method for such repeated multiplications, and $6 \times 6 \times 6 \times 6$ is now written 6^4. The common factor 6 is called the **base,** the smaller raised number 4 is called the **exponent,** and the product $6^4 = 1296$ is called a **power.**

$$\text{base} \rightarrow N^n \leftarrow \text{exponent}$$

$$\text{the power } N^n = \underbrace{N \times N \times \cdots \times N}_{n \text{ factors}}$$

The area of a square is the length of a side multiplied by itself; that is, area $= s \times s = s^2$ (read "s square" or "the square of s"). The product of a number multiplied by itself is called the **square** of that number.

Similarly, the volume of a cube is the product obtained when the length of a side is used as a factor 3 times; that is, $V = s^3$ (read "s cube" or "the cube of s"). The **cube** of a number is the product obtained by using the number as a factor 3 times.

Since there are only three real physical dimensions, no other power has been given a special name. N^n is read "N to the n" or "the nth power of N." For example, 6^4 is read "6 to the fourth" or "the fourth power of 6."

This discussion is limited to exponents that are elements of the set of positive integers. Later in the book the set from which exponents may be selected will be gradually extended until it becomes the set of real numbers.

Since, by definition, $5^4 = 5 \times 5 \times 5 \times 5$ and $5^2 = 5 \times 5$, then $5^4 = 5^2 \times 5^2 = (5^2)^2$. Now, if there is a simple way to find squares, this method can be used twice to obtain squares of squares, or fourth powers.

Similarly, 5^6 means 6 factors of 5 and $5^3 \times 5^3$ also means 6 factors of 5. Then $5^6 = 5^3 \times 5^3 = (5^3)^2$, or the sixth power of 5 is also the square of the cube of 5.

In general, the fourth power of a number is the square of the square of the number, and the sixth power of a number is the square of the cube of the number.

Example 1.4
Find 2^6 in two different ways.

SOLUTION
(1) $2^6 = (2 \times 2 \times 2)(2 \times 2 \times 2) = (2^3)^2 = 8^2 = 64$.
(2) $2^6 = (2 \times 2)(2 \times 2)(2 \times 2) = (2^2)^3 = 4^3 = 64$.

1.14 / Roots

Inverse operations will be met throughout this book. Subtraction is the inverse of addition and a subtraction exercise can be checked by addition. For example,

$$728 - 504 = 224 \quad \text{and} \quad 224 + 504 = 728, \text{ check.}$$

Multiplication and division are also inverse operations. A division is readily checked by the inverse operation of multiplication. For example,

$$\tfrac{148}{12} = 12\tfrac{1}{3} \quad \text{and} \quad 12 \times 12\tfrac{1}{3} = 12 \times \tfrac{37}{3} = 148, \text{ check}$$

or, by using the distributive axiom,

$$12 \times 12\tfrac{1}{3} = 12(12 + \tfrac{1}{3}) = 144 + 4 = 148$$

The root of a number is defined by this idea of inverse operations. To find the square root of a number means to find a number which when multiplied by itself has the given number as the product. To discuss any root, not just the square root, a notational system is needed. The one that has been used for centuries is

radical (root symbol)

index number (which root?) $\sqrt[n]{N}\leftarrow$ radicand (number whose root is wanted)

For example, $\sqrt{4}$, the square root of 4, is 2 since $2 \times 2 = 4$. The index 2 is not written for square roots. Also,

$\sqrt[3]{125}$, the cube root of 125, $= 5$ since $5^3 = 5 \times 5 \times 5 = 125$

$\sqrt[5]{32}$, the fifth root of 32, $= 2$ since $2^5 = 2 \times 2 \times 2 \times 2 \times 2 = 32$

$\sqrt[4]{\frac{1}{16}}$, the fourth root of $\frac{1}{16}$, $= \frac{1}{2}$ since $(\frac{1}{2})^4 = \frac{1}{2} \times \frac{1}{2} \times \frac{1}{2} \times \frac{1}{2} = \frac{1}{16}$

Index numbers are limited to the set of positive integers as were exponents. For now, radicands are limited to the set of nonnegative real numbers and the radical symbol is used to designate only positive roots or 0.

In general, a root of a specified degree of a given positive number is that positive number which if raised to the same power as the index number produces the original number as the result. For positive or zero roots, $\sqrt[n]{(\text{root})^n} = \text{root}$. In symbols, N and x being positive, $\sqrt[n]{N} = x$ if and only if $x^n = N$. Since $N^4 = (N^2)^2$ and $N^6 = (N^3)^2$, then for positive N or $N = 0$,

$$\sqrt[4]{N^4} = \sqrt{\sqrt{N^4}} = \sqrt{N^2} = N$$

$$\sqrt[6]{N^6} = \sqrt{\sqrt[3]{N^6}} = \sqrt{\sqrt[3]{N^2 \times N^2 \times N^2}} = \sqrt{N^2} = N$$

$$\sqrt[6]{N^6} = \sqrt[3]{\sqrt{N^6}} = \sqrt[3]{\sqrt{N^3 \times N^3}} = \sqrt[3]{N^3} = N$$

Therefore, the fourth root of a number is the square root of the square root of the number. The sixth root of a number is the square root of the cube root of the number and also the cube root of the square root of the number.

Example 1.5
Find $\sqrt[6]{729}$ in two different ways.

SOLUTION

(1) $\sqrt[6]{729} = \sqrt[3]{\sqrt{729}} = \sqrt[3]{27} = 3$.

(2) $\sqrt[6]{729} = \sqrt{\sqrt[3]{729}} = \sqrt{9} = 3$.

1.15 / Scientific notation

The technical world has changed drastically these past few years. Today the numbers met in the world of science are often extremely large or exceptionally small. Both a simple way to write such numbers and a method to give them universally accepted names were needed. The International Committee on Weights and Measures has done this.

Any positive real number, large or small, can be written as a number between 1 and 9.999 . . . multiplied or divided by some power of 10. For example,

$$4762 = 4.762 \times 1000 = 4.762 \times 10^3$$

$$12{,}046{,}000{,}000 = 1.2046 \times 10^{10}$$

For any number 10 or larger, a decimal point is placed after the first digit. The power of 10 written is exactly equal to the number of places from this new decimal point to the original one. When the exponent of 10 is 1, it is never written. For example,

$$47.62 = 4.762 \times 10$$

For positive real numbers smaller than 10 and larger than 1, the number is in the proper form and no power of 10 is indicated.

For numbers smaller than 1, the new position of the decimal point is after the first digit different from 0. Starting at the original decimal point and moving to the right, all zeros and the first nonzero digit met are counted. The negative of this count is the exponent of 10.

Using the method described,

$$0.\quad 0 \quad 0 \quad 4 \quad 7 \quad 6 \quad 2 = 4.762 \times 10^{-3}$$
$$-1 \;-2 \;-3$$

The minus sign in front of the exponent means that division is used:

$$0.004\,762 = \frac{4.762}{1000} = \frac{4.762}{10^3} = 4.762 \times 10^{-3}$$

If the first nonzero digit is adjacent to the decimal point, the rule still applies. For example,

$$0.\quad 4 \quad 7 \quad 6 \quad 2 = 4.762 \times 10^{-1}$$
$$-1$$

Rule for Scientific Notation
To write a number in scientific notation,
(1) *Move the decimal point in the ordinary decimal notation to the position after the first nonzero digit, and*
(2) *Multiply this new number by a power of* 10 *whose exponent is*
    (a) n *if the decimal point is moved* n *places to the left, or*
    (b) $-n$ *if the decimal point is moved* n *places to the right.*

This is a very simple and effective system for anyone trained in it. Unfortunately, most of the nontechnical people of the world would not

Table 1.4

Power of 10	Name	Abbreviation	Pronounciation
10^{12}	tera	T	ter' ä
10^9	giga	G	ji' gä
10^6	mega	M	meg' ä
10^3	kilo	K	kil' ō
10^2	hecto	h	hek' tō
10	deka	da	dek' ä
10^{-1}	deci	d	des' i
10^{-2}	centi	c	sen' ti
10^{-3}	milli	m	mil' i
10^{-6}	micro	μ (mu)	$\overline{\text{mi}}$' krō
10^{-9}	nano	n	nan' ō
10^{-12}	pico	p	pē' kō
10^{-15}	femto	f	fem' tō
10^{-18}	atto	a	at' tō

understand what was being said if a newspaper reported that the national debt was about 3×10^{11} dollars. There has grown up a curious blend of two systems. Suppose a newscaster wants to report that the Congress has appropriated \$1,870,000,000. He would probably not read this as one billion, eight hundred seventy million dollars and certainly not as 1.87×10^9 dollars, but blend these two methods and say 1.87 billion dollars.

Americans recognize a million, a billion, and a trillion as names for 10^6, 10^9, and 10^{12}. To people in many other countries these names either have no meaning or they have a different meaning. Therefore, the International Commission has adopted for world-wide use the names listed in Table 1.4. (This table appears also as Table 9 of the Appendix.)

Calculations with powers of ten

1. Products of powers Two powers of 10 are multiplied by adding their exponents. For example,

$$10^2 \cdot 10^3 = 10^{2+3} = 10^5$$

$$(100)(1000) = 100,000 = 10^5$$

In general,

$$10^m \cdot 10^n = 10^{m+n}$$

2. Quotients of powers Two powers of 10 are divided by subtracting the exponent in the denominator from the exponent in the numerator. For example,

$$\frac{10^6}{10^2} = 10^{6-2} = 10^4 \qquad \left(\frac{1,000,000}{100} = 10,000\right)$$

$$\frac{10^3}{10^6} = 10^{3-6} = 10^{-3} \qquad \left(\frac{1000}{1,000,000} = \frac{1}{1000} = 10^{-3}\right)$$

In general,

$$\frac{10^m}{10^n} = 10^{m-n}$$

3. Squares and cubes of powers A square of a power of 10 is obtained by multiplying the exponent by 2. A cube of a power of 10 is obtained by multiplying the exponent by 3. For example,

$$(10^3)^2 = 10^{3\cdot2} = 10^6 \qquad [(1000)^2 = (1000)(1000) = 1,000,000]$$

$$(10^{-2})^3 = 10^{-2\cdot3} = 10^{-6} \qquad \left[\left(\frac{1}{100}\right)^3 = \left(\frac{1}{100}\right)\left(\frac{1}{100}\right)\left(\frac{1}{100}\right) = \frac{1}{1,000,000}\right]$$

In general,

$$(10^n)^2 = 10^{2n} \qquad \text{and} \qquad (10^n)^3 = 10^{3n}$$

Problem Set 1.7

1–20
Write each of the following numbers in scientific notation. Round all data to four significant figures.

Sample
The modern electronic computer can do an arithmetic operation in 0.000 000 002 4 seconds (sec).

SOLUTION
2.4×10^{-9} sec.

1. A British ton contains 2240 lb.
2. Recently, the annual receipts at the Chicago post office were $242,476,184.00. (Round this off to four significant figures as the first step.)
3. The largest dam in the world is the Fort Peck dam, containing 125,600,000 cu yd of earth.
4. The largest Russian dam is at Nurek and contains 75,900,000 cu yd of earth.
5. The angstrom unit is used to measure wavelengths of light. It is 0.000 000 000 1 meter (m).

6. An angstrom in the U.S. system is approximately 0.000 000 004 inch.
7. A millimeter is 0.039 37 in.
8. A micron is 0.000 039 37 in.
9. An International nautical mile is 6076.115 49 ft.
10. A square foot contains 929,030 square centimeter (sq cm).
11. 63/64 is equivalent to 0.984 375.
12. 65/64 is equivalent to 1.015 625.
13. The maximum distance from the sun to the planet Neptune is 2,817,400,000 miles.
14. The planet Saturn is closer to the sun, 935,570,000 miles away, than Neptune.
15. Grover Cleveland received 5,540,050 votes but the Electoral College gave the presidency to Benjamin Harrison, who received 5,444,337 votes.
16. It is estimated that the world population is 3,356,485,000 people, who live on 135,696,590 sq kilometers (km) of land.
17. An electron of an atom has an electrical charge of 0.000 000 000 480 288 electrostatic units (esu).
18. The mass of an electron is 0.000 000 000 000 000 000 000 000 000 910 85 gram (g).
19. The proton of an atom is much heavier than an electron and has a mass of 0.000 000 000 000 000 000 000 001 672 43 g.
20. The neutron of an atom has almost the same mass as a proton, being 0.000 000 000 000 000 000 000 001 674 74 g.

21–30

Express the following statements as numbers in ordinary decimal form.

21. The population of Tokyo is about 14.2 million people.
22. The United States exported annually about 1.771×10^9 dollars worth of finished manufactured goods in the late 1960s.
23. An atom has a radius of 1.5×10^{-8} cm.
24. An atomic nucleus has a radius of 4.1×10^{-13} cm.
25. One million electron volts (1 Mev) is equal to 3.83×10^{-14} calorie (cal).
26. An Mev is equal to 4.45×10^{-20} kilowatt hours (kwh).
27. In recent years, many units have been renamed, often after a famous scientist. FM radio sets have dials graduated from 88 to 108. These were originally a measure of the cycles per second, which have now been renamed hertz (Hz). If a set is tuned to 104.5 megahertz, how many cycles per second does that represent?
28. A force of 1 newton (N) is about one quarter of a pound of force. How many newtons of force is 23.6 kilonewtons?
29. Absolute zero on the Fahrenheit scale is a temperature of -4.60×10^2 °F.
30. Absolute zero on the Celsius scale is a temperature of -2.732×10^2 °C.

31–40

Write the name of each number given in scientific notation by selecting the proper prefix from Table 1.4.

Sample 1
An obsolete name for 4.7×10^{-12} farad (F; the capacitance of a certain condenser) was $4.7\ \mu\mu$F.

SOLUTION
4.7 pF.

Sample 2
An erg is 9.48×10^{-11} British thermal unit (Btu).

SOLUTION
Since there is no prefix for 10^{-11}, either 10^{-9} or 10^{-12} must be selected. Whenever possible, it is customary to select the nearest unit that gives a numerical value greater than 1.0. Since $9.48 \times 10^{-11} = 948 \times 10^{-9}$, this gives 948 nano Btu.

31. The speed of light in a vacuum is 2.99×10^{10} cm/sec.
32. An International Steam Table calorie is 4.197×10^{7} ergs.
33. The average distance of Mars from the sun is 1.41×10^{8} miles.
34. The mean distance of the moon from the earth is 2.389×10^{5} miles.
35. One calorie is equivalent to 2.613×10^{13} Mev.
36. The atomic time unit is 2.419×10^{-17} sec.
37. A constant used by Planck in the study of radiation is 4.9918×10^{-15} erg-sec.
38. The gravitational constant, G, is 6.670×10^{-8} cu cm/(g sec/sec).
39. The mass of an electron is 5.4875×10^{-4} atomic mass unit (amu).
40. The Bohr radius of the circular orbit in which an electron revolves about a proton in a hydrogen atom is 5.29×10^{-11} m.

41–70

Calculate each of the following.

41. 3^4

42. 7^4

43. 5^6

44. 4^6

45. $\sqrt[4]{625}$

46. $\sqrt[4]{81}$

47. $\sqrt[4]{4096}$

48. $\sqrt[4]{10{,}000}$

49. $\sqrt[6]{64}$

50. $\sqrt[6]{4096}$

51. $\sqrt[6]{1{,}000{,}000}$

52. $\sqrt[6]{15{,}625}$

53. $10^4 10^2$

54. $10^3 10^4$

55. $10^5 10^{-3}$

56. $10^{-7} 10^3$

57. $\dfrac{10^8}{10^2}$

58. $\dfrac{10^{12}}{10^4}$

59. $\dfrac{10^5}{10^{-2}}$　　　　**63.** $(10^4)^2$　　　　**67.** $(10^4)^3$

60. $\dfrac{10^4}{10^{-1}}$　　　　**64.** $(10^5)^2$　　　　**68.** $(10^5)^3$

61. $\dfrac{10^{-3}}{10^{-6}}$　　　　**65.** $(10^{-5})^2$　　　　**69.** $(10^{-3})^3$

62. $\dfrac{10^{-4}}{10^{-8}}$　　　　**66.** $(10^{-2})^2$　　　　**70.** $(10^{-4})^3$

1.16 / Use of tables of numbers

Most of the school systems in the United States have abandoned teaching manual methods for finding square and cube roots, and no simple method exists for other roots. In this section, the use of tables of numbers will be studied. The next chapter will cover finding powers and roots on a slide rule, and in Chapter 8 the method for doing these operations by logarithms will be shown. Electric desk calculators are often used if many significant figures are needed.

Handbooks　Four widely used handbooks will be discussed briefly since they differ greatly as to what tables permit direct reading of roots and powers. All these handbooks contain what can be termed the "standard tables." Many other excellent tables are published and their not being listed here does not detract from their excellence.

Engineering and Technical Handbook by D. C. McNeese and A. L. Hoag (Englewood Cliffs, N.J.: Prentice-Hall, Inc., 1957) contains the standard tables giving for each integer from 1 to 999 the following items:

(1) Square.
(2) Cube.
(3) Square root.
(4) Cube root.
(5) Reciprocal.
(6) Circumference of a circle for the listed number as diameter.
(7) Area of a circle for the listed number as diameter.

This handbook contains an additional table giving the same information for fractional and decimal parts of a unit, the fractions varying by $\frac{1}{64}$ths to 1 unit and $\frac{1}{8}$ths from 1 to 6 units. Decimals vary by 0.01 unit.

Standard Mathematical Tables (Cleveland: Chemical Rubber Publishing Company, 1969), includes in its standard tables additional columns that give $\sqrt{10N}$, extending the table from 1 to 9990 by tens, and for cube roots

$\sqrt[3]{10N}$ and $\sqrt[3]{100N}$, extending the table to 99,900 by hundreds. There is an additional table that gives for integers from 1 through 100 the values of the fourth through the ninth powers and for the base 2 the values of all powers from 1 through 101.

The Engineer's Companion by Mott Souders (New York: John Wiley & Sons, Inc., 1966) includes in the standard tables the $\frac{3}{2}$ power and the fifth root. It also has an additional table giving the standard table values as augmented for values $\frac{1}{64}$ to 1 by $\frac{1}{64}$ths and from $1\frac{1}{8}$ to $9\frac{7}{8}$ by $\frac{1}{8}$ths. Another table gives higher powers from the fourth to the eighth for the integers from 1 to 100. A unique table gives for decimals by hundredths from 0.01 to 0.99 their values to decimal powers by tenths from 0.1 to 0.9.

Handbook of Hydraulics by H. W. King and E. F. Brater (New York: McGraw-Hill Book Company, Inc., 5th ed., 1963) contains besides the standard tables some very special tables needed in hydraulic computations. These include $\frac{3}{2}$ powers, $\frac{5}{2}$ powers, 1.47 powers, $\frac{3}{8}$ powers, and $\frac{8}{3}$ powers.

Squares and cubes   Before using the tables, it is recommended that the squares and cubes of the digits be memorized.

Digit	1	2	3	4	5	6	7	8	9
Square	1	4	9	16	25	36	49	64	81
Cube	1	8	27	64	125	216	343	512	729

These values permit rough checking when using the tables. For example, if the square of $7\frac{1}{2}$ is to be found, the result should be between 49 ($= 7^2$) and 64 ($= 8^2$). When the tabular value for the square of 75 is found as 5625, there should be no difficulty in seeing that the result desired is $56\frac{1}{4}$. Scientific notation permits any number to be written as the product of a digit between 1 and 9 and a power of 10. Thus, only the squares and the cubes of the digits are needed for a rough check.

To use the standard tables, often labeled "Functions of Numbers" in a handbook, no instructions are needed for powers and roots of numbers whose significant digits are integral values from 1 to 999. These values are read directly. For other numbers, a simple procedure for squares and cubes is outlined below.

> **Table Method for Squares and Cubes** (using Table 1 of the Appendix):
> (1)   Round off the number to three significant figures and write it in scientific notation.
> (2)   From the table find the power corresponding to the three significant digits. Write this power as a number having three significant figures.

(a) Write a square as a number between 1.00 and 99.0.
(b) Write a cube as a number between 1.00 and 999.
(3) Multiply the exponent of 10 in step 1 by
  (a) 2 for squares, and
  (b) 3 for cubes.
(4) The product of the numbers obtained in steps 2 and 3 is the answer in exponential form. It can be written in ordinary notation or in scientific notation, as desired.

Example 1.6
Square 16,747.

SOLUTION

(1) ⌈ Round off	16,700	
⌊ Scientific notation	1.67×10^4	
(2) Table value of power	2.79	
(3) New power of 10		10^8
(4) Result, exponential	2.79×10^8	
ordinary	279,000,000	
scientific	2.79×10^8	

Example 1.7
Cube 62.401.

SOLUTION

(1) ⌈ Round off	62.4	
⌊ Scientific notation	6.24×10	
(2) Table value of power	243	
(3) New power of 10		$10^3 \ (10 = 10^1)$
(4) Result, exponential	243×10^3	
ordinary	243,000	
scientific	2.43×10^5	

Example 1.8
Square 0.127.

SOLUTION

(1) ⌈ Round off	0.127	
⌊ Scientific notation	1.27×10^{-1}	
(2) Table value of power	1.61	
(3) New power of 10		10^{-2}
(4) Result, exponential ⌉		
scientific ⌋	1.61×10^{-2}	
ordinary	0.0161	

Example 1.9
Cube 0.074 65.

SOLUTION

(1) ⎡ Round off   0.0746
    ⎣ Scientific notation 7.46×10^{-2}
(2) Table value of power   415
(3) New power of 10 10^{-6}
(4) Result, exponential 415×10^{-6}
           ordinary   0.000 415
           scientific 4.15×10^{-4}

Problems should be rough checked to see that the answers are reasonable. For example, look at Example 1.9.

(1) *Digits* Since $7^3 = 343$ and $8^3 = 512$, the cube of 7.46 should be between 343 and 512. The digits 415 meet this requirement.

(2) *Decimal point* $(0.07465)^3 \approx (0.08)^3 \approx (0.1)^3 = 0.001$. The decimal point should give a value near 0.001, and 0.0004 meets this requirement.

Roots The method for roots is almost the same as that for powers. However, the position of the original decimal point has added importance. In the second step, instead of writing the number in scientific notation, it may be necessary to multiply the significant digit portion of the number by either 10 or 100 so that the resulting exponent of 10 is exactly divisible by 2 for square roots or by 3 for cube roots. Then the new exponent of 10 for the root is obtained by dividing the exponent by 2 for square roots and by 3 for cube roots.

A second problem may also appear. The table may not contain the roots of some three-digit numbers. For example, the table does not give the square and cube roots of 12.3 directly. However, the roots can be obtained by using the concept of an inverse operation. The table does give the square root of 12 as 3.46 and the cube root of 12 as 2.29. Squares of numbers around 346 can be found in the table. In this case, $(351)^2$ is 123,201, and thus the desired square root of 12.3 is 3.51. Similarly, cubes of numbers near 229 can be found in the table. The number whose cube is closest to 12,300,000 is 231, and the cube root of 12.3 is 2.31.

Table Method for Square Roots and Cube Roots

(1) Round off to three significant figures, and write in scientific notation.
(2) In order to obtain a new exponent for 10 that is exactly divisible by 2 for square roots or by 3 for cube roots, either
    (a) multiply the digit part by 10 and reduce the exponent of 10 by 1, or
    (b) multiply the digit part by 100 and reduce the exponent of 10 by 2.
(3) (a) Direct method. Write the table value of the root to three significant figures, when this is possible.

(b) Indirect method. If the table value cannot be read directly, find an approximate root of a nearby number by using fewer significant figures. Then use the square or cube column.

(4) Divide the exponent of 10 in step 2 by 2 for square roots and by 3 for cube roots.

(5) The result, in exponential form, is the product of the numbers obtained in steps 3 and 4. It can be rewritten in ordinary or scientific notation, as desired.

Example 1.10

Find $\sqrt{1234}$.

SOLUTION

(1) Round off, scientific notation
(2) Rewritten form

$$\times 10 \begin{cases} 1.23 \times 10^3 \\ 12.3 \times 10^2 \end{cases} \div 10$$

(3) Table value of root, indirect   3.51

(4) New power of 10 $10 \ (10^1 = 10)$

(5) Result, exponential, scientific 3.51×10

        ordinary   35.1

Example 1.11

Find $\sqrt{0.00123}$.

SOLUTION

(1) Round off, scientific notation
(2) Rewritten form

$$\times 10 \begin{cases} 1.23 \times 10^{-3} \\ 12.3 \times 10^{-4} \end{cases} \div 10$$

(3) Table value of root, indirect   3.51

(4) New power of 10 10^{-2}

(5) Result, exponential, scientific 3.51×10^{-2}

        ordinary   0.0351

Example 1.12

Find $\sqrt[3]{12345}$.

SOLUTION

(1) Round off, scientific notation
(2) Rewritten form

$$\times 10 \begin{cases} 1.23 \times 10^4 \\ 12.3 \times 10^3 \end{cases} \div 10$$

(3) Table value of root, indirect   2.31

(4) New power of 10   10

(5) Result, exponential, scientific 2.31×10

        ordinary   23.1

Example 1.13

Find $\sqrt[3]{0.123}$.

SOLUTION
(1) Round off, scientific notation
(2) Rewritten form
(3) Table value of root, direct
(4) New power of 10
(5) Result, exponential, scientific
ordinary

$$\times 100 \begin{Bmatrix} 1.23 \times 10^{-1} \\ 123 \times 10^{-3} \end{Bmatrix} \div 100$$

4.97

10^{-1}

4.97×10^{-1}

0.497

To rough check the result, the digits of the number in ordinary notation are pointed off by groups of two for square roots and by groups of three for cube roots. The grouping always starts at the decimal point and zeros are digits. Then, using the table, the root of the first group containing a nonzero digit is found. A second digit of the root is then easily obtained. The rough checks of the results of Examples 1.10–1.13 are as follows:

Example 1.10
$$\overset{3\ \ 5.}{\sqrt{1234}} \rightarrow \sqrt{12'34.}$$

Example 1.11
$$\overset{0.\ \ 0\ \ 3\ \ 5}{\sqrt{0.00123}} \rightarrow \sqrt{0.00'12'30}$$

Example 1.12
$$\overset{2\ \ \ 3.}{\sqrt[3]{12345}} \rightarrow \sqrt[3]{12'345.}$$

Example 1.13
$$\overset{0.\ \ 4\ \ \ 9}{\sqrt[3]{0.123}} \rightarrow \sqrt[3]{0.123'000}$$

Note that the decimal point is not moved and that one digit is obtained in the answer for each group pointed off.

Fourth and sixth powers and roots Since a fourth power is the square of a square and the sixth power is the square of a cube, the fourth and sixth powers of a number can be obtained by using the method for squares and cubes two times. Similarly, since a fourth root is the square root of a square root and since a sixth root is the square root of a cube root, these roots can be obtained by using the method for square and cube roots two times. The answers are slightly less accurate since numbers are rounded off each time the method is used.

Example 1.14
Find $(747)^4$.

SOLUTION
$$(747)^4 = [(747)^2]^2$$

$$(747)^2 = 5.58 \times 10^5 \qquad \text{(read directly from table,}$$
$$\text{rounded off)}$$

$$(5.58 \times 10^5)^2 = 31.1 \times 10^{10} = 3.11 \times 10^{11}$$

Example 1.15
Find $(0.215)^6$.

SOLUTION
$$(0.215)^6 = [(0.215)^3]^2$$
$$= [(2.15 \times 10^{-1})^3]^2$$
$$= (9.94 \times 10^{-3})^2$$
$$= 99.8 \times 10^{-6} = 9.98 \times 10^{-5} = 0.000\ 099\ 8$$

Example 1.16
Find $\sqrt[4]{0.006\ 718}$.

SOLUTION
$$\sqrt[4]{0.006\ 718} = \sqrt{\sqrt{0.006\ 718}}$$
$$\sqrt{0.006\ 718} = \sqrt{6.72 \times 10^{-3}}$$
$$= \sqrt{67.2 \times 10^{-4}}$$
$$= 8.20 \times 10^{-2} \quad \text{(indirectly from 800 part of table)}$$
$$\sqrt{8.20 \times 10^{-2}} = 2.86 \times 10^{-1} = 0.286$$

Example 1.17
Find $\sqrt[6]{27678}$.

SOLUTION
$$\sqrt[6]{27678} = \sqrt{\sqrt[3]{27678}}$$
$$\sqrt[3]{27678} = \sqrt[3]{2.77 \times 10^4}$$
$$= \sqrt[3]{27.7 \times 10^3}$$
$$= 3.03 \times 10 = 30.3 \quad \text{(indirectly from 300 part of table)}$$
$$\sqrt{30.3} = 5.50 \quad \text{(indirectly from 500 part of table)}$$

In checking, it is well to remember that a root of a number larger than 1 is smaller than the original number, whereas a root of a number between 0 and 1 is always larger than the original number.

Problem Set 1.8

Using Table 1 of the Appendix, find the indicated power or root to three significant figures. Express answers between 0.0001 and 999,999 in ordinary notation; otherwise use scientific notation. Write a rough check for each problem.

1. $(1240)^2$
2. $(67.2)^2$
3. $(9.82)^2$
4. $(0.8767)^2$
5. $(41.7)^3$
6. $(7.83)^3$
7. $(0.9972)^3$
8. $(0.00275)^3$
9. $(0.000047)^3$
10. $(0.00000606)^3$
11. $\sqrt{91700}$
12. $\sqrt{42618}$
13. $\sqrt{9.17 \times 10^5}$
14. $\sqrt{5.11 \times 10^{-3}}$

15. $\sqrt[3]{0.878}$
16. $\sqrt[3]{0.000\,746}$
17. $\sqrt[3]{0.0858}$
18. $\sqrt[3]{0.000\,051\,5}$
19. $\sqrt[3]{10.313}$
20. $\sqrt[3]{78.6422}$
21. $(18)^4$
22. $(24)^6$
23. $(1.32)^6$
24. $(9.87)^4$
25. $(0.0176)^4$
26. $(0.00222)^6$
27. $\sqrt[4]{611}$

28. $\sqrt[6]{759}$
29. $\sqrt[6]{729}$
30. $\sqrt[4]{1.23}$
31. $\sqrt[4]{0.876}$
32. $\sqrt[6]{0.876}$
33. $\sqrt[6]{0.008\,76}$
34. $\sqrt[6]{0.000\,087\,6}$
35. $\sqrt{272\pi}$
36. $\sqrt[3]{314\pi}$
37. $\sqrt{\frac{1}{246}}$
38. $\sqrt{\frac{1}{667}}$
39. $\sqrt[3]{\frac{1}{713}}$
40. $\sqrt[3]{\frac{1}{899}}$

1.17 / Linear interpolation

Mathematical and engineering data are frequently given in tables. Sometimes values are needed for numbers that lie between values listed in a table. The process of finding values between tabular values is called *interpolation*, the prefix "inter" meaning "between."

To Find a Value by Linear Interpolation

(1) *Find the difference between the given value and the smaller of the tabulated entry values just above and just below the given value. Express this difference in tenths.*

(2) *Find the difference between the tabular resulting values by subtracting the value matching the smaller entry value from the value matching the larger entry value.*

(3) *Multiply the differences obtained in steps 1 and 2, and round off to the nearest unit for which the resulting values are tabulated.*

(4) *Add the product obtained in step 3 to the tabular resulting value matching the smaller entry value.*

Example 1.18
Find $(123.4)^2$.

SOLUTION

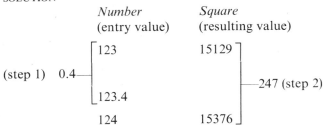

| | Number (entry value) | Square (resulting value) |

(step 1)   0.4 — [123 ... 123.4 ... 124] [15129 ... 15376] — 247 (step 2)

(step 3) $0.4 \times 247 = 98.8 \approx 99$

(step 4) $15129 + 99 = 15228$

$(123.4)^2 = 15228$ (the exact square is 15227.56)

Example 1.19
Find $(0.7566)^2$.

SOLUTION
First, rewrite the problem (see Section 1.16):

$$(0.7566)^2 = (7.566 \times 10^{-1})^2 = (7.566)^2 \times 10^{-2}$$

Now find $(7.566)^2$ by interpolation.

| | Number | Square |

0.6 — [7.560 ... 7.566 ... 7.570] [57.1536 ... 57.3049] — 0.1513

$$0.6 \times 0.1513 = 0.09078 \approx 0.0908$$

$$(7.566)^2 = 57.1536 + 0.0908 = 57.2444$$

$$(0.7566)^2 = 57.2444 \times 10^{-2} = 0.572\ 444 \qquad \text{(the exact square is } 0.572\ 443\ 6\text{)}$$

It should be noted that if three significant figures are adequate, the direct-reading method of Section 1.16 is preferable since it is much faster.

Example 1.20
Find $(0.7566)^2$, assuming that all work is being done to four significant figures and intermediate calculations therefore use five significant figures.

SOLUTION

$(0.7566)^2 = (7.566 \times 10^{-1})^2$

$\left.\begin{array}{l}(7.56)^2 = 57.154 \\ (7.57)^2 = 57.305\end{array}\right]$ 0.151 and $0.6 \times 0.151 \approx 0.091$

$(0.7566)^2 = (57.154 + 0.091) \times 10^{-2} = 57.245 \times 10^{-2}$

$\qquad\qquad\qquad\qquad\qquad\qquad = 0.572\,45$

Notice that the difference between this result and that of Example 1.19 is 0.00001, or 1 part in 57,000, a precision rarely needed in most calculations.

Example 1.21
Cube 6.734, giving the result to four significant figures.

SOLUTION

$\qquad(6.73)^3 = 304.82$
$\qquad\qquad\qquad\qquad\qquad$ (working to five significant figures)
$\qquad(6.74)^3 = 306.18$

$0.4 \times 1.36 \approx 0.54$

$\qquad(6.734)^3 = 304.82 + 0.54 = 305.36 = 305.4$ to four significant
$\qquad\qquad$ figures

Example 1.22
Find $\sqrt{5486} = \sqrt{5.486 \times 10^3} = \sqrt{54.86 \times 10^2} = \sqrt{54.86} \times 10.$

SOLUTION

$\qquad\sqrt{54} = 7.348$
$\qquad\qquad\qquad\qquad 0.068 \times 0.86 \approx 0.058$
$\qquad\sqrt{55} = 7.416$

$\sqrt{5486} = (7.348 + 0.058) \times 10 = 7.406 \times 10 = 74.06$

Inverse method   When the fourth significant figure is of real importance, the inverse method illustrated in Examples 1.23 and 1.24 is slightly better.

Example 1.23
Find $\sqrt{5486}$, using the inverse method of finding roots.

SOLUTION

$\sqrt{5486} = \sqrt{54.86} \times 10.$ Noting that $\sqrt{54} > 7$, use the 700 part of the table.

	Number	*Square*		
$d \times 0.01$ — $\left[\begin{array}{l}\end{array}\right.$	7.400	54.760 $\left.\right]$ —0.10		
		54.860		—0.148
	7.410	54.908		

Letting d be the required distance, expressed as a tenth of the tabulated unit, 0.01,

$$d \times 0.148 = 0.10 \quad \text{and} \quad d = \frac{0.10}{0.148} = 0.7$$

$$d \times 0.01 = 0.7 \times 0.01 = 0.007$$

$$\sqrt{54.86} = (7.40 + 0.007) = 7.407$$

$$\sqrt{5486} = 7.407 \times 10 = 74.07$$

Example 1.24

Find $\sqrt[3]{0.068\ 29}$ to four significant figures.

SOLUTION

$$\sqrt[3]{0.068\ 29} = \sqrt[3]{6.829 \times 10^{-2}} = \sqrt[3]{68.29 \times 10^{-3}}$$

Since $\sqrt[3]{68} > \sqrt[3]{64} = 4$, use the 400 part of the table.

	Number	Cube		
$d \times 0.01 \Big[$	4.08	$67.917 \Big]$	$-0.373 \Big]$	
	___	68.29		-0.500
	4.09	68.417		

$$d \times 0.500 = 0.373 \quad \text{and} \quad d = \frac{0.373}{0.500} \approx 0.7$$

$$d \times 0.01 = 0.7 \times 0.01 = 0.007$$

$$\sqrt[3]{0.06829} = (4.080 + 0.007) \times 10^{-1}$$

$$= 4.087 \times 10^{-1}$$

$$= 0.4087$$

Problem Set 1.9

Find the indicated quantity, giving all results to four significant figures and thus using five significant figures in intermediate steps. Express answers between 0.0001 *and* 999,999 *in ordinary notation; otherwise, use scientific notation.*

1–4
Find the area of a square whose side is given below. $(A = s^2.)$

1. 2468 m
2. 13,570 cm
3. 0.074 57 in.
4. 0.008 263 ft

5–8

Find the volume of a cube whose side is given below. $(V = s^3.)$

5. 3214 m

6. 55,555 cm

7. 0.098 765 ft

8. 0.008 642 1 in.

9–12

Find the side of a square whose area is given below. $(s = \sqrt{A}.)$

9. 12,406 sq cm

10. 224,060 sq m

11. 0.01241 sq ft

12. 0.022 604 sq in.

13–16

Find the side of a cube whose volume is given below. $(s = \sqrt[3]{V}.)$

13. 3333 cu m

14. 5555.5 cu cm

15. 33,333 cu in.

16. 55,555 cu ft

17–26

Calculate.

17. $\sqrt[3]{0.071\ 31}$

18. $\sqrt[3]{0.007\ 131}$

19. $\sqrt[3]{0.000\ 713\ 1}$

20. $\sqrt[3]{0.000\ 071\ 31}$

21. $\sqrt[3]{0.000\ 007\ 131}$

22. $\sqrt[3]{0.000\ 000\ 713\ 1}$

23. $\dfrac{1}{2.174}$

24. $\dfrac{1}{36.93}$

25. $\dfrac{1}{0.1245}$

26. $\dfrac{1}{0.046\ 28}$

27–30

Find the circumference and the area of a circle whose diameter is given.

27. 12.88 in.

28. 3.177 ft

29. 0.029 88 m

30. 0.000 672 8 in.

1.18 / Use of desk calculators

Today most schools and offices have some type of desk calculator. The individual makes and models are so varied that no textbook written solely for such machines could adequately explain how each one functions and is used. The actual manual prepared by the manufacturer is the best possible book.

Desk calculators generally fall into one of the following types:

(1) Low-speed 10-key printing calculator
(2) Low-speed multiple-key rotary calculator
(3) High-speed 10-key printing calculator
(4) High-speed electronic desk calculators, with fixed capabilities of executing special operations in addition to multiplication, division, and square root. These may be operations needed in surveying or statistical calculations.
(5) High-speed electronic calculators that are preprogrammed to execute fairly complex mathematical operations. As an extra feature, they can be programmed by the user to repeat a desired series of these operations. This temporary program is usually on a separate card that is inserted each time that sequence is desired. This is *not* the electronic *computer*, a much larger and much more expensive device that uses a special language between the user and the machine to transmit instructions.

Printing calculators are preferable when a great number of data are entered and the data should be checked on a printed tape. These calculators are used for quantity estimates, cost and payroll computations, and other routine office calculations.

Rotary calculators are preferable when most of the calculations are multiplications and divisions. Additions and subtractions can be readily performed but are not readily checked. Square roots and cube roots can be quickly found using the methods described below. These methods are not usually listed in the manufacturers' manuals and therefore are included here.

To Find a Square Root

(1) From a table of functions of numbers, find the nearest square smaller than the given number. If needed, use powers of 10 in multiples of 2 to handle the decimal point. Let n be the square root of this closest square.
(2) Find the difference between the original number, called N^2, and the table value, n^2.
(3) Divide the difference, $N^2 - n^2$, by twice the value of n. This is the correction which when added to n gives the first approximation to the square root.
(4) Square this approximate root on the desk calculator and see if it is close enough. If not, repeat the above steps. Usually one repetition will give the answer to any meaningful accuracy.

Example 1.25

Find the square root of $9,876,543,210 = N^2$.

SOLUTION

From a table:

$$(99300)^2 = 9,860,490,000 = n^2$$

Difference:

$$N^2 - n^2 = 16,053,210$$

Correction:

$$\frac{N^2 - n^2}{2n} = \frac{16,053,210}{2(99300)} = \frac{16,053,210}{198,600} = 80.8 = c$$

First approximation to root:

$$n + c = 99,300 + 80.8 = 99,380.8$$

Squaring:

$$(99,380.8)^2 = 9,876,543,409$$

This is usually close enough, but if greater accuracy is desired, the steps are repeated.

Difference:

$$N^2 - n^2 = 9,876,543,210 - 9,876,543,409 = -199$$

(The minus sign is important. It means that the first approximation was too large and the next correction must be subtracted.)

Correction:
$$c = \frac{-199}{198,761.6} = -0.001$$

The second (and final) approximation to the square root is 99,380.799.

Division is automatic on most desk calculators, so these large numbers are very easily handled.

To Find a Cube Root

A process similar to the square-root method is used. Use the table of numbers to find n, the table-entry number whose cube is just below the given number. At the same time, write down the value of the square, n^2. Then the correction

$$c = \frac{N^3 - n^3}{3n^2}$$

and $n + c$ is the first approximation to the cube root.

Example 1.26

Find the cube root of $9,876,543,210 = N^3$.

SOLUTION

From a table:

$$(2140)^3 = 9,800,344,000 = n^3 \qquad \text{and} \qquad n^2 = 45,796$$

Correction $\qquad c = \dfrac{9,876,543,210 - 9,800,344,000}{3(45,796)}$

$$= \dfrac{76,199,210}{13,738,800}$$

$$= 5.55$$

First approximation:

$$n + c = 2140 + 5.55 = 2145.55$$

Cubing: $\qquad (2145.55)^3 = 9,876,792,264$

Using the calculator:

$$(2145.55)^2 = 4,603,384.8025 \qquad \text{and} \qquad 3n^2 = 13,810,154$$

Second correction:

$$\dfrac{9,876,543,210 - 9,876,792,264}{13,810,154}$$

$$= \dfrac{-249,054}{13,810,154}$$

$$= -0.018$$

Second approximation:

$$N = 2145.55 - 0.018 = 2145.532$$

The high-speed machines are so completely different that no comments will be made on their use. The important concept is that the principles presented in this text must be understood in order to use these modern calculators.

1.19 / Chapter Review

1. Numbers are considered as collections called sets. The operations performed depend upon the properties of the set containing the numbers as elements.
2. Special sets of numbers are digits, integers, rational numbers, irrational numbers, real numbers, imaginary numbers, and complex numbers.

3. Positive integers are classified as odd or even and as prime or composite.
4. Decimals with a finite number of digits or with repeating digits are rational numbers. Nonterminating, nonrepeating decimals are irrational numbers.
5. In the real number system, addition and multiplication are closed, commutative, and associative. Multiplication can be distributed over addition. Every real number has an opposite, or addition inverse. Every nonzero real number has a reciprocal, or multiplication inverse.
6. Every real number has a unique location on the number line. Every point on the number line is the graph of exactly one real number, its coordinate.
7. The equality laws state that if two real numbers are equal, the results are also equal when the same quantity is added to both sides, subtracted from both sides, used as a multiplier on both sides, or used as a divisor (not 0) on both sides.
8. Counting is exact. All measurements are approximations. Calculations are usually made to three or four significant figures to yield results that match the observed data in precision.
9. Powers indicate that a factor has been used an indicated number of times to obtain a product.
   A root of a number is the factor which if used the indicated number of times yields the stated number.
10. Tables are used to simplify routine calculations. Interpolation is used to find answers in intervals between entries in a table.

Problem Set 1.10 (Chapter Review)

These review problems cover the concepts met in this chapter. No answers are given to any of these problems.

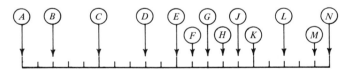

The number line shown above has 20 equal parts.

1–5

Assume that each part of the number line in the above figure represents 0.01 units and that zero is at point K.

1. What is the value for point *E*, expressed as a fraction? State if this value is larger or smaller than that for point *G*.

2. What letter represents a quantity one half of the quantity represented by point M?

3. Write in symbols a statement that set S contains the numerical values that are integers and that correspond to lettered positions on the number line. Use the listing method.

4. What is the distance from point B to point F?

5. Double the real number corresponding to point H. What point is the graph of this new quantity?

6–10

Assume that each part of the number line now represents 3 units and point C corresponds to the value zero.

6. What number and what arithmetic operation would correspond to moving an object on the number line from point M to point A?

7. What point represents the square root of 576? The cube root of 729?

8. What is the square root of the real number represented by point B?

9. List all the prime numbers that fall on this number line, including those that fall between the marked points.

10. List the largest and the smallest cube of an integer that would be plotted anywhere between point C and point N.

11–14

Using Table 1 of the Appendix, find the square, cube, square root, and cube root of each of the following numbers to four significant figures.

11. 2.13×10^4

12. 4.78×10^{-2}

13. 3.142×10^3

14. 7.891×10^{-5}

15–18

Using Table 1 of the Appendix, find the indicated values to three significant figures.

15. $(\frac{3}{8})^4$

16. $\sqrt[4]{\frac{7}{8}}$

17. $(\frac{1}{800})^6$

18. $\sqrt[6]{\frac{1}{407}}$

The slide rule

2.01 / Introduction

In 1617 the Scottish mathematician John Napier published a description of "Napier's Bones," a mechanical device Napier had invented for applying his newly discovered theory of logarithms, a work he had published three years earlier.

An English mathematician, astronomer, and surveyor, Edmund Gunter, devised the logarithmically graduated scale in 1620. There was no slide on "Gunter's Line" and distances were obtained by using a pair of dividers.

In 1622 the English mathematician William Oughtred invented the straight logarithmic slide rule. A description of this, together with that of another of his inventions, a circular slide rule, appeared in print 10 years later.

In 1850 Amédée Mannheim, an officer in the French artillery corps, was motivated by practical applications and he standardized and perfected the slide rule. Mannheim was a true engineer. He took sound mathematical principles and applied them to solve complex projectile-firing problems by a relatively simple method. The slide rule he perfected was so well planned that the basic slide rule used today is called the Mannheim type. This will be the type used for illustration in this chapter.

There are a large number of types of slide rules on the commercial market today. The three major types are the flat, rectangular type (affectionately

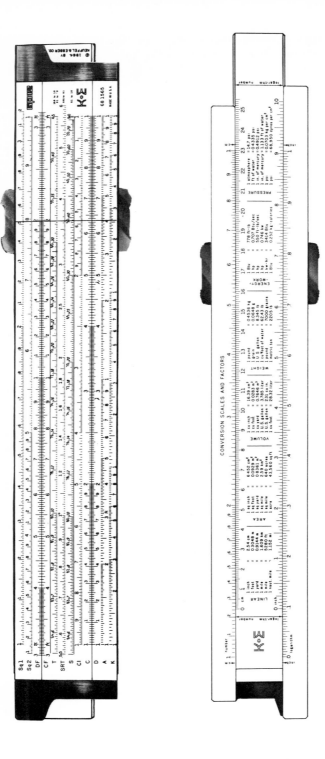

Figure 2.1
Student rule (Courtesy of Keuffel & Esser Co.)

called the "slipstick"); the circular variety; and the cylindrical or Thatcher slide rule. The electric desk calculator spelled the death of the cylindrical rule, which was the equivalent of a 480-in. flat type and could be read to five significant figures but was nonportable. The circular slide rule has its circle of admirers. It is made in two sizes, $4\frac{1}{2}$ and $8\frac{1}{2}$ in. The smaller one readily fits into a coat pocket and this is probably the reason for its popularity. The rectangular variety is still the most widely used and is available in many models. It is usually based upon a 10-in. graduated scale, although some 20-in. models are still made for office use and there are 5- to 6-in. models for pockets. These rules can be divided into five main classes according to their usage.

1. Students The student rule contains the essential scales for multiplication and division (C, D), squares, cubes, square roots, and cube roots (A, B, and K). Trigonometric scales are included. Figure 2.1 is a typical student type. The rule shown is the basic Mannheim type plus the two folded CF and DF scales.

2. Business The business rule is similar to the student rule shown in Figure 2.1 but without the trigonometric scales.

3. Limited purpose The limited-purpose rule is a manufacturer's name for a large group of slide rules that vary in the exact scales provided, but, in general, these rules provide all the scales except the log-log scales. Figure 2.2 illustrates this type.

4. General purpose The general-purpose rule is the ultimate in slide rules, usually the best of each manufacturers' price structure. It contains all scales, including the log-log, that are needed for specialized work involving higher mathematics. Figure 2.3 is an example.

5. Special purpose The special purpose rule contains the C and D scales, plus other special scales needed only in a particular profession. Some examples are the Cooke Radio rule for electronics, the stadia slide rule for surveyors, the Log-Log Duplex Vector for electrical engineering, and the Analon, devised to employ dimensional analysis, as might be met in a physics research project.

All illustrations of problems in this text are made using the Acu-Math 400, with the permission of the Acu-Rule Manufacturing Company, Division of the Sterling Plastics Company. All problems in this text can be solved on this student rule. The more expensive models do permit slightly greater speed and convenience for certain problems.

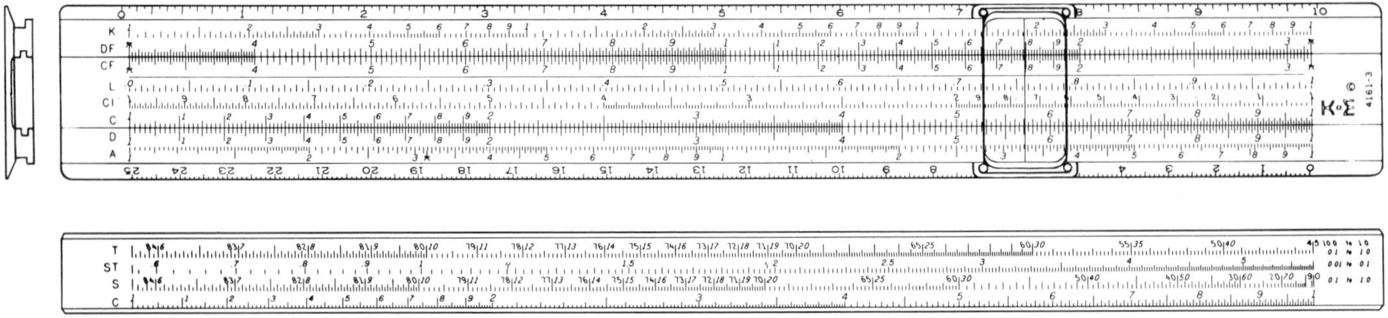

Figure 2.2
Limited-purpose rule (Courtesy of Keuffel & Esser Co.)

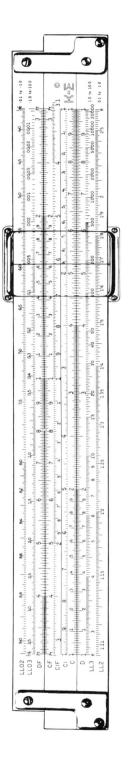

Figure 2.3
General-purpose rule
(Courtesy of Keuffel &
Esser Co.)

2.02 / Identification of parts

Referring to Figure 2.4, the two fixed parallel scales and the fastening devices at their ends constitute the **body** of the slide rule. It is sometimes called the **frame**. The movable set of scales, which can be moved either to the left or the right, is called the **slide**. The plastic or glass movable device is called the **runner**, the **indicator**, or the **cursor**. The thin black vertical line on the runner is called the **indicator hairline,** or more often just the **hairline.** In this book we shall use the terms **runner** and **hairline.**

The two basic scales for calculations are the C and D scales. They are so named on *all* slide rules, including the special-purpose rule. The D scale on the body contains two figure 1's. The one at the left end is called the **left index** and the one at the right end, the **right index.** The two indexes of the C scale are called the **left index of the slide** and the **right index of the slide.** (For the greatest understanding, the student should always use his slide rule along with the figures in the text.)

The A and B scales are similar to the C and D scales, but each contains two full sets of numbers from 1 to 10, called a **cycle,** so that these are two-cycle scales. The A scale is related to the D scale because both are on the fixed portion of the slide rule.

The letters chosen for all other scales indicate their purpose, except that, since C was already used, K was substituted for the "c" of "cube" because it has the k sound. The S and T scales are trigonometric and will be discussed in Chapter 9. The L scale is logarithmic and will be studied in Chapter 8. The CI scale is the C-Inverted scale, explained in the next section. For those owning a rule with CF and DF scales, the F signifies that the original C and D scales were folded at the value of π, or that any value on CF and DF is the product of π and the respective C or D scale value. For any other scale the manufacturer's manual should be consulted.

2.03 / Reading the scales

The scales used for arithmetic computations are the A, B, C, D, CI, and K scales. (Include the CF, DF, and CIF, if these are on your rule.) All these are based upon the one-cycle logarithmic scale and therefore are not uniformly graduated.

There is no zero on a logarithmic scale. Without regard to a decimal point, the leftmost figure 1 is simply the first significant figure. Thus, the left index can represent 1, 10, 1,000,000, or 0.0001. Symbolically, it is $1 \cdot 10^n$, which was defined in Section 1.15 as a number written in scientific notation. The cycle ends at $1 \cdot 10^{n+1}$ or the next multiple of 10. So if in a

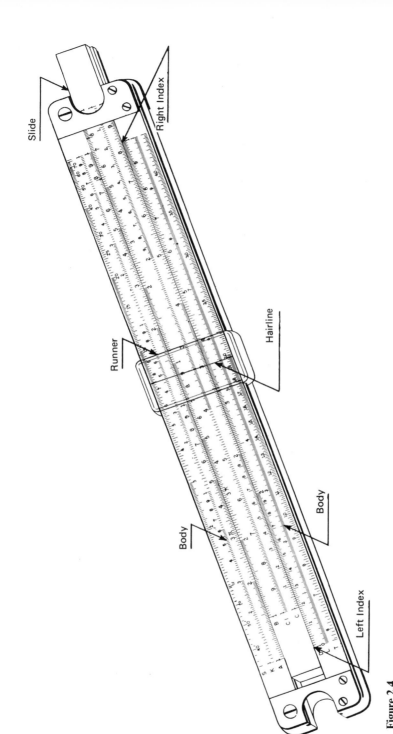

Figure 2.4
Identification of parts

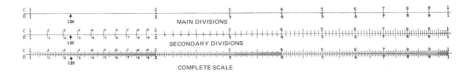

Figure 2.5
Divisions of a slide rule

given problem, the left index represents $1 \cdot 10^1$ or 10, the right index becomes $1 \cdot 10^2$, or 100. The locations of the digits between 1 and 10 are shown in Figure 2.5 as the <u>Main Divisions</u>.

The intervals between the main divisions are all tenths of the main division. On most slide rules, only the tenths between digits 1 and 2 are actually marked in numerical values, as seen in Figure 2.5, where the <u>Secondary Divisions</u> are shown.

The further subdivisions of the secondary divisions differ depending on whether the main division being read is on the left, central, or right portions of the scale. Looking at the <u>Complete Scale</u> on Figure 2.5, the secondary divisions between main divisions 1 and 2 are subdivided into 10 parts, so each small line represents 0.01 of the main division. In this figure, the left index represents 100 and the right index 1000, so the arrow is pointing to 100 plus 2 tens plus 5, or to 125. The slide rule should always be read as three significant digits, with a decimal point assigned later.

From main division 2 to main division 4, the secondary divisions are all divided into five parts, reading directly to 0.02 main division units, and the interval between ruled divisions is easily interpolated so that the third digit can be accurately read to 0.01 unit. Figure 2.6 has the hairline set to 232 (on the C and D scales).

Figure 2.6
Subdivisions of a slide rule between 2 and 4

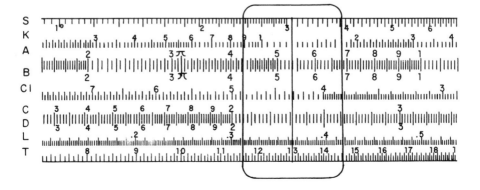

From main division 4 to the right index all secondary divisions are divided into 2 parts, reading directly to 0.05 main division units. From main division 4 to main division 7, it is possible to estimate the third digit with an accuracy of ± 0.01 main division unit. From 7 to the right index, the third digit can be estimated to an accuracy of ± 0.02 main division unit. In Figure 2.7, assuming that the left index has a value of 1.0, the D scale reading is 1.404 ± 0.002. (Individual readings may vary from 1.402 to 1.406, depending on the observer's experience.) Only between 1 and 2 can a fourth significant figure be read. Whether the fourth significant figure should be recorded depends upon the actual problem. If other answers found were in thousandths, such as 0.987 and 0.752, the fourth significant figure is in agreement and can be retained. The C-scale reading in Figure 2.7 is 6.64 ± 0.01, again assuming that the left index has a value of 1.0.

Everything that has been said about scale subdivisions applies to all the *one*-cycle scales: C, D, CI, CF, DF, and CIF. On the CI scale, the scale is inverted. In other words, the CI scale is the C scale reversed, with the main divisions increasing from *right to left*. The CF and DF scales have only one index near the middle, but are read exactly as the C and D scales are.

The A and B scales are two-cycle scales and the K scale is a three-cycle scale. Therefore, less inches are available for each cycle and fewer subdivisions can be expected. However, the subdivisions are always in units of 1, 2, or 5. On the two-cycle A and B scales, there are no subdivisions of the secondary divisions after main division 5. On the three-cycle K scale, there are none after main division 3. In most cases three significant digits can be estimated but with a lowered accuracy. The exception is on the K scale, where only two significant digits should be recorded for numbers beyond main division 6.

For practice in reading slide-rule scales, problems involving reading the L scale are included, because the answers are just numbers. This is the only

Figure 2.7
Subdivisions of a slide rule beyond 4

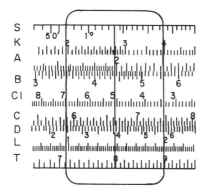

scale on the slide rule that has a decimal point and the scale is uniformly graduated. The readings cover the values 0.000 to 1.000, all readings being direct to three decimal places. Subdivisions are uniform along the entire scale, each line representing 0.002. It is best to read the major division, the nearest secondary division, and then the third digit. Using Figure 2.6, the reading on the L scale is 0.365.

This section may seem somewhat overwhelming at first reading, but if a slide rule is brought to class every day and all possible problems solved on it, everything said here becomes an automatic reflex. Your eye will look at the scale divisions in the area to be read and automatically the proper method of reading the scale will come to your conscious mind. It is very similar to learning to drive a car. The first few trips are frightening, but in a few days you steer and brake without apparent effort.

2.04 / Accuracy

As the ability to estimate the third significant figure on the C and D scales was developed in the previous section, it was shown that the least accurate readings occurred between main division 7 and the right index, where the third digit might be in error by 2 units of the value. Thus, a reading of 702, might be 701, 702, 703, or 704. The values 700 and 705 are marked values and can be read accurately. Accordingly, the maximum error would be 2 parts in 700, or 0.3 per cent. The remainder of the slide rule is read accurately to 0.1 per cent, so for a single overall figure, it is said that the slide rule is accurate to 0.2 per cent. Section 1.10 indicated that if the original data are correct to three significant figures, a slide rule is quite adequate.

There is a tendency for some poorly trained personnel to say "slide-rule accuracy" as an excuse for a poor answer. It is true that if numbers are not carefully aligned and results are not carefully read, an appreciable error can develop. But equally poor results can be achieved by the careless use of any calculating device. This chapter is purposely the second in the book, to relieve the student from arithmetic drudgery. The slide rule is quick and it is accurate when properly used.

2.05 / Multiplication

By using the logarithmically graduated scales, the multiplication of two or more factors is changed to a process of addition. The thinking is identical to the method used to draw a 9-in. line if only a 6-in. ruler is available. On a given straight line, a 6-in. interval would be marked. Then an additional 3-in. interval would be marked, starting at the end of the 6-in. interval.

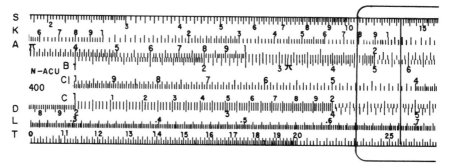

Figure 2.8
Multiplication using left index of slide

Figure 2.8 illustrates this method of addition for the problem 2(24) = 48. The left index of the slide is set over the first factor, 2, on the D scale. The runner is then moved to set the hairline on the second factor, 24, on the C scale. The product is the distance (sum) from the starting point, the left index of D, to the hairline and is read as 480. By inspection, the answer should be near 50, so a decimal point is introduced to give the answer as 48.0.

When the slide rule is positioned as shown in Figure 2.8, 50 on the C scale is over the right index of D since 2(50) = 100. If the second factor had been 63, that number on the C scale is off the D scale. In this case the *right* index of the slide is set over the first factor 2, as shown in Figure 2.9. The remaining procedure is identical; the hairline is set to the second factor 63 on C and the product 126 is read on D. The choice of the proper slide index to use can be made by estimating the answer. Should the wrong index be chosen, simply start the problem again using the other index.

Figure 2.9
Multiplication using right index of slide

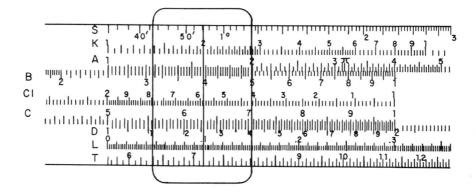

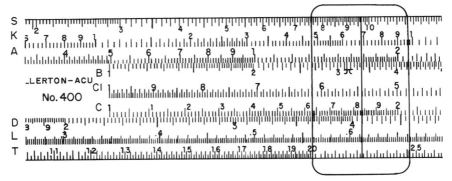

Figure 2.10
Use of a constant multiplier

Some problems involve multiplication by a constant. The procedure is illustrated in Example 2.1.

Example 2.1

One dollar at $5\frac{1}{2}$ per cent compound interest is worth $2.2324765 at the end of 15 years. Find the value at the end of 15 years if the original amount was (a) $1.84; (b) $302; (c) $3680; (d) $10,500.

SOLUTION[1]

(1) Round off the constant factor to 2.23 and set the left index of the slide to this value. (See Figure 2.10.)

(2) Move the hairline to each value of the original amount on C.

(3) Read the future values at the hairline on D.

For (a) shown on Figure 2.10, read 410. By inspection the correct answer is $4.10.

For (b) under 302, read 668 and record $668.

For (c) under 368, read 821 and record $8210.

For (d) under 105, read 234 and record $23,400.

For (d) the location of the decimal point will also be calculated by use of scientific notation. The problem is first rewritten using two significant figures and separating all powers of 10 and placing them on the right to give

$$(2.2)(1.1) \cdot (10^0)(10^4)$$

---

[1] For the remainder of this chapter, the following simplifications will be made:

(1) The word "scale" will be omitted when referring to the A, B, C, D, etc., scales.

(2) "Move the hairline to . . ." will replace "Move the runner so that the hairline is at . . . ."

(3) "Set xxx on C over . . ." will replace "Move the slide so that xxx is over . . . ."

When the factors are multiplied, the exponents of 10 are added. This produces the product

$$2.4 \cdot 10^4 = 24,000$$

Problem Set 2.1

1–8

Prepare a table of answers similar to the sample shown here.

PROBLEM	SCALE				
	A	C	CI	K	L
1.					
2.					
3.					
etc.					

Read the indicated settings on the slide rule and write all the answers to three significant figures. Assume that the left index of the A, C, and K scales is 1.00. Every additional cycle present starts with the next power of 10. The left index of the CI scale is 10 and the values decrease to the right.

1 and 2.

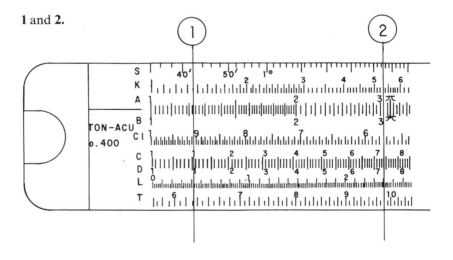

3 and 4.

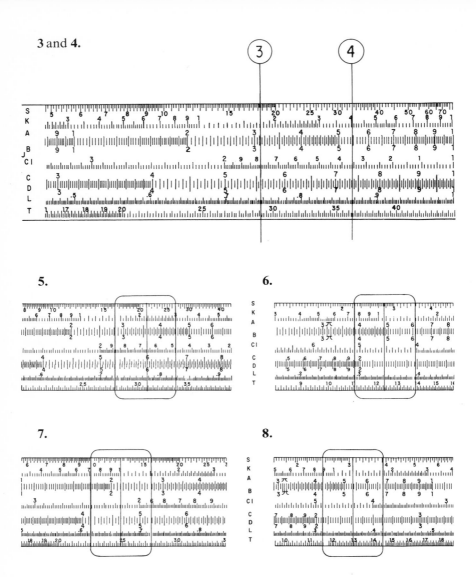

5.

6.

7.

8.

9. Set the left index of C to 1.50 on D. Move the runner so that the hairline is at 3.00 on C. Record the readings on K, A, B, CI, and D.

10. Set the right index of C to 8.25 on D. Move the runner so the hairline is at 6.00 on C. Record the readings on K, A, B, CI, and D.

11–40

Write the answer in scientific notation if the value is 100,000 *or greater, or less than* 0.0001. *Otherwise, write in ordinary decimal notation.* (*Do not forget the initial zero on numbers smaller than* 1.)

11–20

Multiply the two given factors and write the answer to three significant digits.

11. (170)(2.40)   **16.** (29,400)(31,500)
12. (230)(4.20)   **17.** (0.0149)(0.565)
13. (122)(7.50)   **18.** (0.213)(0.0435)
14. (189)(4.60)   **19.** (0.00830)(0.0812)
15. (2450)(37,500)   **20.** (0.0762)(0.00915)

21–30

One mile is approximately 1.61 k. *Find the number of kilometers for the number of miles listed below.*

21. 3.1   **25.** 36.7   **29.** $\frac{1}{2}$
22. 4.1   **26.** 39.7   **30.** $\frac{1}{4}$
23. 1.81   **27.** 647
24. 1.43   **28.** 7470

31–40

A gallon of water weighs 8.345 lb. *Find the total weight of a container that weighs* 10 lb *empty if filled with the given gallonage of water.*

31. 110   **35.** 34.2   **39.** $\frac{1}{4}$
32. 11.9   **36.** 27.9   **40.** $\frac{1}{8}$
33. 6.10   **37.** 0.817
34. 74.0   **38.** 0.972

2.06 / Division

By the use of logarithmically graduated scales, division is changed to the process of subtraction. As in computational arithmetic, division is the inverse operation to multiplication and is performed by changing the sequence of steps. Figure 2.11 indicates the steps in dividing 48 by 2. The number to be divided, the dividend, is located by moving the hairline to 48 on D. The divisor 2 on C is aligned with the hairline by moving the slide. One index of C will always be on D—in this problem, the left index—and the value on D at that index is the quotient 24. Notice that if Figure 2.11 was shown without an explanation, it would not be possible to state whether it was illustrating $\frac{48}{2} = 24$ or 2(24) = 48. Figure 2.12 is a similar illustration of a simple division, $\frac{48}{6} = 8$, but here the right-hand index is available and the answer read below it on D.

Decimal points are handled as in multiplication, by estimating for simple problems and by using scientific notation for complex ones. For problems

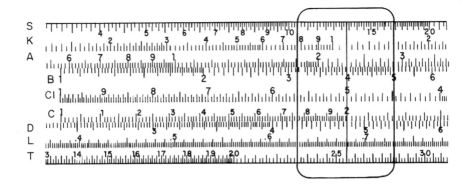

Figure 2.11
Division with result under left index of slide

in division, the sum of the exponents of 10 in the denominator have their sign changed and are added to the sum of the exponents in the numerator.

Division by a constant is a common problem met in finding the percentage composition of compounds and alloys and in related problems. There exists an interesting method of solution not often mentioned in slide-rule manuals. Since division is the same as multiplication by the reciprocal of the divisor, the slide rule is positioned to compute the reciprocal, but the value *is not read*. Instead the remainder of the problem is treated as multiplication by a constant (the unread value) and the hairline moved to successive positions for each dividend.

Figure 2.12
Division with result under right index of slide

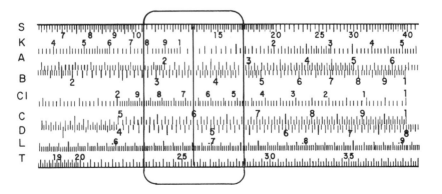

Figure 2.13
Use of a constant divisor

Example 2.2

Change the given areas in square inches to square feet: (a) 8.41;
(b) 165; (c) 2470; (d) 57,200.

SOLUTION

(1) The constant divisor is 144, since 144 sq in. = 1 sq ft. Select the
index of D closest to the divisor, in this case, the left index. (For
all numbers whose significant digits are 315 or less, the index will
be the left index.) Set the divisor 144 directly over the index as
shown in Figure 2.13. Notice that the value of the reciprocal
$\frac{1}{144}$ is not visible in the illustration, but this value, actually
0.00694, is not needed.

(2) Move the hairline to 841 on C. The product of the reciprocal
and 841 is read on D as 583.

(3) To find the decimal point by estimation, write $\frac{8}{160} = \frac{1}{20} = 0.05$.
The answer is therefore 0.0583 sq ft. To find the decimal point
by scientific notation, rewrite the problem as

$$\frac{8.41}{144} \approx \frac{8}{1.6} \cdot \frac{10^0}{10^2} \approx 5 \cdot 10^{-2} = 0.05$$

Thus, the answer is 0.0583 sq ft.

Moving the hairline to the three remaining values of the dividends gives
(b) 1.15 sq ft; (c) 17.1 sq ft; (d) 397 sq ft. Check these values on your slide
rule.

Example 2.3

Find the volume in cubic feet, given the following volumes in
cubic inches: (a) 113; (b) 1670; (c) 12,400; (d) 27,200.

SOLUTION

(1) Since there are 1728 cu in. in 1 cu ft, the constant divisor is
1728, and since it is less than 315, the left index of D would
normally be used. But here three of the given dividends are
less than the constant divisor (without regard to decimal point).
When this occurs, the other index is used for these three values.
Part (d) of this example is a regular division problem and is
done as shown in Example 2.2. Should the dividends be about
equally grouped above and below the constant divisor, simply
use both indexes.
Therefore, 1728 is set over the right index as shown in Figure
2.14. The value of the reciprocal is visible but is not read.

(2) Move the hairline to the value of the first dividend 113 on C.

(3) Read the quotient on D at the hairline as 654.

(4) Find the decimal point by estimation: Write $\frac{100}{2000} = 0.05$.
Therefore, the answer is 0.0654 cu ft.

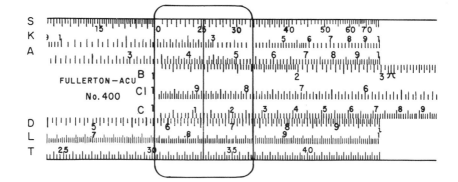

Figure 2.14
Use of a constant divisor and right index

Moving the hairline to the other two dividends gives (b) 0.965 cu ft and
(c) 7.17 cu ft. Dividing 272 by 173 gives (d) 15.7 cu ft.

Problem Set 2.2

*For all problems in this set, give your answer in scientific notation when the
number is 100,000 or larger, or when smaller than 0.0001.*

1. $\dfrac{145}{148}$

2. $\dfrac{247}{261}$

3. $\dfrac{7.47}{39,100}$

4. $\dfrac{0.816}{4770}$

5. $\dfrac{27.6}{0.000\,371}$

6. $\dfrac{0.197}{0.000\,927}$

7. $\dfrac{0.003\,77}{21,500}$

8. $\dfrac{0.002\,89}{8747}$

9. $\dfrac{5670}{\frac{1}{2}}$

10. $\dfrac{0.611}{\frac{1}{4}}$

11–20
*In the United States gasoline is sold by the gallon and in Europe by the liter,
where 3.785 liters equal 1 U.S. gal. Find the number of gallons bought if the
gas pump at a European service station reads in liters:*

11. 40

12. 60

13. 55

14. 75

15. 19

16. 17

17. 12.5   **19.** 22.1

18. 31.7   **20.** 44.4

21. A 1025-g sample of a metallic alloy is analyzed and the following report of its elements given. Find the percentage composition of the alloy, correct to the nearest one-tenth of 1 per cent.

lead	339 g	vanadium	144 g
copper	250 g	antimony	55 g
tin	200 g	bismuth	37 g

22. A commercial vitamin pill on the market contains the following list of ingredients, all weights being in milligrams (mg). Record results correct to the nearest 0.01 per cent.

vitamin A	1.5	vitamin B6	0.5
vitamin C	50.0	vitamin B12	0.002
vitamin D	0.01	niacinamide	20.0
vitamin B1	3.0	calcium pantothenate	5.0
vitamin B2	2.5		

(a) Find the percentage of each in one pill.
(b) What did you record for the B12 percentage? (*Hint:* The smallest amount of rain recorded on a rain gauge is 0.01 in. Sometimes a rain lasts only a minute or two and no rain is recorded on the gauge. What do they put in the daily weather report when this happens?)

2.07 / Combined operations

There are many problems involving both multiplication and division. The outstanding feature of a slide rule, unlike a desk calculator, is that these multiple steps can be performed without ever stopping to read an intermediate answer.

Example 2.4
Find the area of a 17 by 19 in. rectangle in square feet.

SOLUTION

The problem is $\dfrac{17(19)}{144}$. Habitually start all problems in combined operations with a division. Starting with a division will always save one shift of the slide.

(1) Set 144 on C over 170 on D. (For two-digit numbers, use of the runner is optional. It can be used until greater familiarity with scale reading is reached.)

(2) Move the hairline to 19 on C.

(3) Read the answer, 224, on D.

(4) Find the decimal point by estimation, and write the answer, 2.24 sq ft.

(*Note:* Try multiplying 17 by 19 and then dividing that product by 144. The product is not read. The hairline is merely moved to 19 on C. But to perform the division by 144, a *second* movement of the slide is needed. The answer of 224 is read on D under the left index of the slide. Remember: *Division is the first step.*)

Example 2.5

Find $\dfrac{21(142)}{33}$.

SOLUTION

The first operation is the division of 21 by 33. When the second step is attempted, 142 on C is off the scale. There are two possibilities:

(1) If you have the simple Mannheim-type rule, move the hairline to the right index of the slide. Move the slide so that its left index is at the hairline. Now 142 on C is available and the answer 90.4 is read on D.

(2) If your slide rule has CF and DF scales, read the answer on DF by moving the hairline to 142 on CF.

(The manual provided by the manufacturer will describe these scales in detail.)

This process is called **reversal of indexes.**

In more complex problems the decimal point can still be found either by "roughing out" the problem or by using scientific notation. For roughing out, reduction by division is recommended to obtain smaller numbers. However, do not reduce the given factors for the actual slide-rule work. In Example 2.6 it is no more difficult to divide by 792 than by 198, and dividing the numerator and denominator by 4 may introduce an accidental error.

Example 2.6

Find $\dfrac{0.04(2.24)(0.841)}{792(685)(81.2)}$.

SOLUTION

(1) Set 792 on C over 4 on D.

(2) Move the hairline to 224 on C.

(3) Set 685 on C at the hairline.

(4) Move the hairline to 841 on C.

(5) Set 812 on C at the hairline.

(6) Read the answer on D at the right index of slide as 171.

(7) (a) To find the decimal point by roughing out, simplify each set of fractions:

$$\frac{0.04}{792} \cdot \frac{2.24}{685} \cdot \frac{0.841}{81.2} \approx \frac{1}{19,800} \cdot \frac{1}{300} \cdot \frac{1}{100}$$

$$\approx \frac{1}{20,000} \cdot \frac{1}{30,000}$$

$$\approx \frac{1}{6 \cdot 10^8}$$

Answer $= 0.171 \cdot 10^{-8} = 1.71 \cdot 10^{-9}$.

(b) To find the decimal point by using scientific notation, each factor is rewritten with the numerical portion on the left and the power of 10 on the right:

$$\frac{4.0(2.24)(8.41)}{7.92(6.85)(8.12)} \cdot \frac{10^{-2+0-1}}{10^{2+2+1}} \approx \frac{1}{2} \cdot \frac{1}{3} \cdot 1 \cdot 10^{-3-5}$$

$$\approx \frac{1}{6} \cdot 10^{-8}$$

Applying the two rules for multiplication and addition, all the exponents in the numerator were added, giving -3, and the exponents in the denominator were added, giving $+5$. The sign of $+5$ was changed, and -5 added to -3 gave -8, the resulting exponent.

Example 2.7

Find $\dfrac{3.17(16,400)(6820)}{5.65(0.0598)}$

SOLUTION

(1) Move the hairline to 317 on D.

(2) Set 565 on C to the hairline.

(3) LOOK! 164 is off the scale but 682 is not. Move the hairline to 682 on C.

(4) Set 598 on C to the hairline.

(5) Move the hairline to 164 on C.

(6) Read the answer, 105, on D at the hairline.

(7) To find the decimal point, rewrite the problem:

$$\frac{3.17(1.64)(6.82)}{5.65(5.98)} \cdot \frac{10^{0+4+3}}{10^{0-2}} \approx 0.6(2) \cdot 10^{7+2}$$

$$\approx 1.2 \cdot 10^9$$

Thus, the answer is $1.05 \cdot 10^9$.

Problem Set 2.3

For all problems, use scientific notation for your answer if the number is larger than 100,000 or smaller than 0.0001. Locate all decimal points by the scientific-notation method. Show this work, including all steps used. For answers between 1 and 2 main divisions, use four significant figures.

1. $\dfrac{125(775)}{175}$

2. $\dfrac{342(548)}{460}$

3. $\dfrac{745(0.002\ 48)}{6.25}$

4. $\dfrac{5.95(0.004\ 38)}{0.0323}$

5. $\dfrac{5420(74,500)}{0.003\ 52}$

6. $\dfrac{21,400(15,400)}{0.000\ 361}$

7. $\dfrac{49.5(69.3)(845)}{8.35(39.2)}$

8. $\dfrac{6.94(55.5)(10.9)}{44.6(731)}$

9. $\dfrac{0.0241(0.199)(0.0410)}{292(7150)}$

10. $\dfrac{0.006\ 15(1.54)(0.0022)}{5740(4440)}$

11. $\dfrac{3.17(7.64)(44.7)}{52.2(2.53)(8.20)}$

12. $\dfrac{411(5.38)(61.9)}{2.25(771)(111)}$

13. $\dfrac{8.05(41.4)(203)}{0.632(0.0395)(0.009\ 04)}$

14. $\dfrac{92.7(519)(7220)}{0.0844(0.004\ 73)(0.435)}$

15. $\dfrac{6.59(6.64)(1.76)}{4840(37,600)(8450)}$

16. $\dfrac{0.831(0.419)(0.524)}{53,000(29,800)(182)}$

17. $\dfrac{9.22(0.466)(20.7)(35.0)}{5.72(0.395)(9.26)}$

18. $\dfrac{71.3(619)(0.0344)(1.05)}{9.58(1830)(0.0732)}$

19. $\dfrac{742(911)(546)(944)}{0.622(0.0815)(0.573)}$

20. $\dfrac{1.86(1.59)(0.714)(25,200)}{3.28(5530)(3.11)}$

2.08 / The CI scale

As previously mentioned in the discussion of scale reading, the CI scale is the C scale reversed, or the C-inverted scale. It is called inverted because every value of the CI scale is the value of $1/C$, the reciprocal of C. If the left indexes of C and D are matched, CI gives the value of the reciprocal for either C or D. This is the best position for the direct reading of reciprocals.

Example 2.8
Resistances in parallel equal a resistance given by

$$(1) \ \frac{1}{R} = \frac{1}{R_1} + \frac{1}{R_2} \qquad \text{or} \qquad (2) \ R = \frac{R_1 R_2}{R_1 + R_2}$$

Find the total resistance if $R_1 = 2$ ohms (Ω) and $R_2 = 5 \ \Omega$.

SOLUTION
(a) By arithmetic,

$$R = \frac{2(5)}{2 + 5} = \frac{10}{7} = 1.428 \ \Omega \ [\text{using formula (2)}]$$

(b) By slide rule,

$$\frac{1}{R} = \frac{1}{2} + \frac{1}{5} \ [\text{using formula (1)}]$$

Under 2 on CI read 0.5 on C.
Under 5 on CI read 0.2 on C:

$$\text{sum} = 0.7$$

Over 0.7 on C, read 1.428 Ω on CI.

The reciprocal slide-rule method works for any number of resistances (that is, $1/R = 1/R_1 + 1/R_2 + \cdots + 1/R_n$). However, formula (2) is valid for only two resistances.

A most important use of the CI scale occurs in problems involving several multiplications, divisions, or both. If the problem is a series of multiplications, then, since the general principle of combined operations is to start with a division, the first step is to divide by a reciprocal of a factor. The basic idea involved is illustrated by the example $4 \times 2 = 4 \div \frac{1}{2}$.

Multiplying by a number on the CI scale is the same as dividing by that same number on the C scale.

Dividing by a number on the CI scale is the same as multiplying by that same number on the C scale.

Example 2.9
Multiply: $120(0.4)(72.8)(2.17)(92.5)$.

SOLUTION
(1) Start with a division: Set 4 on CI over 120 on D. (See Figure 2.15.)
(2) Move the hairline to 728 on C.
(3) Set 217 on CI to the hairline.
(4) Move the hairline to 925 on C.
(5) Read 700 on D at the hairline.
(6) Estimating the decimal point, the answer is 700,000, written $7.00 \cdot 10^5$.

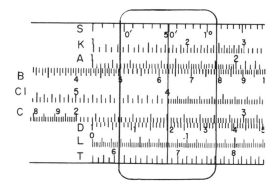

Figure 2.15
Use of CI scale for a series of multiplications

Example 2.10

Find $\dfrac{2.72}{6.09(0.405)(3.02)(0.177)}$.

SOLUTION
(1) Start with a division; set 609 on C over 272 on D.
(2) The rule is positioned to multiply, so multiply by the reciprocal of the next divisor; move the hairline to 405 on CI.
(3) Set 302 on C to the hairline.
(4) Move the hairline to 177 on CI.
(5) Read the answer 206 on D.
(6) Find the decimal point:

$$\frac{3}{6(4)(3)(2)} \cdot \frac{10^0}{10^{0-1+0-1}} \approx \frac{1}{48} \cdot 10^2 \approx 2.00$$

Thus, the answer is 2.06.

For a problem in combined operations there may be an excess of factors in either the numerator or the denominator. The procedure outlined in Section 2.07 required only the C and D scales if the number of factors in the numerator and denominator is alike or if the numerator had an excess of one factor. If the denominator has any excess or if the numerator has an excess of more than one factor, the CI scale is used.

Example 2.11

Find $\dfrac{54.5(627)}{724(73.7)(400)}$.

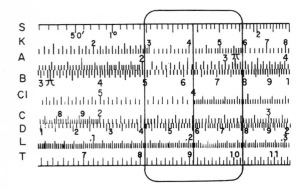

Figure 2.16
Use of CI scale for excess divisors

SOLUTION
(1) Set 724 on C over 545 on D.
(2) Move the hairline to 627 on C.
(3) Set 737 on C to the hairline.
(4) The rule is ready for a multiplication, but a division remains. Use CI scale and multiply by the reciprocal of the last factor in the denominator: move the hairline to 400 on CI. (See Figure 2.16.)
(5) Read the answer, 160, on D at the hairline.
(6) Find the decimal point:

$$\frac{50(600)}{700(75)(400)} = \frac{1}{700} \approx 0.0015$$

Thus, the answer is 0.00160.

For all problems with multiple factors, it is wise to check off each factor as it is used with a plainly visible checkmark. This is particularly important in problems where the factors may not be taken in order.

Problem Set 2.4

By proper use of the CI scale, do all problems without resorting to reversal of indexes.

1. 2.5 (4.6)(8.7)(5.3)

2. 645 (2.28)(6.45)(44.7)

3. 3.33 (51.2)(0.0685)(5.22)

4. 4.27 (615)(0.0552)(0.0343)

5. $\dfrac{8.72}{9.45\ (5.74)(4.37)(2.42)(9.55)}$

6. $\dfrac{5.72}{7.32\ (39.8)(5.75)(29.2)(2.09)}$

7. $\dfrac{1.77}{6.88\ (5.42)(7.75)(1.44)(3.17)}$

8. $\dfrac{745}{2.88\ (1.75)(2.49)(0.545)(0.0837)}$

9. $\dfrac{7.97\ (4.18)}{5.72\ (9.44)(5.59)}$

10. $\dfrac{9.14\ (50.8)}{7.91\ (6.21)(0.0438)}$

11. $\dfrac{8.25\ (303)(1.65)(54.7)}{0.637\ (0.0698)}$

12. $\dfrac{64.2\ (844)(7450)(18,400)}{7.25\ (5.28)}$

13. $\dfrac{5.42\ (1.21)}{6.95\ (595)(295)(1740)}$

14. $\dfrac{4.27\ (5.65)}{2.11\ (8.55)(0.495)(0.0726)}$

15. $\dfrac{5.17\ (6.27)(5.48)}{3.16\ (34.7)}$

16. $\dfrac{0.0622\ (754)(58.2)}{0.442\ (0.0893)}$

2.09 / Squares and cubes

Squares

Just as the use of logarithmically graduated scales permitted multiplication to be performed by an addition on that scale, the arithmetic operation of squaring or cubing a number is performed by a multiplication. Graphically, multiplication can be accomplished by a change of scale. If the C scale represents all numbers from 1 to 10, a C^2 scale would represent all numbers from 1 to 100 (1^2 to 10^2). Thus, if the same space allocated to the C scale is subdivided into two C scales (two cycles identical to each other), the task has been accomplished. This is the B scale. The A scale, which is identical to the B scale, but fixed, matches the fixed D scale. The A–D scale combination permits the direct reading of squares. The decimal point is best found by using scientific notation with the exponent of 10 being multiplied by 2. The two halves of A (or B) are not read alike. The left half represents numbers from 1 to 10; the right half represents numbers from 10 to 100.

Example 2.12
Find the square of 20.

SOLUTION
(1) Move the hairline to 200 on D.
(2) Read 4.0 on A. (See Figure 2.17.)
(3) Find the decimal point:

$$(20)^2 = (2.00 \cdot 10^1)^2 = 4.00 \cdot 10^2 = 400$$

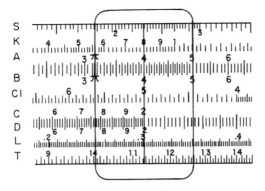

Figure 2.17
Squares and cubes in first cycle of A and K scales

Example 2.13
Find the square of 0.35.

SOLUTION
(1) Move the hairline to 350 on D.
(2) Read 12.25 on A. (See Figure 2.18.)
(3) Find the decimal point:

$$(0.35)^2 = (3.5 \cdot 10^{-1})^2 = 12.25 \cdot 10^{-2} = 0.1225$$

Note that $12.25 \cdot 10^{-2} = 1.225 \cdot 10^{-1}$.

The B scale is used in problems where, after the square has been obtained, it is desired to perform multiplications or divisions. As with other combined operations, the square is not read; only the final answer is read.

Figure 2.18
Squares and cubes in subsequent cycles of A and K scales

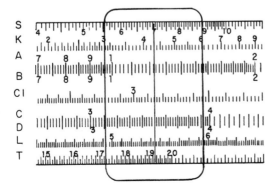

Example 2.14

Find the area of a circle with a radius of 0.157 ft (a) in square feet and (b) in square inches. The area is πr^2.

SOLUTION

(1) Move the hairline to 157 on D.
(2) Set the middle index on B to the hairline.
(3) Move the hairline to the value of π (3.14) on B.
(4) Read the answer to (a) on A as 0.0773 sq ft (decimal point by inspection).

(*Note:* On the Acu-Math slide rule, π is marked on the left B scale; if the π mark is to be used, the left index must be used. Use of the middle index ensures that a full cycle will be available.)

(5) For (b) transfer 773 to the D scale, setting the hairline to that value.
(6) Set 144 on CI to the hairline.
(7) Read the answer at the left index of scale on D as 11.1 sq in.

(*Note:* Using the CI scale saves one step.)

Cubes

Finding cubes is similar to finding squares. The K scale has three cycles, so an answer falling on the left cycle is recorded between 1 and 10, on the middle cycle between 10 and 100, and on the right cycle between 100 and 1000. Scientific notation is again used to locate the decimal point.

Example 2.15

Find the cube of 200. (See Figure 2.17.)

SOLUTION

(1) Move the hairline to 200 on D.
(2) Read the answer, 8, on K.
(3) Find the decimal point:

$$(200)^3 = (2.00 \cdot 10^2)^3 = 8 \cdot 10^6$$

Example 2.16

Find the cube of 0.35. (See Figure 2.18.)

SOLUTION

(1) Move the hairline to 350 on D.
(2) Read the answer, 42.9, on K.
(3) Find the decimal point:

$$(0.35)^3 = (3.5 \cdot 10^{-1})^3 = 42.9 \cdot 10^{-3} = 4.29 \cdot 10^{-2} = 0.0429$$

Powers higher than the cube are not common in engineering. As shown in Chapter 1, fourth powers can be obtained by squaring the square and sixth powers by cubing the square or squaring the cube.

Problem Set 2.5

1–10
Find the indicated power. Show how the decimal point was determined.

1. $(4.9)^2$	**5.** $(0.0522)^2$	**9.** $(0.00714)^3$
2. $(6.3)^2$	**6.** $(0.00745)^2$	**10.** $(0.00821)^3$
3. $(12.2)^2$	**7.** $(2.61)^3$	
4. $(27.5)^2$	**8.** $(3.87)^3$	

11–16
Find the area in square inches of the circle whose radius is given.

11. 0.642 in.	**13.** 31.7 in.	**15.** 8 ft $5\frac{1}{2}$ in.
12. 0.867 in.	**14.** 55.4 in.	**16.** 12 ft $1\frac{1}{4}$ in.

17–20
Find the volume in cubic inches of a cube having one edge of the given length.
$(V = s^3.)$

17. 0.75 in.	**19.** 3.68 in.
18. 0.88 in.	**20.** 6.82 in.

2.10 / Square roots

Roots were introduced in Section 1.14 and the methods for finding them from tables was explained in some detail. This is the best method, but tables may not be available, whereas a slide rule is highly portable. Finding square roots is simple on the slide rule, the only drawback being that only three significant figures can be found. The first step is to point off the given number, as in Section 1.16. If the leftmost group contains only one digit, the left cycle of A is used. If this group contains two digits, the right cycle of A is used. The hairline is set to the given number on the proper cycle of A and square root is read on D. The pointing off also locates the decimal point, with the three significant figures read being placed over the three leftmost groups.

Example 2.17
Find the square root of 36017.9. (See Figure 2.19.)

SOLUTION
(1) Round off the given number to three significant figures: 36000.

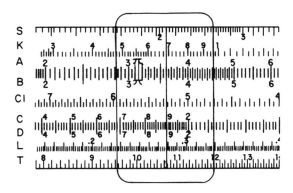

Figure 2.19
Square root using left cycle of A scale

(2) Point off in pairs from the decimal point:

$$\begin{array}{c} \text{x x x.} \qquad \text{(answer)} \\ \sqrt{3'60'00.} \qquad \text{(given number)} \end{array}$$

(3) Move the hairline to 360 on the *left* cycle of A.
(4) Read the answer, 190, on D. (Note that the decimal point was found in step 2.)

Example 2.18
Find the square root of 0.003 601 79. (See Figure 2.20.)

SOLUTION
(1) Round off the given number to three significant figures: 0.003 60.

Figure 2.20
Square root using right cycle of A scale

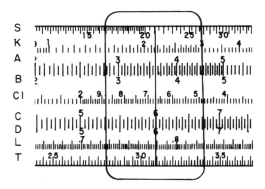

(2) Point off in pairs from the decimal point:

$$. \; \text{x} \; \text{x} \; \text{x} \qquad \text{(answer)}$$
$$\sqrt{0.00'36'00} \qquad \text{(given number)}$$

(3) Move the hairline to 360 on the *right* cycle of A.
(4) Read the answer, 0.060, on D. (Note that the decimal point was found in step 2.)

It should be noted in Example 2.18 that for every pair of zeros before the first significant figure, one zero is obtained in the answer. It should also be remembered that roots of numbers smaller than 1 are always larger than the given number.

2.11 / Cube roots

The process for cube roots is very similar to that for square roots. Pointing off in triplets from the decimal point not only locates the decimal point but also determines which cycle of K should be used. One digit in the leftmost group indicates that the left cycle of K should be used, two digits in this group indicates that the middle cycle should be used, and three digits in this group indicates that the right cycle should be used. The next three examples will show how each of these cycles of K is used.

Example 2.19
Find the cube root of 2.16. (See Figure 2.21.)

SOLUTION
(1) Point off in triplets from the decimal point:

$$\text{x.} \; \; \text{x} \; \; \text{x} \qquad \text{(answer)}$$
$$\sqrt[3]{2.160'000'} \qquad \text{(given number)}$$

Figure 2.21
Cube root using left cycle of K scale

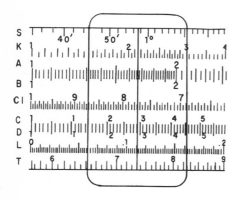

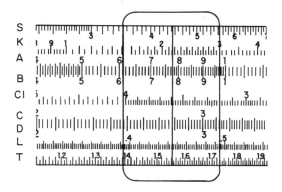

Figure 2.22
Cube root using middle cycle of K scale

(2) Move the hairline to 216 on the *left* cycle of K.
(3) Read the answer, 1.29, on D.

Example 2.20
Find the cube root of 21,600,000. (See Figure 2.22.)

SOLUTION
(1) Point off in triplets from the decimal point:

$$\begin{array}{ccc} x & x & x. \end{array} \quad \text{(answer)}$$
$$\sqrt[3]{21'600'000.} \quad \text{(given number)}$$

(2) Move the hairline to 216 on the *middle* cycle.
(3) Read the answer, 278, on D.

Example 2.21
Find the cube root of 0.000 216. (See Figure 2.23.)

Figure 2.23
Cube root using right cycle of K scale

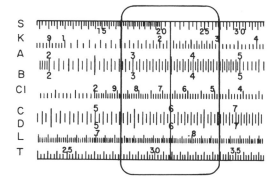

SOLUTION

(1) Point off in triplets from the decimal point:

$$\begin{array}{r} . \quad x \quad x \quad x \qquad \text{(answer)} \\ \sqrt[3]{0.000'216'000'} \qquad \text{(given number)} \end{array}$$

(2) Move the hairline to 216 on the *right* cycle.

(3) Read the answer, 0.060, on D.

Since both square roots and cube roots are read on the D scale, subsequent operations of multiplication or division can be performed. If both multiplication and division are involved, start with a division. If only multiplication is involved, start with the CI scale.

Example 2.22

In flow through an orifice, the theoretical velocity for a head of h ft is $V = 8.02\sqrt{h}$, V being in feet per second. Find the velocity for a head of 8.0 ft.

SOLUTION

(1) Move the hairline to 8 on the left cycle of A.

(2) Set 802 on CI to the hairline.

(3) Read the answer, 227, on D at the left index of the slide.

(4) Obtain the decimal point by inspection. $V = 22.7$ ft/sec.

Problem Set 2.6

Evaluate.

1. $\sqrt{8649}$

2. $\sqrt{6724}$

3. $\sqrt{47.27}$

4. $\sqrt{77.8}$

5. $\sqrt{0.006\,79}$

6. $\sqrt{0.000\,063\,2}$

7. $\sqrt[3]{132.65}$

8. $\sqrt[3]{172.81}$

9. $\sqrt[3]{0.0544}$

10. $\sqrt[3]{0.000\,011}$

11. $179\dfrac{\sqrt{6667}}{588}$

12. $0.202\dfrac{\sqrt{49,500,000}}{313}$

13. $\dfrac{\sqrt[3]{270}}{198}$

14. $\dfrac{0.0498\sqrt{0.0832}}{1.42}$

15. $\dfrac{17}{45}\sqrt{7.45}$

16. $\dfrac{\sqrt[3]{0.027}}{2.02}$

17. $8.27\sqrt[3]{61.1}$

18. $0.0749\sqrt[3]{0.749}$

19. $\dfrac{6.42\sqrt[3]{5.55}}{2.33}$

20. $\dfrac{4.37\sqrt[3]{0.000\ 008\ 4}}{6.98}$

21. Using the method shown in Example 2.22, find the theoretical velocity through an orifice for $h = 12.2$ ft.

22. Solve Problem 21 if $h = 2.78$ ft.

23. If metric units are used, the velocity in meters per second for a head of h m is $4.43\sqrt{h}$. Find the velocity for $h = 3.64$ m.

24. Solve Problem 23 if $h = 16.6$ m.

2.12 / Proportions

Proportions occur in both engineering and basic science and are readily solved on a slide rule. A simple example from chemistry will be used to illustrate this type of problem.

> **Example 2.23**
> Water is the product when gaseous hydrogen and oxygen are combined by a source of energy, such as an electric spark. The chemical equation is
>
> $$2H_2 + O_2 \rightarrow 2H_2O$$
>
> $$\quad 4 \qquad 32 \qquad 36$$
>
> The numbers under the chemical symbols are obtained from the atomic weights and yield the proportion. For every 36 parts by weight of water produced, 32 parts will be oxygen. If 100 lb of water was so produced, how many pounds of oxygen would be needed?
>
> SOLUTION
> (1) Set 32 on C over 36 on D. (This is the given ratio.)
> (2) Read the answer, 88.8, on C over 100 on D.

Note that the two values forming the given ratio must be in the same units, in this case atomic weights. Similarly, the value calculated must agree with the value given; in this case 88.8 lb will always be in the same units (pounds) as the given known quantity, 100 lb in this example.

Example 2.24

Carpenters identify a roof slope as the number of inches the roof rises in a 12-in. horizontal distance called the run. If a building has a 4:12 rise/run ratio, how wide is a roof that rises 6 ft?

SOLUTION

(1) Set 4 on C over 12 on D.
(2) Read the answer, 18 ft, on D under 6 on C.

Notice that in Example 2.23 the answer was found on C, but in Example 2.24 it was found on D. The correct scale to use can easily be seen if the actual proportion is written out:

$$\text{scale C:} \quad \frac{\text{given rise} \quad (4)}{\text{given run} \quad (12)} = \frac{\text{rise known} \quad (6)}{\text{run wanted} \quad (\text{on D})} \quad \text{scale D:}$$

In some problems a number of values are wanted for a fixed ratio of proportionality. If some of the knowns fall off the scale, skip these problems and do not check them off. When the list of given values has been completed, reverse the indexes of C and find the values for the unchecked knowns. In Example 2.24, readings cannot be found for rises smaller than 3.33 ft. If the value of the run for a 2-ft rise was needed, the indexes of the slide would be reversed and the value 6 ft could then be read.

Up to this point, all proportions have been **direct proportions.** In a direct proportion, as one value increases, so does the other. In the roof problem, the larger the run, the larger the rise, and thus this is a direct proportion. Some problems may involve an **inverse proportion;** that is, as one value increases, the other decreases.

Example 2.25

Eight machinists can complete a certain work project in 10 days. Find the number of machinists needed to complete the same project in 6 days. (Assume that all machinists work at the same rate.)

SOLUTION

The number of days has been made smaller and the number of machinists must be increased. This is an inverse proportion and, before doing the slide-rule work, it is better to write out the proportion to be solved:

$$\text{scale C:} \quad \frac{\text{original number of days}}{\text{new number of days}} = \frac{\text{new number of machinists}}{\text{original number of machinists}} \quad \text{scale D:}$$

Note that on the right side the ratio is inverted and that the original value is now in the denominator. Setting this on the slide rule:

(1) Set the original days, 10, on C over the new days, 6, on D.
(2) Move the hairline to the original number of machinists, 8, on D.
(3) Read the answer, 14, on C. (Note that an answer of 13.4 machinists makes no sense.)

2.13 / Combined A, K, and D scale operations

A number of routine engineering calculations require squaring or cubing a given set of arithmetic computations. For this type of problem, all the arithmetic operations are executed first. The answer to these is not read, but the result is transferred from the hairline or an index of a scale to the A scale or the K scale, where the answer is read.

Example 2.26

Find $\left(\dfrac{2.72(41.6)}{7.89}\right)^2$.

SOLUTION
(1) Start with a division! Set 789 on C over 272 on D.
(2) Move the hairline to 416 on C.
(3) Read the answer, 206, on A at the hairline.
(4) Find the decimal point:

$$\left(\frac{3(4)}{8} \cdot \frac{10^{0+1}}{10^0}\right)^2 \approx (1.5 \cdot 10^1)^2 \approx 2.2 \cdot 10^2 = 220$$

Thus, the answer is 206.

Example 2.27

Find $\left(\dfrac{0.472(0.0812)}{6.56(3.69)}\right)^3$.

SOLUTION
(1) Set 656 on C over 472 on D.
(2) Move the hairline to 812 on C.
(3) Set 369 on C to the hairline.
(4) Move the hairline to the left index of the slide.
(5) Read the answer, 3.96, on K.
(6) Find the decimal point:

$$\left(\frac{5(8)}{6(4)} \cdot \frac{10^{-1-2}}{10^{0+0}}\right)^3 = \left(\frac{5}{3} \cdot 10^{-3}\right)^3 = \frac{125}{27} \cdot 10^{-9} \approx 4 \cdot 10^{-9}$$

Thus, the answer is $3.96 \cdot 10^{-9}$.

In Problem Set 2.6 problems were worked with a subsequent multiplication or division being made on a root. Since the root was found on D, normal procedures were used. If the given problem involves a multiplication or division *before* taking the root, the intermediate answer must be read and transferred to the A or K scale. Another case that requires reading intermediate answers is the root of an addition or subtraction, most commonly met as $\sqrt{a^2 + b^2}$.

Example 2.28

Find $\sqrt{\dfrac{41.7(812)}{0.685}}$.

SOLUTION
(1) Set 685 on C over 417 on D.
(2) Move the hairline to 812 on C.
(3) Read the answer, 495, on D.
(4) Estimate the decimal point; the answer is 49,500.
(5) Point off this intermediate answer as 4′95′00. One digit in the left block means to use the left cycle.
(6) Move the hairline to 495 on the left cycle of A.
(7) Read the answer, 222, on D.

Example 2.29

Find $\sqrt{(0.472)^2 + (0.682)^2}$.

SOLUTION
(1) Move the hairline to 472 on D.
(2) Read the square, 22.3, on A.
(3) Determine the decimal point; write the answer, 0.223.
(4) Move the hairline to 682 on D.
(5) Read the square, 46.5, on A.
(6) Determine the decimal point; write the answer, 0.465.
(7) Add the two squares, obtaining 0.688.
(8) Point off this sum as 0.68′80′. There are two digits in the left block; use the right cycle.
(9) Move the hairline to 688 on the right cycle of A.
(10) Read the answer, 0.830, on D.

Problem Set 2.7

1. Concrete is specified as a ratio of cement to sand to rock. For 1 : 3 : 5 concrete, 1 bag of cement (approximately 1 cu ft) would be mixed with 3 cu ft of sand and 5 cu ft of rock. If 78 bags of cement are to be used, how many cubic feet of sand and how many cubic feet of rock are needed?

2. A highway grade is given as a percentage and means the number of feet it changes in elevation in 100 ft measured horizontally. If a

highway has a $-3\frac{1}{2}$ percent grade, how much does it drop in a 1-mile stretch?

3. A speed of 60 mph is equal to a speed of 88 fps (feet per second). Make a table of equivalents in fps (correct to nearest tenth) for 10-mph increments from 0 to 60 mph.

4. Slaked lime is calcium oxide (lime) mixed with water. In chemical symbols the reaction is written

$$CaO + H_2O \rightarrow Ca(OH)_2$$

$$56 \qquad 18 \qquad 74$$

(a) What weight of water would be required to slake 100 lb of lime?
(b) How much slaked lime would result?

5. The Golden Ratio is supposed to yield the most pleasing proportions to the human eye. It is approximately 89 : 144. What is the area of a rectangle meeting this requirement if the short side is 12 in.?

6. Water pipes should have as a minimum fall a fall of $\frac{1}{4}$ in. per foot of run. If in a certain house a waterline is 83 ft 6 in. long, how many inches will it fall at this minimum slope?

7. In perfect gases, two pressures and two volumes form an inverse proportion. A certain tubeless automobile tire has 4500 cu in. of air in it at the normal inflation of 30 pounds per square inch (psi). How many cubic feet of air must be added to raise the tire pressure to 36 psi?

8. The concentrated load a beam can carry varies inversely as the distance between supports. (Two loads and their two distances form an inverse proportion.) A certain beam can carry 3850 lb if the supports are 16 ft apart. What is the maximum load for the same beam if the supports are 24 ft apart?

9–20

Evaluate.

9. $\left(\dfrac{7.47\,(6.62)}{4.83}\right)^2$

10. $\left(\dfrac{8.38\,(4.89)}{3.87}\right)^2$

11. $\left(\dfrac{0.0627\,(0.001\,44)}{9.85\,(5.11)}\right)^2$

12. $\left(\dfrac{0.005\,73\,(0.0133)}{8.37\,(7.62)}\right)^2$

13. $\left(\dfrac{273\,(787)}{5.42\,(0.179)}\right)^3$

14. $\left(\dfrac{3670\,(213)}{6.85\,(0.001\,66)}\right)^3$

15. $\sqrt{\dfrac{9.12\,(5.15)}{4.04}}$

16. $\sqrt{\dfrac{7.9\,(82.3)}{5.26}}$

17. $\sqrt{\dfrac{0.0246\,(0.0642)}{331}}$

18. $\sqrt{\dfrac{0.003\,57\,(0.001\,59)}{579}}$

19. $\sqrt[3]{\dfrac{142\,(758)}{0.293\,(0.534)}}$

20. $\sqrt[3]{\dfrac{2110\,(8430)}{0.394\,(0.667)}}$

2.14 / Arrangement of calculations

All industrial and scientific organizations generally require that the calculations of one employee be independently checked by another. It is

Figure 2.24
Sketch of commercial paper and how it is used

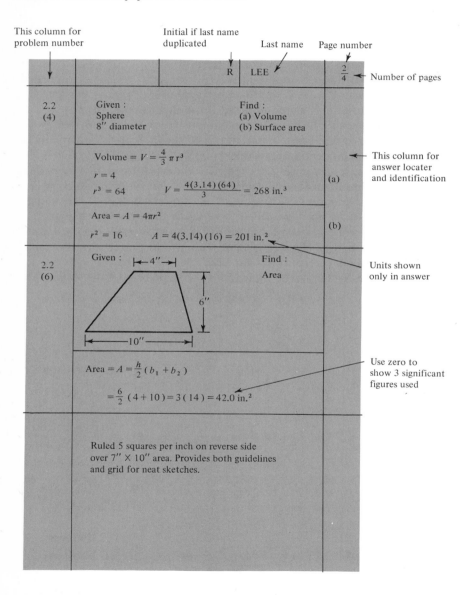

This column for problem number

Initial if last name duplicated

Last name

Page number

Number of pages

This column for answer locater and identification

Units shown only in answer

Use zero to show 3 significant figures used

important, therefore, that what is recorded is legible; that every item and every step is identified clearly; that when assumptions are made, they are stated; and that when formulas are used, they are written out in full. One technician might compute the volume of a sphere by using $V = \frac{4}{3}\pi r^3$ and another by using $V = 0.523d^3$. Neither would recognize what the other was doing unless the formula was written with the calculation.

Figure 2.24 is a possible arrangement of a page of calculations. Given information should be recorded, either as a list or as a well-drawn, well-labeled sketch. This should be checked with the assigned problem before any work is done. Listing what is to be found in the simplest way possible focuses attention on the elements that must be considered. Preruled paper, such as that shown, is available in pads at most college bookstores.

One should do all work on the paper to be submitted. Use of the slide rule should eliminate the need for scratch-paper calculations. The transferring of calculations and results from scratch paper has been found to be a potent source of error, and, in many cases, vital intermediate steps are not shown, making the work impossible to check.

Units of length, weight, and other quantities are normally shown in the "given" data and in the final answer but are rarely written during intermediate calculations. If there is any chance that a calculation is not self-evident, a note can be added. A highly unique and original solution may be misunderstood for lack of a note.

Work should be done using a sharp, soft lead. HB or No. 1 pencils are suggested. Ballpoint pens should be avoided because the ink cannot be erased easily. A good-quality eraser is needed because errors will occur.

2.15 / Reasonableness of results

One of the many virtues expected in a proficient technician is not that he never make a mistake, but rather that he has trained himself to find most of his own errors.

The basic test of any solution to a real problem is to see if the answer found is logical. If, for example, the problem involves a rise in temperature, we can expect a rise in the pressure, an expansion of a material object, or a rise in energy levels. Getting the opposite effect is an indicator of an error, probably in the sign of some quantity.

Other illogical answers indicating trouble include those that are senseless, such as the weight of a pilot being 473 lb, a tire pressure being 1242 psi, or a student's age being 217 years. Common sense dictates the range of reasonable solutions.

Roughing out a problem to find the decimal point will also give a good approximation of the numerals in the answer. If the roughing out gave an answer of $\frac{1}{4}$ and the slide-rule answer is 748, there must be a bad error in one of the two.

One reason for accurately drawn sketches is that the answer can be scaled for many problems. Whenever possible, this check should be made to verify that the calculations are correct.

In some types of problems values from a given formula for different values of the literal value may be the requirement. For example, the area of a circle may be requested for radii of 2, 6, 9, and 14 in. Plotting these results may show that all but one answer falls on a smooth curve. That value should be immediately rechecked. Plotting will be covered in detail in Chapter 7, but many students have had some experience in simple plotting in high school, so it is mentioned here.

Finally, many problems involve finding numerical values that meet specified conditions. For example, the problem might involve finding quantities of various-sized bolts whose unit price is given. The total number of bolts and their total worth may be the specified values. It should seem obvious that after calculations for the number of each size has been made, the problem should be checked by finding the total number and total worth. Unfortunately, many students ignore this vital check and often turn in a completely wrong solution.

2.16 / Chapter Review

1. Slide rules are as accurate as most engineering data and greatly reduce the time required for arithmetic calculations.
2. To obtain excellent results, all settings must be made with care. Readings must be made with equal care. Good results require familiarity with the scales and their subdivisions, and this is obtained by daily use.
3. Most calculations require use of only the C, D, and CI scales. Roots and powers require the A and K scales.
4. Decimal points are found by estimation or by using scientific notation. Roughing out a complex problem can give a good approximation to the answer, both as to numerical value and as to the decimal point.
5. All combined operations begin with a division.
6. The CI scale is normally used when the slide rule is positioned for either a multiplication or a division and only factors requiring the inverse operation are available.
7. Proportions require that each ratio involve the same units. Writing out the proportion indicates the scale to use.
8. Roots require pointing off the original number to determine the proper cycle to be used and to find the decimal point.

Problem Set 2.8 (*Chapter Review*)

The bulk of the problems in this set are verbal; that is, a series of statements are given containing the needed information. The student should, as the first step, put the information into a computational form before doing any slide-rule work. Supervisors do not write out tasks in problem-solving form but will dictate to the technician the basic facts and expect him to jot down the data and to solve the problem.

1. Find the three quotients: 52 divided by (a) 17.3; (b) 0.144; (c) 3760.

2. Find $\dfrac{7.22\,(0.0104)}{0.003\,61\,(9890)(0.000\,845)}$.

3. Find $\dfrac{0.06\,(0.007\,07)}{0.004\,11\,(0.698)(0.021\,15)(0.000\,001\,243)}$.

4. Find the quotient of $\dfrac{1.0 \cdot 10^{-8}}{4.67 \cdot 10^{-7}}$ divided by $5.67 \cdot 10^{-9}$.

5. Find $\sqrt{5.72} \cdot \sqrt[3]{0.000\,615}$.

6. Find $\dfrac{\sqrt{0.617} \cdot \sqrt[3]{125}}{11.6\,(0.089)}$.

7. Find $\sqrt{\dfrac{411\,(231)}{168} \div \dfrac{73\,(173)}{22}}$.

8. Find $\dfrac{77.63\,(75.17)(\sqrt{0.613})(219.3)}{6.5 \cdot 10^{3}(5.17 \cdot 10^{3})(174.3)}$.

9. Find the cost of a rug to cover a floor 12 ft by 17 ft if the rug sells for $8.25/sq yd.

10. How long will it take to dig a 1200-ft sewer line if the work output is constant and the first 315 ft were dug in $1\frac{3}{4}$ days?

11. Sound travels at 332 m/sec at 0°C. A meter is 39.37 in. Find the speed of sound in mph at 0°C.

12. A cylinder has a volume equal to the area of the base (which is a circle) times the altitude. Find the amount of gasoline that can be stored in a cylindrical tank 4 ft in diameter and 10 ft long if 1 cu ft equals 7.48 gal.

13. Using the information in Problem 12 as needed, find the diameter of a tank that will hold 5000 gal and be 8 ft long.

14. Chelated iron is fed to lawns, crops, and plants at the agricultural rate of 1 lb/100 gal of water. If 1 teaspoon of this chemical weighs 0.12 ounces (oz), how many teaspoons per gallon should the home gardener use? (16 oz = 1 lb.)

15. Find the area in square inches, square feet, and square yards of a standard piece of plywood 4 by 8 ft.

16. The torque (T) transmitted by a ring-disc clutch plate is given by the formula

$$T = \frac{2}{3} fP \frac{R_o^3 - R_i^3}{R_o^2 - R_i^2}$$

where f = coefficient of friction = 0.3
P = pressure on plate = 500 lb
R_o = outer radius of ring = 8.15 in.
R_i = inner radius of ring = 2.88 in.

Compute T in inch-pounds.

17. The temperature (t) of air leaving a rectangular duct is given by

$$t = \frac{t_e(y - 1) + 2t_a}{y + 1} \qquad \text{where } y = \frac{28.8AVd}{UPL}$$

Given t_e = temperature of air entering the duct = 123.7°F
t_a = temperature of air surrounding the duct = 40.0°F
A = area of duct, sq ft (use a duct 24 by 36 in.)
V = mean velocity of air, ft per min, = 1200 fpm
d = density of air, in pounds per cu ft, = 0.0749 pcf
U = heat-transmission coefficient = 0.49 Btu
P = perimeter of duct, ft
L = length of duct, ft = 70 ft

Find t for the data given.

18. Three condensers in series have a total capacitance C, where

$$\frac{1}{C} = \frac{1}{C_1} + \frac{1}{C_2} + \frac{1}{C_3}$$

If C_1 = 2.5 millifarads (mF), C_2 = 3.75 mF, and C_3 = 6.45 mF, find C.

19. The distance a body freely falls in t seconds is $\frac{1}{2}gt^2$, where g = 32.2 when the distance is measured in feet. Find the distance for a 200-lb block falling for 9.25 sec.

20. A given alloy is 30 per cent bronze, 42 per cent brass, 24 per cent tin, and 4 per cent nickel. If 685 lb of the alloy is needed, how many pounds of each metal are needed?

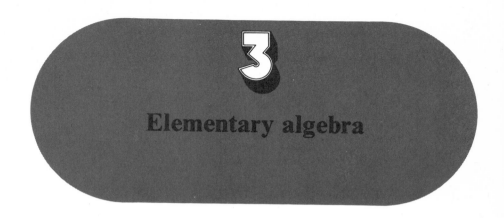

3.01 / Concept of algebra

Elementary algebra is a logical study of numbers and their properties with the use of symbols an important feature. Algebra is actually arithmetic that has been generalized so that the number properties can be readily recognized and understood. By using algebra, engineering and scientific personnel can find general relationships that then can be applied to many specific cases.

The reader is probably familiar with the use of symbols in stating mathematical relationships. In elementary grades it is shown that the area of a rectangle is found by multiplying its length by its width. To save time in writing this statement and to see at a glance what it says, symbols are used; that is, $A = L \times W$. This kind of statement is called a *formula*, because it is a general rule stated in symbols. Later it is usually shown that this formula may be written as $A = LW$, with the multiplication sign omitted. Two letters placed side by side are used to indicate a multiplication.

As another example of a formula, the area of a circle can be expressed as $A = \pi r^2$. The Greek letter π, used as the name of a fixed number, is called a *constant* because it always designates exactly one number. It is desirable to use the letter π because the number π occurs so often and because π is an irrational real number with a never-ending decimal form: $\pi = 3.14159265\ldots$. In applications, the user approximates the exact number π by selecting as many decimal places as are needed for the problem. The letter r, designating the radius of a circle, is called a *variable* because the value of *r* changes or varies for circles of different sizes.

3.02 / Terminology of algebra

Literal numbers

Literal numbers are numbers that are named by using letters. Any letter of the English alphabet, or any Greek letter, for that matter, may be used as the name of a number.

A **variable** is a letter whose value is unspecified but is restricted to a certain set that contains more than one number. Letters near the end of the alphabet, such as x, y, and z, are usually used for variables.

A **constant** is a numeral or letter whose value may be unspecified, but each constant is restricted to have exactly one value. Letters at the beginning of the alphabet, such as a, b, and c, are commonly used for constants.

In practical problems, the values for the variables may be limited to a special set of numbers either by the physical conditions of what is being investigated or by the conditions imposed by the person giving a particular assignment. For example, in area problems, only positive rational numbers would be considered as admissible values since these are the values obtained by actual measurements.

Subscripts

Subscripts are often used when there are several similar unspecified quantities. For example, if three forces were acting on a beam, they could be labeled F_1, F_2, and F_3 (read "F sub one, F sub two, and F sub three"). If there were an unspecified number of forces, then the three-dot symbol would be used with F_n naming the last one. For example, $F_1, F_2, \ldots, F_n$ (read "F sub one, F sub two, through F sub n"). When there can be no misunderstanding, these are read "F one, F two, through F n."

Algebraic expressions

There are six algebraic operations that can be performed on numbers: addition, subtraction, multiplication, division, raising to a power, and root extraction. An **algebraic expression** is a numeral, a letter, or any set of symbols indicating one or more algebraic operations.

A **term** is a numeral, a letter, or an algebraic expression indicating a number obtained by multiplication, division, raising to a power, or root extraction. The numbers combined by addition or subtraction are called the terms of the operation. For example,

$$3 \quad \text{is a term}$$

$$x \quad \text{is a term}$$

$$3x \quad \text{is a term}$$

$$\frac{x^3\sqrt{2x}}{y} \quad \text{is a term}$$

$$2x - 5 \quad \text{is an expression having two terms}$$

$$x^2 - 5x + 6 \quad \text{is an expression having three terms}$$

The special terms x, x^2, x^3, x^4, x^5, and so on, are called **natural powers** of the variable x since each exponent is a natural number. (Recall that $x^1 = x$.)

A **power term** is either a constant or a product of a constant and a natural power of the variable. For example, 3, x, $3x$, x^2, $3x^2$, and so on, are power terms.

The **degree** of a power term is the exponent of the variable, with the degree of a constant assigned the value 0 for convenience.

A **polynomial in one variable** is a power term or a sum of power terms. (A polynomial does not have a variable in a denominator, under a radical sign, or in an exponent.)

The **degree of a polynomial in one variable** (Table 3.1) is the largest degree of any of its terms. Note that although the constant a must not be zero, one or more of the other constants may be 0.

Table 3.1
Polynomials in one variable

Degree	General form $(a \neq 0)$	Example
0	a	5
1	$ax + b$	$3x - 2$
2	$ax^2 + bx + c$	$4.2x^2 + 1.7x - 3.9$
3	$ax^3 + bx^2 + cx + d$	$x^3 - \sqrt{2x} + \frac{1}{2}$
4	$ax^4 + bx^3 + cx^2 + dx + e$	$2x^4 + x^3 - 3x^2 - 7$

Some examples of expressions that are *not* polynomials are the following:

$$\frac{x^2 + 1}{x} \quad \text{because the variable } x \text{ is in the denominator}$$

$$x^2 + 3\sqrt{x} \quad \text{because the variable } x \text{ is under the radical sign}$$

$$2^x - 5x \quad \text{because the variable } x \text{ appears in an exponent}$$

A **polynomial in two or more variables** is a power term of any one variable, a product of power terms of two or more variables, or a sum of these types of terms.

The **degree of a power term containing two or more variables** is the sum of the degrees of its variable factors. The **degree of a polynomial in two or more variables** is the largest degree of any of its terms. As examples,

$$x + y \qquad \text{is a polynomial in two variables, of degree 1}$$

$$x^2 - 2xy + y^2 \qquad \text{is a polynomial in two variables, of degree 2}$$

$$x^5 - 4y^2 \qquad \text{is a polynomial in two variables, of degree 5}$$

$$3x + 6y + 9z \qquad \text{is a polynomial in three variables, of degree 1}$$

$$x^2 + 2xy^2 + y^2 - z^2 \qquad \text{is a polynomial in three variables, of degree 3}$$

A **monomial** ("mono" means "one") is a polynomial having exactly one term. For example, $3x^4$.

A **binomial** ("bi" means "two") is a polynomial having exactly two terms. For example, $x + y$ and $x^2 - 9$.

A **trinomial** ("tri" means "three") is a polynomial having exactly three terms. For example, $x^2 + 2xy + y^2$ and $2x^6 - 6x^3 + 4$.

Any factor of a product is called a **coefficient** of the other factors of the product. For example, for the monomial $3xyz$,

$$3xy \qquad \text{is the coefficient of } z$$

$$x \qquad \text{is the coefficient of } 3yz$$

$$3 \qquad \text{is the } \textbf{numerical coefficient} \text{ of } xyz$$

The coefficient of the term of highest degree of a polynomial in one variable is called the **leading coefficient.** For example,

$4a$ is the leading coefficient of $4ax^3 + 3bx - 7c$

1 is the leading coefficient of $x^2 - 2x + 3$

5 is the leading coefficient of $3x^2 - 2x + 5x^3 - 7 = 5x^3 + 3x^2 - 2x - 7$

If a polynomial in two or more variables is considered as a polynomial in one of the variables, the leading coefficient is the coefficient of the term of highest degree for this variable. For example,

$4a$ is the leading coefficient of $4ax^4 + bx^3y + cx^2y^2$ when this polynomial is considered as a polynomial in x

cx^2 is the leading coefficient of $4ax^4 + bx^3y + cx^2y^2$ when this polynomial is considered as a polynomial in y

3.03 / Algebraic operations and grouping symbols

Since elementary algebra is generalized arithmetic, all the arithmetic concepts of addition, subtraction, multiplication, division, raising to a power, and root extraction apply. Addition is indicated by the $+$ sign and subtraction by the $-$ sign. Multiplication is indicated by the $\cdot$ symbol, as in $3 \cdot 5 = 15$; by the use of parentheses, as in $3(5) = 15$; and by placing the factors side by side, as in $3x$ or xy. The arithmetic multiplication symbol $\times$ is avoided because the letter x is used as the name of a number. The division symbol $\div$ is rarely used in algebraic operations, because the fractional notation meaning a quotient is simpler and more convenient. Just as $3 \div 4$ has the same meaning as $\frac{3}{4}$, the quotient $x \div y$ is usually written as $\frac{x}{y}$.

The electronic computer is programmed to multiply before adding unless it receives other instructions. If a computer is required to find the value of 3 times 4 plus 2, it will always obtain 14 for the answer. To a person this may not be a clear statement since it is possible to do the computation in two different ways as follows.

$$3 \cdot 4 + 2$$

may be

$$(3 \cdot 4) + 2 = 12 + 2 = 14$$

or

$$3(4 + 2) = 3 \cdot 6 = 18$$

The parentheses are used to indicate that the operation within the parentheses is to be done first. Therefore, to make statements clear, grouping symbols are used. The most common ones are

the **parentheses** ( )

the **brackets** [ ]

the **braces** { }

It is customary to use the grouping symbols in the order listed above; that is, parentheses first, then brackets, and then braces:

$$\{[( )]\}$$

Example 3.1
Simplify: $\{4[3(5 + 2) + 1] - 7\}$.

SOLUTION

$$= \{4[3(7) + 1] - 7\} \quad \text{First, do operation inside ( )}$$

$$= \{4[21 + 1] - 7\} \quad \text{Second, do operations inside [ ]}$$

$$= \{4[22] - 7\}$$

$$= \{88 - 7\} \quad \text{Third, do operations inside \{ \}}$$

$$= 81$$

To avoid misunderstanding when a writer of a mathematical statement has omitted adequate grouping symbols, there is an agreement as to the order of operations to be done. This order agrees with the order the modern electronic computer would do the operation under these same circumstances.

Agreement
Unless grouping symbols indicate otherwise, operations will be done in the following order : raising to a power, root extraction, multiplication, division, addition, subtraction.

Example 3.2
For each indicated calculation listed, the meaning with grouping symbols is given, and then, using the order stated in the above agreement, the meaning without grouping symbols is given.

With grouping symbols	*No grouping symbols*
(a) $(2 + 3)x = 5x$	$2 + 3x$ (cannot be simplified)
(b) $(1 + 2)3^2 = 3(9) = 27$	$1 + 2 \cdot 3^2 = 1 + 2 \cdot 9 = 1 + 18 = 19$
(c) $1 + (2 \cdot 3)^2 = 1 + 6^2 = 1 + 36 = 37$	$1 + 2 \cdot 3^2 = 1 + 2 \cdot 9 = 19$
(d) $(1 + 2)^2 3 = 3^2 \cdot 3 = 9 \cdot 3 = 27$	$1 + 2^2 \cdot 3 = 1 + 4 \cdot 3 = 1 + 12 = 13$
(e) $(3x + 1)^2 = 9x^2 + 6x + 1$	$3x + 1^2 = 3x + 1$
(f) $(5x)^3 = 125x^3$	$5x^3$ (cannot be simplified)

Example 3.3
Simplify $1 + (2 \cdot 3)^2$.

SOLUTION

$$1 + (2 \cdot 3)^2 = 1 + 6^2 \quad \text{first, do operation inside ( )}$$

$$= 1 + 36 \quad \text{second, square}$$

$$= 37 \quad \text{third, add}$$

Example 3.4
Simplify $(1 + 2) \cdot 3^2$.

SOLUTION

$$(1 + 2) \cdot 3^2 = 3 \cdot 3^2 \qquad \text{first, do operation inside ( )}$$

$$= 3 \cdot 9 \qquad \text{second, square}$$

$$= 27 \qquad \text{third, multiply}$$

3.04 / Addition and subtraction of signed numbers

The set of real numbers contains both positive and negative numbers. This quality of a number is indicated by a $+$ or $-$ symbol. These same symbols are also operators, indicating an addition or a subtraction. To prevent misunderstanding, a negative number may be enclosed within parentheses. For example, the subtraction of minus 2 from 4 is written $4 - (-2)$. Since $+4$ and 4 are names for the same number, $+4 = 4$, the plus sign of quality is usually omitted as being understood.

When, in practical problems, a positive answer means a tension, an uphill slope, or any other interpretation whose positive quality has special significance, the plus sign is written. As examples,

Force is $+800$ lb (meaning tensile stress)

slope is $+21\%$ (meaning up)

sum of latitudes is $+20°$ (meaning north)

Since a \$5 gain ($+5$) followed by a \$4 gain ($+4$) results in a gain of \$9 ($+9$) and since a \$5 loss (-5) followed by a \$4 loss (-4) results in a loss of \$9 (-9), the addition of numbers having the same signs is defined to retain this meaning.

The sum of numbers with like signs is the sum of their absolute values prefixed by their common sign.

Example 3.5

$$(+5) + (+4) = +(5 + 4) = +9$$

or $\qquad\qquad 5 + 4 = 9$

Example 3.6

$$(-5) + (-4) = -(|-5| + |-4|) = -(5 + 4) = -9$$

Since a gain of \$6 ($+6$) followed by a loss of \$2 (-2) results in a net gain of \$4 ($+4$), and since a loss of \$6 (-6) followed by a gain of \$2 ($+2$) results in a net loss of \$4 (-4), the sum of numbers having unlike signs is defined to retain this meaning.

The sum of numbers with unlike signs is the result obtained by subtracting the smaller absolute value from the larger absolute value and prefixing the result with the sign of the number with the larger absolute value.

Example 3.7
$$(+6) + (-2) = +(|+6| - |-2|) = +(6 - 2) = +4 = 4.$$

Example 3.8
$$(-6) + (+2) = -(|-6| - |-2|) = -(6 - 2) = -4.$$

The rules for the addition of signed numbers can also be understood by referring to their graphical representation on the number line, as shown in Figure 3.1. Note that the addition operator moves the terminal point in the *same* direction as the sign of the term being added.

Since $a - b = a + (-b)$, subtraction is the same as the addition of the opposite of the number being subtracted.

To subtract signed numbers, change the sign of the number to be subtracted and add, following the rules for the addition of signed numbers.

Example 3.9
$$(+6) - (+2) = (+6) + (-2) = 4.$$

Example 3.10
$$(+6) - (-2) = (+6) + (+2) = 8.$$

Figure 3.1
Addition of signed numbers

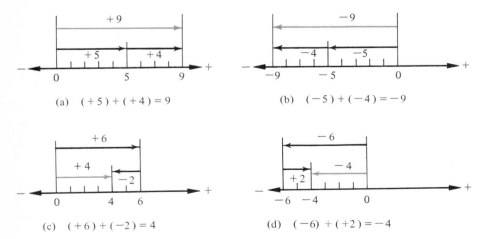

(a) $(+5) + (+4) = 9$

(b) $(-5) + (-4) = -9$

(c) $(+6) + (-2) = 4$

(d) $(-6) + (+2) = -4$

(a)　$(+6) - (+2) = 4$　　　　　　(b)　$(-6) - (-2) = -4$

Figure 3.2
Subtraction of signed numbers

Example 3.11
$(-6) - (+2) = (-6) + (-2) = -8.$

Example 3.12
$(-6) - (-2) = (-6) + (+2) = -4.$

The rule for subtraction is illustrated on the number line in Figure 3.2. Note that the subtraction operator moves the terminal point in the *opposite* direction to the sign of the term to be subtracted.

Since addition and subtraction are inverse operations, any subtraction problem can always be checked by addition.

Example 3.13
Check that $(+6) - (+2) = 4.$

SOLUTION
$4 + (+2) = 6.$

Example 3.14
Check that $(-6) - (-2) = -4.$

SOLUTION
$(-4) + (-2) = -6.$

Summary　Let a and b be any positive real numbers.

	General definitions	*Examples*
Addition	$(+a) + (+b) = +(a + b)$	$7 + 3 = 10$
	$(-a) + (-b) = -(a + b)$	$(-7) + (-3) = -10$
	$(+a) + (-b) = +(a - b)$ if $a > b$	$(+7) + (-3) = 4$
	$(+a) + (-b) = -(b - a)$ if $b > a$	$(+3) + (-7) = -4$
Subtraction	$(+a) - (+b) = a + (-b)$	$3 - 7 = 3 + (-7) = -4$
	$(+a) - (-b) = a + (+b)$	$3 - (-7) = 3 + 7 = 10$
	$(-a) - (+b) = -a + (-b)$	$-3 - 7 = -3 + (-7) = -10$
	$(-a) - (-b) = -a + (+b)$	$-3 - (-7) = -3 + 7 = 4$

Problem Set 3.1

1–10

(a) *State whether each of the following is a polynomial or not; if not, state the reason.*

(b) *Find the value of each algebraic expression for $x = 3$ and $y = 2$.*

Sample

$$\frac{4x}{y} + xy.$$

SOLUTION

(a) Not a polynomial; involves division by a variable.

(b) Replace x by 3 and y by 2 and calculate the value:

$$\frac{4 \cdot 3}{2} + 3 \cdot 2 = \frac{12}{2} + 6 = 6 + 6 = 12$$

1. $x^2 - 2x + 5$

2. $\dfrac{12}{x} + \dfrac{x}{12}$

3. $\frac{1}{2}x^3 - \frac{3}{4}$

4. $x^4 + 9$

5. $\dfrac{30}{x - 1} + x - 1$

6. $\frac{2}{3}x^2 - \frac{2}{9}$

7. $5 - \sqrt{5(x + y)}$

8. $x^2 - 2xy + y^2$

9. $x^3 - y^3$

10. $\sqrt{x^2 + 4y^2} - 4$

11–20

(a) *State whether each of the following is a monomial, binomial, trinomial, or none of these.*

(b) *State the coefficient of the power of x for the term of highest degree containing x.*

(c) *State the numerical coefficient of the term containing the highest power of x.*

11. $2x^2y - 3y^3$

12. $x^2 + 2y^2 + 3z^2$

13. $4y^2 - 4xy^2 - x^2$

14. $8x^3y - 27y^3$

15. $0.5x^3y^2z$

16. $x^4 - x^3 - 2x + 2$

17. $\frac{1}{2}x + \frac{1}{2}y$

18. $1.25x^5y^5$

19. $4x^4 - 2x^2y^3 + 9y^2 - 25$

20. $\frac{1}{4}x^2 - \frac{1}{4}y + \frac{1}{8}xy^2$

21–30

State the leading coefficient of each of the following polynomials.

21. $5x^3 - 6x^2 + 2x + 10$

22. $x + 3x^3 - 4x^4 - 5x^2$

23. $7a + y^2 - 6ay$

24. $cy^5 - c^2y^4 + c^3y^3 - c^4y$

25. $2x^3y^2 + 9x^4y - 8x^2y^3$ (considered as a polynomial in x)
26. $2x^3y^2 + 9x^4y - 8x^2y^3$ (considered as a polynomial in y)
27. $ay^2 + bxy + cx^2 + dx + ey + f$ (considered as a polynomial in y)
28. $ay^2 + bxy + cx^2 + dx + ey + f$ (considered as a polynomial in x)
29. $xyz - 5x^2y^2z^2 + 4x^3y^3z^3$ (considered as a polynomial in z)
30. $ax^2yz + bxy^2z + cxyz^2$ (considered as a polynomial in z)

31–40

Insert parentheses, if necessary, so that the resulting statement is a true statement.

31. $20 - 10 - 5 = 15$ **35.** $5 \cdot 6 + 4 = 50$ **39.** $9 - 3^2 = 36$
32. $36 \div 12 \div 3 = 1$ **36.** $5 \cdot 6 + 4 = 34$ **40.** $10 - 3 - 2^2 = 9$
33. $2 \cdot 3^2 = 18$ **37.** $7 - 2 \cdot 4 - 1 = 1$
34. $2 \cdot 3^2 = 36$ **38.** $8 + 3 \cdot 5 - 2 = 17$

41–50

Simplify.

41. $17 - [2(5 - 3)]$
42. $2[1 + 3(7 - 2)]$
43. $10 - \{8 - [6 - (4 - 2)]\}$
44. $2\{9 + [7 - (5 - 3)]\}$
45. $1 - (1 - \{1 - [1 - (1 - 1)]\})$
46. $2(9 - 4) - 3(5 - 3)$
47. $3(8 - 1) - 2(3 + 2)$
48. $2 + \{2 - [2 + (2 - 2)]\}$
49. $5[(2 + 3)^2 - (2 + 1)^2]$
50. $[(5 + 1) + (5 - 1)] \cdot [(5 + 1)^2 - (5 + 1)(5 - 1) + (5 - 1)^2]$

51–70

Express each of the following as a single number.

51. $6 + (-3)$ **58.** $(-7) - (-9)$ **65.** $(6 - 9) + (8 - 6)$
52. $(-6) + (-3)$ **59.** $(-3) - (-4)$ **66.** $(10 - 8) + (7 - 12)$
53. $(-6) + (+3)$ **60.** $(-3) - (-2)$ **67.** $(5 - 10) - (10 - 5)$
54. $(-8) + (+5)$ **61.** $7 + (2 - 5)$ **68.** $(11 - 4) - (4 - 11)$
55. $(-8) + (-5)$ **62.** $8 + (4 - 9)$ **69.** $(3 - 8) - (2 - 9)$
56. $8 + (-5)$ **63.** $(1 - 8) + (-4)$ **70.** $(7 - 4) - (9 - 1)$
57. $(-7) - (-4)$ **64.** $(3 - 7) + (-5)$

71–80

Find the sum of each number pair.

71. $3\frac{5}{8}, -5\frac{3}{4}$ **72.** $-8\frac{7}{9}, +2\frac{5}{6}$

73. $-7\frac{3}{16}$, $-4\frac{1}{2}$

74. $-6\frac{7}{12}$, $-5\frac{11}{18}$

75. $+95.25$, -123.62

76. -45.37, $+36.98$

77. -1.004, -2.015

78. -0.146, -0.099

79. $-0.000\,92$, $+0.000\,54$

80. $+0.000\,029$, $-0.000\,071$

81–90

Find the difference between each number pair in problems 71–80 if the second number is subtracted from the first.

91. The entries on a certain bank statement are recorded as positive numbers for a deposit and as negative numbers for a withdrawal. Find the balance for the following entries: $+150.00$, $+27.50$, -52.30, $+210.00$, -37.40, -19.25.

92. The daily changes in weight for a person on a diet were recorded, a positive number for a gain and a negative number for a loss. Find the weight at the end of the week if the person originally weighed 185 lb: Mon. $+1$, Tues. 0, Wed. $-\frac{1}{2}$, Thurs. $-\frac{3}{4}$, Fri. -2, Sat. $+\frac{1}{4}$, Sun. $-1\frac{1}{2}$.

93. A certain stock having an original value of $100 was reported in the newspaper as having the following changes in value: $+\frac{3}{4}$, $+1\frac{1}{8}$, $-\frac{5}{8}$, $-\frac{1}{4}$, $+1\frac{3}{8}$, $-2\frac{1}{2}$, $+\frac{7}{8}$. A positive number indicates an increase, a negative number indicates a decrease, and a fractional value such as $\frac{3}{4}$ means $\frac{3}{4}$ of a dollar, or 75 cents. In dollars and cents, what was the value of the stock at the end of the week?

94. While in possession of the ball for a certain sequence of plays, a football team made the following gains (positive numbers) and losses (negative numbers) in yardage: $+5$, $+2\frac{1}{2}$, $+6$, -12, -3, $+9$, -4. If the team started on its own 45-yd line, where was the ball at the end of this sequence?

95. The high and low temperatures for different cities on a certain day were recorded as shown. Find the difference between the high and low temperatures for each city.

City	High	Low
(a) Sacramento	75°	57°
(b) Chicago	25°	$-4°$
(c) Nome	$-12°$	$-35°$

96. How many years elapsed between each of the following pairs of dates where a negative number means time B.C. and a positive number means time A.D.? Note that there was no year 0; that is, the year 1 A.D. followed the year 1 B.C. (The number 0 had not been invented at the time of the calendar reform.)

(a) -3000 to -600 (b) -300 to $+400$ (c) $+825$ to $+1250$

97. A particle in a cloud chamber in a physics laboratory is moving back and forth on a line in the east–west direction. If a positive number means the number of millimeters it moves to the east and a negative number means the number of millimeters it moves to the west, what is its final position with respect to its starting point (0) for the following account of its motion? $+100, -50, +75, -120, +30, -90$.

98. In the game of pinochle, a player on each round may gain points, lose points, or obtain no points. A loss is indicated by enclosing the number of points lost in a circle. What is the final score of each of the players whose scores on each round are given as follows?

Al: 18, ㉟, 19, 16, 37, 18, 22
Bill: 22, 15, 5, ㉘, 12, 7, 12
Carl: 8, 12, ㉙, 14, 5, ㉗, 4

3.05 / Multiplication and division of signed numbers

Assume that the *directed distance* of a car from a city is positive ($+$) or negative ($-$) according as it is east or west of the city.

The *velocity* of the car is positive ($+$) if it is moving toward the east and negative ($-$) if it is moving toward the west.

The *directed time* is counted from noon with positive numbers indicating time after noon (P.M.) and with negative numbers indicating time before noon (A.M.), as shown in the table.

Clock time	9 A.M.	10 A.M.	11 A.M.	12 noon	1 P.M.	2 P.M.	3 P.M.
Directed Time	-3	-2	-1	0	$+1$	$+2$	$+3$

The formula for the directed distance for uniform motion is

directed distance = (directed time) (velocity)

$$d = tv$$

Now, assume that a car is in the city at noon. Then its position at 3 P.M. when moving 40 mph eastward is

$$d = (+3)(+40) = +120,$$ or 120 miles east of the city [see Figure 3.3(a)]

Still assuming that the car is at the city at noon, its position at 3 P.M. if it is moving 40 mph westward is

$$d = (+3)(-40) = -120,$$ or 120 miles west of the city [see Figure 3.3(b)]

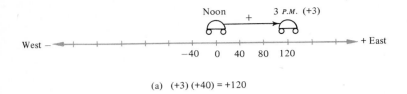

(a) $(+3)(+40) = +120$

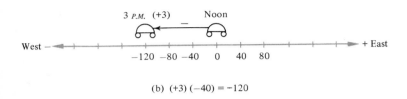

(b) $(+3)(-40) = -120$

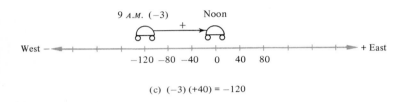

(c) $(-3)(+40) = -120$

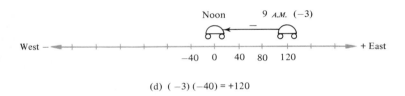

(d) $(-3)(-40) = +120$

Figure 3.3
Directed movements

Changing the situation now, assume that the car arrives at the city at noon. Then the position of the car at 9 A.M. if it is moving 40 mph eastward is

$$d = (-3)(+40) = -120,$$ or 120 miles west of the city [see Figure 3.3(c)]

The position of the car at 9 A.M. if it is moving 40 mph westward is

$$d = (-3)(-40) = +120,$$ or 120 miles east of the city [see Figure 3.3(d)]

Generalizing this special case, a definition can be stated.

Definition:

Let a and b be positive real numbers. Then

General cases	Special examples
$(+a)(+b) = +ab$	$(+2)(+3) = +6 = 6$
$(-a)(-b) = +ab$	$(-2)(-3) = +6 = 6$
$(+a)(-b) = -ab$	$(+2)(-3) = -6$
$(-a)(+b) = -ab$	$(-2)(+3) = -6$

Rule

The product of two numbers having the same sign is positive. The product of two numbers having unlike signs is negative.

On the number line, multiplication may be represented by repeated additions followed by a rotation. If the multiplier is positive, the rotation is 0°, or no movement. If the multiplier is negative, the rotation is 180°, or to the opposite side of the origin. This graphical interpretation is shown in Figure 3.4.

In Section 1.09 it was seen that every nonzero real number has a reciprocal. This property permits any division problem to be considered as a multiplication problem. Recall that this was done when the CI scale was used on the slide rule. Since a division is the same as a multiplication by the

Figure 3.4
Multiplication of signed numbers

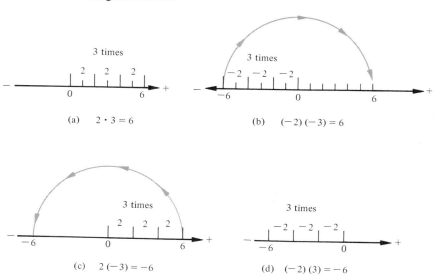

(a) $2 \cdot 3 = 6$

(b) $(-2)(-3) = 6$

(c) $2(-3) = -6$

(d) $(-2)(3) = -6$

reciprocal of the divisor, the rules for the signs are the same. Also, since multiplication and division are inverse operations, every division problem can be checked by multiplication.

Division of signed numbers   Let a and b be positive real numbers.

General case	Example	Check
$\dfrac{+a}{+b} = +\dfrac{a}{b}$	$\dfrac{+10}{+5} = 10\left(\dfrac{1}{5}\right) = 2$	$(+2)(+5) = +10 = 10$
$\dfrac{-a}{-b} = +\dfrac{a}{b}$	$\dfrac{-10}{-5} = (-10)\left(-\dfrac{1}{5}\right) = 2$	$(+2)(-5) = -10$
$\dfrac{+a}{-b} = -\dfrac{a}{b}$	$\dfrac{+10}{-5} = 10\left(-\dfrac{1}{5}\right) = -2$	$(-2)(-5) = +10 = 10$
$\dfrac{-a}{+b} = -\dfrac{a}{b}$	$\dfrac{-10}{+5} = (-10)\left(\dfrac{1}{5}\right) = -2$	$(-2)(+5) = -10$

3.06 / Operations with zero

It was stated in Section 1.09 that the addition or subtraction of zero does not change the original number. This property is stated by using a literal number.

$$x + 0 = x \quad \text{and} \quad x - 0 = x$$

For example, if you earn nothing or if you spend nothing, you have the same amount of money.

If zero is a factor of a product, the product is zero.

$$x \cdot 0 = 0 \cdot x = 0$$

The commutative law for multiplication states that $x \cdot 0 = 0 \cdot x$, and if multiplication is thought of as a repeated addition, then no matter how many times zero is added to itself, the result is zero.

$$x \cdot 0 = 0 + 0 + \cdots + 0 = 0$$

For example, if you have no money, 10 times what you have still leaves your pocket empty.

The quotient of one number divided by another, $\dfrac{a}{b}$, is the number c if and only if there is *exactly one* number c so that $bc = a$. For example,

$$\frac{12}{3} = 4 \qquad \text{because 4 is the only number such that } 3 \cdot 4 = 12$$

$$\frac{0}{3} = 0 \qquad \text{because 0 is the only number such that } 3 \cdot 0 = 0$$

On the other hand, expressions like $\frac{3}{0}$ and $\frac{0}{0}$ are meaningless or undefined.

If $\frac{3}{0} = c$, then $0 \cdot c = 3$. However, $0 \cdot c = 0$ and $3 \neq 0$. Thus, there is no number c and $\frac{3}{0}$ is meaningless.

If $\frac{0}{0} = c$, then $0 \cdot c = 0$. This time, there are too many numbers available for c, because $0 \cdot c = 0$ for all real numbers c. The definition requires that there be exactly one number c. Suppose that $\frac{0}{0} = 0$ and $\frac{0}{0} = 1$. Then it would follow that $0 = 1$, since $\frac{0}{0} = \frac{0}{0}$. But $0 \neq 1$ and there is a contradiction. To avoid contradictions, each symbol must mean exactly one number. Therefore, $\frac{0}{0}$ is considered as a meaningless symbol, or as undefined.

In summary, if x is any real number such that $x \neq 0$, then

$$\frac{0}{x} = 0$$

$$\frac{x}{0} \text{ is meaningless, or undefined}$$

$$\frac{0}{0} \text{ is meaningless, or undefined}$$

In any algebraic problem, division by zero must be excluded. This is done by listing the restrictions on the variables so that the divisor is not 0.

Example 3.15
In the solution of a certain problem, one obtains

$$\frac{(y - 1)(y - 2)(y - 3)}{x - 3} = 0$$

It has been shown that if one factor of a product is zero, the product is zero. The values $y = 1$, $y = 2$, or $y = 3$ do give a zero in the numerator. However, if $x = 3$, there is a zero in the denominator, which gives a meaningless answer no matter what value y may have. Thus, for this problem, the solution would be written $y = 1, 2,$ or 3 and $x \neq 3$.

Problem Set 3.2

1–50

Multiply or divide as indicated, if possible. If an expression is meaningless, write "undefined."

1. $(+5)(-4)$

2. $(-7)(+8)$

3. $(-9)(-6)$

4. $(-12)(-11)$

5. $(-\frac{3}{8})(-\frac{5}{8})$

6. $(+\frac{7}{9})(-\frac{3}{4})$

7. $(-\frac{5}{7})(+\frac{21}{35})$

8. $(-\frac{9}{16})(-\frac{2}{3})$

9. $(-0.125)(8)$

10. $16(-0.375)$

11. $(-2.625)(-4.00)$

12. $(-0.008)(-750)$

13. $(-2)(-2)(-2)$

14. $(-\frac{1}{2})(-\frac{1}{2})(-\frac{1}{2})$

15. $(-\frac{3}{4})(\frac{8}{9})(-\frac{2}{5})$

16. $(0.25)(-3.12)(-0.04)$

17. $(12.34)(0)(-6.73)$

18. $(-9.87)(0)(-8.76)$

19. $(-\frac{1}{2})(-\frac{2}{3})(-\frac{3}{4})(-\frac{4}{5})$

20. $(-0.5)(-0.4)(-0.3)(-0.2)$

21. $\dfrac{+72}{-9}$

22. $\dfrac{-56}{+8}$

23. $\dfrac{-52}{-4}$

24. $\dfrac{-56}{-4}$

25. $\dfrac{-\frac{1}{32}}{625}$

26. $\dfrac{\frac{1}{64}}{-125}$

27. $\dfrac{-\frac{35}{48}}{-\frac{7}{8}}$

28. $\dfrac{-\frac{15}{16}}{-\frac{45}{56}}$

29. $\dfrac{1.0101}{-0.5}$

30. $\dfrac{-111}{0.5}$

31. $\dfrac{(-3\frac{1}{8})(+8)}{-3}$

32. $\dfrac{(-5\frac{2}{5})(-4\frac{3}{4})}{-1\frac{1}{2}}$

33. $\dfrac{(-7.2)(-1.1)}{-0.05}$

34. $\dfrac{(-0.375)(0.160)}{-0.025}$

35. $\dfrac{-0.56}{-0.0001}$

36. $\dfrac{-0.56}{-0.000\,01}$

37. $\dfrac{0.56}{-0.000\,001}$

38. $\dfrac{0.56}{-0.000\,000\,1}$

39. $\dfrac{3-3}{-3.333\,33}$

40. $\dfrac{12-12}{4-4}$

41. $(-8)(-0.375) - (2 - 2)$

42. $\dfrac{5-5}{-9.9999}$

43. $\dfrac{-12 + (8 + 4)}{(-6 - 2) + 8}$

44. $\dfrac{-2.5}{(8 + 6) - 14}$

45. $\dfrac{3.5}{4 - 4}$

46. $\dfrac{(-3)(0)(-5)}{(-5)(0)(-3)}$

47. $(1.01)(-5) + (-5)(0)$

48. $(0.0220)(-6) + (-6)(0)$

49. $\dfrac{(-2)(-6)(0)}{2(-6)(0)}$

50. $(-16)(-0.875) - (5 - 5)$

51–60

Assuming that the directed distance of an airplane is positive $(+)$ or negative $(-)$ according as it is north or south of an airport, that the directed time is counted from noon with $+$ meaning time P.M. and $-$ meaning time A.M., and that the velocity of the airplane is positive if flying north and negative if flying south, find the position of each airplane at the stated time and velocity if the airplane is at the airport at noon.

51. 2:30 P.M. flying 500 mph south
52. 9:30 A.M. flying 500 mph south
53. 9:30 A.M. flying 500 mph north
54. 2:30 P.M. flying 500 mph north
55. 10:45 A.M. flying 600 mph south
56. 10:45 A.M. flying 600 mph north
57. 1:45 P.M. flying 600 mph north
58. 1:45 P.M. flying 600 mph south
59. 11:15 A.M. flying 560 mph south
60. 11:15 A.M. flying 640 mph south

61–68

A seesaw is an everyday example of a lever, a rigid rod with an upright support called a fulcrum. The moment, M, of a force about the fulcrum is a measure of the turning effect of the force or torque and is given by the formula

$$moment = (directed\ distance\ from\ fulcrum)\ (directed\ force)$$

$$M = dF$$

A counterclockwise ↺ moment is positive (+).
A clockwise ↻ moment is negative (−).
A distance to the right of the fulcrum is positive.
A distance to the left of the fulcrum is negative.
A force applied upward is positive.
A force applied downward is negative.

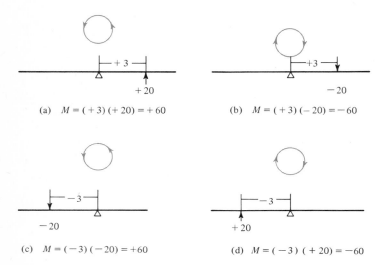

(a) $M = (+3)(+20) = +60$

(b) $M = (+3)(-20) = -60$

(c) $M = (-3)(-20) = +60$

(d) $M = (-3)(+20) = -60$

Figure 3.5
Signed moment products

Find the moments for each of the following, explaining the meaning of each numerical product in words.

Sample
$F = -20\ lb,\ d = -3\ ft.$

SOLUTION
$M = (-3)(-20) = +60$, a 60 ft-lb counterclockwise torque.

61. $F = 30\ lb,\ d = 5\ ft$

62. $F = 30\ lb,\ d = -5\ ft$

63. $F = -30\ lb,\ d = 5\ ft$

64. $F = -30\ lb,\ d = -5\ ft$

65. $F = -25\ lb,\ d = -4\ ft$

66. $F = -25\ lb,\ d = 4\ ft$

67. $F = 25\ lb,\ d = -4\ ft$

68. $F = 25\ lb,\ d = 4\ ft$

3.07 / Addition and subtraction of polynomials

When algebraic terms are added or subtracted, only like terms can be combined. **Like terms** are terms whose literal factors are identical. For example,

$$2x \quad \text{and} \quad 3x \qquad \text{are like terms}$$

$$2x^2 \quad \text{and} \quad -3x^2 \qquad \text{are like terms}$$

$$-2xy \quad \text{and} \quad 3xy \qquad \text{are like terms}$$

Terms whose literal factors are *not* identical are called **unlike terms.** For example,

$$2x \quad \text{and} \quad 2x^2 \qquad \text{are unlike terms}$$

$$3x \quad \text{and} \quad 3y \qquad \text{are unlike terms}$$

There is no possible way to add 2 screws to 3 bolts unless both are called fasteners and then the sum is 2 fasteners + 3 fasteners or 5 fasteners. Similarly, $2x + 3y$ cannot be combined into a single term. However, the sum $2x + 3x$ can be combined into a single term by using the distributive law.

The Distributive Law: $\qquad ac + bc = (a + b)c$

Examples: $\qquad 2x + 3x = (2 + 3)x = 5x$

$$2x + x = (2 + 1)x = 3x$$

$$2x - 3x = 2x + (-3x) = (2 - 3)x = -x$$

$$2x - x = (2 - 1)x = x$$

If algebraic expressions containing several unlike terms are to be added, it is best to rearrange the terms by the commutative and associative laws so that the like terms are together.

Example 3.16
Add: $(5x^2 + 2x - 3) + (2x^2 - 4x - 5)$.

SOLUTION

$$(5x^2 + 2x^2) + (2x - 4x) + (-3 - 5)$$

$$= (5 + 2)x^2 + (2 - 4)x + (-8)$$

$$= 7x^2 - 2x - 8$$

If many quantities are to be added, it is often more convenient to arrange the work vertically with like terms in the same column and with the literal terms arranged alphabetically according to descending powers of one of the variables, usually the variable appearing first in the alphabet.

Example 3.17

Add: $(3x^3 + 2xy + 7y^2) + (2x^2 - 3xy + 4) + (x + xy - y^2)$.

SOLUTION

$$
\begin{array}{lll}
3x^3 & & 2xy + 7y^2 \\
 & 2x^2 & \quad - 3xy \qquad + 4 \\
 & & x + xy - y^2 \\
\hline
3x^3 + 2x^2 + x & & \quad + 6y^2 + 4
\end{array}
$$

Horizontal addition is more common in algebraic problems than vertical addition. When many terms are present, overlooking one term is a very common error. To prevent this, each term can be checkmarked as it is written in the rearrangement of the problem.

Example 3.18

Add: $3x^2 + 2x - 7 - 2x + 4 + 18 - 6x - x^2 - 6 + x$.

SOLUTION

First step: $3x^2 + 2x - 7 - 2x + 4 + 18 - 6x - x^2 - 6 + x$

$= (3x^2 - x^2) +$ other terms

Second step: $3x^2 + 2x - 7 - 2x + 4 + 18 - 6x - x^2 - 6 + x$

$= (3x^2 - x^2) + (2x - 2x - 6x + x) +$ other terms

Third step: $3x^2 + 2x - 7 - 2x + 4 + 18 - 6x - x^2 - 6 + x$

$= (3x^2 - x^2) + (2x - 2x - 6x + x) + (-7 + 4 + 18 - 6)$

$= 2x^2 - 5x + 9$

Problems involving decimals or fractions are usually easier if arranged vertically, because this permits proper alignment for decimals and the selection of the proper denominator for fractions. Problems with unusual fractional numerical coefficients should be converted to decimal equivalents by use of the slide rule.

Example 3.19

Add: $4x^2 + 0.2x + 4.71$, $2x - \frac{17}{83}$, and $3.97x^2 - 0.001x - \frac{18}{61}$.

SOLUTION

$$
\begin{array}{l}
4.00x^2 + 0.200x + 4.710 \\
 2.000x - 0.205 \\
3.97x^2 - 0.001x - 0.295 \\
\hline
7.97x^2 + 2.199x + 4.210
\end{array}
$$

Subtracting a number is the same as adding the additive inverse of the number; that is, $a - b = a + (-b)$. Subtraction problems in algebra may involve the additive inverses of sums and differences.

$$-(a + b) = (-1)(a + b) = (-a) + (-b)$$

$$-(a - b) = (-1)(a - b) = -1[a + (-b)] = (-a) + (+b)$$

Consequently, to subtract one polynomial from another, the sign of *each* term in the subtrahend is changed and the resulting polynomial is then added.

Example 3.20
Subtract: $5x - (2x + 3)$.

SOLUTION
$$5x - (2x + 3) = 5x + (-2x - 3) = 3x - 3.$$

Example 3.21
Subtract: $5x - (2x - 3)$.

SOLUTION
$$5x - (2x - 3) = 5x + (-2x + 3) = 3x + 3.$$

Example 3.22
Subtract $(3x^2 - 4x + 8)$ from $(7x^2 - 3x + 5)$.

SOLUTION   (Horizontal arrangement)

Subtract b from a means
$a - b$:

$$(7x^2 - 3x + 5) - (3x^2 - 4x + 8)$$

Change sign of each term in subtrahend:

$$= (7x^2 - 3x + 5) + (-3x^2 + 4x - 8)$$

Collect like terms:

$$= (7x^2 - 3x^2) + (-3x + 4x) + (5 - 8)$$

$$= 4x^2 + x - 3$$

Example 3.23
Subtract $(3x^2 - 4x + 8)$ from $(7x^2 - 3x + 5)$.

SOLUTION   (Vertical arrangement)

$$\begin{array}{r} 7x^2 - 3x + 5 \\ - \underline{3x^2 - 4x + 8} \end{array} \rightarrow + \begin{array}{r} 7x^2 - 3x + 5 \\ \underline{-3x^2 + 4x - 8} \\ 4x^2 + x - 3 \end{array}$$

It is desirable to develop the ability to perform the sign changes mentally and to write only the result. After sufficient practice, the problem should be written as shown in Example 3.24.

Example 3.24

Subtract $(3x^2 - 4x + 8)$ from $(7x^2 - 3x + 5)$.

SOLUTION

$$
\begin{array}{r}
7x^2 - 3x + 5 \\
-\;\underline{3x^2 - 4x + 8} \\
4x^2 + \;\;x - 3
\end{array}
$$

Example 3.25

Add $(5x^4 - 3x^2y^2 - y^4)$ to $(2y^4 + 2y^2x^2 - 4x^4)$.

SOLUTION

$$
\begin{array}{r}
5x^4 - 3x^2y^2 - \;\;y^4 \\
\underline{-4x^4 + 2x^2y^2 + 2y^4} \\
x^4 - \;\;x^2y^2 + \;\;y^4
\end{array}
$$

Problem Set 3.3

1–10
Add.

1. $2x - 3y$, $-3x + 5y$, $2x - y$. Check, letting $x = 2$ and $y = 1$.
2. $x^2 + 3x$, $5x^2 - 7x$, $-6x^2 + 3x$. Check, letting $x = 2$.
3. $\frac{1}{3}x^2 + \frac{1}{2}x - 1$, $x^2 + \frac{1}{4}$, $\frac{1}{3}x - \frac{3}{4}$. Check, letting $x = 6$.
4. $\frac{1}{5}y^2 - \frac{3}{2}y + 2$, $\frac{1}{5}y + 1$, $\frac{5}{2}y^2 - 3$. Check, letting $y = 10$.
5. $4a^2 + b^2 - 3ab$, $2b^2 - a^2 + ab$, $2ab - 3a^2$
6. $9c^3 + 8c - 10$, $2 + c^2 - 4c$, $5c^2 - 2 - c^3$
7. $2x^3 - x^2y + xy^2 - y^3$, $2x^2y - 3xy^2 + 2y^3$, $x^3 - 2xy^2 - 2y^3$
8. $5a - 3b + 4c$, $2b - 3c - 4a$, $c + 2a - b$
9. $5x^2 - 0.544x + 0.70$, $3x - 0.190$, $1.02x^2 + 0.005x - 1.75$
10. $1.25x^3y - 0.317x^2y$, $0.212xy^2 - 0.021x^2y$, $2xy^2 - 0.007x^3y$

11–20
Perform the indicated operations.

11. From $3x^3 - 7x^2 - 5x + 2$, subtract $x^3 - 4x^2 + 3x - 5$.
12. Subtract $5x - 5y + 5z$ from $4x + 2y - 4z$.
13. Subtract $2a + 6b - 4c$ from $3a + 6b - 5c$.
14. From $a^3 + 2a^2b - 3ab^2 - 4$, subtract $2a^3 + 3a^2b - ab^2 - 5$.
15. $[(x^2 - 2x + 3) - (2x^2 + 3x - 5)] + (x^2 - 4x + 1)$
16. $[(r^2 + 3r - 5) + (2r^2 - 4r - 1)] - (4r^2 - r + 2)$
17. $(2x^3 - x - 1) - \{(x^3 - 5x^2 + 2) - (x^2 + 2x - 3)\}$
18. $(xy + 2x - 5) - \{(x + 2y - 4) - (2xy - 3y + 2)\}$
19. $\{-x - [3x + (-x + 2)]\} - [x - (x + 1)]$
20. $1 - \{5x^2 - [-(x^2 - 2) + x] - 2x\}$

3.08 / Multiplication by monomials

The multiplication of two monomials often involves powers of a variable. Now,

$$x^2 x^3 = (xx)(xxx) = x^5 = x^{2+3}$$

In general,

$$x^m x^n = (xx \ldots \text{to } m \text{ factors})(xx \ldots \text{to } n \text{ factors}) = x^{m+n}$$

Also,

$$(x^2)^3 = (x^2)(x^2)(x^2) = (xx)(xx)(xx) = x^6 = x^{2 \cdot 3}$$

In general,

$$(x^m)^n = x^m x^m \ldots \text{to } n \text{ factors} = x^{m+m+\cdots \text{to } n \text{ terms}} = x^{mn}$$

Exponent Law 1
To multiply two powers having the same base, keep the same base and add the exponents.

Exponent Law 2
To raise a power to a power, keep the same base and multiply the exponents.

The product of monomials involving a combination of numerals and letters is obtained by applying the commutative and associative laws to rearrange the factors.

Example 3.26
Multiply: $2x^3 \cdot 3x^4$.

SOLUTION

$$\begin{aligned} 2x^3 3x^4 &= (2 \cdot 3)(x^3 x^4) \qquad \text{commutative and associative laws} \\ &= 6x^{3+4} \qquad \text{exponent law 1} \\ &= 6x^7 \end{aligned}$$

If a product is raised to a power, each factor of the product is raised to the power. For example,

$$(2x)^4 = (2x)(2x)(2x)(2x) = (2)(2)(2)(2)xxxx = 2^4 x^4$$

In general,

$$(xy)^n = (xy)(xy) \ldots \text{to } n \text{ factors} = (xx \ldots \text{to } n \text{ factors})(yy \ldots \text{to } n \text{ factors})$$

$$= x^n y^n$$

Exponent Law 3
To raise a product to a power, raise each factor to the power.

Example 3.27
Simplify: $(2x^3)^4$.

SOLUTION

$$(2x^3)^4 = 2^4(x^3)^4 \qquad \text{exponent law 3}$$
$$= 16x^{12} \qquad \text{exponent law 2}$$

Example 3.28
Simplify: $2(x^3)^4$.

SOLUTION

$$2(x^3)^4 = 2x^{12} \qquad \text{(since 2 is not inside the parentheses,}$$

2 is *not* raised to the fourth power)

Example 3.29
Multiply: $(5xy^2z^3)(3xy^2)(2x^2z)$.

SOLUTION

$$= (5 \cdot 3 \cdot 2)(xxx^2)(y^2y^2)(z^3z)$$
$$= 30x^{1+1+2}y^{2+2}z^{3+1}$$
$$= 30x^4y^4z^4$$

Example 3.30
Simplify: $(\frac{1}{2}xy^2z^3)^3$.

SOLUTION

$$= (\tfrac{1}{2})^3(x)^3(y^2)^3(z^3)^3$$
$$= \tfrac{1}{8}x^3y^{2 \cdot 3}z^{3 \cdot 3}$$
$$= \tfrac{1}{8}x^3y^6z^9$$

Example 3.31
Simplify: $(-2x^2y^3)^5$.

SOLUTION

$$= [(-1)(2x^2y^3)]^5$$
$$= (-1)^5 2^5(x^2)^5(y^3)^5$$
$$= (-1)(32)x^{10}y^{15}$$
$$= -32x^{10}y^{15}$$

The distributive law is used to obtain the product of a polynomial multiplied by a monomial.

Example 3.32
Multiply: $2.1x^2y^3(4.2xy - 0.3x^3)$.

SOLUTION

$$= (2.1x^2y^3)(4.2xy) - (2.1x^2y^3)(0.3x^3)$$
$$= 8.82x^3y^4 - 0.63x^5y^3$$

Example 3.33
Multiply: $-3st(r^2 + 2s^2 + 3t^2 - 4u^2)$.

SOLUTION

$$= -3r^2st - 6s^3t - 9st^3 + 12stu^2$$

Problem Set 3.4

1–6
Write each product using exponents.

Sample
$2 \cdot 2 \cdot 2\ xxxx = 2^3x^4$.

1. $5 \cdot 5 \cdot 5 \cdot 5\ xxyyy$
2. $3 \cdot 3 \cdot 3 \cdot 3\ xxxxxyy$
3. $(5axxy)(5aaxyyy)$

4. $(4bbxyyy)(4bxyyy)$
5. $(7rrsssss)(49rs)$
6. $(13tttssss)(169tss)$

7–10
Express each of the following as a single power.

Sample
$$\frac{(2)(2)(2)xxx}{(3)(3)(3)} = \left(\frac{2x}{3}\right)^3.$$

7. $(-2)(-2)(-2)(-2)xxxx$

8. $(-3)(-3)(-3)(-3)(-3)(-3)yyyyyy$

9. $\dfrac{(-5)(-5)(-5)rrr}{(2)(2)(2)}$

10. $\dfrac{(-8)(-8)(-8)(-8)(-8)bbbbb}{(5)(5)(5)(5)(5)}$

11–60
Simplify by doing all possible multiplications.

11. $5x^2 \cdot 3y^2 \cdot 2xy$

12. $2x^3 \cdot 7xy^2 \cdot 5x^2y$

13. $(2x^2)^5$

14. $(3x^3)^4$

15. $-25(4x^3)^2$

16. $(-25 \cdot 4x^3)^2$

17. $(-xy^4)^3$

18. $-x(y^4)^3$

19. $\left(\dfrac{-3a^2}{2}\right)^5$

20. $\left(\dfrac{-2a^3}{3}\right)^3$

21. $(-4a^2bc)(-3abc^2)(-2a^3b^2c^2)$

22. $(-5rst^3)(-6r^2s^2t^2)(-7r^3st)$

23. $(-\frac{1}{4}x^3y^2z)^4$

24. $(-\frac{2}{5}x^2y^3z^4)^3$

25. $(-3x^2y^4)^5$

26. $(-10x^3y)^6$

27. $3x^2y(0.50x^3 - 0.25y^3)$

28. $-5x^2y^3(0.04xy + 0.06x^2y^2)$

29. $-4abc(0.15a^2b^2c^2 + 0.45a^3b^3c^3)$

30. $0.125rs(80r^5 - 160s^5)$

31. $-0.002t^5(1.25t^3 - 3.75t^2 + 0.25)$

32. $-0.004d^7(5.00d^2 + 2.50d - 1.25)$

33. $7x^2(2x^2 + 5x - 2)$

34. $6x^3(4x^2 - 3x + 1)$

35. $abcd(a + b - c - d)$

36. $qrst(q^2 - r^2 + s^2 - t^2)$

37. $2x(4x^2 - 6xy + 9y^2) + 3y(4x^2 - 6xy + 9y^2)$

38. $5x(25x^2 + 10xy + 4y^2) - 2y(25x^2 + 10xy + 4y^2)$

39. $x(x^4 + x^3 + x^2 + x + 1) - (x^4 + x^3 + x^2 + x + 1)$

40. $y(y^4 - y^3 + y^2 - y + 1) + (y^4 - y^3 + y^2 - y + 1)$

41. $(x^a)^b + (x^b)^a$

42. $(y^m)^{3n} + (y^n)^{3m}$

43. $3a^2(a^2 - 2b^2) + 4b^2(a^2 + b^2)$

44. $x(x + y) + y(x - y)$

45. $3x(x - 2y) + 2y(y - 3x)$

46. $5a^2(a^2 - 2b^2) + 2b^2(b^2 - 5a^2)$

47. $z^n(z - 1) + z(z^{n-1} - 1)$

48. $z^{m-1}(z + 1) - z(z^m + 1)$

49. $(3^x)^2(3^2)^x$

50. $(5^{3y})^2(5^{2y})^3$

51. $2[2x(3x - 2) - 3x(x + 3)]$

52. $3y[x(4y + 1) - 2y(x - 2)]$

53. $x^2 - \{5x[(x + 1)x - (x - 1)x] - x^2\}$

54. $6xy - \{2[x + y] + 2[x(y - 1) + y(x - 1)]\}$

55. $x(x^2 - 2x + 4) + 2(x^2 - 2x + 4)$

56. $y(y^2 + 3y + 9) - 3(y^2 + 3y + 9)$

57. $x(y + z) + y(x + z) + z(x - y)$

58. $x^2(y^2 - z^2) + y^2(z^2 - x^2) + z^2(x^2 - y^2)$

59. $[(x + y) - (x - y)] \cdot [(x + y) + (x - y)]$

60. $[(x^3 + x^2) - (x^3 - x^2)] \cdot [(x^3 + x^2) + (x^3 - x^2)]$

3.09 / Multiplication of polynomials

The multiplication of polynomials involves a repeated application of the distributive law. The algebraic process is the same as that used in arithmetic in the multiplication of two numbers each having more than one digit. In the multiplication problem

$$
\begin{array}{r}
45 \\
\times \quad 23 \\
\hline
15 \\
120 \\
100 \\
800 \\
\hline
1035
\end{array}
$$

all the zeros are written and each partial product is written with the carry operation omitted. Rewriting this problem horizontally,

$$(23 \cdot 45) = (20 + 3)(40 + 5)$$

$$= 20(40 + 5) + 3(40 + 5)$$

$$= (20 \cdot 40) + (20 \cdot 5) + (3 \cdot 40) + (3 \cdot 5)$$

$$= \quad 800 \quad + \quad 100 \quad + \quad 120 \quad + \quad 15$$

$$= 1035$$

Similarly,

$$(a + b)(c + d) = a(c + d) + b(c + d) = ac + ad + bc + bd$$

This concept can be extended to two factors each having any number of terms in its sum.

Example 3.34
Multiply: $(2x^2 - 3x + 1)(3x^2 - 4x - 1)$.

SOLUTION

$$= 2x^2(3x^2 - 4x - 1) - 3x(3x^2 - 4x - 1) + 1(3x^2 - 4x - 1)$$

$$= 6x^4 - 8x^3 - 2x^2 - 9x^3 + 12x^2 + 3x + 3x^2 - 4x - 1$$

$$= 6x^4 + (-8x^3 - 9x^3) + (-2x^2 + 12x^2 + 3x^2) + (3x - 4x) - 1$$

$$= 6x^4 - 17x^3 + 13x^2 - x - 1$$

For problems involving polynomials other than binomials, a vertical arrangement tends to reduce errors. Example 3.34 could also be done as shown in Example 3.35.

Example 3.35

Multiply: $(2x^2 - 3x + 1)(3x^2 - 4x - 1)$.

SOLUTION

$$
\begin{array}{r}
2x^2 - 3x + 1 \\
3x^2 - 4x - 1 \\
\hline
6x^4 - 9x^3 + 3x^2 \\
- 8x^3 + 12x^2 - 4x \\
- 2x^2 + 3x - 1 \\
\hline
6x^4 - 17x^3 + 13x^2 - x - 1
\end{array}
$$

Note that the signs in the upper line of this problem are $+ - +$. Each of the three lines for the partial products obtained during the multiplication must have either exactly this same pattern, $+ - +$, or else its opposite, $- + -$. The eye can quickly check to make sure that no errors in signs have been made. This concept applies to any given sign pattern since a positive multiplier will keep the same pattern and a negative multiplier will change the sign of each term.

Problem Set 3.5

Multiply and simplify.

1. $(x + 3)(x - 2)$
2. $(x - 4)(x + 5)$
3. $(x + 2)(x + 5)$
4. $(x - 3)(x - 4)$
5. $(x - 5)(x - 6)$
6. $(x + 5)(x + 7)$
7. $(x + 3)(x - 3)$
8. $(y + 5)(y - 5)$
9. $(2x - 5y)(2x + 5y)$
10. $(3x - 4y)(3x + 4y)$
11. $(5x + 3)(5x + 3)$
12. $(7x - 2)(7x - 2)$
13. $(6x - 5y)(6x - 5y)$
14. $(8x + 3y)(8x + 3y)$
15. $(2x - 1)(3x + 4)$
16. $(5x + 2)(3x - 5)$
17. $(6y - 7)(7y - 6)$
18. $(4y - 9)(9y - 4)$
19. $(25x + 2y)(4x + 5y)$
20. $(3x + 7y)(2x + 3y)$

21. $(x - 2)(x^2 + 2x + 4)$
22. $(x + 3)(x^2 - 3x + 9)$
23. $(y + 5)(y^2 - 5y + 25)$
24. $(y - 7)(y^2 + 7y + 49)$
25. $(a + b + c)(a - b - c)$
26. $(a^2 - b^2 + c^2)(a^2 + b^2 - c^2)$
27. $(x^2 + 2x - 3)(x^2 - 2x - 3)$
28. $(y^2 + 2y + 2)(y^2 - 2y + 2)$
29. $(x - 3)(y + 2)$
30. $(x + 4)(y - 5)$
31. $(x^2 + 1)(x - 7)$
32. $(y^2 - 1)(y + 6)$
33. $(y^3 - 1)(y^2 - 9)$
34. $(x^3 - 8)(y^2 - 4)$
35. $(2y - 1)(4x^2 - 9)$
36. $(2x + 3y)(x^3 - 8y^3)$
37. $(x + y)(x - y)(x^2 + y^2)$
38. $(x^2 + 2y^2)(x^2 - 2y^2)(x^4 + 4y^4)$
39. $(x^2 + 4x + 4)(x^2 + 4x + 4)$
40. $(y^2 - 6y + 9)(y^2 - 6y + 9)$

3.10 / Division of monomials

Since

$$\frac{2^7}{2^3} = \frac{2 \cdot 2 \cdot 2 \cdot 2 \cdot 2 \cdot 2 \cdot 2}{2 \cdot 2 \cdot 2} = 2 \cdot 2 \cdot 2 \cdot 2 = 2^4 = 2^{7-3}$$

if n is larger than m,[1] the operation in general form is

$$\frac{x^n}{x^m} = \frac{(xx \ldots \text{to } n \text{ factors})}{(xx \ldots \text{to } m \text{ factors})} = xx \ldots \text{to } n - m \text{ factors} = x^{n-m}$$

Exponent Law 4

To divide powers having the same base, subtract the exponents and keep the common base.

If $n = m$, then $\dfrac{x^n}{x^n} = 1$, since $x^n = 1 \cdot x^n$, just as $\dfrac{2^5}{2^5} = \dfrac{32}{32} = 1$. If exponent law 4 were applied to this special case, $\dfrac{2^5}{2^5}$ would equal $2^{5-5} = 2^0$ and in general, $\dfrac{x^n}{x^n} = x^{n-n} = x^0$. Since in all cases where $x \neq 0$, $\dfrac{x^n}{x^n} = 1$, it is convenient to define the value of x^0 as 1.

Definition of x^0

If $x \neq 0$, then $x^0 = 1$.

Example 3.36

Simplify: $\dfrac{36x^4 y^2 z}{-4xyz}$.

SOLUTION

$$\frac{36x^4 y^2 z}{-4xyz} = \left(\frac{36}{-4}\right)\left(\frac{x^4}{x^1}\right)\left(\frac{y^2}{y^1}\right)\left(\frac{z^1}{z^1}\right)$$

$$= -9x^{4-1} y^{2-1} z^{1-1} \qquad \left.\begin{array}{l} \\ \\ \\ \\ \\ \end{array}\right\} \text{done mentally}$$

$$= -9x^3 y^1 z^0$$

$$= -9x^3 y$$

---

[1] The case m larger than n will be discussed later.

3.11 / Division of polynomial by monomial

The division of a polynomial by a monomial is done by using the distributive law, and considering division as a multiplication by a reciprocal.

$$\frac{a + b}{c} = (a + b)\left(\frac{1}{c}\right) = a\left(\frac{1}{c}\right) + b\left(\frac{1}{c}\right) = \frac{a}{c} + \frac{b}{c}$$

$$\frac{a + b + c}{d} = (a + b + c)\left(\frac{1}{d}\right) = \frac{a}{d} + \frac{b}{d} + \frac{c}{d}$$

Rule for Division of a Polynomial by a Monomial
Divide each term of the polynomial by the monomial divisor.

Example 3.37
Simplify: $\dfrac{12x^3 - 9x^2 + 15x}{3x}$.

SOLUTION

$$\frac{12x^3 - 9x^2 + 15x}{3x} = \frac{12x^3}{3x} - \frac{9x^2}{3x} + \frac{15x}{3x}$$

$$= 4x^2 - 3x + 5$$

Problem Set 3.6

Divide as indicated.

1. $\dfrac{72x^5y^3z^2}{18x^2y^2z^2}$

2. $\dfrac{52x^4y^3z}{13x^3y^3z}$

3. $\dfrac{-76a^4b^6c^8}{19ab^2c^4}$

4. $\dfrac{0.343r^9s^6t^3}{-0.049r^3s^2t}$

5. $\dfrac{-9.99P^7Q^5}{-0.37P^4Q^4}$

6. $\dfrac{-7.68I^{12}J^{16}}{0.24I^6J^8}$

7. $\dfrac{10.2r^{10}s^8t^6}{-1.7r^2s^2t^6}$

8. $\dfrac{-260a^6b^6c^6}{-65a^6b^2c}$

9. $\dfrac{(3x^2y^3)^2(-2xy^3)^3}{(2xy^2)^4(-3xy^2)^2}$

10. $\dfrac{(-5x^3y^3)^2(2x^2y)^4}{(-2x^2y)^3(5x^4y^3)^2}$

11. $\dfrac{5x^2 - 45x}{5x}$

12. $\dfrac{9x^3 - 18x^2}{9x}$

13. $\dfrac{35x^2y^2 - 42xy}{-7xy}$

15. $\dfrac{9.1x^2 - 6.5x + 5.2}{-1.3}$

14. $\dfrac{54a^3b^2 - 90a^2b^3}{-18a^2b^2}$

16. $\dfrac{-10.2x^3 + 8.5x^2 - 6.8x}{-1.7x}$

17. $\dfrac{-1.33x^4 + 1.14x^3 - 7.6x^2}{-0.19x^2}$

18. $\dfrac{0.138y^5 - 9.2y^4 + 0.115y^2}{-0.023y^2}$

19. $\dfrac{2.56a^3b^2c + 1.28a^2bc^3 - 0.64ab^3c - 0.32abc}{-0.016abc}$

20. $\dfrac{2.43r^4s^2t^2 - 0.81r^2s^4t^2 + 0.27r^2s^2t^4 - 0.9r^2s^2t^2}{-0.15r^2s^2t^2}$

3.12 / Special products

Certain products appear so often in mathematics that their forms should be memorized. These forms are listed in Table 3.2. When the forms are memorized, the special products can be written immediately, which saves much time and effort.

Table 3.2

Name of factors	Factors	Product	Name of product
Sum and difference	$(A + B)(A - B)$	$= A^2 - B^2$	Difference of squares
Square of binomial	$(A + B)(A + B)$	$= A^2 + 2AB + B^2$	Perfect square
	$(A - B)(A - B)$	$= A^2 - 2AB + B^2$	
Simple binomials	$(x + A)(x + B)$	$= x^2 + (A + B)x + AB$	Simple trinomial
General binomials	$(Ax + B)(Cx + D)$	$= ACx^2 + (AD + BC)x + BD$	General trinomial
Unrelated binomials	$(A + B)(C + D)$	$= AC + AD + BC + BD$	Double distributive
Binomial–trinomial	$(A + B)(A^2 - AB + B^2)$	$= A^3 + B^3$	Sum of cubes
	$(A - B)(A^2 + AB + B^2)$	$= A^3 - B^3$	Difference of cubes

Example 3.38
Multiply: $(x + 5y)(x - 5y)$.

SOLUTION

$$(A + B)(A - B) = A^2 - B^2 \qquad \text{(form is recognized)}$$
$$(x + 5y)(x - 5y) = x^2 - 25y^2$$

Example 3.39
Multiply: $(x - 5y)^2$.

SOLUTION

$$(A - B)(A - B) = A^2 - 2AB + B^2$$
$$(x - 5y)(x - 5y) = x^2 - 10xy + 25y^2$$

Example 3.40
Multiply: $(x - 5)(x + 6)$.

SOLUTION

$$(x + A)(x + B) = x^2 + (A + B)x + AB$$
$$(x - 5)(x + 6) = x^2 + (-5 + 6)x + (-5)(6)$$
$$= x^2 + x - 30$$

Example 3.41
Multiply: $(2x + 3)(3x - 5)$.

SOLUTION

$$(Ax + B)(Cx + D) = ACx^2 + (AD + BC)x + BD$$
$$(2x + 3)(3x - 5) = (2 \cdot 3)x^2 + (-10 + 9)x + 3(-5)$$
$$= 6x^2 - x - 15$$

Note that in Example 3.41 the first term of the product is the product of the first terms of the factors. The third term of the product is the product of the last terms of the factors. The middle term of the product is the sum of the inner and outer products:

$$(2x + 3)(3x - 5)$$

$9x$	inner product
$-10x$	outer product
$-x$	sum of inner and outer products

Example 3.42
Multiply: $(2x + 3)(3y - 5)$.

SOLUTION

$$(A + B)(C + D) = AC + AD + BC + BD$$
$$(2x + 3)(3y - 5) = 2x(3y) + 2x(-5) + 3(3y) + 3(-5)$$
$$= 6xy - 10x + 9y - 15$$

Example 3.43
Multiply: $(2x + 3)(4x^2 - 6x + 9)$.

SOLUTION

$$(A + B)(A^2 - AB + B^2) = A^3 + B^3$$
$$(2x + 3)(4x^2 - 6x + 9) = (2x)^3 + (3)^3$$
$$= 8x^3 + 27$$

Example 3.44
Multiply: $(2x - 3)(4x^2 + 6x + 9)$.

SOLUTION

$$(A - B)(A^2 + AB + B^2) = A^3 - B^3$$
$$(2x - 3)(4x^2 + 6x + 9) = (2x)^3 - 3^3$$
$$= 8x^3 - 27$$

Problem Set 3.7

Multiply by recognizing a special product.

1. $(3x - 4y)(3x + 4y)$

2. $(7x + 6y)(7x - 6y)$

3. $(5xy + 1)(5xy - 1)$

4. $(9ab - 1)(9ab + 1)$

5. $(9ab - 1)(9ab - 1)$

6. $(7xy + 1)(7xy + 1)$

7. $(2x + 3y)(2x + 3y)$

8. $(6x - 5y)(6x - 5y)$

9. $(x - 0.4)(x + 30)$

10. $(x - 0.3)(x + 0.04)$

11. $(y - 0.3)(y - \frac{1}{25})$

12. $(y - 0.06)(y - \frac{1}{5})$

13. $(2x + 3)(5x + 2)$

14. $(3x - 4)(2x - 3)$

15. $(5y - 2)(y + 6)$

16. $(4y + 7)(y - 2)$

17. $(0.2x + 0.3)(0.3y - 0.5)$

18. $(x - 0.06)(y + 0.07)$

19. $(1.1 - 3.0y)(1.0 - 0.4x)$

20. $(2.1 - 6.0x)(1.1 - 1.0y)$

21. $(x + 5)(x^2 - 5x + 25)$

22. $(x - 2)(x^2 + 2x + 4)$

23. $(3x - 1)(9x^2 + 3x + 1)$

24. $(4x + 1)(16x^2 - 4x + 1)$

25. $(x - 4)(x^2 + 4)$

26. $(y + 7)(y^2 - 7)$

27. $(x + 6)(y + 6)$

28. $(y - 5)(x - 5)$

29. $(9x^3 - y^2)(9x^3 + y^2)$

30. $(1.1x^5 + y^4)(1.1x^5 + y^4)$

31. $(0.13a^2b^3 - 0.8c^4)(0.13a^2b^3 - 0.8c^4)$

32. $(1.5r^3t^6 + 2.1)(1.5r^3t^6 - 2.1)$

33. $(x^4 - 8)(x^8 + 8x^4 + 64)$

34. $(y^3 + 9)(y^6 - 9y^3 + 81)$

35. $(0.1r^6 + 0.4)(0.01r^{12} - 0.04r^6 + 0.16)$

36. $(2.5a^8 - \frac{1}{2})(6.25a^{16} + 1.25a^8 + \frac{1}{4})$

37. $(x + y + 1)(x + y - 1)$

38. $(x^2 + 2 + 2x)(x^2 + 2 - 2x)$

39. $(x - 3y)(x + 3y)(x^2 + 9y^2)$

40. $(x^3 + 1)(x^3 - 1)(x^6 + 1)$

3.13 / Factoring

The fundamental theorem of arithmetic states that any positive integer can be expressed as a product of primes in exactly one way, disregarding the order of the factors. For example,

$$200 = 2 \cdot 2 \cdot 2 \cdot 5 \cdot 5$$

Although $200 = 5 \cdot 40$ and $200 = 8 \cdot 25$, the numbers 40, 8, and 25 are not primes and $2 \cdot 2 \cdot 2 \cdot 5 \cdot 5$ is the only prime factorization, where each factor is a prime number.

If rational numbers are permitted as factors, the factorization is no longer unique. For example,

$$20 = \frac{1}{2} \cdot 2 \cdot 2 \cdot 2 \cdot 5$$

$$20 = \frac{1}{3} \cdot 3 \cdot 2 \cdot 2 \cdot 5$$

$$20 = \frac{1}{7} \cdot 7 \cdot 2 \cdot 2 \cdot 5 \qquad \text{and so on}$$

For this reason, unless it is otherwise stated, the factorization of a polynomial is restricted to polynomial factors whose coefficients are integers.

An **integral polynomial** is a polynomial whose coefficients are integers.

A **prime polynomial** is an integral polynomial that has no integral polynomial factors except itself and ± 1.

Note the similarity to the terms integer and prime integer, since a prime integer has no integers for factors except itself and ± 1.

Examples:

Prime polynomials:

$$2x - 5, \ x^2 + 9, \ 4x^2 - 6xy + 9y^2$$

Polynomials, not prime:

$$4x - 10 \qquad \text{since } 4x - 10 = 2(2x - 5)$$

$$x^2 - 9 \qquad \text{since } x^2 - 9 = (x - 3)(x + 3)$$

$$4x^2 - 12xy + 9y^2 \qquad \text{since this equals } (2x - 3y)^2$$

The instruction "**factor**," unless otherwise stated, means "express an integral polynomial as a product of prime polynomials."

The prime factors of a polynomial are obtained by first using the distributive law to find the highest common monomial factor if there is one, and by then recognizing the resulting polynomial as a special product.

Example 3.45
Factor: $14x^2y - 63xy^2 + 49xy$.

SOLUTION

Recognizing a common monomial factor, apply the distributive law:

$$14x^2y - 63xy^2 + 49xy = 7xy(2x - 9y + 7)$$

Example 3.46
Factor: $2x^2 - 18y^2$.

SOLUTION

Using the distributive law: $\qquad 2x^2 - 18y^2 = 2(x^2 - 9y^2)$

Noting the difference in squares: $\qquad\qquad = 2(x + 3y)(x - 3y)$

Example 3.47
Factor: $9x^2 - 12xy + 4y^2$.

SOLUTION

Recognizing the form: $\quad A^2 \quad - \quad 2AB \quad + \quad B^2 = (A - B)^2$

$$(3x)^2 - 2(3x)(2y) + (2y)^2 = (3x - 2y)^2$$

Example 3.48
Factor: $x^2 + x - 12$.

Discussion   The form to be used is $x^2 + (A + B)x + AB = (x + A)(x + B)$.

From the memorized special products the coefficient of the middle term is an algebraic sum and the coefficient of the last term is an algebraic product. The signs of these two coefficients permits reduction of the number of combinations of integers that must be tested.

Rule 1

For the third term, a positive sign states that the integers sought have the same sign; a negative sign states that the integers differ in sign.

Rule 2

The sign of the middle term is the sign of both integers sought if alike, and of the one having the larger absolute value if different.

In this example, the positive integral factors of 12 are 1 and 12, 2 and 6, 3 and 4. Rule 1 states signs are unlike, and thus the absolute values are subtracted. Rule 2 states that the larger in absolute value is positive. This narrows the choice to three possibilities:

$$12 - 1 = 11, \qquad 6 - 2 = 4, \qquad 4 - 3 = 1$$

The last combination is the one sought, because the coefficient of the middle term is 1.

SOLUTION

$$x^2 + x - 12 = (x + 4)(x - 3).$$

For factoring the general trinomial, a large number of possible combinations may exist, since all combinations of integral factors of the first and third term must be investigated. Again, using the sign rules will reduce the number of trials. An arithmetic arrangement can be used as an aid as shown in Example 3.49.

Example 3.49

Factor: $6x^2 - 11x - 10$.

SOLUTION

$$ACx^2 + (AD + BC)x + \quad BD \quad = (Ax + B)(Cx + D)$$
$$6x^2 + \quad (-11)x \quad + (-10) = (\quad)(\quad)$$

The factors of 6 are (1 and 6) and (2 and 3). The factors of 10 are (1 and 10) and (2 and 5). Therefore, the possible factors producing the first and third terms are as follows:

$(x + 1)(6x - 10)$, $(x - 1)(6x + 10)$, $(x + 2)(6x - 5)$, $(x - 2)(6x + 5)$

$(x + 10)(6x - 1)$, $(x - 10)(6x + 1)$, $(x + 5)(6x - 2)$, $(x - 5)(6x + 2)$

$(2x + 1)(3x - 10)$, $(2x - 1)(3x + 10)$, $(2x + 2)(3x - 5)$, $(2x - 2)(3x + 5)$

$(2x - 10)(3x + 1)$, $(2x + 10)(3x - 1)$, $(2x - 5)(3x + 2)$, $(2x + 5)(3x - 2)$

Since factorization over the integers is unique, exactly one of these combinations produces the correct middle term. The possibilities must be tried until the right one is found. The number of trials may be reduced as follows:

Since the middle coefficient (-11) is negative, the inner and outer products are unlike in sign and the larger in absolute value is negative. The first and third coefficients are written in vertical form and added. If the result is not the value of the second coefficient, divide one coefficient by any of its integral factors and multiply the other by the same number. For this example,

$$
\begin{array}{rrr}
-10 & +5 & -15 \\
+6 & -12 & +4 \\
\hline
-4 & -7 & -11
\end{array}
$$

The combination $-15 + 4 = -11$ produces the correct middle coefficient and the factorization has the following form:

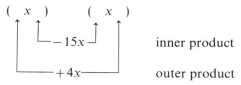

$$\text{inner product}$$

$$\text{outer product}$$

The factors of 15 and 4 are obtained and then grouped as follows:

$$
\begin{array}{l}
(1 \text{ and } 15) \text{ with } (1 \text{ and } 4) \\
(1 \text{ and } 15) \text{ with } (2 \text{ and } 2) \\
(3 \text{ and } 5) \text{ with } (1 \text{ and } 4) \\
(3 \text{ and } 5) \text{ with } (2 \text{ and } 2)
\end{array}
$$

It is noted that the first coefficient 6 can be formed only by the factors 3 and 2. Therefore,

$$6x^2 - 11x - 10 = (2x - 5)(3x + 2)$$

Factorization may always be checked by multiplication, either horizontally or vertically. Checking Example 3.49, horizontally,

$$(2x - 5)(3x + 2) = (2x - 5)3x + (2x - 5)2$$
$$= 6x^2 - 15x + 4x - 10$$
$$= 6x^2 - 11x - 10$$

Vertically,

$$
\begin{array}{r}
2x \ - \ 5 \\
3x \ + \ 2 \\
\hline
6x^2 \ - \ 15x \\
+ \ 4x - 10 \\
\hline
6x^2 \ - \ 11x - 10
\end{array}
$$

Example 3.50

Factor: $2x^3 - 6x^2 + x - 3$.

SOLUTION

Since four terms are seen, the double distributive special product is tried.

$$2x^3 - 6x^2 + x - 3 = (2x^3 - 6x^2) + (x - 3) \quad \text{grouping 2 by 2}$$
$$= 2x^2(x - 3) + 1 \cdot (x - 3) \quad \text{factoring each group}$$
$$= (x - 3)(2x^2 + 1) \quad \text{distributive law}$$

Example 3.51

Factor: $27x^3 - y^3$.

SOLUTION

$$A^3 - B^3 = (A - B)(A^2 + AB + B^2)$$
$$(3x)^3 - y^3 = (3x - y)(9x^2 + 3xy + y^2)$$

Example 3.52

Factor: $125x^3 + 343$.

SOLUTION

$$A^3 + B^3 = (A + B)(A^2 - AB + B^2)$$
$$(5x)^3 + 7^3 = (5x + 7)(25x^2 - 35x + 49)$$

Problem Set 3.8

Factor. If not possible, write "no solution."

1. $5x - 20y$
2. $12x + 54y$
3. $28x^3 + 8x^2y - 4x^2$
4. $24x^2y - 8xy^2 + 8xy$
5. $26x^6y^3 + 104x^4y^5$
6. $34x^7y^5 - 51x^5y^7$
7. $4a^2bc - 8ab^2c + abc^2$
8. $7a^4b^2c^2 + 21a^3b^3c^3 - 7a^2b^2c^4$
9. $r + rst$
10. $k - klm$
11. $x^2 - 9$
12. $y^2 - 36$
13. $25x^2 - 4y^2$
14. $49x^2 - 64y^2$
15. $81a^2 - 1$

16. $121b^2 - 1$
17. $4x^3 - 9$
18. $196k^2 - 225n^4$
19. $16r^4 - t^2$
20. $36x^2 + 1$
21. $x^6 - 400y^8z^4$
22. $y^5 - x^2$
23. $y^2 + 64$
24. $256x^8 - 169y^{10}z^{12}$
25. $x^2 - 14x + 49$
26. $y^2 + 16x + 64$
27. $9a^2 + 6a + 1$
28. $36b^2 - 12b + 1$
29. $25r^2 - 20rs + 4s^2$
30. $16k^2 - 88kt + 121t^2$

31. $x^2 + 2x + 4$
32. $100y^6 - 20y^3 + 1$
33. $81x^4 + 18x^2 + 1$
34. $Y^2 + 4Y - 4$
35. $a^{10} + 169 - 26a^5$
36. $Y^2Z^2 - 6YZ + 36$
37. $a^2b^2 + 14ab - 49$
38. $b^{12} + 225 - 30b^6$
39. $x^2 - 5x + 6$
40. $y^2 - 5x - 6$
41. $x^4 + 4x^2y - 21y^2$
42. $x^6 - 10x^3y + 21y^2$
43. $x^2 - 7x + 5$
44. $a^2 - 2a - 8$
45. $t^2 - 7t - 60$
46. $x^2 + 5x - 2$
47. $b^2 - 70bc^3 + 1200c^6$
48. $k^2 - 50kn^4 + 600n^8$
49. $3x^2 + 5x - 2$
50. $7x^2 - 20x - 3$
51. $6y^2 - 5y + 1$
52. $10y^2 - 9y + 2$
53. $8a^2 + 5ab - 3b^2$
54. $6x^2 - x + 1$
55. $5x^2 + 3x + 2$
56. $2a^2 + 5ab + 2b^2$
57. $3c^4 - c^2 - 4$
58. $5c^6 + 14c^3 - 3$
59. $6x^8 + 6 - 13x^4$
60. $9y^4 + 10 - 21y^2$

61. $12x^2 - 7xy - 45y^2$
62. $20x^2 + xy - 12y^2$
63. $x(y + 2) + 3(y + 2)$
64. $y(x - 3) + 5(x - 3)$
65. $5xy(x^2 + 1) + (x^2 + 1)$
66. $3y^2(y - 1) + (y - 1)$
67. $2a^3(a + 2) - (a + 2)$
68. $7b^2(b - 4) - (b - 4)$
69. $xy - 12 - 4x + 3y$
70. $xy - 5y - 2x + 10$
71. $3x + 3y + xy + y^2$
72. $3x - 6y + xy - 18$
73. $x^3 - x^2 + x - 1$
74. $2y^3 - y + 2y^2 - 1$
75. $3a^3 - 6a^2 - a + 2$
76. $10b^3 + 15b^2 - 2b - 3$
77. $x^6y^4 + x^4y^6 - 5x^2 - 5y^2$
78. $x^6y^3 + 7x^3y^3 - 4x^3 - 28$
79. $x^3 + 8$
80. $x^3 - 27$
81. $343y^3 - 1$
82. $216y^3 + 1$
83. $125x^3 - 64y^3$
84. $169x^3 + 243y^3$
85. $27y^6 + 64z^9$
86. $8y^9 - 125z^{12}$
87. $8x^8 - 1$
88. $27y^{10} + 1$
89. $(a + b)^3 + (a - b)^3$
90. $(a + b)^3 - (a - b)^3$

3.14 / Techniques of factoring

Some products require more than one application of a special product.

Example 3.53
Factor: $4x^4 - 64y^4$.

SOLUTION

$$4x^4 - 64y^4 = 4(x^4 - 16y^4) \qquad \text{distributive law}$$
$$= 4(x^2 - 4y^2)(x^2 + 4y^2) \qquad \text{difference of squares}$$
$$= 4(x - 2y)(x + 2y)(x^2 + 4y^2) \qquad \text{difference of squares}$$

A polynomial is not completely factored unless each factor is either a monomial or a prime integral polynomial. The highest common monomial should always be found first, since this simplifies the later factorization when it is needed. As a general rule, apply the 3 R's:

R_1 remove highest common factor (HCF)
R_2 recognize a special product
R_3 rearrange terms if necessary

One method for recognizing a special product is to count the number of terms. If there are two terms, the product may be a difference of squares, a sum of cubes, or a difference of cubes. If there are three terms, the product may be a perfect square or a product of two related binomial factors. If four or more terms are present, the terms should be grouped to recognize either the double distributive product or one or more perfect-square trinomials.

Example 3.54
Factor: $6x^3 + 6x^2 - 72x$.

SOLUTION

$6x^3 + 6x^2 - 72x = 6x(x^2 + x - 12)$ remove HCF

$= 6x(x + 4)(x - 3)$ recognize simple trinomial

Example 3.55
Factor: $x^6 - y^6$.

SOLUTION

$x^6 - y^6 = (x^3 - y^3)(x^3 + y^3)$

$= (x - y)(x^2 + xy + y^2)(x + y)(x^2 - xy + y^2)$

Compare the solution of Example 3.55 with the factorization

$x^6 - y^6 = (x^2)^3 - (y^2)^3$

$= (x^2 - y^2)(x^4 + x^2y^2 + y^4)$

$= (x - y)(x + y)(x^4 + x^2y^2 + y^4)$

Since factorization over the integers is unique, there can be exactly one set of prime factors for $x^6 - y^6$. Therefore,

$x^4 + x^2y^2 + y^4$ must equal $(x^2 + xy + y^2)(x^2 - xy + y^2)$

This statement may be verified by direct multiplication. However, the process of factoring involved here is more difficult than the other methods used so far.

$$x^4 + x^2y^2 + y^4 = (x^4 + \qquad + y^4) + x^2y^2$$

$$= (x^4 + 2x^2y^2 + y^4) + x^2y^2 - 2x^2y^2 \rightarrow \quad \text{0 is added in}$$
the form
$$2x^2y^2 - 2x^2y^2$$
$$= (x^2 + y^2)^2 - x^2y^2 \qquad\qquad\qquad\qquad \text{to obtain a}$$
perfect square

$$= (x^2 + y^2 - xy)(x^2 + y^2 + xy) \qquad\qquad \text{difference of}$$
squares

Note that the objective here was to obtain a difference of squares by obtaining a group of three terms that was a perfect-square trinomial. The principle of zero was also used; that is, any number plus its addition inverse is equal to zero: $x + (-x) = 0$.

Example 3.56
Factor: $x^4 + 5x^3 + x + 5$.

SOLUTION

Since four terms are present and there are *not* two perfect-square terms, a 2 by 2 grouping is tried.

$$x^4 + 5x^3 + x + 5 = (x^4 + 5x^3) + (x + 5)$$
$$= x^3(x + 5) + 1(x + 5) \qquad \text{factor each group}$$
$$= (x + 5)(x^3 + 1) \qquad\qquad \text{distributive law}$$
$$= (x + 5)(x + 1)(x^2 - x + 1) \qquad \text{sum of two cubes}$$

Example 3.57
Factor: $x^2 - 2xy + 1 - y^2 - 6y - 9$.

SOLUTION

$$x^2 - 2xy + 1 - y^2 - 6y - 9$$
$$= (x^2 - 2xy + 1) - (y^2 + 6y + 9) \qquad \text{recognize perfect squares}$$
$$= (x - 1)^2 - (y + 3)^2$$
$$= [(x - 1) + (y + 3)] \cdot [(x - 1) - (y + 3)] \quad \text{difference of squares}$$
$$= (x - 1 + y + 3)(x - 1 - y - 3)$$
$$= (x + y + 2)(x - y - 4)$$

Problem Set 3.9

Factor. If not possible, write "no solution."

1. $6x^2 - 24$
2. $x^2 - 9x$
3. $x^3 - 64x$
4. $100x^2 - 4y^2$
5. $2x^5 - 162x$
6. $5x^2 - 4x + 1$
7. $2x^7 + 128x$
8. $2x^7 - 128x$
9. $2x^2 + 3x + 2$
10. $5x^5 + 625x^2$
11. $x^4 + 5x^2 - 36$
12. $3x^4 - 39x^2 + 108$
13. $7x^6 - 7x^3 - 14$
14. $6x^6 + 42x^3 - 48$
15. $4x^4y^2 - 104x^2y^4 + 100y^6$
16. $3x^4y^4 - 60x^2y^6 + 300y^8$
17. $5y^4 + 5y^3 - 20y^2 - 20y$
18. $7y^5 - 21y^4 + 7y^2 - 21y$
19. $32(x + y)^2 - 8(x - y)^2$
20. $9(x^2 + 3)^2 - 36x^2$
21. $64x^2 - 16(x^2 + 5)^2$
22. $75x^2 - 3(x^2 - 2)^2$
23. $x^2 - 14x + 49 - y^2$
24. $x^4 - y^2 - 10y - 25$
25. $16x^4 + 64$

26. $16x^2 + 25$
27. $27x^3 + y^5$
28. $2x^4 + 5000$
29. $x^2 - 16x + 64 - y^2 - 12y - 36$
30. $y^2 + 18y + 81 - x^2 + 14x - 49$
31. $12x^9y^2z - 12xy^6z$
32. $80x^7y^3z^3 - 5x^3y^{11}z^3$
33. $x^2 + y^2 - z^2$
34. $x^2 - y^2 - z^2$
35. $x^7 + 8x^4 - 25x^3 - 200$
36. $x^7 + 27x^4 - 4x^3 - 108$
37. $x^5 + 500 - 4x^3 - 125x^2$
38. $2x^5 + 18 - 18x^3 - 2x^2$
39. $4x^2 - 9y^2 - 12x - 6y + 8$
40. $25x^2 - y^2 - 20x - 8y - 12$
41. $x^2 - 4y^2 - 4x - 8y$
42. $x^2 - 9y^2 - 6x + 18y$
43. $x^3 + 6x^2 + 12x + 8$
44. $x^3 + 9x^2 + 27x + 27$
45. $x^4 + x^3 + x^2 + x^2y^2 + xy^2 + y^2$
46. $x^2y^2 - x^2y + x^2 + y^4 - y^3 + y^2$
47. $60a^2x^2 + 20a^2x - 200a^2 - 15b^2x^2$
    $- 5b^2x + 50b^2$
48. $36a^2x^2 - 45a^2x - 54a^2 - 36b^2x^2$
    $+ 45b^2x + 54b^2$

3.15 / Factoring with nonintegral coefficients

In actual solutions of engineering problems, expressions may be found with coefficients in fractional or decimal form. Two courses of action exist:
(1) Multiply and divide the given expression by an integer so that the resulting expression is the product of a rational number and a polynomial with integral coefficients, or
(2) Factor the given expression directly by using the procedures of the previous sections, if the given expression is quickly recognized as a special product.

Example 3.58

Can $x^2 + \frac{1}{2}x + \frac{1}{16}$ be factored?

SOLUTION   Method 1:

$$x^2 + \tfrac{1}{2}x + \tfrac{1}{16} = \tfrac{1}{16}(16x^2 + 8x + 1) = \tfrac{1}{16}(4x + 1)^2$$

Method 2:

$$x^2 + \tfrac{1}{2}x + \tfrac{1}{16} = (x + \tfrac{1}{4})^2$$

recognizing that $\frac{1}{4} + \frac{1}{4} = \frac{1}{2}$ and $\frac{1}{4} \cdot \frac{1}{4} = \frac{1}{16}$.

Example 3.59

Can $x^2 + 0.3x + 0.02$ be factored?

SOLUTION   Method 1:

$$x^2 + 0.3x + 0.02 = \tfrac{1}{100}(100x^2 + 30x + 2)$$
$$= \tfrac{1}{50}(50x^2 + 15x + 1)$$
$$= \tfrac{1}{50}(10x + 1)(5x + 1)$$

Method 2:

$$x^2 + 0.3x + 0.02 = (x + 0.1)(x + 0.2)$$

recognizing that $0.1 + 0.2 = 0.3$ and $0.1 \cdot 0.2 = 0.02$.

Example 3.60

Can $0.704x^2 + 0.084x - 0.098$ be factored?

SOLUTION

$$0.704x^2 + 0.084x - 0.098 = \tfrac{1}{1000}(704x^2 + 84x - 98)$$
$$= \tfrac{1}{500}(352x^2 + 42x - 49)$$

$+352$	using 7	$+2464$	using 8	$+308$	using 2	$+154$
-49		-7		-56		-112
$+303$		$+2457$		$+252$		$+42$

$$154 = \boxed{7} \cdot 2 \cdot 11$$
$$112 = \boxed{7} \cdot 2^4$$
$$49$$

$$\tfrac{1}{500}(22x - 7) \qquad (16x + 7)$$

$$0.704x^2 + 0.084x - 0.098 = \tfrac{1}{500}(22x - 7)(16x + 7)$$

The numbers in this example are too large to use method 2.

Problem Set 3.10

Factor.

1. $x^2 + \frac{3}{4}x + \frac{1}{8}$
2. $x^2 + \frac{1}{4}x + \frac{1}{64}$
3. $y^2 - \frac{5}{6}y + \frac{1}{6}$
4. $y^2 - \frac{7}{12}y + \frac{1}{12}$
5. $x^2 + 0.20x + 0.01$
6. $x^2 + 0.40x + 0.04$
7. $3.0t^2 + 2.1t + 0.3$
8. $7.00t^2 + 3.50t + 0.42$
9. $0.50x^2 - 0.25x - 0.03$
10. $0.50x^2 - 0.15x - 0.05$
11. $\frac{1}{9}x^2 - \frac{2}{3}x + 1$

12. $\frac{1}{16}x^2 - \frac{1}{2}x + 1$

13. $0.04x^2 + 0.40x + 1.00$

14. $0.01x^2 + 0.20x + 1.00$
15. $0.03z^2 - 0.01z - 0.02$
16. $0.60z^2 + 0.25z - 0.10$
17. $0.391x^2 - 0.030x - 0.025$
18. $0.768x^2 + 0.088x - 0.121$
19. $0.091y^2 + 0.061y - 0.072$
20. $0.186y^2 - 0.640y - 0.154$
21. $5.76t^2 - 9.12t + 3.61$
22. $0.6845t^2 - 1.8870t + 1.3005$
23. $0.405x^4 - 0.080y^4$
24. $0.030\,25x^4 - 0.042\,25y^4$

25. $\dfrac{xy}{12} + \dfrac{x}{4} + \dfrac{y}{6} + \dfrac{1}{2}$

26. $2.10xy + 0.70x - 1.05y - 0.35$

3.16 / Chapter Review

1. Elementary algebra is generalized arithmetic in which letters are used as the names of numbers and symbols are used to indicate the six operations: addition $(+)$, subtraction $(-)$, division $(\div)$, multiplication $(\cdot)$, raising to a power $[(\ )^n]$, root extraction $(\sqrt[n]{\ })$.
2. Grouping symbols are used to indicate the order in which operations are to be performed. The most common ones are parentheses $(\ )$, brackets $[\ ]$, and braces $\{\ \}$.
3. Signed numbers are used for the measurement of quantities opposite in nature.
4. The sum of two signed numbers having the same sign is the sum of their absolute values prefixed by their common sign.
5. The sum of two signed numbers having opposite signs is the difference of their absolute values prefixed by the sign of the number having the larger absolute value.
6. To subtract signed numbers, change the sign of the subtrahend and add the resulting signed numbers.
7. The product or quotient of two signed numbers having the same sign is positive $(+)$.
8. The product or quotient of two signed numbers having opposite signs is negative $(-)$.

9. In the addition and subtraction of polynomials, the like terms can be combined by using the distributive law.
10. The exponent for the product of powers having the same base is the sum of the exponents of the factors: $b^x b^y = b^{x+y}$.
11. The exponent for a power of a power is the product of the exponents: $(b^x)^y = b^{xy}$.
12. If a product is raised to a power, each factor of the product is raised to that power: $(ab)^x = a^x b^x$.
13. The exponent for the quotient of powers having the same base is the difference of the exponents: $\dfrac{b^x}{b^y} = b^{x-y}$.
14. Polynomials are multiplied or divided by applying the distributive law and the properties of exponents.
15. Certain special products occur frequently and the memorization of their forms permits rapid writing of either the product or the factors of the product.
16. Special products summarized:

$$A^2 - B^2 = (A + B)(A - B)$$
$$A^3 - B^3 = (A - B)(A^2 + AB + B^2)$$
$$A^3 + B^3 = (A + B)(A^2 - AB + B^2)$$
$$A^2 + 2AB + B^2 = (A + B)^2$$
$$A^2 - 2AB + B^2 = (A - B)^2$$
$$x^2 + (A + B)x + AB = (x + A)(x + B)$$
$$ACx^2 + (AD + BC)x + BD = (Ax + B)(Cx + D)$$
$$AC + AD + BC + BD = (A + B)(C + D)$$

Problem Set 3.1 (Chapter Review)

1 and 2
Name the operations in the order in which they must be done for each of the following. State the result.

1. $\dfrac{\sqrt{(7 + 5)(7 - 4)}}{2}$

2. $5\left(\dfrac{\sqrt{25} - 1}{2}\right)^3$

3–5
Simplify. (Do not factor.)

3. $7x - 2\{x - 2[x - 2(x - 2)]\}$
4. $[2(3x - 4) - (2x + 1)] - [3(x + 2) - 2(x - 3)]$
5. $[(y + 1) - (y - 1)] \cdot [(y + 1)^2 + (y + 1)(y - 1) + (y - 1)^2]$

6. From the sum of $4x - (2y - z)$ and $-(2y - 5x) - 9z$ subtract $-4x - (3z + y)$.
7. Subtract $-6c - (7b - 2a)$ from $-3b - (-2c + 9a)$ and add the difference to $5a - (7c + 4b)$.
8. Subtract $x^3 - 2x^2y + 2xy^2 - y^3$ from $2x^3 - x^2y + 2xy^2 - 2y^3$. Check, letting $x = 2$ and $y = 1$.
9. Multiply $x^4 - 2x^2 + 2$ by $x^4 + 2x^2 + 2$. Check, letting $x = 3$.
10. Multiply $3(4y - x)$ by $x^2 + xy + y^2$. Check, letting $x = 3$ and $y = 2$.
11. Multiply $a - b$ by $a^2 - 2ab + b^2$.
12. Simplify: $12x\left(x^2 - \dfrac{x}{6}\right) - 5x\left(2x^2 - \dfrac{2}{5}\right) + 6x\left(\dfrac{x}{2} - \dfrac{2}{3}\right)$.
13. Simplify: $(2x^2y^3)^3(5xy)^2$.

14. Simplify: $\dfrac{18x^7 - 36x^5 + 45x^3}{9x^3}$

15. Simplify: $\dfrac{(-5x^2y^3)^4(2x^3y)^5}{(-2xy^2)^3(5x^2y^3)^2}$.

16–23
Factor.

16. $36x - 3x^5 + 3x^3$
17. $a^8b^4 - 39\frac{1}{16}$
18. $x^2y^2 + 6xy^3 - 77x^3y$
19. $4a - 3b - 6ab + 2$
20. $100x^2 - 25x$
21. $64x^3 - 36x$
22. $x^6y^6 - 64$
23. $(x + 1)^3 - (x - 1)^3$

24. The area A of an annulus (the ring between two concentric circles is given by

$$A = \pi r_o^2 - \pi r_i^2$$

(a) Express A in factored form.
(b) Using the factored form, calculate the area of an annulus whose outer radius $r_o = 37$ in. and whose inner radius $r_i = 35$ in. (Use $\pi = 3.14$.)

25. The moment of a hollow square about a side is found as follows:

$$M = \tfrac{1}{2}a^3 - \tfrac{1}{2}ab^2$$

(a) Write M in factored form.
(b) Evaluate M if the side of the outer square $a = 3.75$ in. and the side of the inner square $b = 3.25$ in.

26. Write in factored form the volume V of a spherical shell if

$$V = \tfrac{4}{3}\pi R_o^3 - \tfrac{4}{3}\pi R_i^3$$

27. The bending moment for a certain beam of length L, uniformly loaded w lb per unit length, at a distance x from one end is given by

$$M = \tfrac{1}{2}wx^2 - \tfrac{5}{8}wLx + \tfrac{1}{8}wL^2$$

Write M in factored form.

28. The bending moment for a certain beam is given by

$$M = \tfrac{1}{2}wx^2 - 5.2wx + 9.0w$$

Write M in factored form.

29. The area of a circular segment with central angle $30°$ is given by

$$A = \frac{\pi r^2}{12} - \frac{r^2}{4}$$

Write A in factored form, then find A for $r = 1.5$ ft, $\pi = 3.14$.

30. The work W done in stretching a spring of stiffness k from a length $L + s_1$ to a length $L + s_2$, where L is the natural length of the spring, is given by

$$W = \tfrac{1}{2}ks_2^2 - \tfrac{1}{2}ks_1^2$$

Write W in factored form.

31. $(-7.481 \times 10^{-9})t^3 + (4.9651 \times 10^{-6})t^2 - (4.217 \times 10^{-4})t$ is an expression for the difference between the temperatures registered on the thermodynamic scale and the International scale. Write this expression in factored form.

32–40

Write each of the following expressions in factored form.

32. $\dfrac{W}{8EI}cL^2 - \dfrac{W}{2EI}c^2L + \dfrac{W}{2EI}c^3$, the maximum deflection of a certain beam.

33. $\dfrac{S^4}{12} - \dfrac{s^4}{12}$, a moment of inertia of a hollow square.

34. $cT_1^{\,4} - cT_2^{\,4}$, the net change of radiant energy of a body having temperature T_1 in a container whose walls have temperature T_2. Calculate this net change if $c = 1.70 \times 10^{-12}$, $T_1 = 400°K$, and $T_2 = 300°K$.

35. $4e\left(\dfrac{s}{r}\right)^{12} - 4e\left(\dfrac{s}{r}\right)^{6}$, a function used to express the potential energy of interaction between two molecules.

36. $-16t^2 + 2000t - 62{,}500$, an expression used to find the time that a certain projectile is in flight.

37. $4x^3 - 2wx^2 - 2lx^2 + wlx$, the volume of a box made by cutting squares of side x from each corner of a rectangular sheet l by w.

38. $c_m T_0 - c_g T_0 + c_m T_1 - c_g T_1$, the interface stress in the glass member of a glass–metal cylindrical seal.

39. $\dfrac{k}{L} D_1{}^3 - \dfrac{k}{L} D_2 D_1{}^2 - \dfrac{k}{L} D_1 D_2{}^2 + \dfrac{k}{L} D_2{}^3$, the conductance for the flow of gases through a long duct of length L and diameters D_1 and D_2.

40. $b^2 x^2 - a^2 x^2 + 2a^2 dx - a^2 d^2$, an expression used to find the distance x

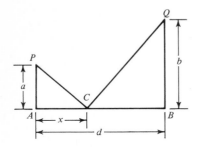

in the figure above so that the sum of the distances, $PC + QC$, is as small as possible.

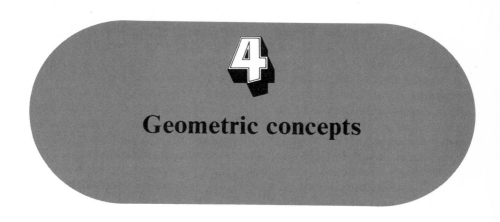

Geometric concepts

4.01 / Role of geometry

The origins of geometry have been traced to Egyptian and Babylonian documents dated 2200–1600 B.C. These ancient Orientals developed methods for computing lengths, areas, and volumes in order to solve problems related to agriculture and engineering. By 300 B.C., the Greeks had clarified the geometric concepts, arranged them in a logical order, and established valid proofs. The geometric principles are timeless and still widely used in solving real problems. The important principles, with applications, will be presented in this book but proofs will be omitted. If a proof is desired, it can be found in almost any elementary textbook devoted solely to geometry.

The technician will find that many problems he faces can be solved with a scaled sketch. Each student should own a ruler with decimally graduated scales (a triangular engineering drafting scale), a protractor (4 to 5 in. wide) for measuring angles, and a compass. Drafting triangles, 30° and 45°, are useful additional equipment. In general, if a given problem can be drawn to scale, it is often possible to find a solution by using scaled measurements. In many cases, the procedures used in the preparation of the scaled sketch will indicate a method for computing a solution.

4.02 / Points and lines

A **point** is a location without dimension. Although a point is usually drawn as a dot, having a finite size, this is just the picture of a point and not the real point. The location of a point can be determined by its co-ordinate on a number line. A point is named by a capital letter, such as point *A* or point *B*.

A **line** has length but no width. The drawn line does have a finite width but this is just a picture of a line. A line can be straight or curved. To avoid confusion, the word "line" will be used for a straight line and the word "curve" for a curved line. A line is infinitely long and may be named by

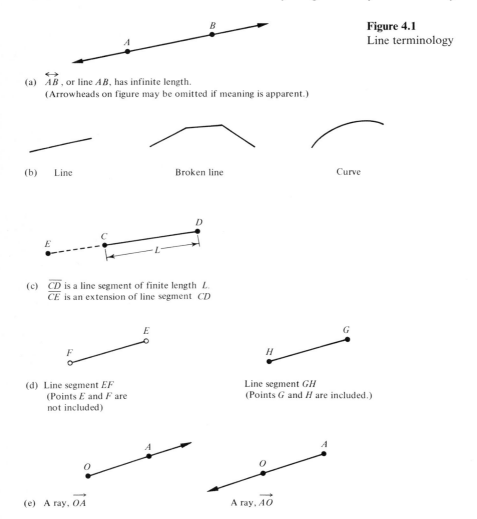

Figure 4.1
Line terminology

(a) $\overleftrightarrow{AB}$, or line *AB*, has infinite length.
(Arrowheads on figure may be omitted if meaning is apparent.)

(b)   Line   Broken line   Curve

(c) $\overline{CD}$ is a line segment of finite length *L*.
$\overline{CE}$ is an extension of line segment *CD*

(d) Line segment *EF*   Line segment *GH*
(Points *E* and *F* are   (Points *G* and *H* are included.)
not included)

(e) A ray, $\overrightarrow{OA}$ A ray, $\overrightarrow{AO}$

drawing a double-headed arrow over two capital letters that name any two points on the line. For example, if A and B are any two points on a line, the line is referred to as $\overleftrightarrow{AB}$, or as line AB, or as line A–B. Figure 4.1(a) shows the correct graphical representation of a line AB.

A **line segment** is a finite length of a given line. In symbols, $\overline{AB}$ is the name of a line segment whose endpoints are A and B. The endpoints (also called *terminal points*) are usually shown as small dots, solid if included and open if excluded.

A **ray** is a part of a line consisting of a fixed initial point, called the *endpoint of the ray*, and all the points on the line on a given side of the endpoint. In symbols, $\overrightarrow{OA}$ names a ray with O the endpoint of the ray and A any other point on the ray. The arrow indicates that the ray extends infinitely in the direction from O to A. See Figure 4.1(e). Also illustrated is $\overrightarrow{AO}$, the opposite ray having A as its fixed endpoint and passing through point O extending infinitely in the direction from A to O.

Any two lines that intersect have a common point called the **point of intersection.** Two intersecting lines determine a **plane,** easily visualized as a flat surface of no thickness. Any three points in space, not all on the same

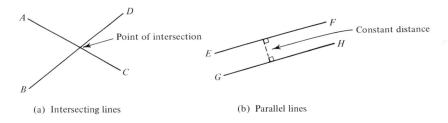

(a) Intersecting lines   (b) Parallel lines

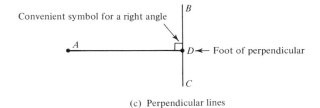

(c) Perpendicular lines

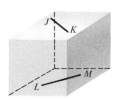

Figure 4.2
Types of lines   (d) Skew lines

line, also determine a plane. Thus, a particular plane may be defined by selecting the point of intersection of two lines and a known point on each of these lines.

Parallel lines are lines in the same plane that never intersect, no matter how far they are extended. Parallel lines are a constant distance apart.

If two lines are in the same plane and are not parallel, they intersect and have a common point, although this point may be off the paper that is used.

Perpendicular lines are two lines in the same plane that intersect and form

Figure 4.3
Constructing perpendiculars

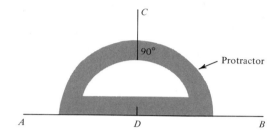

(a) Erecting a perpendicular *CD* to line *AB* at point *D*

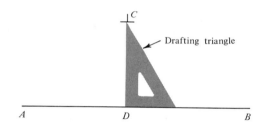

(b) Erecting a perpendicular *CD* to line *AB* through point *C*

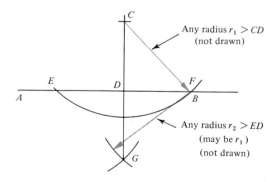

(c) Erecting a perpendicular *CD* to line *AB* using a compass

a right angle, the name given an angle of 90°. The point of intersection of a line through a given point and perpendicular to a given line is called the **foot of the perpendicular.**

Lines that are not in the same plane and do not intersect are called **skew lines.** A telephone line crossing a power cable provides an example of a pair of skew lines.

To construct a perpendicular line to another line, a protractor can be used and a 90° angle drawn. If the line must pass through a given point, a drafting triangle can be used to construct the line. An exact method of construction is shown in Figure 4.3. The choice of method depends on the accuracy required.

To draw a line parallel to another, erect two perpendiculars to one line and measure off the desired distance between the parallels along these perpendiculars. Using three such perpendiculars provides a good check.

4.03 / Angles

An **angle** is the figure formed by two rays having a common endpoint. The common point is called the **vertex** of the angle, and the two rays are called the **sides** of the angle. An angle may be designated by stating the capital letter that names the vertex; by listing a point on each ray and placing the vertex designation between these; or by stating a Greek letter, usually θ (theta) or ϕ (phi). On figures, angles may also be designated by numerals. To indicate that an angle is under discussion, the printed symbol $\angle$ is used; in handwritten work the symbol is often written ⋌ to prevent confusion with the letter L, so often used for length.

An angle may be described by its size, using a 90° angle (perpendicular rays) as a reference. If the angle is less than 90°, it is called **acute;** if exactly 90°, it is called a **right angle;** and if greater than 90° but less than 180°,

Figure 4.4
Names of angles

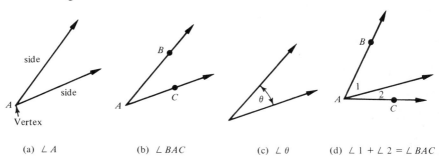

(a) $\angle A$ (b) $\angle BAC$ (c) $\angle \theta$ (d) $\angle 1 + \angle 2 = \angle BAC$

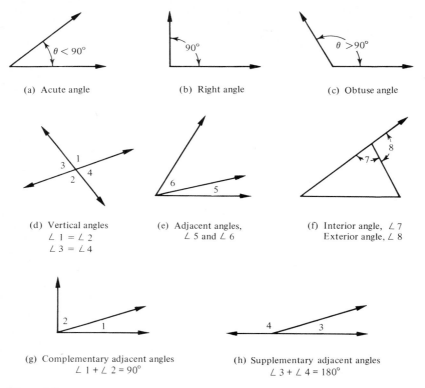

(a) Acute angle

(b) Right angle

(c) Obtuse angle

(d) Vertical angles
$\angle 1 = \angle 2$
$\angle 3 = \angle 4$

(e) Adjacent angles,
$\angle 5$ and $\angle 6$

(f) Interior angle, $\angle 7$
Exterior angle, $\angle 8$

(g) Complementary adjacent angles
$\angle 1 + \angle 2 = 90°$

(h) Supplementary adjacent angles
$\angle 3 + \angle 4 = 180°$

Figure 4.5
Classification of angles

it is called an **obtuse angle.** An angle having exactly 180° is called a **straight angle.** If an angle has more than 180° but less than 360°, it is called a **reflex angle.**

A pair of angles may be named by their position. If angles are formed by two intersecting lines, each opposite pair is called a pair of **vertical angles.** In Figure 4.5(d), $\angle 1$ and $\angle 2$ are a pair of vertical angles. Also $\angle 3$ and $\angle 4$ are a pair of vertical angles.

Two angles having a common vertex and a common ray between them are called **adjacent angles,** such as $\angle 5$ and $\angle 6$ in Figure 4.5(e).

The angle between two sides of a closed figure is called an **interior angle,** shown in Figure 4.5(f). An angle between two sides, one of which has been extended, is called an **exterior angle,** also shown in Figure 4.5(f). Surveyors call an exterior angle a *deflection angle*

A pair of angles may be named by their sum. Two angles are **complementary** if their *sum* is 90°. If they are also adjacent angles, their exterior rays form a right angle.

Two angles are **supplementary** if their *sum* is 180°. If they are also adjacent angles, their exterior rays form a straight line. Since the two rays of an angle of 180° form a straight line, a 180° angle is also called a **straight angle.**

The size of an angle may be considered as the amount of rotation from one side of the angle to the other. The ray from which the rotation is measured is called the *initial side;* the final ray is called the *terminal side.* The terms *clockwise* and *counterclockwise* are often used to describe rotations. In mathematics and a number of engineering subjects, counterclockwise rotations, abbreviated CCW, are considered positive and clockwise rotations are considered negative.

Angles may be measured by a variety of units. Surveying, one of the oldest forms of engineering, uses 360° to represent one full revolution of the terminal side. This system, a heritage from the Babylonian system that used the base 60, makes each quadrant (one fourth of a circle) 90°, or a right angle. The degree is divided into 60 minutes (') and each minute into 60 seconds ("). In recent years, a purely decimal degree notation has been used, as it aids computations on simple devices such as a slide rule and on complex ones such as an electronic computer. In this notation, an angle of 36°28'48" would be written 36.480°.

In some European countries that have adopted the decimal metric system, a quadrant is divided into 100 equal parts, the unit division being called a **grade.** The U.S. artillery uses a quadrant of 1600 units called **mils,** 1 mil moving the impact of a shell 1 yd laterally at a range of 1000 yd. Mathematicians use a unit called the **radian,** which will be studied under trigonometry in Chapter 9. For now, 1 radian (rad) is approximately 57.3°.

If an accuracy of $\frac{1}{2}°$ is acceptable, the quickest and easiest method of measuring an angle is with a protractor. Care must be taken to align the 0–180° line exactly along one ray and to align the tick mark exactly on the vertex. Frequently one or both rays must be extended to permit reading the graduation on the circumference of the protractor. Protractors with vernier scales are manufactured to read to 1' intervals, but the width of pencil lines and the inaccuracies of drafting make any scaled reading under 10' open to suspicion.

A number of geometric solutions depends upon finding equal angles. One configuration that yields a number of equal angles is that of two parallel lines cut by a third line called a **transversal.**

Corresponding angles of parallel lines, two nonadjacent angles on the same side of the transversal with one angle between the parallel lines and the other not between the parallel lines, are equal. For example, in Figure 4.6(a), $\angle 1 = \angle 5$, $\angle 2 = \angle 6$, $\angle 3 = \angle 7$, and $\angle 4 = \angle 8$.

Alternate interior angles, two nonadjacent angles between the parallel lines and on opposite sides of the transversal, are equal. For example, in Figure 4.6(b), $\angle 3 = \angle 6$ and $\angle 4 = \angle 5$.

Alternate exterior angles, two nonadjacent angles on opposite sides of the transversal and not between the parallel lines, are equal. For example, in Figure 4.6(c), $\angle 1 = \angle 8$ and $\angle 2 = \angle 7$.

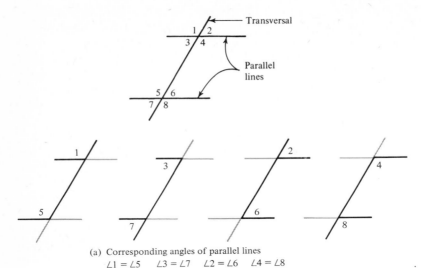

(a) Corresponding angles of parallel lines

$\angle 1 = \angle 5 \qquad \angle 3 = \angle 7 \qquad \angle 2 = \angle 6 \qquad \angle 4 = \angle 8$

(b) Alternate interior angles of parallel lines

$\angle 3 = \angle 6 \qquad \angle 4 = \angle 5$

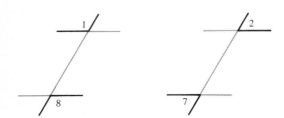

(c) Alternate exterior angles of parallel lines

$\angle 1 = \angle 8 \qquad \angle 2 = \angle 7$

Figure 4.6
Parallel lines cut by a transversal

If two lines are cut by a transversal, the two lines are parallel if
(1) A pair of corresponding angles are equal,
(2) A pair of alternate interior angles are equal,
(3) A pair of alternate exterior angles are equal, or
(4) Two interior angles on the same side of the transversal are supplementary.

Figure 4.7
Angles with mutually perpendicular sides, $\theta = \phi$

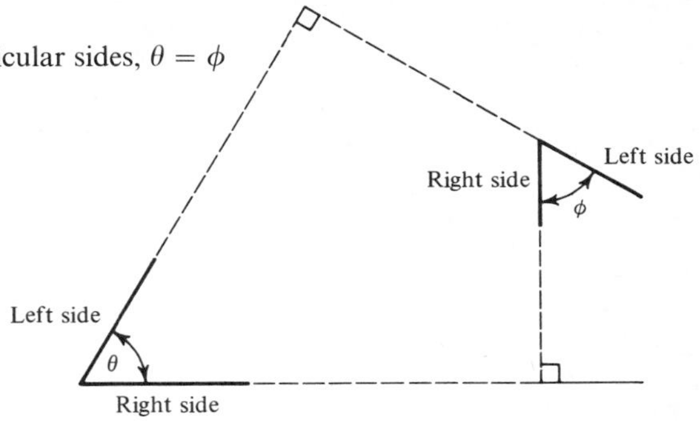

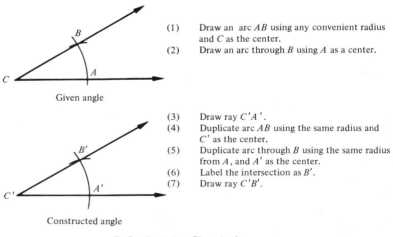

If two angles, when each is viewed with the vertex pointing toward the viewer, have their left sides perpendicular and also their right sides perpendicular, these two angles are equal. For example, in Figure 4.7, $\theta = \phi$, because the sides of these angles are perpendicular right to right and left to left. This relationship may occur when the mutually perpendicular lines are some distance apart and may not be drawn as intersecting. Recognition of this situation may yield a quick and easy solution to what might appear to be a baffling problem. If a relationship, such as this one, is not obvious, it is advised that the figure be sketched and measured.

Two graphical techniques are shown in Figure 4.8; the duplication of a given angle and the bisection of a given angle. To bisect an angle means to divide the angle into two equal angles. Although both of these problems can be solved using a protractor, the errors inherent in reading the protractor may make these constructions more desirable.

Figure 4.8
Angular geometric constructions

(1) Draw an arc AB using any convenient radius and C as the center.
(2) Draw an arc through B using A as a center.

Given angle

(3) Draw ray $C'A'$.
(4) Duplicate arc AB using the same radius and C' as the center.
(5) Duplicate arc through B using the same radius from A, and A' as the center.
(6) Label the intersection as B'.
(7) Draw ray $C'B'$.

Constructed angle

To Duplicate Any Given Angle

Figure 4.8 (continued)

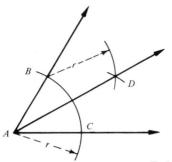

(1) Draw arc *BC* using any convenient radius *r* and *A* as the center. *B* and *C* are the intersections of this arc and the sides.
(2) Using the same radius *r*, draw an arc using *C* as the center.
(3) Using the same radius *r*, draw an arc using *B* as the center, and intersecting the first arc from *C* at *D*.
(4) Draw the ray *AD*. This is the bisector of the given angle *BAC*.

To Bisect Any Given Angle

Problem Set 4.1

Problems 1–4 are based on the following figure.

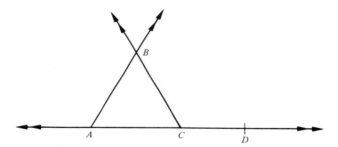

1. List five line segments, using proper symbols.
2. Using proper symbols, list three rays that have a common endpoint.
3. Using proper symbols, list two rays that form an obtuse angle.
4. List two line segments whose sum appears on this plot.

5. Draw a horizontal line segment *AB* 4 in. long. Using a radius of 3 in. and *A* as a center, draw arcs above and below $\overline{AB}$. With the same radius and *B* as a center, draw two arcs that intersect the first two arcs at points *C* and *D*. Draw $\overline{CD}$ intersecting $\overline{AB}$ at *E*. Measure $\overline{AE}$, $\overline{EB}$, $\angle AEC$, and $\angle CEB$. Record these measurements and suggest an appropriate description of line *CD*.
6. Draw a circle with a 2-in. radius. Select any point on the circle as point *A* and with the same radius draw two arcs with *A* as a center, intersecting the circle at points *B* and *C*. Using a 3-in. radius and points *B* and *C* in turn as centers, draw two arcs that intersect inside the circle at

point *D*. Draw line *AD*. Measure and record ∠*BAD* and ∠*DAC*. Suggest an appropriate description of line *AD*.

7. Draw angle *BAC* equal to 30°, with side *AC* horizontal. From point *D*, 2 in. to the right of *A* and on *AC*, draw a perpendicular to *AB*, intersecting *AB* at *F*. From point *E*, 6 in. to the right of *A* and on *AC* draw a perpendicular to *AB*, intersecting *AB* at *G*. From point *D* draw a perpendicular to *EG*, intersecting *EG* at *H*.
   (a) Measure ∠*ADF* and ∠*DEG* and record results.
   (b) Describe the relationship between *DF* and *EG*.
   (c) Describe the relationship of angles *ADF* and *DEG* with respect to lines *DF* and *EG*.
   (d) Measure and record lengths of line segments $\overline{FG}$ and $\overline{DH}$.
   (e) Describe the results obtained in part (d) with respect to lines *DF* and *EG*.

8. Draw a horizontal line segment $\overline{AB}$ measuring 2 in. Draw a horizontal line *CD* so that *C* is 1 in. below *A* and *D* is to the right. Draw a horizontal line segment $\overline{EF}$ measuring 2 in. so that *E* is 2 in. below *A*. Draw $\overline{BE}$ intersecting *CD* at *G*.
   (a) Measure ∠*ABE* and ∠*BEF* and record results.
   (b) Describe the relationship of these two angles with respect to lines *AB* and *EF*.
   (c) Measure and record the length of $\overline{BG}$ and $\overline{GE}$.
   (d) Since *ACE* and *BGE* are both transversals of parallel lines, deduce a relationship for all transversals of the same parallel lines. Draw any other transversal and verify this statement.

9–24

Use the figure below where FOA is a straight line and DO is perpendicular to OA. In Problems 9–14, use O A as the initial side of the angle to be named.

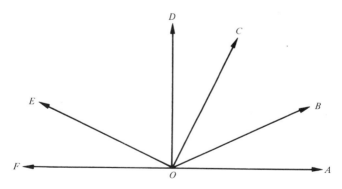

9. Name an acute angle.
10. Name an obtuse angle.
11. Name a right angle.

12. Name a straight angle.

13. Name an angle adjacent to $\angle BOC$.

14. Name an angle adjacent to $\angle COE$.

15. Name an angle complementary to $\angle DOC$.

16. Name an angle complementary to $\angle EOF$.

17. Name an angle supplementary to $\angle AOB$.

18. Name an angle supplementary to $\angle EOF$.

19. Name an angle equal to $\angle COD$ if $\angle COE$ is a right angle.

20. Name an angle equal to $\angle AOC$ if $\angle COE$ is a right angle.

21–24

Using a protractor, measure to the nearest $\frac{1}{2}°$.

21. $\angle AOB$ **22.** $\angle BOE$ **23.** $\angle AOE$ **24.** $\angle DOC$

25. Draw a pair of two complementary adjacent angles, bisect each angle of the pair, and determine the measure of the angle formed by the two bisecting lines.

26. Draw a pair of two supplementary adjacent angles, bisect each angle of the pair, and determine the measure of the angle formed by the two bisecting lines.

Problems 27–34 are based on the figure opposite, where ABCD, AFG, BFH, and ECG are straight lines; AFG is perpendicular to ABCD and to HG, ECG is perpendicular to ED, and FB is parallel to ECG.

27–34

Complete each of the following.

27. A pair of alternate interior angles are $\angle FBC$ and _____.

28. A pair of corresponding angles are $\angle FBC$ and _____.

29. A pair of corresponding angles are $\angle AFB$ and _____.

30. A pair of alternate interior angles are $\angle HFG$ and _____.

31. A pair of alternate exterior angles are $\angle ECD$ and _____.

32. A pair of vertical angles are $\angle ECD$ and _____.

33. A pair of angles with mutually perpendicular sides are $\angle CDE$ and _____.

34. A pair of angles with mutually perpendicular sides are $\angle HFG$ and _____.

35. Referring to the figure opposite, where AD is parallel to BC and BAE is a straight line, find the exact number of degrees in $\angle EAD$, $\angle DAC$, and $\angle BAC$.

36. Referring to the figure opposite where AD, BE, and CF are all parallel to each other and ABC and FCG are straight lines, find the exact number of degrees in $\angle EBC$, $\angle BCG$, and $\angle BCF$.

Problems 27–34

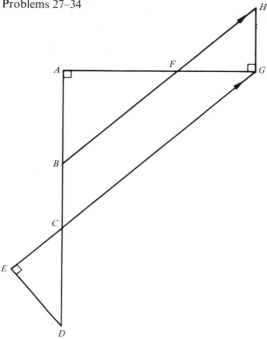

Problem 35

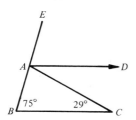

Problem 36

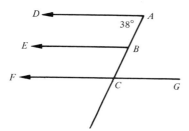

4.04 / Triangles

A **triangle** is a closed plane figure formed by three line segments. A triangle has three *sides* (the three line segments) and three *angles*, each formed by two sides of the triangle. An *exterior angle* of a triangle is an angle formed by one side of the triangle and the extension of another side through the point of intersection of the two sides.

An **included angle** of two sides of a triangle is the angle formed by these two sides.

An **included side** of two angles of a triangle is the common side of these two angles.

An angle is **opposite** a side of a triangle if the side of the triangle is not a side of the angle.

It is convenient to designate the sides of a triangle as a, b, and c and their respective opposite angles as $\angle A$, $\angle B$, and $\angle C$, with $\angle C$ the largest angle and side c the longest side.

A triangle may be classified by its number of equal sides or by the size

Figure 4.9
Classification of triangles

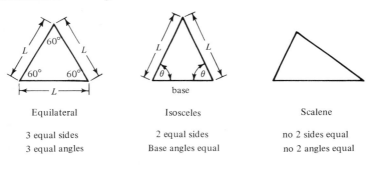

Equilateral	Isosceles	Scalene
3 equal sides	2 equal sides	no 2 sides equal
3 equal angles	Base angles equal	no 2 angles equal

(a) By Number of Equal Sides

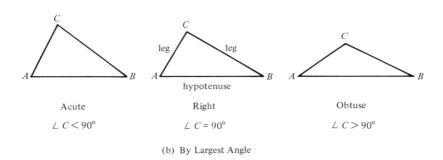

Acute	Right	Obtuse
$\angle C < 90°$	$\angle C = 90°$	$\angle C > 90°$

(b) By Largest Angle

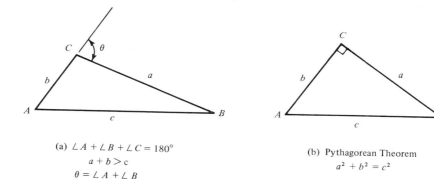

(a) $\angle A + \angle B + \angle C = 180°$
$a + b > c$
$\theta = \angle A + \angle B$

(b) Pythagorean Theorem
$a^2 + b^2 = c^2$

Figure 4.10
Basic triangle relationships

of its largest angle. A triangle with three equal sides is called **equilateral.** An equilateral triangle is also equiangular with each angle equal to 60°.

A triangle with two equal sides is called **isosceles.** The third side of an isosceles triangle is called the *base.* Base angles of an isosceles triangle are equal.

A triangle with no two sides equal is called **scalene.**

A **right triangle** is a triangle whose largest angle is a right angle, that is, exactly 90°. The side opposite the right angle of a right triangle is called the **hypotenuse.** The two sides forming the right angle are often called the *legs* of the triangle.

An **acute triangle** is a triangle whose largest angle is acute, that is, less than 90°. An **obtuse triangle** is a triangle whose largest angle is obtuse, that is, greater than 90°.

Important triangular relations are the following (see Figure 4.10):

The sum of the angles of a triangle is 180°.

The sum of two sides of a triangle is greater than the third side.

An exterior angle of a triangle is equal to the sum of the two nonadjacent interior angles of the triangle.

A triangle is a right triangle if and only if the sum of the squares of two sides of the triangle is equal to the square of the third side. (This is the theorem of Pythagoras.)

When the three angles of a triangle are measured to the nearest $\frac{1}{2}°$ by using a protractor, the sum of the three angles may differ from 180° by $\frac{1}{2}°$. In this case, the largest angle is adjusted by $\frac{1}{2}°$.

Two common engineering applications involve right triangles whose sides are natural numbers: $a = 3, b = 4, c = 5$ (or multiples of these numbers) for the first triangle and $a = 5, b = 12, c = 13$ (or multiples of these numbers) for the second triangle. In rough construction work such as land clearing, a right triangle can be laid out by using one of these triangles and then the right angle may be checked by using the other triangle.

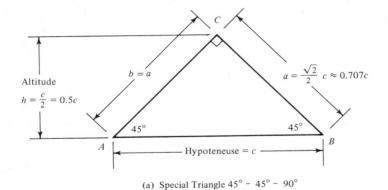

(a) Special Triangle 45° – 45° – 90°

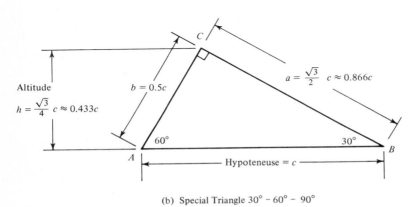

(b) Special Triangle 30° – 60° – 90°

Figure 4.11
Special right triangles

Two special right triangles occur frequently in real engineering problems and even more frequently in engineering textbook problems. These are the 45°–45°–90° triangle and the 30°–60°–90° triangle, the standard triangles used by draftsmen. The relationships of the sides and the altitude upon the hypotenuse of these special triangles are given in Figure 4.11. Values are also given to three significant figures to permit slide-rule calculations. These values will be derived in Chapter 9.

The **graphical construction of a triangle** is possible if
(a) Three sides are given and the sum of the two shorter lengths is greater than the longest length,
(b) One side and two angles are given and the sum of the two angles is less than 180°, or
(c) Two sides and their included angle are given.
(d) (Ambiguous Case.) Two sides and an angle not included are given; then either two triangles or one triangle or no triangle may be possible. Figure 4.12 illustrates these four cases.

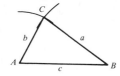

Point C is the intersection of two arcs, having radii a and b, respectively.
(Note there is no intersection if $a + b \leq c$.)

(a) Given: Three sides, a, b, and c.

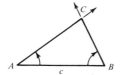

Point C is the intersection of the terminal sides of $\angle A$ and $\angle B$, constructed at the endpoints of side c.
(Note there is no intersection if $\angle A + \angle B \geq 180°$.)

(b) Given: Side c and two angles, $\angle B$ and $\angle A$.

(If $\angle C$ and $\angle A$ are given, then $\angle B = 180° - \angle A - \angle C$.)

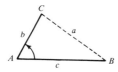

Side a is obtained by connecting B and C.

(c) Given: Two sides, b and c, and their included angle, $\angle A$.

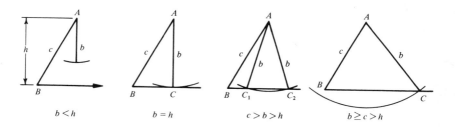

$b < h$ $b = h$ $c > b > h$ $b \geq c > h$

(d) Given: Two sides, b and c, and an angle not included, $\angle B$.

Figure 4.12
Graphical construction of triangles

If three angles are given, it is possible to construct infinitely many triangles, all having the same shape but differing in size.

The **area of a triangle** can be computed if a base b (any side of the triangle) and its corresponding altitude h are known:

$$A = \tfrac{1}{2}bh$$

If the lengths of the three sides of the triangle are known, Heron's formula can be used to find the area. Using s to represent the semiperimeter, the area is given by

$$A = \sqrt{s(s - a)(s - b)(s - c)} \qquad \text{where } s = \tfrac{1}{2}(a + b + c)$$

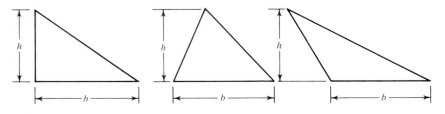

(a) These 3 triangles have the same area, $A = \frac{1}{2} bh$

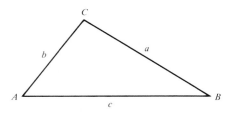

(b) Area $= \sqrt{s\,(s-a)\,(s-b)\,(s-c)}$, where s = semiperimeter $= \frac{1}{2}\,(a + b + c)$

Figure 4.13
Area of a triangle

The word *congruent* in geometry means an exact duplicate. Two congruent line segments have exactly the same length although they may be in different positions. Two congruent triangles may be in different positions but they have the same size and shape. By *definition*, **two triangles are congruent** *if and only if their corresponding angles are equal and their corresponding sides are equal.* Referring to the graphical construction of triangles as shown in Figure 4.12, each set of conditions that has a single, unique solution leads to a set of *conditions for congruent triangles.*

Two triangles are congruent if
(1) **SSS** Three sides of one are equal respectively to three sides of the other.
(2) **AAS** One side and two angles of one are equal respectively to the corresponding side and angles of the other.
(3) **SAS** Two sides and the included angle of one are equal respectively to two sides and the included angle of the other.

Similar triangles have the same shape although they may differ in size. By *definition*, **two triangles are similar** *if and only if their corresponding angles are equal and their corresponding sides are proportional.* Figure 4.14 shows a standard photographic enlarger and illustrates the basic principles of similar triangles.

Three conditions for determining if two triangles are similar are as follows:
(1) Two angles of one are equal respectively to two angles of the other.
(2) The corresponding sides of the two triangles are proportional.

Figure 4.14
Similar triangles

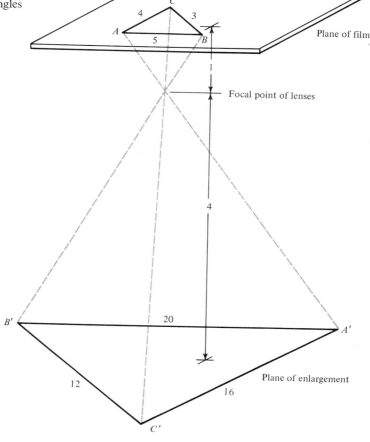

Schematic concept of photoenlarger

$\angle A = \angle A'$
$\angle B = \angle B'$
$\angle C = \angle C'$

$\dfrac{AB}{A'B'} = \dfrac{AC}{A'C'} = \dfrac{BC}{B'C'} = K$

$\dfrac{5}{20} = \dfrac{4}{16} = \dfrac{3}{12} = \dfrac{1}{4}$

(3) One angle of one triangle is equal to an angle of the other triangle and the including sides of these angles are proportional.

If each of the three angles of any triangle is bisected, the three bisectors meet at a common point. Since any point on an angle bisector is equidistant from the two sides that include that angle, the intersection of all three bisectors must be equidistant from all three sides of the triangle. This point is, therefore, the center of a circle that can be drawn entirely within the triangle and the radius of the circle is the perpendicular distance from this point to one of the sides. This circle, touching each side at exactly one point, is called the **inscribed circle,** illustrated in Figure 4.15.

Figure 4.15
Inscribed and circumscribed circles

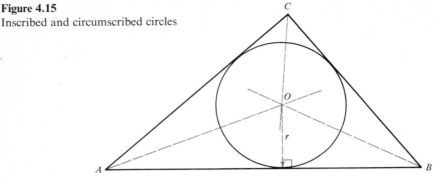

Bisectors of angles A, B, and C meet at O.
Perpendicular distance from O to any side is radius.

(a) Drawing an Inscribed Circle

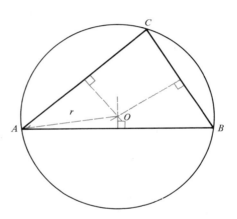

Perpendicular bisectors of 3 sides meet at O.
Distance from O to any vertex is radius.

(b) Drawing a Circumscribed Circle.

Similarly, if upon each side of a triangle, the perpendicular bisector is erected, these three lines meet at a common point. Any point on the perpendicular bisector of a line segment is equidistant from the endpoints of the segment, in this case two vertices of the triangle. Thus, the intersection of the three perpendicular bisectors is equidistant from all three vertices, and a circle can be drawn through all three vertices using the intersection as center and the distance from the intersection to any vertex as the radius. This circle is called the **circumscribed circle,** also illustrated in Figure 4.15.

A problem frequently met in engineering is to pass a circle through three known points. If lines are drawn connecting the three points, the solution is to draw the circumscribed circle for the triangle just formed.

Figure 4.16
Medians of a triangle

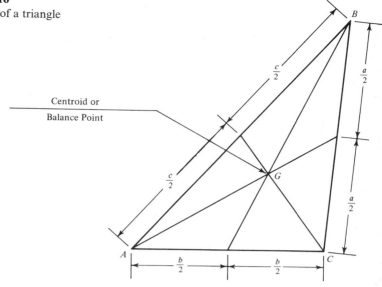

A median connects a vertex with midpoint of the side opposite.
Medians intersect at G, the centroid.

A **median of a triangle** is a line segment drawn from any vertex to the midpoint of the opposite side. A median divides a triangle into two parts equal in area. Note that for the two triangles formed by a median, each has a base of one-half the side of the original triangle, $\frac{b}{2}$, and a common altitude, h, and thus both triangles have a common area of $\frac{1}{4}bh$.

If two median lines are drawn, they trisect each other; that is, each median is divided into two parts, one being twice the size of the other. All three medians of a triangle intersect in a point called the **centroid** of the triangle. If the triangle were cut out of heavy cardboard and if a sharp straight pin were inserted through the centroid, the triangle would balance. There would be no tendency for the cardboard to rotate, because the centroid point is the true "middlemost" point of the triangle. The medians and the centroid are shown in Figure 4.16.

Problem Set 4.2

1–10
Determine which of the following triangles are right triangles if the three numbers listed represent sides a, b, and c, respectively. (Hint: Use a table of squares.)

1. 6, 13, 15
2. 7, 15, 17
3. 7, 24, 25
4. 8, 15, 17
5. 11, 60, 61

6. 1.2, 3.5, 3.7
7. 4.4, 11.7, 12.5
8. 1.5, 2.0, 2.5
9. 2.5, 4.0, 5.5
10. 0.875, 3.000, 3.125

11–22

Find to three significant figures the area of each triangle, having the dimensions as listed.

11. $b = 17, h = 47$
12. $b = 17.5, h = 46.5$
13. $b = \sqrt{2}, h = \sqrt{5}$
14. $b = \sqrt{3}, h = \sqrt{7}$
15. $a = 2, b = 3, c = 4$
16. $a = 3, b = 5, c = 9$

17. $a = 2.2, b = 4.2, c = 6.4$
18. $a = 3.6, b = 6.8, c = 8.6$
19. $\angle A = 30°, \angle C = 90°, c = 12$
20. $\angle A = 60°, \angle C = 90°, c = 18$
21. $\angle A = \angle B = 45°, c = 15$
22. $\angle A = 45°, \angle C = 90°, c = 25$

23–36

Find the missing data on each line of the following table by drawing the triangle, using five squares to the inch. Use the 50 scale on the engineer drafting scale to measure distances, and read the protractor to the nearest $\frac{1}{2}°$. (Note that a number 6 in this table means six squares, not 6 in.)

	a	b	c	A	B	C
23.	6	8	11			
24.			8	38°	32°	
25.				20°	60°	100°
26.	7	9	13			
27.	9			45°	27°	
28.		7	10	53°		
29.	7	11				95°
30.	5	9	15			
31.			12	40°		100°
32.		10		67°	21°	
33.	8	10	19			
34.	4	10		31°		
35.		10.0	12.5	37°		
36.	8.4		12.6		40.5°	

37 and 38

Three sides of a triangle are given. Using a drawing, find the perpendicular distance from side b to the centroid. All units are in inches.

37. $a = 2.0, b = 4.8, c = 5.2$ 38. $a = 6.8, b = 5.1, c = 8.5$

39. A company is planning to manufacture a prefabricated cattle-feeding trough. The sides are each two 2- by 12-in. planks (which actually measure $1\frac{5}{8}$ by $11\frac{1}{2}$ in.) set at a 90° angle. The ends are galvanized sheet

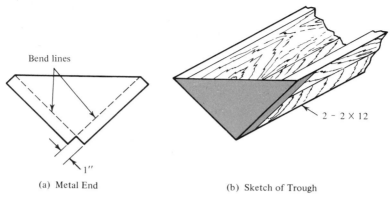

Bend lines

1"

(a) Metal End

(b) Sketch of Trough

2 - 2 × 12

metal with a 1-in. flap on both of the sides for nailing. If sheet metal costs 10 cents/sq ft for the thickness chosen, and 20 per cent must be added to the actual area for wastage in cutting, find the cost of 500 ends.

40. A series of campus sidewalks form a triangle as shown in the sketch. It is to be filled with an ivy ground cover that costs $2.95 a flat. Each flat will cover 5 sq ft. Find the cost of planting this area. Ignore the small curves at the intersections. Nurseries will only sell full flats.

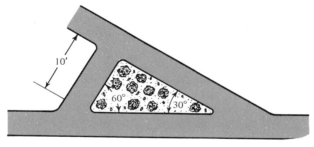

10'

60° 30°

41 and **42.** Find the number of acres in each plot of land shown below by subdividing it into convenient rectangles and triangles.

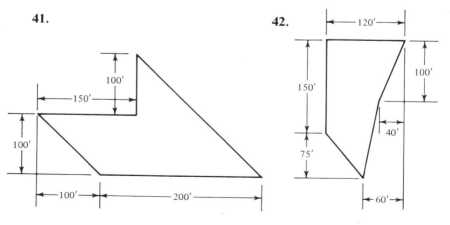

41.

100'

150'

100'

100'

100'

200'

42.

120'

150'

100'

75'

40'

60'

43. Draw an equilateral triangle with 4-in. sides and draw its inscribed circle. Find the radius of the inscribed circle to the nearest 0.01 in. by scaling.
44. Repeat Problem 43 using an equilateral triangle with $4\frac{7}{8}$-in. sides.
45. Given an isosceles triangle with 4-in. equal sides and a 3-in. base. Find the radius of the circumscribed circle to the nearest 0.01 in.
46. Repeat Problem 45 using 5-in. equal sides and a 3-in. base.
47. By a construction, find the centroid of a triangle having sides
    (a) $a = 6, b = 8, c = 9$
    (b) $a = 6, b = 8, c = 10$
    (c) $a = 6, b = 8, c = 12$
48. By a construction, find the centroid of a triangle having sides
    (a) $a = 9, b = 12, c = 13$
    (b) $a = 9, b = 12, c = 15$
    (c) $a = 9, b = 12, c = 17$
49. Classify each of the triangles in Problem 47 by the largest angle.
50. Classify each of the triangles in Problem 48 by the largest angle.
51. By a construction, find the orthocenter, the intersection of the three altitudes, for each of the triangles in Problem 47.
52. By a construction, find the orthocenter, the intersection of the three altitudes, for each of the triangles in Problem 48.

53–58
A, B, C, a, b, and c designate the parts of one triangle and A', B', C', a', b', and c' designate the corresponding parts of a similar triangle.

53. If $a = 12, b = 15$, and $a' = 8$, find b'.
54. If $c = 7, \angle C = 70°, c' = 14$, find $\angle C'$.
55. If $\angle B = 10°$ and $\angle C = 100°$, find $\angle A'$.
56. If $b = 12, c = 16$, and $c' = 20$, find b'.
57. If $a = 1.4, b = 4.8, c = 5.0$, and $a' = 0.7$, find the area and the perimeter of triangle $A'B'C'$.
58. If $\angle A = \angle B = 45°, c = 12$, and $c' = 8$, find the area and the perimeter of triangle $A'B'C'$.

59. Two foresters on an exploratory trip through a newly acquired wilderness area find a wide river. They would like to report its approximate width but have no measuring equipment other than a pocket 100-ft metallic cloth tape and a chalk line. They devise this scheme. A sighting bar is made by nailing a straight piece of wood to a sturdy staff cut from a branch. Two feet back from the edge of the river stake A is driven, and moving 60 ft parallel to the bank a similar stake B is driven. Sixteen feet from stake A on line AB stake D is driven. Holding their tape with the 20-ft mark on the stake at D, an arc is scratched on the ground in the vicinity of point C. Similarly, holding the 12-ft mark on A, another arc is swung and stake C is driven at the intersection of these two arcs.

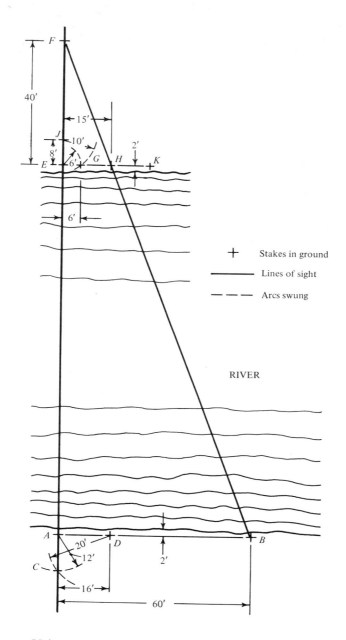

Using the sighting bar at C, and aligning it on A, the one forester who has crossed the river in their inflatable skiff is aligned and drives stake E 2 ft from the edge of the river. He is again aligned when he sets stake F exactly 40 ft from E. Next a random line EK is located using 6- and 10-ft arcs as shown in the sketch. A straight branch with a handkerchief tied to it for visibility is placed at F. The near-bank forester moves his sighting bar to B, and sighting on F locates his partner at H on line EK, marked by the chalkline. Line segment EH is found to be 15 ft.

(a) Identify angle EAB and give a reason for the statement made.

(b) Identify angle AEK and give a reason for the statement made.

(c) Find the relationship between angle FHE and angle HBA, and give the reason for the statement made.

(d) Calculate the width of the river to the nearest foot.

60. Repeat Problem 59 if the arc swung at point E is 24 ft, point J is 10 ft from point E, and the arc swung from J is 26 ft. In this problem EH is measured as 17 ft $1\frac{1}{2}$ in.

61. A much easier method to measure the width of the river is possible if a right angle can be turned. For a reconnaissance survey, either a Brunton compass or a right-angled surveying prism can be used; both fit into a pocket. As shown in the figure, a stake C is driven on one shore, 3 ft back from the river bank, and marked with a flagged stake for visibility. Both men cross the river, set stake B 3 ft back from the bank, and sight a right-angled line to A, which is located a convenient distance, say 90 ft. The midpoint M is also marked at this time. Another right angle is turned at A and several random stakes set on line near point D. Using an improvised sighting bar held at M, point C is sighted and then line CM extended to locate D. The distance AD is measured and found to be 93 ft 9 in.

(a) State a relationship between triangles DAM and MBC, giving reasons.

(b) Find the width of the river.

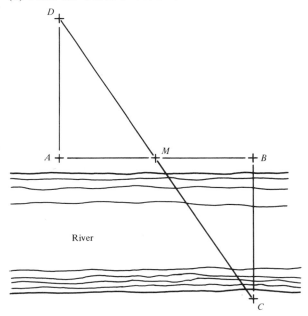

62. Assume that the area behind A is limited by a stand of trees so that M is located 60 ft from B and 30 ft from A. Answer the same two questions as in Problem 61 for this changed situation, this time AD being measured as 37 ft 2 in.

63. A tide gate consists of an isosceles triangle with a 2-ft base and 3-ft sides, hinged along its base, and hanging point downward. The base is 12 ft below the water surface at the critical condition being investigated. The total force acting upon this gate is the product of the area of the gate by the water pressure at the centroid. This water pressure will be 62.4h, where h is the distance from the water surface to the centroid. Find force F acting on this gate. (*Note :* The dimensions given for the gate represent the area exposed to the water pressure; the actual gate would be slightly larger.)

64. Repeat Problem 63 using a scalene triangle with a base of 2 ft, one side $2\frac{1}{2}$ ft, and the third side $3\frac{1}{2}$ ft.

65. A logging road is being laid out. The road must have its centerline pass through points A, B, and C in order to clear certain obstacles. A circular curve is desired. Point B is 400 ft due east of point A, and point C is 100 ft east and 400 ft south of point B. Find the radius of the circular curve and the distance to its center, given as a distance east and south of point A.

66. In a similar situation to that of Problem 65, the road must pass through points D, E, and F. Point D is the reference point. Point E is 700 ft due east and 100 ft north of point D. Point F is 200 ft due east and 400 ft south of point E. Find the radius and the location of the center with reference to point D.

67. A manhole cover, 4 ft in diameter, is reinforced with three structural

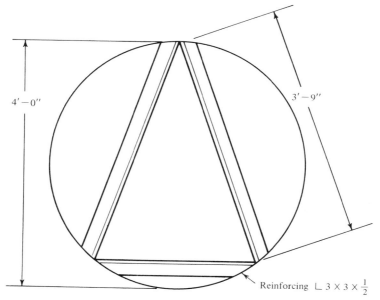

4'−0"

3'−9"

Reinforcing L 3 X 3 X $\frac{1}{2}$

steel angles, 3 by 3 by $\frac{1}{2}$ in., two of which are cut with the vertical leg 3 ft 9 in. long, as shown in the figure on the preceding page. Find the largest circular hole that can be cut in the triangular area bounded by these three angles.

68. A roof truss has its top members sloped 4 on 12, as shown in the figure. The first vertical post is 4 ft 0 in. from the junction of the two truss members. It is desired to run an air-conditioning return duct in the open space. These sheet-metal ducts are made in increments of 2-in. diameters, starting with an 8-in. duct, and require an external wrapping of $\frac{3}{4}$ in. of fiberglass insulation around the circumference. What is the largest duct that can be installed in this truss?

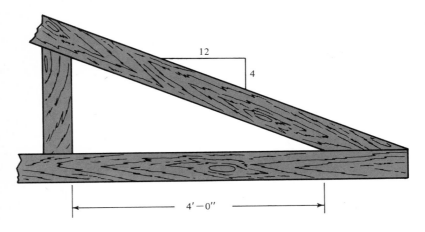

4.05 / Polygons

A **polygon** is a closed broken-line figure lying in a plane. The line segments that form the polygon are called the **sides** of the polygon and the endpoints of the sides are called the **vertices** of the polygon. A **diagonal** of a polygon is a line segment whose endpoints are two nonconsecutive vertices of the polygon.

A polygon is called **convex** if each of its interior angles is less than 180°. If an interior angle of a polygon is greater than 180°, the polygon is called **concave.**

The sum of the exterior angles of a convex polygon is 360°. Traversing the perimeter of any polygon is like traversing any closed loop, and since a circle contains 360°, the sum of 360° should seem reasonable.

The sum of the interior angles of a convex polygon having n sides is $(n - 2)180°$. The interior of a convex polygon having n sides can be subdivided into $n - 2$ triangles by drawing the diagonals from one vertex of the polygon. Since the sum of the interior angles of each triangle is 180°

Table 4.1

Regular polygons and properties (L = length of one side)

Number of sides	Name	Area	Radius of inscribed circle	Radius of circumscribed circle
3	Equilateral triangle	$0.4330L^2$	$0.2887L$	$0.5774L$
4	Square	$1.000L^2$	$0.5000L$	$0.7071L$
5	Pentagon	$1.720L^2$	$0.6882L$	$0.8506L$
6	Hexagon	$2.598L^2$	$0.8660L$	$1.000L$
7	Heptagon	$3.640L^2$	$1.038L$	$1.152L$
8	Octagon	$4.828L^2$	$1.207L$	$1.306L$
9	Nonagon	$6.182L^2$	$1.374L$	$1.462L$
10	Decagon	$7.694L^2$	$1.539L$	$1.618L$
11	Undecagon	$9.366L^2$	$1.703L$	$1.775L$
12	Dodecagon	$11.196L^2$	$1.866L$	$1.932L$
20	Duodecagon	$18.628L^2$	$3.156L$	$3.196L$

and since there are $n - 2$ triangles, the sum of the interior angles of the polygon is $(n - 2)180°$.

A **regular polygon** is a polygon whose sides are equal in length and whose interior angles are equal.

A circle can be inscribed in any regular polygon. The *center* of the inscribed circle is the point of intersection of the perpendicular bisectors of any two sides of the polygon. The *radius* is the perpendicular distance from the center to a side.

A circle can be circumscribed about any regular polygon. The *center* of the circumscribed circle is the center of the inscribed circle. The *radius* is the distance from the center to a vertex of the polygon.

The most common regular polygons, their names, areas, and radii of inscribed and circumscribed circles are listed in Table 4.1.

Although the areas of regular polygons are given in Table 4.1, there is no simple formula for the area of an irregular polygon. However, the interior of any polygon can be divided into triangles and the area of the polygon can be calculated as the sum of the areas of these triangles.

A **quadrilateral** is a polygon having four sides. The quadrilaterals are widely used shapes. These figures and their properties are shown in Figure 4.17 on the following page.

Figure 4.17
The family of quadrilaterals

No Sides Parallel

General Quadrilateral
(Trapezium)

No side parallel
No sides equal

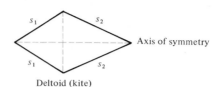

Axis of symmetry

Deltoid (kite)

No sides parallel
Two adjacent sides equal

$$\text{Area} = \frac{d_1 d_2}{2} \quad (\tfrac{1}{2} \text{ product of diagonals })$$

Diagonals are perpendicular

Two Sides Parallel

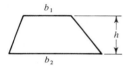

General Trapezoid
No sides equal

$$\text{Area} = \tfrac{1}{2} h (b_1 + b_2)$$

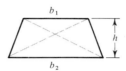

Isosceles Trapezoid
Nonparallel sides equal
Base angles are equal
Diagonals are equal

Parallelograms (Opposite Sides Parallel)

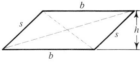

General Parallelogram

Opposite sides parallel
Opposite sides equal
Diagonals bisect each other
Area = bh

Rhombus

All properties of
parallelogram
All sides equal
Perpendicular diagonals

$$\text{Area} = \tfrac{1}{2} d_1 d_2 = bh$$

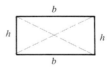

Rectangle

All properties of
parallelogram
Each angle = 90°
Equal diagonals
Area = bh

Square

All properties of parallelogram
All properties of rhombus
All properties of rectangle
Area = s^2 and area = $\tfrac{1}{2} d^2$

Problem Set 4.3

1. A surveyor has measured all but the last exterior angle of a polygon. His survey notes indicate that at this point he has turned a total of 290°. What should this last angle measure if no errors have been made?

2. The figure below indicates the original centerline of a proposed road. Point B is the point of intersection of two straight lines called tangents. The office engineers have decided to put a circular curve from point A, 200 ft before B to point C, 200 ft past point B. If lines perpendicular to the two tangents are drawn at A and C, they will intersect at point O, the center of the circular arc. The external angle at B, also called the deflection angle, was measured as $117°14'$. Find the central angle AOC.

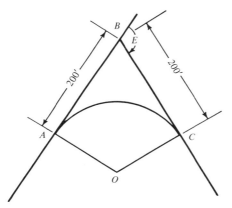

3. The sketch indicates a plot plan of a portion of a new subdivision. Swimming in Blue Lake has become so popular that an extension of 4th Avenue to Highway 101 is necessary. From the information shown on the sketch, find the angle between the east side of 4th Avenue and the highway.

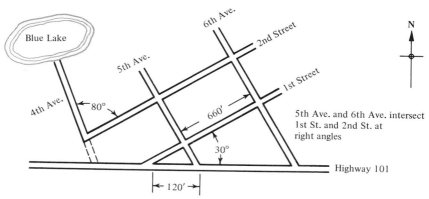

4. The sketch shows the base traverse of a proposed nature trail in a state park. Starting at the park headquarters (HQ), the angles shown were measured. Unfortunately, although the flagpole can be seen from the base of the tallest redwood tree, the dense woods prevent seeing the HQ building. What interior angle should be measured at the base of the tree station to permit a clearing crew to work toward the HQ and meet another group cutting along the same line from the west edge of the woods?

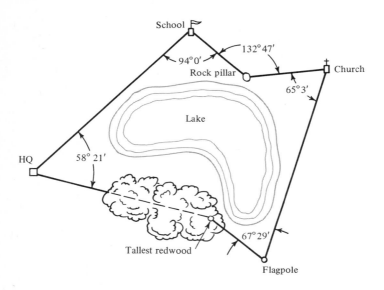

School

132° 47′

94° 0′

Rock pillar

Church

65° 3′

Lake

HQ

58° 21′

67° 29′

Tallest redwood

Flagpole

5. The Pentagon (a regular polygon) in Washington, D.C., measures 921 ft on a side. How many acres does it cover? (If you do not remember the number of square feet in an acre, use Table 10 of the Appendix.)

6. The inner pentagonal court (a regular polygon) of the Pentagon is a grassy, open plot containing 5 acres. What is the length of each side?

7. A regular hexagon with 2-in. sides is cut out of a square piece of metal with two opposite vertices of the hexagon lying on sides of the square. How many square inches of metal are wasted?

8. A new garden area to be paved measures 5 ft $0\frac{1}{2}$ in. wide by 7 ft $11\frac{1}{4}$ in. long. The plan is to use precast concrete blocks $5\frac{1}{2}$ in. on a side, made in the shape of a regular hexagon. The long dimension is to be positioned across the width and the dimension across the flats is to be positioned across the length. Half-blocks may be used, as shown in the figure. The small triangle, shown shaded, needed to complete the rectangle will be filled with newly mixed concrete.

(a) Find the dimensions across the corners and across the flats.

(b) Find the total number of full blocks needed.

(c) Find the area to be filled with concrete in square feet.

Problem 8

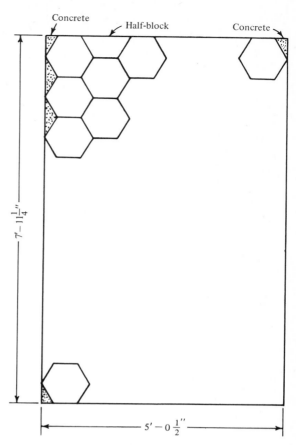

Concrete

Half-block

Concrete

$7'-11\frac{1}{4}''$

$5'-0\frac{1}{2}''$

9. A fraternity house on a college campus was designed in the shape of their pin, a regular octagon. The gross area of the main floor at ground level is 2414 sq ft. The outer face of the foundation walls was protected with a plastic film sold from continuous rolls containing 500 lineal feet. How many lineal feet should be ordered if a 5-ft overlap is specified?

10. A square gazebo has a floor that is made of 16 red concrete regular

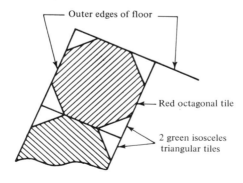

Outer edges of floor

Red octagonal tile

2 green isosceles
triangular tiles

octagons and green isosceles triangular tiles, as shown in the figure. Each octagonal tile contains 173.8 sq in. of surface. Find (a) the outside dimensions of the gazebo floor; (b) the area of one green triangle; (c) the total number of green triangular tiles required.

11 and **12.** The two figures below represent plots of irregular land tracts in an assessor's office, drawn to a scale of 1 in. = 200 ft. Draw each plot to scale on paper ruled five squares to the inch and measure all distances to the nearest 0.01 in. Find the area of each figure to the nearest quarter-acre and compute the tax if the current rate is $6.00/quarter-acre.

11.

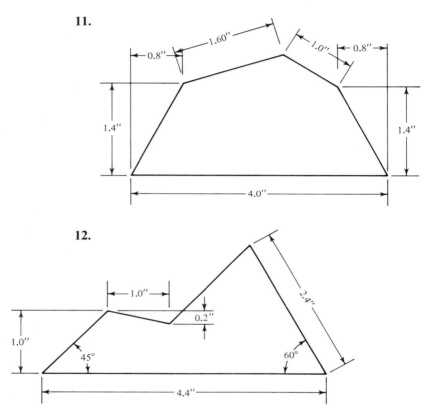

12.

13. Find the weight of a piece of 26-gage galvanized iron cut in the shape of a deltoid with a $6\frac{1}{4}$-in. short side and a 13-in. long side. The shorter diagonal is 10 in. (26-gage metal weighs $14\frac{1}{2}$ oz/sq ft.)

14. A deltoid-shaped kite whose short side is $8\frac{3}{4}$ in. and whose long side is 25 in. and whose shorter diagonal is 14 in. is exposed to a maximum air pressure of 1.75 psi. If the kite string must be twice as strong as the expected pull, what is the minimum strength string that can be used, assuming that it is manufactured in 10-lb increments of tensile strength?

15. The two trapezoids shown below, which are the same height, each represent the cross section of a coal storage pile. If the volume is the cross-sectional area times the length, in this case 200 ft, compare the volumes of the two piles.

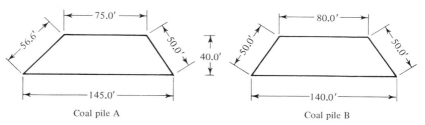

Coal pile A

Coal pile B

16. Referring to the subdivision shown in Problem 3, find the number of acres, to two decimal places, contained in the block bounded by 5th and 6th Avenues, 1st Street, and Highway 101.

17. An instructor has made the model shown to illustrate the instability of an unbraced parallelogram. The four bolted joints are loose. He moves the members from position (a) to position (b). Find the areas in each position, neglecting the narrow width of each bar.

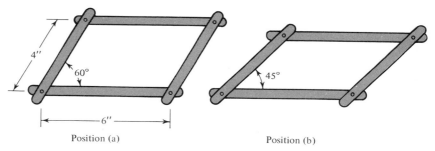

Position (a)

Position (b)

18. A pedestrian crossing of a major street, as shown in the figure, was experimentally painted with a fluorescent paint. This special paint and a wear-resistant plastic coating cost 50 cents/sq ft. What did this test material cost to the nearest dollar?

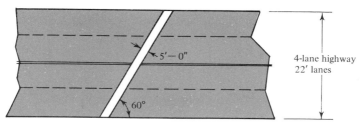

19. A rhombic antenna has 172 ft between opposite masts. For protection, an additional 128 ft to a barbed-wire fence was provided as shown in the sketch. (a) If the land fenced in is to be leased at $2.00/acre or any fractional part thereof, per month, find the annual rental. (b) Find the lineal feet of barbed wire required if a three-strand fence is erected around the perimeter.

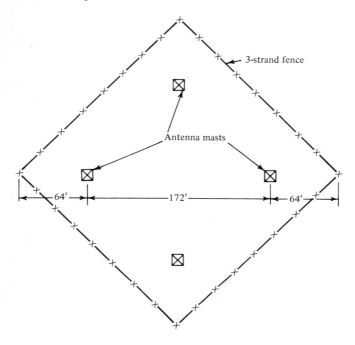

20. A street caution sign denotes reduced speed and is a yellow rhombus measuring $42\frac{1}{2}$ in. across the horizontal line and the vertical line joining the corners. A stop sign is a red octagon, with each side 10 in. long. If both are made of 10-gage black sheet metal weighing 5.625 lb/sq ft and if the paint weighs 0.28 lb per sign for the octagon and 0.52 lb per sign for the rhombus, find (a) the weight of 100 caution signs; (b) the weight of 100 stop signs; (c) whether a $\frac{3}{4}$-ton pickup, a $1\frac{1}{2}$-ton, $2\frac{1}{2}$-ton, or a 5-ton truck should be used to carry 100 caution signs and 100 stop signs.

21.

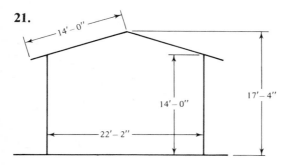

21. An advertising company has rented the end of a barn at a cost of 10 cents/sq ft. From the given dimensions, find the rental cost to the nearest dollar.

22. The volume of a swimming pool is based on finding the cross-sectional area. From the sketch, find the cross-sectional area of this pool.

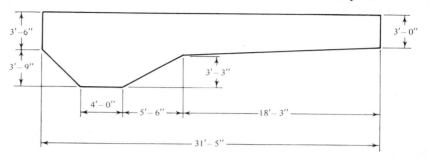

23. Compute the cross-sectional area of the three structural shapes shown.

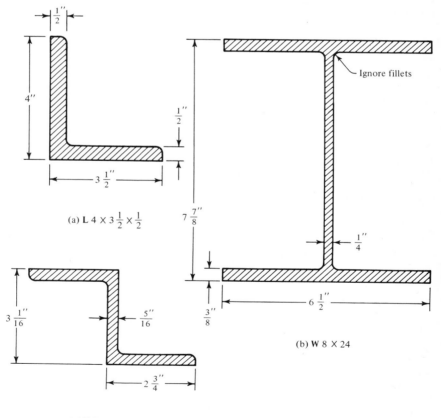

(a) **L** 4 X 3 $\frac{1}{2}$ X $\frac{1}{2}$

(b) **W** 8 X 24

(c) **Z** 3 X 6.7

24. The sketch below represents a half-section of a common type of reinforced floor. It is customary to find the weight of a unit width, that is, using a 1-ft dimension perpendicular to the cross-sectional area drawn. If concrete weighs 150 lb/cu ft, what does this floor weigh per unit width?

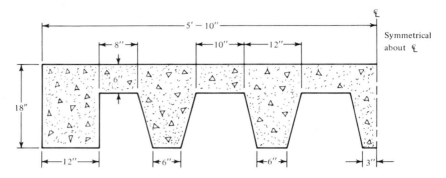

4.06 / Circles

A **circle** is the set of all points, in a plane, that are at a given fixed distance from a given point in the plane. The given point is called the **center.** The given fixed distance is called the **radius.**

Two **circles** are **congruent** (or equal) if their radii are equal.

Concentric circles are circles that have the same center. The ring-shaped space between concentric circles is called an **annulus** or an **annular ring.**

A **chord** is a line segment whose endpoints are points of the circle, such as AB in Figure 4.18. A **diameter** is a chord that contains the center of the circle, such as CD in Figure 4.18. A **secant** is a line that contains a chord. For example, $\overleftrightarrow{ED}$ is a secant because it contains the chord $\overline{ED}$.

A **central angle** of a circle is an angle whose vertex is the center of the circle, for example $\angle DOF$ in Figure 4.18. An **arc** is a part of a circle; for example the portion of the circle between points A and B is an arc, written $\overparen{AB}$ or arc AB. The chord joining points A and B is called the chord subtending arc AB. The arc consisting of those points that are interior to a central angle is called the **intercepted arc** of the central angle; for example, in Figure 4.18, arc DF is the intercepted arc of central angle DOF. When needed for clarity, the shorter arc between two points on a circle is called the *minor arc* and the longer arc is called the *major arc*. If necessary, an arc may be named by three letters, such as $\overparen{AEB}$, the major arc shown in Figure 4.18. A **semicircle** is one of the two equal arcs cut off by a diameter of a circle. The length of the entire circle is called the **circumference,** which means the perimeter of a circular area.

Figure 4.18
Nomenclature of circles

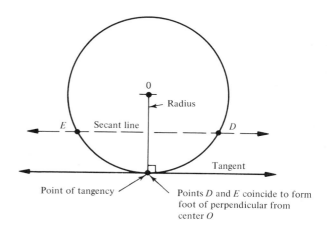

If the secant *ED* is gradually moved downward, point *E* becomes closer and closer to point *D* until they become the same point. The resulting line, shown in Figure 4.19, contains exactly one point of the set of points forming the circle and is called a *tangent* to the circle. The point common to the tangent line and the circle is called the **point of tangency** (often abbreviated P.T.). If this point is given a letter name, such as *D*, the line is said to be *tangent to the circle at D*. If a perpendicular is erected at *D*, it will pass through the center of the circle. A tangent line is always perpendicular to the radius drawn to the point of tangency.

If the point of tangency is known, the tangent line is obtained by drawing

Figure 4.19
Tangent line

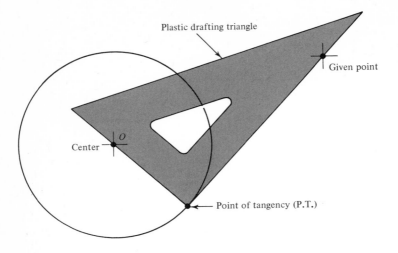

Plastic drafting triangle

Given point

Center

O

Point of tangency (P.T.)

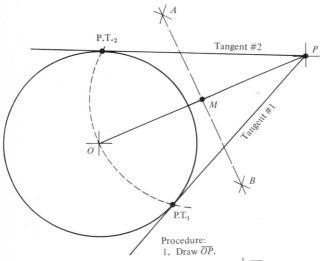

A

P.T.$_2$

Tangent #2

P

M

Tangent #1

O

B

P.T.$_1$

Procedure:
1. Draw $\overline{OP}$.
2. With radius $> \frac{1}{2}\,\overline{OP}$, O and P as centers, swing arcs intersecting at A and B.
3. Draw $\overline{AB}$, the perpendicular bisector of $\overline{OP}$.
4. With M as a center, OM as a radius, swing arc locating two points at tangency.
5. Draw tangents.

Figure 4.20
Constructing tangents

the radius to the point and then drawing a perpendicular to the radius at the point of tangency. The perpendicular is the tangent line and the radius at the P.T. is called the *normal*, a line perpendicular to a tangent of a curve.

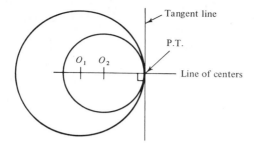

(a) Internally Tangent Circles

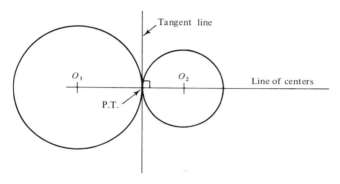

(b) Externally Tangent Circles

Figure 4.21
Tangent circles

It is more difficult to draw a tangent from a given point P off the circle. In many cases only a scaled sketch is required. Figure 4.20 shows a rapid method if any object with a right-angled corner is available.

Figure 4.20 illustrates the use of a small drafting triangle, but an ordinary 3- by 5-in. file card can be used. The lower figure shows the precise construction using a compass.

Extending the concept of tangency, two **circles are tangent** if they have the same point of tangency on a given tangent line (see Figure 4.21). Circles are called **internally tangent** if their centers are on the same side of the tangent line. In this case one circle is within the other. If the centers are on opposite sides of the tangent line, the circles are called **externally tangent** circles.

The line joining the centers of two circles is called the **line of centers.** If two circles are tangent, the line of centers contains the point of tangency and is perpendicular to the common tangent line.

The following are some important fundamental properties of circles, illustrated in Figure 4.22.

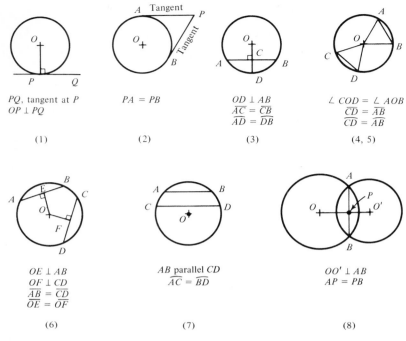

Figure 4.22
Basic properties of circles

(1) A tangent to a circle is perpendicular to the radius drawn to the point of tangency.
(2) The two tangents to a circle from an external point are equal.
(3) A radius perpendicular to a chord bisects the chord and its arc.
(4) In the same circle or in equal circles, central angles are equal if and only if their intercepted arcs are equal.
(5) In the same circle or in equal circles, two arcs are equal if and only if their chords are equal.
(6) In the same circle or in equal circles, two chords are equal if and only if they are equidistant from the center of the circle.
(7) The arcs between two parallel chords are equal.
(8) If two circles intersect and are not tangent, the line of centers is the perpendicular bisector of their common chord.

An angle whose sides intersect a circle may be measured by one or two arcs of the circle, depending upon the location of the vertex of the angle. If the vertex is at the center of the circle, the angle is a central angle and it is measured by its intercepted arc. In Figure 4.23(a), central angle AOB is measured by its intercepted arc AB, both being measured in degrees.

Arc AB is said to *subtend* angle AOB. Chord AB also subtends angle AOB. Since a chord can be expressed as a linear distance, it is sometimes used to identify a particular central angle; for example angle *GOK* subtended by a 2-in. chord.

If the vertex of an angle formed by two secants is on the circumference, this angle is called an **inscribed angle,** and is measured by one half of its

Figure 4.23
Angles in circles

θ is a central $\angle$

$\theta = $ arc *AB*

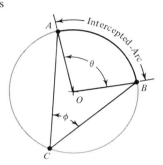

ϕ is an inscribed $\angle$

$\phi = \dfrac{1}{2}$ arc *AB*

(a) Central and Inscribed Angles

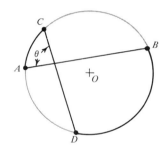

$\theta = \dfrac{1}{2}$ (arc *AC* + arc *BD*)

(b) Angle Between Chords

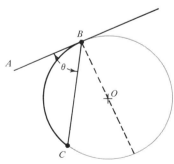

$\theta = \dfrac{1}{2}$ arc *BC*

(c) Angle Between Tangent and Chord

intercepted arc. For example, $\angle ACB = \frac{1}{2}\widehat{AB}$, in degrees. By observation, note that $\angle ACB = \frac{1}{2}\angle AOB$.

A useful fact following from the measure of an inscribed angle is that **any angle inscribed in a semicircle is a right angle.**

If the vertex of an angle lies within the circle but not at the center, the angle is measured by the average of its intercepted arc and the arc intercepted by its vertical angle, as shown in Figure 4.23(b).

Figure 4.24
Angles external to circle

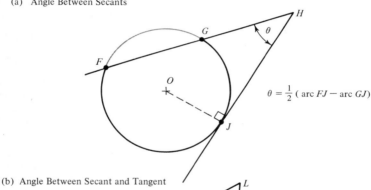

$\theta = \frac{1}{2} (\text{ arc } AE - \text{ arc } BD)$

(a) Angle Between Secants

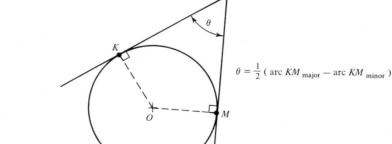

$\theta = \frac{1}{2} (\text{ arc } FJ - \text{ arc } GJ)$

(b) Angle Between Secant and Tangent

$\theta = \frac{1}{2} (\text{ arc } KM_{major} - \text{ arc } KM_{minor})$

(c) Angle Between Tangents

In all three cases θ is measured as $\frac{1}{2}$ the difference of intercepted arcs.

One special case with the vertex on the circle, but with the angle partially outside the circle, is the **angle between a tangent and a chord,** shown in Figure 4.23(c). Like an inscribed angle, it is measured by one half of its intercepted arc.

There are three types of angles that can be formed when the vertex is outside the circle. These angles are described by the kinds of lines forming the sides of the angles:

(a) **The angle between two secants.**

(b) **The angle between a secant and a tangent.**

(c) **The angle between two tangents.**

Fortunately, the same rule applies to the measure of the angle in all three cases, that is, the average of the *difference* of the two intercepted arcs. Figure 4.24 clearly indicates which arcs are used.

Often the area within a circle is called colloquially a circle, rather than a circular area or the area within a circle. The **area of a circle** of radius r is πr^2, where π is the nonterminating decimal $3.14159\ldots$. For rough calculations, $\frac{22}{7}$ can be used as an approximation to π. The **circumference of a circle** of radius r is $2\pi r$. Many slide rules have a special mark at π, and sometimes at $\pi/4$, since the area of a circle in terms of the diameter is $\frac{1}{4}\pi d^2$.

Figure 4.25
Circle, sector, segment, and annulus measurements

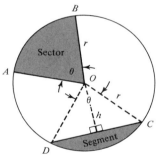

Area of circle $= \pi r^2$

Area of sector $= \dfrac{\theta}{360}\, \pi r^2$

Circumference $= 2\pi r$

Length of arc $AB = \dfrac{\theta}{180}\, \pi r$

Area of segment $= \dfrac{\theta}{360}\, \pi r^2 - \dfrac{1}{2}\, hL$, where L is the length of CD.

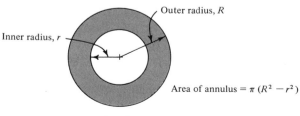

Outer radius, R

Inner radius, r

Area of annulus $= \pi\,(R^2 - r^2)$

Annulus

Just as two radii 90° apart intercept a quadrant, or an arc of one fourth of a circle, the area of a quadrant is one fourth of the area of the circle. A **sector** is the area bounded by any two radii and their included arc. If a sector has a central angle of θ degrees, the area of the sector and the length of its arc are given by

$$\text{area of sector} = \frac{\theta}{360}\pi r^2$$

$$\text{arc length} = \frac{\theta}{180}\pi r$$

Figure 4.25 shows a sector and another area of interest, a **segment** of a circle. A segment is the area between a chord and its intercepted minor arc. The area of a segment is the difference between the area of the associated sector and the area of the triangle formed by the chord of the segment and the radii of the sector.

Also shown in Figure 4.25 is an annulus. Its area is obtained by subtracting the area of the smaller circle from the area of the larger circle.

Problem Set 4.4

Exercises involving drawing scaled sketches should be drawn on quadrilled ruled paper divided five squares to the inch. Use a decimal scale ruler if needed. If the sketch is used only for visualizing the problem, a reduced-size sketch may be appropriate, say two small squares representing 1 in.

1. Within a 2-in.-diameter circle, inscribe an equilateral triangle and find the length of a side.
2. Within a 2-in.-diameter circle, inscribe an isosceles triangle with a 1.20-in. base and find the length of one of the equal sides.
3. Within a 2-in.-diameter circle, inscribe a 45°–45°–90° triangle and find the length of the shortest side.
4. Within a 2-in.-diameter circle, inscribe a 30°–60°–90° triangle and find the length of the longest side.
5. Within a 2-in.-diameter circle, inscribe a trapezium and find the sum of the opposite angles. Give a reason that will explain your findings.
6. Within a 2-in.-diameter circle, inscribe a trapezoid and compare the lengths of the nonparallel sides. Give a reason that will explain your findings.
7. Within a 2-in.-diameter circle, inscribe a parallelogram with one side = 1.60 in. and find the length of an adjacent side.
8. Within a 2-in.-diameter circle, inscribe a parallelogram with equal sides and find the length of a side.

9. An inscribed quadrilateral $ABCD$ subtends arc $AC = 74°$, arc $BC = 82°$, and arc $CD = 96°$.
   (a) Find the number of degrees in arc AD.
   (b) Find the number of degrees in each angle of the quadrilateral.
   (c) Find the number of degrees in the smaller angle formed by the diagonals of the quadrilateral.
10. A circle is divided into four arcs whose lengths, taken in consecutive order, are $\widehat{AB} = 3$ in., $\widehat{BC} = 4$ in., $\widehat{CD} = 7$ in., and $\widehat{DA} = 10$ in.
    (a) Find the number of degrees in each of these four arcs.
    (b) Find the number of degrees in each angle of triangle ABC.
    (c) Find the number of degrees in the smaller angle formed by chords AC and BD.
11. A circle is inscribed in a triangle. The consecutive arcs determined by the points of tangency measure 2 cm, 3 cm, and 4 cm, respectively.
    (a) Find the number of degrees in each of these three arcs.
    (b) Find the number of degrees in each angle of the triangle.
    (c) Find the number of degrees in each angle of the triangle formed by the chord of the largest arc and the tangents at the endpoints of this chord.
12. The angle between two equal chords AB and AC is 70°. Tangents are drawn at points B and C, intersecting at point D.
    (a) Find the number of degrees in arcs BC, AB, and AC.
    (b) Find the number of degrees in angles ABD and ACD.
    (c) Find the number of degrees in angle BDA.
13. A regular octagon with consecutive vertices $ABCDEFGH$ is inscribed in a circle. Sides AB and GH extended meet at P. The tangent at B meets the extension of GH at Q.
    (a) Find the number of degrees in each arc subtended by the sides of the octagon.
    (b) Find the number of degrees in angle APH.
    (c) Find the number of degrees in angle BQH.
14. In circle O, diameter CD is perpendicular to chord AB with arc $AD = 55°$. The extensions of chords CA and BD meet outside the circle at E. The tangent at B meets the extension of CD at F. Find the number of degrees in
    (a) arcs DB, BC, and CA.
    (b) angle AEB.
    (c) angle CFB.
15. The figure on the next page shows a fragment of a gear wheel. AB is measured as 6 in. and CD, the perpendicular bisector of AB, is measured as 4 in. Find the diameter of the original circle. (*Hint:* Copy the sketch, complete the circle, and extend CD to meet the circle at E. Show that triangle ACD is similar to triangle ACE and use a proportion to find the diameter.)

Problem 15

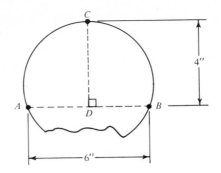

16. An uncrossed belt tautly surrounds a 3-in.-diameter pulley and a 12-in.-diameter pulley whose centers are 9 in. apart. Find the length of the belt.

17. A 3-in.-diameter pitch circle of one gear is internally tangent to a 5-in.-diameter pitch circle of another gear.
    (a) Find the distance between the centers of these two gears.
    (b) Find the length of a tangent to the smaller circle from the opposite endpoint of the diameter on the line of centers.

18. A roller with a 3-in.-diameter is externally tangent to another roller with a 4-in.-diameter when a certain sheet-metal roll is in the fully closed position. Point P, the pivot point of the two roller axle arms, lies on the line tangent at the common point of tangency and is 4 in. from the line of centers. Find the perimeter of the triangle formed by the pivot point and the centers of the two rollers by scaling and verify this result by calculations.

19. Find the diameter of one circular duct that will supply approximately the same cross-sectional area as three circular ducts having diameters 2.5, 5, and 5 in., respectively.

20. Find the diameter of a pipe at a point where the linear speed of the water is 2 ft/sec and the flow of the water past this point is 44.14 gal/sec. (*Hint:* The flow, Q, in cu ft/sec is equal to the linear speed in ft/sec multiplied by the cross-sectional area in sq ft; $Q = AV$. Also, 1 gal = 0.1337 cu ft.)

21. Find the number of square feet in a semicircular field if 610 ft of fencing are needed to enclose it.

22. Find the length of a metal band needed to encircle a 12-in.-diameter duct surrounded by insulation 1 in. thick, allowing 2 in. extra for the clamping device.

23. A newly erected circular water-storage tank is 120 ft in diameter. It is planned to grass the area extending 20 ft beyond the tank. If a new lawn requires 1 lb of grass seed per 250 sq ft of lawn, how many pounds of seed should be ordered?

24. A circular hospital is being planned as an annulus, with an open inner court 100 ft in diameter. If a gross floor space of 21,000 sq ft is desired,

what should the outside diameter of the building be to the nearest integral value in feet?

25. During atomic testing, the circular area around the tower holding the nuclear device is divided into sectors, which are allocated to the many government agencies participating. For one particular test, the critical overpressures extended out $\frac{3}{4}$ mile from the tower. The General Services Administration was allocated a 30° sector for testing commercial trucks. How many square feet were in this sector?

26. During the same test described in Problem 25, the Air Force had a 42° sector allocated for testing nose hangers. If each hanger site required 24,000 sq ft, how many hangers could be tested, assuming that 10 per cent of the land assigned is too close to the tower for test purposes?

27 and 28

To obtain needed angles and distances, draw accurate-scaled sketches covering about one fourth of a sheet of paper.

27. The counterweight on a movable bridge is made of concrete cast in the shape of a segment of a circle. If the circular radius is 40 ft and the chord distance is 50 ft, find the weight in tons of this 1-ft-thick counterweight. Concrete weighs 150 lb/cu ft.

28. A counterweight similar to the one described in Problem 27 has a radius of 50 ft and a chord distance of 45.4 ft. It is made of a mixture of concrete and scrap iron weighing 220 lb/cu ft. Find the weight in tons of this counterweight.

4.07 / Ellipses and parabolas

Ellipses and parabolas are found in a number of natural phenomena. The advent of the space age has made every newspaper reader familiar with the elliptical orbits of satellites and space vehicles. For several centuries, astronomers have been calculating the elliptical orbits of the planets, including the earth, about the sun. Parabolas are seen in daily life but are not often recognized and identified as such. Automobile headlights have parabolic reflectors, and the cables of large suspension bridges hang in parabolas. Almost all highways use parabolic curves to change the vertical slope of the road. In this geometric chapter, emphasis will be on the nomenclature of these two curved lines and a few of their properties.

An **ellipse** is the set of points in a plane such that the sum of the distances from any point on the curve to two fixed points, called the *foci*, is a constant. If a string of fixed length is fastened at its two endpoints to two pins separated a distance less than the length of the string, then, holding a pencil against

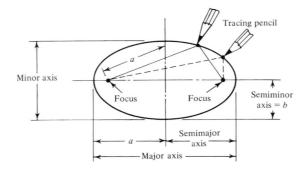

String and Pencil Method: Construction of Ellipse

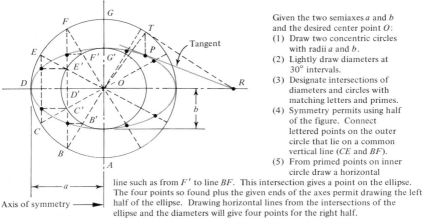

Given the two semiaxes a and b and the desired center point O:

(1) Draw two concentric circles with radii a and b.
(2) Lightly draw diameters at 30° intervals.
(3) Designate intersections of diameters and circles with matching letters and primes.
(4) Symmetry permits using half of the figure. Connect lettered points on the outer circle that lie on a common vertical line (CE and BF).
(5) From primed points on inner circle draw a horizontal line such as from F' to line BF. This intersection gives a point on the ellipse. The four points so found plus the given ends of the axes permit drawing the left half of the ellipse. Drawing horizontal lines from the intersections of the ellipse and the diameters will give four points for the right half.

To draw a tangent to the ellipse at any point P:
(1) Draw a vertical line from P to the outer circle at T.
(2) Draw the tangent to this circle at T, and find point R on the extension of the major axis.
(3) Line RP is the desired tangent.

Figure 4.26
Ellipses and tangents

the string and keeping the string taut, the pencil will trace an ellipse. Figure 4.26 illustrates this construction and also another method for constructing an ellipse.

The longest diameter of the ellipse is called the *major axis*, whether horizontal, vertical, or oblique. The shortest diameter is called the *minor axis*. In many calculations, halves of these diameters, called *semiaxes*, are used. The semimajor axis and the semiminor axis are designated as a and b, respectively.

A line tangent to an ellipse is similar to a line tangent to a circle in that it contains one and only one point common to both the tangent line and the

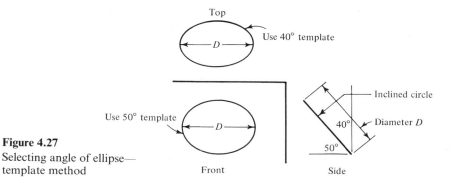

Figure 4.27
Selecting angle of ellipse—
template method

ellipse. A method for drawing a tangent line to an ellipse at a given point P on the ellipse is shown in Figure 4.26.

Today most ellipses are drawn by using factory-made plastic templates. These templates usually have ellipses for every 5° of inclination of the basic circle. The meaning of this angle for the ellipse is shown in Figure 4.27.

On a template, the diameters vary by $\frac{1}{32}$ in. for very small ellipses, then by $\frac{1}{16}$-in. increments up to 1 in., and then by $\frac{1}{8}$-in. increments. The error from a maximum possible angular inclination error of $2\frac{1}{2}°$ is not noticeable. A special template is made for the isometric projection of circles (the most widely used) since the true angular inclination is 35°16'.

The **area within an ellipse** is given by $A = \pi ab$. Since a circle can be thought of as an ellipse where $a = b = r$, this formula is valid for all positive values for a and b.

The **perimeter of an ellipse** is given by $P = \pi(a + b)k$. If a is less than $2b$, then the constant k is approximated by

$$k = 1 + \frac{m^2}{4} \qquad \text{where } m = \frac{a - b}{a + b}$$

If a is greater than $2b$ and an error of 2 per cent is not acceptable, k may be approximated by

$$k = 1 + \frac{m^2}{4} + \frac{m^4}{64}$$

For most applications, the approximation $k = 1 + (m^2/4)$ is adequate. More than three terms are given in handbooks but are needed only when a is much larger than b $(a > 5b)$.

A **parabola** is the set of points in a plane such that the distance from any point on the parabola to a fixed line, called the *directrix*, is equal to the distance from this same point on the parabola to a fixed point, called the *focus*.

The focus of a parabola has certain mathematical properties that will be studied later. Physically, it is the point where a headlight bulb is placed to

Figure 4.28

Elements of a parabola

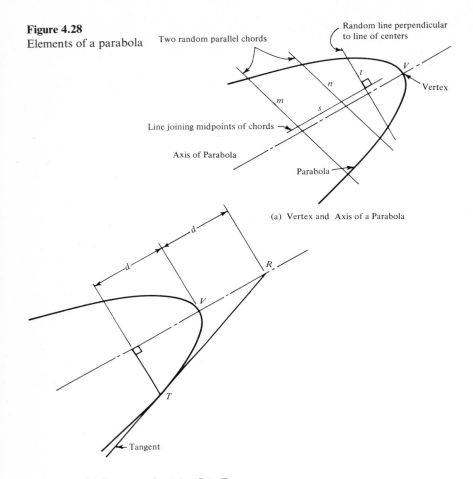

(a) Vertex and Axis of a Parabola

(b) Tangent to a Parabola at Point T

produce parallel rays of light. Any ray of light from the focus is reflected parallel to the axis of the parabola.

A general case of a parabolic curve is shown in Figure 4.28(a), where initially it is assumed that only the parabola itself is given. To locate the axis of the parabola (its line of symmetry) and the vertex of the parabola (the point of the parabola on its axis), two parallel random chords m and n are drawn. (A chord is a line segment joining two points on the curve.) The midpoints of the chords are found either by a geometric bisection or by using a finely divided decimal scale. Line s is drawn through these midpoints. At any convenient point on s, a perpendicular chord t is erected and then bisected. This bisector is the axis of the parabola and any perpendicular to this axis will cut the parabola at points equidistant from the vertex, the point where the axis intersects the parabola.

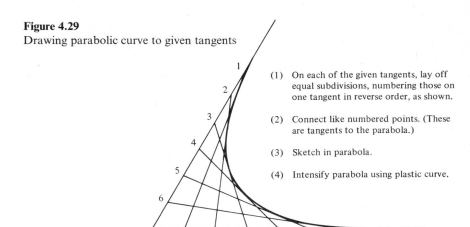

Figure 4.29
Drawing parabolic curve to given tangents

(1) On each of the given tangents, lay off equal subdivisions, numbering those on one tangent in reverse order, as shown.

(2) Connect like numbered points. (These are tangents to the parabola.)

(3) Sketch in parabola.

(4) Intensify parabola using plastic curve.

To draw a *tangent* to a parabola (a line containing exactly one point common to the line and the parabola) at a designated point T on the parabola, drop a perpendicular to the axis and measure the distance d to the vertex. Extend the axis an equal distance past the vertex to the point R. Then RT is the tangent desired. [See Figure 4.28(b).]

The method shown in Figure 4.29 can be used when it is desired to join two intersecting tangents with a parabolic curve. The lines drawn joining like numbered points are tangents to the parabola desired and thus this method produces an approximation to the parabolic curve. Once a suitable curve is drawn, the methods shown in Figure 4.28 can be used to locate the axis or vertex, if these are desired.

A fairly common engineering problem is to draw a parabolic curve through a given vertex and two other points, usually selected as the terminal points of the desired curve. In Figure 4.30, it is assumed that these points, V, A, and B, are given.

The horizontal distance $A'V$ is divided into a convenient number of equal parts. Since it usually represents a real distance, the engineer decimally

Figure 4.30
Drawing a parabola

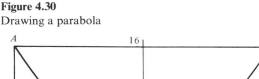

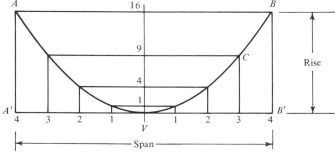

divided drafting scale is convenient. (The geometric method shown in Review Problem 11 can be used if desired.) Square the number that represents the number of equal parts into which $A'V$ has been divided, and divide the vertical distance from V to the horizontal line through AB into that number of parts. In the example shown in Figure 4.30, the half-span $A'V$ is divided into 4 equal parts, so the rise is divided into 4^2, or 16, parts. A point on the parabola is found above each horizontal division point at a vertical distance equal to the square of the horizontal unit number times the unit distance found for the vertical measurement. Since this parabola is symmetrical, the rise is divided at 1, 4, 9, and 16 units, the squares of the four horizontal divisions.

When referring to hanging cables, the distance marked "Rise" is frequently called "Sag." The method described above can also be applied when A and B are at different heights. However, the vertex will not be at midspan, so a different number of parts may be used for the $A'V$ and $B'V$ subdivisions, but the unit distance for each subdivision should be maintained, since the parabolic curve will be symmetrical about the vertex to the lower of the two heights.

Often, when the area bounded by a parabola is cited, there is one side that is not given. It is customary to choose a line perpendicular to the axis of the parabola as the closing side. Using Figure 4.30 as an example, the area bounded by the parabola would be the area bounded by arc AVB and line segment AB and is given by

$$\text{area} = \tfrac{2}{3}(\text{rise})(\text{span})$$

The area between the parabola, a perpendicular to the axis passing through the vertex, and two line segments parallel to the axis is called the area of a *parabolic spandrel*; for example, the area bounded by arc AVB and line segments AA', BB', and $A'VB'$. This area is given by

$$\text{area of spandrel} = \tfrac{1}{3}(\text{rise})(\text{span})$$

The *distance*, s, along a parabolic curve is found by an approximation. For a symmetrical parabolic curve with a span L and a rise R and with $m = R/L$,

$$s = L\left(1 + \frac{8m^2}{3}\right) \qquad \text{if } m \text{ is less than } 0.05$$

$$s = L\left(1 + \frac{8m^2}{3} - \frac{32m^4}{5}\right) \qquad \text{if } m \text{ is greater than } 0.05 \text{ but less than } 0.16$$

$$s = L\left(1 + \frac{8m^2}{3} - \frac{32m^4}{5} + \frac{128m^6}{7}\right) \qquad \text{if } m \text{ is greater than } 0.16$$

If the parabolic curve is not symmetrical, the length can be found as the sum of two half parabolas, being careful to remember that L is the *full* span, or the double of the distance from the vertex to the point of support on each side.

Problem Set 4.5

1–6

Draw each ellipse using a compass and the method shown in Figure 4.26. Paper ruled five squares to the inch is recommended.

1. Draw an ellipse whose axes are 3 and 4 in., respectively, with the shorter axis horizontal.
2. Draw an ellipse whose axes are 4 and 6 in., the major axis being horizontal.
3. Draw the ellipse that depicts a 4-in. circle tilted 45°.
4. Draw the ellipse that depicts a 4-in. circle inclined 60° from the horizontal.
5. Draw the ellipse with its major axis horizontal, given $a = 2\frac{1}{2}$ in. and $b = 2$ in. Locate foci F_1 and F_2. Draw a tangent at a point on the ellipse to the left of the minor axis and 1 in. above the major axis.
6. Draw an ellipse inscribed on the vertical face of a 3-in. cube, drawn isometrically. Locate the foci F_1 and F_2. If the eccentricity of an ellipse is defined as the quotient obtained by dividing the distance from the center of the ellipse to a focus by the length of the semimajor axis, what is the eccentricity of this ellipse? (The center of an ellipse is the point of intersection of its major and minor axes.)

7. The Colosseum in Rome is an ellipse 617 ft long and 512 ft wide. What is the gross area in square feet, and what is the external perimeter?
8. The Blue Room of the White House in Washington, D.C., is used for major receptions. It is oval (elliptical), measuring 39 ft by 29 ft 6 in. If 7 sq ft is required for each person by the fire safety code and 10 per cent of the total floor area is taken up by furniture, what is the maximum number of people that can be invited to a function?
9. If a new scuff plate (a molding at the base of a wall) is to be installed in the Blue Room described in Problem 8 and 5 per cent of the perimeter is doorways where no molding is used, how many feet are required?
10. The orbit of the earth is an ellipse with the sun at one focus. The major axis is 185.8 million miles, and the eccentricity (see Problem 6) is $\frac{1}{60}$. Find the greatest and the least distance of the earth from the sun.
11. The Brooklyn Bridge has a main span of 1600 ft and the low point of the cable is 140 ft below the top of the towers. Draw the parabolic form of the main cable and, by scaling, find the cable height above the low point at the quarter point of the span.
12. How long is the main cable in Problem 11?
13. Pipelines are often carried across a wide river by hanging them with short cables called "hangers" from a heavy main cable. A 200-ft river with towers set back 25 ft from the waterline is to be crossed, with the tops of the towers 50 ft above high water. The lowest point of the pipeline

must be 10 ft above high water and attached to the main cable by a 5-ft hanger at midspan. If the other hangers are spaced every 25 ft, find by scaling the total length of hanger cable needed. Allow 5 per cent for waste and fastening. No hanger is used at the tower. (*Note:* To obtain a reasonable answer, draw half of this parabola to the largest convenient scale that will fit on an $8\frac{1}{2}$- by 11-in. paper.)

14. Referring to Problem 13, calculate the sum of the hanger cable lengths.
15. Find the cubic feet of concrete in the arch bridge in the figure if the curved opening is a true parabola. (The volume is the area of the face multiplied by the thickness of 20 ft.)

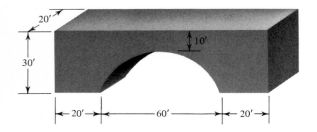

16. Two planned streets intersect at 45°. It is planned to use a parabolic cutoff as shown in the figure, the centerlines each being tangent to the parabola 100 ft from the original point of intersection. Draw this intersection to scale and measure the approximate length of the curve. Find the number of square yards of asphalt needed, assuming the area is the length of the curve multiplied by the roadway width. (*Note:* The R/L ratio is so large that the formulas given in the text cannot be used.)

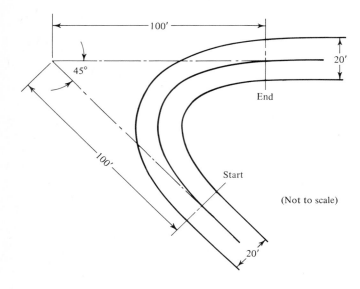

4.08 / Solids with plane sides

A **polyhedron** is a closed surface bounded by plane polygons, called the **faces** of the polyhedron. The intersections of the faces are called the **edges** and the points of intersection of the edges are called the **vertices**.

A **regular polyhedron** is a polyhedron whose faces are congruent regular polygons. There are only five regular polyhedrons and these are called the five regular solids, illustrated in Figure 4.31.

The names and properties of the regular polyhedrons are given in Table 4.2.

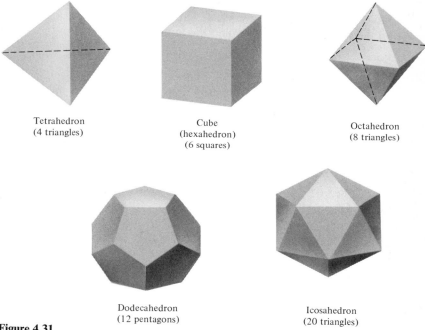

Tetrahedron
(4 triangles)

Cube
(hexahedron)
(6 squares)

Octahedron
(8 triangles)

Dodecahedron
(12 pentagons)

Icosahedron
(20 triangles)

Figure 4.31
The five regular solids

Table 4.2
Properties of regular solids (L = length of one edge)

Name	Nature of surface	Surface area	Volume
Tetrahedron	4 equilateral triangles	$1.732L^2$	$0.1178L^3$
Cube	6 squares	$6.000L^2$	$1.0000L^3$
Octahedron	8 equilateral triangles	$3.464L^2$	$0.4714L^3$
Dodecahedron	12 pentagons	$20.646L^2$	$7.6631L^3$
Icosahedron	20 equilateral triangles	$8.6603L^2$	$2.1817L^3$

With the exception of the cube, these solids are not met too frequently. Recently, however, heavy concrete tetrahedrons have been widely used for protecting shorelines and riverbanks from erosion. In the field of mineralogy, all these solids appear in studying crystalline structures.

Commercially, these shapes are beginning to appear more and more. Individual cream containers, used on airplanes and in some restaurants, have the form of a regular tetrahedron. The dodecahedron is used as a calendar, with each of the 12 months appearing on one of its 12 pentagonal faces. Many pieces of jewelry and works of sculpture exhibit these five regular solids.

A **pyramid** is a polyhedron one of whose faces is a polygon, called the **base** of the pyramid, and whose other faces are triangles having a common vertex, called the **vertex** of the pyramid. The triangles are called the **lateral faces** and their intersections are called the **lateral edges.**

Figure 4.32
Pyramids

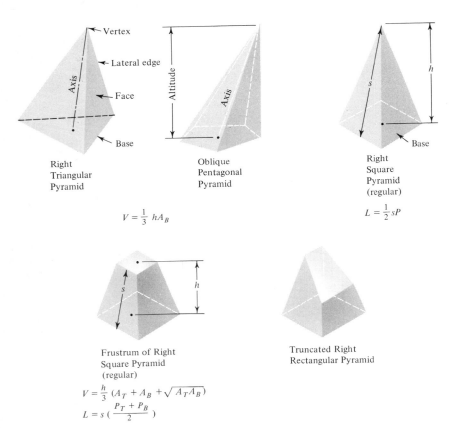

Right Triangular Pyramid

Oblique Pentagonal Pyramid

$$V = \frac{1}{3} hA_B$$

Right Square Pyramid (regular)

$$L = \frac{1}{2} sP$$

Frustrum of Right Square Pyramid (regular)

$$V = \frac{h}{3} (A_T + A_B + \sqrt{A_T A_B})$$
$$L = s \left(\frac{P_T + P_B}{2} \right)$$

Truncated Right Rectangular Pyramid

The **altitude** of a pyramid is the perpendicular distance from its vertex to its base.

A **regular pyramid** is a pyramid whose base is a regular polygon and whose altitude passes through the center (centroid) of its base. The **slant height** of a regular pyramid is the common altitude of its congruent triangular faces.

A line from the vertex of a pyramid to the center (centroid) of its base is called the **axis** of the pyramid. If the axis is perpendicular to the base, the pyramid is called a **right pyramid.** If the axis slopes, the pyramid is called an **oblique pyramid.** Any section cut off by a plane perpendicular to the axis is called a **right section.**

If the top of a pyramid has been cut off by a plane parallel to the base of the pyramid, the resulting solid is called a **frustrum** of a pyramid. If the top has been cut off by a plane inclined to the base, the resulting solid is called a **truncated pyramid.**

Examples of pyramids and portions of pyramids are illustrated in Figure 4.32.

The **volume of any pyramid** having h as its altitude and A_B as the area of its base is given by

$$V = \tfrac{1}{3}hA_B$$

The **volume of a frustrum of a pyramid** having h as its altitude, A_T as the area of its top polygon, and A_B as the area of its base is given by

$$V = \frac{h}{3}(A_T + A_B + \sqrt{A_T A_B})$$

The **lateral surface area,** A_L, of a pyramid is the sum of the areas of its lateral faces. The **total surface area,** S, is the sum of the lateral surface area and the area of the base. For a regular pyramid,

$$A_{L_{\text{regular pyramid}}} = \tfrac{1}{2}sP$$

where s is the slant height and P is the perimeter of the base.

For the frustrum of a regular pyramid, the lateral area is the product of the average perimeter by the intercepted slant height, or

$$A_{L_{\text{frustrum of regular pyramid}}} = s\frac{P_T + P_B}{2}$$

For nonregular pyramids or truncated pyramids, a development (a plane drawing which, when folded on the lateral edges, forms the lateral surface) will give the dimensions of the polygons that form the lateral faces.

The prisms constitute another important family of polyhedrons. A **prism** is a polyhedron two of whose faces, called **bases,** are congruent polygons lying in parallel planes and whose other faces (the lateral faces) are parallelograms. Each lateral edge of a prism is parallel to the other lateral edges.

If the lateral edges are perpendicular to the bases, the prism is called a **right prism.** If the lateral edges are oblique to the bases, the prism is called an **oblique prism.** Prisms are also classified according to the shapes of their bases. For example, a right triangular prism is a right prism whose bases are triangles. If the bases are parallelograms, the prism is also called a **parallelepiped.**

The **altitude** of a prism is the perpendicular distance between its parallel bases. A **right section** of a prism is a section cut off by a plane perpendicular to the lateral edges. Examples of prisms are illustrated in Figure 4.33.

The **volume of a prism** is the product of the area of the base and the altitude; that is,

$$V = hA_B$$

The **lateral area of a prism** is the sum of the areas of its lateral faces. Since these faces are parallelograms, with the altitude of the prism also the

Figure 4.33
Prisms

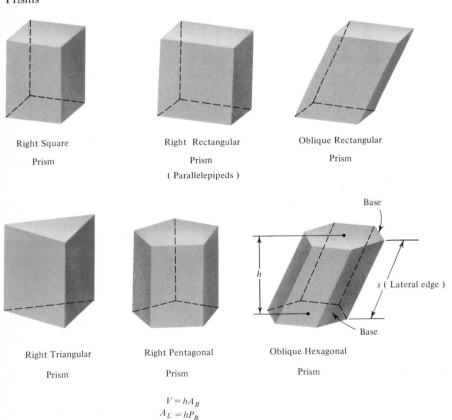

Right Square

Prism

Right Rectangular

Prism

(Parallelepipeds)

Oblique Rectangular

Prism

Base

h

s (Lateral edge)

Base

Right Triangular

Prism

Right Pentagonal

Prism

Oblique Hexagonal

Prism

$$V = hA_B$$
$$A_L = hP_B$$

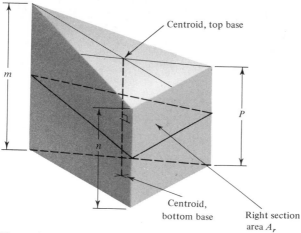

Figure 4.34

Truncated right triangular prism, $V = A_r \dfrac{m + n + p}{3}$

altitude of each parallelogram, the lateral area is the product of the perimeter of the base and the altitude; that is,

$$A_L = hP_B$$

The **total surface area of a prism** is the sum of the lateral area and the areas of the two congruent bases; that is,

$$s = hP_B + 2A_B$$

A **truncated prism** is the solid that results when the top of a prism has been cut off by a plane that is not parallel to the bases. As a general rule, it is necessary to make exact drawings of a truncated prism in order to compute its volume and area. The centroids of the bases are found by drawing axes of symmetry and locating their intersection. A line is drawn joining these two centroids and the area of a section taken at right angles to this line is found. The volume of the truncated prism is the product of this area and the length of the line joining the centroids. The total surface area can be obtained by drawing the development.

Figure 4.34 illustrates a truncated right triangular prism. For this solid, there is a slightly simpler solution. The volume is the product of the area of the right section, A_r, and the mean lateral edge; that is,

$$V = A_r \frac{m + n + p}{3}$$

A **prismatoid**, illustrated in Figure 4.35, is a polyhedron all of whose vertices lie in one or the other of two parallel planes. The faces in the parallel planes are called the *bases*. The *altitude* of a prismatoid is the perpendicular

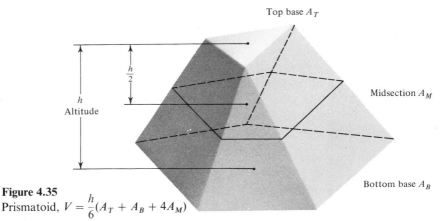

Top base A_T

$\dfrac{h}{2}$

h
Altitude

Midsection A_M

Bottom base A_B

Figure 4.35
Prismatoid, $V = \dfrac{h}{6}(A_T + A_B + 4A_M)$

distance between the bases. Each lateral face of a prismatoid is a triangle, a parallelogram, or a trapezoid.

A development must usually be drawn to find the surface area of a prismatoid. The volume, however, can be computed by using the **prismoidal formula,**

$$V = \frac{h}{6}(A_T + A_B + 4A_M)$$

where h is the altitude, A_T and A_B are the areas of the top and bottom bases, and A_M is the area of a right section taken at midaltitude. In many problems, A_M is found by careful drafting methods when it cannot be calculated readily.

The prismoidal formula is widely used in computing volumes of earthwork. The cross section for a highway, a railroad, or an irrigation ditch is measured, say, every 50 ft along its length. The shape of these sections is drawn as an eight-sided polygon based on measuring the elevation of the ground at five points and computing two points for the desired finished surface. The area of this polygon is either measured mechanically using a device called a planimeter or by computations explained in more advanced texts. This computational method can easily be run on an electric computer and large offices have eliminated thereby this time-consuming arithmetic operation.

4.09 / Solids with curved sides

There are three important types of solids with curved sides: cylinders, cones, and solids of revolution.

A **cylinder** is the surface generated by a line segment that remains parallel to a fixed line, called the **generatrix,** and that traces a plane curve, called the

directrix. The directrix and its interior are called the **base,** or lower base, of the cylinder. The cylinder also has an upper base congruent to the lower base.

The **altitude** of a cylinder is the perpendicular distance between its parallel bases. The *axis* of a cylinder is the line segment joining the centers (centroids) of the bases. A **right section** is a section cut off by a plane perpendicular to the axis.

A cylinder is called a **right cylinder** or an **oblique cylinder** according as its axis is perpendicular or oblique to its bases. Cylinders are also classified by the shape of their bases. For example, a right circular cylinder has a circle for its base and a right elliptic cylinder has an ellipse for its base. Examples of cylinders are shown in Figure 4.36.

The **volume of a cylinder** can be obtained either as the product of the area of the base and the altitude or as the product of a right section and the **slant height** (the length of a line segment on the cylinder parallel to the generatrix):

$$V = hA_B \qquad \text{or} \qquad V = sA_r$$

The **lateral surface area** is the product of the perimeter of a right section and the slant height:

$$A_L = sP_r$$

A **truncated cylinder** is the solid that results when the top of a cylinder has been cut off by a plane that is not parallel to the bases. The **volume** of a truncated right cylinder or a truncated oblique cylinder whose top base is a right section can be computed as the product of the area of the base and the average of the minimum and maximum heights:

$$V = \tfrac{1}{2}(h_1 + h_2)A_B$$

For any truncated cylinder, a method similar to that shown in Figure 4.34 can be used, that is,

$$V = A_r d_c$$

Figure 4.36
Cylinders

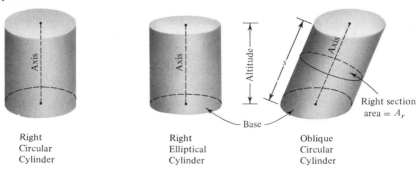

Right
Circular
Cylinder

Right
Elliptical
Cylinder

Oblique
Circular
Cylinder

Right section
area $= A_r$

Base

Volume: $V = hA_B$ or $V = sA_r$

Lateral Area: $A_L = sP_r$

Figure 4.37
Ungula of a cylinder

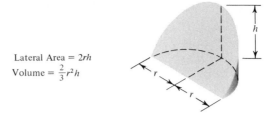

Lateral Area $= 2rh$

Volume $= \frac{2}{3}r^2h$

(a) Special Ungula

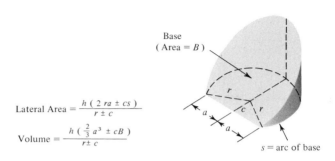

Base
(Area $= B$)

Lateral Area $= \dfrac{h\,(\,2\,ra \pm cs\,)}{r \pm c}$

Volume $= \dfrac{h\,(\frac{2}{3}\,a^3 \pm cB\,)}{r \pm c}$

$s =$ arc of base

(b) Any Ungula

where d_c is the distance between the centroids of the two bases. The **lateral area** of circular or elliptical truncated cylinders can be obtained by multiplying the perimeter of a right section by the average of the minimum and maximum slant heights:

$$A_L = \tfrac{1}{2}(s_1 + s_2)P_r$$

In general, a truncated oblique cylinder can be divided into two truncated oblique cylinders each having a right section for one of its bases. The volume and lateral area of each of the two parts can be obtained by the method just described. If necessary, the developed surface can be drawn and the area measured mechanically.

When a cylinder is truncated by a plane that passes through one of the bases, the resulting wedgelike shape is called an **ungula.** Examples of ungulas and their volume and surface area formulas are illustrated in Figure 4.37.

A **cone** is the surface generated by a line segment (called the **generatrix**) that passes through a fixed point (called the **vertex**) and traces the perimeter of a closed curve (called the **directrix**). The *axis* of a cone is the line segment joining the vertex and the center (centroid) of the base (the plane surface bounded by the directrix). The **altitude** of a cone is the perpendicular distance from the vertex to the base. Cones are classified by using the same adjectives to describe the shape of the base and the inclination of the axis as were used for the cylinders. Examples of cones and portions of cones are illustrated in Figure 4.38.

The **volume** of a cone or a frustrum of a cone is obtained by using the same formulas as those used for a pyramid.

The **slant height,** s, of a right circular cone is the length of the generatrix and can be calculated from the altitude, h, and the radius, r, of the base as follows:

$$s = \sqrt{h^2 + r^2}$$

For a **frustrum of a right circular cone,** the intercepted slant height is given by

$$s = \sqrt{(r_B - r_T)^2 + h^2}$$

Figure 4.38
Cones and sections of cones

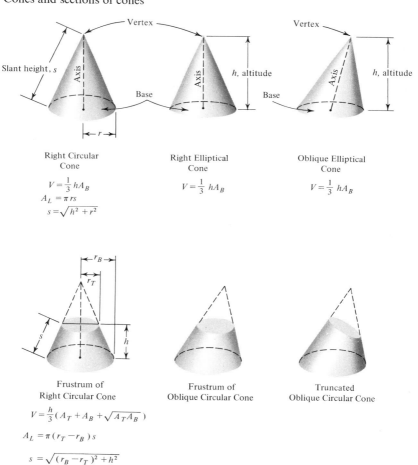

Right Circular Cone

$V = \frac{1}{3} hA_B$
$A_L = \pi r s$
$s = \sqrt{h^2 + r^2}$

Right Elliptical Cone

$V = \frac{1}{3} hA_B$

Oblique Elliptical Cone

$V = \frac{1}{3} hA_B$

Frustrum of Right Circular Cone

$V = \frac{h}{3}(A_T + A_B + \sqrt{A_T A_B})$

$A_L = \pi (r_T - r_B) s$

$s = \sqrt{(r_B - r_T)^2 + h^2}$

Frustrum of Oblique Circular Cone

Truncated Oblique Circular Cone

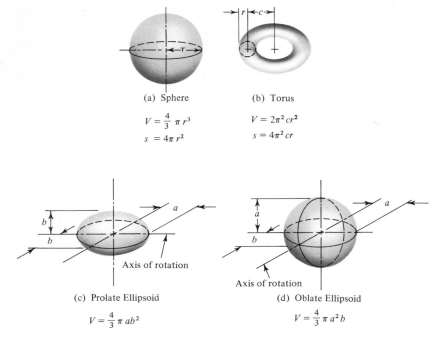

(a) Sphere

$$V = \frac{4}{3} \pi r^3$$

$$s = 4\pi r^2$$

(b) Torus

$$V = 2\pi^2 cr^2$$

$$s = 4\pi^2 cr$$

(c) Prolate Ellipsoid

$$V = \frac{4}{3} \pi ab^2$$

(d) Oblate Ellipsoid

$$V = \frac{4}{3} \pi a^2 b$$

Figure 4.39
Solids of revolution

where h is the altitude of the frustrum, r_B is the radius of the bottom circular base, and r_T is the radius of the top circular base.

The **lateral area** of a right circular cone or a frustrum of a right circular cone is obtained by multiplying the slant height by half the perimeter of the base for the cone and by multiplying the slant height by the perimeter of the average base for the frustrum.

A solid of revolution is formed by revolving a closed curve about a chosen line called the **axis of revolution.** If the closed curve is a circle and the chosen axis is a diameter, the resulting solid is a **sphere.** If a circle is revolved about a line that does not intersect the circle, the resulting doughnut-shaped solid is called a **torus.** A sphere and a torus are shown in Figure 4.39. The last two solids shown in Figure 4.39 are created by revolving an ellipse first about its minor axis to form the **oblate ellipsoid,** and second about its major axis to form the **prolate ellipsoid.** Formulas for the surface areas of the ellipsoids, not shown on Figure 4.39 since they involve terms not yet discussed, will be presented in Chapter 10.

4.10 / Relationships of a sphere

Since the earth is almost a perfect sphere (it is slightly flattened at the north and south poles), the nomenclature of a sphere has crept into the common speech of man. If a sphere is cut by a plane perpendicular to a diameter of the sphere, the cut section is a circle. The two points where any

Figure 4.40

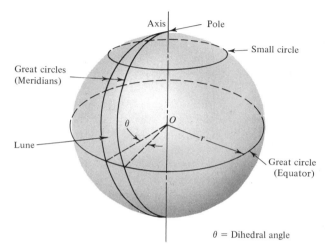

(a) Nomenclature of a Sphere

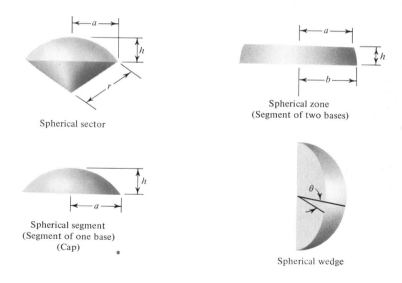

Spherical sector

Spherical zone
(Segment of two bases)

Spherical segment
(Segment of one base)
(Cap)

Spherical wedge

(b) Spherical Solids

diameter cuts the surface of a sphere are called **poles.** The north and south poles are the ends of that particular diameter about which the earth rotates. A circle cut off by a plane containing a diameter is called a **great circle.** The shortest distance between any two points on the earth's surface is the great circle through these two points. Most major airlines fly great-circle routes across the two oceans. The meridians of longitude by which man locates himself east or west of a selected reference meridian are all great circles through the north pole. Most of the nations of the world signed an international agreement in 1884 to use the meridian through Greenwich, England, as the reference meridian.

Circles cut by planes not containing the center of the sphere are called small circles. The surface of the earth is covered by a geographic grid system using meridians and small circles perpendicular to the polar axis, known as the **parallels** of latitude, north or south. The zero latitude is called the **equator,** the great circle parallel to these small circles.

The angle between any two planes forming meridian great circles is called a **dihedral angle.** This same name is used for the angle between any two planes. The dihedral angle is very widely used in aeronautics.

The surface area between two meridians is called a **lune.** The solid so formed is called a **spherical wedge.**

The solid created by a plane intersecting a sphere in a small circle is called a **spherical segment,** or **cap,** as shown in Figure 4.40.

A **spherical sector** is formed by adding a spherical segment to a cone whose vertex is the center of the sphere and whose base is the small circle forming the base of the spherical segment.

That portion of a sphere between two parallel planes intersecting the sphere in circles is called a **spherical zone.**

Table 4.3 gives the volumes and surface areas of these portions of a sphere, using the dimensions identified on Figure 4.40.

Table 4.3
Areas and volumes of spherical solids

	Sector	Zone	Segment	Segment (Alternate)	Wedge
Volume	$\frac{2}{3}\pi r^2 h$	$\frac{\pi h}{6}(3a^2 + 3b^2 + h^2)$	$\frac{\pi h}{6}(3a^2 + h^2)$	$\frac{\pi h^2}{3}(3r - h)$	$\frac{\pi r^3 \theta}{270}$
Spherical surface area	$2\pi r h$	$2\pi r h$	$\pi(a^2 + h^2)$	$2\pi r h$	$\frac{\pi r^2 \theta}{90}$
Total surface area	$\pi r(2h + a)$	$\pi(2rh + a^2 + b^2)$	$\pi(2a^2 + h^2)$	$\pi(2rh + a^2)$	$\pi r^2\left(1 + \frac{\theta}{90}\right)$

Problem Set 4.6

1. To protect river banks and ocean frontage against erosion, various methods of placing heavy rock have been tried. One of the better methods found was using concrete tetrahedrons weighing several tons. Further experimentation showed that the efficiency generally rose with the increase in the ratio of the surface area divided by the volume. For a regular concrete tetrahedron with 6-ft sides, find the weight in tons and the area/volume ratio. Concrete weighs 150 lb/cu ft.

2. Referring to Problem 1, a concrete tetrapod was another innovation used in shore protection. A tetrapod is a regular tetrahedron with an identical tetrahedron attached to each face. Find the weight in tons and the area/volume ratio for a concrete tetrapod with 4-ft sides.

3. A desk calendar has the shape of a regular dodecahedron measuring $2\frac{1}{2}$ in. on each edge.
   (a) Find the number of square inches required to make this calendar.
   (b) Find the volume of this solid that could be filled to give it additional weight.

4. An individual cream container has the shape of a regular tetrahedron $1\frac{1}{2}$ in. long on each side.
   (a) Find the number of ounces this container holds.
   (b) Find the number of square inches of material required to make this container.

5. Some diamond crystals and some quartz crystals have essentially the shape of a regular octahedron, although slightly modified. A crystal of this type weighs 1.2 g and measures 9 mm along each edge. If the specific gravity of diamond is about 3.5 and the specific gravity of quartz is about 2.6, determine whether this crystal is quartz or diamond. (1 cu cm of water weighs 1 g.)

6. The main part of each one of a pair of earrings has the shape of a regular octahedron, each side of which is 2.5 cm long. Find the amount of plastic required to make these two main parts if
   (a) the parts are hollow made from sheet plastic.
   (b) the parts are solid.

7–12

A manufacturer of games of chance for carnivals has decided to innovate and replace conventional pairs of dice with other regular polyhedrons. To solve these problems, draw a plane development of each polyhedron indicating how the edges are to be joined to form the polyhedron.

7. These polyhedrons are to be made of thin-gage sheet metal, with mating edges soldered. For a dodecahedron, how many lineal inches of soldering are required if each side is 2 in.?

8. How many lineal inches of soldering are required for an icosahedron if each side is 2 in.?

9. Each polyhedron is to be covered with an abrasive-resistant material with a self-adhering backing. The dice will be die punched in quantity from the most economical rectangular shape. For the dodecahedron, each side of which is 2 in., find the actual area needed and the rectangular shape to use, giving the dimensions of the latter to the nearest $\frac{1}{8}$ in.

10. Solve Problem 9 if an icosahedron with 2-in. sides is used instead of a dodecahedron.

11. To give these polyhedrons more stability when rolled, it is decided to completely fill them with water, soldering the filling hole so that the water cannot evaporate or leak out. Ignoring this thin metal, find the weight of water added to the dodecahedron.

12. Referring to Problem 11, find the weight of water added to the icosahedron.

13. Many small-home builders rest the 4- by 4-in. posts supporting the floor on a frustrum of a concrete pyramid to obtain a larger bearing area on the ground. If a nominal 4- by 4-in. post actually measures $3\frac{1}{2}$ by $3\frac{1}{2}$ in., these forming the dimensions of the upper base of the pyramid, and the bearing area is a square 81 sq in., what would be the weight of a 6-in.-high block? Concrete weighs 150 lb/cu ft.

14. Find the cost of paving a driveway 30 ft long, 16 ft wide, and 4 in. deep if concrete costs $20/cu yd.

15. Find the weight of a sheet of metal that is 6 by 4 ft and $\frac{3}{8}$ in. thick if the metal weighs 490 lb/cu ft.

16. A roof of a building has the shape of a frustrum of a right rectangular pyramid. The bottom base is 30 by 20 ft, the top base is 20 by 10 ft, and the altitude is 8 ft.
   (a) Find how many full squares of shingles are needed to cover the lateral surface area. (One square of shingles is the amount necessary to cover 100 sq ft.)
   (b) For the purpose of ventilation, it is necessary to know the volume of air within the roof area. Find this volume.

17. A storage bin for grain has the shape of a right regular hexagonal prism 10 ft high. Each side of the hexagonal base is $3\frac{1}{2}$ ft long.
   (a) Find the volume (in bushels) that the bin will hold.
   (b) Find to the nearest tenth the number of gallons of paint required to paint the lateral surface if 1 gal covers 200 sq ft.

18. A water trough 20 ft long has the shape of a right trapezoidal prism. Each of the parallel bases is an isosceles trapezoid whose bases are 5 ft and 3 ft and whose sides are 4 ft.
   (a) Find how many gallons of water the trough holds when full.
   (b) Find the number of square feet of metal needed to make the trough.

19. The Great Pyramid of Egypt, built around 2900 B.C., was originally

481 ft high and 756 ft long on each side of its square base. Excepting for the funeral chamber and a few passages, the pyramid was solid, formed by limestone blocks each having a volume of about 40 cu ft.

(a) Find the approximate number of these blocks needed to build a solid pyramid of this size, ignoring all wastage.

(b) Find the approximate number of polished blocks that originally formed the casing of the Great Pyramid if the polished rectangular face showing of each block was 5 by 4 ft.

20. The main portion of a round file has the shape of a frustrum of a cone, 10 in. long. The diameter of the tip end is $\frac{1}{4}$ in., the diameter at the butt end is $\frac{3}{8}$ in., and the tang of the file at the butt end is a right regular hexagonal pyramid $2\frac{1}{2}$ in. long. The hexagon forming the base of this pyramid is inscribed in the $\frac{3}{8}$-in. circular base of the butt end. Find the weight of this file if it is made of steel weighing 490 lb/cu ft.

21. Coal, piled using an elevating grader, tends to form a triangular prism, but the top sluffs off and approximates a horizontal plane. In this storage area (see illustration), the pile, now 12 ft high, has the dimensions shown. If this coal averages 90 lb/cu ft, how many tons are in this pile? (*Hint:* The solid is a prismatoid.)

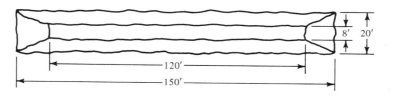

22. A 36- by 18-ft rectangular swimming pool is 3 ft deep along the shallow end and 10 ft deep along the deep end. The bottom of the pool is a rectangle of width 16 ft.

(a) Find the number of gallons of water needed to fill the pool 6 in. from the top.

(b) Find the surface area that will require painting.

23. A tool shed has the shape of a truncated right square prism with base 8 by 8 ft, minimum height 5 ft, and maximum height 7 ft.

(a) Find the number of square feet of lumber required to build the shed.

(b) Find the volume of the shed.

24. (a) Compute the total surface area and the volume of a sphere 6 in. in diameter.

(b) Compute the total surface area and the volume of a right circular cylinder 6 in. in diameter and 6 in. high.

(c) Find the ratio of the area to a unit volume for the sphere and for the cylinder.

(d) Determine the annual maintenance cost for painting per unit of volume for each shape and compare.

25. A funnel has the shape of one frustrum of a right circular cone on top of another frustrum of a right circular cone. The diameter at the top of the funnel is 5 in., at the juncture of the two frustrums $\frac{3}{4}$ in., and at the bottom $\frac{3}{8}$ in. The altitude of the top frustrum is $3\frac{1}{2}$ in. and of the bottom frustrum 2 in.

(a) Find the capacity of the top frustrum of the funnel.

(b) Find the amount of metal needed to make the whole funnel.

26. An air duct has the shape of a truncated oblique elliptical cylinder. The major and minor axes of the ellipse are 12.5 and 10 in., respectively. The truncated face is a circular right section of diameter 10 in. The maximum and minimum slant heights are 20 and 12.5 in., respectively.

(a) Find the number of square feet of sheet metal required to make this duct.

(b) Find the volume of air in cubic feet contained within this duct.

27. The commercial Hortonsphere is a municipal water tank in the shape of a sphere. If, in a certain city, a 60-ft-diameter tank was built:

(a) How many gallons will it hold when full?

(b) How many gallons will it hold when the water is 15 ft deep? (*Hint:* Use a spherical sector and subtract a cone.)

(c) How many gallons of paint would be needed to give two coats of paint to this tank if 1 gal will cover 200 sq ft?

28. Given a sphere, a hollow right circular cylinder, and a hollow right circular cone. Ignoring the very thin thickness of the metal from which these hollow forms are made, all diameters and heights are $2r$ units. The sphere is placed inside the cylinder, the cone is filled with water, and the water poured into the cylinder. In terms of r units, how much below the top of the cylinder is the water surface?

29. (a) An oblique elliptical cylinder forms part of a dust-exhaust duct, with the dimensions shown in the sketch on the opposite page. Using the right section find the external area in square feet that will require red lead paint to reduce corrosion.

(b) Find the volume by (1) using the elliptical base and (2) using the right section.

(c) If the dust-laden air is changed every 2 sec, compute the cubic feet of air moved per minute.

30. A Whispering Gallery shaped as a prolate ellipsoid is 20 ft wide and 40 ft long. It is desired to change the air every 15 min, since smoking is permitted. Ignoring efficiency losses, how many cfm should the exhaust fan be rated?

31. To hold a memorial plaque, a marble cylinder 2 ft in diameter and 6 ft high is cut by a plane containing a diameter of the top base, and cutting the lateral surface at a maximum depth of 2 ft below the top base. What is the weight of the lower portion if marble weighs 170 pcf?

32. (a) A heavy-duty life-saving ring is a canvas-covered cork torus, with an inner diameter of 20 in. and a maximum external diameter of 36 in. Find the square feet of canvas needed to cover it, if 11 per cent must be added to cover overlapping and seams.

(b) Find the weight that just submerges this life-saving ring if the weight W is given by

$$W = \text{volume (density of water} - \text{density of cork)}$$

The density of water is 62.4 pcf; of cork, 15 pcf.

33. A right-circular-cylindrical water tank 3 ft 10 in. high has a diameter of 1 ft 4 in.

(a) Find the number of gallons of water the tank will hold.

(b) Find the number of square feet of insulation needed to cover the lateral surface and the top of the tank.

34. A vinyl plastic garden hose is 50 ft long and has an inside diameter of $\frac{5}{8}$ in. Find the volume in cubic feet carried by the hose.

35. A butane storage tank has the shape of a 5-ft-long cylinder with a hemispherical cap on each end. The diameter of the cylinder is 3 ft.

(a) Find the volume of the tank.

(b) Find the amount of metal needed to make the tank.

36. A silo has the shape of a 20-ft-diameter cylinder 20 ft high surmounted by a conical top 4 ft high.

(a) Find the volume inside the silo.

(b) Find the total number of square feet in the lateral cylindrical surface and the conical top.

Problem 29

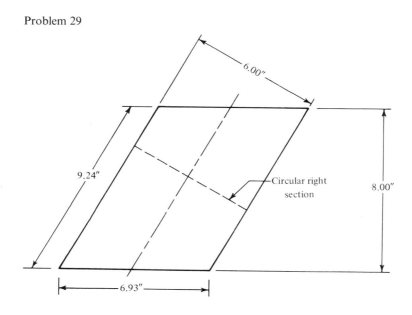

37. A truncated right square pyramid has the dimensions shown in the sketch. Find (a) the volume and (b) the lateral area. (*Hint*: To obtain needed dimensions, sketch the section cut by a vertical plane containing the axis, and use similar-triangle ratios.)

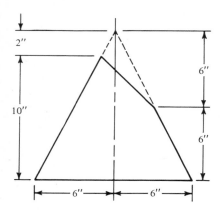

38. A California city, entering a float for their Orange Queen, plans to use as a background for the throne six segments of an orange, whose actual shape will be that of a spherical wedge. Each segment is from a 9-ft sphere, with a dihedral angle of 30°. They are to be made from styrofoam, which weighs 1.85 pcf.
(a) Find the weight of one.
(b) Find the total amount of orange spray coating, if this coating covers 100 sq ft/gal.

39. To develop arm muscles, dumbbells are used in gymnasiums. The sketch gives the dimensions of a common type, made from oak weighing 47 lb/cu ft. Find the weight of this dumbbell.

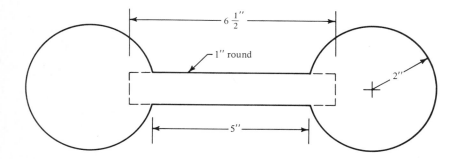

40. For developing shoulder and arm muscles used in weight-lifting, barbells are used. The one shown at the top of the next page is made of steel, with a 28-in.-long 1-in.-round bar drilled 1 in. into the end weights, which are

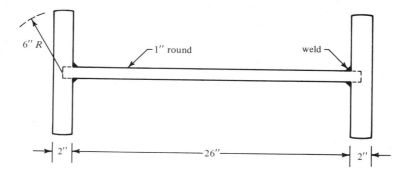

true spherical zones made from a 12-in. sphere. Ignoring the minute weight of the weld, find the total weight of this barbell to the nearest pound using steel at 490 lb/cu ft.

4.11 / Chapter Review

This chapter cannot be summarized, for the entire chapter is itself a summary of plane and solid geometry. The student should know the names of the common plane shapes and common solid forms, and should also know that specific information about most given shapes and solids is to be found in this chapter.

The review problems that comprise the next problem set are intended to see if the many rules and formulas can be properly located and applied. Throughout the remainder of the book, geometric concepts may be needed to solve more advanced topics. Geometry often gives basic relationships upon which other mathematical operations can be performed.

Again the importance of well-drawn scaled sketches is stressed. The mere drawing of the conditions of a problem may indicate the method of solution. Clarity of labeling and neatness of drawing should not be reserved for drafting classes. Both in this chapter and in subsequent chapters where dimensions are calculated, the use of a properly constructed geometric sketch should indicate that the calculated answer is correct or grossly in error.

Problem Set 4.7 (Chapter Review)

Sketches should be made using the decimally graduated engineer scale, using the 50-parts-to-the-inch scale when feasible. Angles should be laid off using a protractor, estimating to the nearest $\frac{1}{2}°$. All calculations should be made on the slide rule and answers should be identified by the unit of measurement.

1. Redraw the traverse shown in the figure below, which would be used to avoid a marsh on a survey. Compute all the interior angles of the triangles formed, giving as the solution the size of angle x. Check the solution by scaling.

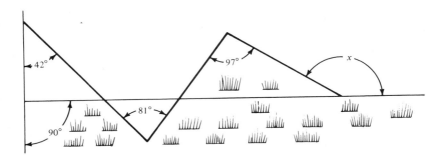

2. The pin E attaches levers EB and EC to a rotating disc. To analyze the conformation shown in the figure below, angle x is needed. Copy the sketch and indicate on it the angles or arcs needed for the solution. Check by scaling and list both scaled and computed values of angle x.

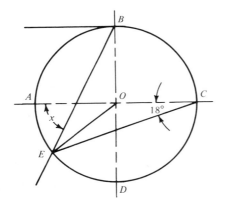

3. Find the area of a sheet metal square with a 12-inch diagonal.
4. Find the area of the concrete ramp shown in the figure.

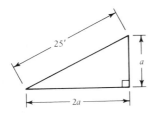

5. Find the size of angle x in the figure below. Copy the sketch and indicate on it the angles or arcs computed for the solution. Check by scaling.

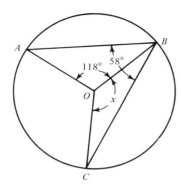

6. The focal length of an aerial camera is the distance from the lens to the film, for high-altitude photography. Using similar triangles, find the actual width of a river in feet if in a photograph taken at 20,000 ft the river measures 0.25 in. on the finished print and if the focal length of the lens is $f = 11$ in.

7. For the plywood panel with equal sides shown below, find the length of the stiffener BC and find the number of square feet of plywood required.

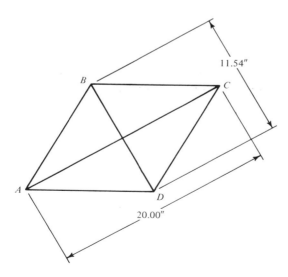

8. It is necessary to shift a highway 100 ft to the north but on an alignment parallel to the original one. Given the desired radii of the two circular arcs forming the reverse curve connecting the two centerlines, find the distance, D, between centers as shown in the figure.

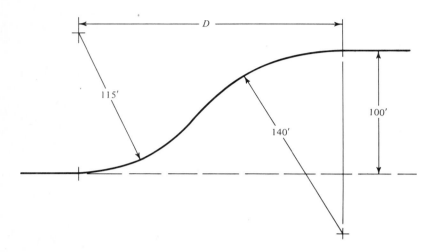

9. Find the area of the circular segment shown in the figure.

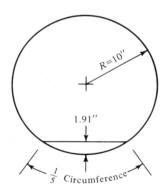

10. Find the perimeter of an ellipse whose two axes are 8 and 10 in., respectively, approximating k first by using two terms and second by using three terms. Assuming that the result using three terms is closer to the true value, what is the percentage error in using two terms?

11. Divide a line 4 in. long into exactly seven equal parts, using a simple geometric construction based upon similar triangles. (Accurate parallel lines can be drawn using two plastic triangles.) Using the decimal scale divided 50 parts to the inch, record the scaled answer to the nearest 0.01 in. that can be read.

12. A less accurate approximation for the length of a parabolic curve than that given in the text is

$$s = \sqrt{L^2 + \frac{16R^2}{3}}$$

For a parabola with a 100-ft span and a 20-ft rise, what is the percentage error using this formula if the series approximation given in Section 4.07 is considered correct?

13. Find the area of a trapezoid whose altitude is 10 in., whose upper base is 15 in., and whose lower base angles are 45° and 30°.

14. A $\frac{9}{16}$-in. semifinished hexagonal nut has a tapped diameter of $\frac{9}{16}$ in. Each side of the hexagon is 0.5 in. and the thickness of the nut is 0.5 in. Find the weight of 1000 of these nuts if they are made of brass weighing 530 pcf.

15. In hoisting heavy loads, a large pulley is fastened to the end of a beam, as shown in the sketch. For the given arrangement, find the distance *AD*. (*Hint*: Draw *AC*.)

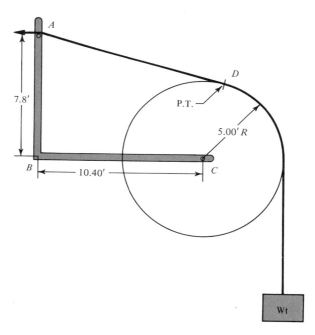

16. A certain church and school lie on a line parallel to a riverbank and 57 ft from it. The line between them has a bearing of N10°W (this is the angle from the north–south meridian) and is measured with a steel tape as 424 ft in length. A point *A* is selected on the line of sight from a hilltop across the river to the church. The distance from *A* to the riverbank is

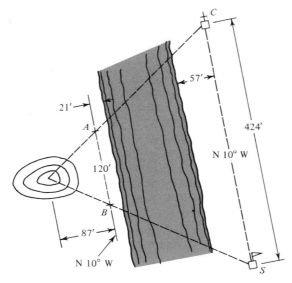

measured and found to be 21 ft. A random line is then laid out from *A*
southward at the reverse bearing, and actually marked on the ground
with white tape beginning about 100 ft from *A*. A line of sight is then
taken on the school and the point where this line crosses the white tape
marked *B*. The bearing of *BA* is taken and verified as N10°W, so that
line *AB* is parallel to line *CS*. The distance *AB* is taped and found to be
120 ft. How wide is the river?

17. Taper is defined by machinists as the change in diameter in inches per
foot of length of a shaft. A No. 5 Morse taper used in a machine shop
has a taper of 0.630. Find the volume of a tapered pin made using this
taper if the large diameter is 1.50 in. and the pin is 3 in. long.

18. The upper base of a frustrum of a right square pyramid has a 4-in. side,
is 3 in. below the original vertex, and is 6 in. above the lower base. The
ratio of the areas of the two bases written as a number less than 1 and
multiplied by the load in psi on the smaller area gives the resulting load
in psi on the larger base. If the larger base rests upon soil safe at 7 psi,
what is the psi loading that can be put on the upper base?

19. A study of atomic collisions is being photographed in a nearly perfect
vacuum chamber, spherical in shape, and made of a special flint glass
0.214 in. thick. If the chamber holds exactly 2000 cu in., find
(a) the internal and external diameters of the sphere.
(b) the weight of the container if this flint glass weighs 259 pcf.
(c) the total area (both inside and outside) that must be treated with a
special cleanser to ensure accurate photography. Assume that the
container is mounted on a round pedestal with an area of contact
of 3.14 sq in. and that 12.86 sq in. are covered by an insert panel for
the instrumentation.

20. A chute from a bulk cement hopper is shown below. If, when in use, the cement dust would completely fill this chute in 2.2 sec, and the dust contains 82 per cent cement and 18 per cent air, how many seconds (to the nearest tenth) would it take to load $\frac{1}{4}$ cu yd of cement (the amount used in a 1 : 2 : 4 mix of concrete measuring 1 cu yd)?

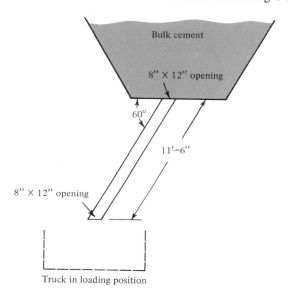

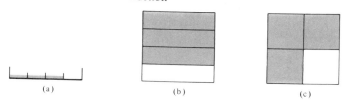

5

Algebraic fractions

5.01 / Arithmetic fractions

Arithmetic fractions, the quotients of counting numbers, were first introduced to obtain refinement in measurement. In surveying a plot of land, if the length of a line segment did not measure an exact number of feet, it was necessary to subdivide one foot into an equal number of parts and then to indicate how many of these equal parts were needed to record the measurement. The Romans divided their basic unit into 12 equal parts which they called "uncias." From this word is derived our modern words "inches" and "ounces."

To illustrate a fraction geometrically, a unit line segment or a unit square is subdivided into d equal parts, called *subunits*. By shading n of these equal subunits, a geometric model for the fraction $\frac{n}{d}$ is obtained. The upper number n is called the **numerator** of the fraction, and the lower number d is called the **denominator** of the fraction. Figure 5.1 shows models for the fraction $\frac{3}{4}$.

Figure 5.1
Geometric models of a fraction

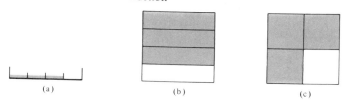

(a)   (b)   (c)

233

Figure 5.2
Fundamental principle of fractions

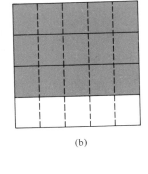

(a)

(b)

$$\frac{3}{4} = \frac{3 \cdot 5}{4 \cdot 5} = \frac{15}{20}$$

Fundamental principle of fractions

Since there are many ways to subdivide a basic unit into an equal number of parts, there are many different numbers that may be used for the denominator of a fraction, and for each of these denominators there is a corresponding numerator that does not change the value of the fraction.

If each of the d equal parts of a basic unit is further divided into k equal parts, the basic unit is now divided into a total of dk subunits. Each of the n equal parts corresponding to the numerator is similarly divided into k equal parts producing a total of nk subunits. Thus, the fraction n/d may now be written as nk/dk. The statement

$$\frac{n}{d} = \frac{nk}{dk}$$

is called the **fundamental principle of fractions.** Figure 5.2 illustrates this principle for the fraction

$$\frac{3}{4} = \frac{3 \cdot 5}{4 \cdot 5} = \frac{15}{20}$$

Example 5.1
Rewrite the fraction $\frac{2}{3}$ so that the new denominator is 12.

SOLUTION

$$\frac{2}{3} = \frac{?}{12}$$

The "build-up" factor is $\dfrac{\text{new denominator}}{\text{old denominator}} = \dfrac{12}{3} = 4.$

$$\frac{2}{3} = \frac{2 \cdot 4}{3 \cdot 4} = \frac{8}{12}$$

Example 5.2

Simplify the fraction $\frac{15}{36}$ so that the new denominator has no factor in common with the new numerator. (This process is called "simplification" or "reducing the fraction to lowest terms.")

SOLUTION

$$\frac{15}{36} = \frac{3 \cdot 5}{2^2 \cdot 3^2}$$ expressing numerator and denominator as products of prime factors

$$= \left(\frac{5}{2^2 \cdot 3}\right)\frac{3}{3}$$ rearranging by noting the common factor

$$= \frac{5}{12}$$ applying the fundamental principle of fractions

For some problems, including Example 5.2, it may not be necessary to actually write the entire denominator in prime numbers, since the numerator consists of the two primes 3 and 5, and inspection shows that 5 is not a factor of 12. Using this observation, the problem would be written

$$\frac{15}{36} = \frac{3 \cdot 5}{3 \cdot 12} = \frac{5}{12}$$

Multiplication and division of fractions

The meaning of the multiplication of two fractions is suggested by the word "of" in the problem "Find $\frac{2}{3}$ of $\frac{4}{5}$." The fraction $\frac{4}{5}$ is to be divided into three equal parts, and then two of those three equal parts is the quantity desired. (See Figure 5.3.)

In general, to multiply two fractions, multiply the numerators to obtain the new numerator and multiply the denominators to obtain the new

Figure 5.3

Multiplication of fractions

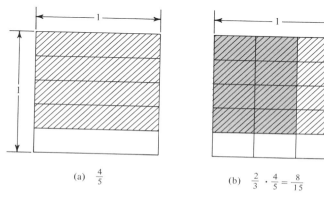

(a) $\frac{4}{5}$

(b) $\frac{2}{3} \cdot \frac{4}{5} = \frac{8}{15}$

denominator. In symbols,

$$\frac{a}{b} \cdot \frac{c}{d} = \frac{ac}{bd}$$

The quotient of two fractions is obtained by using the fact that multiplication and division are inverse operations and multiplication by the reciprocal of the divisor is the same as division by the number that is the divisor. In symbols,

$$\frac{a}{b} \div \frac{c}{d} = \frac{a}{b} \cdot \frac{d}{c} = \frac{ad}{bc}$$

Example 5.3
How many quarters are in 1 dollar?

SOLUTION
Using fractions,

$$\frac{1}{\frac{1}{4}} = 1 \cdot \frac{4}{1} = 4$$

Example 5.4
Simplify: $\dfrac{15}{16} \div \dfrac{3}{4}$.

SOLUTION

$$\frac{15}{16} \div \frac{3}{4} = \frac{15}{16} \cdot \frac{4}{3} = \frac{15(4)}{16(3)} = \frac{5(3 \cdot 4)}{4(3 \cdot 4)} = \frac{5}{4}$$

Addition and subtraction of fractions

Since only the same kinds of units can be combined by addition or subtraction, to express the sum or difference of two fractions as a single fraction requires that the two fractions be rewritten so they have the same denominator. Then, in symbols,

$$\frac{a}{c} + \frac{b}{c} = \frac{a+b}{c} \qquad \text{and} \qquad \frac{a}{c} - \frac{b}{c} = \frac{a-b}{c}$$

Example 5.5
Write as a single fraction: $\dfrac{2}{3} + \dfrac{3}{5}$.

SOLUTION

$$\frac{2}{3} + \frac{3}{5} = \frac{2(5)}{3(5)} + \frac{3(3)}{5(3)} = \frac{10}{15} + \frac{9}{15} = \frac{19}{15}$$

In Example 5.5 a common denominator was found by multiplying the two denominators. If the original denominators have one or more factors in common, the computation can be simplified by finding a smaller denominator than the product of the two denominators. The smallest common denominator possible is called the least common denominator (LCD).

To obtain the LCD, factor each denominator into prime factors and use, as a factor of the new denominator, each prime the greatest number of times it occurs in one of the original denominators.

Example 5.6

Write as a single fraction: $\dfrac{13}{24} - \dfrac{7}{18}$.

SOLUTION

(1) Find the LCD:

$$24 = 2^3 \cdot 3 \quad \text{and} \quad 18 = 2 \cdot 3^2$$

$$\text{LCD} = 2^3 \cdot 3^2 = 8 \cdot 9 = 72$$

(2) Build up each fraction:

$$\frac{72}{24} = 3 \quad \text{and thus} \quad \frac{13}{24} = \frac{13(3)}{24(3)} = \frac{39}{72}$$

$$\frac{72}{18} = 4 \quad \text{and thus} \quad \frac{7}{18} = \frac{7(4)}{18(4)} = \frac{28}{72}$$

(3) Subtract new numerators and place over LCD:

$$\frac{13}{24} - \frac{7}{18} = \frac{39}{72} - \frac{28}{72} = \frac{11}{72}$$

(4) If possible, simplify the result. (There is no simplification possible in this case.)

Since elementary algebra is generalized arithmetic, the principles of arithmetic fractions also apply to algebraic fractions. A computation with algebraic fractions will be better understood by keeping this fact in mind and by recalling the method used for the similar arithmetic problem.

It should be noted that the fractions of arithmetic and their negatives belong to the set of real numbers, and, therefore, the commutative, associative, and distributive properties apply when three or more fractions are combined.

Example 5.7

Simplify: $7\left(\dfrac{3}{56} + \dfrac{4}{7}\right) + \dfrac{5}{8}$.

SOLUTION

(1) Expand:

$$7\left(\frac{3}{56} + \frac{4}{7}\right) + \frac{5}{8} = \left(\frac{7}{1}\cdot\frac{3}{56} + \frac{7}{1}\cdot\frac{4}{7}\right) + \frac{5}{8}$$

(2) Factor nonprime denominator and rearrange:

$$\left(\frac{7\cdot 3}{7\cdot 8} + \frac{7\cdot 4}{7\cdot 1}\right) + \frac{5}{8}$$

(3) Simplify by division of like factors

$$\left(\frac{3}{8} + 4\right) + \frac{5}{8}$$

(4) Rearrange for addition of fractions:

$$4 + \left(\frac{3}{8} + \frac{5}{8}\right)$$

(5) Complete addition:

$$4 + 1 = 5$$

Problem Set 5.1

1–10

Reduce to lowest terms.

1. $\dfrac{8}{12}$

2. $\dfrac{28}{35}$

3. $\dfrac{17}{68}$

4. $\dfrac{23}{69}$

5. $\dfrac{150}{400}$

6. $\dfrac{180}{600}$

7. $\dfrac{222}{74}$

8. $\dfrac{483}{161}$

9. $\dfrac{437}{943}$

10. $\dfrac{221}{255}$

11–20

Build up by supplying the missing numerator or denominator.

11. $\dfrac{1}{2} = \dfrac{?}{16}$

12. $\dfrac{1}{3} = \dfrac{?}{42}$

13. $\dfrac{5}{6} = \dfrac{?}{72}$

14. $\dfrac{7}{8} = \dfrac{?}{120}$

15. $6 = \dfrac{?}{5}$

16. $7 = \dfrac{?}{8}$

17. $\dfrac{4}{5} = \dfrac{16}{?}$

18. $\dfrac{3}{7} = \dfrac{9}{?}$

19. $8 = \dfrac{24}{?}$ **20.** $9 = \dfrac{108}{?}$

21–26

A fraction may be thought of as a quotient. Rewrite each of the indicated divisions below as a fraction and then simplify by using the fundamental principle of fractions.

21. $963 \div 642$ **23.** $484 \div 847$ **25.** $6461 \div 923$
22. $1225 \div 735$ **24.** $2600 \div 2925$ **26.** $6976 \div 872$

27–32

A fraction may be thought of as the ratio of two numbers. For example, if the length of a rectangle is 7 ft 6 in. and its width is 4 ft 6 in., the ratio of the length to the width is

$$7\,ft\;6\,in. : 4\,ft\;6\,in. = \frac{90\;in.}{54\;in.} = \frac{5(18)}{3(18)} = \frac{5}{3}$$

or a ratio of 5 to 3. An alternative and equally correct solution is

$$\frac{7\frac{1}{2}\,ft}{4\frac{1}{2}\,ft} = \frac{15}{2} \cdot \frac{2}{9} = \frac{3(5)}{3(3)} = \frac{5}{3}$$

Write each of the following ratios as fractions and then reduce to lowest terms.

27. $2.25 : 75$ cents   **30.** 2 hr 15 min : 1 hr 30 min
28. 90 cents : $3   **31.** $15°20' : 11°30'$
29. 3 ft 4 in. : 5 ft 10 in.   **32.** 60 mph : 1 ft/sec (1 mile $=$ 5280 ft)

33–60

Simplify by rewriting each of the following as a single fraction in lowest terms.

33. $\dfrac{1}{2} \cdot \dfrac{1}{3}$ **38.** $\dfrac{7}{9} \cdot \dfrac{12}{49}$ **43.** $\dfrac{1}{5} \div \dfrac{1}{7}$

34. $\dfrac{1}{5} \cdot \dfrac{1}{7}$ **39.** $\dfrac{30}{77} \cdot \dfrac{176}{225}$ **44.** $\dfrac{1}{2} \div \dfrac{1}{3}$

35. $\dfrac{2}{3} \cdot \dfrac{5}{7}$ **40.** $\dfrac{36}{65} \cdot \dfrac{75}{90}$ **45.** $\dfrac{9}{16} \div \dfrac{45}{64}$

36. $\dfrac{3}{4} \cdot \dfrac{7}{11}$ **41.** $\dfrac{1560}{3773} \cdot \dfrac{3087}{3432}$ **46.** $\dfrac{25}{32} \div \dfrac{225}{960}$

37. $\dfrac{5}{6} \cdot \dfrac{12}{35}$ **42.** $\dfrac{872}{923} \cdot \dfrac{6461}{6976}$ **47.** $\dfrac{912}{1371} \div \dfrac{1653}{914}$

48. $\dfrac{831}{1960} \div \dfrac{1385}{2352}$

49. $\dfrac{1}{4} + \dfrac{1}{28}$

50. $\dfrac{1}{6} + \dfrac{1}{18}$

51. $\dfrac{5}{6} + \dfrac{3}{4}$

52. $\dfrac{4}{9} + \dfrac{5}{21}$

53. $\dfrac{3}{56} + \dfrac{5}{98}$

54. $\dfrac{5}{54} + \dfrac{7}{72}$

55. $\dfrac{1}{4} - \dfrac{1}{5}$

56. $\dfrac{1}{2} - \dfrac{1}{3}$

57. $\dfrac{2}{45} - \dfrac{2}{75}$

58. $\dfrac{5}{24} - \dfrac{5}{54}$

59. $\dfrac{3}{296} - \dfrac{5}{666}$

60. $\dfrac{7}{258} - \dfrac{1}{301}$

61–70
Rewrite each of the following as a single fraction or integer in lowest terms. Use the commutative, associative, and distributive laws to simplify the computation when convenient.

61. $\left(\dfrac{7}{16} + \dfrac{5}{24} \right) + \dfrac{9}{16}$

62. $\left(\dfrac{25}{36} - \dfrac{143}{144} \right) + \dfrac{47}{36}$

63. $\left(\dfrac{2}{3} \cdot \dfrac{4}{5} \right) \div \dfrac{4}{3}$

64. $\left(\dfrac{2}{5} \div \dfrac{9}{7} \right) \cdot \dfrac{5}{7}$

65. $\dfrac{36}{77} \left(\dfrac{7}{12} - \dfrac{11}{18} \right)$

66. $\dfrac{15}{16} \left(\dfrac{32}{45} + \dfrac{64}{75} \right)$

67. $\dfrac{723}{964} \cdot \dfrac{242}{247} + \dfrac{723}{964} \cdot \dfrac{5}{247}$

68. $\dfrac{377}{544} \cdot \dfrac{119}{277} - \dfrac{100}{277} \cdot \dfrac{119}{544}$

69. $\dfrac{1}{42} + \left[\dfrac{1}{86} + \left(\dfrac{1}{129} + \dfrac{1}{301} \right) \right]$

70. $\left(\dfrac{1}{24} + \dfrac{1}{58} \right) + \left(\dfrac{1}{174} + \dfrac{1}{232} \right)$

Applications

71–82
Solve each of the following.

71. Find the volume of a sphere whose radius r is $\frac{9}{2}$ in. Use $V = \frac{4}{3}\pi r^3$ with π approximated as $\frac{22}{7}$.

72. Find the volume of a cone whose radius r is $1\frac{1}{2}$ in. and whose height h is $\frac{7}{16}$ in. Use $V = \frac{1}{3}\pi r^2 h$ with π approximated as $\frac{22}{7}$.

73. The amount of gold in an alloy is expressed in carats where pure gold is 24 carats. How much gold is in $6\frac{2}{3}$ lb of an 18-carat alloy?

74. In photography, the "short-stop" bath into which prints are dipped after developing is 28 per cent glacial acetic acid. Express this strength as a ratio.

75. A 16-ft-long piece of lumber is cut into five pieces. Four of the pieces are 2 ft $10\frac{1}{2}$ in. each in length. If $\frac{1}{16}$ in. is lost by each sawcut, what is the length of the fifth piece?

76. The changes in the price of a stock worth $\$66\frac{3}{4}$ on Monday were reported in the newspaper as follows:

$$\text{Tuesday } +1\tfrac{5}{8} \quad \text{Wednesday } -1\tfrac{1}{2} \quad \text{Thursday } -1\tfrac{1}{4} \quad \text{Friday } +\tfrac{7}{8}$$

What was the price of the stock at closing time on Friday?

77. A truck that averages $11\frac{3}{4}$ miles/gal of gasoline was driven 230 miles. How much money was spent on gasoline if the cost of gasoline was $33\frac{9}{10}$ cents/gal?

78. How many $4\frac{1}{4}$- by $4\frac{1}{4}$-in. tiles are needed to cover three kitchen counters having dimensions 3 ft $2\frac{1}{4}$ in. by 4 ft 3 in., 3 ft $2\frac{1}{4}$ in. by 6 ft $4\frac{1}{2}$ in., and 4 ft 3 in. by $12\frac{3}{4}$ ft, respectively?

79. How many cubic yards of concrete should be ordered to make a patio 12 by 20 ft if the concrete is laid 4 in. deep? (Concrete is sold by the cubic yard.)

80. A man earns $\$3.25$/hr for a 40-hr week and his overtime pay over 40 hr is $1\frac{1}{2}$ times this rate. What is his pay for the week where his time report is as follows?

$$\text{Monday } 8 \text{ hr } 30 \text{ min} \quad \text{Tuesday } 7 \text{ hr } 45 \text{ min} \quad \text{Wednesday } 8 \text{ hr}$$

$$\text{Thursday } 9 \text{ hr } 20 \text{ min} \quad \text{Friday } 10 \text{ hr } 25 \text{ min}$$

81. In a threaded hole such as on an automobile engine block, the threaded length L is given by $L = 1\frac{1}{2}D + (4/n)$, where D is the diameter of the fastener and n is the number of threads per inch. The lead of a thread is the amount the fastener moves forward in one complete revolution and is the reciprocal of the number of threads per inch. If a certain engine head uses $\frac{3}{8}$-in. stud bolts with 24 threads per inch, how many complete turns are needed to completely seat the bolt?

82. Repeat Exercise 81 using $\frac{5}{8}$-in. stud bolts with 18 threads per inch.

5.02 / Simplification of fractions

If a fraction is negative, there are three positions where the minus sign may be placed: in front of the fraction, in the numerator, or in the denominator. In symbols,

$$-\frac{n}{d} = \frac{-n}{d} = \frac{n}{-d}$$

As a general rule, the minus sign is placed in the numerator since this practice tends to reduce errors.

The negative of a binomial can be rewritten by using the following forms:

$$-(a + b) = -a - b \qquad \text{negative of a sum}$$

$$-(a - b) = \quad b - a \qquad \text{negative of a difference}$$

Example 5.8

Rewrite $\dfrac{1}{3 - x}$ with denominator $x - 3$.

SOLUTION

$$\frac{1}{3 - x} = \frac{1}{-(x - 3)} = \frac{-1}{x - 3}$$

Algebraic fractions are simplified by using the fundamental principle of fractions,

$$\frac{nk}{dk} = \frac{n}{d}$$

To apply this principle, it is necessary that the numerator and denominator be completely factored into primes so that the common factors can be recognized.

Example 5.9

Simplify: $\dfrac{x^2 + 2x}{4 + 2x}$.

SOLUTION

$$\frac{x^2 + 2x}{4 + 2x} = \frac{x(x + 2)}{2(2 + x)} \qquad \text{factor numerator and denominator}$$

$$= \frac{x(x + 2)}{2(x + 2)} \qquad \text{commutative law, addition } (2 + x = x + 2)$$

$$= \frac{x}{2} \qquad \text{fundamental principle of fractions}$$

Example 5.10

Simplify: $\dfrac{x^2 - 25}{5 - x}$.

SOLUTION

$$\frac{x^2 - 25}{5 - x} = \frac{(x + 5)(x - 5)}{5 - x} \qquad \text{factor numerator and denominator}$$

$$= \frac{(x + 5)(x - 5)}{-(x - 5)} \qquad b - a = -(a - b)$$

$$= \frac{(x + 5)(x - 5)}{(-1)(x - 5)} \qquad -ab = (-a)(b)$$

$$= \frac{x + 5}{-1} \qquad \text{fundamental principle of fractions}$$

$$= \frac{-(x + 5)}{1} \qquad \frac{a}{-b} = \frac{-a}{b}$$

$$= -(x + 5) \qquad \frac{a}{1} = a$$

or if useful,

$$= -x - 5 \qquad -(a + b) = -a - b$$

Example 5.11

Simplify: $\dfrac{8x^4 + 8x^3 - 160x^2}{4x^5 + 40x^4 + 100x^3}$.

SOLUTION

$$\frac{8x^4 + 8x^3 - 160x^2}{4x^5 + 40x^4 + 100x^3} = \frac{8x^2(x^2 + x - 20)}{4x^3(x^2 + 10x + 25)}$$

$$= \frac{8x^2(x - 4)(x + 5)}{4x^3(x + 5)(x + 5)}$$

$$= \frac{4x^2(x + 5)2(x - 4)}{4x^2(x + 5)x(x + 5)}$$

$$= \frac{2(x - 4)}{x(x + 5)}$$

Note that the answer is left in the factored form, because this is the most useful form for later applications.

WARNING! Do NOT draw a line through a term of a sum or a difference even if this term appears in both the numerator and denominator. The fundamental principle of fractions states that only common *factors* of the numerator and denominator can be eliminated. Lining out a common factor means that the numerator and denominator are each *divided* by this common factor.

Problem Set 5.2

1–20

Find the missing numerator or denominator for each of the following.

1. $\dfrac{x}{-3} = \dfrac{?}{3}$

2. $\dfrac{5}{-y} = \dfrac{-5}{?}$

3. $\dfrac{2x}{-3y} = \dfrac{-2x}{?}$

4. $\dfrac{4a}{-7b} = \dfrac{?}{7b}$

5. $\dfrac{1}{2x-7} = \dfrac{?}{7-2x}$

6. $\dfrac{-1}{9-x^2} = \dfrac{?}{x^2-9}$

7. $\dfrac{-9}{9-y^2} = \dfrac{?}{y^2-9}$

8. $\dfrac{2}{2-y} = \dfrac{?}{y-2}$

9. $\dfrac{-(x+4)}{4-x} = \dfrac{?}{x-4}$

10. $\dfrac{-(5+y)}{5-y} = \dfrac{?}{y-5}$

11. $\dfrac{6-y}{5-y} = \dfrac{?}{y-5}$

12. $\dfrac{t-3}{3-s} = \dfrac{?}{s-3}$

13. $\dfrac{-1}{3-x} = \dfrac{?}{x^2-9}$

14. $\dfrac{-1}{5-x} = \dfrac{?}{x^2-25}$

15. $\dfrac{4-t}{4+t} = \dfrac{t^2-16}{?}$

16. $\dfrac{3-5r}{3+5r} = \dfrac{25r^2-9}{?}$

17. $\dfrac{49-a^2}{a^2-49} = \dfrac{16-b^2}{?}$

18. $\dfrac{b^2-64}{64-b^2} = \dfrac{4.7-2.1a}{?}$

19. $\dfrac{(x+2)(x-3)}{(2-x)(3-x)} = \dfrac{?}{x-2}$

20. $\dfrac{(x-4)(x+5)}{(4-x)(5-x)} = \dfrac{?}{x-5}$

21–52

Simplify.

21. $\dfrac{4.5x^3y^4}{6.3x^2y^5}$

22. $\dfrac{0.42x^4y^5}{0.54x^5y^4}$

23. $\dfrac{1.20a^3b^6c^9}{-1.05a^9b^6c^3}$

24. $\dfrac{12.50r^4s^8t^{12}}{-17.50r^8s^8t^4}$

25. $\dfrac{-1.62x^6y^6z^6}{-0.81x^3y^2z^6}$

26. $\dfrac{-3.43x^4y^8z^4}{-0.49x^2y^4z^4}$

27. $\dfrac{x^2 + 6x}{x^2 + 3x}$

28. $\dfrac{y^2 - 10y}{y^2 - 5y}$

29. $\dfrac{y^2 - 4y}{16 - 4y}$

30. $\dfrac{x^2 - 9x}{81 - 9x}$

31. $\dfrac{x^2 - 7x}{49 - x^2}$

32. $\dfrac{y^2 - 64}{8y^2 - y^3}$

33. $\dfrac{x^2 - x - 6}{x^2 - 5x + 6}$

34. $\dfrac{x^2 - 9x + 20}{x^2 - x - 20}$

35. $\dfrac{4 - x^2}{4 + 4x + x^2}$

36. $\dfrac{9 - x^2}{9 - 6x + x^2}$

37. $\dfrac{64x - 4x^3}{x^4 - 256}$

38. $\dfrac{x^4 - 81}{9x^4 + 54x^3 + 81x^2}$

39. $\dfrac{4x^2 - 100y^2}{2x^2 - 5xy - 25y^2}$

40. $\dfrac{6x^3y + 15x^2y^2 - 9xy^3}{6x^3y - x^2y^2 - xy^3}$

41. $\dfrac{x^3 - 8}{x^3 + 2x^2 + 4x}$

42. $\dfrac{8x^3 + 8}{16x^3 - 16x^2 + 16x}$

43. $\dfrac{20x^2 - 30xy + 45y^2}{8x^3 + 27y^3}$

44. $\dfrac{100x^3 + 20x^2y + 4xy^2}{250x^3 - 2y^3}$

45. $\dfrac{x^3 + x^2 - x - 1}{x^3 - x^2 + x - 1}$

46. $\dfrac{x^3 - 2x^2 + 4x - 8}{x^3 + 2x^2 - 4x - 8}$

47. $\dfrac{32mv^2 - 50m}{16mv^2 - 40mv + 25m}$

48. $\dfrac{\pi R_1{}^2 - \pi R_2{}^2}{2\pi R_1{}^2 + 4\pi R_1 R_2 + 2\pi R_2{}^2}$

49. $\dfrac{\pi R^3 h - \pi r^3 h}{3R - 3r}$

50. $\dfrac{KT^4 - KT_0{}^4}{LT^6 - LT_0{}^6}$

51. $\dfrac{c_1{}^2 F_1{}^4 - c_2{}^2 F_2{}^4}{c_1{}^2 F_1{}^3 + c_1 c_2 F_1 F_2{}^2 - c_1 c_2 F_1{}^2 F_2 - c_2{}^2 F_2{}^3}$

52. $\dfrac{v_0{}^3 t^3 + v_0{}^2 t^2 + v_0 t + 1}{v_0{}^3 t^3 + v_0{}^2 t^2 - v_0 t - 1}$

5.03 / Multiplication and division of fractions

The multiplication and division of algebraic fractions involve the same methods that are used for arithmetic fractions.

To Multiply Fractions

(1) Factor each numerator and each denominator.
(2) Reduce each fraction to lowest terms.
(3) (a) Multiply the resulting numerators to obtain the new numerator. Leave this product in factored form.
  (b) Multiply the resulting denominators to obtain the new denominator. Leave this product in factored form.
(4) Reduce the resulting fraction to lowest terms, when possible, by dividing out like factors.

Example 5.12

Simplify: $\dfrac{9ab^3}{4a^3b} \cdot \dfrac{10a^2}{15ab}$.

SOLUTION

(1) $\qquad\qquad\qquad \dfrac{3 \cdot 3abbb}{2 \cdot 2aaab} \cdot \dfrac{2 \cdot 5aa}{3 \cdot 5ab}$

(2) $\qquad\qquad\qquad \dfrac{3 \cdot 3bb}{2 \cdot 2aa} \cdot \dfrac{2a}{3b}$

(3) $\qquad\qquad\qquad \dfrac{3 \cdot 3 \cdot 2abb}{2 \cdot 2 \cdot 3aab}$

(4) $\qquad\qquad\qquad \dfrac{3b}{2a}$

Example 5.13

Simplify: $\dfrac{rs + s^2}{r^2 + rt} \cdot \dfrac{2r + 2t}{rs - s^2}$.

SOLUTION

(1) $\qquad\qquad\qquad \dfrac{s(r + s)}{r(r + t)} \cdot \dfrac{2(r + t)}{s(r - s)}$

(2) Each fraction is in lowest terms.

(3) $\qquad\qquad\qquad \dfrac{2s(r + s)(r + t)}{rs(r + t)(r - s)}$

(4) $\qquad\qquad\qquad \dfrac{2(r + s)}{r(r - s)}$

Example 5.14

Simplify: $\dfrac{3x^2 - 7xy + 2y^2}{3x^2 - 5xy - 2y^2} \cdot \dfrac{18x^2 + 24xy + 6y^2}{18x^2 - 24xy + 6y^2}$.

SOLUTION

(1)
$$\frac{(3x - y)(x - 2y)}{(3x + y)(x - 2y)} \cdot \frac{6(3x + y)(x + y)}{6(3x - y)(x - y)}.$$

(2)
$$= \frac{(3x - y)}{(3x + y)} \cdot \frac{(3x + y)(x + y)}{(3x - y)(x - y)}$$

(3)
$$= \frac{(3x - y)(3x + y)(x + y)}{(3x + y)(3x - y)(x - y)}$$

(4)
$$= \frac{x + y}{x - y}$$

To divide one fraction by a second fraction, multiply the first fraction by the reciprocal of the second fraction. ("Invert the divisor and multiply.")

Example 5.15

Simplify: $\dfrac{8xy - 4y^2}{4x^3 - xy^2} \div \dfrac{8xy + 4y^2}{4x^2 + 4xy + y^2}.$

SOLUTION

$$\frac{8xy - 4y^2}{4x^3 - xy^2} \div \frac{8xy + 4y^2}{4x^2 + 4xy + y^2}$$

$$= \frac{8xy - 4y^2}{4x^3 - xy^2} \cdot \frac{4x^2 + 4xy + y^2}{8xy + 4y^2}$$

$$= \frac{4y(2x - y)}{x(2x + y)(2x - y)} \cdot \frac{(2x + y)(2x + y)}{4y(2x + y)}$$

$$= \frac{4y}{x(2x + y)} \cdot \frac{2x + y}{4y}$$

$$= \frac{4y(2x + y)}{x(2x + y)4y}$$

$$= \frac{1(4y)(2x + y)}{x(4y)(2x + y)}$$

$$= \frac{1}{x}$$

Problem Set 5.3

Simplify.

1. $\dfrac{15x^3y}{18xy^3} \cdot \dfrac{14xy^2}{35x^2y}$

2. $\dfrac{12abc}{16a^5b^3c^2} \cdot \dfrac{4a^4b^2c^4}{18a^2c^5}$

3. $\dfrac{\pi R_1{}^2h}{\pi R_2{}^2h} \cdot \dfrac{R_1R_2{}^2}{R_1{}^2R_2}$

4. $\dfrac{F_1{}^4F_2{}^8}{36c^4d^4} \cdot \dfrac{27c^3d^5}{F_1{}^6F_2{}^4}$

5. $\dfrac{21P^4}{20V^5T^3} \cdot \dfrac{12V^3T^3}{35P^3}$

6. $\dfrac{4xy^3}{9x^3z} \cdot \dfrac{15x^2z^4}{35x^2y^4}$

7. $\dfrac{at - bt}{at + bt} \cdot \dfrac{a^2 + ab}{a^2 - ab}$

8. $\dfrac{F_1 - F_2}{F_2 + F_3} \cdot \dfrac{F_2 - F_3}{F_2 - F_1}$

9. $\dfrac{x^2 + 2x}{x^2 - 3x} \cdot \dfrac{9 - 3x}{6 - 3x}$

10. $\dfrac{4x^2 - 2xy}{4x^2 - y^2} \cdot \dfrac{4xy + 8y^2}{8xy}$

11. $\dfrac{F_1{}^2 - F_2{}^2}{(F_1 - F_2)^2} \cdot \dfrac{F_1{}^2 + F_2{}^2}{(F_1 + F_2)^2}$

12. $\dfrac{cT^2 - cS^2}{c^2T^2 + c^2S^2} \cdot \dfrac{4S^2T^2}{2S^2 - 2T^2}$

13. $\dfrac{x^2 - 4}{x^2 - 9} \cdot \dfrac{2x^2 - 7x + 3}{2x^2 + 3x - 2}$

14. $\dfrac{9x^2 - 1}{16x^2 - 25} \cdot \dfrac{20x^2 + 9x - 20}{15x^2 - 17x + 4}$

15. $\dfrac{8x^3 - y^3}{x^3 + 8y^3} \cdot \dfrac{x^4y^2 - 2x^3y^3 + 4x^2y^4}{4x^4y^2 + 2x^3y^3 + x^2y^4}$

16. $\dfrac{125x^3 + y^3}{(5x + y)^3} \cdot \dfrac{75x^2 + 30xy + 3y^2}{75x^2 - 15xy + 3y^2}$

17. $\dfrac{RT - 1 - R + T}{RT - 1 + R - T} \cdot \dfrac{R^2 - 1}{T^2 - 1}$

18. $\dfrac{W^2 + rW + sW + rs}{W^2 + rW + tW + rt} \cdot \dfrac{W^2 - t^2}{W^2 + sW - tW - st}$

19. $\dfrac{u^2 - 1 + 6v - 9v^2}{u^2 - 1 + 6uv + 9v^2} \cdot \dfrac{u^2v^3 + 3uv^4 + uv^3}{u^4v^2 - 3u^3v^3 + u^3v^2}$

20. $\dfrac{x^4 + x^3 - x - 1}{4x^4 - 4} \cdot \dfrac{28x^3 + 28x^2}{7x^3 + 7x^2 + 7x}$

21. $\dfrac{0.12a^2b^2}{0.45a^4c^4} \div \dfrac{0.84a^3b^6c^3}{1.40a^6b^4c^6}$

22. $\dfrac{1.80m^2n}{4.20n^2p^2} \div \dfrac{1.65mn^2}{0.77m^2p^2}$

23. $\dfrac{xy - x^2}{x^2 - y^2} \div \dfrac{x^2y - 2xy^2}{xy + y^2}$

24. $\dfrac{a^2b - a}{ab - b^2} \div \dfrac{b - ab^2}{ab - a^2}$

25. $\dfrac{25v^2}{v^2 + 2v - 15} \div \dfrac{50v^2}{v^2 - 8v + 15}$

26. $\dfrac{r^2 + 4r}{r^2 - 10r + 24} \div \dfrac{r^2 - 4r}{r^2 - 2r - 24}$

27. $\dfrac{4x^2 - 1}{4x^2 - 9} \div \dfrac{2x^2 - 11x + 5}{2x^2 - 13x + 15}$

28. $\dfrac{9x^2 - 25}{15x^2 + 16x - 15} \div \dfrac{9x^2 - 1}{15x^2 - 14x + 3}$

29. $\dfrac{h_1{}^3 h_2{}^2}{R_1{}^2 R_2{}^3} \div \dfrac{h_1{}^2 h_2}{R_1 R_2{}^2}$

30. $\dfrac{P_1{}^3 P_2{}^4}{T_1{}^3 T_2{}^2} \div \dfrac{P_1{}^2 P_2{}^4}{T_1{}^2 T_2{}^2}$

31. $\dfrac{m_1 v_1{}^2 - m_1 v_2{}^2}{m_2 v_1{}^2 + m_2 v_2{}^2} \div \dfrac{m_1 v_2 - m_1 v_1}{m_2 v_2{}^2 + m_2 v_1{}^2}$

32. $\dfrac{c_1{}^2 c_2}{c_1{}^2 F_1{}^2 - c_2{}^2 F_2{}^2} \div \dfrac{c_1 c_2{}^2}{c_2 F_2 - c_1 F_1}$

33. $\dfrac{a^3 - b^3}{a^4 - b^4} \div \dfrac{4a^2 + 4ab + 4b^2}{8a^3 b + 8ab^3}$

34. $\dfrac{27x^3 + 1}{3x^2 - 8x - 3} \div \dfrac{81x^3 - 27x^2 + 9x}{9x^2 - 28x + 3}$

35. $\dfrac{4x^4 - 80x^3}{x^4 - 5x^3 + x - 5} \div \dfrac{4x^4 - 60x^3 - 400x^2}{x^3 + x^2 - 25x - 25}$

36. $\dfrac{8y^3 - 1728}{16y^2 + 576} \div \dfrac{6y^2 - 35y - 6}{12y^4 + 2y^3 + 432y^2 + 72y}$

37. $\dfrac{r_1{}^4 - r_2{}^4}{r_1{}^2 - r_2{}^2} \div \dfrac{r_1{}^6 - r_2{}^6}{r_1{}^3 - r_2{}^3}$

38. $\dfrac{s_1{}^3 + s_2{}^3}{s_1{}^6 - s_2{}^6} \div \dfrac{s_1{}^7 + s_1{}^6 s_2 + s_1 s_2{}^6 + s_2{}^7}{s_1{}^{12} - s_2{}^{12}}$

39. $\dfrac{x^2 - y^2 - 10y - 25}{x^2 + y^2 - 2xy - 25} \div \dfrac{5x^2 y^2 + 5xy^3 + 25xy^2}{25x^3 y - 25x^2 y^2 + 125x^2 y}$

40. $\dfrac{x^2 + y^2 - 2xy - 16}{48 - 12x + 12y} \div \dfrac{x^2 - y^2 + 8y - 16}{72 - 18x - 18y}$

41. $\dfrac{x^2 - 9}{3x^2 - 8x - 3} \cdot \dfrac{6x^2 + 8x + 2}{6x^2 - 12x} \div \dfrac{x^2 + 4x + 3}{2x^3 - 3x^2 - 2x}$

42. $\dfrac{3y - 3}{4y^2 - 4} \cdot \dfrac{2y^2 - 2y}{3y^2} \div \dfrac{1 - y}{1 + y}$

43. $\dfrac{2v + v^2}{8 - 4v} \cdot \dfrac{v^2 - 2v}{4v^2 - 16} \div \dfrac{4v}{4v - 8}$

44. $\dfrac{3t^2 - 4t + 1}{t^3 - 5t^2 + 6t} \cdot \dfrac{10t^2 - 20t}{10t^2 + 5t} \div \dfrac{12t^2 - 16t + 4}{2t^2 - 5t - 3}$

5.04 / Addition and subtraction of fractions

The addition and subtraction of algebraic fractions involve the same methods that are used for arithmetic fractions.

> **To Add or Subtract Fractions**
> (1) Reduce each fraction to lowest terms.
> (2) Factor each denominator.
> (3) Find the LCD.
> (4) Rewrite each fraction so its new denominator is the LCD. Write each new numerator as the product of the original numerator multiplied by the quotient of the LCD divided by the original denominator.
> (5) Add or subtract the resulting numerators, placing the result over the LCD.
> (6) Reduce the resulting fraction to lowest terms.

Example 5.16

Simplify: $\dfrac{4xy}{24x^2y^2} + \dfrac{15y}{36xy^2} + \dfrac{4x}{60x^2y}$.

SOLUTION

(1) $\qquad \text{Sum} = \dfrac{1}{6xy} + \dfrac{5}{12xy} + \dfrac{1}{15xy}$

(2) $\qquad = \dfrac{1}{2 \cdot 3xy} + \dfrac{5}{2^2 3xy} + \dfrac{1}{3 \cdot 5xy}$

(3) $\qquad \text{LCD} = 2^2 \cdot 3 \cdot 5xy = 60xy$

(4) $\qquad \text{Sum} = \dfrac{1(10) + 5(5) + 1(4)}{60xy}$

(5) $\qquad = \dfrac{39}{60xy}$

(6) $\qquad = \dfrac{13(3)}{20xy(3)} = \dfrac{13}{20xy}$

Example 5.17

Express as a single fraction: $\dfrac{12}{x^2 - 9} - \dfrac{10}{x^2 + x - 6}$.

SOLUTION

(1) Each fraction is in lowest terms, so no reduction is necessary.

(2)
$$x^2 - 9 = (x + 3)(x - 3)$$
$$x^2 + x - 6 = (x + 3)(x - 2)$$

(3)
$$\text{LCD} = (x + 3)(x - 3)(x - 2)$$

(4)
$$\frac{12}{(x + 3)(x - 3)} - \frac{10}{(x + 3)(x - 2)}$$
$$= \frac{12(x - 2)}{\text{LCD}} - \frac{10(x - 3)}{\text{LCD}}$$

(5)
$$= \frac{12x - 24 - 10x + 30}{\text{LCD}}$$
$$= \frac{2x + 6}{\text{LCD}}$$

(6)
$$= \frac{2(x + 3)}{(x + 3)(x - 3)(x - 2)}$$
$$= \frac{2}{(x - 3)(x - 2)}$$

A computation involving fractions may be checked by substituting a numerical value for a variable. Any value can be used as long as this value does not make a denominator zero. Avoid using 0 or 1.

In order to check Example 5.17, x may be chosen to be any value different from -3, 3, and 2. Selecting $x = 4$,

$$\frac{12}{x^2 - 9} - \frac{10}{x^2 + x - 6} = \frac{12}{16 - 9} - \frac{10}{16 + 4 - 6} = \frac{12}{7} - \frac{10}{14} = \frac{24 - 10}{14} = 1$$

and

$$\frac{2}{(x - 3)(x - 2)} = \frac{2}{(4 - 3)(4 - 2)} = 1$$

Since $1 = 1$, a check has been established.

This method of checking does not guarantee that no errors have been made, but it does provide an assurance that the work is probably correct. It is wise to avoid doing the same type of operations as were used in the solution, and to always use the given fractions before any reduction was made.

Problem Set 5.4

Simplify.

1. $\dfrac{3b}{10x} + \dfrac{2b}{15x} + \dfrac{4b}{45x}$

2. $\dfrac{5a}{14y} + \dfrac{4a}{21y} + \dfrac{7a}{24y}$

3. $\dfrac{6x}{40x^2y} + \dfrac{5y}{100xy^2} + \dfrac{12xy}{250x^2y^2}$

4. $\dfrac{5a}{165a^3b^2} + \dfrac{2ab}{198a^3b^3} + \dfrac{3b}{726a^2b^3}$

5. $\dfrac{1}{x} + \dfrac{1-x}{x^2} + \dfrac{2-x}{x^3}$

6. $\dfrac{2}{y^2} + \dfrac{3-2y^2}{y^4} + \dfrac{4-3y^2}{y^6}$

7. $\dfrac{6y-1}{6y} - \dfrac{2y^2+y}{2y^2} + \dfrac{2}{9y^3}$

8. $\dfrac{x-2}{5x^3} + \dfrac{3x+5}{10x^3} - \dfrac{x+5}{10x^4}$

9. $\dfrac{x+y}{ky} - \dfrac{x-y}{kx}$

10. $\dfrac{ax+b}{ax} - \dfrac{bx-a}{bx}$

11. $\dfrac{a-b}{ab} + \dfrac{b-c}{bc} + \dfrac{c-a}{ac}$

12. $\dfrac{x+y}{xy} - \dfrac{y+z}{yz} + \dfrac{x-z}{xz}$

13. $\dfrac{1}{2x-6} + \dfrac{1}{5x-15}$

14. $\dfrac{1}{3x+12} + \dfrac{1}{7x+28}$

15. $\dfrac{2}{3y^2+6y} - \dfrac{4}{9y+18}$

16. $\dfrac{3}{2y-10} - \dfrac{1}{y^2-5y}$

17. $\dfrac{4}{x-y} + \dfrac{3}{y-x}$

18. $\dfrac{a}{a-b} + \dfrac{b}{b-a}$

19. $\dfrac{a}{a-b} - \dfrac{b}{a+b}$

20. $\dfrac{y}{x+y} - \dfrac{x}{x-y}$

21. $\dfrac{3}{x} - \dfrac{2}{x-2} + \dfrac{4}{x^2-2x}$

22. $\dfrac{5}{y} - \dfrac{4}{y+3} - \dfrac{12}{y^2+3y}$

23. $\dfrac{x-2}{(x+2)^2} + \dfrac{x+6}{x+2}$

24. $\dfrac{y+2}{y+1} + \dfrac{y-1}{(y+1)^2}$

25. $\dfrac{y-2}{y-3} + \dfrac{y+1}{y+3} - \dfrac{12}{y^2-9}$

26. $\dfrac{x+1}{x+5} + \dfrac{x-2}{x-5} - \dfrac{30}{x^2-25}$

27. $x+y+\dfrac{y^2}{x-y}$

28. $a-b+\dfrac{b^2}{a+b}$

29. $\dfrac{x^2-10}{x^2+2x-8} + \dfrac{x-3}{2-x}$

30. $\dfrac{x^2-5}{x^2+2x-3} + \dfrac{x-2}{1-x}$

31. $\dfrac{x}{x+4} + \dfrac{x}{x-4} - \dfrac{x^2}{x^2-16}$

32. $\dfrac{6}{y-6} - \dfrac{6}{y+6} + \dfrac{2y}{y^2-36}$

33. $\dfrac{x+5}{x-5} - \dfrac{x-5}{x+5}$

34. $\dfrac{x-11}{x+11} - \dfrac{x+11}{x-11}$

35. $\dfrac{2}{x^2+3x-10} - \dfrac{3}{x^2+2x-15}$

36. $\dfrac{5}{x^2+2x-35} - \dfrac{4}{x^2+3x-28}$

37. $\dfrac{1}{r^6} + \dfrac{1-r}{r^7}$

38. $\dfrac{r+1}{r^6} - \dfrac{1}{r^5}$

39. $\dfrac{a^5+b^5}{a^5-b^5} - \dfrac{a^5-b^5}{a^5+b^5}$

40. $\dfrac{c^6+d^6}{c^6-d^6} + \dfrac{c^6-d^6}{c^6+d^6}$

41. $\dfrac{x+3}{2x^2+3x-20} + \dfrac{x-4}{2x^2-11x+15} - \dfrac{2x+5}{x^2+x-12}$

42. $\dfrac{x-9}{3x^2-23x+14} - \dfrac{x+7}{3x^2+25x-18} + \dfrac{3x+2}{x^2+2x-63}$

43. $\dfrac{r^2+1}{r^3-r^2+r-1} - \dfrac{r^2-1}{r^3+r^2-r-1}$

44. $\dfrac{v^2-2}{v^3+v^2-2v-2} - \dfrac{v^2-1}{v^3-2v^2-v+2}$

45. $\dfrac{1}{(v_1-v_2)(v_1-v_3)} + \dfrac{1}{(v_2-v_3)(v_2-v_1)} + \dfrac{1}{(v_3-v_1)(v_3-v_2)}$

46. $\dfrac{t_1}{(t_1-t_2)(t_1-t_3)} + \dfrac{t_2}{(t_2-t_3)(t_2-t_1)} + \dfrac{t_3}{(t_3-t_1)(t_3-t_2)}$

47. $\dfrac{R+L}{(R-K)(K-L)} + \dfrac{K+L}{(R-K)(R-L)} + \dfrac{R+K}{(R-L)(K-L)}$

48. $\dfrac{R-L}{(R+K)(K+L)} + \dfrac{L-K}{(R+K)(R+L)} + \dfrac{K-R}{(R+L)(K+L)}$

49. $3 + \dfrac{x}{x+1} - \dfrac{x}{x-1}$

50. $1 + \dfrac{2x}{1-x} - \dfrac{x+1}{x-x^2}$

51. $\dfrac{0.4y^2+0.5}{2y^2+y-1} + \dfrac{0.1y-0.2}{y^2+y} - 0.2$

52. $\dfrac{5y^3+0.04}{125y^3+1} - \dfrac{0.2}{25y^3-5y^2+y} - 0.04$

53. $\left(a-b+\dfrac{4ab}{a-b}\right)\dfrac{b-a}{b+a}$

54. $\left[\left(\dfrac{z}{2}-\dfrac{1}{2z}\right)^2+1\right]\dfrac{2z}{z^2+1}$

55. $\dfrac{6t}{9t^2 + 6t + 1}\left[\left(\dfrac{3t}{2} + \dfrac{1}{6t}\right)^2 - 1\right]$ **57.** $\dfrac{1}{x^5 - y^5}\left(\dfrac{x}{y^4} + \dfrac{x - y}{x^4 - y^4}\right)$

56. $\left(m - 3 + \dfrac{12m - 1}{3m + 1}\right)\dfrac{3m + 1}{3m - 2}$ **58.** $\left(\dfrac{x^2 - y^2}{y^2} + \dfrac{x^5 + y^5}{x^5}\right)\dfrac{1}{x^7 + y^7}$

5.05 / Complex fractions

A **simple fraction** is one that does not have a fraction in its numerator or denominator.

A **complex fraction** is a fraction that has one or more fractions in its numerator or denominator (or both). Some examples of complex fractions are

$$\dfrac{x + \dfrac{1}{x}}{2}, \quad \dfrac{1}{\dfrac{1}{x} + \dfrac{1}{y}}, \quad \dfrac{\dfrac{x}{3} - \dfrac{3}{x}}{\dfrac{1}{3} - \dfrac{1}{x}}$$

A **simple complex fraction** is a complex fraction that does not have another complex fraction in its numerator or denominator.

A simple complex fraction may be simplified by using the fundamental principle of fractions:

$$\dfrac{n}{d} = \dfrac{nk}{dk}$$

In other words, the numerator and denominator are each multiplied by the same number, the LCD of all the fractions in the numerator and denominator of the fraction to be simplified.

Example 5.18

Simplify: $\dfrac{\dfrac{5}{12x}}{\dfrac{5}{18y}}$.

SOLUTION

(1) The LCD of $12x$ and $18y$ is $36xy$.

(2) Multiply numerator and denominator by $36xy$:

$$\dfrac{\left(\dfrac{5}{12x}\right)36xy}{\left(\dfrac{5}{18y}\right)36xy} = \dfrac{5(3)y}{5(2)x}$$

(3) Reduce the resulting simple fraction to lowest terms:

$$\frac{5(3)y}{5(2)x} = \frac{3y}{2x}$$

ALTERNATIVE SOLUTION
Treating the complex fraction as a quotient:

$$\frac{\dfrac{5}{12x}}{\dfrac{5}{18y}} = \frac{5}{12x} \div \frac{5}{18y} = \frac{5}{12x} \cdot \frac{18y}{5} = \frac{3y}{2x}$$

To avoid errors, it is suggested that the student draw a double line or a much longer line to replace the thicker line used in the text for the main line of the fraction.

Example 5.19

Simplify: $\dfrac{\dfrac{x}{3} - \dfrac{3}{x}}{\dfrac{1}{3} - \dfrac{1}{x}}$.

SOLUTION
(1) Multiplying by the LCD $= 3x$:

$$\frac{\left(\dfrac{x}{3} - \dfrac{3}{x}\right)3x}{\left(\dfrac{1}{3} - \dfrac{1}{x}\right)3x} = \frac{\left(\dfrac{x}{3}\right)3x - \left(\dfrac{3}{x}\right)3x}{\left(\dfrac{1}{3}\right)3x - \left(\dfrac{1}{x}\right)3x}$$

$$= \frac{x^2 - 9}{x - 3}$$

(2) Reducing to lowest terms:

$$\frac{x^2 - 9}{x - 3} = \frac{(x + 3)(x - 3)}{1(x - 3)}$$

$$= \frac{x + 3}{1}$$

$$= x + 3$$

Example 5.20

Check that $\dfrac{\dfrac{x}{3} - \dfrac{3}{x}}{\dfrac{1}{3} - \dfrac{1}{x}} = x + 3$ by letting $x = 2$.

SOLUTION

$$\frac{\dfrac{x}{3} - \dfrac{3}{x}}{\dfrac{1}{3} - \dfrac{1}{x}} = \frac{\dfrac{2}{3} - \dfrac{3}{2}}{\dfrac{1}{3} - \dfrac{1}{2}} = \frac{\dfrac{4}{6} - \dfrac{9}{6}}{\dfrac{2}{6} - \dfrac{3}{6}} = \frac{-\dfrac{5}{6}}{-\dfrac{1}{6}} = \frac{5}{6} \cdot \frac{6}{1} = 5$$

$$x + 3 = 2 + 3 = 5$$
$$5 = 5, \text{ check}$$

If a fraction has one or more complex fractions in its numerator or denominator, a simple complex fraction appearing is first reduced to a simple fraction and then the resulting fraction is simplified. It is best to do a *single* operation at a time and to use a double line to clearly indicate the numerator and denominator of the main fraction. If both numerator and denominator are complex, one step at a time may be done in each.

Example 5.21

Simplify $\dfrac{1}{1 - \dfrac{1}{1 - x}}$.

SOLUTION
Multiplying the *main* numerator and *main* denominator by the LCD $= 1 - x$:

$$\frac{1 \cdot (1 - x)}{\left(1 - \dfrac{1}{1 - x}\right)(1 - x)} = \frac{1 - x}{1(1 - x) - \left(\dfrac{1}{1 - x}\right)(1 - x)}$$

$$= \frac{1 - x}{1 - x - 1}$$

$$= \frac{1 - x}{-x}$$

$$= \frac{x - 1}{x}$$

Example 5.22

Simplify: $\dfrac{1}{1 - \dfrac{1}{1 - \dfrac{1}{1 - x}}}$

SOLUTION

$$\frac{1}{1 - \dfrac{1}{1 - \dfrac{1}{1 - x}}} = \frac{1}{1 - \dfrac{1}{\dfrac{1 - x - 1}{1 - x}}}$$

$$= \frac{1}{1 - \dfrac{1}{\dfrac{-x}{1 - x}}}$$

$$= \frac{1}{1 - \dfrac{x - 1}{x}}$$

$$= \frac{1}{\dfrac{x - x + 1}{x}}$$

$$= \frac{1}{\dfrac{1}{x}}$$

$$= x$$

Problem Set 5.5

Simplify.

1. $\dfrac{\dfrac{3}{20}}{\dfrac{21}{50}}$

2. $\dfrac{\dfrac{4}{45}}{\dfrac{32}{75}}$

3. $\dfrac{\dfrac{3x}{4y}}{\dfrac{9x}{8y}}$

4. $\dfrac{\dfrac{2a}{7b}}{\dfrac{5a}{14b}}$

5. $\dfrac{\dfrac{a^2}{b^2}}{a^2}$

6. $\dfrac{\dfrac{x^2}{y^2}}{x^2}$

7. $\dfrac{\dfrac{1}{2}+\dfrac{1}{3}}{1-\dfrac{1}{6}}$

8. $\dfrac{\dfrac{1}{3}-\dfrac{1}{4}}{1+\dfrac{1}{12}}$

9. $\dfrac{\dfrac{1}{a}-b}{a-\dfrac{1}{b}}$

10. $\dfrac{x-\dfrac{1}{x}}{x-1}$

11. $\dfrac{\dfrac{x}{2}-\dfrac{x}{8}}{\dfrac{x}{2}+\dfrac{x}{4}}$

12. $\dfrac{\dfrac{x}{6}-\dfrac{x}{9}}{\dfrac{x}{3}-\dfrac{x}{18}}$

13. $\dfrac{x+\dfrac{1}{y}}{x^2+\dfrac{x}{y}}$

14. $\dfrac{x+\dfrac{x}{y}}{2+\dfrac{2}{y}}$

15. $\dfrac{3-\dfrac{1}{t}}{9-\dfrac{1}{t^2}}$

16. $\dfrac{r-\dfrac{4}{r}}{1+\dfrac{2}{r}}$

17. $\dfrac{\dfrac{1}{R_1}-\dfrac{R_1}{R_2{}^2}}{\dfrac{1}{R_1{}^2}+\dfrac{1}{R_1 R_2}}$

18. $\dfrac{\dfrac{4F_2}{F_1}-\dfrac{4F_1}{F_2}}{\dfrac{1}{8F_1}-\dfrac{F_2{}^2}{8F_1{}^3}}$

19. $\dfrac{r_n-\dfrac{1}{r_n}}{r_n{}^2-\dfrac{1}{r_n{}^2}}$

20. $\dfrac{\dfrac{d}{r_1}-\dfrac{d}{r_2}}{\dfrac{d}{r_1}+\dfrac{d}{r_2}}$

21. $\dfrac{2d}{\dfrac{d}{r_1}+\dfrac{d}{r_2}}$

22. $\dfrac{v_0{}^2-\dfrac{1}{v_0{}^2}}{v_0+\dfrac{1}{v_0}}$

23. $\dfrac{1-\dfrac{4}{x^2}}{x+\dfrac{8}{x^2}}$

24. $\dfrac{x-\dfrac{125}{x^2}}{1-\dfrac{25}{x^2}}$

25. $\dfrac{x+3-\dfrac{10}{x}}{x-9+\dfrac{14}{x}}$

26. $\dfrac{x-1-\dfrac{12}{x}}{x-5-\dfrac{24}{x}}$

27. $\dfrac{1-\dfrac{9x^2}{4y^2}}{x+2y-\dfrac{6x^2}{y}}$

28. $\dfrac{3 + \dfrac{y}{x} - \dfrac{4y^2}{x^2}}{1 - \dfrac{16y^2}{9x^2}}$

29. $\dfrac{\dfrac{2}{x^2 - a^2}}{\dfrac{1}{x - a} - \dfrac{1}{x + a}}$

30. $\dfrac{\dfrac{x - y}{x + y} - \dfrac{x + y}{x - y}}{\dfrac{4}{x^2 - y^2}}$

31. $\dfrac{\dfrac{kx + ky}{R^2 + RL}}{\dfrac{Rx + Ry}{kR + kL}}$

32. $\dfrac{\dfrac{nx - ny}{C^2 - CF}}{\dfrac{Cx - Cy}{nC + nF}}$

33. $\dfrac{x + 7 - \dfrac{x - 29}{x - 5}}{x + 3 + \dfrac{x + 3}{x - 3}}$

34. $\dfrac{y + 3 - \dfrac{y - 12}{y - 4}}{y - 3 - \dfrac{y - 6}{y + 2}}$

35. $\dfrac{\dfrac{x - 1}{x + 1} + \dfrac{x + 1}{x - 1}}{\dfrac{1 + x}{1 - x} - \dfrac{1 - x}{1 + x}}$

36. $\dfrac{\dfrac{x^2 - 4}{x^2 + 4} - \dfrac{x^2 + 4}{x^2 - 4}}{\dfrac{x - 2}{x + 2} - \dfrac{x + 2}{x - 2}}$

37. $\dfrac{1}{1 + \dfrac{1}{1 + \dfrac{1}{1 + \frac{1}{2}}}}$

38. $\dfrac{1}{1 - \dfrac{1}{1 - \dfrac{1}{1 - \frac{1}{2}}}}$

39. $1 - \dfrac{1}{1 - \dfrac{1}{1 + \dfrac{1}{x - 1}}}$

40. $1 + \dfrac{1}{\dfrac{1}{x} - \dfrac{1}{x + \dfrac{x}{x - 1}}}$

41. $\dfrac{x - \dfrac{2}{\dfrac{1}{x} + \dfrac{1}{y}}}{y - \dfrac{2}{\dfrac{1}{x} + \dfrac{1}{y}}}$

42. $\dfrac{\dfrac{1}{x} - \dfrac{1}{y}}{\dfrac{1}{x} - 1} \cdot \dfrac{\dfrac{1}{x} + \dfrac{1}{y}}{\dfrac{x}{y} - 1}$

5.06 / Chapter Review

1. Algebraic and arithmetic fractions may be reduced to lowest terms or built up to higher terms by using the *fundamental principle of fractions*:

$$\frac{n}{d} = \frac{nk}{dk}$$

2. For the *product of two fractions*, the numerators are multiplied to obtain the numerator of the product and the denominators are multiplied to obtain the denominator of the product:

$$\frac{a}{b} \cdot \frac{c}{d} = \frac{ac}{bd}$$

3. To *divide one fraction by another*, invert the divisor and multiply:

$$\frac{\dfrac{a}{b}}{\dfrac{c}{d}} = \left(\frac{a}{b}\right)\left(\frac{d}{c}\right)$$

4. To *add (or subtract) fractions*, first rewrite the fractions so that the new denominator of each is the LCD. Then add (or subtract) the new numerators:

$$\frac{a}{b} + \frac{c}{d} = \frac{ad + bc}{bd}$$

5. A *simple complex fraction* may be simplified by multiplying both the numerator and the denominator by the LCD of all fractions appearing in the numerator and denominator of the complex fraction.

6. A *complex complex fraction* (a complex fraction with one or more complex fractions in its numerator or denominator) may be simplified by using a logical sequence of operations, beginning with a simple complex fraction in the numerator or denominator and doing one step at a time.

Problem Set 5.6 (*Chapter Review*)

1–22

Simplify.

1. $\dfrac{225a^3b^4c^6}{375a^2b^5c^6}$

2. $\dfrac{27x^3 - 9x^2}{27x^3 - 3x}$

3. $\dfrac{35 + 2r - r^2}{42 - 13r + r^2}$

4. $\dfrac{x^3 + 64}{4x^3 - 16x^2 + 64x}$

5. $\dfrac{a^2 - b^2 + c^2 - 2ac}{a + b - c}$

6. $\dfrac{x - 3}{6x - 30} + \dfrac{x - 8}{9x - 45}$

7. $\dfrac{x^2 + x}{4x^2 + 28x} - \dfrac{3x^2 - x}{12x^2 + 84x}$

8. $\dfrac{4x^2 - 9}{3x^2 + 8x + 4} \cdot \dfrac{x^3 + 2x^2 + x + 2}{2x^3 - 3x^2 + 2x - 3}$

9. $\left(\dfrac{1}{x} + \dfrac{1}{x + 1}\right)\left(\dfrac{1}{x} + 1\right)$

10. $\dfrac{4\pi(r_1 - r_2)^2}{32r_2} \div \dfrac{\pi(r_1^2 - r_2^2)}{8r_1}$

11. $\dfrac{x - 3}{x^2 + 3x} - \dfrac{x + 7}{x^2 - 7x} - \dfrac{x - 17}{x^2 - 4x - 21}$

12. $\dfrac{27x^3 - 3x}{4x^2 + 100x} \cdot \dfrac{36x^4 + 12x^3 + 4x^2}{27x^3 - 81x^3 + 3x - 9} \div \dfrac{27x^6 - x^3}{x^3 + 22x^2 - 75x}$

13. $\left(\dfrac{x^2 + y^2}{xy} + 2\right) \div \left(\dfrac{x^2 + y^2}{xy} - 2\right)$

14. $\left(\dfrac{1}{x} + \dfrac{1}{y}\right) \div \left(\dfrac{1}{x} - \dfrac{1}{y}\right)$

15. $\dfrac{x^2 - y^2}{(x - y)^2} \cdot \left(\dfrac{x^2}{y^2} - \dfrac{2x}{y} + 1\right)$

16. $\dfrac{\dfrac{1}{7x} - \dfrac{1}{49}}{\dfrac{x}{49} - \dfrac{7}{x^2}}$

17. $\dfrac{1 - \dfrac{1}{v_1 v_2}}{1 - \dfrac{1}{v_1^2 v_2^2}}$

18. $\dfrac{(r_1 - r_2)\left(\dfrac{1}{r_1} + \dfrac{1}{r_2}\right)}{(r_1 + r_2)\left(\dfrac{1}{r_1} - \dfrac{1}{r_2}\right)}$

19. $\dfrac{\dfrac{1}{1 + a} + \dfrac{1}{m - 1}}{\dfrac{1}{1 - m} + \dfrac{1}{1 + a}}$

20. $\dfrac{\dfrac{1}{x^3} + \dfrac{1}{y^3}}{\dfrac{1}{x^6} - \dfrac{1}{y^6}} \cdot \dfrac{\dfrac{1}{x^3} - \dfrac{1}{y^3}}{\dfrac{1}{x} + \dfrac{1}{y}}$

21. $2 - \dfrac{x}{2 + \dfrac{x}{2 - \dfrac{x}{2}}}$

22. $1 - \dfrac{x - 1 + \dfrac{x}{x + 1 + \dfrac{1}{x - 1}}}{x - 1}$

23. The torque transmitted by two ring friction disks is

$$T = \frac{2}{3} fP \frac{R_o^3 - R_i^3}{R_o^2 - R_i^2}$$

Find the torque T if the coefficient of friction $f = 0.3$, the total pressure $P = 2000$ lb, the outer radius $R_o = 8.25$ in., and the inner radius $R_i = 3.75$ in. (*Hint:* Simplify the fraction before substituting.)

24. An important engineering concept is called the *radius of gyration* (k) and is defined as follows: $k = \sqrt{\dfrac{I}{A}}$. For an annulus (ring) of outer radius r_o and inner radius r_i,

$$I = \frac{\pi(r_o^4 - r_i^4)}{4} \quad \text{and} \quad A = \pi(r_o^2 - r_i^2)$$

(a) Express k^2 as a simplified fraction.
(b) Evaluate k for $r_o = 12$ in. and $r_i = 5$ in.

First-degree equations and inequalities

6.01 / Equations

An equation is a statement stating that whatever is to the left of the equality symbol (=) names the same thing as whatever is to the right of the symbol. There is nothing in this statement that requires it to be true. A mathematical equation may be always true, always false, or true sometimes and false other times. These types of mathematical equations may be better understood if they are paralleled by similar types of English sentences (Table 6.1).

The equation $2 + 4 = 6$ is called a *true statement* since it is known that $2 + 4 = 6$. Since it is a known fact that bronze is an alloy of copper and tin, this, too, is a true statement.

Table 6.1

Type of Equation	Mathematical	English
True	$2 + 4 = 6$	Bronze is an alloy of copper and tin.
False	$3 + 5 = 7$	The boiling point of water is 40°F.
Identity (or open)	$x + x = 2x$	A man is mortal.
Conditional (or open)	$x + 5 = 13$	Some size of schedule 50 cast-iron pipe weighs 25.9 lb/ft.

The equation $3 + 5 = 7$ is called a *false statement* since the sum of 3 and 5 is known to be 8. Similarly, "The boiling point of water is 40°F" is a false statement because the boiling point of water is known to be 212°F.

An *open equation* is an equation that contains a variable. It is neither true nor false but may become true or false when the variable is replaced by a constant.

The statement $x + x = 2x$ is called an *identity* because this open equation becomes a true statement no matter what number is used to replace x; that is, $3 + 3 = 2(3)$, $4 + 4 = 2(4)$, and so on. Also, "A man is mortal" is true no matter what man is selected; that is, Richard Nixon is mortal, Isaac Newton is mortal, and so on.

The equation $x + 5 = 13$ is called *conditional* because this open equation becomes true on the condition that a certain number is the replacement value for x. This particular conditional equation becomes true for $x = 8$. On the other hand, if x is replaced by 2, the statement becomes false, since $2 + 5 = 13$ is a false statement. In a similar way, the statement about schedule 50 pipe is true only if 6-in. pipe is used.

Some open equations become false no matter what number is used as the replacement value for the variable; for example, $x + 2 = x + 3$ is false for all values of x.

Finding all the values of the variable that change the given conditional equation to a true statement is called **solving the equation.** The replacement values that may be substituted for the variable are usually in the set of real numbers, but in many problems, only certain values, called **admissible values,** may be used. The values of the variable that create true equations are called **roots, solutions,** or **elements of the solution set.** Each root is said to satisfy the equation. Substituting each root into the original equation should produce a true equation and this operation is called **checking** the solution.

Every open equation has a solution set. It may be the null (empty) set as for an always false equation, it may have one or a finite number of elements, or it may have an infinite number of elements, as for the identity $x + x = 2x$. In this last case, the solution set is written R, meaning the entire set of real numbers.

The degree of an algebraic polynomial equation is the highest degree of any term in it. A first-degree equation in one variable, also called a *linear equation*, is an equation that can be reduced to the form $Ax + B = 0$, where A and B are constants and $A \neq 0$. Since the number of elements in the solution set of any conditional polynomial equation in one variable is equal to or is less than the degree of the equation, a first-degree conditional equation in one variable has either one element or no elements in its solution set.

Problem Set 6.1

1–10
Identify each of the following equations as a true statement, a false statement, an identity, or a conditional equation by using T, F, I, or C.

1. $3(x - 4) = 3x - 12$

2. $7x - 11 = 11 - 7x$

3. $\sqrt{16 + 9} = 7$

4. $\dfrac{22.4(4.11)}{5.62(5.17)} = 0.317$

5. $\dfrac{17.2(31.6)}{4.17(5.42)} = 24.0$

6. $x(8 - 2) = 6x$

7. $4x - 5 = 5 - 4x$

8. $\sqrt{40 + 41} = -9$

9. $x = 0$

10. $\sqrt[3]{7 - 34} = -3$

11–20
Determine whether the number following each equation is a root of the equation.

11. $7x - 11 = 17; \{4\}$

12. $13x - 25 = 40; \{5\}$

13. $\sqrt{144} + 2x = 34; \{-2\}$

14. $17.29x - 14.77 = 252; \{0\}$

15. $1.2x + 3.7 = -6.1; \{-2\}$

16. $\frac{7}{8} - \frac{3}{4}x = 2\frac{1}{8}; \{4\}$

17. $(2x - 4)(2x + 4) = 0; \{-2\}$

18. $\sqrt{24x - 9} = -9; \{-3\}$

19. $1.76x^2 - 5.85x = 1.71; \{-3\}$

20. $(5x - 2)(6x + 7) = 187; \{-3\}$

21–30
From the set $\{-4, -3, -2, -1, 0, 1, 2, 3, 4\}$, select those numbers that are solutions to the given equation.

21. $2x - 5 = 7 - x$

22. $6 + (2 - x) = 6 - (x - 2)$

23. $x^2 - x - 6 = 0$

24. $x^3 = 4x$

25. $2(5 - 3x) = 3(5 - 2x)$

26. $x^2 + 3x - 4 = 0$

27. $x^3 = x$

28. $(x - 2)(x - 1) = x - 2(x - 1)$

29. $x(x^2 - 1) - 2(x^2 - 1) = (x - 2)(x^2 - 1)$

30. $x^2 + 2x = 2x^2 - (x^2 - 2x + 4)$

6.02 / Solving conditional first-degree equations

In solving a conditional equation, it is necessary to find the solution set whose elements are in another set, the set of replacement values. This set may differ from the set of real numbers in that the replacement set contains only **admissible values.** The admissible values are those that meet the particular conditions of the applied problem and that exclude impossible mathematical operations. Table 6.2 gives examples of admissible values.

The equality axioms that are used in solving conditional linear equations are stated below.

1. Symmetric Axiom

The right- and left-hand sides of an equation may be exchanged. (If $A = B$, then $B = A$.)

2. Addition Axiom

If the same number is added to both sides of an equation, the resulting sums are equal. (If $A = B$, then $A + C = B + C$.)

3. Subtraction Axiom

If the same number is subtracted from both sides of an equation, the resulting differences are equal. (If $A = B$, then $A - C = B - C$.)

4. Multiplication Axiom

If both sides of an equation are multiplied by the same number, the resulting products are equal. (If $A = B$, then $AC = BC$.)

5. Division Axiom

If both sides of an equation are divided by the same number (different from zero), the resulting quotients are equal. (If $A = B$ and $C \neq 0$, then $\dfrac{A}{C} = \dfrac{B}{C}$.)

Table 6.2

Problem Involves	*Admissible Values*
$\dfrac{x + a}{x + b}$	$\{x \mid x \in R \text{ and } x \neq -b\}$ or $R - \{-b\}$
$\sqrt{x + a}$	$\{x \mid x \in R \text{ and } x + a \geq 0\}$
Weight of a person in pounds	All positive rational numbers < 400
A low temperature in °C	All negative rational numbers > -273
Value of coins in pennies	Selected integers

It should be noted that multiplication by a factor containing the variable may introduce a false root and division by a factor containing the variable may lose a true root.

General Procedure for Solving First-Degree Equations
(1) Remove any grouping symbols. If any fractional terms are involved, reduce these to lowest terms.
(2) List as inadmissible values those values of the variable that would make a divisor equal to zero, if there are any.
(3) Use the equality axioms to clear the equation of any fractions.
(4) Use the equality axioms to collect all variable terms on one side of the equal sign and all numerals on the other.
(5) Use the equality axioms and then solve the equation resulting from step (4).
(6) Check the solution in the *original* equation. (Checking any derived equation may be quicker, but it will not disclose an error made in obtaining that derived form nor will it disclose a false root if multiplication by a variable term was used.)

Example 6.1
Find the solution set of $x^2 + 7x - 18 = (x - 11)(x - 2)$.

SOLUTION
(1) Removing parentheses, $x^2 + 7x - 18 = x^2 - 13x + 22$.
(2) All values are admissible.
(3) No fractions are involved.
(4) By using the addition and subtraction equality axioms, all literal terms are placed on one side of the equation and the numerical terms on the other side. Subtracting x^2 and adding $13x + 18$ to both sides,

$$
\begin{aligned}
x^2 + 7x - 18 &= x^2 - 13x + 22 \\
-x^2 + 13x + 18 &= -x^2 + 13x + 18 \\
\hline
20x \quad\quad &= \quad\quad 40
\end{aligned}
$$

(*Note :* If the coefficients are simple integers, then, with practice, this middle step involving addition and subtraction can be done mentally.)
(5) Solving the equation just found by dividing both sides by 20,

$$20x = 40$$

$$x = \frac{40}{20} = 2$$

(6) Checking for $x = 2$,

$$\text{left side} = 4 + 14 - 18 = 0$$

$$\text{right side} = (2 - 11)(2 - 2) = -9(0) = 0 \qquad \text{thus, } 0 = 0.$$

Therefore, the solution set is $\{2\}$.

Example 6.2

Find the root of $\dfrac{3x + 1}{5} - 1 = \dfrac{x}{2}$.

SOLUTION

(1) Writing the left side as a single fraction:

$$\frac{3x + 1 - 5}{5} = \frac{x}{2}$$

$$\frac{3x - 4}{5} = \frac{x}{2}$$

(2) All values are admissible.

(3) Multiplying both sides by 10, the LCD, to clear of fractions:

$$\frac{10(3x - 4)}{5} = \frac{10x}{2}$$

$$2(3x - 4) = 5x$$

Removing parentheses:

$$6x - 8 = 5x$$

(4) Adding 8 to both sides and subtracting $5x$ from both sides so that the literal terms are on the left and the numerals are on the right:

$$
\begin{array}{rcl}
6x - 8 & = & 5x \\
-5x + 8 & = & -5x + 8 \\
\hline
x & = & 8
\end{array}
$$

(5) No further operations are necessary.

(6) Checking in the original equation:

$$\frac{3(8) + 1}{5} - 1 \overset{?}{=} \frac{8}{2}$$

$$\frac{24 + 1}{5} - 1 \overset{?}{=} 4$$

$$5 - 1 \overset{?}{=} 4$$

$$4 = 4$$

Therefore, the root is 8.

Example 6.3

Find the solution set of $\dfrac{2x^2 - 3x + 13}{x + 3} = 2(x - 4).$

SOLUTION

(1) Remove parentheses:

$$\frac{2x^2 - 3x + 13}{x + 3} = 2x - 8$$

(2) The inadmissible value is $x = -3$.

(3) Clearing of fractions:

$$2x^2 - 3x + 13 = (2x - 8)(x + 3)$$
$$2x^2 - 3x + 13 = 2x^2 - 2x - 24$$

(4) Collecting literal terms on left and numerals on right:

$$
\begin{array}{rcl}
2x^2 - 3x + 13 &=& 2x^2 - 2x - 24 \\
-2x^2 + 2x - 13 &=& -2x^2 + 2x - 13 \\
\hline
-x &=& -37
\end{array}
$$

(5) Solving:

$$-x = -37$$
$$x = 37$$

(6) Checking:

Left Side	Right Side
$\dfrac{2(37)^2 - 3(37) + 13}{37 + 3}$	$2(37 - 4)$
$\dfrac{2(1369) - 111 + 13}{40}$	$2(33)$
$\dfrac{2738 - 98}{40} = \dfrac{2640}{40}$	66
$66 = 66$	

Therefore, the solution set is $\{37\}$.

Problem Set 6.2

State any inadmissible values and find the solution set. Check all solutions.

1. $4r - 5 = 7$

2. $7s + 2 = 16$

3. $5t - 4 = 3t - 28$

4. $11u + 7 = 7(u - 3)$

5. $2v = 5v + 12$

6. $5w = 2(3w + 17)$

7. $\dfrac{x}{4} - 1 = \dfrac{3}{4}$

8. $\dfrac{2u}{3} + 2 = \dfrac{2}{3}$

9. $\dfrac{3z - 2}{4} = 4$

10. $\dfrac{4(r + 1)}{5} = 4$

11. $\dfrac{2(x + 4)}{2} = 8$

12. $\dfrac{5x + 7}{9} = 4$

13. $2.2x - 7.4 = 11.6$

14. $3.14x + 3.09 = 14.29$

15. $7.11x - 13.74 = 3.89x + 7.21$

16. $14.48x + 12.56 = 4(2.06x + 3.14)$

17. $\dfrac{x^2 - 5x + 19}{x + 2} = -7$

18. $\dfrac{x^2 + 5x - 19}{x + 3} = x - 5$

19. $\dfrac{3x^2 - 2x - 2}{5 - x} = 5 - 3x$

20. $\dfrac{x^2 - 13x + 17}{4 - x} = 9 - x$

6.03 / Fractional equations

A fractional equation is an equation whose terms are rational expressions. In the previous section the simplest types were met. This section will cover the more complex types.

To solve these more complex types of fractional equations, it is necessary to multiply both sides of the equation by the least common multiple (LCM) of all denominators. The LCM is identical with the LCD found in Section 5.01, Example 5.5. The procedure is basically unchanged. The steps are as follows:

(1) Find inadmissible values.
(2) Find LCM.
(3) Multiply both sides by LCM to clear of fractions.
(4) Expand as required.
(5) Collect and simplify.
(6) Solve.
(7) Check.

It should be noted that the multiplication axiom requires *both* sides of the equation to be multiplied by the LCM. A very common error is to forget to multiply the right-hand side of the equation, especially if it contains no literal terms.

Example 6.4

Solve and check: $\dfrac{(x - 1)}{(x - 2)} + \dfrac{(x + 3)}{(x + 7)} = 2$.

SOLUTION

(1) Inadmissible values are $x = 2$ and $x = -7$.

(2) LCM is $(x - 2)(x + 7) = x^2 + 5x - 14$.

(3) Clearing:

$$(x - 1)(x + 7) + (x + 3)(x - 2) = 2(x^2 + 5x - 14)$$

(4) Expanding:

$$x^2 + 6x - 7 + x^2 + x - 6 = 2x^2 + 10x - 28$$

(5) Collecting:

$$
\begin{array}{rcl}
2x^2 + 7x - 13 &=& 2x^2 + 10x - 28 \\
-2x^2 - 10x + 13 &=& -2x^2 - 10x + 13 \\
\hline
-3x &=& -15
\end{array}
$$

(6) Solving: $x = 5$.

(7) Checking:

$$\frac{x - 1}{x - 2} + \frac{x + 3}{x + 7} = \frac{5 - 1}{5 - 2} + \frac{5 + 3}{5 + 7}$$

$$= \frac{4}{3} + \frac{8}{12} = \frac{4}{3} + \frac{2}{3} = \frac{6}{3} = 2 \qquad \text{and thus } 2 = 2$$

The solution set is $\{5\}$.

Example 6.5

Find the solution set of $\dfrac{x^2 + 7x - 18}{x - 2} = x - 11$.

SOLUTION

(1) The inadmissible value is $x = 2$.

(2) LCM $= x - 2$.

(3) Clearing: $x^2 + 7x - 18 = (x - 2)(x - 11)$.

(4) Expanding: $x^2 + 7x - 18 = x^2 - 13x + 22$.

(5) Collecting:

$$
\begin{array}{rcl}
x^2 + 7x - 18 &=& x^2 - 13x + 22 \\
-x^2 + 13x + 18 &=& -x^2 + 13x + 18 \\
\hline
20x &=& 40
\end{array}
$$

(6) Solving: $x = \frac{40}{20} = 2$.

(7) Checking is not required, because 2 is inadmissible.

Therefore, the solution set is $\varnothing$.

Problem Set 6.3

State any admissible values and find the solution set. Check all solutions.

1. $\dfrac{n-1}{n} + \dfrac{n-2}{2n} = 1$

2. $\dfrac{z-3}{z} + \dfrac{z+1}{2z} = 1$

3. $\dfrac{p+6}{p+5} + \dfrac{p+4}{p+5} = 2$

4. $\dfrac{13}{y-2} - \dfrac{9}{y-3} = -\dfrac{9}{y^2 - 5y + 6}$

5. $\dfrac{8}{r+4} + \dfrac{4}{r+3} = -\dfrac{8}{r^2 + 7r + 12}$

6. $\dfrac{2}{x-3} - \dfrac{2}{x} = \dfrac{19}{x^2 - 3x}$

7. $\dfrac{5}{6(s-2)} - \dfrac{3}{2(s+3)} = \dfrac{s-2}{6(s-2)(s+3)}$

8. $\dfrac{7}{4(w+5)} + \dfrac{5}{2(w-4)} = \dfrac{4w+5}{w^2 + w - 20}$

9. $\dfrac{6}{2t-3} - \dfrac{2}{6t^2 - 13t + 6} = \dfrac{8}{3t-2}$

10. $\dfrac{3}{4v-3} - \dfrac{2v+21}{28v^2 - 9v - 9} = \dfrac{5}{7v+3}$

11. $\dfrac{2.4}{0.1u} - \dfrac{1.2}{0.2u} + \dfrac{0.6}{0.4u} = 7.8$

12. $\dfrac{3.6}{0.2u} + \dfrac{4.8}{0.4u} - \dfrac{4.8}{0.5u} = 1.02$

13. $\dfrac{v-2}{v-1} + \dfrac{v+6}{v-4} = 2$

14. $\dfrac{t+1}{t+3} + \dfrac{2t-1}{t-1} = 3$

15. $\dfrac{w+1.5}{w+0.5} + \dfrac{1.5w}{w+1.0} = 2.5$

16. $\dfrac{2s + 1.20}{s + 0.40} - \dfrac{0.8s + 3.12}{s + 2.40} = 1.20$

17. $\dfrac{x - 7}{x - 5} - \dfrac{x + 7}{x + 5} = \dfrac{3x}{25 - x^2}$

18. $\dfrac{r + 3}{r + 6} - \dfrac{r - 5}{r - 6} = \dfrac{8r - 15}{36 - r^2}$

19. $\dfrac{t - 0.60}{t - 0.80} + \dfrac{t + 2.60}{t + 0.80} = \dfrac{2t^2 - 0.56}{t^2 - 0.64}$

20. $\dfrac{2p - 0.15}{0.5p + 2.00} + \dfrac{2p + 0.25}{0.5p - 2.00} = \dfrac{2p^2 + 0.05p + 0.80}{0.25p^2 - 4.00}$

6.04 / Literal equations

In most handbooks and manuals prepared for workers in engineering and science, formulas are given for the many relations that exist. These are given with a number of literal symbols that represent the variables involved. Some formulas contain numerical constants. All these formulas are equations since each one contains the equality symbol.

In many cases the given formula is not in the correct form for the problem at hand. In Example 6.6, the length of a rod and the temperature are related by a formula based upon knowing the coefficient of expansion determined from the measured length before and after heating. To change the given formula into the form desired, the same principles used in solving a conditional equation are used. The literal value desired is treated as the variable and all other literal symbols are treated as constants. The last step, the check, may be awkward but it should be made. If the solution obtained should not check, one could try substituting numerals for the letters, as explained in Section 5.04, Example 5.17.

Example 6.6
Solve for α, the coefficient of linear expansion:

$$L = L_0(1 + \alpha t)$$

SOLUTION

(1) Divide by L_0: $\qquad\qquad \dfrac{L}{L_0} = 1 + \alpha t$

(2) Subtract 1: $\qquad\qquad \dfrac{L}{L_0} - 1 = \alpha t$

(3) Combine left side: $\qquad \dfrac{L - L_0}{L_0} = \alpha t$

(4) Divide by t:
$$\alpha = \frac{L - L_0}{L_0 t}$$

(5) Check:
$$L = L_0\left(1 + \frac{L - L_0}{L_0 t}t\right) = L_0\left(1 + \frac{L - L_0}{L_0}\right) = L_0\frac{L_0 + L - L_0}{L_0}$$

$$= L_0\frac{L}{L_0} = L$$

Occasionally, a given formula may be used to derive an associated relation-ship.

Example 6.7
Using the formula given in Example 6.6, find the percentage change in length.

SOLUTION
The percentage change in length is the change in length divided by the original length and multiplied by 100:

$$\text{percentage change} = 100\left(\frac{L - L_0}{L_0}\right) = 100\left(\frac{L}{L_0} - 1\right)$$

$$= 100\left[\frac{L_0(1 + \alpha t)}{L_0} - 1\right]$$

$$= 100[(1 + \alpha t) - 1] = 100\alpha t$$

Thus, the percentage change $= 100\alpha t$.

Problem Set 6.4

This problem set consists of five subsections, each representing a commonly found type of technology. A very condensed title is given each formula cited to identify the formula, but no attempt is made to identify the literal symbols used. All formulas are taken from contemporary publications, which can be found in any technical library. Solve each formula for the variable desired.

Basic physics

Title	Formula	Variable desired
1. Law of small prisms	$D = A(n - 1)$	n
2. Elastic collision	$e = \dfrac{U_2 - U_1}{v_1 - v_2}$	v_2

Title	Formula	Variable desired
3. Volume expansion	$\beta = \dfrac{V_i - V_o}{V_o(T_2 - T_1)}$	T_1
4. Absolute temperature	$P_t = \dfrac{P_o}{273}(273 + t)$	t
5. Gas law	$\dfrac{P_1 V_1}{m_1 t_1} = \dfrac{P_2 V_2}{m_2 t_2}$	m_1
6. Thermometer scales	$F = \dfrac{9}{5}\,C + 32$	C
7. Specific heats	$Q = mc(t_f - t_1)$	t_1
8. Heat of fusion	$Q = m_i L_i + m_i c_w t_f$	m_i
9. Doeppler effect	$f' = \left(\dfrac{v_o}{v_o - v_s}\right) f$	v_o
10. Law of lenses	$\dfrac{1}{D_O} + \dfrac{1}{D_I} = \dfrac{1}{f}$	f

Mechanical technology

11. Locknut pitch diameter	$p = E_1 + \dfrac{0.3125}{n}$	n
12. Three-wire measure of pitch diameter	$E = M + \dfrac{0.866}{n} - 3G$	n
13. Pulley speed	$R = \dfrac{D_R S}{D_N}$	D_N
14. Velocity of pollutants	$v_c = v_s \dfrac{1 + 1.72\lambda}{D}$	D
15. Shafts in torsion	$K = q(K_{ts} - 1) + 1$	K_{ts}
16. Cylindrical journal bearings	$A = \dfrac{132}{D}(m^2 \times 10^6)\dfrac{P}{ZN}$	N
17. Lubricant supply	$Q_M = K_M urml$	u
18. Low-pressure turbines	$A = \dfrac{Q_v}{25V}$	V

Title	Formula	Variable desired
19. Steam enthalpy	$h_2 = \dfrac{Wh_1 - 3413P_g}{W}$	W
20. Surface condensers	$Q = 500Gc_p(T_0 - T_1)$	T_0

Electrical technology

Title	Formula	Variable desired
21. Resistance–temperature relationship	$R' = R[1 + (t_2 - t_1)]$	t_1
22. Local circuit method	$R = \dfrac{E}{A}\left(\dfrac{M}{N} - 1\right)$	N
23. Transformer ratio	$T = \left(\dfrac{R + r_v}{r_v}\right)\dfrac{x_1}{x_2}$	r_v
24. Sensitivity-reduction factor	$P = \dfrac{nr}{r - 1}$	r
25. Open-circuit damping	$R_x = R_1\dfrac{r_1 - r_0}{r_x - r_0}$	r_0
26. Slip in motors	$S = \dfrac{N_S - N}{N_S}$	N_S
27. Power-factor leakage	$b = a\left(1 + \dfrac{ab}{4}\right)$	b
28. Band-pass filters	$L_1 = \dfrac{(f_{ch} - f_{cl})R}{4\pi f_{cl}f_{ch}b}$	f_{cl}
29. Varley loop	$\dfrac{a + b}{b} = \dfrac{x + y + L + r}{y + L}$	b and L (in turn)
30. Gain in circuit	$G = \dfrac{G_0}{1 - G_0 f}$	G_0

Surveying

Title	Formula	Variable desired
31. Tape correction, tension	$c_p = \dfrac{(p - p_0)L}{AE}$	p
32. Tape correction, temperature	$c_t = 0.000\,006\,5L(T - T_0)$	T_0
33. Peg adjustment	$d' = c + \dfrac{(a - b) + (d - c)}{2}$	c

Title	Formula	Variable desired
34. Slope stakes	$d = \dfrac{w}{2} + hs$	s
35. Stadia	$D = ks + (f + c)$	s
36. Simpson's rule	$A_{1,2} = \dfrac{d}{3}(h_1 + 4h_2 + h_3)$	h_1
37. Earthwork	$V = \dfrac{L}{6}(A_1 + 4A_m + A_2)$	A_m
38. Verniers	$L = D - \dfrac{n-1}{n}D$	D
39. Change of grade	$r = \dfrac{g_2 - g_1}{L}$	g_1
40. Photogrammetry	$s = \dfrac{f}{H - h}$	h

Heating and ventilating technology

41. Partial water vapor pressure	$p_s = \dfrac{n_s}{n_s + n_a}p$	n_a
42. Dalton's rule	$V_T = \dfrac{(n_a + n_w)RT}{P}$	n_a
43. Adiabatic mixing	$\dfrac{h_2 - h_3}{h_3 - h_1} = \dfrac{G_1}{G_2}$	h_3
44. Degree of saturation	$H = \dfrac{S}{1 - (1 - S)f_s\dfrac{P_s}{P_a}}$	S
45. Mach number	$M^2 = 2\dfrac{p_1 - p_2}{kp_1}$	p_1
46. Thermal convection	$\dfrac{q}{A} = h_c(t_s - t_f)$	t_f
47. Thermal conduction	$R = \dfrac{\dfrac{1}{r_1} - \dfrac{1}{r_0}}{4\pi k}$	r_0
48. Combustion*	$A = \dfrac{34.56}{100}\left[\dfrac{C}{3} + \left(H - \dfrac{O}{8}\right) + \dfrac{S}{8}\right]$	H

*Note: O in this formula is not zero but the symbol for oxygen.

Title	Formula	Variable desired

49. Expansion tank

$$V_t = \frac{E}{\dfrac{P_a}{P_f} - \dfrac{P_a}{P_0}}$$

P_a

50. Chimney size

$$H = \frac{D_r}{2.96B_0\left(\dfrac{P_0}{T_0} - \dfrac{P_c}{T_c}\right) - \dfrac{0.184fp_cB_0V^2}{T_cd}}$$

P_c

6.05 / Stated problems

Stated problems, sometimes called verbal problems or word problems, are the essence of this course. In actual on-the-job situations, the engineer or team leader states only the known facts. The ability to develop a proper mathematical relationship from information pertaining to a specific situation is the most important aspect of all applied mathematics. The method of approach is the same regardless of how the algebraic relation is solved. Ability to quickly and easily derive a mathematical relationship for problems leading to first-degree equations in one variable guarantees that later equations involving more than one variable or terms of higher degree can be handled just as easily.

The noted mathematician G. Polya published a book* devoted exclusively to problem-solving techniques. First he stresses the importance of reading the entire problem to determine what the general subject is. Is it a problem about numbers, about investment, or perhaps about geometric relations? Then the problem should be reread to find out what information is given and what values are wanted. In many problems, a relation is most easily found when a letter is chosen to represent the answer to the question asked in the problem.

To reduce chances for error, Polya suggests always picking a meaningful letter for the variable. If a problem deals with two numbers, b for bigger and s for smaller might be used. If there is just one number, using n could indicate *number* and that *nothing* is known about the number. For geometric problems one might use the initial letter of the thing described; a for altitude, b for base, c for circumference, d for diameter, and so on. It is important that there be a complete statement of what the letter chosen represents. Statements should both identify the item and give the units used. For

---

* G. Polya, *How to Solve It*. Princeton, N.J.: Princeton University Press, 1945. (A 1948 paperback edition is available.)

example,

$$\text{Let } c = \text{time in hours for } car \text{ going one way}$$
$$\text{Then } c - 10 = \text{time in hours for motorcycle going one way}$$
$$\text{And } c + 20 = \text{time in hours for bicycle going one way}$$

The real key to solving a problem is finding a relationship. Polya suggests that you try to think of a related problem previously solved. What was done there and can it be applied to this new problem? For example, many problems involving two circles are solved by drawing a line through their centers. This same idea might be used in a new problem involving two or more circles.

Another excellent technique in getting a correct relationship is to write the words of the problem as a terse English sentence and then make direct substitutions under this sentence. For example,

product   is   ten more than   difference

$$b(24 - b) = 10 \quad + \quad b - (24 - b)$$

It is wise when setting up a relationship for a problem involving the words "larger," "smaller," "exceeds," "is less than," and so on that the smaller item be identified and something *added* to establish the equality. This technique tends to eliminate negative signs. If the relationship involves multiples such as "twice as big," "4 times as much," "tripled," and so on, pick as the variable the smallest item in order to avoid fractions.

Many of the problems met can be solved by remembering this simple memory device and understanding what it means:

Two gallons of gasoline at 40 cents per gallon costs 80 cents.

The 2 gallons represent an *amount*, a quantity. The 40 cents per gallon is a *rate*; this term can usually be recognized by the word "per," sometimes as *per*centage. The 80 cents represents a *total*. This kind of relationship can be

Table 6.3

Subject	Amount	×	Rate	=	Total
Travel	time traveling	×	speed per unit time	=	distance
Alloy	gross weight	×	purity of metal, %	=	weight of pure metal
Sales	number of items	×	price per item	=	total sales
Investment	amount invested	×	earning rate, %	=	income
Savings	principal	×	interest rate, %	=	interest
Work	time worked	×	output per unit of time	=	amount of job finished
Solution	volume of solution	×	strength of component, %	=	volume of pure component

written briefly as

$$\text{amount} \times \text{rate} = \text{total}$$

In symbols, $A \times R = T$. Table 6.3 provides a partial list of common relationships of this type.

For problems based on this multiplicative relationship, there are three methods for developing the actual equation to be solved, as will be illustrated in the examples that follow.

Method I Use of concise statements, useful for all problems.
Method II Use of a table, especially suited to mixtures, alloys, and financial types of problems.
Method III Use of a well-labeled sketch, particularly suited to motion problems.

Example 6.8
A man having $9000 invested at 5 per cent wants to convert part of this amount into high-yield second-mortgage bonds paying 8 per cent so that his total income will be $600. How much should he convert into mortgages?

SOLUTION (Using the method of statements)
(1) Select letter:

Let m = amount converted into mortgages at 8%
Then $9000 - m$ = amount retained at 5%

(2) Use formula: amount $\times$ per cent = income:

$$0.08m = \text{income from mortgages}$$

$$0.05 (9000 - m) = \text{income from bonds}$$

(3) Derive relation and solve:

$$\text{income from mortgages} + \text{income from bonds} = \text{total income}$$

$$0.08m + 0.05 (9000 - m) = 600$$

$$0.08m + 450 - 0.05m = 600$$

$$0.03m + 450 = 600$$

$$0.03m = 150$$

$$m = \$5000 \text{ (answer)}$$

(4) *Check*

$$0.08 (5000) = \$400$$

$$0.05 (4000) = \$200$$

$$\overline{\$600}$$

Example 6.9

Resolve Example 6.8 by using a table.

SOLUTION

(The table is always formed with four rows and four columns.)

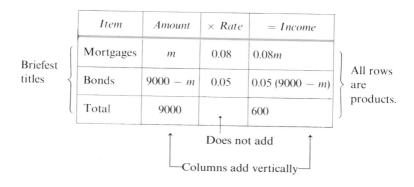

The equation to be solved is the sum of the fourth column:

$$0.08m + 0.05 (9000 - m) = 600$$

This equation is identical to that solved in Example 6.8 and the remainder of the work is not repeated.

For all problems involving percentages, the percentages should be written as decimals when entered in a table. For amounts less than $1 or amounts in dollars and cents, it is best to express all amounts in pennies instead of dollars in decimal form.

Some problems may involve more difficult arithmetical operations than those of Example 6.8. If a slide rule is used, only three significant figures can be obtained. In this case a check is established if the results agree when rounded off to three significant figures.

Example 6.10

Albany and Beacon are two towns, 240 miles apart. A motorist leaves Albany at 7 A.M. to drive to Beacon and averages 60 mph. Another motorist leaves Beacon for Albany at the same time, but he has motor trouble and averages only 40 mph. At what time do they meet? (Remember that if two motorists meet, it must be at the same clock time.)

SOLUTION   (Using a labeled sketch)
The uniform motion relation is

$$\text{time} \times \text{speed} = \text{distance} \qquad \text{or} \qquad T \cdot S = D$$

	Albany		Meeting		Beacon
	$0700 \rightarrow$				$\leftarrow 0700$
Time		t hr		t hr	
Speed		60 mph		40 mph	
Distance		$60t$		$40t$	
			240 miles		

The equation is obtained from the fact that the sum of the distances the motorists travel must equal the distance between the two cities, as may be seen from the sketch.

$$60t + 40t = 240$$
$$100t = 240$$
$$t = 2.4 \text{ hr} = 2 \text{ hr } 24 \text{ min}$$
$$\text{starting time} = 7 \text{ hr}$$

$$\text{meeting time} = 9 \text{ hr } 24 \text{ min}$$

Answer: They meet at 9:24 A.M.

Check:

$$2.4(60) = 144 \text{ miles}$$
$$2.4(40) = 96 \text{ miles}$$

$$\overline{240 \text{ miles}}$$

Note that the sketch for Example 6.10 is *not* a scaled sketch but rather a convenient method to display information so that relationships can be seen.

Example 6.11

Forty years ago, State College was 5 times older than City Hall. Ten years from now, State College will be only $\frac{5}{3}$ older than City Hall. When will State College celebrate its 100th birthday?

SOLUTION   (Using the method of statements)
This example illustrates the type of problem where it is not convenient to let a letter be the answer to the question. Instead a letter is chosen

to represent the age of one of the institutions because then the sentences can be directly translated into symbols. By choosing a letter as the age of the younger institution, a fraction can be avoided. Thus,

$$\text{Let } s = \text{age of City Hall now}$$

$$\text{Then } s - 40 = \text{age of City Hall 40 years ago}$$

$$5(s - 40) = \text{age of State College 40 years ago}$$

$$s + 10 = \text{age of City Hall 10 years from now}$$

and

$$5(s - 40) + 50 = 5s - 150 = \text{age of State College 10 years from now}$$

$$(40 + 10 = 50)$$

The ratio of ages 10 years from now is $\frac{5}{3}$, or

$$\frac{5s - 150}{s + 10} = \frac{5}{3}$$

$$15s - 450 = 5s + 50 \qquad \text{(clearing of fractions)}$$

$$10s = 500$$

$$s = 50$$

$$5(s - 40) = 5(50 - 40) = 50 \qquad \text{age of State College 40 years ago}$$

$$50 + 40 = 90 \qquad \text{age of State College now}$$

Since State College is 90 years old now, it will celebrate its 100th birthday 10 years from now.

Check:

Time	City Hall	College	
40 yr ago	10	50	ratio is 5 to 1
now	50	90	
10 yr from now	60	100	ratio is 5 to 3

Example 6.11 brings out two points. Note that the answer is not the value of the variable but requires one more simple step to obtain it. Also note that instead of trying to find the age of State College now and adding 10 to it, 50 years were added to the age 40 years ago. These types of variations do not require great mathematical skill, merely sound common sense.

Problem Set 6.5

Problems involving numbers

Example 6.12

A certain fraction has a numerator that is one less than the denominator. If 5 is added to the numerator and 4 is subtracted from the denominator, the new fraction becomes the integer 3. What is the original fraction?

SOLUTION

Let $\qquad n =$ numerator, since the numerator is the smaller number

Then $\qquad n + 1 =$ denominator

$$\text{original fraction} = \frac{n}{n + 1}$$

$$\text{new fraction} = \frac{n + 5}{n + 1 - 4} = \frac{n + 5}{n - 3} = 3$$

Clearing of fractions:

$$n + 5 = 3(n - 3)$$
$$n + 5 = 3n - 9$$
$$2n = 14$$
$$n = 7$$

Original fraction is $\frac{7}{8}$.

Check:

$$\frac{7 + 5}{8 - 4} = \frac{12}{4} = 3$$

1. If a certain number is increased by 2, then 3 times the new number equals 4 less than 4 times the original number. Find the original number.
2. If the difference between $\frac{4}{5}$ and $\frac{1}{3}$ of a certain number is 42, find the number.
3. Two less than 4 times a certain number is equal to 4 more than 3 times the number. Find the number.
4. The difference between two numbers is 6 and their quotient is equal to $\frac{2}{3}$. What are these two numbers?
5. If 42 is added to a certain number to obtain a sum and if 18 is subtracted from this same number to obtain a difference, the quotient obtained by dividing the sum by the difference is 4. Find this number.

6. One quarter of the excess of a certain number over 10 is one sixth of the number. Find the number.

7. The denominator of a fraction exceeds the numerator by 3. If the numerator and denominator are each increased by 5, the new fraction has the value $\frac{3}{4}$. Find the original fraction.

8. The denominator of a certain fraction is 2 more than twice the numerator. If the numerator is increased by 2 and if the denominator is tripled, the new fraction is $\frac{2}{9}$ less than the original fraction. What is the original fraction?

9. Find two consecutive even numbers whose squares differ by 212.

10. Find two consecutive odd numbers whose squares differ by 184.

Problems involving geometry

Example 6.13
Find the radius of the circle.

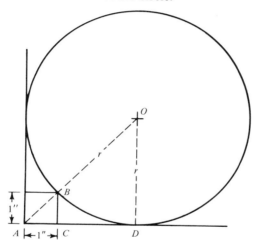

SOLUTION

In Chapter 4, the special 45°–45°–90° triangle was introduced. It has a hypotenuse approximately 1.414 times a leg. For the small triangle ABC, AB is 1.414 (1.0), or 1.414. For the large triangle AOD, $AO = r + 1.414$, by adding the two line segments. By using the property of the hypotenuse, $AO = 1.414r$. This gives the equation sought:

$$1.414r = r + 1.414$$

$$0.414r = 1.414$$

$$r = 3.42 \text{ in.}$$

The best check would be a scaled sketch, which does verify the radius computed.

11. A rectangle is 4 times as long as it is wide. If the perimeter is 160 ft, what are the dimensions of the rectangle?

12. The perimeter of a triangle is 78 ft. The longest side is 3 times the shortest. The remaining side is 6 ft longer than twice the shortest side. Find the length of each side.

13. Find the radius of a circle if the radius in feet is numerically the same as the area in square feet.

14. Twenty per cent of a fencepost should be in the ground for stability. The lower wire (horizontal) should be 1 ft above ground to permit farm dogs to pass under the fence. If the distance from the lower wire to the top of the post is 60 per cent of the length, how long should the post be?

15. Find the angles of a triangle if one angle is 4 times the second and 0.4 of the third.

16. Lots are often sold by the front foot—a foot of width on the street side. One lot containing 7200 sq ft sold for $120 per front foot. A more shallow lot, only $\frac{3}{4}$ as deep, contained 6300 sq ft and sold for $100 per front foot. The sale of these two lots netted $14,200. Find the dimensions of each lot. (Assume that each lot is a rectangle.)

17. One square has an area 54 sq in. larger and a perimeter 12 in. longer than another square. Find the side of each square.

18. Two rectangles each have their height half of their length. The difference in their perimeters is 15 in. and the difference in their areas is 95 sq in. What are the dimensions of each rectangle?

19. Two cylinders resting on a horizontal plane are just touching each other, as shown below. The larger cylinder has a radius twice that of the smaller one. If the horizontal distance between their centers is 5.66 in., what is the radius of the larger cylinder?

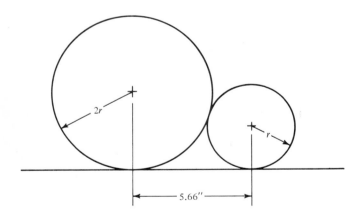

20. For the structure shown in the figure and using the given dimensions and slopes, find the length in feet and inches of members *AD* and *DC*.

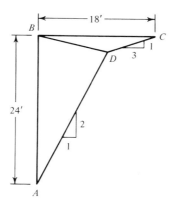

Problems involving uniform motion

Example 6.14

A flight from Portland to Sacramento, which makes two stops of 22 min each, takes a total time of 2 hr when traveling against a headwind. (A headwind blows against the direction of travel.) The nonstop flight from Sacramento to Portland traveling with the same wind, now a tailwind (a tailwind blows with the direction of travel), requires 1 hr 12 min. If the average speed in still air of both planes is 555 mph, find the speed of the wind.

SOLUTION

(1) Let w = speed of wind in mph. If speed of a craft in still $\begin{cases} \text{air} \\ \text{water} \end{cases}$ is x and speed of $\begin{cases} \text{wind} \\ \text{current} \end{cases}$ is y, then

$$x - y = \text{speed against the wind or water current}$$

$$x + y = \text{speed with the wind or water current}$$

Thus,

$$555 - w = \text{speed against the headwind}$$

$$555 + w = \text{speed with the tailwind}$$

(2) Using a sketch and the formula: rate × time = distance,

	Portland	Portland
Rate	$555 - w$	$555 + w$
Time	$2 - \dfrac{2(22)}{60} = \dfrac{19}{15}$	$1\frac{12}{60} = \frac{6}{5}$
Distance	$\frac{19}{15}(555 - w)$	$\frac{6}{5}(555 + w)$
	Sacramento	Sacramento

(3) Since the distances are equal,

$$\tfrac{6}{5}(555 + w) = \tfrac{19}{15}(555 - w)$$

$$18(555 + w) = 19(555 - w)$$

$$18w + 19w = 19(555) - 18(555)$$

$$37w = 555$$

$$w = 15 \text{ mph}$$

21. Jet planes cut 4 hr off the trip time of the propeller-driven planes on the San Francisco–Chicago run. The old planes averaged 250 mph and the jets average 650 mph.
(a) How long does the trip by jet take?
(b) What was the time for the trip by the old planes?
(c) How far apart are the two airports?
22. Two freight trains traveling the same length of time cover 300 and 350 miles, respectively. If the one train is traveling 8 mph slower than the other,
(a) Find their speeds.
(b) Find how long each has been traveling.
23. A plane made a flight with a 40-mph headwind in 4 hr. On the return trip, the wind increased to a 50-mph tailwind and the flight took only 3 hr 6 min. Find the still air speed of this plane.
24. A hurricane-hunter airplane has a speed in still air of 600 mph. A storm is reported due south of the airbase, and the airplane takes off with a tailwind of 20 mph. If the wind remains relatively constant on the basis of an average effect, and the mission is photographic so that the flight altitude is above the intense winds of the hurricane, how far from the airbase can this plane go if the plane must be back in 3 hr to permit processing the pictures for the next forecast period?
25. Selma and Taylor are 250 miles apart. A truck left Selma at 8 A.M. and traveled at an average speed of 48 mph, with a rest stop of 20 min after $1\tfrac{1}{2}$ hr of driving. A motorist left Taylor at 8 A.M. headed for Selma and he averaged 66 mph. What time did they pass each other?
26. A machine shop had some parts on order in a large city 225 miles away. An important repair job was being held up for lack of some of these parts, so the owner phoned and found that they had been sent that morning at 8 A.M. on the XYZ motor freight line. The owner decided to intercept the truck and was on his way by 10 A.M. He drove an average of 25 mph faster than the truck. When they met, there was a 15-min delay in getting the parts transferred. The owner was back at his shop at 12:15 P.M. Find the speed of the truck.
27. To get to a triangulation station, a survey party rowed upstream for 3 hr 20 min, then hiked uphill 6 miles to the station, and arrived at 12:20 P.M., somewhat hungry because they had left at 6 A.M. They finished

their survey work and headed back at 2 P.M. and were docked at 6 P.M. They could row in still water at 6 mph, walk uphill at 2 mph, and walk downhill at 3 mph. What was the rate of the current in the river?

28. A sound is heard at Station A $2\frac{1}{2}$ sec after it is heard at Station B, which is 5 miles due north of Station A. If sound travels in air at 1056 fps for the ambient temperature and the sound is known to come from a rocket test stand due east of Station B, find the distance to this test stand from Station B.

29. A forest-ranger station maintains a microphone in the water near the shoreline of a large lake to help detect illegal fishing with dynamite. When it detects a large sound impulse, it rings an alarm and starts an accurate timer. The ranger on duty notes that the sound of an explosion is heard 3.2 sec after the alarm sounds. The speed of sound in air that afternoon is 1140 fps; in water it is 4788 fps. How many feet from the station is the illegal fisherman?

30. Two stock cars traveling 60 and 75 mph, respectively, are moving in the same direction around a 2-mile oval track. If they were together at noon, what time do they next meet?

Problems involving mixtures

Example 6.15

Type 1A solder (ASTM Specification B32-21) contains 50 per cent tin and 50 per cent lead. Class 4A solder contains 37.5 per cent tin and 62.5 per cent lead. How many pounds of each are required to make 68 lb of solder containing 40 per cent tin?

SOLUTION (Use of a table is indicated, since this is a mixture problem.)

Item	Weight of Alloy	× Percentage of Tin	= Weight of Tin
Type 1A	$68 - x$	0.50	$0.50 (68 - x)$
Class 4A	x	0.375	$0.375x$
40% tin	68	0.40	$0.40 (68)$

Obtaining the equation from the fourth column,

$$0.50 (68 - x) + 0.375x = 0.40 (68)$$
$$34.00 - 0.50x + 0.375x = 27.20$$
$$-0.125x = -6.80$$
$$x = 54.4 \text{ lb of Class 4A}$$
$$68 - x = 13.6 \text{ lb of Type 1A}$$

(Note in this problem that the letter x was selected to represent the item having the more awkward percentage, thus simplifying the multiplication.)

31. Type 1A solder (ASTM Specification B32-21) contains 50 per cent tin and 50 per cent lead. Type 5A contains 33 per cent tin and 67 per cent lead. How many pounds of each are required to make 68 lb of solder containing 40 per cent tin?
32. Redimix grout is a mixture of sand and cement. If sand costs 55 cents for 100 lb and cement costs $1.90 for a 94-lb sack, what is the weight of sand and cement in a 40-lb Redimix bag that costs 37 cents to prepare? Give answers to the nearest half-pound.
33. Type 301 AISI stainless steel averages 7 per cent nickel; Type 316 averages 12 per cent nickel and Type 347 averages 11 per cent nickel. How many pounds of Type 301 should be combined with 800 lb of Type 316 to approximate the nickel content of Type 347?
34. How many pounds of yellow brass containing 65 per cent copper should be combined with 330 lb of commercial bronze containing 90 per cent copper to approximate low brass that contains 80 per cent copper?
35. An increase of 8 per cent in the methanol content of an antifreeze will depress the freezing point 18°F. A car has 14 per cent methanol in its cooling system, which holds 13 quarts (qt), and is safe to $+14°F$. How much of the current coolant must be drained out and replaced with methanol so that the car is safe to $-4°F$? (*Warning*: Do not ignore the loss of methanol as coolant is drained.)
36. When glycerol is used as the antifreeze agent, an increase of 12 per cent glycerol content depresses the freezing point 18°F. A car with 30 per cent glycerol in its 13-qt cooling system is safe to $+14°F$. How much coolant must be drained out and replaced with glycerol so that the car is safe to $-4°F$?
37. A paint manufacturer uses 16.9 lb of pigment to 83.1 lb vehicle for one product. If the cost of the finished product cannot exceed $397 for materials and if the vehicle costs 71 cents/lb, what is the maximum price that can be paid for the pigment?
38. If 2000 cc of 4 per cent alcohol was combined with 400 cc of 10 per cent alcohol, how much of a solution of 50 per cent alcohol should be added to make a solution of 20 per cent alcohol?
39. A student attended a college where an A was 4 grade points, a B was 3, and a C was 2. At the end of his first semester he obtained a GPA (grade-point average) of 3.33. He had twice as many units of A as of B. He had one less unit of C than B. How many units did he have in each grade?
40. A custodian had a 15- and a 25-gal tank. The first had 10 gal of water in it and the other 20 gal of water. Four gallons of an insecticide was added to *each* tank. A request was received for 5 gal of a 20 per cent spray. How many gallons should be drawn from each tank?

Problems involving work

Example 6.16

A sump on a construction site collects underground water at an average rate of 2 cfm. When the sump contains 200 cu ft of water, two pumps are actuated by a float switch. One pump alone could empty the sump in 2 hr; the other pump alone would require 4 hr. How long would it take both pumps working together to drain the sump?

SOLUTION

(Use formula: time worked × output per unit time = amount of job finished.)

Each hour, $60(2) = 120$ cu ft of water enter the sump. The large pump has an output rate of

$$\frac{200 + 2(120)}{2} = 220 \text{ cu ft/hr}$$

The small pump has an output rate of

$$\frac{200 + 4(120)}{4} = 170 \text{ cu ft/hr}$$

Let t = time in hours for both pumps to drain the sump.

Then
$$220t + 170t = 200 + 120t$$
$$270t = 200$$
$$t = 0.74\,h = 44\tfrac{1}{2}\,\text{min}$$

41. A master machinist can complete 20 pulleys in a regular 8-hr work day. His apprentice can produce 12. A rush order for 40 is received. How many hours overtime must they work to fill this order?

42. One survey party in rugged terrain averages 6 days to map a square mile. A new crew took 9 days to do the same job. If on a priority job both crews are used, how long would it take them to map a square mile?

43. A factory has two multiple drill presses. An order for 720 plates is received and given to an operator. Later the purchaser calls and offers to pay a premium for a quick delivery. After the first operator has worked for 2 hr and finished 160 plates, a second drill press begins operation. Four hours later the job was done. How long would it have taken each operator alone?

44. A bricklayer built a certain brick wall in 32 hr. He and a younger, less-experienced man volunteered to put up an identical wall only twice as long across the rear of a neighborhood playground. Together they took 38 hr 24 min to build this wall. How long would it have taken the younger man to build half of this wall by himself?

45. A new machine takes one third the time to complete the same amount of work as each of two older machines. On a certain rush order, all three machines were used, but one of the older ones broke down at the

end of 1 hr, when half of the work was completed. Find the time it took the other two machines to complete the work.

46. Three men volunteered to fry hamburgers for a union picnic lunch. Alone each would have taken 5 hr. The first man began at 10:00 A M., the next joined him at 10:20, and the third came at 10:40. What time did they finish?

47. One pipe can fill a certain water tank in 9 hr while a second pipe can fill this tank in 3 hr. Find the time it would take a third pipe to fill the tank so that when all three pipes are open, the tank is filled in $1\frac{1}{2}$ hr.

48. A 2-in. pipe is delivering 0.1 cfs and a $1\frac{1}{2}$-in. pipe is draining 0.06 cfs at a settling basin. An automatic switch opens a second $1\frac{1}{2}$-in. drain when the tank holds 240 cu ft.
   (a) How long a time elapses between the initial input of water and the first operation of the automatic switch?
   (b) If the settling basin has an automatic switch that closes the second drain when the tank holds 120 cu ft, how long is the second drain in operation?

49. A large battery is used to operate a monitoring device. It is charged by a selenium rectifier that could fully charge it in 6 hr. The control system turns off the rectifier when the battery is fully charged and turns it on when the ampere-hour capacity has fallen to 25 per cent of capacity. The drain from the monitoring system is constant and would completely discharge the battery in 10 hr. If the battery is fully charged at the start of a test period, find the time that elapses until it is again fully charged.

50. A large storage tank is connected to three sources of water. A well is connected by a 2-in. pipe and can fill the tank in 6 hr. A nearby stream is connected by a $2\frac{1}{2}$-in. pipe and can fill the tank in 3 hr. A stream condensing pool is connected by a $1\frac{1}{2}$-in. pipe and can fill the tank in 10 hr 12 min. If all three sources are used, how long would it take to fill a half-empty tank? Give your answer in hours, minutes, and seconds.

Miscellaneous problems

51. Four years ago a father was twice as old as his son. Eight years from now the father will be but $\frac{8}{5}$ as old. How old is the father now?

52. If Fahrenheit and Celsius temperatures are related by $F = \frac{9}{5}C + 32$, at what temperature are the readings alike?

53. A can was used to collect shipping bolts received on incoming orders. After several months an inventory was taken. The can contained 100 bolts. Some were $\frac{3}{16}$-in. bolts worth 8 cents each, some were $\frac{1}{4}$-in. bolts worth 12 cents each, and some were $\frac{5}{16}$-in. bolts worth 15 cents each. The number of $\frac{3}{16}$-in. bolts and $\frac{1}{4}$-in. bolts turned out to be the same. If the whole collection was worth $12.80, how many bolts of each size were in the can?

54. In Alaska there are extensive coal mines near the one and only railroad. Coal prices at the mine vary, depending largely on the distance from

Anchorage, Alaska. One mine 190 miles north of Anchorage charges $17.75/ton while another mine 70 miles north of Anchorage charges $17.55/ton. Shipping coal costs $\frac{1}{4}$ cent/ton-mile. Find the distance from Anchorage on the railroad between the two mines where the cost from either mine is the same.

55. Resistances in parallel can be replaced by a single resistance whose reciprocal is the sum of the reciprocals of each resistance in parallel. If a circuit has three resistors in parallel, the second being twice the number of ohms as in the first, and the third being half the number of ohms of the first, find the ohms in each resistor if the total circuit has an 8-Ω resistance.

56. A contractor who had set $640 aside to provide guides over a 4-hr period each day found that the actual cost was $20/day higher than he had estimated. He therefore curtailed the number of days he employed them by 25 per cent and ended up with $40 unspent. What was his original number of days that he planned to furnish guides and how much had he planned to pay them per day?

57. In mechanics (also called statics) the moment of any force about a moment center is the product of the magnitude of the force and the perpendicular distance from that force to the moment center. In the figure below, find the distance d from the moment center at A for the 500-lb force so that equilibrium exists; that is, there is a zero total moment. (Counterclockwise moments are positive and clockwise moments are negative.)

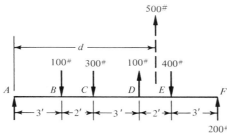

58. Find the distance x to produce equilibrium. Use point A as the moment center.

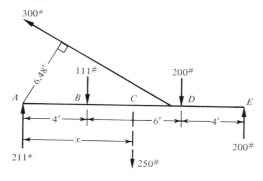

59. A local resident, foreseeing the growth of a city, bought a large tract of land for $640,000. In 20 years the land doubled in value. The owner sold a portion of it for $576,000 and had 880 acres left. Find what he originally paid per acre and what acreage he bought.

60. If land for a subdivision can be purchased at $5000/acre when bought in large tracts, what acreage must a speculator buy if he wants a $1\frac{1}{2}$-acre homesite without cost to himself, and expects to sell the remaining property at $2500 for each quarter-acre lot after spending $2500/acre for streets, sewers, and other improvements?

6.06 / Linear inequalities

The set of real numbers possesses order; that is, if any two real numbers a and b are compared, a is either greater than b, equal to b, or less than b. If a is greater than b, then point a is to the right of point b on the number line. If a is equal to b, then point a and point b are identical. If a is less than b, then point a is to the left of point b.

Up to now in this chapter only the equality relation has been considered. However, in daily living there are numerous cases where the nonequal or order relations, called **inequalities,** are met. For example, driving on a freeway, a person can be arrested for driving below a set minimum speed or for exceeding a set maximum speed. In traffic-flow studies for special sites, such as long bridges or tunnels, the maximum capacity is maintained when the traffic flow is kept between calculated minimum and maximum speeds. If the speed of a vehicle is designated as s, the cases just cited could be written

	Symbol	*Meaning*
Obstructing traffic	$s < 20$	Speed is less than 20 mph
Speeding	$s > 70$	Speed is greater than 70 mph
Ideal traffic flow	$30 < s < 60$	Speed is greater than 30 mph and less than 60 mph

Inequalities are used in programming the modern electronic computer. The IF statement in one of the most widely used programming languages asks "Is $x > y$, $x = y$, or $x < y$?" For each possibility, the computer has instructions as to what step to execute next.

Table 6.4 summarizes those inequalities most commonly met.

As with equations, many inequalities are **conditional**; that is, they are true only for certain values of the replacement set. For example, the inequality $x + 4 > 10$ is true only for those real numbers greater than 6. In this example the solution set involves an inequality $\{x \mid x > 6\}$. Other

Table 6.4

Symbol	Meaning
$x > a$	x is greater than a
$x < a$	x is less than a
$x \geq a$	x is greater than a or equal to a
$x \leq a$	x is less than a or equal to a
$x \not> a$	x is not greater than a
$x \not< a$	x is not less than a
$a < x < b$	x is between a and b
$x > 0$	x is positive
$x < 0$	x is negative
$x \not> 0$	x is not positive
$x \not< 0$	x is not negative

inequalities are always true no matter what replacement values are used, such as $x^2 + 3 > 0$. The latter types are called **absolute inequalities.**

The number line provides a means to visualize inequalities. For example, the graph of the inequality $x < 4$ (all real numbers less than 4) is shown in Figure 6.1.

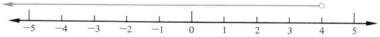

Figure 6.1

$x < 4$

The open circle over the numeral 4 means that 4 is *not* in the solution set. The graph is the half-line starting at 4 (but not including 4) and extending indefinitely to the left, as indicated by the arrow.

The graph of the inequality $x \geq -1$ (all real numbers greater than or equal to -1) is shown in Figure 6.2.

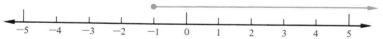

Figure 6.2

$x \geq -1$

The solid circle over the numeral -1 means that -1 *is* in the solution set. The graph is the ray starting at -1 (including -1) and extending indefinitely to the right, as indicated by the arrow.

The graph of the inequality $-1 < x \leq 4$ (all numbers between -1 and 4 and including 4) is shown in Figure 6.3.

Figure 6.3

$-1 < x \leq 4$

Inequalities, unlike equations, are not symmetric. In an equation, if $a = b$, then $b = a$. However, in an inequality, if $a > b$, then $b \ngtr a$. On the other hand, whenever $a > b$, it is proper to write $b < a$; that is, if a is larger than b, then b is less than a.

When comparing two inequalities, if the inequality symbols point in the same direction, the inequalities are said to be of the **same order** or the **same sense**. For example, $x + 4 > 10$ and $x > 6$ are inequalities of the same sense. If the inequality symbols point in opposite directions, the inequalities are said to be of the **opposite order** or the **opposite sense**. For example, $a > b$ and $b < a$ are inequalities of the opposite sense.

To solve conditional inequalities, there are inequality axioms similar to the equality axioms but with some modifications. No change is needed for the addition or subtraction of equal quantities to both members of an inequality.

$$\text{If } 5 > 3, \text{ then } 5 + 2 > 3 + 2$$

$$\text{If } 5 > 3, \text{ then } 5 - 2 > 3 - 2$$

$$\text{If } 6 < 9, \text{ then } 6 + 9 < 9 + 9$$

$$\text{If } 6 < 9, \text{ then } 6 - 9 < 9 - 9$$

For the multiplication and division operations, an inequality of the same sense will result only when both sides are multiplied or divided by a *positive* number.

If $5 > 3$, $2(5) > 2(3)$ or $10 > 6$. But $(-2)5 \ngtr (-2)3$ since this yields $-10 > -6$, which is not true. On the other hand, if $5 > 3$, $(-2)5 < (-2)3$, since $-10 < -6$. When both sides of an inequality are multiplied or divided by the same *negative number*, the sense of the inequality is changed.

As for an equation, the actual technique of solving a conditional inequality can be put into standard steps. The objective is to obtain the variable on the left side and only numerals on the right side.

Procedure for Solving Linear Inequalities
(1) Simplify each side; that is, remove grouping symbols and reduce fractions to lowest terms, if this is necessary.
(2) a. Add or subtract the same number on both sides, or
    b. Multiply or divide both sides by the same *positive* number, or
    c. Multiply or divide both sides by the same *negative* number *and reverse the sense* of the inequality.
(3) State the solution set.
(4) Check in the original statement, using an integral value of the variable, if possible, that is in the solution set and that is close to the numerical value stated in the solution.
(*Note:* The order of the operations in step 2 depends on the particular inequality being solved. This will vary from problem to problem.)

Example 6.17

Solve $\dfrac{2(x-3)}{5} > 4$ and graph the solution set on a number line.

SOLUTION

(1) Remove parentheses: $\dfrac{2x-6}{5} > 4$

(2) Multiply by 5: $2x - 6 > 20$

    Add 6: $2x > 26$

    Divide by 2: $x > 13$

(3) The solution set is $\{x \mid x > 13\}$.

Figure 6.4
$x > 13$

(4) Check, using $x = 14$:

$$\frac{2(x-3)}{5} = \frac{2(14-3)}{5} = \frac{2(11)}{5} = \frac{22}{5} = 4\tfrac{2}{5} \text{ and } 4\tfrac{2}{5} > 4.$$

(*Note:* 4 is not greater than 4. If 13 is used to check, the result is $4 > 4$, which is not true.)

Example 6.18

Solve $5(4 - 3x) < 7(x + 4)$.

SOLUTION

(1) Remove parentheses: $20 - 15x < 7x + 28$

(2) Subtract 20: $-15x < 7x + 8$

    Subtract $7x$: $-22x < 8$

    Divide by -22 *and* reverse sense: $x > -\dfrac{8}{22}$

$$x > -\frac{4}{11}$$

(3) The solution set is $\left\{x \mid x > -\dfrac{4}{11}\right\}$.

(4) Check, using $x = 1$:

$$5(4 - 3x) = 5[4 - 3(1)] = 5 \cdot 1 = 5$$
$$7(x + 4) = 7(1 + 4) = 7(5) = 35$$

$5 < 35$ is true.

Example 6.19

Solve $\dfrac{5 - 2x}{3} \geq 4$ and graph the solution set on a number line.

SOLUTION
(The $\geq$ and $\leq$ inequalities are solved in exactly the same way as the $>$ and $<$ inequalities.)

(1) No simplification is necessary: $\qquad\qquad \dfrac{5 - 2x}{3} \geq 4$

(2) Multiply by 3: $\qquad\qquad\qquad\qquad\quad 5 - 2x \geq 12$

    Subtract 5: $\qquad\qquad\qquad\qquad\qquad -2x \geq 7$

    Divide by -2 and reverse sense: $\qquad\quad x \leq -\dfrac{7}{2}$

(3) The solution set is $\left\{ x \mid x \leq -\dfrac{7}{2} \right\}$.

Figure 6.5
$x \leq \frac{7}{2}$

(4) Check, using $x = -4$:

$$\frac{5 - 2x}{3} = \frac{5 - 2(-4)}{3} = \frac{5 + 8}{3} = 4\tfrac{1}{3}$$

and $4\tfrac{1}{3} \geq 4$ is true since $4\tfrac{1}{3} > 4$.

Check, using $x = -\dfrac{7}{2}$:

$$\frac{5 - 2x}{3} = \frac{5 - 2(-7/2)}{3} = \frac{5 + 7}{3} = 4$$

and $4 \geq 4$ is true since $4 = 4$.

Example 6.20

Solve $-2 \le \dfrac{3x - 2}{4} \le 2$ and graph the solution set on a number line.

SOLUTION

(This is actually a combination of two inequalities:

$$-2 \le \frac{3x - 2}{4} \quad and \quad \frac{3x - 2}{4} \le 2$$

Thus, there are two problems to solve. However, for the "less than" relation and *only* for this relation, both of these can be solved at the same time, as shown below.)

(1) Given: $\qquad\qquad\qquad -2 \le \dfrac{3x - 2}{4} \le 2$

(2) Multiply by 4: $\qquad\quad -8 \le 3x - 2 \le 8$

      Add 2: $\qquad\qquad\quad\; -6 \le 3x \le 10$

      Divide by 3: $\qquad\quad\; -2 \le x \le \dfrac{10}{3}$

(3) The solution set is $\left\{ x \mid -2 \le x \le \dfrac{10}{3} \right\}$.

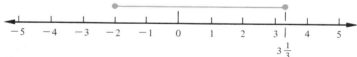

Figure 6.6
$-2 \le x \le \frac{10}{3}$

(4) Check, using $x = 3$:

$$\frac{3x - 2}{4} = \frac{3(3) - 2}{4} = \frac{7}{4} = 1\tfrac{3}{4}$$

and $-2 \le 1\tfrac{3}{4} \le 2$ is true.

6.07 / Absolute-value relations

The concept of absolute value was introduced in Chapter 1 as a convenient way to describe distances on a number line. In Figure 6.7 it may be seen that point 4 and point -4 are on opposite sides of the origin but their distances from the origin is the same; that is, $|4| = |-4| = 4$.

If $a > b$, point a is to the right of point b and the difference $a - b$, being positive, is the distance between these two points. For example, $-2 > -5$ and $-2 - (-5) = -2 + 5 = 3$ is the distance between point -2 and point -5. (See Figure 6.7.)

Figure 6.7
Absolute values

On the other hand, if $a < b$, point a is to the left of point b and the difference $a - b$, being negative, cannot designate the distance. However, the absolute value of this difference $|a - b|$ is positive and can be used as the distance. For example, $3 < 5$ and $|3 - 5| = |-2| = 2$ is the distance between point 3 and point 5. (See Figure 6.7.)

In general, $|a - b|$ is the *distance* between point a and point b no matter if point a is to the left or the right of point b.

A more precise way of stating that the absolute value of a number is the number stripped of its sign is given in the following definition.

Definition of Absolute Value $|x|$

$$|x| = x \qquad \text{if } x \geq 0$$

$$|x| = -x \qquad \text{if } x < 0$$

The definition states that if a number is positive or zero, its absolute value is that number. For example, $|5| = 5$ and $|0| = 0$. It also states that if a number is negative, its absolute value is the addition inverse (opposite) of that number. For example, $|-5| = -(-5) = 5$.

If a variable appears within the absolute-value symbol, it is possible for the number inside to be either positive or negative. This means that in the solution of an equation or inequality involving absolute value, there are always two cases to be considered. The absolute-value term is replaced first by whatever is inside the symbol and then second by the negative of what is inside. Two equations (or two inequalities) result and each of these is solved in turn.

Example 6.21

Solve $|3x - 6| = 9$.

SOLUTION

Case 1	*Case 2*
$|3x - 6| = 3x - 6$	$|3x - 6| = -(3x - 6)$
$3x - 6 = 9$	$-(3x - 6) = 9$
$3x = 15$	$3x - 6 = -9$
$x = 5$	$3x = -3$
	$x = -1$

The solution set is $\{5, -1\}$.

Check: If $x = 5$:

$$|3x - 6| = |3(5) - 6| = |15 - 6| = |9| = 9$$

If $x = -1$:

$$|3x - 6| = |3(-1) - 6| = |-3 - 6| = |-9| = 9$$

Example 6.22

Solve $\left|\dfrac{2x - 7}{3}\right| > 2$ and graph the solution set on a number line.

SOLUTION

Case 1	*Case 2*
$\dfrac{2x - 7}{3} > 2$	$-\left(\dfrac{2x - 7}{3}\right) > 2$
$2x - 7 > 6$	$\dfrac{2x - 7}{3} < -2$
$2x > 13$	$2x - 7 < -6$
$x > \frac{13}{2}$	$2x < 1$
$x > 6\frac{1}{2}$	$x < \frac{1}{2}$

The solution set is $\{x \mid x < \frac{1}{2} \text{ or } x > 6\frac{1}{2}\}$.

Figure 6.8

$x < \frac{1}{2}$ or $x > 6\frac{1}{2}$

Check: Using $x = -1$:

$$\left| \frac{2(-1) - 7}{3} \right| = \left| \frac{-9}{3} \right| = |-3| = 3 \text{ and } 3 > 2 \text{ is true}$$

Using $x = 7$:

$$\left| \frac{2(7) - 7}{3} \right| = \left| \frac{7}{3} \right| = 2\tfrac{1}{3} \text{ and } 2\tfrac{1}{3} > 2 \text{ is true}$$

Example 6.23
Solve $|7 - 2x| \le 3$ and graph the solution set on a number line.

SOLUTION
Since this is a "less than" relation, both cases may be solved at the same time. First note, however, that $|7 - 2x| = |-(7 - 2x)| = |2x - 7|$, and thus the problem can be rewritten as

$$|2x - 7| \le 3$$

This technique simplifies the problem by eliminating the minus sign in front of the variable term. Combining the two cases,

$$-3 \le 2x - 7 \le 3$$

Add 7: $\qquad\qquad\qquad\quad 4 \le 2x \le 10$

Divide by 2: $\qquad\qquad\qquad 2 \le x \le 5$

The solution set is $\{x \mid 2 \le x \le 5\}$.

Figure 6.9
$2 \le x \le 5$

Check: For $x = 2$:

$|7 - 2x| = |7 - 2(2)| = 3$ and $3 \le 3$ is true.

For $x = 4$:

$|7 - 2x| = |7 - 2(4)| = |-1| = 1$ and $1 \le 3$ is true.

For $x = 5$:

$|7 - 2x| = |7 - 2(5)| = |7 - 10| = |-3| =: 3$ and $3 \le 3$ is true.

Problem Set 6.6

1–20

Find the solution set, check by using an integer near the critical value, and graph the solution set on a number line.

1. $\dfrac{2x - 5}{3} > 1$

2. $\dfrac{3x + 5}{7} \geq 2$

3. $\dfrac{5(3 - 2x)}{4} \geq 3 - x$

4. $8 - 3x > 2(x - 2)$

5. $2 < 2x + 1 < 8$

6. $-3 < 3x + 2 \leq 7$

7. $-3 \leq 1 - 2x < 5$

8. $1 \leq 1 - 4x \leq 17$

9. $\dfrac{4}{(2x + 1)^2} \geq \dfrac{9}{(3x - 2)^2}$

10. $\dfrac{x + 1}{x} + \dfrac{2x + 2}{x^2} > \dfrac{3x - 1}{3x}$

11. $|x - 2| = 5$

12. $|x + 4| = 7$

13. $|5 + 3x| = 2$

14. $|6 - \frac{1}{4}x| = \frac{3}{4}$

15. $|x - 2| > 2$

16. $|x + 3| < 3$

17. $4|2x - 3| \leq 16$

18. $6|3x + 7| \geq 12$

19. $|8 - 5x| < 7$

20. $|9 - 4x| > 1$

21. To close the sale of a mine, it was agreed that five samples must average between 10 and 15 per cent metallic ore. If the first four samples ran 13.2, 9.7, 8.6, and 14.2 per cent, what is the permissible range for the last sample?

22. The Scleroscope and the Brinell hardness tests of metal are approximately related by

$$S = \tfrac{1}{8}B + 3$$

For Scleroscope readings ranging from 20 to 30, what is the matching range of Brinell numbers?

23. A measurement written as $m = k \pm e$ can also be written as the inequality $k - e \leq m \leq k + e$. For example, $R = 645 \pm 3$ can also be written as $645 - 3 \leq R \leq 645 + 3$ or $642 \leq R \leq 648$. Write each of the following measurements as inequalities.
(a) $t = 23.5 \pm 0.2$
(b) $P = 1.78 \pm 0.01$
(c) $q = (8.32 \pm 0.5) \times 10^{-9}$
(d) $v = (6.91 \pm 0.25) \times 10^{12}$

24. Express each of the relations in Problem 23 by using the absolute-value symbol. For example, for $R = 645 \pm 3$, this becomes $|R - 645| \leq 3$.

25. Express as an inequality the measure of angle C of a triangle if angle $A = 25°$ and angle B is such that
   (a) $0° < B \leq 90°$ (c) $120° \leq B < 180°$
   (b) $90° \leq B < 180°$ (d) $45° \leq B \leq 90°$
26. In constructing a 45°–45°–90° triangle with one leg exactly 4 ft long, it is necessary that the perimeter be correct to within $\frac{1}{16}$ in.
   (a) Find the range of values allowable in the measurement of each of the other two sides.
   (b) Find the range of values in the computation of the area.
27. Two resistors in parallel have a total resistance R given by

$$\frac{1}{R} = \frac{1}{R_1} + \frac{1}{R_2}$$

If $R_1 = 20\,\Omega$, what values are possible for R_2 so that R is between 10 and 15 Ω?
28. A contractor must get a certain job done in four or less 8-hr days. One laborer could do the job alone in 25 days. Working conditions will not permit over 15 men on the site. Union rules require a 6-man minimum crew. All men must be hired for a full 8-hr day, even if there is less than a full 8-hr of work.
   (a) Write an inequality that expresses the minimum and maximum number of laborers that can be used, assuming that all laborers work at the same rate.
   (d) Determine the number of laborers and working days that produce the least excess man-hours.

6.08 / Chapter Review

1. An equation is a statement stating that whatever is to the left of an equal sign names the same thing as whatever is to the right of the sign.
2. Equations can be true or false or conditional statements. Statements that are always true for all values of the variable are called identities. Statements that are only true for selected values of the variable are called conditional or open equations.
3. Conditional equations are solved by finding the values that make them true statements. These values are called the roots or solutions of an equation and are said to satisfy the equation. All roots of an equation form the solution set.
4. Solution sets may be empty, have just one element, or have many elements. Some values may not be admissible as solutions according to the conditions imposed by the problem.

5. Conditional linear equations in one variable are solved by applying the equality axioms. Roots so found are substituted in the original equation as a check.

6. Literal equations are solved as all other conditional equations by selecting the desired literal term as the variable and treating all others as constants.

7. Verbal problems are practical applications of algebra. Common sense is the most important factor in obtaining correct solutions. Techniques taught in this chapter will solve most verbal problems met during the remainder of the course.

8. Inequalities recognize that given two unequal real numbers, one is always greater than the other. Solving conditional inequalities is very similar to solving conditional equations if only positive multipliers and divisors are used. Should a negative multiplier or divisor be used, the sense of the inequality is reversed.

9. Absolute-value equations and inequalities are solved by replacing the absolute-value term first by what is inside the absolute value symbol and second by the negative of what is inside the absolute-value symbol and then solving the resulting relations.

Problem Set 6.7 (Chapter Review)

1. Solve for x: $(x - 6)(x + 6) = x(x - 9) - 3(x - 44)$.
2. Solve for r: $0.1r - 1.1 = 1.1 - 0.1r$.
3. Sound travels approximately 1080 fps and light travels 186,000 mps. If thunder is heard 5 sec after lightning is seen, how many miles away is the storm? Give your answer to the nearest tenth.
4. Divide 144 into five parts such that the first increased by one third of itself, the second less 24, the third plus 30, the fourth multiplied by 8, and the fifth divided by $\frac{1}{4}$ are all equal.
5. Solve for s:

$$\frac{2s}{4s^2 - 9} = \frac{3}{2s - 3} + \frac{3}{4s^2 - 9}$$

6. Three common alloys used in the printing industry are

	Tin, %	Antimony, %	Lead, %
Electrotype metal	3	3	94
Linotype metal	4	12	84
Monotype metal	8	16	76

In an emergency, it is decided to approximate linotype metal, temporarily not available, by combining the other two. The antimony content, which influences the hardness, is deemed critical.

(a) Determine how much of the other metals to use to produce 600 lb of a 12 per cent antimony alloy.

(b) Find the percentage of tin and lead in that alloy.

7. Solve:

$$\frac{2(3x - 5)}{7} - 2 \text{ is positive}$$

8. A 16-qt cooling system contains 20 per cent ethylene glycol and is safe to $+16°F$. To make the coolant safe to $-12°F$, the ethylene content must be raised to 40 per cent. How much antifreeze must be drained and replaced with pure ethylene glycol to reach this level?

9. In air conditioning, the usual working range of temperatures is from 60 to 80°F. If a contract is obtained for a European country using the Celsius scale, write the inequality for the corresponding range of Celsius temperatures. Use $F = \frac{9}{5}C + 32$. Express the final result using integers so that the inequality includes the given range of temperatures.

10. A new study of viscosity in rotating fluids revealed positive and negative viscosities. In deriving part of the data the calculation sheet read

$$\left| \frac{7 - 4v}{3} \right| \leq 5$$

Find the range of values for the viscosity, v, under these test conditions.

11. In photoelasticity, the observed stress is

$$\sigma_2 = \frac{F}{1 - \mu}[1.5(1 + \mu)N_0 - (2 + \mu)N_n]$$

Find the value of Poisson's ratio μ.

12. The form factor for a hollow rectangular beam of width t_2 is

$$F = 0.5 + 0.5\left[\frac{k(t_2 - t_1)}{t_2} + \frac{t_1}{t_2}\right]$$

Find an expression for t_2.

Relations, functions, and their graphs

7.01 / Basic concepts

Consider a simple equation such as $2x - 12 = y$. If a solution were to be attempted by selecting random values for x and calculating the result, this would be the same as finding pairs of values, a value for x and a corresponding value for y so that the equation $2x - 12 = y$ becomes a true statement. There are infinitely many pairs of values that make the above equation true, since x may be any real number and since multiplying any real number by 2 and then subtracting 12 always produces a real number for y. Let set P represent all possible pairs of values for x and y that *satisfy this equation*: that is, that make it true. The symbol (x, y) designates an **ordered pair**, since it is agreed that the first value (also called the first component) will always be the value for x and the second value (or second component) will always be the value for y. Now set P can be written:

$$P = \{(x, y) \mid y = 2x - 12\}$$

In the dictionary sense of the word, there is obviously some sort of relationship between x and y in the above example. Mathematicians call this kind of relationship a *relation*. If the universal set is the set of real numbers (R), a **relation** is defined as a subset of the infinite set of ordered pairs of real numbers.

The **domain** of a relation is the set of real numbers that are assigned as values of the variable x. The **range** of a relation is the set of real numbers that are assigned as values of the variable y.

For the relation P above, the domain is R and the range is R.

As another example, consider air temperatures and the related work outputs of a healthy male. Although theoretically the air temperatures may span from $-460°F$ to an infinite positive value, there would be no valid meaning for temperatures below $-40°F$ or above $130°F$, the approximate limits of human endurance. In this case, the domain is the set of real numbers from -40 to 130; that is, those values corresponding to practical temperatures. The range is the set of real numbers representing the related work outputs.

A particular relation may be defined by an equation such as $2x - 12 = y$, by listing all the ordered pairs of the relation, or by other methods that will be presented later in this chapter. The method for finding the second component of an ordered pair given the first component is called the **rule of correspondence**, or, if there is no ambiguity, just the rule.

A **function** is a relation such that there is exactly one second component for each first component. Since a function is a relation, it has a domain, a range, and a rule of correspondence.

Example 7.1
For the relation defined by the rule $y = \sqrt{x}$:
(a) State the domain.
(b) State the range.
(c) List the ordered pairs of integers that belong to the relation and such that $-10 \le x \le 10$.

SOLUTION
(a) The domain is the set of nonnegative real numbers; that is, $x \ge 0$.
(b) The range is the set of nonnegative real numbers; that is, $y \ge 0$.
(c) $\{(0,0), (1,1), (4,2), (9,3)\}$.

Example 7.2
A certain finite relation is defined by the following list of ordered pairs:

$$\{(1,1), (-1,1), (2,4), (-2,4), (3,9), (-3,9)\}$$

(a) State the domain of the relation.
(b) State the range of the relation.
(c) State whether or not the relation is a function.

SOLUTION
(a) The domain is the set of the first components of the ordered pairs; that is, $\{-3, -2, -1, 1, 2, 3\}$.
(b) The range is the set of the second components of the ordered pairs; that is, $\{1, 4, 9\}$.

(c) The relation is a function since exactly one second component is paired with each first component.

Example 7.3
State whether the relation below is a function or not.

$$\{(1,1), (1,-1), (4,2), (4,-2), (9,3), (9,-3)\}$$

SOLUTION
The relation is *not* a function since each first component is paired with two second components. It should be noted that, although in this case each first component is paired with two second components, there only needs to be one first component paired with more than one second component to disqualify the relation from being a function.

Problem Set 7.1

1–12
For the given defining rule, (a) state the domain and range of the relation, (b) state whether or not the relation is a function, and (c) list the ordered pairs of integers that belong to the relation and such that $-9 \le x \le 0$ and $-4 \le y \le 4$.

1. $y = 2x$
2. $y = \frac{1}{2}x$

3. $y > \dfrac{x}{5}$

4. $y < \dfrac{x}{6}$

5. $y = x^2$
6. $x = y^3$

7. $y^2 = x$
8. $y^2 = -x$

9. $y = \sqrt[3]{x}$

10. $y = \sqrt[3]{-x}$

11. $x = |y|$
12. $y = |2x|$

13–20
Determine if the given data represent merely a relation or a function, when the first quantity listed is taken as the first component of the relation.

13. In 1969 local parcel post rates were 4 cents for 2 oz, 2 cents for each additional ounce up to and including 15 oz, and from then on, according to the table:

Weight, lb	2	3	4	5	6	7	8	9	10
Postage, cents	40	40	45	45	45	50	50	55	55

14. To mail a 20-lb package, the post office charges as follows:

Zone destination	Local	1	2	3	4	5
Postage, cents	75	140	140	165	195	250

15. Antifreeze is sold by the quart. The service-station table shows the following data for a 12-qt cooling system currently protected to $+10°F$:

Safe temp., °F	0	-10	-20	-30	-40	-50
Quarts added	2	2	3	4	5	5

16. The change in density of water with temperature is

Density	0.999 87	0.999 93	0.999 97	0.999 99	1.000 00
Temp., °C	0	1	2	3	4
Density	0.999 99	0.999 97	0.999 93	0.999 88	
Temp., °C	5	6	7	8	

17. An electromagnet was being magnetized by an electric current measured in amperes per meter, and the magnetism measured in webers per square meter. The test results were

Amp/m	0	250	500	750	1000	750	500	250	0
Webers/m²	0	0.8	1.2	1.4	1.5	1.4	1.3	1.2	1.0

18. An airfoil was tested in a wind tunnel with these results:

Lift, C_L	-0.8	-0.4	0	$+0.4$	$+0.8$	$+1.2$
Drag, C_D	0.020	0.012	0.0095	0.0105	0.0145	0.0305

19. A NASA air-temperature/elevation test gave these results:

Air temp., °F	59	0	-68	-68	0	$+110$	$+170$
Altitude, thousands of ft	0	15	32	106	120	150	165

20. A stress-deformation plot for steel gave

Unit deformation, in./in.	0.0000	0.0005	0.0010	0.0015	0.0020
Stress, psi	0	16,000	31,000	40,000	40,000

Figure 7.1
The XY coordinate plane

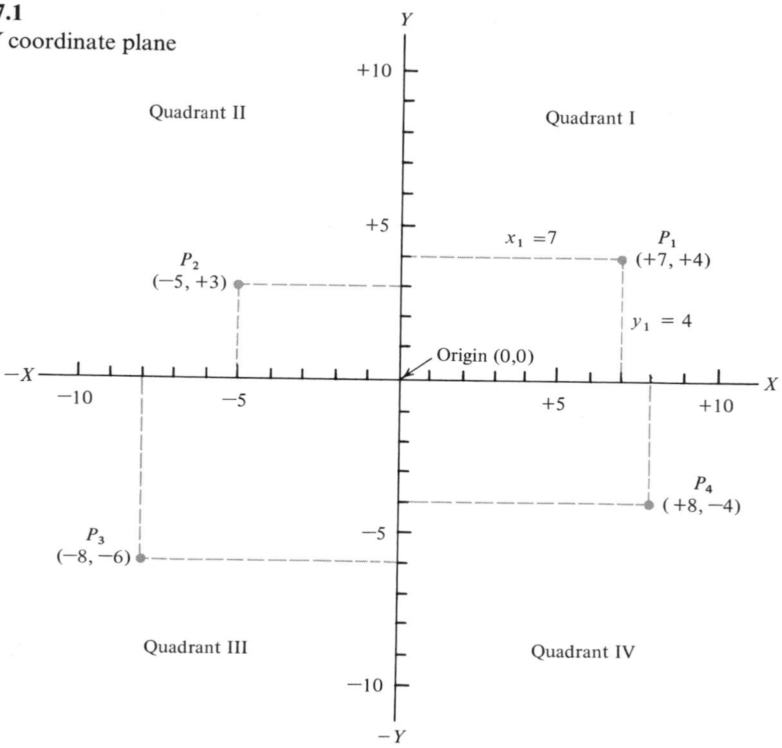

7.02 / Rectangular coordinates

The set of ordered pairs of real numbers is graphically illustrated by using a plane infinite in size to obtain a two-dimensional space. Starting with a horizontal number line, another number line is drawn perpendicular to the original one, with the two lines intersecting at their zero points, as shown in Figure 7.1.

The two perpendicular number lines are called the **axes** and their point of intersection is called the **origin**. In abstract algebraic problems where x is the independent variable and y the dependent variable, the horizontal number line is called the X *axis* and the vertical number line is called the Y *axis*.

A point in the coordinate plane thus produced is associated with a given pair of real numbers (x_1, y_1) by drawing a vertical line through the point x_1 on the X axis and a horizontal line through the point y_1 on the Y axis. These two lines intersect in exactly one point, the graph of the ordered pair (x_1, y_1). The values x_1 and y_1 are called the **rectangular coordinates** of the point on the plane. The x coordinate is also called the **abscissa** and the y coordinate the **ordinate**.

If a point on the coordinate plane is given, exactly one ordered pair of real numbers is assigned to this point by drawing a horizontal line and a vertical line through the point. The intersection of the vertical line with the X axis determines the x coordinate and the intersection of the horizontal line with the Y axis determines the y coordinate.

The origin corresponds to the ordered pair (0,0), any point on the X axis corresponds to an ordered pair of the form $(x,0)$, and any point on the Y axis corresponds to an ordered pair of the form $(0,y)$.

By the above procedure, every point in the infinite XY plane corresponds to exactly one ordered pair (x,y) of real numbers, its rectangular coordinates, and every ordered pair of real numbers corresponds to exactly one point, its graph. The system thus generated is called a **rectangular coordinate system.**

The axes divide the XY plane into four subareas called **quadrants** (from ancient navigational terminology). These quadrants are usually numbered using Roman numerals. Quadrant I is the quadrant where both variables are positive, that is, the upper right-hand area. The numbering progresses counterclockwise, as shown in Figure 7.1. Figure 7.1 also illustrates the graphing of four points, one in each quadrant; that is, $P_1 : (7,4)$, $P_2 : (-5,3)$, $P_3 : (-8,-6)$, and $P_4 : (8,-4)$.

7.03 / Graphs from observed data

Many of man's achievements in science and engineering have come from patient observation and recording of data. Modern technology has increased the precision of the observations and the ease of recording and plotting, although there has been no real change in the use of recorded data.

In an applied problem, the letters x and y are not ordinarily used to designate practical quantities. Therefore, it is better to think of the horizontal axis as the values of the independent variable and the vertical axis as the values of the dependent variable. The initial step in graphing observed data is to select the independent variable. Normally it is the variable controlled by the experimenter or observer. It might be the altitude of an aircraft, the speed of a motor, or the force being exerted. When time is a variable, it is almost always the independent variable. Next the domain and range are selected. In many cases, lacking a rule of correspondence, the maximum range cannot be computed, but, based upon prior observations, a good approximation can be made. The domain and range accepted will dictate the feasible scales. Subdivisions in multiples of 1, 2, or 5 units are usually used. The scales on the two axes do not need to be identical.

In many practical problems, the origin (0,0) is far away from the values being considered and a **false origin** is used. For example, in a study of the heat of steam and the resulting pressures, there would be no values below 212°F.

Whether the true origin or a false origin is to be used will depend upon the purpose of the graph. If purely pictorial, the origin is unimportant; if needed for subsequent mathematical operations, it may be vital. The electronic computer program known as COGO computes and adjusts surveying traverses. Failure to use a false origin may result in a negative coordinate, and this renders the program useless.

With suitable axes and scales, the observed ordered pairs are plotted. Usually a fine dot is placed at the true coordinates and a larger, darker circle drawn about it for increased visibility. If several experiments are plotted on the same sheet, data points are usually marked in the preference ⊙, ⊡, △, as shown in Figure 7.2.

Each axis should bear a title and a statement of the unit plotted. Avoid excess zeros by using units in thousands, millions, hundredths, and so on, but avoid using scientific notation if possible, since nontechnical personnel may have trouble reading it.

Initially, connect the data points with a lightly drawn line, which is primarily for ease of eye travel. This is called a **broken-line plot.** Any violent displacement should be immediately checked for a possible error in plotting. A little reflection should indicate whether this series of line segments does give a true concept of the relation being plotted. If the data are probably not mathematically related to the independent variable, as the daily variation of maximum temperatures, this broken-line plot is the *best* plot. In contrast, a plot of temperatures taken every 30 min in a single day would tend to be a

Figure 7.2

Effect of holes in flat wrought steel plates
(Adapted from Steel Founder's Society of
America Design Rules.)

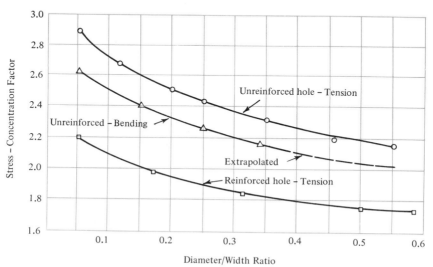

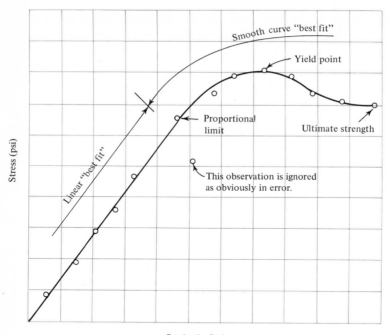

Figure 7.3
Linear and smooth-curve "best-fit" plotting from observed data

smooth transition, and then the broken-line plot is replaced by a smooth curve.

A smooth curve is called a **best-fit curve** if it passes through or nearby the data points in such a way that the sum of distances to data points above the curve is approximately the same as the sum of distances to data points below the curve. Drawing this best-fit curve is usually done visually without calculations. The best-fit curve may be a straight line. Examples of best-fit curves are shown in Figure 7.3.

If the observations are not too widely separated, values between observations can be read by **interpolation,** exactly as interpolation was used to read values in tables in Chapter 1. **Extrapolation,** or obtaining values outside the actual observed domain by extending the plot, can be quite dangerous and should be used solely to predict further values to study in subsequent tests. Figure 7.4 shows both interpolation and extrapolation and the possible errors in the use of the latter.

Since each ordered pair does define exactly one point on an infinite plane, a machine can be directed to move a tool or a pen to a location given by its coordinates. Machines called digitizers are now manufactured that permit a relatively unskilled operator to place a stylus on a drawing of a desired shape and read directly the *x,y* coordinates of that location with reference to

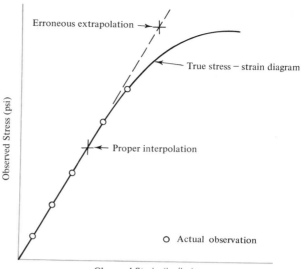

Figure 7.4
Interpolation and extrapolation

Observed Strain (in./in.)
Stress-Strain Diagram for Cast Iron

a selected origin. Digitized data can be given to the machine by a punched tape or magnetic tape if the machine is made to accept numerical control information. Numerical control can be used to produce drawings, to bore holes, to shape metal, and to perform similar tasks on drill presses, milling machines, shapers, and lathes.

Problem Set 7.2

1–8

Paper ruled five squares to the inch is recommended. Show axes, origin, and subdivide axes so that not over five printed squares are unlabeled. Look over the domain and range and select a good scale. Use identical scales for the two axes in each of these problems. Identify the plotted points by the letter assigned in the problem.

1. $A : (3,4)$, $B : (4, -5)$, $C : (-5,4)$, $D : (-4, -3)$, $E : (0,4)$, $F : (-4,0)$.
2. Plot $A : (\frac{1}{2}, \frac{7}{8})$, $B : (\frac{3}{4}, -\frac{3}{8})$, $C : (-\frac{1}{2}, -\frac{3}{4})$, $D : (0, -\frac{5}{8})$, $E : (-\frac{9}{8}, 1)$, $F : (-\frac{7}{8}, 0)$.
3. $A : (2\frac{1}{4}, 2)$, $B : (-1\frac{1}{2}, -1\frac{1}{2})$, $C : (0, -2)$, $D : (1\frac{3}{4}, -\frac{3}{4})$, $E : (2,0)$, $F : (-\frac{1}{4}, \frac{1}{4})$.
4. Plot $A : (1.2,1.2)$, $B : (-1.4,0.8)$, $C : (2.1, -1.1)$, $D : (0.1,0)$, $E : (-0.4, -0.6)$, $F : (0.2,2.0)$.
5. Plot $A : (70,95)$, $B : (50, -20)$, $C : (-40,45)$, $D : (-20, -30)$, $E : (-30, -20)$, $F : (55,5)$.

6. Plot $A : (20,000,15,000)$, $B : (-15,000, -15,000)$, $C : (25,000, -5000)$, $D : (-5000,35,000)$.
7. Plot $A : (192.5,16.1)$, $B : (194.1,15.7)$, $C : (191.9,19.7)$, $D : (193.5,16.0)$.
8. Plot $A : (-10.2,0.22)$, $B : (-8.7,0.34)$, $C : (-11.3,0.14)$, $D : (-9.7,0.27)$.

9. Given two sets X and Y, select from the available elements the values needed to plot the stated requirement. (Select x from X and y from Y.)

$$X = \{-3, -2, -1,0,1,2,3\}, \qquad Y = \{-4, -2, -1, -\tfrac{1}{2},2,4\}$$

Plot (x,y) such that
(a) x and y are negative and equal.
(b) x and y are equal in absolute value but opposite in sign.
(c) x is the reciprocal of y.
(d) $y = 2x$ and $y < 0$.
(e) $y = \frac{2}{3}x$ and $y > 0$.
(f) x and y negative, consecutive, and $|y| > |x|$.
(g) $y = x + 7$.
(h) $\dfrac{x}{y} = -6$.

10. The compensation for basic engineering services was compiled by the magazine *Civil Engineering*. Plot their findings.

Construction cost (Millions of Dollars)	Compensation as percentage of cost
0.1	10.6
0.2	9.4
0.3	8.7
0.4	8.2
0.5	7.8
1.0	6.8
2.0	6.3
5.0	5.9

11. The number of students attending college in U.S. was collected. Plot these findings.

Year	Students (in Millions)
1930	2.30
1935	2.35
1940	2.48
1945	2.32
1950	2.05
1955	2.20
1960	2.82
1965	3.50
1970	3.78

12. A detailed study of the income-tax returns of individuals for a recent year gave the following data. Plot on the same graph the number of taxpayers and the average tax paid, using income as the independent variable for each.

Income, $	Number of Taxpayers	Average Tax, $
Under 5000	19,600,000	0.25
5000 to 10,000	23,000,000	0.65
10,000 to 15,000	7,700,000	1.41
15,000 to 20,000	1,800,000	2.34
20,000 to 50,000	1,400,000	5.30
50,000 to 100,000	190,000	19.15
100,000 to 500,000	43,000	65.10
500,000 to 1,000,000	1,400	282.00
Over 1,000,000	600	960.00

(*Hints:* Two different vertical scales are proper; show one on the left margin and the other on the right. Devise a way of obtaining x values since you cannot plot the bracketed value as given. These are authentic data. Note that the average tax is not the tax paid by the average citizen, but the average of the entire group.)

13. For a furnace bonnet temperature of 200°F, the delivery temperature is given as a function of the distance away. In addition, the data gives the register delivery volume in cfm per 1000 Btuh. Plot both on the same graph. (Data adapted from A.S.H.R.A.E. Guide and Data Book.)

Distance, ft	Delivery Temp., °F	cfm
20	187	9.2
40	176	9.9
60	167	10.7
80	158	11.6
100	151	12.4
120	144	13.4
140	138	14.4

14. The properties of water change with temperature.

Temp., °F	Pressure, psia	Density, lb/cu ft
212	14.7	59.9
220	17.2	59.7
240	25.0	59.2
260	35.4	58.6
280	49.2	58.0
300	67.0	57.4
350	134.6	55.6
400	247.2	53.6

Plot the above data and draw "best-fit" curves.

15. The U.S. Bureau of Reclamation ran a series of tests on concrete. One test related the change in compressive strength as the water–cement ratio was increased. These were the test observations:

Water–cement ratio	0.45	0.55	0.60	0.65	0.69	0.75	0.80
Compressive strength, psi	5750	4300	3950	3850	3600	2350	2800

A theoretical relationship has been determined from prior tests, and three calculated values were

Water–cement ratio	0.465	0.640	0.815
Compressive strength, psi	6000	4000	2000

Plot this information, using a solid line for the theoretical relationship, a dashed line for the broken-line observed plot, and a long-and-short dashed line for the "best-fit" line. Use a horizontal scale of 1 in. = 0.10 for the water–cement ratio and a vertical scale of 1 in. = 2500 psi.

16. As part of the same Bureau of Reclamation program as in Problem 15, a 1-year shrinkage study was made. The test specimens were cured in 100 per cent relative humidity for 90 days and then in a 50 per cent relative humidity for the rest of the year. These were the test observations:

Age, days	90	120	180	210	280	300	365
Shrinkage, %	+0.010	−0.034	−0.0515	−0.062	−0.0665	−0.062	−0.068

Plot this information using a dashed line for the broken-line observed plot and a solid line for the "best-fit" line. Use a horizontal scale of 1 in. = 100 days and a vertical scale of 1 in. = 0.02 per cent.

7.04 / Functions

When a relation has been found to be a function, it is convenient to have a simple usable notation for the unique value of y that is paired with each x. This notation is written $f(x)$, read either as "f of x" or "the value of f at x." If a situation involves several functions, the y values may be written as $g(x)$, $h(x)$, $F(x)$, $G(x)$, or $\phi(x)$. Actually any letter may be used to designate the function, but the ones listed here are among the most common.

If there is a functional relationship, there is a unique y_1 associated with a specific x_1. When x_1 is given in the domain of the function, the value of $f(x_1)$ is that unique y_1 of the ordered pair (x_1, y_1). In other words, $y_1 = f(x_1)$ and, in general, $y = f(x)$.

Since a value may be arbitrarily assigned to the x component, x is called the *independent variable*. Knowing the x component, the y component of the ordered pair can be found by the rule of correspondence, so y is called the *dependent variable*. The notation $f(x)$ is further explained in Example 7.4, where the letter designating the independent variable is first replaced by open parentheses and then a given value is inserted within these parentheses.

Example 7.4

Using the rule of correspondence for Fahrenheit and Celsius temperatures, find the Fahrenheit equivalent of 10°C and 25°C.

SOLUTION

(1) State the rule: $\quad\quad\quad\quad\quad\quad\quad\quad\quad F = f(C) = \frac{9}{5}C + 32$

(2) Rewrite with open parentheses: $\quad F = f(\ ) = \frac{9}{5}(\ ) + 32$

(3) Insert first given value of the
independent variable; $\quad\quad\quad\quad\quad F = f(10) = \frac{9}{5}(10) + 32 = 50°$

(4) Repeat, using second value: $\quad\quad F = f(25) = \frac{9}{5}(25) + 32 = 77°$

Sometimes it is desirable to express a function of a function. The volume of a sphere is a function of its radius and the area of a great circle of that sphere is also a function of that radius. Moreover, the radius of the sphere is a function of the area of a great circle. Therefore, it is possible to express the volume as a function of the great-circle area. Using the functional notation, $V = f(r)$ and $r = g(A)$ and thus $V = f(g(A))$, a function of a function.

Example 7.5

Given the volume of a sphere $V = \frac{4}{3}\pi r^3$ and the area of a great circle $A = \pi r^2$, write the volume of a sphere as a function of the area of a great circle.

SOLUTION

(1) Expressed as a function: $\quad\quad V = f(r) = \frac{4}{3}\pi r^3$

(2) Solving $A = \pi r^2$ for r: $\quad\quad r = \sqrt{\frac{A}{\pi}} = g(A)$

(3) Using open parentheses: $\quad\quad V = f(\ ) = \frac{4}{3}\pi(\ )^3$

(4) Inserting functional value: $\quad V = f(g(A)) = \frac{4}{3}\pi\left(\sqrt{\frac{A}{\pi}}\right)^3$.

Since a function is defined as a relation with exactly one second component (y value) for each first component (x value), the graph of a function is such that each vertical line intersects the graph in at most one point. For example, the relation defined by $y = x^2$ is a function since, as illustrated in Figure 7.5(a), each vertical line intersects the graph in exactly one point. On the other hand, the relation defined by $x = y^2$ is not a function since, as illustrated in Figure 7.5(b), there is a vertical line that intersects the graph in more than one point.

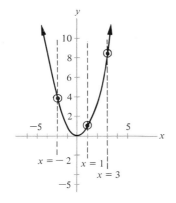

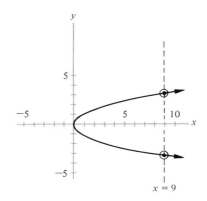

(a) Graph of a function, $y = x^2$ (b) Graph of a relation, not a function, $x = y^2$

⊙ is used to indicate points computed in plotting the curve, but properly should not appear visually on actual plot.

Figure 7.5

Problem Set 7.3

1-10

Find the indicated functional values, if they exist.

1. Given $f(p) = 3p - 4$, find $f(3)$, $f(4)$, and $f(-4)$.

2. Given $f(r) = 4r - 3$, find $f(\frac{4}{3})$, $f(\frac{3}{4})$, and $f(0)$.

3. Given $f(s) = \dfrac{s^2 + 4}{s^2 - 4}$, find $f(2)$, $f(-2)$, and $f(0)$.

4. Given $g(t) = t(t - 2)(t - 4)$, find $g(0)$, $g(2)$, and $g(4)$.

5. Given $g(u) = \dfrac{u(u - 1)}{(u - 2)(u - 3)}$, find $g(0)$, $g(1)$, $g(2)$, and $g(3)$.

6. Given $h(v) = \dfrac{v^2 - 4}{v + 2}$, find $h(0)$, $h(2)$, and $h(-2)$.

7. Given $h(w) = \dfrac{3w^2 + 2w - 4}{w^2 - 4}$, find $h(0)$, $h(2)$, and $h(10)$.

8. Given $F(x) = \dfrac{81x^2 - 169}{9x^2 + 5x - 26}$, find $F(-2)$, $F(\frac{1}{3})$, and $F(0)$.

9. Given $F(y) = y + \dfrac{1}{y}$, find $F(x^2)$, $F\left(\dfrac{1}{x}\right)$, and $F\left(\dfrac{1}{x^2}\right)$.

10. Given $G(z) = \dfrac{1}{z^2} - z$, find $G(y^3)$, $G\left(\dfrac{1}{y^2}\right)$, and $G(0)$.

11–20 Illustrative Example

Given $f(x) = \dfrac{1 + x}{1 - x}$, *find* $f(x + 1)$, $f\left(\dfrac{1}{x}\right)$, *and* $f(f(x))$.

SOLUTION Using open parentheses:

$$f(\ ) = \frac{1 + (\ )}{1 - (\ )}$$

For $f(x + 1)$:

$$\frac{1 + (x + 1)}{1 - (x + 1)} = \frac{2 + x}{-x} = -\frac{x + 2}{x}$$

For $f\left(\dfrac{1}{x}\right)$:

$$\frac{1 + \left(\dfrac{1}{x}\right)}{1 - \left(\dfrac{1}{x}\right)} = \frac{\dfrac{x + 1}{x}}{\dfrac{x - 1}{x}} = \frac{x + 1}{x - 1}$$

For $f(f(x))$:

$$\frac{1 + \left(\dfrac{1 + x}{1 - x}\right)}{1 - \left(\dfrac{1 + x}{1 - x}\right)} = \frac{\dfrac{1 - x + 1 + x}{1 - x}}{\dfrac{1 - x - 1 - x}{1 - x}} = \frac{2}{-2x} = -\frac{1}{x}$$

11. Given $f(p) = a^2 - p^2$, find $f(a^2)$, $f(p^2)$, and $f(a^2 - p^2)$.

12. Given $f(r) = r^2 - b^2$, find $f(b)$, $f(b^2)$, and $f(b^2 r^2)$.

13. Given $g(s) = s^3$, find $\dfrac{g(s + h) - g(s)}{h}$.

14. Given $g(t) = \dfrac{1}{t}$, find $\dfrac{g(t + k) - g(t)}{k}$.

15. Given $A(r) = \pi r^2$, find $\dfrac{A(r + 0.001) - A(r)}{0.001}$.

16. Given $P(V) = \dfrac{k}{V}$, find $\dfrac{P(T - 0.001) - P(T)}{0.001}$.

17. Given a volume of a cube $V = f(s) = s^3$ and the area of a face $A = s^2$, letting $s = g(A)$, find $f(g(A))$ and $f(g(\tfrac{9}{16}))$.

18. Given $s = f(t) = -\tfrac{1}{2}gt^2 + v_0 t$ and $v = -gt + v_0$ and letting $t = h(v)$, find $f(h(v))$ and $f(h(36.5))$ for $g = 32.2$ and $v_0 = 44$.

19. Given $y = f(x) = x^3$.
   (a) If $x = g(t) = 3t$, find $f(g(t))$.
   (b) If $x = h(y) = \sqrt[3]{y}$, find $f(h(y))$.
20. Given $y = f(x) = 4x - 5$.

   (a) If $x = g(t) = \dfrac{1}{t} + 1$, find $f(g(t))$.

   (b) If $x = h(y) = \dfrac{y + 5}{4}$, find $f(h(y))$.

21. From the graphs shown below, select those that are the graphs of functions.

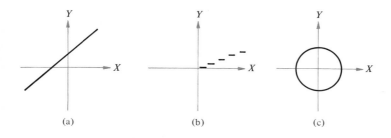

     (a)   (b)   (c)

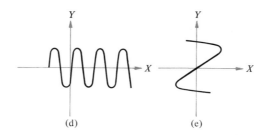

     (d)   (e)

22. From the graphs shown at the top of the next page, select those that are the graphs of functions.

7.05 / Functions of several variables

Although there are many relations in science and engineering that involve finding the fundamental rule between two variables, the technology of today may require many variables to express the actual function. In purely geometric problems, area relations are usually functions of two variables and volumetric ones usually involve three variables. On the other hand, in modern aerodynamics, a horsepower requirement was found to be:

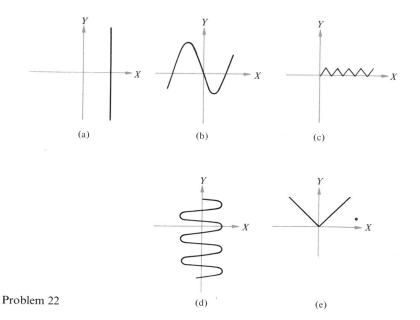

(a)

(b)

(c)

Problem 22

(d)

(e)

$HP = f(A_T, R_L, L, G, M, T_i, T_0)$, that is, a function of a total of seven independent variables.

In a laboratory situation, it is desirable to keep as many of the variables constant as possible in order to determine a rule of correspondence between just two or three variables. Many experiments are planned at constant temperature, constant pressure, or constant humidity, in fact, whatever can be conveniently maintained at a constant level. Section 7.12 will show engineering applications of this concept.

Common notations that are used for functions involving more than two variables are as follows:

| $z = f(x,y)$ | where x and y are the independent variables and z is the dependent variable |
| $w = f(x,y,z)$ | where x, y, and z are the independent variables and w is the dependent variable |

When the rule of the function is given and when values are specified for the independent variables, the value of the dependent variable can be calculated by using the rule.

Example 7.6

Given $f(x,y) = x - y + \dfrac{x}{y}$, find $f(5,2)$.

SOLUTION

(1) Write the rule: $f(x,y) = x - y + \dfrac{x}{y}$

(2) Replace x by open parentheses: $f(\ ,y) = (\ ) - y + \dfrac{(\ )}{y}$

(3) Insert 5 in the x position: $f(5,y) = 5 - y + \dfrac{5}{y}$

(4) Replace y by open parentheses: $f(5,\ ) = 5 - (\ ) + \dfrac{5}{(\ )}$

(5) Insert 2 in the y position: $f(5,2) = 5 - 2 + \frac{5}{2}$

(6) Simplify: $f(5,2) = 3 + 2.5 = 5.5$

7.06 / Inverse functions

The rule of a function is written in the form most frequently used. The volume of a cube is usually written as $V = f(s) = s^3$. The function is $\{(s,V)|V = s^3\}$. When a function is such that there is exactly one value of the dependent variable for each value of the independent variable and also exactly one value of the independent variable for each value of the dependent variable, the function has an inverse function. When a rule relating the variables is known, a rule for the inverse function can be written. In the preceding example, a rule can be written for finding a side given the volume; that is, $s = g(V) = \sqrt[3]{V}$. The inverse function is $\{(V, s)|s = \sqrt[3]{V}\}$.

The notation $f^{-1}(V) = \sqrt[3]{V}$ is used instead of $g(V) = \sqrt[3]{V}$ to indicate that g is the inverse function of f. In general, if $y = f(x)$ defines a function that has an inverse function $x = g(y)$, this inverse function is indicated by $x = f^{-1}(y)$.

Examples of functions and their inverses used a number of times in this book are those of powers and roots. For the squaring function, $s = f(n) = n^2$. For positive numbers n, the square-root function is the inverse function with the rule $n = f^{-1}(s) = \sqrt{s}$.

For a function of several variables, an inverse function may be obtained by considering all but one of the dependent variables as constant or by reducing the given function to a function of one variable. The second alternative is used when it is possible to express the other dependent variables as functions of just one dependent variable.

Example 7.7
Given $A = f(w,h) = wh$. Find the rule for the inverse function
(a) if h is considered constant.
(b) if h is 3 times the width.

SOLUTION

(a) Since $A = wh$, $w = f^{-1}(A) = \dfrac{A}{h}$.

(b) Since $A = wh$ and $h = 3w$, $A = w(3w) = 3w^2$. Thus, $w = f^{-1}(A)$

$$= \sqrt{\frac{A}{3}}.$$

Problem Set 7.4

Problems involving geometric shapes should be solved by reference to Chapter 4 or to an appropriate handbook.

1–6
Find the indicated functional values, if they exist.

1. Given $h(u,v) = u^2 - v^2$, find $h(1,2)$, $h(-1,-2)$, $h(2,-1)$, and $h(-2,-1)$.

2. Given $h(v,w) = \dfrac{v + w}{v - w}$, find $h(3,2)$, $h(3,5)$, $h(-3,-5)$, and $h(1,1)$.

3. Given $F(x,y) = \dfrac{1}{x} - \dfrac{1}{y}$, find $F(1,1)$, $F(2,1)$, $F(2,-1)$, and $F(2,-2)$.

4. Given $F(y,z) = \dfrac{1}{y^2} - \dfrac{1}{z^2}$, find $F(1,a)$, $F(a,-1)$, $F(3,3)$, and $F(0,3)$.

5. Given $G(r,s) = \dfrac{r}{s}$, find $G\left(\dfrac{b}{a}, \dfrac{a}{b}\right)$, $G(ab,1)$, and $G\left(\dfrac{a}{b}, \dfrac{b}{a}\right)$.

6. Given $H(t,u) = \dfrac{t - u}{u}$, find $H(6a,2b)$, $H\left(\dfrac{a}{b}, \dfrac{c}{b}\right)$, and $H\left(\dfrac{a + b}{b}, \dfrac{a - b}{a}\right)$.

7–24
Write the rule for each relation first by using functional notation and then by using the expression needed for calculations.

Example
Find the relation between the volume of a right rectangular prism and its dimensions.

SOLUTION $V = f(w,l,d)$ and $V = wld$.

7. Find the relation between the area of a trapezoid and its dimensions using three independent variables.

8. Repeat Problem 7 using two independent variables.
9. Find the relation between the length of the diagonal of a square and its perimeter.
10. Find the rule for the inverse function of that in Problem 9.
11. Find the relation between the area of an isosceles triangle and its sloping sides if the altitude of the triangle is one half of the base.
12. For the triangle described in Problem 11, find the relation between the perimeter and one of its sloping sides.
13. Find the relation that will give the length s of the arc intercepted by a 30° inscribed angle as a function of the radius of the circle.
14. A perpendicular is erected at some point P on the diameter of a circle. Point P divides the diameter into two line segments of lengths a and b. Find the relation between the height of the perpendicular and the lengths a and b.
15. Find a relation between the volume of a pyramid and its dimensions using two independent variables, and then find the inverse relation for the altitude.
16. Find a relation between the volume of a rectangular pyramid and its dimensions using three independent variables, and then find the inverse relation for the altitude.
17. Find a relation between the volume of an elliptic cone and its dimensions using three independent variables, and then find the inverse relation for the altitude.
18. Find a relation expressing the volume of a circular cylinder as a function of two variables, and then find the inverse function for the radius.
19. Name a solid whose volume can be expressed as a function of one variable. Find the function and then find its inverse function.
20. A piece of heavy wire n inches long is cut into two pieces, one twice as long as the other. The shorter one is formed into a circle, the longer one into a square. Find a relation between n and (a) the *total* area and (b) the *total* perimeter.
21. A wire n inches long forms a circle. It is carefully straightened and formed into a square. Find a relation between the original area of the circle and the area of the square.
22. Referring to Problem 21, find the relation between the original area and the perimeter of the square.
23. Find the relation that expresses the side of a regular tetrahedron as a function of the surface area A.
24. Find the relation that expresses the side of a regular dodecahedron as a function of the surface area A.

7.07 / Graphs from algebraic relations

Although many of the concepts that apply to graphs based upon physical observation also apply to the graphs of algebraic relations, there are some fundamental differences. In physical observations, the domain is often limited by the possible physical conditions that can exist. For example, a large number of physical quantities can not have negative values and others are by their nature limited to integers (a solution could not be $2\frac{2}{3}$ men). The graphs of algebraic relations tend to form smooth curves and there will be a point on the graph for each real number in the domain of the relation. For this reason, the actual points calculated to plot the graph are not identified by any symbol. Also, any sharp breaks or irregularities are immediately checked for a possible error in calculation. These features do exist for certain functions and, in later chapters, they will be identified and located. Since many algebraic graphs are infinite in extent, the whole graph cannot be drawn, and an arrowhead is placed at the end or ends of the plot to indicate that the graph does not terminate there.

Extremely useful points on graphs are those points where the graph crosses the axes. For this reason the true origin is used whenever possible, since the crossing of an axis drawn through a false origin is not meaningful. The x value of a point where a graph crosses the X axis is called an **x intercept.** If this point has coordinates $(a,0)$, a is an x intercept. Similarly, the y value of a point where the graph crosses the Y axis is called a **y intercept.** If this point has coordinates $(0,b)$, b is the y intercept.

If the graph is that of a function whose rule is $y = f(x)$, the zeros of $f(x)$, those values of x for which $f(x) = 0$, are the x intercepts. Graphically, this means that every point where the graph touches or crosses the X axis has coordinates of the form $(x,0)$. If a graph never touches the X axis, then $f(x) = 0$ has no solution in the set of real numbers.

7.08 / Graphs of linear equations in two variables

Any first-degree polynomial equation in two variables is called a linear equation, because its graph is an infinite straight line. If this first-degree equation is written in the form $Ax + By + C = 0$, it is called an *implicit* equation, since the relation between x and y is implied. In contrast, if the equation is written as $y = mx + b$, it is called an *explicit* equation, since y can be found directly when x is known. It can easily be seen that if $B \neq 0$, any implicit linear equation can be readily transformed into the explicit form.

The graph of any relation whose ordered pairs are of the form (x,y) is the set of points in the XY plane whose coordinates are these given pairs. From a purely geometric viewpoint, any two given points define a unique line. If two ordered pairs, (x_1,y_1) and (x_2,y_2), are known, the graph of the linear equation they define can be drawn. A straight line is drawn joining the two points that have these ordered pairs for their coordinates. Since man does make errors, usually three points are used to check that no error was made in arithmetic.

The two easiest ordered pairs to find are those for the x and y intercepts and they should be used whenever possible. In some problems the area of interest is far from the true origin so that the intercept points may be off the paper. In a few problems the intercept points will both fall close to the origin and, if the distance between them is small, a graphical distortion in connecting them will probably result. For both of these two cases, additional values should be assigned to the independent variable to obtain suitable plotting points.

Example 7.8
Plot $x + 2y - 4 = 0$.

SOLUTION
(1) Find the intercept points: If $x = 0$, $y = 2$ and if $y = 0$, $x = 4$.
(2) The intercept points (0,2) and (4,0) are well spaced, so they are plotted, and the line joining them is drawn.
(3) As a check point, use $(-4,4)$. (If $x = -4$, then $y = 4$.) The check point should be selected so that it is not too close to the two plotted points.
The desired plot is shown in Figure 7.6.

Figure 7.6
Plot of
$x + 2y - 4 = 0$

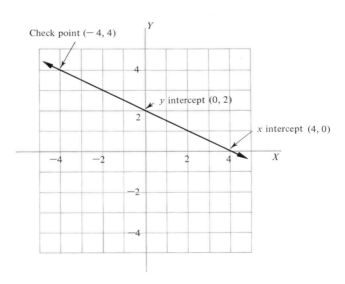

Check point $(-4, 4)$

y intercept $(0, 2)$

x intercept $(4, 0)$

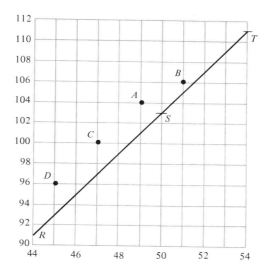

Figure 7.7

Example 7.9

Determine graphically if $y = 2x + 3$ passes through any of these four points:

$$A : (49,104), \ B : (51,106), \ C : (47,100), \ D : (45,96)$$

SOLUTION

(Avoid the intercept points because they are too far from the four given points.)

(1) Select three points in the area of interest by assigning values to x:

For point R, if $x = 44$, $y = 2(44) + 3 = 91$ and R is (44,91)

For point S, if $x = 50$, $y = 2(50) + 3 = 103$ and S is (50,103)

For point T, if $x = 54$, $y = 2(54) + 3 = 111$ and T is (54,111)

(2) Plot points A through D and R through T. Draw a line through R and T. The resulting plot is shown on Figure 7.7. Note that the origin does not need to appear on the plot; a false origin of (44,90) was used.

From the figure it is seen that $y = 2x + 3$ does *not* pass through any of the four given points.

Example 7.10

Plot $3x + 4y - 2 = 0$.

SOLUTION

(1) By inspection, for $x = 0$, $y = \frac{1}{2}$ and for $y = 0$, $x = \frac{2}{3}$.

Figure 7.8
Plot of
$3x + 4y - 2 = 0$

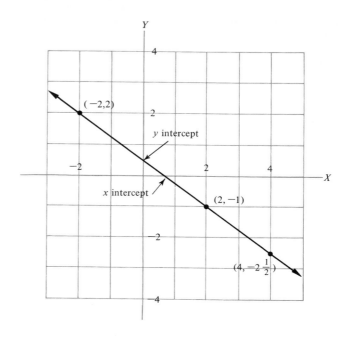

(2) The intercept points are too close together for a good plot. One of them can be used, say $(0,\frac{1}{2})$ and two other points are chosen so that the x values are not too close to 0. For $x = 2$, $y = -1$ and for $x = -2$, $y = 2$.

The desired plot is shown in Figure 7.8.

Problem Set 7.5

Plot the given equation for the indicated domain. Indicate the scale used on each axis by numerical values along the axis, as shown in Figures 7.1 and 7.5. If the plotted equation appears to have intercept points, indicate their coordinates on the graph, designating the x intercept point as A and the y intercept point as B. (Note: Some nonlinear algebraic relations, discussed in Section 7.07, are included in this problem set. Plot points using integers for x and join these points with a smooth curve.)

1. $5x - 4y = 0$ for domain $-4 \le x \le 5$
2. $2x + 3y = 0$ for domain $-5 \le x \le 5$
3. $y = \frac{2}{5}x + 2$ for domain $-5 \le x \le 5$
4. $y = \frac{3}{4}x - 2$ for domain $-5 \le x \le 5$
5. $4y = 8x + 3$ for domain $-2 \le x \le 2$
6. $12x - 28y = 21$ for domain $-2 \le x \le 2$

7. $x - 5y + 5 = 0$ for domain $-10 \leq x \leq 0$

8. $4x - y - 12 = 0$ for domain $-4 \leq x \leq 4$

9. $x - y - 40 = 0$ (appropriate domain to be selected by student)

10. $2x + y - 110 = 0$ (appropriate domain to be selected by student)

11. $y = x^2$ for domain $-4 \leq x \leq 4$

12. $y = -x^2$ for domain $-4 \leq x \leq 4$

13. $y = x^2 + 2$ for domain $-4 \leq x \leq 4$

14. $y = -x^2 - 2$ for domain $-4 \leq x \leq 4$

15. $y = x + \dfrac{1}{x}$ for domain $0 < x \leq 10$

16. $y = x - \dfrac{1}{x}$ for domain $0 < x \leq 10$

17. $y = \sqrt{x}$ for domain the largest possible subset of $-100 \leq x \leq 100$

18. $y = -\sqrt{x}$ for domain the largest possible subset of $-100 \leq x \leq 100$

19. $y = -\sqrt{-x}$ for domain the largest possible subset of $-100 \leq x \leq 100$

20. $y = -|-x|$ for domain $-4 \leq x \leq 4$

7.09 / Graphs of linear inequalities in two variables

Since an inequality is a statement of order or size, an instinctive concept of a pictorial representation might be something above, something coincident, or something below another thing. This is exactly what a graph of a linear inequality in two variables shows. The graph of the equality $y = x$ is shown in Figure 7.9(a). If the inequality to be graphed is $y > x$, the graph must be the set of ordered pairs, $\{(x, y) \mid y > x\}$; that is, each point on the graph has a y coordinate greater than its corresponding x coordinate. For the case $y > x$, the graph is the area above the $y = x$ line, since for any given point, say (a,a), on the line, the point (a,y) is above the line when $y > a$.

The line $y = x$ is included in the graphs of the inequalities $y \geq x$ and $y \leq x$ and it is excluded from the graphs of the inequalities $y > x$ and $y < x$. When it is included, the line $y = x$ is drawn as a solid line as shown in Figure 7.9(b), the graph of the inequality $y \geq x$. When the line is excluded, a dashed line is used as shown in Figure 7.9(c), the graph of $y > x$.

Finally, if the sense is reversed and y is less than x, the area desired is below the line for the equality, as shown in Figure 7.9(d), the graph of $y < x$.

The area that represents the solution is usually lightly cross-sectioned. Diagonal lines on about a 45° slope and $\frac{1}{8}$ in. apart are suggested. When there are numerous lines that demark the area solution, the diagonal lines need not cross the entire area but are drawn perhaps $\frac{3}{8}$ in. long, enough to show on which side of a given line the solution lies.

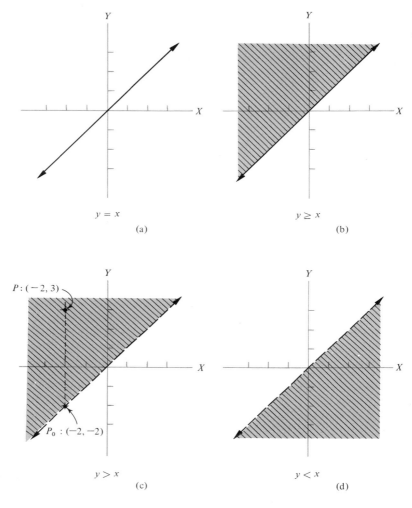

Figure 7.9

The plot of an inequality can be readily checked for a gross error by picking a point in the shaded area, reading its coordinates, and seeing if they meet the stated conditions. Thus, in Figure 7.9(c) point P has coordinates $(-2, 3)$ and 3 is greater than -2. A vertical line dropped from P to P_0 merely checks that the line for the equality was correctly plotted. Both the area and the equality line are infinite, but no symbolism is used to show the infinite extent of the area.

Example 7.11
Graph $3x + 2y \leq 6$.

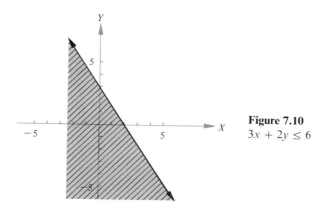

Figure 7.10
$3x + 2y \leq 6$

SOLUTION

(1) Solve the inequality for y: $y \leq 3 - \frac{3}{2}x$.
(2) Graph the line $y = 3 - \frac{3}{2}x$ using a solid line. (Why?)
(3) Shade the area below this line. (See Figure 7.10.)

Example 7.12
Graph $2x - y < 5$.

SOLUTION

(1) Solve the inequality for y: $-y < -2x + 5$
$$y > 2x - 5$$
   (Remember that multiplying both sides of an inequality by a negative number reverses the sense.)
(2) Graph the line $y = 2x - 5$ using a dashed line. (Why?)
(3) Shade the area above this line. (See Figure 7.11.)

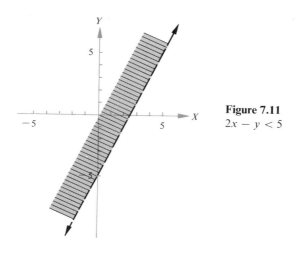

Figure 7.11
$2x - y < 5$

Problem Set 7.6

Graph each of the following. For all problems use a domain of $-6 \leq x \leq 6$ *unless otherwise directed by the instructor. Identical scales should be used for both axes, but one printed square may be assigned any desired value. Paper ruled five squares to the inch is recommended.*

1. $y < 2x$

2. $y > 2x$

3. $y \leq 3x - 5$

4. $y \leq x - 6$

5. $3x + 4y > 0$

6. $2x + 3y < 0$

7. $2x + 5y < 0$

8. $3x - 5y > 0$

9. $\frac{1}{2}y \geq x - 1$

10. $\frac{1}{3}y \leq x + 2$

11. $0.7y \leq 0.4x$

12. $0.71y \leq 0.57x$

13. $1.1y - 2 > 0.63x$

14. $2.7y - 4.11 \leq 2.17x$

15. $\frac{1}{2}(0.46y - 2.72) \geq \dfrac{x}{3}$

16. $\frac{1}{3}(2.16y + 1.72) \geq 2x - 0.33$

17. $0.77x < 1.83y - 2$

18. $6x + y > 2.32 - 1.47y$

19. $1.12x - 2.17y$ is positive

20. $3.37x + 4.24y$ is negative

21. $\{(x,y) \mid y > 2\}$

22. $\{(x,y) \mid y \leq -2\}$

23. $\{(x,y) \mid x \leq -1\}$

24. $\{(x,y) \mid x > 3\}$

25. $\{(x,y) \mid -2 \leq x < 3\}$

26. $\{(x,y) \mid x < -1 \text{ or } x \geq 4\}$

27. $\{(x,y) \mid |x| \geq 2\frac{1}{2}\}$

28. $\{(x,y) \mid |x| \leq 5\}$

29. $|x - y| < 5$

30. $|x + y| > 1$

7.10 / Simple parametric equations: a functional concept

In many situations it is desirable to express each component of an ordered pair (x,y) of a relation in terms of a third variable, usually the time t. This produces a pair of equations $x = f(t)$ and $y = g(t)$ that represent the graph of the relation. The two equations are called **parametric equations.** If the rule of a relation is given as a pair of parametric equations, it is often possible to eliminate the parameter t and obtain the rectangular equation involving only x and y.

Parametric equations are quite useful in describing the complex paths traversed by particles, since they permit the x and y coordinates to be expressed at any instant of time. They are of limited value for the first-degree equations being studied. If it does appear that the relationship is linear, three

Figure 7.12
Parametric equations

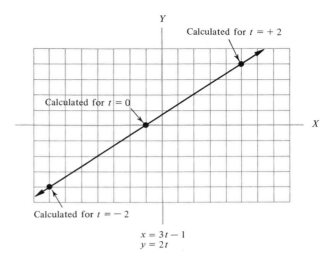

Y

Calculated for $t = +2$

Calculated for $t = 0$

X

Calculated for $t = -2$

$$x = 3t - 1$$
$$y = 2t$$

selected values of t should be adequate to obtain the plot. Note that the values of t do *not* appear on the plot; only the computed values of x and y appear.

Example 7.13
Given the parametric equations $x = 3t - 1$ and $y = 2t$;
(a) Plot the function defined by these equations.
(b) Find the rectangular equation for this function.

SOLUTION
(a) For $t = -2$: $x = -7$ and $y = -4$, giving the point $(-7, -4)$
   For $t = 0$: $x = -1$ and $y = 0$, giving the point $(-1, 0)$
   For $t = 2$: $x = 5$ and $y = 4$, giving the point $(5, 4)$
   The desired plot is shown in Figure 7.12.

(b) Solving $y = 2t$ for t, then $t = \dfrac{y}{2}$. Substituting this value for t into

the equation for x, $x = 3\left(\dfrac{y}{2}\right) - 1$ and thus $2x - 3y + 2 = 0$.

7.11 / Ratios and conversion tables

The concept of a ratio was first met when rational numbers were defined. A ratio is simply a quotient. When any two variables are so related that $y = kx$, a linear function, the ratio $y/x = k$ is a constant. Ratios abound in the field of mensuration. Chapter 2 showed how problems involving ratios were readily solved on the slide rule. The major purpose of this section is to emphasize the many conversion constants that are published. They appear in many handbooks and manufacturers' literature, and each student should collect those pertinent to his chosen field.

If there is any doubt as to how to calculate a quantity using a coefficient from a handbook, the ratios involved can be written, using a literal symbol for the desired quantity.

Example 7.14
Find (a) the number of inches in 7 ft and (b) the number of feet in 2 in.

SOLUTION
$$\frac{\text{inches}}{\text{feet}} = \frac{12}{1}$$

For (a): $\frac{12}{1} = \frac{x}{7}$; multiplying both sides by 7, $x = 7(12) = 84$ in.

For (b): $\frac{12}{1} = \frac{2}{x}$; multiplying both sides by x, $12x = 2$ and
$$x = 0.167 \text{ ft.}$$

Example 7.15
Maps published by the U.S. government are identified by their rational fraction (R.F.), that is, the ratio of 1 in. on the map to inches on the ground. An R.F. of 1 : 25,000 means that 1 in. on the map represents 25,000 in. on the ground. Four of the common scales used are 1 : 25,000, 1 : 50,000, 1 : 62,500, and 1 : 125,000. Express these ratios as approximations of the number of miles represented by 1 in., and for scales equal to or larger than 1 in. equal to 1 mile, give in addition the number of inches representing 1 mile.

SOLUTION
$12(5280) = 63,360$ in./mile

$\frac{25,000}{63,360} \approx 0.39$ miles/in. $\approx 2\frac{1}{2}$ in./mile

$\frac{50,000}{63,360} \approx 0.79$ miles/in. $\approx 1\frac{1}{4}$ in./mile

$\frac{62,500}{63,360} \approx 1$ mile/in.

$\frac{125,000}{63,360} \approx 2$ miles/in.

(*Note:* The U.S. Coast and Geodetic Survey maps are published at R.F. = 1 : 63,360.)

Example 7.15 should have brought to mind the method of using a constant divisor on the slide rule as illustrated in Chapter 2.

Example 7.16

A common-sized room air conditioner is rated at 13,500 Btuh, this being the amount of heat it will remove in that period of time. Using conversion tables, find (a) the gram calories (gm-cal) per hour removed; (b) the foot-pounds of work performed per hour; (c) the kilowatt-hours consumed; (d) the horsepower required.

SOLUTION

From Table 10 of the Appendix, these constants were obtained:

$$1 \text{ Btu} = 252 \text{ gm-cal.} = 778 \text{ ft lb}$$

$$1 \text{ Btuh} = 2.93 \times 10^{-4} \text{ kwh}$$

$$1 \text{ Btu/min} = 0.0236 \text{ horsepower}$$

(a) $\dfrac{\text{Btu/hr}}{\text{gm-cal/hr}} = \dfrac{1}{252} = \dfrac{13,500}{x}$ and $x = 252(13,500)$

$$= 3.40 \times 10^6 \text{ gm-cal.}$$

(b) $\dfrac{\text{Btu/hr}}{\text{ft lb/hr}} = \dfrac{1}{778} = \dfrac{13,500}{y}$

$$y = 778(13,500) = 1.05 \times 10^7 \text{ ft lb}$$

(c) $\dfrac{\text{Btu/hr}}{\text{kwh}} = \dfrac{1}{2.93 \times 10^{-4}} = \dfrac{13,500}{z}$

$$z = 13,500(2.93 \times 10^{-4}) = 3.96 \text{ kwh}$$

(d) $\dfrac{\text{Btu/min}}{\text{hp}} = \dfrac{1}{0.0236} = \dfrac{13,500}{60 \text{ hp}}$

$$\text{hp} = \dfrac{13,500}{60}(0.0236) = 5.31 \text{ hp}$$

7.12 / Variation: a functional concept

The equation $y = f(x)$, which has been treated with respect to the mathematical concept of a function, states that y varies as x; that is, if x changes, then y also changes. In this section the rule is selected as that for a proportion. This means that there is a constant of proportionality k that yields the value of y when k is multiplied by the value of $f(x)$. In symbolic form,

y varies with x	$y \sim x$
y is proportional to x	$y = kx$
y varies with a function of x	$y \sim f(x)$
y is proportional to a function of x	$y = kf(x)$

Example 7.17
A 2 by 4-in. timber is laid across two blocks of wood 10 ft apart and a row of bricks is placed on the timber. Discuss the amount the 2 by 4 bends downward in terms of the distance between the blocks. (See Figure 7.13.)

SOLUTION
(1) In extremely general terms, the downward movement D, called the *deflection*, can be said to be a **direct variation** of the distance between the blocks, s, called the *span*. The adjective "direct" means that if the span is increased, the deflection is increased. This statement is entirely qualitative and gives no clue as to the size of the deflection or as to how it changes with the span change. In symbols, $D \sim f(s)$.
(2) If the principles of mechanics are known, it is possible to state more precisely that the deflection varies directly with the fourth power of the span. In symbols, $D \sim f(s) \sim s^4$ and $D = ks^4$.

Figure 7.13
A variation: $D \sim f(s)$

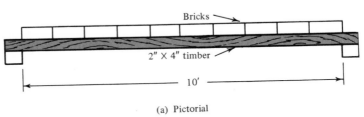

Bricks

2" X 4" timber

10'

(a) Pictorial

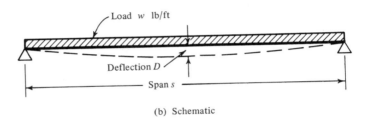

Load w lb/ft

Deflection D

Span s

(b) Schematic

(3) **By** applying the principles of strength of materials, an exact relationship can be stated. For a rectangular cross section b units wide and d units deep, k is known to be

$$\frac{w}{7.7 \times 10^6 bd^3} = \frac{w}{(7.7 \times 10^6)(2)(4^3)} = \frac{w}{10^9}$$

for this 2 by 4-in. timber, where w is the weight of the load per foot of the timber. In symbols, $D = \dfrac{ws^4}{10^9}$.

Variations can be direct or inverse and singly or joint. As already seen, items that vary directly increase as the other variable increases. An **inverse variation** means that the first variable decreases as the second variable increases. A **single variation** is one in which one variable is a function of one other variable. In a **joint variation**, one variable is a function of two or more variables.

Example 7.18

The exact relationship for the deflection of a simple beam carrying a uniform load of w pounds per linear foot, as in Example 7.17, is

$$D = \frac{5ws^4}{384EI}$$

where E = the modulus of elasticity of the material of the beam; for wood, it is about 1.2×10^6 psi

I = a measure of the stiffness, called the moment of inertia; for a rectangle, it is $\frac{1}{12}bd^3$.

w = the weight per lineal foot of beam
= $w_0 c$, where w_0 is the weight per square foot and c is the spacing, ft

Discuss the types of variations apparent in this relationship.

SOLUTION

The deflection D varies jointly with the load w, the span s, the material E, and the stiffness I. The deflection varies directly with the load w and directly with the fourth power of the span s^4. The deflection varies inversely with the modulus of elasticity E, the width b, and the cube of the depth d^3.

All the discussion so far has been preliminary to the real topic, the variation of one variable with respect to just one other variable. This is significant in engineering, for it focuses attention on those factors that radically affect a relationship.

Suppose that a beam was being selected to carry a certain load and the first selection proved unsatisfactory. (Most cities require that for a plastered ceiling, the deflection should be less than 1/360 of the clear span.) What should be done to find a suitable solution? It would be possible to write:

(a) $D \sim w \sim cw_0$

(b) $D \sim s^4$

(e) $D \sim \dfrac{1}{E}$

(c) $D \sim \dfrac{1}{I} \sim \dfrac{1}{d^3}$

(d) $D \sim \dfrac{1}{I} \sim \dfrac{1}{b}$

Usually choices (b) and (c) are investigated since a small change in either produces a large change in D. In many problems there is not a free choice of values for the variables. In a problem such as this one, the architect may have definite limitations on the permissible minimum span, and the depth of the beam is limited to those commercially produced by sawmills.

Example 7.19
A wood-framed structure must conform to a city code of a deflection less than $\frac{1}{360}$ of the span. The architect has selected 20 ft for clear spans. The roof loading, including its own weight, is 120 psf, and the spacing between roof joists is 2 ft. The contractor has suggested using 2 by 8-in. joists of Ponderosa pine ($E = 1.26 \times 10^6$ psi). What action should be recommended if the computed deflection is 0.82 in.?
(*Note:* The fact that a 2 by 8 actually is smaller due to milling processes is ignored in this problem.)

SOLUTION

The allowable deflection is $\dfrac{20(12)}{360} = 0.67$ in. ($\frac{1}{360}$ of span). Of the five choices listed above, only the values of c and d can be changed in this problem.

$$D = \frac{k_1}{d^3} \quad \text{or} \quad D = k_2 c$$

where c is the spacing between joists. If d is changed, $k_1 = 0.82(8)^3 = 418$.

$$(d')^3 = \frac{418}{0.67} = 625 \quad \text{and} \quad d' = 8.8 \text{ in.}$$

Ten inches is the nearest depth on the market. If c is changed,

$$k_2 = \frac{0.82}{24} = 0.0342 \quad \text{(using } c \text{ in inches).}$$

$$c' = \frac{0.67}{0.0342} = 19.6 \text{ in.}$$

There are two possible recommendations: to space the joists at

20-in. centers or to use 2 by 10-in. joists. Since labor costs dictate, the probable choice would be the deeper joists, because fewer would require placement.

In many problems where the function of the independent variable is a power function, arithmetic calculations are minimized if k is merely indicated instead of being computed. For joint variations, this method is equally useful.

Example 7.20

The frictional loss H_f of pressure in air flowing through a duct is given in inches of water as

$$H_f = \frac{f L V^2}{4005 D}$$

where f = coefficient of friction
L = length of duct, ft
V = velocity of air, in fpm
D = duct diameter, ft

(a) The frictional loss for a 120 ft duct was 0.048 in. of water. What would the loss be if the duct was shortened to 88 ft?

(b) If the frictional loss is 0.5 in. of water for a 6-in.-diameter duct, what would it be if a 1-ft duct was substituted?

(c) The air velocity in a certain duct is reduced from 242 to 181 cfm. What percentage effect does this have on the frictional loss of head?

SOLUTION

(Avoid finding the constant of proportionality.)

(a) All variables are constant except H_f and L.

$$H_{f_1} = k L_1 \qquad \text{and} \qquad H_{f_2} = k L_2$$

Therefore,

$$\frac{H_{f_2}}{H_{f_1}} = \frac{k L_2}{k L_1} \qquad \text{and} \qquad H_{f_2} = H_{f_1}\left(\frac{L_2}{L_1}\right)$$

Substituting the given values,

$$H_{f_2} = 0.048\left(\frac{88}{120}\right) = 0.0352 \text{ in. of water}$$

(b) All variables are constant except H_f and D.

$$H_{f_1} = \frac{K}{D_1} \qquad \text{and} \qquad H_{f_2} = \frac{K}{D_2}$$

Therefore,

$$H_{f_2} = H_{f_1}\left(\frac{D_1}{D_2}\right) = 0.50\left(\frac{\frac{1}{2}}{1}\right) = 0.25 \text{ in. of water}$$

(c) $$H_{f_1} = k(V_1)^2 \qquad \text{and} \qquad H_{f_2} = k(V_2)^2$$

Therefore,

$$\frac{H_{f_2}}{H_{f_1}} = \frac{k(V_2)^2}{k(V_1)^2} = \left(\frac{V_2}{V_1}\right)^2 = \left(\frac{181}{242}\right)^2$$

$$= (0.748)^2 = 0.56 = 56\% \text{ reduction}$$

(*Note:* In all quotients of powers relationships, do not raise the variables to the given power, but find the quotient and raise the quotient to the desired power.)

Problem Set 7.7

1–8

(a) *Plot each pair of parametric equations, using as domain the largest possible subset of $|x| \le 5$.*

(b) *Find the rectangular equation for each pair.*

1. $x = 2t$, $y = \frac{1}{2}t$
2. $x = 3t - 1$, $y = 3t + 1$
3. $3x = 4 - t$, $2y = 5 + t$
4. $x = \frac{1}{3}t + 3$, $3y = t$
5. $x = t^2$, $y = 1 - t^2$
6. $x = t^3 - 4$, $y = t^3 + 6$
7. $x = \sqrt{t}$, $y = \sqrt{t} - 1$
8. $x = \frac{1}{2}t^2 + 2$, $y = 2t^2 - 3$

9–20

Find all values to three significant figures and include the proper units in your answer.

9. Two cities are exactly 20 miles apart. Find this distance in (a) feet; (b) yards; (c) kilometers; (d) nautical miles.

10. The weather report from San Francisco, California, frequently gives the wind velocity in knots. For a 20-knot wind, find the equivalent in (a) mph; (b) fps; (c) meters per second (mps).

11. Roofing material is sold by the square, which is 100 sq ft. Convert this to (a) square yards; (b) square meters; (c) square inches.

12. A European highway was 15 m wide, 23.5 k long, and paved with 2 deci's (decimeters) of concrete. Restate these facts in appropriate U.S. measurements.

13. State the volume of a quart of water in (a) ounces; (b) gallons; (c) cubic inches; (d) cubic centimeters; (e) liters.

14. A circular mil is the area of a circle 1 mil (0.001 in.) in diameter. Number 00 wire has a diameter of 365 mils. Find its area in (a) circular mils; (b) square inches; (c) square millimeters.

15. Using the metric ton as unity, express as a percentage (a) the current U.S. ton; (b) the British long ton.

16. Using a kilogram as unity, express as a percentage (a) 1 oz; (b) 1 lb; (c) 1 milligram (mg); (d) the druggist's grain.

17. Change 11.2 g/cc to (a) kilograms per cubic meter; (b) pounds per cubic inch; (c) pounds per cubic foot.

18. One standard atmosphere is a barometric reading of 76 cm of mercury at 0°C. Give its equivalent in (a) inches of mercury; (b) feet of water; (c) psi; (d) psf; (e) kg/m^2.

19. A pipe discharging 5 gpm is delivering how many (a) cubic inches per second? (b) cfm? (c) cubic centimeters per second? (d) liters per minute?

20. A legal speed of 65 mph is how many (a) fpm? (b) fps? (c) km/hr? (d) meters per second?

21–30

Use three significant figures for all answers. Note that not all problems are proportional variations.

21. The inductance L of an air-core coil is

$$L = \frac{rN^2}{9r + 10l}$$

where r = mean radius of core, in.
  N = total number of turns of wire
  l = length of the coil, in.

A certain coil was wound on a cardboard tube 4 in. in diameter and 6 in. long, and contained 240 turns of wire. What is the percentage *change* in the inductance if
(a) 360 turns were used?
(b) an 8-in. coil length had been used?
(c) a 6-in.-diameter tube had been used?
For each part, only change the one variable mentioned and retain all others at their original value.

22. Petroff's equation for the frictional force on a lightly loaded journal bearing is

$$F = 4\pi^2 \mu r^2 h_s \frac{L}{c}$$

If r, the shaft radius, is made 3 times as large and c, the clearance between the shaft and the bearing, is changed from 0.003 to 0.005 in., what is the percentage *change* in F?

23. Thin-walled cylinders collapse under a critical pressure w_c, where

$$w_c = KE\left(\frac{t}{d}\right)^3 \text{ psi}$$

A satisfactory design used $\frac{1}{16}$ in. material for a cylinder 3 in. in diameter. It was decided to double the working pressure w_c. To retain the $\frac{1}{16}$ in. material, what diameter tube should be used?

24. The Vickers hardness number of metals is given by $V = \dfrac{P}{0.593d^2}$, where d is the diagonal of the impression of a diamond point under a load of P kilograms. A test of two metals gave a diagonal measurement 2.32 times larger for metal A under a 50-kg load than for metal B under a 120-kg load. What is the ratio of the Vickers number of metal A to that of metal B?

25. In vibration studies the following relationship is found:

$$d_d = d_s \frac{1}{1 - \left(\dfrac{w}{w_n}\right)^2}$$

Find the value of $\dfrac{w}{w_n}$ if $\dfrac{d_s}{d_d}$ is doubled and $\dfrac{w}{w_n}$ was originally a frequency ratio of $3 : 1$.

26. A formula in the hydraulics of closed conduits is

$$\frac{D^5}{f} = \frac{8LQ^2}{h_f \pi^2 g}$$

Find the percentage *change* in h_f if D is doubled and Q is halved.

27. The power output of an aircraft propeller is given by

$$P = C_p \rho n^3 D^5$$

where D is the propeller diameter and n is the speed of rotation, $n = \text{rpm}/88$. If a planned propeller diameter is increased by 50 per cent and the available horsepower is kept constant, what is the effect on the engine speed in rpm?

28. A column of mercury at a height h cm at a temperature $t°C$ is converted to standard conditions ($t = 0°C$) by

$$h_0 = h\left[1 - \frac{(m - L)t}{1 + mt}\right]$$

$$\text{where} \quad m = 0.000\,182$$

$$L = 1.84 \times 10^{-5}$$

If t is 40°C, find h_0 for an observed h of 72 cm.

29. Centrifugal force varies directly with the mass m, the radius of curvature r, and the square of the angular velocity v_a. It varies inversely with the gravitational constant g. If all quantities are doubled except the gravitational constant, which is decreased 1 per cent because of an increase in the elevation, what is the ratio of the new centrifugal force to the original one?

30. The deflection of a helical spring varies directly with the force F, the cube of the radius r of the helix, and its active number of coils n. It varies inversely as the modulus of rigidity G and the fourth power of the spring wire diameter d. G is affected by temperature and, for stainless steel, drops from 9.9×10^6 psi at 200°F to 9.6×10^6 psi at 400°F. If the wire diameter is increased by 10 per cent, does the new spring at 400°F deflect more or less than the original one at 200°F, and by what percentage?

7.13 / Chapter Review

1. A *relation* is a set of *ordered pairs* (x,y).

   To find the second component y, there is a *rule of correspondence* that may be a list, a graph, or a method of calculation.

   If every first component in a relation has exactly one second component, this particular relation is called a *function* and the second component may be written as $f(x)$.

2. The *domain* of a relation is the set of elements that form the replacement set for the first component of the ordered pairs of the relation.

   The *range* of a relation is the replacement set for the second component. The domain and range may be the set of real numbers or they may be limited by the conditions of the problem.

3. The first component of the ordered pair of a relation is called the *independent* variable, since values are assigned to it.

   The second component, found by the rule of correspondence, is called the *dependent* variable.

4. An *inverse* function of a given function interchanges the dependency; that is, the independent variable becomes the dependent variable and the dependent variable becomes the independent variable.

5. A function can be a relation of two or more variables.

6. A *coordinate grid* formed by two perpendicular number lines permits plotting all ordered pairs of real numbers on an XY plane. The graph of a function so plotted has a unique vertical y coordinate for every value of x in the domain.

7. *Observed data* may be just a series of points designated by their coordinates and connected by a line for the convenience of the travel of the eye.

Calculated data tend to form a smooth curve (including the straight line). In these cases any point on the curve has a meaningful interpretation.

8. *Inequalities in two variables* are graphed as areas since they represent all possible values of the second component of an ordered pair that are greater or less than the selected first component. The applicable area is shaded or cross-sectioned. When the line of the equality is included, it is drawn as a solid line and when it is excluded, it is drawn as a dashed line.

9. *Parametric equations* permit stating a functional relationship between two variables in terms of a third variable. Time is one of the most common interpretations of a parameter.

10. If variables are related, but the exact relationship is not known, they form a *variation*. A variation may be singly between two variables or jointly between several variables.

    A *direct variation* is one in which the dependent variable increases with the increase of the independent variable.

    An *inverse variation* is one in which the dependent variable decreases with the increase of the independent variable.

    Variations can be converted to equations by introducing a constant of proportionality.

Problem Set 7.8 (Chapter Review)

1. In testing air for radioactivity, it is blown through two identical filters. The actual level of radioactivity A is found by

$$A = \frac{n_1{}^2}{n_1 - n_2}$$

where n_1 and n_2 represent the levels measured on each filter, respectively. If the Geiger count for filter 2 is one third of that for filter 1, what is the total count A in terms of n_1?

2. Two hardness scales in current use are the Brinell and the Rockwell. Plot the given data and estimate if a linear relationship appears likely.

Brinell number	495	477	415	375	285	255
Rockwell number	52	50	45	40	30	25

3. Plot $y > |x|$ for $-4 \le x \le 4$.

4. Eddy current in thin metal sheets produce power losses given as

$$P_e = \frac{(\pi t f B)^2}{6\rho 10^{16}} \qquad \text{watts/cm}^3$$

where t = the thickness of the metal in cm, and will be doubled

f = the cycles per second, and will be tripled

ρ = the specific resistance, and will be halved

What is the ratio $P_{e_{new}}/P_{e_{old}}$?

5. Plot $x = 2t^3 - 5$ and $y = 5t^3 - 2$ for the domain $-3 \le x \le 2$.
6. Plot a relation such that any point P lies on the line $2x + y = 0$ and the coordinates of P satisfy the inequality $(x - 2) > y > (x - 4)$.
7. In an imperfect impact, the energy loss Q is

$$Q = \frac{(v_1 - v_2)^2(1 - e^2)m_1 m_2}{2(m_1 + m_2)}$$

(a) Find m_1 as a function of m_2.
(b) What is the effect on Q if the coefficient of restitution e is changed from 0.745 to 0.484, all other terms being unchanged?

8. A wheel of radius r and a moment of inertia I has a cable wrapped around it holding a mass M. The change in the velocity of the mass, called the acceleration a, is given by

$$a = g\frac{M}{M + \dfrac{I}{r^2}}$$

(a) Find M as a function of a.
(b) If g is the gravitational constant, 32.2 ft/sec^2,

I is 4 ft-lb sec^2.

M is $\dfrac{\text{weight}}{g} = \dfrac{W}{g}$

r is 2 ft

plot the acceleration a for the domain $10 \le W \le 60$ lb in increments of 10 lb.
(c) What is the percentage change in M if the only change made is to reduce the radius to one half its present size? (This can be done by changing the mass of the wheel.)

9. Distance in rectilinear motion is given by

$$s = v_0 t + \tfrac{1}{2}at^2$$

(a) What is the distance when the time is $(t_0 + h)$?
(b) Find a as a function of s.
(c) Given $v = v_0 + at$, express s as a function of v, and write the result in simplified form.

10. A sonic nondestructive testing machine determines the modulus of elasticity E of various metals as

$$E = \frac{W}{g}\left(\frac{2\pi L^2 N}{m^2 k}\right)^2$$

(a) Find the natural frequency N of the specimen as a function of the length L of the specimen.

(b) The radius of gyration k is a dimension based upon the shape of the specimen. If k and L are doubled, what is the new natural frequency N' in terms of the original one if all other values remain unchanged?

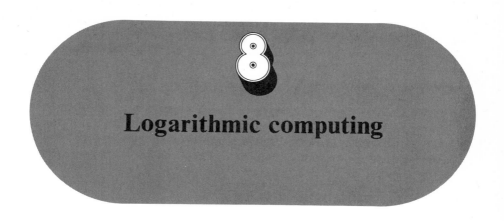

Logarithmic computing

8.01 / Introduction

Just as the use of the slide rule was presented in Chapter 2, without developing the theory, this chapter will cover the use of logarithmic tables to perform certain types of calculations. For almost 400 years logarithms were used primarily for ease in the trigonometric calculations of surveying, navigation, astronomy, and warfare. Today these tedious calculations are quickly and easily performed on the electric desk calculator. The newer models, which tend to be somewhat expensive, are even preprogrammed to solve these types of problems with only the depression of one or two keys.

However, there remain three excellent reasons for retaining the ability to calculate by logarithms. Survey parties in highly inaccessible locations usually want to partially check their observations before making the arduous trip back. Navigators of small craft may still make sun or star observations for finding their latitude and longitude and they lack electric calculators. Isolation is thus the first reason.

In a surprising number of fields of modern technology, as subsequent problem sets will show, logarithms are needed to find decimal powers or roots of numbers. Although the general-purpose slide rule with the log-log scales can quickly perform this type of calculation, the scales on those slide rules are not easily read. Only two significant figures are meaningful for answers over 50 and the graduated interval between 5000 and 10,000 is 500 units.

Finally, modern technology has found many natural phenomena are logarithmic relations. The relationship cannot be used unless the technician can quickly and correctly find the numerical value of the logarithm of a given quantity.

This chapter will therefore concentrate on these three aspects of logarithmic calculations, with the exception that calculations involving trigonometry will be deferred to a later chapter. Problems involving simple multiplications and divisions will be minimized, as these should habitually be done on the desk calculator or by slide rule whenever possible.

8.02 / Common logarithms

Theoretically, there are infinitely many logarithmic systems that could be devised. Only two have proved necessary for modern mathematics, natural logarithms and common logarithms. This chapter deals exclusively with common logarithms, based upon the number 10, the same base as the decimal system of enumeration used in arithmetic.

Scientific notation, met in Section 1.15, is closely related to common logarithms. If the number 27,642 was a factor in a problem, it could be written in scientific notation as 2.7642×10^4, where the first portion identifies the digits of the number without regard to size and 10^4 gives its size. All that is needed to convert this scientific-notational form to common-logarithmic form is to find what power of 10 is exactly 2.7642. The common logarithm of a given number is the exponent of 10 that yields the given number. In symbols, if $10^x = 2.7642$, then x is the common logarithm of 2.7642.

By inspection, the exponent must be greater than 0, since $10^0 = 1$, and less than 1, since $10^1 = 10$. If a table of the powers of 10 for 0.1 increments of the exponent between 0 and 1 is prepared, it looks like this:

Exponent, x	0	0.1	0.2	0.3	0.4	0.5	0.6	0.7	0.8	0.9	1.0
Power, 10^x	1.00	1.26	1.58	2.00	2.51	3.16	3.98	5.01	6.31	7.94	10.00

These values are plotted in Figure 8.1.

Looking at the graph, the exponent for the power of 10 near 2.7642 appears to be near 0.44. So a new table of powers of 10 for exponents from 0.4410 to 0.4420 by increments of 0.0002 gives these values:

Exponent, x	0.4410	0.4412	0.4414	0.4416	0.4418	0.4420
Power, 10^x	2.761	2.762	2.763	2.764	2.766	2.767

If the problem warrants greater accuracy, the following values can be computed to six places and rounded to five places for use:

Exponent, x	0.441 538	0.441 554	0.441 570
Power, 10^x	2.7640	2.7641	2.7642

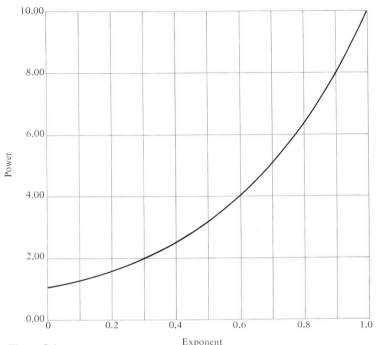

Figure 8.1
Powers of 10

Restating these findings,

$$27{,}642 = 2.7642 \times 10^4 = 10^{0.44157} \times 10^4 = 10^{0.44157 + 4} = 10^{4.44157}$$

To avoid having to write the base 10 over and over again when calculations are performed, logarithmic notation is used. In this notation, $27{,}642 = 10^{4.44157}$ is written as

$$\log 27{,}642 = 4.441\ 57$$

read "the logarithm of 27,642 is 4.441 57."

If for any reason the base of the logarithm needs to be written, it is shown as a subscript after the word log, as $\log_{10} 27{,}642 = 4.44157$.

Knowing that $\log 27{,}642 = \log 2.7642 \times 10^4 = 0.44157 + 4$, it is very easy to find the logarithms of other numbers having these same digits for significant figures. For example,

$$\log 276.42 = \log 2.7642 \times 10^2 = 0.44157 + 2$$

$$\log 2.7642 = \log 2.7642 \times 10^0 = 0.44157$$

$$\log 0.27642 = \log 2.7642 \times 10^{-1} = 0.44157 - 1$$

$$\log 0.002\ 764\ 2 = \log 2.7642 \times 10^{-3} = 0.44157 - 3$$

The number 10 is called the *base* for the common logarithms. The *logarithm* of a number is the exponent of the base to obtain the number.

For base 10, there are two important parts of a logarithm. The *characteristic* is the integer part, which is identical to the exponent of 10 in the scientific notation for the number. The *mantissa* (meaning "extra portion" in Latin) is the positive decimal part between 0 and 1, which is the exponent of 10 for the part of the number between 1 and 10 when the number is written in scientific notation. For example,

$$\log 0.002\,764\,2 = \log(2.7642 \times 10^{-3}) = \log(10^{0.44157} \times 10^{-3}) = 0.44157 - 3$$

where the mantissa is 0.44157 and the characteristic is -3.

The number of decimal places in the mantissa are referred to as the *place value* of the table of logarithms. For example, a *five-place table* has *five digits* in the mantissa and can be used to identify a number with *five significant figures*.

8.03 / Rules for characteristics

Since the characteristic of a common logarithm is identical to the exponent given the 10 factor of scientific notation, any number written in that notation yields the characteristic by inspection.

Example 8.1
Find the characteristic of the common logarithm of (a) 3.562; (b) 356,000; (c) 0.03562.

SOLUTION
Write each number in scientific notation.
(a) $3.562 = 3.562 \times 10^0$. The characteristic $= 0$.
(b) $356,000 = 3.562 \times 10^5$. The characteristic $= 5$.
(c) $0.03562 = 3.562 \times 10^{-2}$. The characteristic $= -2$.

A negative characteristic causes certain computational difficulties since the mantissa is always a positive number. There are two actions that can be taken and the choice depends upon why the logarithms are being used.

Case 1
If the logarithms are to be used to perform calculations, including finding powers and roots, rewrite the negative characteristic by adding and subtracting a multiple of 10.

Thus -1 is replaced by $-1 + 10 - 10 = 9 - 10$ and 0.xxxxx $- 1$ is replaced by 9.xxxxx $- 10$, where xxxxx represents the mantissa. Similarly,

0.xxxxx − 4 is written as 6.xxxxx − 10. Since the mantissa for 2 is 0.3010, the logarithm of 0.2 would be written as 9.3010 − 10 and the logarithm of 0.0002 as 6.3010 − 10.

In some problems, such as root extractions, the computation may require the division of a logarithm by an integer. In these cases, instead of adding and subtracting 10, add and subtract 10 times the divisor. For roots, the divisor is the index number (the number that indicates what root is being extracted.)

Example 8.2

Given that $\log 2 = 0.3010$, find the best form of the logarithm for each of these root extractions: (a) $\sqrt{2.0}$; (b) $\sqrt{0.2}$; (c) $\sqrt[3]{0.02}$; (d) $\sqrt[4]{0.002}$.

SOLUTION

(a) $\log 2.0 = 0.3010$. (Since no negative characteristic is involved, no adjustment is made on the characteristic.)
(b) $\log 0.2 = 0.3010 − 1$ and the index number for square roots is 2. Since $2(10) = 20$ and $−1 + 20 − 20 = 19 − 20$, the best form for the logarithm of 0.2 is $19.3010 − 20$.
(c) $\log 0.02 = 0.3010 − 2$ and the index number is 3. Since $3(10) = 30$ and $−2 + 30 − 30 = 28 − 30$, the best form for the logarithm of 0.02 is $28.3010 − 30$.
(d) $\log 0.002 = 0.3010 − 3$ and the index number is 4. Since $4(10) = 40$ and $−3 + 40 − 40 = 37 − 40$, the best form for the logarithm of 0.002 is $37.3010 − 40$.

Case 2

If a logarithm with a negative characteristic is to be substituted into a formula, the entire logarithm is changed into a negative number.

Example 8.3

A formula for sound intensity is $D = 20 \log \dfrac{I_1}{I_2}$. Find D for $\dfrac{I_1}{I_2} = 0.02$.

SOLUTION

$$D = 20 \log 0.02$$

$$\log 0.02 = 0.3010 − 2 = −2.0000 + 0.3010 = −1.6990$$

$$D = 20(−1.6990) = −33.98 = −34 \text{ (rounded off)}$$

Problem Set 8.1

1–6

Determine the size (number of places) of logarithmic table that should be used for each of the following computations. (It is recommended that Section 1.11 be reviewed. As additional information, the commonly available logarithmic tables run from three to six places. Tables of seven or more places exist but are not readily available.)

1. The following sum is to be multiplied by another factor using logarithms:
$$2.1746 + 34.172\ 65 + 1,276,000 + 0.074$$

2. The following difference is to be multiplied by another factor using logarithms:
$$(36.22 + 150.78) - (92.14 + 13.67)$$

3. 3.1416 is to be multiplied by 2222.
4. 3.1416 is to be multiplied by 2.2222.
5. 3.1416 is to be divided by 2222.
6. 3.1416 is to be divided by the product of 2222 and 3.

7 and 8

Write, as a single integer, the characteristic of the logarithm of the given number.

7. (a) 100　　　　　　　(d) 0.0001　　　　　　(g) $\dfrac{1}{10}$

　　(b) 10,000　　　　　(e) 1,000,000　　　　(h) 100,000,000

　　(c) 0.01　　　　　　(f) 0.000 001　　　　(i) $\dfrac{1}{1000}$

8. (a) 2000　　　　　　　(d) 200　　　　　　　(g) $\dfrac{2}{10}$

　　(b) $\dfrac{1}{20}$　　　　　　(e) 2,000,000　　　　(h) $\dfrac{2}{100}$

　　(c) $\dfrac{1}{200}$　　　　　(f) $\dfrac{1}{2,000,000}$　　(i) 20

9–17

Given that the mantissa of 4 is 0.6021, write the best form of the logarithm of the given number, assuming that a multiplication is the assigned arithmetic computation.

9. 0.40	**12.** 4000	**15.** 4,000,000,000
10. 0.040	**13.** 0.004 00	**16.** 4.000×10^{-12}
11. 4.000	**14.** 0.000 040 000 0	**17.** $\frac{1}{25}$

18–26

Roots are being extracted using logarithms. Write the best form of the logarithm of the given number whose root is desired. The five-place mantissa for 6 is 0.77815.

18. $\sqrt{60}$	**21.** $\sqrt{0.06\ 000}$	**24.** $\sqrt[3]{0.600\ 00}$
19. $\sqrt{6000}$	**22.** $\sqrt[3]{6}$	**25.** $\sqrt[4]{0.600\ 00}$
20. $\sqrt{0.6000}$	**23.** $\sqrt[3]{0.0600}$	**26.** $\sqrt[4]{0.060\ 000\ 0}$

27–34

Given that $\log 6 = 0.77815$, write in the best form the logarithm that appears in each of the following.

27. $25 \log 0.60$

28. $\dfrac{25}{\log 0.06}$

29. $\dfrac{1.7248 + \log 60.000}{3.5291}$

30. $492.35 - \dfrac{\log 60,000}{2.0335}$

31. $\dfrac{3.1416 + \log 0.060\ 00}{\log 0.060\ 00}$

32. $\dfrac{0.752\ 43}{0.752\ 43 - \log 0.600\ 00}$

33. $\sqrt[3]{\log 0.000\ 600}$

34. $\sqrt[5]{\log 0.006\ 000}$

8.04 / Rules for mantissas

There are three basic facts about the mantissa of a logarithm:
(1) It is the exponent of 10 to produce a number between 1 and 10.
(2) It is always a positive decimal between 0 and 1.
(3) The mantissa of a logarithm is found in tables.

Example 8.4
Using Table 7 of the Appendix, find (a) log 2.2060; (b) log 673,000; (c) log 0.094510.

SOLUTION

(a) 1. Write the number in scientific notation:

$$\log 2.2060 = \log(2.2060 \times 10^0)$$

2. Find the characteristic:

$$\log 2.2060 = (\log 2.2060) + 0$$

3. Find the mantissa from table:

$$\log 2.2060 = 0.34361 + 0 = 0.34361$$

(b) 1. $\qquad \log 673{,}000 = \log(6.7300 \times 10^5)$

2. $\qquad\qquad\qquad = (\log 6.7300) + 5$

3. $\qquad\qquad\qquad = 0.82802 + 5$

Thus, $\log 673{,}000 = 5.82802$.

(c) 1. $\qquad \log 0.094510 = \log(9.4510 \times 10^{-2})$

2. $\qquad\qquad\qquad = (\log 9.4510) - 2$

3. $\qquad\qquad\qquad = 0.97548 - 2$

Thus,

$$\log 0.094510 = 0.97548 - 2$$

$$= 8.97548 - 10 \qquad \text{(computational form)}$$

$$= -1.02452 \qquad \text{(formula form)}$$

A mantissa should never contain more digits than the given data warrants. The principle established in Chapter 1 was to calculate to one more significant figure than the least accurate data and then to reduce the answer to the correct number of significant figures for that data. Three-place tables are the least accurate tables that are used.

As a general rule, published logarithmic tables read *directly* to one less significant figure than the number of places. Thus, a four-place table reads directly to the first three significant figures and a five-place table directly to four. The most widely available seven-place table reads directly to only five significant figures and it is quite a thick volume. A new table published by the National Bureau of Standards as *AMS 55* has a 10-place table, but reads directly to but three significant figures. The two most common handbooks discussed in Chapter 1, the CRC and McNeese and Hoag, both contain five-place tables, as does the Appendix of this book.

Since most tables read directly to one less significant figure than the number of places, the value for the final significant digit is found by interpolation. Figure 8.1 shows clearly that the logarithmic function is certainly nonlinear. Figure 8.2 has been drawn for just a small portion of that function, specifically for the domain $1010 \le x \le 1020$. (Mantissas are not affected by a decimal point.)

Figure 8.1 shows that the function of $\log x$ has its greatest curvature at the left end of the plot, so this was the reason for selecting the domain

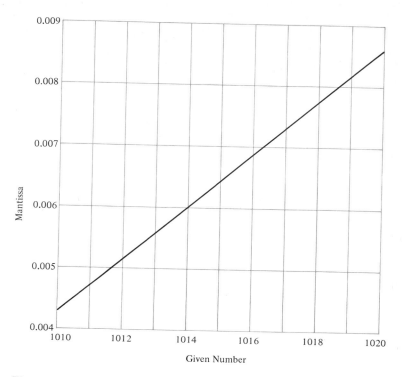

Figure 8.2
Values of mantissa—five-place table

chosen. However, the graph shown in Figure 8.2 is linear for all practical purposes. This means that using a five-place table, linear interpolation is accurate for mantissas with five significant figures. This finding cannot be extended; that is, it would be incorrect to try and find a six-place mantissa by interpolating from a four-place table.

Linear interpolation was explained in detail in Section 1.17 and the same technique is used here. Most logarithmic tables of five or more places carry on the right side a wide column headed "Proportional Parts," which greatly simplifies the process of interpolation. An example follows which first reviews interpolation and then repeats the same problem using these proportional parts.

TABLE 7
Five-Place Mantissas for Common Logarithms†

N	0	1	2	3	4	5	6	7	8	9
100	00 000	043	087	130	173	217	260	303	346	389
101	00 432	475	518	561	604	647	689	732	775	817
102	00 860	903	945	988	*030	*072	*115	*157	*199	*242
103	01 284	326	368	410	452	494	536	578	620	662
104	01 703	745	787	828	870	912	953	995	*036	*078
105	02 119	160	202	243	284	325	366	407	449	490
106	02 531	572	612	653	694	735	776	816	857	898
107	02 938	979	*019	*060	*100	*141	*181	*222	*262	*302
108	03 342	383	423	463	503	543	583	623	663	703
109	03 743	782	822	862	902	941	981	*021	*060	*100
110	04 139	179	218	258	297	336	376	415	454	493
111	04 532	571	610	650	689	727	766	805	844	883
112	04 922	961	999	*038	*077	*115	*154	*192	*231	*269
113	05 308	346	385	423	461	500	538	576	614	652
114	05 690	729	767	805	843	881	918	956	994	*032
115	06 070	108	145	183	221	258	296	333	371	408
116	06 446	483	521	558	595	633	670	707	744	781
117	06 819	856	893	930	967	*004	*041	*078	*115	*151
118	07 188	225	262	298	335	372	408	445	482	518
119	07 555	591	628	664	700	737	773	809	846	882
120	07 918	954	990	*027	*063	*099	*135	*171	*207	*243
121	08 279	314	350	386	422	458	493	529	565	600
122	08 636	672	707	743	778	814	849	884	920	955
123	08 991	*026	*061	*096	*132	*167	*202	*237	*272	*307
124	09 342	377	412	447	482	517	552	587	621	656
125	09 691	726	760	795	830	864	899	934	968	*003
126	10 037	072	106	140	175	209	243	278	312	346
127	10 380	415	449	483	517	551	585	619	653	687
128	10 721	755	789	823	857	890	924	958	992	*025
129	11 059	093	126	160	193	227	261	294	327	361
130	11 394	428	461	494	528	561	594	628	661	694
131	11 727	760	793	826	860	893	926	959	992	*024
132	12 057	090	123	156	189	222	254	287	320	352
133	12 385	418	450	483	516	548	581	613	646	678
134	12 710	743	775	808	840	872	905	937	969	*001
135	13 033	066	098	130	162	194	226	258	290	322
136	13 354	386	418	450	481	513	545	577	609	640
137	13 672	704	735	767	799	830	862	893	925	956
138	13 988	*019	*051	*082	*114	*145	*176	*208	*239	*270
139	14 301	333	364	395	426	457	489	520	551	582
140	14 613	644	675	706	737	768	799	829	860	891
141	14 922	953	983	*014	*045	*076	*106	*137	*168	*198
142	15 229	259	290	320	351	381	412	442	473	503
143	15 534	564	594	625	655	685	715	746	776	806
144	15 836	866	897	927	957	987	*017	*047	*077	*107
145	16 137	167	197	227	256	286	316	346	376	406
146	16 435	465	495	524	554	584	613	643	673	702
147	16 732	761	791	820	850	879	909	938	967	997
148	17 026	056	085	114	143	173	202	231	260	289
149	17 319	348	377	406	435	464	493	522	551	580
150	17 609	638	667	696	725	754	782	811	840	869
N	0	1	2	3	4	5	6	7	8	9

Prop. Pts.

	44	43	42
1	4.4	4.3	4.2
2	8.8	8.6	8.4
3	13.2	12.9	12.6
4	17.6	17.2	16.8
5	22.0	21.5	21.0
6	26.4	25.8	25.2
7	30.8	30.1	29.4
8	35.2	34.4	33.6
9	39.6	38.7	37.8

	41	40	39
1	4.1	4.0	3.9
2	8.2	8.0	7.8
3	12.3	12.0	11.7
4	16.4	16.0	15.6
5	20.5	20.0	19.5
6	24.6	24.0	23.4
7	28.7	28.0	27.3
8	32.8	32.0	31.2
9	36.9	36.0	35.1

	38	37	36
1	3.8	3.7	3.6
2	7.6	7.4	7.2
3	11.4	11.1	10.8
4	15.2	14.8	14.4
5	19.0	18.5	18.0
6	22.8	22.2	21.6
7	26.6	25.9	25.2
8	30.4	29.6	28.8
9	34.2	33.3	32.4

	35	34	33
1	3.5	3.4	3.3
2	7.0	6.8	6.6
3	10.5	10.2	9.9
4	14.0	13.6	13.2
5	17.5	17.0	16.5
6	21.0	20.4	19.8
7	24.5	23.8	23.1
8	28.0	27.2	26.4
9	31.5	30.6	29.7

	32	31	30
1	3.2	3.1	3.0
2	6.4	6.2	6.0
3	9.6	9.3	9.0
4	12.8	12.4	12.0
5	16.0	15.5	15.0
6	19.2	18.6	18.0
7	22.4	21.7	21.0
8	25.6	24.8	24.0
9	28.8	27.9	27.0

† From P. R. Rider. *Plane and Spherical Trigonometry*. New York: The Macmillan Company, 1965.

Figure 8.3

A sample page from a five-place logarithmic table

Example 8.5

Using a five-place table, find log 1.2886. (See Figure 8.3.)

FIRST SOLUTION

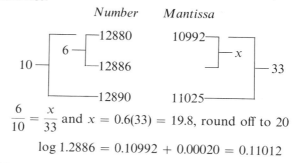

Number   Mantissa

$\dfrac{6}{10} = \dfrac{x}{33}$ and $x = 0.6(33) = 19.8$, round off to 20

$$\log 1.2886 = 0.10992 + 0.00020 = 0.11012$$

ALTERNATIVE SOLUTION

From the table, log 1.2880 = 0.10992.

From the proportional parts section of Figure 8.3, under 33, find the value for the fifth digit, 6. It is 19.8 and this value is rounded off to 20.

$$\log 1.2880 = 0.10992$$
$$\text{value under 33 for } 6 = \underline{20}$$
$$\log 1.2886 = 0.11012$$

Note that the difference between the mantissa of 1.2880 and the next one in sequence will be in the right-hand column near that mantissa. Subtracting only the last digits of these mantissas, $5 - 2 = 3$, so 33 is used for the difference. The asterisk (*) in front of *025 indicates that the first two digits of the mantissa have changed from 10 to the next number, 11.

If the decimal portion of the proportional-parts table is rounded off, the obvious question is why is it given. It is *never* used in finding a mantissa. It will be used frequently in the next section when the inverse operation of finding a number from the mantissa is studied.

There should be no feeling that using a three-place logarithmic table is some sort of a mathematical sin. Many problems warrant a slide-rule solution and three-place logarithms are adequate. Using a logarithmic table with more places than are warranted merely results in a loss of time with no gain whatsoever.

Problem Set 8.2

1–50

Using Table 7 in the Appendix, find the logarithm of each of the following to five places.

Problems 1–20 are direct-reading problems and Problems 21–40 require interpolation.

For Problems 1–40, use only a positive characteristic, followed by a subtraction where needed.

For Problems 41–50, show the entire logarithm of any number smaller than 1 as a completely negative number.

1. 214	**14.** 0.9772	**27.** 0.184 56	**39.** 3.9804×10^{-2}
2. 6.89	**15.** 0.1002	**28.** 0.016 756	**40.** 3.6303×10^{-4}
3. 6491	**16.** 95.50	**29.** 1.2499	**41.** 0.25
4. 47.92	**17.** 2.17×10^{-10}	**30.** 114.88	**42.** 0.38
5. 5,808,000	**18.** 0.1024	**31.** 14.466	**43.** 0.0881
6. 0.0537	**19.** 7.008	**32.** 1.2357	**44.** 0.000 794
7. 0.899	**20.** 4.08×10^{-9}	**33.** 195.08	**45.** 0.007 591
8. 85,290,000	**21.** 58,057	**34.** 15.598	**46.** 0.066 07
9. 2884	**22.** 68,036	**35.** 0.199 54	**47.** 0.000 398 1
10. 39,820	**23.** 7.0088	**36.** 0.016 212	**48.** 2.88×10^{-4}
11. 0.003 635	**24.** 550.82	**37.** 1.8692×10^{3}	**49.** 0.351 51
12. 0.3163	**25.** 209.73	**38.** 2.0411×10^{6}	**50.** 0.002 345 6
13. 7.94	**26.** 2.4495		

51–60

Find the four-place logarithm of the given number.

51. 1.741	**54.** 4.074	**57.** 6,919,000	**59.** 0.4898
52. 3.742	**55.** 0.4651	**58.** 0.4063	**60.** 0.000 631
53. 457	**56.** 0.006 761		

61–70

Find the three-place logarithm of the given number.

61. 75,000	**64.** 0.0618	**67.** 408	**70.** 0.0302
62. 6.0	**65.** 37.8	**68.** 12,345	
63. 0.687	**66.** 0.0202	**69.** 0.000 182	

8.05 / Antilogarithms

An **antilogarithm** is the number whose logarithm is known. Since log 2 is 0.3010, the antilogarithm of 0.3010 is 2. Antilogarithm is usually shortened to antilog in computational headings.

In finding antilogarithms, linear interpolation is again used and the tabulation of proportional parts reduces the arithmetic.

Example 8.6
Find the antilog of 0.41162.

SOLUTION

The mantissa 41162 appears in a five-place table, so the correct answer can be written without calculations. The digits of the answer are 25800. The characteristic, 0, gives the decimal point after the first significant digit.

$$\text{Thus, antilog } 0.41162 = 2.5800 \times 10^0 = 2.5800$$

(Note that the use of a five-place mantissa has been taken to indicate that five significant figures are desired in the result.)

Example 8.7
Find the antilog of 3.17032.

SOLUTION

Using a five-place table, the closest smaller mantissa listed is 17026, corresponding to the number 1480. The difference to the next-listed mantissa is 30 and the difference to the given mantissa is 6. In the table of proportional parts under 30, 6 appears to the right of the digit 2. The digits of the answer are 14802. Since the characteristic is 3, the number desired, antilog $3.17032 = 1.4802 \times 10^3 = 1480.2$.

The problem would actually be done by tabulation as follows:

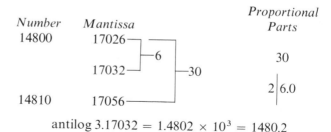

$$\text{antilog } 3.17032 = 1.4802 \times 10^3 = 1480.2$$

Example 8.8
Find the antilog of 8.74616 − 10.

SOLUTION

The nearest smaller mantissa is 74609, corresponding to the number 5574. The difference between adjacent mantissas is 7 and to the given mantissa 6. Under 7 in the table of proportional parts, 6.3 is closest to 6, so the fifth digit is 9. The digits of the answer are 55749. Thus, antilog $8.74616 = 5.5749 \times 10^{-2} = 0.055\,749$.

Example 8.9
Find the antilog of −2.14156.

SOLUTION

This logarithm must be rewritten so that the decimal part is positive. Adding and subtracting 10 gives $7.85844 - 10$:

$$\begin{array}{r} 10.00000 - 10 \\ - 2.14156 \\ \hline 7.85844 - 10 \end{array}$$

The nearest smaller mantissa is 85842, corresponding to the number 7218. The difference between adjacent mantissas is 6 and to the given mantissa, 2. Under 6 in the table of proportional parts, 1.8 is closest, so the fifth digit is 3. The digits of the answer are 72183. Thus, antilog $7.85844 - 10 = 7.2183 \times 10^{-3} = 0.007\,218\,3$.

Problem Set 8.3

Find the antilogarithm of each number. (Problems 1–20 are direct reading while 21–50 require interpolation. Note that problems 51–60 are completely negative logarithms.)

1. 0.4133	**16.** $9.82000 - 10$	**31.** 0.56000	**46.** 2.46802
2. 0.8202	**17.** 0.8456	**32.** 0.47000	**47.** 3.69120
3. 2.0013	**18.** 3.7852	**33.** 9.23075	**48.** $0.40145 - 10$
4. $9.405 - 10$	**19.** 6.7701	**34.** $2.19210 - 10$	**49.** $9.24000 - 10$
5. $7.3032 - 10$	**20.** $9.4863 - 10$	**35.** 2.17050	**50.** 10.20000
6. 8.4014	**21.** 0.98902	**36.** 5.17320	**51.** -1.09691
7. $8.4442 - 10$	**22.** 0.97910	**37.** 1.25400	**52.** -1.06890
8. 1.233	**23.** $9.93104 - 10$	**38.** 3.24282	**53.** -0.56400
9. $8.935 - 10$	**24.** 4.90310	**39.** 1.11111	**54.** -3.180
10. 6.0026	**25.** 3.74040	**40.** $6.66666 - 10$	**55.** -4.19997
11. 0.2878	**26.** 8.70080	**41.** 1.23456	**56.** -1.96900
12. 3.2760	**27.** 0.75010	**42.** 3.45678	**57.** -2.66999
13. $9.24030 - 10$	**28.** 1.68000	**43.** $9.87654 - 10$	**58.** -4.21000
14. 2.29070	**29.** $9.66465 - 10$	**44.** 6.54023	**59.** -3.95740
15. 1.5800	**30.** 8.60200	**45.** 8.76543	**60.** -2.99801

8.06 / Logarithmic computations

Logarithmic computations are based upon these four principles:
(1) The logarithm of the product of several factors is the sum of the logarithms of the factors of the product. For example, $\log(3.2)(0.57) = \log 3.2 + \log 0.57$. In symbols,

$$\log abc = \log a + \log b + \log c$$

(2) The logarithm of the quotient of two numbers is the logarithm of the dividend minus the logarithm of the divisor. If there are multiple divisors, the logarithm of each divisor is subtracted. For example, $\log \dfrac{3.2}{0.57} = \log 3.2 - \log 0.57$. In symbols,

$$\log \frac{a}{b} = \log a - \log b$$

$$\log \frac{a}{bcd} = \log a - \log b - \log c - \log d$$

(3) The logarithm of the nth power of a number is n times the logarithm of the number. For example, $\log(3.2)^5 = 5 \log 3.2$. In symbols,

$$\log a^n = n \log a$$

(4) The logarithm of the nth root of a number is the logarithm of the number divided by n. For example, $\log \sqrt[3]{3.2} = \frac{1}{3}(\log 3.2)$ In symbols,

$$\log \sqrt[n]{a} = \frac{\log a}{n}.$$

It should be noted that when logarithms are used for computations, the *logarithm* of the arithmetic answer will be obtained first, *not* the arithmetic answer. Therefore, in solving arithmetic problems by logarithmic computations, the final step is always finding an antilogarithm.

Example 8.10
Using four place logarithms, find (a) 4 times 2; (b) 4 divided by 2; (c) 4 squared; (d) the square root of 4.

SOLUTION

(a)
$$\log 4 = 0.6021$$
$$\log 2 = 0.3010$$
$$\text{sum} = \log(4 \cdot 2) = 0.9031$$
$$\text{antilog} = 4 \cdot 2 = 8.000$$

(b)
$$\log 4 = 0.6021$$
$$\log 2 = 0.3010$$
$$\text{difference} = \log \frac{4}{2} = 0.3011$$

$$\text{antilog} = \frac{4}{2} = 2.001$$

(c)
$$\log 4 = 0.6021$$
$$2 \log 4 = 1.2042$$
$$\text{antilog} = 4^2 = 16.00$$

(d)
$$\log 4 = 0.6021$$
$$\tfrac{1}{2}\log 4 = 0.3010 \text{ (rounding off even)}$$
$$\text{antilog} = \sqrt{4} = 2.000.$$

The fact that the answer to part (b) is in error by 1 part in 2000 is no cause for alarm. Chapter 1 stressed the importance of selecting the degree of precision warranted. If 1 part in 2000 is not acceptable, a five-place table must be used.

Example 8.11
Using a five-place logarithmic table, find (a) the product of 0.2 and 0.4; (b) the quotient of 0.2 divided by 0.4; (c) the square of 0.4; (d) the square root of 0.4.

SOLUTION

(a)
$$\log 0.2 = 9.30103 - 10$$
$$\log 0.4 = 9.60206 - 10$$
$$\text{sum} = \log 0.2(0.4) = 18.90309 - 20$$
$$\log 0.2(0.4) = 8.90309 - 10 \quad \text{(characteristic simpli-}$$
$$\text{antilog} = 0.2(0.4) = 0.080\,000 \quad \text{fied by subtracting 10}$$
from both sides)

(b)
$$\log 0.2 = 19.30103 - 20 \quad \text{(characteristic adjusted}$$
$$\log 0.4 = 9.60206 - 10 \quad \text{so that the subtraction}$$
yields a positive man-
$$\text{difference} = \log \frac{0.2}{0.4} = 9.69897 - 10 \quad \text{tissa)}$$

$$\text{antilog} = \frac{0.2}{0.4} = 0.500\,00$$

(c)
$$\log 0.4 = 9.60206 - 10$$
$$2\log 0.4 = 19.20412 - 20$$
$$\log(0.4)^2 = 9.20412 - 10$$
$$\text{antilog} = (0.4)^2 = 0.160\,00$$

(d)
$$\log 0.4 = 9.60206 - 10$$
$$\log 0.4 = 19.60206 - 20 \quad \text{(characteristic adjusted}$$
$$\log \sqrt{0.4} = \tfrac{1}{2}\log 0.4 = 9.80103 - 10 \quad \text{for division by the index}$$
2)
$$\text{antilog} = \sqrt{0.4} = 0.632\,46$$

To increase the accuracy of the work and to further the concept that engineering calculations must be readily checkable, the labeling of each line should be done except in the few rare cases where it is obvious, such as in the adjustment of characteristics in Example 8.11(d). In most problems, the work will be clarified and the page turning in the tables will be minimized if the entire left-hand side of the problem is completed before any logarithm is found.

For problems involving both multiplication and division of three or more numbers, the logarithmic computation is complicated by the fact that some logarithms are added and others are subtracted. This can be avoided by using the **cologarithm,** which is the logarithm of the reciprocal of a number. If a cologarithm (abbreviated colog) is used, division by a number is replaced by multiplication by the reciprocal of the number and the logarithmic computation involves addition only. To find a cologarithm, the logarithm of a divisor is subtracted from the logarithm of 1, which is 0.00000. Replacing this 0 by $9.99999 + 0.00001 - 10$, which can be written as $9.9999(10) - 10$, for a problem involving a division by 2, the cologarithm of 2 is obtained as follows:

$$
\begin{array}{r}
\log 1 = 9.9 \quad 9 \quad 9 \quad 9(10) - 10 \\
-\log 2 = 0.3 \quad 0 \quad 1 \quad 0 \quad 3 \\
\hline
\text{colog } 2 = \log \tfrac{1}{2} = 9.6 \quad 9 \quad 8 \quad 9 \quad 7 - 10
\end{array}
$$

The above computation is not actually written, but the value of any logarithm found in the table is changed mentally to its cologarithm by subtracting, left to right, each digit in the table from 9 except the "last" digit, which is subtracted from 10. The "last" digit may not be the fifth digit; it is the last nonzero digit.

Example 8.12
Find the cologs of (a) 922.47; (b) 0.084 623; (c) 36.450; (d) 0.6223.

SOLUTION
(a)
$$\log 922.47 = 2.96496$$
$$\text{colog } 922.47 = 7.03504 - 10$$

(b)
$$\log 0.084623 = 8.92748 - 10 \qquad \text{(round even)}$$
$$\text{colog } 0.084623 = 1.07252$$

(c)
$$\log 36.450 = 1.56170 \qquad \text{(see Note)}$$
$$\text{colog } 36.450 = 8.43830 - 10$$

(d)
$$\log 0.6223 = 9.7940 - 10 \qquad \text{(see Note)}$$
$$\text{colog } 0.6223 = 0.2160$$

[*Note:* When no interpolation is required, cologs can be written by inspection from the table after the characteristic has been written. The actual logarithm would not be transcribed as it has been done in Example 8.12(c) and (d).]

8.07 / Suggestions on computations

All the basic principles needed for even highly complex calculations have been introduced. All that remains is to devise the easiest and best way to use them in solving a real problem.

Since many engineering and scientific problems involve the constant π, it is suggested that the student, on the proper page of his own table of five-place logarithms, pencil in neatly the logarithms of π, π^2, and $1/\pi$ given below.

$$\log \pi = 0.49715$$

$$\log \pi^2 = 0.99430$$

$$\log \frac{1}{\pi} = 9.50285 - 10$$

Example 8.13
(From the study of diffusion in gases.) Using five-place logarithms, find the value of t_{opt} if

$$t_{opt} = \frac{4L^2}{\pi^2 D}$$

where L = length of tube used = 50 cm
D = diameter of tube used = 0.1640 cm

SOLUTION
(This will be done in multiple steps so that the arrangement of the work is clarified before the actual calculations begin.)

Step 1
Write the logarithmic equation.

$$\log t_{opt} = \log 4 + 2 \log L + \operatorname{colog} \pi^2 + \operatorname{colog} D$$

$$\log t_{opt} = \log 4 + 2 \log 50 + \operatorname{colog} \pi^2 + \operatorname{colog} 0.1640$$

Step 2
Prepare a format for the work as follows:
(a) List above a double line all factors to be raised to a power, or to have a root extracted, or whose colog is needed and interpolation is required.
(b) Below the double line, provide a line and a title for every needed entry, including the answer.
(c) Draw a vertical line to represent the decimal point.
(d) Write all characteristics.

$$\log 50 = 1.$$
$$\log \pi^2 = 0.$$

$\log 4 = 0$		
$2 \log 50 = 3$		
$\text{colog } \pi^2 = 9$	-10	
$\text{colog } 0.1640 = 0$		
sum $= \log t_{opt} =$		
antilog $= t_{opt} =$		

Step 3

Using tables, find all mantissas and do the indicated operations. Align the mantissas vertically with care. The completed problem looks as follows:

$$\log 50 = 1.69897$$
$$\log \pi^2 = 0.99430$$

$\log 4 =$	0	60206	
$2 \log 50 =$	3	39794	
$\text{colog } \pi^2 =$	9	00570	$- 10$
$\text{colog } 0.1640 =$	0	78516	
sum $= \log t_{opt} =$	13	79086	$- 10$
antilog $= t_{opt} =$	6178 sec	$\approx$ 6180 sec	

Comment 1 The 50-cm length of tubing is really a conventional stock size rather than an exact measurement, and its precision must be estimated. It is assumed that it is correct to three significant figures. The diameter is correct to four significant figures.

Comment 2 Since most of the data are to four significant figures, or exact, five-place logarithms were used, but the final answer rounded off to 3, since 2 sec is not meaningful in this type of experiment.

Comment 3 Note that no calculations have been done on scratch paper. The colog 0.1640 can be read directly from the tables.

Example 8.14

The vibration of a circular steel rod in cycles per second is given by

$$\text{cps} = \frac{11.0}{2\pi} \sqrt{\frac{EI}{mL^4}}$$

where E = Young's modulus = 29.3×10^6 psi for spring steel

I = moment of inertia = $\frac{1}{4}\pi r^4$, in.^{4}

m = mass per unit length = $\dfrac{\pi r^2 \rho}{g}$

and for steel, with all units in inches $\dfrac{\rho}{g} = 7.33 \times 10^{-4}$

$$r = \text{radius of rod} = 0.031\ 12 \text{ in.}$$

$$L = \text{rod length} = 4.0200 \text{ in.}$$

Using logarithms, find the value of cps.

SOLUTION

Before any calculations are done, the problem is simplified.

$$\text{cps} = \frac{11.0}{2\pi}\sqrt{\frac{EI}{mL^4}} = \frac{11.0}{2\pi}\sqrt{\frac{29.3 \times 10^6(\frac{1}{4}\pi r^4)}{\frac{\rho}{g}\pi r^2 L^4}}$$

$$= \frac{1.1 \times 10^4}{2\pi}\sqrt{\frac{29.3 r^2}{4\frac{\rho}{g}L^4}} = \frac{1.1 \times 10^4 r}{4\pi L^2}\sqrt{\frac{29.3}{7.33 \times 10^{-4}}}$$

Finally,

$$\text{cps} = \frac{1.1 \times 10^6(0.031\ 12)}{4\pi(4.0200)^2}\sqrt{\frac{29.3}{7.33}}$$

$$\log \text{cps} = \log(1.1 \times 10^6) + \log 0.03112 + \text{colog } 4 + \text{colog } \pi$$
$$+\ 2\,\text{colog } 4.02 + \tfrac{1}{2}(\log 29.3 - \log 7.33)$$

$\log 4.0200 =$	0.60423
$2 \log 4.0200 =$	1.20846

$\log 29.3 =$	1.46687
$\log 7.33 =$	0.86510
difference $=$	0.60177

$\frac{1}{2}$ difference $=$	0|30084
$\log 1.1 \times 10^6 =$	6|04139
$\log 0.03112 =$	8|49304 $-$ 10
colog $4 =$	9|39794 $-$ 10
colog $\pi =$	9|50285 $-$ 10
2 colog $4.02 =$	8|79154 $-$ 10

$$\text{sum} = \log \text{cps} = \quad 42|52760 - 40 = 2.52760$$
$$\text{antilog} = \text{cps} = 337.0$$

Comment 1 For this problem, deciding on the correct number of significant figures in the data given is difficult. The value of the constant 11.0 is probably purely experimental in origin. The terms under the radical are of less importance since the square root of the quotient is used. Therefore, looking at the data outside the radical, r and L were given to four significant figures. Four significant figures were arbitrarily chosen as controlling, so five-place logarithms were used and the final answer given to four significant figures.

Comment 2 Again note that by using the double-line technique twice, every logarithm is found without using scratch paper.

Example 8.15
Evaluate $1.7264\sqrt{(3.1187)^2 - (0.87421)^2}$.

SOLUTION

Any problem containing internal additions or subtractions cannot normally be worked by logarithms unless separated into steps where arithmetic values are first obtained before adding or subtracting. The two squares could have been found by logarithms and then the antilogarithms subtracted. However, this case, the difference of two squares, is an exception since this is an algebraic special product. So the problem is rewritten as follows:

$$\text{answer} = 1.7264\sqrt{(3.1187 + 0.8742)(3.1187 - 0.8742)}$$

$$\text{answer} = 1.7264\sqrt{(3.9929)(2.2445)}$$

$$\log \text{answer} = \log 1.7264 + \tfrac{1}{2}(\log 3.9929 + \log 2.2445)$$

$$
\begin{array}{rl}
\log 3.9929 = & 0|60129 \\
\log 2.2445 = & 0|35112 \\
\hline
\text{sum} = & 0|95241 \\
\hline
\tfrac{1}{2}\,\text{sum} = & 0|47620 \\
\log 1.7264 = & 0|23714 \\
\hline
\text{sum} = \log \text{answer} = & 0|71334 \\
\text{antilog} = \text{answer} = & 5.1682
\end{array}
$$

Example 8.16
Using logarithms, find (a) 3.468(4.689); (b) 2.865(4.689).

SOLUTION

A number of situations arise, particularly in trigonometry, where one constant is multiplied by two different factors, as in this example. For compactness, write the common factor in the middle and work in both directions, upward and downward.

$$
\begin{array}{rl}
\text{answer (a)} = & 16.26 \\
\log \text{answer (a)} = & 1|2112 \\
\log 3.468 = & 0|5401 \\
\log 4.689 = & 0|6711 \quad\text{—add upward} \\
\log 2.865 = & 0|4571 \quad\text{—add downward} \\
\log \text{answer (b)} = & 1|1282 \\
\text{answer (b)} = & 13.44
\end{array}
$$

Problem Set 8.4

Use the logarithmic table with the number of places consistent with the given data, and show the correct number of significant figures in the final answer. If directed, check your answer to three significant figures using a slide rule.

1.* The Knoop hardness number is given by

$$HK = \frac{P}{0.070\,28d^2}$$

where P = load, kg
    d = diagonal of the indentation, mm
Find the Knoop hardness if a 1000-g load made an indentation with a diagonal of 0.0710 mm.

2.* The Vickers hardness number is given by

$$HV = \frac{1.8544P}{d^2}$$

where P = load, kg
    d = diagonal of the indentation, mm
Find the Vickers hardness under a 1-kg load if the diagonal of the indentation is 0.0499 mm.

3. The moment of inertia I of a triangle about its base is

$$I = \frac{bh^3}{12} \quad in.^4$$

Find I if b is 2.0475 in. and h is 4.7216 in.

4. The moment of inertia I of an elliptical quadrant about its minor axis is

$$I = \frac{\pi a^3 b}{16}$$

Find I if $a = 6.2728$ and $b = 3.1789$.

5.† The circular equivalent of a rectangular air duct, to obtain approximately the same frictional losses and the same mean velocity of the air flow, is given by

$$d_c = 1.30 \sqrt[8]{\frac{(ab)^5}{(a+b)^2}}$$

Find the circular equivalent of a 10- by 14-in. duct.

6.† Repeat Problem 5 for an 18- by 24-in. duct.

---

* Problems 1 and 2 are adapted from ASTM Standard 6-66, which indicates the difference in the shape of the diamond point used to make the indentations and when each test is best used.
† Problems 5 and 6 are adapted from material in the ASHRAE Guide.

7. The natural frequency f_n of vibration in cycles per minute of a machine on its support is

$$f_n = \frac{1}{2\pi}\sqrt{\frac{g}{d}}$$

where g = gravitational constant = 32.2 ft/sec²
d = static deflection of the support, ft
Find the natural frequency for a deflection of 0.985 in.

8. The centripetal acceleration toward the center of a rotating body is

$$a_c = \frac{4\pi r^2}{t^2} \text{ ft/sec}^2$$

Find the acceleration if r is 8.978 in. and t is 0.017 47 sec.

9. The draft lost in a chimney, measured in inches of water, is

$$h_c = \frac{fW^2CH}{A^3}$$

where W = weight of gases expelled, lb/sec
f = constant for the material of the chimney = 0.0015 for steel
C = chimney perimeter, ft
H = chimney height, ft
A = chimney area, sq ft
Find the draft lost per boiler horsepower if 120 lb of gas per minute are produced per boiler horsepower and if this chimney is cylindrical, 6 ft in diameter and 120 ft high.

10. The current concern over pollution usually discusses pollutants in parts per million (ppm). Express the following amounts as ppm.
(a) 1 ounce in 32.43 tons
(b) $\frac{63}{64}$ inch in 15 miles
(c) 1 gram in an English long ton (2240 lb)

11. A study made by Iowa State University on retaining walls gave for the stress in the X direction, σ_x:

$$\sigma_x = \frac{3Px^2z}{2\pi R^5}$$

where x = distance in the x direction = 2.50 ft
z = depth below load P = 1.78 ft
$R = \sqrt{x^2 + y^2 + z^2}$
Find σ_x if $y = \frac{7}{8}$ ft and P = 2000 lb
(Adapted from *Bulletin 140*, Iowa State College, Ames, Iowa.)

12. McMath's formula, used in estimating storm-water runoff, is

$$Q = Aci \sqrt[5]{\frac{S}{A}} \text{ in cfs}$$

where A = drainage area in acres = 2074

c = a coefficient, here 0.735

i = intensity of rainfall, in./hr; use a moderate storm of 1.75 in./hr

S = ground slope in ft/1000 ft = 18.27

Find Q in cfs.

13. The ratio between two similar right triangles is 1 : 1.746. The smaller triangle has a hypotenuse AC of 7.464 in. and one leg AB of 3.892 in. Find the length of the leg in the larger triangle corresponding to leg BC of the smaller.

14. Kinetic energy, the energy due to motion, is given by

$$KE = \frac{WV^2}{2g}$$

where W = weight, lb

V = velocity, ft/sec

What would be the kinetic energy of an automobile weighing 3878 lb travelling at 65 mph? Use $g = 32.2$ ft/sec^2. (WARNING: All units must agree. Give your result in pound-feet.)

15. For a simple beam with a load at its center, the deflection D is given by

$$D = \frac{PL^3}{48EI}$$

Find the deflection if $P = 2.47$ kips, $L = 12.48$ ft, $E = 29.86 \times 10^6$ psi, and $I = 232.2$ in.^{4}. (Watch the units used!) (Kip is an abbreviation for a kilopound, 1000 lb.)

16. For the same beam as that in Problem 15 but with the load at the left third point, the maximum deflection is

$$D_{max} = \frac{Pab(a + 2b)\sqrt{3a(a + 2b)}}{27EIL}$$

where $a = L/3$

$b = 2L/3$.

Find the deflection for the same conditions as given in Problem 15, determine which loading produces the greater deflection, and find the percentage by which the larger exceeds the smaller deflection.

17. The maximum shearing stress of a rectangular bar in torsion is

$$s_{max} = \frac{M_t}{k_2(2a)^2(2b)}$$

where a and b are the half-width and half-height, k_2 is a function of a/b. and M_t is the torque. Find s_{max} in psi if $a = 1.754$ in., $b = 3.505$ in., $k_2 = 0.246$, and $M_t = 12,042$ in.-lb.

18. The continual increase in truck size has made many pavements obsolete, since the increase requires that an additional thickness be added. Charts

exist that give the total required thickness h for a given truck load and given soil conditions. For an existing 6-in. slab in poor condition, the added thickness required h_r is

$$h_r = \sqrt{h^2 - 0.36h_e^2}$$

where h_e is the existing thickness and 0.36 is the coefficient for a poor condition. From a design chart, h is 9.25 in. Find h_r. (Note that h is *not* $h_e + h_r$ but the thickness if a new pavement had been constructed.) (Adapted from data from the Portland Cement Association, Chicago, publication on Design and Resurfacing Old Pavements.)

8.08 / Logarithms of logarithms

In the newer fields of technology, there are ever-growing numbers of formulas involving numbers with decimal fractions being raised to a power with the exponent expressed as a number containing a decimal fraction. There is no change in the theoretical concept that $\log a^n$ is $n \log a$, but if n has six significant figures and a six-place logarithmic table is used, the arithmetic multiplication is arduous without a desk calculator. Logarithms can be used to perform this multiplication.

Several earlier references have been made to log-log scales on a slide rule. It was indicated in Chapter 2 that the slide rule uses scales graduated logarithmically; the log-log scales are graduated in the logarithms of logarithms.

Since a logarithm is an exponent of a chosen base, it is just an element of the set of real numbers and can be treated as any other element. Thus, there is no reason why the logarithm of this real number cannot be found and treated as the logarithm of any other number.

Example 8.17
Find the logarithm of the logarithm of 2.

SOLUTION
$$\log 2 = 0.3010$$

$$\text{log-log } 2 = \log 0.3010 = 9.4786 - 10 \qquad \text{(computational form)}$$

$$= -0.5214 \qquad \text{(formula form)}$$

It may be necessary to work certain practical problems involving negative numbers by using logarithms. A difficulty arises because a negative number does *not* have a logarithm. Any power of 10 always yields a positive result: $10^{-2} = +0.01$, $10^0 = +1$, and $10^3 = +1000$. Suppose it is desired to find the product $3.5(-0.6990)$ by using logarithms. The logarithmic equation would be log product $= \log 3.5 + \log(-0.6990)$ involving the logarithm of a negative number which does not exist. On the other hand, $3.5(-0.6990) = -(+3.5)(+0.6990)$, where positive factors are preceded by a minus sign. The product of the positive factors *can* be found by using logarithms and then the minus sign can be inserted at the end of the problem. That this is to be done can be indicated by the artificial convention of $[-]$.

In this book brackets enclosing a minus sign, $[-]$, will mean "Do not use this minus sign until the final answer is written." Thus, if some logarithmic operation was to be performed on -0.02, instead of writing $\log(-0.02)$, a meaningless expression, one can write $[-]\log 0.02 = [-] 8.3010 - 10$. The minus sign is inserted at the end of the problem after an antilogarithm has been found.

Example 8.18
Using logarithms, find $3.5(\log 0.2)$.

SOLUTION
Noting that $3.5(\log 0.2) = 3.5(-0.6990) = (+)(-) = -(+)(+)$, the computation is written as follows:

$$\log 0.2 = 9.3010 - 10 = -0.6990$$

$[-]$ log-log $0.2 = [-]\log 0.6990 =$	$9.8445 - 10$
$\log 3.5 =$	0.5441
$[-]$ sum $=$	0.3886
$[-]$ antilog $=$	2.45
answer $= -$	2.45

Example 8.19
Find the value of $(2.7183)^{1.4672}$.

SOLUTION
$$\log(2.7183)^{1.4672} = 1.4672(\log 2.7183)$$

$$\log[\log(2.7183)^{1.4672}] = \log 1.4672 + \text{log-log } 2.7183$$

$$\log 2.7183 = 0.43430$$

$$\log 0.43430 = 9.63779 - 10$$
$$\log 1.4672 = 0.16670$$

$$\text{sum} = \log(n \log a) = 9.80449 - 10$$
$$\text{antilog} = n \log a = 0.63751$$
$$\text{antilog} = a^n = 4.3402$$

It is important to remember that *two* antilogarithms must be found.

Example 8.20
Find the value of $(0.047215)^{3.2468}$.

SOLUTION

$$\text{log power} = 3.2468(\text{log } 0.047215)$$

$$[-]\text{log-log power} = \text{log } 3.2468 + [-]\text{log-log } 0.047215$$

$$\text{log } 0.047215 = 8.67408 - 10 = -1.32592$$

$$[-]\text{log } 1.3259 = [-]0.12248$$
$$\text{log } 3.2468 = 0.51145$$

$$\text{sum} = [-]\text{log-log power} = [-]0.63393$$
$$-\text{antilog} = \text{log power} = -4.3046 = 5.6954 - 10$$
$$\text{antilog} = \text{power} = 0.000\,049\,59$$

In Example 8.20, changing the logarithm of data with five significant figures to the negative form yields six significant figures, which can not be used with a five-place table and require a roundoff. Similarly, one significant digit is lost when the antilog of the product is taken, since one significant digit becomes the characteristic, leaving a four-place mantissa.

This loss of significant figures is of some importance when the calculations are done using a slide rule, as will be shown in the next section. If there is a need for these significant figures, logarithmic calculations should be used, with the multiplication by the exponent done on a desk calculator. When any constant in the basic formula has been found experimentally with a very low precision, no such arithmetic refinement is warranted. In the fields of both hydraulics and friction, the constants lack precision and rarely are two or more significant figures in an answer meaningful.

8.09 / Decimal exponents using a Mannheim slide rule

No attempt will be made to discuss the use of log-log scales found on the more expensive slide rules. The manufacturers' manuals are adequate. However, Example 8.20 cannot be solved on such a rule since the answer falls outside the graduated limits.

Using the Mannheim type of slide rule, the actual procedure is almost identical with the preceding section with these two changes:
(1) The mantissa to three significant figures is read directly on the L scale by setting the hairline to the given number on D. Antilogs are read by setting the hairline to the mantissa on L and reading the antilog on D.
(2) After the characteristic has been added to the mantissa, the multiplication by the exponent is done conventionally using the C and D scales.

Example 8.21

Using the C, D, and L scales, evaluate $(45.7)^{1.47}$.

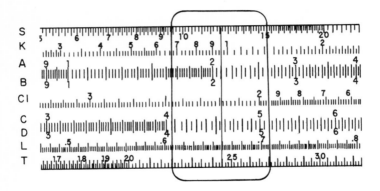

Figure 8.4
Finding the mantissa.

SOLUTION
(1) The characteristic of 45.7 is 1. Set hairline to 457 on D, read 0.660 on L. (See Figure 8.4.) Note that the L scale has a decimal point.
(2) Set the left index of the slide to the exponent 147 on D. Move the hairline to the value of the complete logarithm, 1.660 on C.
(3) Read the product 244 on D and introduce the correct decimal point by inspection, giving 2.44. (See Figure 8.5.)
(4) Using the two-place mantissa, set the hairline to 0.44 on L and read the antilog 276 on D. (See Figure 8.6.)
(5) Insert the correct decimal point from the characteristic of 2, giving 276 as the final answer.

Figure 8.5
Finding the product

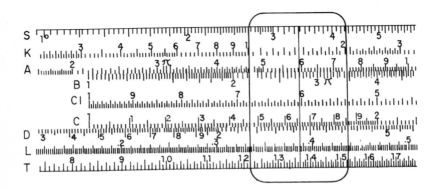

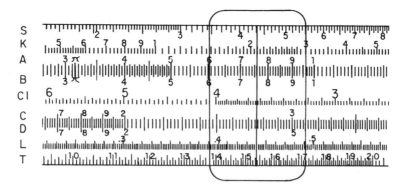

Figure 8.6
Finding the antilogarithm

Had the need existed to find this value by use of five-place tables, the answer would have been 275.47. This happens to be a formula from hydraulics and the exponent was found experimentally. The final answer would have been a flow in cubic feet per second and would have been given to the nearest cubic foot. In step 2 there is no significance to setting the index to the value of the exponent; it is equally correct to choose the other factor if desired.

Example 8.22
For a Mach number of 1.0, the critical pressure ratio in a compressible fluid is found by

$$\text{critical ratio} = \frac{P_s}{P_t} = \left(\frac{2}{\gamma + 1}\right)^{\gamma/(\gamma - 1)}$$

where γ is the ratio of specific heats, $\frac{c_p}{c_v}$. For carbon dioxide $\gamma = 1.28$. Using the C, D, and L scales of the slide rule, find the critical pressure ratio.

SOLUTION
(1) Substituting and simplifying:

$$\frac{P_s}{P_t} = \left(\frac{2}{2.28}\right)^{1.28/0.28}$$

(2) Performing both divisions using the C and D scales gives

$$\frac{P_s}{P_t} = (0.877)^{4.57}$$

    (a) Do the division for the exponent first, recording the result, 4.57.

(b) For the second division, the result need not be read; set the hairline to the right index and read the mantissa on L as 0.943.
(3) The characteristic, by inspection, is -1. The complete logarithm is $-1 + 0.943$ or -0.057. Set the right index to 57 on D and under 457 on C read the product 260 on D.
(4) The product is negative. Changing the result to the conventional form: $-0.260 = 9.740 - 10$. Set the hairline to 0.740 on L; read 550 on D.
(5) Insert the correct decimal point from the characteristic, giving 0.550 as the final answer.

(*Note:* The result using the log-log LL02 scale is 0.549. Using five-place logarithms, the result is 0.54940.)

Problem Set 8.5

1 and 2
Tests on 90° V-notched weirs at the University of Michigan gave $Q = 2.52H^{2.47}$. Later tests substituting polished brass for the commercial steel weir gave for the same conditions a discharge of $Q = 2.48H^{2.48}$, where Q is in cfs.

1. Using both formulas, compute the discharge for $H = 1.5$ ft.
2. Using both formulas, compute the discharge for $H = 0.85$ ft.

3–6
The basic theoretical discharge of a rectangular weir is $Q = \frac{2}{3}\sqrt{2g}LH^{3/2}$, where g is the acceleration due to gravity (32.2 ft/sec²), L is the length of the weir in feet, and H is the head or height of water above the bottom of the notch in feet. The unit for Q is cfs.

3. Find Q for $L = 3.0$ ft and $H = 1.25$ ft.
4. Find Q for $L = 3.5$ ft and $H = 1.50$ ft.
5. Find Q for $L = 2.5$ ft and $H = 0.75$ ft.
6. Find Q for $L = 2.75$ ft and $H = 0.85$ ft.

7–10
One of the oldest experimental formulas for the same weir, ignoring the velocity of approach, was found by Francis about 1850 and is $Q = 3.33LH^{3/2}$. Later tests by Horace King gave $Q = 3.34LH^{1.47}$. Using both of these formulas, compute the discharge for a rectangular weir 8.00 ft long if the head is

7. $H = 2.2$ ft
8. $H = 1.89$ ft

9. $H = 0.47$ ft
10. $H = 0.89$ ft

11–14

Radiant heating by pipes in the floor is frequently used in modern homes. The heat output of such a system, q_c, is measured in Btu/hr/sq ft and is given by

$$q_c = \frac{0.39(t_f - t_a)^{1.31}}{D_e^{0.08}}$$

where $(t_f - t_a)$ is the difference in $°F$ of the temperature of the floor and the room air, and $D_e = $ equivalent diameter $= \dfrac{4(\text{floor area})}{\text{perimeter of room}}$ in feet. Find q_c for each of the following conditions.

	Room Width, ft	Room Length, ft	Floor Temp., °F	Air Temp., °F
11.	12	16	90	70
12.	10	14	92	68
13.	16	20	88	72
14.	12	18	90	67

(Adapted from the ASHRAE Guide.)

15–18

In testing nozzles used for rocket propulsion, the ratio of the pressure P at the nozzle tip to the pressure P_0 in the combustion chamber for a velocity of Mach 1 at the throat is given by

$$\frac{P}{P_0} = \left(1 + \frac{\lambda - 1}{2}\right)^{-\lambda/(\lambda - 1)}$$

where λ is the adiabatic constant. Compute the pressure ratio for the given value of the adiabatic constant.

15. $\lambda = 1.40$ **17.** $\lambda = 1.34$
16. $\lambda = 1.38$ **18.** $\lambda = 1.28$

19. The absolute pressure of the atmosphere at H ft above sea level is

$$p = p_0(1 - 6.87H \times 10^{-6})^{5.256}$$

Find the pressure at 10,000 ft above sea level if $p_0 = 2116.22$ psf.

20. The density of the atmosphere at H ft above sea level is

$$d = d_0(1 - 6.87H \times 10^{-6})^{4.256}$$

Find the density at 20,000 ft above sea level if d_0 is 0.002 378 slug/cu ft.

8.10 / Formulas involving logarithms

The third reason given for obtaining familiarity with logarithms was the large number of formulas in engineering and science where one or more of the factors are logarithms. Once these factors have been converted to their logarithmic value, they become ordinary numbers and in all subsequent operations are treated as any other numerical factor. There will be no need to find an antilogarithm in this type of problem.

Depending upon the complexity of the arithmetic operations required by the given formula, a decision is made as to whether arithmetic or logarithmic calculations are warranted. If an electric desk calculator is available, there is no need for logarithms in this second phase. Whenever it is possible, the slide rule should be used. In some formulas, the use of decimal exponents may require the additional use of logarithms to evaluate those expressions. Since these problems really involve no new concepts, only one example will be shown.

Example 8.23
The area A of the inside surface of a heating coil to heat a given quantity of water a specified number of degrees is given by

$$A = Q \frac{8.33(t_h - t_c)}{U t_m}$$

where Q = quantity of water to be heated, gal/hr, = 80
t_h = temperature at hot-water outlet, °F, = 190°
t_c = temperature of cold-water inlet, °F, = 50°
t_m = logarithmic mean temperature, defined as

$$t_m = \frac{t_h - t_c}{2.3 \log \dfrac{t_h}{t_c}}$$

U = coefficient of heat transmission (for copper coils heating water, U = 100)

SOLUTION
Find t_m first.

$$t_m = \frac{190 - 50}{2.3 \log \dfrac{190}{50}} = \frac{140}{2.3 \log 3.8} = \frac{140}{2.3(0.58)} = 105$$

$$A = \frac{80(8.33)(140)}{100(105)} = 8.9 \text{ sq ft}$$

Generally, for data to two significant figures, there is no justification for calculations by logarithms, and a slide rule should be used.

Problem Set 8.6

1. The mean effective pressure in a steam engine is computed from the engine indicator diagram and is calculated from

$$P_m = \frac{P}{R}(1 + 2.3 \log R)$$

where P = initial pressure = 184 psi
R = ratio of expansion = 4.44
Find the value of P_m.

2. The inductance L in henrys of a coil wound on a torus with a rectangular cross section h cm high and w cm wide containing N turns on a mean radius r is

$$L = 2N^2 w \left(2.3 \log \frac{r + h}{r - h}\right) \times 10^{-9}$$

Find the inductance if h is 2.54 cm, w is 3.16 cm, and there are 1208 turns on a mean radius of 7.87 cm. (Adapted from a Bureau of Standards Scientific Paper.)

3. The reactance X of a single-phase overhead power line for a 60-Hz supply in ohms per 1000 ft of line is given by

$$X = 0.0529 \log \frac{s}{0.3894d}$$

where s = spacing of wire centers, in.
d = diameter of wire, in.
Find the reactance for two No. 0 wires 18 in. apart. Number 0 wire has a diameter of 325 mils. (s and d must be in like units.)

4. Flow into a gravity-fed well is computed using the draw-down curve, that is, the level of the water table when the well is pumped, which slopes in a smooth curve from the original water level to the actual level at the well. The flow in gpm is

$$Q = K \frac{h_e^2 - h_x^2}{\log \frac{r_e}{r_x}}$$

where h_e = distance from original groundwater level to collection point
h_x = distance from a test point on the draw-down curve to the collection point
r_e = maximum radius of draw-down curve at original groundwater level
r_x = radius to draw-down curve at test point
Given $K = 0.143$, $r_e = 80$ ft, $r_x = 0.5$ ft, $h_e = 160$ ft, and $h_x = 120$ ft, compute Q.

5. The inductance L of a single-phase overhead power line for a 60-Hz supply is in henrys.

$$L = M\left(0.161 + 1.48 \log \frac{d}{r}\right) \times 10^{-3} \quad \text{H}$$

where M = length of power line = 10.58 miles
     d = distance between centers of conductors = 24 in.
     r = radius of wire, in.; use No. 000 wire, which has a radius of 205 mils

Find the inductance of this power line.

6. The elapsed time for a given temperature change in motionless water in a pipe is

$$t = 2.3\left(\frac{q}{k}\right)\left|\log \frac{T_2}{T_1}\right|$$

where t = time, hours, that water is not moving
      q = weight of water, kilograms, in a length of 1 meter; use a 6-inch water main, inside diameter 6.065 in. (water weighs 62.4 lb/cu ft)
      k = loss of heat, in kilogram-calories/hour/meter/°C; use 0.47
     T_2 = final difference in temperature between water and surrounding air, °C
     T_1 = initial difference in temperature between water and surrounding air, °C

Find how long it would take water to reach the freezing point if it entered the water main at 44.7°F and the average air temperature is -5°F.

7. For SAE 4130 steel, normalized and annealed, the cycles to failure by fatigue (the reversal of stress from tension to compression and back) is a function of the imposed stress s in psi and is given by

$$s = 62,500 - 2650 \log \text{cycles}$$

What is the maximum stress to ensure a fatigue life of 10 million cycles?

8. The true fracture strain e in a tensile test is

$$e = 2.3 \log \frac{\text{original cross-sectional area}}{\text{cross-sectional area at failure}}$$

If a certain test specimen had an initial cross-sectional area of 0.787 sq in. and had a 62.7 per cent reduction of area, what was the true fracture strain?

9. The capacitance C in microfarads of the same power line described in Problem 5 is

$$C = \frac{0.0194M}{\log \dfrac{d}{r}}$$

Find the value of C for the same line described in Problem 5.

10. The time t required for an airplane to climb to its cruising altitude h is

$$t = 2.303 \left(\frac{H}{r_0}\right) \log \frac{H}{H - h}$$

where H = absolute ceiling for that plane, ft

r_0 = rate of climb at sea level

Find the time for a plane to reach its cruising elevation of 24,000 ft if its absolute ceiling is 47,000 ft and its sea-level rate of climb is 1450 fpm.

11. The parasite drag C_{DF} of a smooth, flat plate in turbulent flow is a function of the Reynold's number R:

$$C_{DF} = \frac{0.91}{\log R^{2.58}}$$

Find the drag coefficient for a Reynold's number of 875,000.

12. The capacitance C of a cable laid in a metal sheath is

$$C = \frac{0.0388kM}{\log \dfrac{d_1}{d_2}} \mu F$$

where k = dielectric constant of insulation

M = length of the cable, miles

d_1 = inside diameter of sheath

d_2 = diameter of conductor

Find C if No. 4 wire ($d = 204$ mils) is encased in $\frac{1}{8}$ in. of rubber insulation ($k = 2.8$) in a cable 217 miles long.

13. The total force P that a journal bearing will sustain is

$$P = \frac{6\mu U L^2}{(c_1 - c_2)^2} \left(2.31 \log \frac{c_1}{c_2} - 2.00 \frac{c_1 - c_2}{c_1 + c_2}\right)$$

where μ = kinematic viscosity = 1.666×10^{-3} lb-sec/ft^2

L = length of bearing surface = 6.13 in.

U = velocity = 4.17 ft/sec

c_1 = maximum clearance = 0.002 76 in.

c_2 = minimum clearance = 0.000 89 in.

Find P for this bearing.

14. Rateau's formula for the discharge m of saturated steam through an orifice is

$$m = AP(16.367 - 0.96 \log P) \times 10^{-3} \quad \text{lb}$$

where A = area of orifice, sq in.

P = pressure, psia

A rough check can be made using Grashof's formula: $m = 0.0165AP^{0.97}$.

Find m and rough check it for an orifice $\frac{7}{8}$ in. in diameter and with a steam pressure of 120 psia.

15. Entropy is a term found in the study of heat transfer and may be considered unavailable energy. If heat transfer is occurring in a closed chamber, the volume of gas remains constant and the change of entropy is

$$S_f - S_i = 2.3 M c_v \left| \log \frac{T_2}{T_1} \right|$$

where $S_f - S_i$ = change in entropy
M = weight of the gas under consideration
c_v = specific heat of the gas under constant-volume conditions
T_1 = initial temperature, degrees Rankine
($°R = 460° + T°F$)
T_2 = final temperature, °R

Find the change in entropy for 0.0907 lb of air whose specific heat is 0.173, initially at 104°F and cooled to 68°F.

16. Polytropic changes in a gas involve a specific heat found by

$$c_n = c_v \frac{k - n}{1 - n}$$

where k is the universal gas constant, 1.4, and n is found by

$$n = \frac{\log P_2 - \log P_1}{\log V_1 - \log V_2}$$

Find c_n if $P_1 = 20.7$ psia, $P_2 = 99.6$ psia, $V_1 = 4.395$ cu ft, $V_2 = 1.276$ cu ft, and $c_v = 0.173$.

17. The resistance to heat flow R in $\dfrac{°F\text{-}hr}{Btu}$ in an insulated pipe is approximately

$$R = \frac{2.3 \log \dfrac{r_o}{r_i}}{2\pi k N}$$

where r_i and r_o = inner and outer radii of the pipe, in.
k = thermal conductivity = 0.031
N = length of the pipe, ft

Find R for 207 ft of $2\frac{1}{2}$-in. API standard pipe [outside diameter (OD) = 2.875 in., and inside diameter (ID) = 2.469 in.].

18. If a given installed fan is replaced by another, the noise level of the new fan can be estimated from the measured noise level of the original fan by

$$\text{change in noise level} = 70 \log \frac{d_2}{d_1} + 50 \log \frac{s_2}{s_1}$$

where d = fan diameter, in.
s = fan speed, rpm

An 18-in. attic fan operating at 1200 rpm produces a noise level of 60 decibels (db), which is above the recommended limit of 35 to 40 db for sleeping areas. If it is replaced by a 24-in. fan running at 500 rpm, which will move the same volume of air, compute the new noise level, and determine if it is acceptable.

8.11 / Chapter Review

1. The use of logarithms simplifies arithmetic calculations, but for the ordinary arithmetic processes they have largely been replaced by the electric desk calculator.
2. Logarithms are still used in isolated locations where no calculators are available, they are used to find nonintegral powers and roots of numbers, and they appear in formulas in many fields of engineering and science.
3. A logarithm is the exponent of a chosen base that will yield the desired number. This chapter has been limited to common logarithms, which use the base 10.
4. A common logarithm consists of an integer called the characteristic and another number, a positive decimal, called the mantissa. The characteristic indicates the size of the given number and may be positive or negative or zero. The mantissa is a unique designation of the digits of the number and it is always positive. The number of figures in a mantissa are called the number of places. Logarithmic tables range from 3 to 10 places. Five-place tables are most commonly used.
5. The common logarithm of a number greater than 1 is positive.
   The common logarithm of 1 is 0.
   The common logarithm of a number between 0 and 1 is negative.
   A negative logarithm may be written as an indicated subtraction by using a negative characteristic and a positive mantissa or as a single negative number.
   The common logarithm of a negative number does not exist. For practical problems, there are special techniques for using logarithms in calculations where the result is negative.
6. The antilogarithm is the number represented by a given logarithm. It may be necessary to use linear interpolation for finding both logarithms and antilogarithms. Using a table of logarithms that contains a column of proportional parts simplifies this work.
7. The basic concepts for logarithmic computations are as follows:
   (a) A logarithm of a product is the sum of the logarithms of the factors:

   $$\log ab = \log a + \log b$$

(b) A logarithm of a quotient is the difference of two logarithms:

$$\log \frac{a}{b} = \log a - \log b$$

(c) A logarithm of a power is a multiple of a logarithm:

$$\log a^n = n \log a$$

(d) A logarithm of a root is the quotient of the logarithm of the radicand divided by the index:

$$\log \sqrt[n]{a} = \frac{\log a}{n}$$

8. A cologarithm is the logarithm of the reciprocal of a given number. It permits converting combined arithmetic multiplication and division to logarithmic addition.

9. Logarithms of logarithms are used when a number with four to six significant figures is raised to a power or a root is extracted with an exponent or index involving a similar number of digits and an electric desk calculator is not readily available.

10. Formulas with one or several factors given as logarithms are evaluated by finding the logarithm indicated and, in all subsequent operations, treated as any other numerical factor. The majority of these formulas contain a constant with two or three significant figures, which indicates the use of a slide rule for the arithmetic steps.

Problem Set 8.7 (*Chapter Review*)

1. Average annual rainfall runoff I can be calculated approximately by

$$I = 0.943 \frac{R^2}{T} S^{0.155} \qquad \text{in.}$$

where R = annual rainfall, in. = 35 in.
$\quad\quad\quad T$ = mean annual temperature, °F, = 51.7°F
$\quad\quad\quad S$ = average slope of drainage area = 0.018
Find the average annual rainfall runoff.

2. A rough estimate of the water requirement W in gallons per capita per day is

$$W = 54 P^{0.125}$$

For a city with a projected population of 250,000, what is the 24-hr requirement of the city for water in millions of gallons per day (mgd)?

3.*The American Society of Testing Materials has established grain-size numbers based upon a basic magnification M_B of 75 to 100 diameters. If some other magnification M is used, a correction factor Q is added to the grain size, where

$$Q = 0.006\ 64 \log \frac{M}{M_B} \quad \text{mm} \quad (\text{use } M_B = 100)$$

A particle was measured as 0.0172 mm at 200 times magnification. The ASTM grain sizes in this vicinity are

ASTM 8	0.0224 mm
ASTM 8.5	0.0189 mm
ASTM 9.5	0.0159 mm

Find the Q factor to be added to the apparent size, and by linear interpolation obtain the ASTM grain size to two decimal places.

4. The grain size N, described in Problem 3, can also be established as

$$N = \frac{\log m}{\log 2} - 2.9541$$

where m = grain count per sq mm at no magnification, $= m_i M^2$
        m_i = grain count per sq mm at magnification used
        M = magnification used

At 200 times magnification the grain count per sq mm was 0.076. Find N.

5. A certain city had a demographic study made that gave for its future population P expected in y years from now

$$P = 20,000(1 + y)^{0.32}$$

(a) Find the population expected in 5 years.
(b) Find the number of years until the population is expected to double.

6. Babcock's equation for the pressure drop in steam pipes is

$$p = 0.000\ 131 \left(1 + \frac{3.6}{D_i}\right) \frac{W^2 V_g L}{D_i^{\,5}}$$

where p = pressure drop, psi
        W = weight of steam passing, lb/min
        V_g = specific volume of steam
        D_i = ID of pipe, in.
        L = length of pipe, ft

(a) Introduce a constant K so that the equation becomes $p = KW^2 V_g L$.

---

* Problems 3 and 4 are based upon ASTM Standard 112–63.

(b) Find the value of K for the following sizes of standard-weight ASA pipe:

$$3\text{-in. pipe, ID} = 3.068 \text{ in.}$$

$$5\text{-in. pipe, ID} = 5.047 \text{ in.}$$

$$6\text{-in. pipe, ID} = 6.065 \text{ in.}$$

7. The piston displacement V_p of an automobile engine is

$$V_p = \frac{\pi D^2 LNn}{4(1728)}$$

where D = bore, in., = 3.80
$\quad\quad L$ = stroke, in., = 3.85
$\quad\quad N$ = rpm (maximum) = 4600
$\quad\quad n$ = number of cylinders = 8

Find V_p.

8. The Colebrook formula for the friction factor for turbulent flow is

$$\frac{1}{\sqrt{f}} = -2\log\left(\frac{2.51}{R\sqrt{f}} + \frac{r}{3.7}\right)$$

where f = friction factor, $0.01 \le f \le 0.10$
$\quad\quad R$ = Reynold's number, $10^4 \le R \le 10^8$
$\quad\quad r$ = relative roughness, $0.001 \le r \le 0.05$

Solve for the value of f if R is 3×10^5 and r is 0.01. Note that this equation cannot be solved directly, but by choosing a few values of f, the solution can be closely approximated.

9. The time t to establish a flow of V in a pipeline L ft in length under a head of H ft with a final velocity of V_f is

$$t = \frac{1.15LV_f}{gH}\log\frac{V_f + V}{V_f - V}$$

Find the time to establish a flow of 3 fps if the final velocity is 5.22 fps, the constant head is 18.78 ft, and the line is 2117 ft long. Use $g = 32.2$ ft/sec^2.

10. The flow in an open channel is

$$Q = \frac{1.486}{n}AR^{0.667}S^{0.5} \quad\quad \text{in cfs}$$

where n = roughness factor = 0.025
$\quad\quad A$ = cross-sectional area = 192.2 sq ft
$\quad\quad R$ = hydraulic radius = 3.06 ft
$\quad\quad S$ = slope of channel = 0.0009

Compute the flow Q.

11. The glare factor, G, is

$$G = \frac{AB^2}{D^2 a^2 S^{0.6}}$$

where A = area of light source, sq in.
B = brightness of source, ft-lumens $\times$ 10^{-3}
D = distance, source to eye, ft $\times$ 10^{-1}
a = angle above horizontal, degrees $\times$ 10^{-1}
S = surrounding brightness, ft-lumens $\times$ 10^{-1}

Find the glare from a 40 sq-in. source of 4900 ft-lumens eminating from a distance of 10 ft and located 40° above the horizontal, with the surrounding brightness being 100 ft-lumens. (Notice that this formula, unlike the others, requires reducing the given data by divisions of specified powers of 10.)

12. The heat loss from the flow of a hot fluid through a metal, uninsulated pipe running horizontally is approximately

$$H = \frac{1.016L}{D^{0.2}T^{0.181}}(T_p - T_a)$$

where L = length of pipe, ft
$T_p - T_a$ = difference in temperature between the pipe and the surrounding air, °R ($= T°F + 460°$)
D = nominal pipe diameter, in.
T = room air temperature, °R (absolute temperature)

Find H for a 4 in. pipe 118 ft long carrying hot water at 180°F in a room at 70°F.

13. The friction loss for a round air duct made from galvanized iron is

$$L_0 = 0.027\left(\frac{L}{d^{1.22}}\right)\left(\frac{V}{1000}\right)^{1.82}$$

where L_0 = friction loss, in. of water
L = duct length, ft
d = duct diameter, in.
V = air velocity, fpm

Find L for a duct 87 ft long, 12 in. in diameter, carrying air at 1600 fpm.

14. The flow of water in pipes, Q, can be found using the Hazen–Williams formula, which for vitrified pipes is

$$Q = 145r^{0.63}s^{0.54}A$$

where r = hydraulic radius, ft; for circular pipes flowing full, $r = \frac{1}{4}$ID, ft
s = slope of pipe, expressed as a decimal; assume a fall in energy of $\frac{1}{4}$ in./ft
A = cross-sectional area of pipe, sq ft

Find the discharge Q in cfs for a 2-in. schedule 80 pipe with ID $= 1.939$ in. (*Note :* The slope is the energy fall per foot, not the physical fall.)

15. Using the Manning formula, the required size of a pipe to carry a stated flow Q in cfs is given by

$$d_i = \left(\frac{1630Qn}{s^{0.5}}\right)^{3/8} \quad \text{in.}$$

Find the size of pipe needed to deliver 85 cfs for a slope s of 0.0016 if the roughness factor n is 0.014.

9

Trigonometric functions and their graphs

9.01 / Introduction

Trigonometry is a very ancient branch of mathematics, about 3000 years old and originally devoted to astronomy and land measurement. It was so intimately connected with triangles that its very name comes from the Greek word for triangles. It is hoped that this chapter and the following one will give a full appreciation of the role that trigonometric functions play in modern technology. Many of the concepts met in Chapter 4 will be found in this chapter. However, they will be considered here from a more mature mathematical viewpoint, because many mathematical skills have been learned since Chapter 4 was studied. The important message of this introduction is that modern trigonometry is a study of functions of real numbers. These functions may be interpreted as functions of an arc length, an angle with a specified unit of measure, a unit of time, or any quantity measured by a real number.

9.02 / Nomenclature

Figure 9.1 shows an angle formed by two rays OX and OQ, having the common endpoint O. Lines OX and OY are the x and y axes of the standard rectangular coordinate system whose origin is at O. Ray OX is considered as the initial position of a ray rotating about the origin, and ray OQ is considered

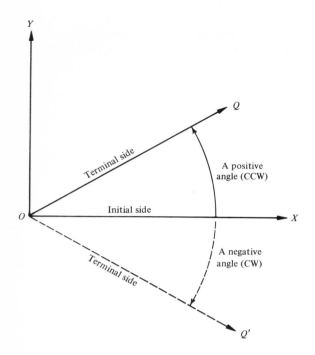

Figure 9.1
An angle in the standard position

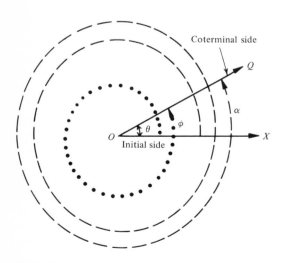

Figure 9.2
Three angles with a coterminal side

the final position of that rotating ray. Therefore, ray OX is called the **initial side** of angle QOX and ray OQ is called the **terminal side** of angle QOX. When the initial side is the positive half of the x axis and the vertex is at the origin, the angle is said to be in **standard position.**

If the rotating ray is moving counterclockwise, the angle generated is said to be a **positive angle.** If the rotation is clockwise, the angle is said to be a **negative angle.** Angle $Q'OX$ in Figure 9.1 is an example of a negative angle.

No limitation is placed upon the rotation of OQ, so there are an infinite number of angles that have the same terminal side, depending upon how many times the rotating ray has crossed the positive x axis. These angles are said to be **coterminal,** and they have a **coterminal side,** as shown in Figure 9.2.

Designating angles was discussed in Section 4.03. In this chapter, a Greek letter will be used for a general angle and a capital letter when there is a geometric figure involved and the vertices of the angles are alphabetically marked. For example, the three coterminal angles in Figure 9.2 are angles θ, ϕ, and α. In a triangle ABC, the angles would be named A, B, and C.

9.03 / The unit circle

In Figure 9.3, a point P with rectangular coordinates (x,y) has been chosen so that the distance OP is 1. An angle θ has been formed by the positive x axis and the ray OP, the terminal side of the angle. Line segment OP has a magnitude of 1 and a direction given by angle θ. Thus, line segment OP belongs to the type of directed line segments called **vectors.** Since OP begins at the origin, it is a special type of vector called a **radius vector.**

A circle has been drawn using the origin as the center and the radius vector OP as its radius. This circle is called a **unit circle** since its radius is 1 unit. If the point where this circle intersects the positive x axis is named R, then arc RP is the arc intercepted on the unit circle by angle θ.

The unit circle permits point P to be described in three different ways. Using rectangular coordinates P is (x,y). Given any ordered pair of real numbers, (x,y), with $x^2 + y^2 = 1$, exactly one point P can be located on the unit circle.

Using the radius vector and the notation commonly used in electrical or electronic engineering, P can be written as $r\underline{/\theta}$, or as $1\underline{/\theta}$ in this case, since $r = 1$, where the number r in front of the angle symbol is the magnitude of the radius vector and the number θ inside the symbol is the measure of the angle θ. When a point P is located by this method, it is called location by **polar coordinates,** written as (r,θ) using the notation common in pure mathematics. Again, given any real number for the measure of θ, an angle in standard position, exactly one point can be located on the unit circle. The converse of this statement is not true, as Figure 9.2 indicates, because infinitely many

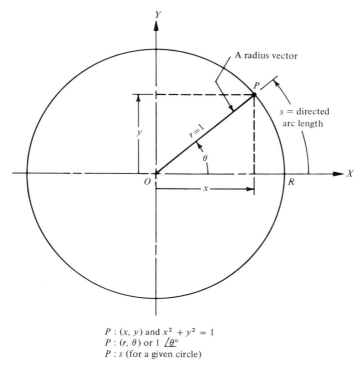

$P : (x, y)$ and $x^2 + y^2 = 1$
$P : (r, \theta)$ or $1 \,/\underline{\theta^\circ}$
$P : s$ (for a given circle)

Figure 9.3
The unit circle

angles have the same terminal side, any two of which differing by one or more full rotations of the unit circle.

Finally, and what is most important, point P can be uniquely located by stating a real number as the measure of a directed arc length on the unit circle. If the actual arc RP in Figure 9.3 could be straightened out and measured, it would have a specific length, which will be designated s, the **arc length.** (Methods for calculating s will be shown in Section 9.06.) Given a positive real number for s as the measure of an arc on the unit circle measured counterclockwise from the point of intersection of the unit circle and the positive x axis, exactly one point P is located on the unit circle as the terminal point of this arc. If $s = 0$, P is the point on the unit circle on the positive x axis. The variable s may also be given a negative value, meaning that the arc length is measured clockwise on the unit circle beginning at the positive x axis. Note that the converse of the unique location of a point P on the unit circle by a directed arc length s is *not* true, because infinitely many arcs terminate at a given point P, any two differing by one or more full circumferences of the unit circle.

Problem Set 9.1

1–20

Draw each of the following angles in standard position. Use paper ruled five squares to the inch and a protractor. Label the X and Y axes. For angles less than one full rotation, use one set of axes for every two assigned problems, identifying the first angle as θ and the second as ϕ.

1. 30°	**6.** 255°	**11.** $-120°$	**16.** 900°
2. 45°	**7.** 285°	**12.** $-220°$	**17.** $-420°$
3. 105°	**8.** 300°	**13.** 700°	**18.** $-870°$
4. 175°	**9.** $-60°$	**14.** 1215°	**19.** $-3000°$
5. 185°	**10.** $-75°$	**15.** 450°	**20.** $-4000°$

21–40

For each point P, one set of coordinates are given. Find the other two types of coordinates that identify the same point. Write each answer as point P with a subscript of the problem number, followed by the three locating values, such as $P_{15}(0.6, 0.8)$, $(1/37°)$, $(s = 0.65)$. Use paper ruled five squares to the inch and draw the unit circle using a radius of ten squares. Set a pair of dividers to exactly one square width, representing 0.1 unit, and mark off the circumference of the unit circle to find the value of s for each given point P. Unless otherwise instructed, solve three assigned problems on each unit circle drawn. Read angles to the nearest degree, read x and y values using the 1 : 50 decimal drafting scale to the nearest 0.01 unit, and estimate s to the nearest 0.01 unit. For Problems 21–26, express the angle between 0° and 360°, and express the arc length between 0 and 2π.

21. $(0.71, 0.71)$	**28.** $1 \;/\!\!-245°$	**35.** $s = -2.70$
22. $(-0.64, 0.77)$	**29.** $1/440°$	**36.** $s = -8.12$
23. $(-0.91, -0.42)$	**30.** $1/705°$	**37.** $s = 1.00$
24. $(0.85, -0.53)$	**31.** $1 \;/\!\!-\;540°$	**38.** $s = -4.00$
25. $(0, -1)$	**32.** $1/1080°$	**39.** $s = 1.57$
26. $(-1, 0)$	**33.** $s = 3.84$	**40.** $s = 3.14$
27. $1/\!\!-150°$	**34.** $s = 0.87$	

9.04 / The trigonometric functions

The concept of similar triangles, introduced in Section 4.04, is illustrated in Figure 9.4, where it is shown that corresponding angles are equal and corresponding sides are proportional. Triangles *ADE*, *ABC*, and *AFG* are

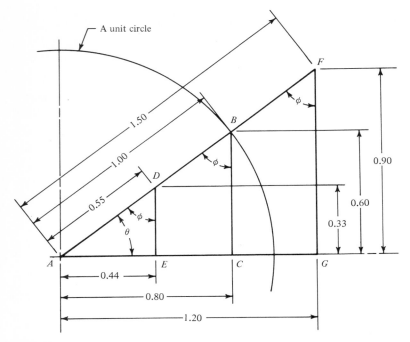

Figure 9.4
Establishing trigonometric ratios

similar triangles and a quick slide-rule check will verify that the corresponding sides are proportional.

$$\frac{DE}{AD} = \frac{0.33}{0.55} = \frac{BC}{AB} = \frac{0.60}{1.00} = \frac{FG}{AF} = \frac{0.90}{1.50} = 0.60$$

$$\frac{AE}{AD} = \frac{0.44}{0.55} = \frac{AC}{AB} = \frac{0.80}{1.00} = \frac{AG}{AF} = \frac{1.20}{1.50} = 0.80$$

$$\frac{DE}{AE} = \frac{0.33}{0.44} = \frac{BC}{AC} = \frac{0.60}{0.80} = \frac{FG}{AG} = \frac{0.90}{1.20} = 0.75$$

Definitions of Basic Trigonometric Functions

*If $P:(x, y)$ is any point on the terminal side of an angle θ in standard
position, then*

(1) *The ratio $\dfrac{y}{r}$ shall be named the* **sine** *of angle θ. In symbols,*

$$\sin \theta = \frac{y}{r}.$$

(2) *The ratio* $\dfrac{x}{r}$ *shall be named the* **cosine** *of angle* θ. *In symbols,*

$$\cos \theta = \frac{x}{r}.$$

(3) *The ratio* $\dfrac{y}{x}$ *shall be named the* **tangent** *of angle* θ. *In symbols,*

$$\tan \theta = \frac{y}{x}.$$

By the similar-triangle concept, the value of each of these three ratios is independent of the size of the triangle considered. Therefore, these three newly named ratios are functions of θ. Given any real number as the value of the independent variable θ, there is exactly one value for $\sin \theta$, exactly one value for $\cos \theta$, and exactly one value for $\tan \theta$, no matter if $P : (x,y)$ is selected on the unit circle or not. It is important to note, however, that if $P : (x,y)$ is on the unit circle, then $r = 1$ and

$$\sin \theta = \frac{y}{1} = y$$

and
$$\cos \theta = \frac{x}{1} = x$$

In other words, $(x,y) = (\cos \theta, \sin \theta)$ for the unit circle.

The three trigonometric functions defined above constitute the basis of all trigonometry and their definitions must be memorized. For convenience, the reciprocal of each of these three basic functions has been named and given a shortened form. By definition, these are as given in Table 9.1.

9.05 / Signs of the trigonometric functions

The signs of the values of the six trigonometric functions are automatically given by the basic coordinate system. Sketching any angle in its proper quadrant gives the proper signs for the x and y coordinates of P and the

Table 9.1

Basic function	Ratio	Name of reciprocal	Shortened written form	Ratio
Sine	$\dfrac{y}{r}$	Cosecant	$\csc \theta$	$\dfrac{r}{y}$
Cosine	$\dfrac{x}{r}$	Secant	$\sec \theta$	$\dfrac{r}{x}$
Tangent	$\dfrac{y}{x}$	Cotangent	$\cot \theta$	$\dfrac{x}{y}$

value of r is always positive. The rules from algebra still apply: Like signs in a ratio (a division) give a positive result, and unlike signs give a negative result.

Figure 9.5 does reveal some useful information. All six functions are positive in the first quadrant. In each of the other quadrants, one of the three basic functions is positive and, automatically, its reciprocal must have the same sign. Therefore, there are exactly two positive functions in each of these three quadrants; sine and cosecant are positive in quadrant II, tangent and cotangent are positive in quadrant III, and cosine and secant are positive in quadrant IV.

Figure 9.5
Signs of the trigonometric functions

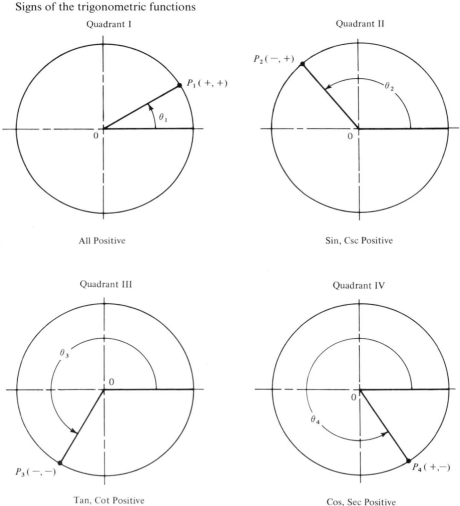

Problem Set 9.2

For each set of values for x, y, and r, calculate the values of the six trigonometric functions. Do this by preparing a table with seven columns. Put the assigned problem number in the first column; head the remaining six columns sin, cos, tan, cot, sec, csc; and record the values of the functions under these headings. Do all calculations by slide rule and give the value of each ratio to three significant figures.

1. $x = 3.0, y = 4.0, r = 5.0$
2. $x = 5.0, y = 12.0, r = 13.0$
3. $x = 7.0, y = 24.0, r = 25.0$
4. $x = 8.0, y = 15.0, r = 17.0$
5. $x = 9.0, y = 40.0, r = 41.0$
6. $x = 12.0, y = 35.0, r = 37.0$
7. $x = -12.22, y = 1.72, r = 12.35$
8. $x = -0.082, y = -0.415, r = 0.423$
9. $x = -0.669, y = -0.743, r = 1.000$
10. $x = -0.731, y = 0.682, r = 1.000$
11. $x = 0.239, y = -0.450, r = 0.510$
12. $x = 5070, y = -4410, r = 6720$
13. $x = 9360, y = 5870, r = 11,050$
14. $x = 14,750, y = 17,520, r = 22,900$
15. $x = 359, y = -532, r = 642$
16. $x = -523, y = 186, r = 555$
17. $x = -0.002\ 77, y = -0.009\ 40, r = 0.009\ 80$
18. $x = 0.006\ 98, y = -0.001\ 34, r = 0.007\ 11$
19. $x = -2.36, y = 52.3, r = 52.4$
20. $x = -7.96, y = -2.52, r = 8.35$

9.06 / Angular measure

The angular measures that are commonly used are
(1) The degree, minute, second with 360° per circumference.
(2) The degree, written as a decimal fraction.
(3) The French grade, 400 per circumference, subdivided into 100 minutes, each of which is subdivided into 100 seconds. (This is also called the *centesimal system*.)
(4) The military mil, 6400 per circumference, selected because the chord at 1000 yd is 1 yd for a 1-mil angle.
(5) The *radian*, with 2π radians per circumference.

The first four measures were introduced in Section 4.03. The radian measure, now introduced, is important in mathematics because it simplifies many formulas, including ones that are used in engineering and science. Just as the other measures of an angle are defined by a unit that indicates into how many parts the circumference of a circle has been divided, the radian is defined by dividing the circumference into 2π units.

Since the circumference of a circle is $C = 2\pi r$ and since, as was shown in Chapter 4, a central angle is measured by its intercepted arc on the circumference, 1 radian (rad) $= \dfrac{1}{2\pi}(2\pi r) = r$. In other words, the arc intercepted by a central angle of 1 rad is equal in length to the radius. In the unit circle where $r = 1$, a central angle of 1 rad intercepts an arc whose length is exactly 1 unit. For radian measure and for radian measure only, the numerical value of the length of an arc on the unit circle is *exactly* equal to the numerical radian measure of its central angle.

If θ is the measure of an angle in radians and if s is the length of its intercepted arc on a circle of radius r,

$$\frac{\theta}{2\pi} = \frac{s}{2\pi r} \qquad \text{and thus} \qquad s = r\theta$$

This means that any arc length of a circle can be computed as the product of r and θ when θ is in radians.

On the other hand, if θ is measured in degrees,

$$\frac{\theta°}{360°} = \frac{s}{2\pi r} \qquad \text{and} \qquad s = \frac{\pi}{180}r\theta° \approx 0.017\ 45r\theta°$$

These two formulas for the arc length provide an example illustrating that the formula using radian measure, $s = r\theta$, is much simpler than its corresponding formula using degree measure, $s \approx 0.017\ 45r\theta$. Also note that in a unit circle, a central angle of 1° intercepts an arc whose length is 0.017 45 unit, approximately.

The fact that 2π radians measure the circumference of any circle and 360° measures the same arc permits writing:

$$2\pi \text{ rad} = 360°$$

$$\pi \text{ rad} = 180°$$

$$1 \text{ rad} = \frac{180°}{\pi} \approx 57.296° \qquad \text{(given as 57.3° in Chapter 4)}$$

$$\approx 57°17'44.8''$$

Conversion from one type of angular measure to another is arithmetically awkward. Angles given with minutes and seconds must be converted to minutes and decimal of a minute before they can be changed to decimals of a degree. Using radian measure, 1 degree is approximately 0.017 453 29 rad. For these reasons, Table 2 of the Appendix contains six sections that will permit rapid and easy conversions between degree-minute-second notation, decimal degree notation, or radian measure.

The conversion from the degree to the grade is the simple ratio of $\frac{10}{9}$, and from the degree to the mil the ratio is $\frac{160}{9}$. The only time mils would be converted to degrees would probably be in a problem involving the use of maps, where $\frac{1}{4}°$ is about the smallest angle plottable, so a low degree of computational precision is adequate. Examples follow showing the use of the six tables that comprise Table 2 of the Appendix.

Example 9.1

Convert $57°17'44.8''$ to decimals of a degree.

SOLUTION (Use Table 2A.)

$$
\begin{array}{rr}
\text{the } 57° \text{ remains unchanged} = & 57.000\ 00 \\
\text{from the table,} \qquad 17' = & 0.283\ 33 \\
44'' = & 0.012\ 22 \\
0.8'' = & 0.000\ 22 \\
\hline
\text{Final answer} = & 57.295\ 77°
\end{array}
$$

Example 9.2

Convert $57.2958°$ to degrees, minutes, and seconds.

SOLUTION (Use Table 2B.)

$$
\begin{array}{rr}
\text{the } 57° \text{ remains unchanged} = & 57° \\
\text{from the table} \qquad 0.29° = & 17'24'' \\
0.005° = & 18'' \\
0.0008° = & 2.9'' \\
\hline
\text{Final answer} = & 57°17'44.9''
\end{array}
$$

(The difference of $0.1''$ between Example 9.1 and 9.2 is the effect of the roundoff of 0.000 77 to 0.0008.)

Example 9.3

Convert 2.7146 rad to degrees, minutes, and seconds.

SOLUTION (Use Table 2C.)

$$
\begin{array}{rlr}
2 & \text{rad} = 114° & 35'\ 29.6'' \\
0.7 & = \quad 40 & 6\ 25.4 \\
0.01 & = & 34\ 22.6 \\
0.004 & = & 13\ 45.1 \\
0.0006 & = & 2\ \ 3.8 \\
\hline
2.7146\ \text{rad} & = 154° & 80'\ 126.5'' \\
& = 155° & 22'\quad 6.5''
\end{array}
$$

Example 9.4
Convert 2.7146 rad to degrees and decimals of a degree.

SOLUTION (Use Table 2D.)

$$
\begin{array}{lll}
2 & \text{rad} = 114.5916° \\
0.7 & = 40.1070 \\
0.01 & = 0.5730 \\
0.004 & = 0.2292 \\
0.0006 & = 0.0344 & \text{(use } \tfrac{1}{10} \text{ of the value for 0.006)} \\
\hline
2.7146 \text{ rad} & = 155.5352°
\end{array}
$$

Example 9.5
Convert 92°14′38.8″ to radians.

SOLUTION (Use Table 2E.)
To find the values for the digits 1 through 9, shift the decimal point one place.

$$
\begin{array}{rl}
90° & = 1.570\ 796\ 3 \text{ rad} \\
2° & = 0.034\ 906\ 6 \\
10' & = 0.002\ 908\ 9 \\
4' & = 0.001\ 163\ 6 \\
30'' & = 0.000\ 145\ 4 \\
8'' & = 0.000\ 038\ 8 \\
0.8'' & = 0.000\ 003\ 9 \\
\hline
& 1.609\ 963\ 4 \text{ rad}
\end{array}
$$

Example 9.6
Convert 425.1847° to radians.

SOLUTION (Use Table 2F.)

$$
\begin{array}{lll}
400 & ° = 6.981\ 32 & \text{(10 times 40°)} \\
20 & = 0.349\ 066 \\
5 & = 0.087\ 266 \\
0.1 & = 0.001\ 745 \\
0.08 & = 0.001\ 396 \\
0.004 & = 0.000\ 070 \\
0.0007 & = 0.000\ 012 & (\tfrac{1}{10} \text{ of 0.007}) \\
\hline
425.1847° & = 7.420\ 876 \text{ rad}
\end{array}
$$

(*Note:* The value of 400° to six decimal places is 6.981 317, making this answer 0.000 003 rad high. For practical applications, this answer would more likely be rounded to five significant figures at the most, that is, to 7.4209 rad.)

In modern trigonometry, the trigonometric functions have been generalized so that they are considered as functions of real numbers that do not have to necessarily be interpreted as angles. This generalization has important practical significance because it permits these functions to be used for the description of many types of natural phenomena that may not involve an angle. A trigonometric function of a real number is defined as the value of that function for the angle having this real number as its radian measure. For example, $\sin 2 = \sin 2\,\text{rad} = \sin 114.592°$, approximately.

Problem Set 9.3

1–10

Convert the given angle to degrees and decimal parts.

1. 32°12'24"	4. 137°7'55"	7. 271°36'48.8"	9. −372°14'22"
2. 77°58'47"	5. 191°47'12.1"	8. 323°43'39.7"	10. −498°37'49"
3. 122°22'22"	6. 178°31'31.6"		

11.20

Convert the given angle to degrees, minutes, and seconds.

11. 37.123°	14. 292.746°	17. 364.2279°	19. −72.8537°
12. 48.874°	15. 3.1748°	18. 111.9864°	20. 458.8597°
13. 269.837°	16. −32.3472°		

21–30

Convert the given angle in radians to degrees, minutes, and seconds.

21. 2.1	24. 3.78	27. 4.679	29. −0.8246
22. 0.37	25. $\dfrac{\pi}{6}$	28. $\dfrac{\pi}{7}$	30. 1.0476
23. 0.426	26. −0.987		

31–40

Repeat Exercises 21–30 but obtain the answers in degrees and decimal parts by using Table 2D. If so directed by the instructor, check your answer by converting it to degrees, minutes, and seconds using Table 2B.

41–50

Convert the given angle to radians, correct to five decimal places.

41. 37°12'	44. 315°39'39"	47. 3.6142°	49. 177.7586°
42. 168°38'	45. −2°54'41.7"	48. 224.2242°	50. −415.2747°
43. 292°41'12"	46. 16°59'51.9"		

51–56

Compute, correct to four decimal places, the length of the arc intercepted by the given central angle on the circle whose radius r is also given.

51. (a) $30°, r = 1$ in.; (b) $30°, r = 5$ in.
52. (a) $45°, r = 1$ in.; (b) $45°, r = 8$ in.

53. (a) $\dfrac{\pi}{3}$ rad, $r = 10$ ft; (b) $\dfrac{\pi}{3}$ rad, $r = 25$ ft

54. (a) $\dfrac{\pi}{2}$ rad, $r = 100$ ft; (b) $\dfrac{\pi}{2}$ rad, $r = 340$ ft

55. (a) 2 rad, $r = 1$ m; (b) $2°, r = 1$ m
56. (a) 5 rad, $r = 1$ mm; (b) $5°, r = 1$ mm

57. If the end of a 32-in. pendulum swings through an arc of 4 in, find the number of radians and the number of degrees and minutes in the angle through which the pendulum swings.
58. If a pendulum 28 in. long swings through an angle of 0.173 rad, find the length of the arc described by the pendulum.
59. Find the length of the center line on the curve of a highway if this line is the arc of a circle of radius 750 ft and has a central angle of 20°27′.
60. Find in degrees and decimals, and in radians, the angle through which a 6-in.-diameter pulley turns as 10 ft of rope pass over it.
61. Assuming that the earth is 92,000,000 miles from the sun and that the earth has a circular orbit requiring $365\frac{1}{4}$ days to traverse, find
  (a) the distance the earth moves in its orbit in 1 hr.
  (b) the radian measure of the central angle through which the earth moves per hour.
62. Assuming that the earth is a sphere with a diameter of 8000 miles, find in miles and in radians the distance a point on the equator moves in 1 hr as the earth rotates on its axis. (Assume that one rotation = 24 hr.)

9.07 / Quadrantal angles

A **quadrantal angle** is an angle whose terminal side lies on either the x or y axis. Within one full positive rotation of the terminal side, the quadrantal angles are 0°, 90°, 180°, 270°, and 360°, or in radian measure, 0, $\pi/2$, π, $3\pi/2$, and 2π.

For all quadrantal angles, either the x or the y coordinate is 0 and it is possible for the denominator of the ratios for the tangent, cotangent, secant, or cosecant to become 0. Mathematically, any fraction with a zero denominator is called "undefined."

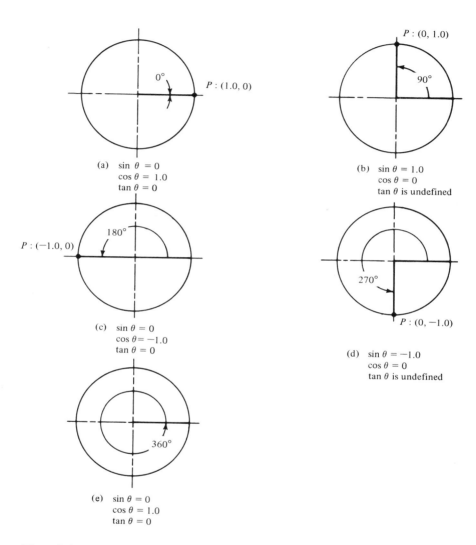

(a) sin $\theta = 0$
     cos $\theta = 1.0$
     tan $\theta = 0$

(b) sin $\theta = 1.0$
     cos $\theta = 0$
     tan θ is undefined

(c) sin $\theta = 0$
     cos $\theta = -1.0$
     tan $\theta = 0$

(d) sin $\theta = -1.0$
     cos $\theta = 0$
     tan θ is undefined

(e) sin $\theta = 0$
     cos $\theta = 1.0$
     tan $\theta = 0$

Figure 9.6
Quadrantal angles

The undefined functions of angles within one full positive rotation are as follows:

undefined values: cot 0°, tan 90°, cot 180°, tan 270°, cot 360°

csc 0°, sec 90°, csc 180°, sec 270°, csc 360°

The symbol ∞ can be used to describe the behavior of a trigonometric function near a quadrantal angle where the function is undefined. Using a unit circle, for the tangent function with $\tan \theta = \dfrac{y}{x}$, as θ varies from 0° to 90°, the numerator y increases from 0 to 1 while the denominator x decreases from 1 to 0. As a result, the ratio $\dfrac{y}{x}$ becomes a larger and larger positive number. For example, $\tan 89° = 57.290$, $\tan 89°30' = 114.59$, $\tan 89°55' = 687.55$, and $\tan 89°59' = 3437.7$. The term "positive infinity," written $+\infty$, is used to describe the fact that nearby values are very large positive numbers. Similarly, the term "negative infinity," written $-\infty$, means that nearby values are very small negative numbers (but large in absolute value). It must be emphasized that the symbols $+\infty$ and $-\infty$ are *not* real numbers, but they are used to indicate whether a ratio is becoming larger than any positive real number or smaller than any negative real number. Some trigonometric tables may print the infinity symbol; others may leave a blank space or put a line across the space for the undefined quadrantal values.

Great care must be taken in handling functions of quadrantal values since they may yield a legitimate solution to a problem or indicate there is no solution. No arithmetic operation can be performed on an undefined value. The expression $\tan \dfrac{\pi}{2} + 1$ is meaningless but it should not be confused with $\tan\left(\dfrac{\pi}{2} + 1\right) = -1.54$ approximately, a real number.

9.08 / Functions of special angles

Three angles, or multiples of them, appear in many problems. These angles are 30°, 45°, and 60°, or, in radian measure, $\dfrac{\pi}{6}, \dfrac{\pi}{4}$, and $\dfrac{\pi}{3}$. They were given special treatment in geometry, as shown in Figure 4.11, where the values of the sides of the 30°–60°–90° and 45°–45°–90° triangles were introduced.

Figure 9.7 shows the first quadrant of a unit circle, with the bisector of the 90° quadrantal angle passing through point P. A vertical line tangent to the circle at R is extended until it intersects ray OP at point Q. Triangle ORQ is an isosceles right triangle, since angle ORQ is a right angle and angle

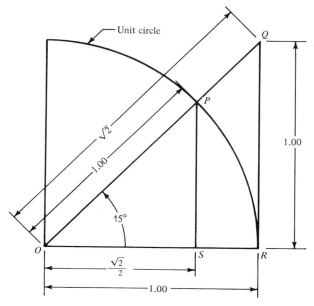

Figure 9.7
The 45°–45°–90° triangle

QOR is 45°. Therefore, the two legs OR and QR are each equal to 1, the unit radius. By the Theorem of Pythagoras, OQ is the square root of the sum of the squares of the legs, or $\sqrt{2}$. Triangle OPS is similar to triangle ORQ, so corresponding sides have equal ratios. Using Figure 9.7, the values of the six trigonometric functions can be calculated and they are listed below in both the radical and the decimal form.

$$\sin 45° = \frac{\sqrt{2}}{2} \approx 0.707\,11 \qquad\qquad \csc 45° = \sqrt{2} \approx 1.414\,21$$

$$\cos 45° = \frac{\sqrt{2}}{2} \approx 0.707\,11 \qquad\qquad \sec 45° \approx 1.414\,21$$

$$\tan 45° = 1 = 1.00000 \qquad\qquad \cot 45° = 1 = 1.00000$$

The radical form is called the *exact* value of the function. Since $\sqrt{2}$ is an irrational number, any decimal form is only an approximation. Both forms should be memorized. The three-place decimal form is used in slide-rule work. The radical form is kept in an equation until all simplifications have been made.

Figure 9.8 illustrates the 30°–60°–90° triangle. First, an equilateral triangle ABC is used since each of its interior angles is 60°. The bisector of angle B also bisects the base AC, so AC was made 2 units long to make AD 1 unit in length. By the Theorem of Pythagoras, $(BD)^2 + 1^2 = 2^2$, $(BD)^2 =$

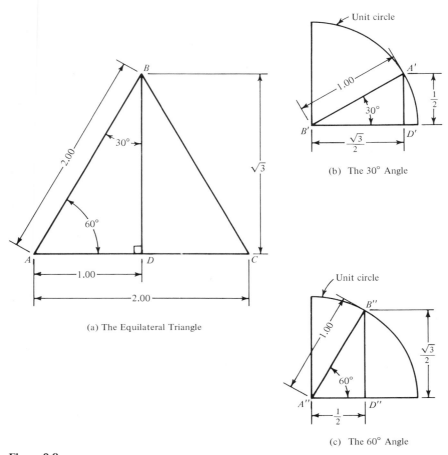

(a) The Equilateral Triangle

(b) The 30° Angle

(c) The 60° Angle

Figure 9.8
The 30°–60°–90° triangle

$4 - 1 = 3$, and thus $BD = \sqrt{3}$. The ratios found in triangle ABD are then transferred to the unit circle, first with 30° in standard position and second with 60° in standard position. The values of the trigonometric functions can be calculated by using these figures.

$$\sin 30° = \frac{1}{2} = 0.500\,00 \qquad \csc 30° = \frac{2}{1} = 2.000\,00$$

$$\cos 30° = \frac{\sqrt{3}}{2} \approx 0.866\,03 \qquad \sec 30° = \frac{2}{\sqrt{3}} \approx 1.154\,67$$

$$\tan 30° = \frac{1}{\sqrt{3}} \approx 0.577\,35 \qquad \cot 30° = \frac{\sqrt{3}}{1} \approx 1.732\,05$$

$$\sin 60° = \frac{\sqrt{3}}{2} \approx 0.866\,03 \qquad \csc 60° = \frac{2}{\sqrt{3}} \approx 1.154\,67$$

$$\cos 60° = \frac{1}{2} = 0.500\,00 \qquad \sec 60° = \frac{2}{1} = 2.000\,00$$

$$\tan 60° = \frac{\sqrt{3}}{1} \approx 1.732\,05 \qquad \cot 60° = \frac{1}{\sqrt{3}} \approx 0.577\,35$$

A very important principle may be seen in this tabulation. A 30° angle and a 60° angle are complementary angles; that is, their sum is 90°. For a pair of complementary angles, any function of one is the cofunction of its complement.

$$\sin 30° = \cos 60° \qquad \text{In general, } \sin \theta = \cos(90° - \theta)$$

$$\tan 30° = \cot 60^0 \qquad \qquad \tan \theta = \cot(90° - \theta)$$

$$\sec 30° = \csc 60° \qquad \qquad \sec \theta = \csc(90° - \theta)$$

The above relations can be derived from the definitions of the functions. They are important because a table of trigonometric functions needs to run from 0° to 45° only. The values for 45° to 90° can be found from these complementary-angle relations. Later sections will show how the values of the functions are obtained for negative angles and for positive angles larger than 90°, when the use of tables is required.

Problem Set 9.4

1–6

Express each of the following angles in radians in terms of π units.

1. 30°, 45°, 60°, 90°
2. 120°, 135°, 150°, 180°
3. 210°, 225°, 240°, 270°
4. 300°, 315°, 330°, 360°
5. −45°, −60°, −150°, −180°
6. −30°, −90°, −135°, −270°

7–22

If they are defined, find both the exact value and an approximate value to three significant figures for each of the following. If undefined, write "undefined." (Sketch each angle in standard position, find exact coordinates on the terminal side of the angle, and use the definitions of the functions to find the values required.)

7. $\sin \dfrac{11\pi}{3}$

11. $\tan \dfrac{13\pi}{4}$

15. $\sec \dfrac{11\pi}{2}$

19. $\tan\left(-\dfrac{17\pi}{3}\right)$

8. $\cos \dfrac{8\pi}{3}$ **12.** $\cot\left(-\dfrac{5\pi}{4}\right)$ **16.** $\tan\left(-\dfrac{7\pi}{2}\right)$ **20.** $\cot \dfrac{19\pi}{6}$

9. $\cos\left(-\dfrac{9\pi}{4}\right)$ **13.** $\csc\left(-\dfrac{7\pi}{6}\right)$ **17.** $\sin \dfrac{25\pi}{6}$ **21.** $\sec \dfrac{21\pi}{4}$

10. $\sin\left(-\dfrac{15\pi}{4}\right)$ **14.** $\sec \dfrac{13\pi}{6}$ **18.** $\cos \dfrac{13\pi}{3}$ **22.** $\csc\left(-\dfrac{7\pi}{3}\right)$

9.09 / Use of trigonometric tables:
$0° < \theta < 90°$

Most handbooks contain tables of natural trigonometric functions and tables of logarithms of trigonometric functions. This chapter will limit itself to natural functions; logarithmic tables will be fully utilized in the next chapter. Most handbooks list in their main table just four functions: the sine, cosine, tangent, and cotangent. Several contain a separate table for secants and cosecants, but these two functions are omitted from the tables in many books because they are reciprocals and can be calculated easily by using a slide rule or a desk calculator.

Most modern handbooks (and this book) contain a table by degrees and minutes and another by degrees and tenths, the latter often called a *decitrig* table. Some handbooks also contain tables for the trigonometric functions for angles in radian measure, but the need for these tables is limited. Table 2 permits rapid conversion of angles to and from radian measure.

In the tables of natural trigonometric functions, the values of these functions are listed in decimal form, the decimal equivalents of the ratios found by using the definitions of the functions. As with logarithmic tables, the term "place" indicates the number of significant figures used. Currently, five-place tables are the most common form, but tables are also available in four, six, and ten places. "Significant figures" should not be confused with "decimal places," for although these terms are interchangeable for tables of sines and cosines, the tangents and cotangents have only one decimal place at values near certain quadrantal angles.

Figure 9.9 is a page from Table 3 of the Appendix. For angles between 0° and 45°, the boldfaced number in the *upper left* corner gives the angle in degrees. The *left*-hand column reading *down* gives the number of minutes and the *upper* headings are used for the functions.

For angles between 45° and 90°, the boldfaced number in the *lower right* corner gives the angle in degrees, the *right*-hand column reading *up* gives the number of minutes, and the *lower* headings are used for the functions. Note the perfect match between the location of the angle and which column heading to use.

	Sin	Tan	Cot	Cos	Sec	Csc	
0	0.224 95	0.230 87	4.331 5	0.974 37	1.026 3	4.445 4	60
1	0.225 23	0.231 17	4.325 7	0.974 30	1.026 4	4.439 8	59
2	0.225 52	0.231 48	4.320 0	0.974 24	1.026 4	4.434 2	58
3	0.225 80	0.231 79	4.314 3	0.974 17	1.026 5	4.428 7	57
4	0.226 08	0.232 09	4.308 6	0.974 11	1.026 6	4.423 1	56
5	0.226 37	0.232 40	4.302 9	0.974 04	1.026 6	4.417 6	55
6	0.226 65	0.232 71	4.297 2	0.973 98	1.026 7	4.412 1	54
7	0.226 93	0.233 01	4.291 6	0.973 91	1.026 8	4.406 6	53
8	0.227 22	0.233 32	4.285 9	0.973 84	1.026 9	4.401 1	52
9	0.227 50	0.233 63	4.280 3	0.973 78	1.026 9	4.395 6	51
10	0.227 78	0.233 93	4.274 7	0.973 71	1.027 0	4.390 1	50
11	0.228 07	0.234 24	4.269 1	0.973 65	1.027 1	4.384 7	49
12	0.228 35	0.234 55	4.263 5	0.973 58	1.027 1	4.379 2	48
13	0.228 63	0.234 85	4.258 0	0.973 51	1.027 2	4.373 8	47
14	0.228 92	0.235 16	4.252 4	0.973 45	1.027 3	4.368 4	46
15	0.229 20	0.235 47	4.246 8	0.973 38	1.027 3	4.363 0	45
16	0.229 48	0.235 78	4.241 3	0.973 31	1.027 4	4.357 6	44
17	0.229 77	0.236 08	4.235 8	0.973 25	1.027 5	4.352 2	43
18	0.230 05	0.236 39	4.230 3	0.973 18	1.027 6	4.346 9	42
19	0.230 33	0.236 70	4.224 8	0.973 11	1.027 6	4.341 5	41
20	0.230 62	0.237 00	4.219 3	0.973 04	1.027 7	4.336 2	40
21	0.230 90	0.237 31	4.213 9	0.972 98	1.027 8	4.330 9	39
22	0.231 18	0.237 62	4.208 4	0.972 91	1.027 8	4.325 6	38
23	0.231 46	0.237 93	4.203 0	0.972 84	1.027 9	4.320 3	37
24	0.231 75	0.238 23	4.197 6	0.972 78	1.028 0	4.315 0	36
25	0.232 03	0.238 54	4.192 2	0.972 71	1.028 1	4.309 8	35
26	0.232 31	0.238 85	4.186 8	0.972 64	1.028 1	4.304 5	34
27	0.232 60	0.239 16	4.181 4	0.972 57	1.028 2	4.299 3	33
28	0.232 88	0.239 46	4.176 0	0.972 51	1.028 3	4.294 1	32
29	0.233 16	0.239 77	4.170 6	0.972 44	1.028 3	4.288 9	31
30	0.233 45	0.240 08	4.165 3	0.972 37	1.028 4	4.283 7	30
31	0.233 73	0.240 39	4.160 0	0.972 30	1.028 5	4.278 5	29
32	0.234 01	0.240 69	4.154 7	0.972 23	1.028 6	4.273 3	28
33	0.234 29	0.241 00	4.149 3	0.972 17	1.028 6	4.268 1	27
34	0.234 58	0.241 31	4.144 1	0.972 10	1.028 7	4.263 0	26
35	0.234 86	0.241 62	4.138 8	0.972 03	1.028 8	4.257 9	25
36	0.235 14	0.241 93	4.133 5	0.971 96	1.028 8	4.252 7	24
37	0.235 42	0.242 23	4.128 2	0.971 89	1.028 9	4.247 6	23
38	0.235 71	0.242 54	4.123 0	0.971 82	1.029 0	4.242 5	22
39	0.235 99	0.242 85	4.117 8	0.971 76	1.029 1	4.237 5	21
40	0.236 27	0.243 16	4.112 6	0.971 69	1.029 1	4.232 4	20
41	0.236 56	0.243 47	4.107 4	0.971 62	1.029 2	4.227 3	19
42	0.236 84	0.243 77	4.102 2	0.971 55	1.029 3	4.222 3	18
43	0.237 12	0.244 08	4.097 0	0.971 48	1.029 4	4.217 3	17
44	0.237 40	0.244 39	4.091 8	0.971 41	1.029 4	4.212 2	16
45	0.237 69	0.244 70	4.086 7	0.971 34	1.029 5	4.207 2	15
46	0.237 97	0.245 01	4.081 5	0.971 27	1.029 6	4.202 2	14
47	0.238 25	0.245 32	4.076 4	0.971 20	1.029 7	4.197 3	13
48	0.238 53	0.245 62	4.071 3	0.971 13	1.029 7	4.192 3	12
49	0.238 82	0.245 93	4.066 2	0.971 06	1.029 8	4.187 3	11
50	0.239 10	0.246 24	4.061 1	0.971 00	1.029 9	4.182 4	10
51	0.239 38	0.246 55	4.056 0	0.970 93	1.029 9	4.177 4	9
52	0.239 66	0.246 86	4.050 9	0.970 86	1.030 0	4.172 5	8
53	0.239 95	0.247 17	4.045 9	0.970 79	1.030 1	4.167 6	7
54	0.240 23	0.247 47	4.040 8	0.970 72	1.030 2	4.162 7	6
55	0.240 51	0.247 78	4.035 8	0.970 65	1.030 2	4.157 8	5
56	0.240 79	0.248 09	4.030 8	0.970 58	1.030 3	4.152 9	4
57	0.241 08	0.248 40	4.025 7	0.970 51	1.030 4	4.148 1	3
58	0.241 36	0.248 71	4.020 7	0.970 44	1.030 5	4.143 2	2
59	0.241 64	0.249 02	4.015 8	0.970 37	1.030 5	4.138 4	1
60	0.241 92	0.249 33	4.010 8	0.970 30	1.030 6	4.133 6	0
	Cos	Cot	Tan	Sin	Csc	Sec	′

Figure 9.9
Sample page of Table 3, Appendix

To obtain values for increments of angles smaller than 1', linear interpolation is used, exactly as taught in Chapters 1 and 8. The use of a slide rule may be warranted if working to tenths of seconds and the function is changing rapidly. Interpolation is not valid for some functions near the quadrantal angles and special methods for these will be covered in Section 9.15 for angles closer than 3° to any quadrantal angle.

Example 9.7
Find the sine of 13°46'.

SOLUTION (Use Figure 9.9.)
The answer is read directly from the table using the left column and top headings.

$$\sin 13°46' = 0.237\,97$$

Example 9.8
Find the cosine of 12°22'14".

SOLUTION
cos 12°22' is read directly as 0.976 80.

$$14'' = \frac{14'}{60} = 0.23'$$

The change in cosine for 1' is −0.000 07 (from 0.976 73 to 0.976 80).
The change in cosine for 0.23' is −0.000 02.
Thus, cos 12°22'14" = 0.976 78.

Example 9.9
Find the cotangent of 13°31'30.6".

SOLUTION
cot 13°31' is read directly as 4.1600.

$$30.6'' = \frac{30.6'}{60} = 0.51'$$

The change in cot for 1' is −0.0053.
The change in cot for 0.51' is −0.0027 (slide rule used).
Thus, cot 13°31'30.6" = 4.1573.

Example 9.10
Find the tangent of 77°46'.

SOLUTION
The answer is read directly from the table using the *right* column reading *up* for the minutes and the *lower* headings, since 77° is in the lower right corner.
Thus, tan 77°46' = 4.6122.

Example 9.11

Find the tangent of 76°2′48.9″.

SOLUTION

tan 76°2′ is read directly as 4.0207.

$$48.9'' = \frac{48.9'}{60} = 0.81'$$

The change in tan for 1′ is 0.0050.
The change in tan for 0.81′ is 0.0040.
Thus, tan 76°2′48.9″ = 4.0247.

It should be noted that between 0° and 90° the sine, tangent, and the secant increase as the angle increases so the increment for seconds is added. On the other hand, the cofunctions cosine, cotangent, and cosecant decrease and the increment is subtracted.

Use of the decitrig tables is similar to the use of Table 3. Figure 9.10 shows a sample page from Table 5 of the Appendix. The examples that follow are based upon that page. Note that the table is to tenths of a degree. Linear interpolation is still within acceptable limits of precision, but the increments for a tenth are larger than for 1′ and more slide-rule multiplication may be needed. Only two examples are given because much of the work is identical to that in the previous examples.

Example 9.12

Find the sine of 31.942°.

SOLUTION

sin 31.9° is read directly as 0.528 44.
The change in sin for 0.1° is 0.001 48.
The change in sin for 0.042° = 0.42(0.001 48) = 0.000 62.
Thus, sin 31.942° = 0.529 06.

Example 9.13

Find the tangent of 65.76°.

SOLUTION

tan 65.7° is read directly as 2.2148. (Notice that the angle is in the right-hand column, which is read *upward*, and the *lower* headings are used for that column.)
The change in tan for 0.1° is 0.0103.
0.6(0.0103) = 0.0062.
Thus, tan 65.76° = 2.2210.

θ°	Sin	Tan	Cot	Cos		θ°	Sin	Tan	Cot	Cos	
24.0	0.406 74	0.445 23	2.246 0	0.913 55	66.0	30.0	0.500 00	0.577 35	1.732 1	0.866 03	60.0
24.1	0.408 33	0.447 32	2.235 5	0.912 83	65.9	30.1	0.501 51	0.579 68	1.725 1	0.865 15	59.9
24.2	0.409 92	0.449 42	2.225 1	0.912 12	65.8	30.2	0.503 02	0.582 01	1.718 2	0.864 27	59.8
24.3	0.411 51	0.451 52	2.214 8	0.911 40	65.7	30.3	0.504 53	0.584 35	1.711 3	0.863 40	59.7
24.4	0.413 10	0.453 62	2.204 5	0.910 68	65.6	30.4	0.506 03	0.586 70	1.704 5	0.862 51	59.6
24.5	0.414 69	0.455 73	2.194 3	0.909 96	65.5	30.5	0.507 54	0.589 05	1.697 7	0.861 63	59.5
24.6	0.416 28	0.457 84	2.184 2	0.909 24	65.4	30.6	0.509 04	0.591 40	1.690 9	0.860 74	59.4
24.7	0.417 87	0.459 95	2.174 2	0.908 51	65.3	30.7	0.510 54	0.593 76	1.684 2	0.859 85	59.3
24.8	0.419 45	0.462 06	2.164 2	0.907 78	65.2	30.8	0.512 04	0.596 12	1.677 5	0.858 96	59.2
24.9	0.421 04	0.464 18	2.154 3	0.907 04	65.1	30.9	0.513 54	0.598 49	1.670 9	0.858 06	59.1
25.0	0.422 62	0.466 31	2.144 5	0.906 31	65.0	31.0	0.515 04	0.600 86	1.664 3	0.857 17	59.0
25.1	0.424 20	0.468 43	2.134 8	0.905 57	64.9	31.1	0.516 53	0.603 24	1.657 7	0.856 27	58.9
25.2	0.425 78	0.470 56	2.125 1	0.904 83	64.8	31.2	0.518 03	0.605 62	1.651 2	0.855 36	58.8
25.3	0.427 36	0.472 70	2.115 5	0.904 08	64.7	31.3	0.519 52	0.608 01	1.644 7	0.854 46	58.7
25.4	0.428 94	0.474 83	2.106 0	0.903 34	64.6	31.4	0.521 01	0.610 40	1.638 3	0.853 55	58.6
25.5	0.430 51	0.476 98	2.096 5	0.902 59	64.5	31.5	0.522 50	0.612 80	1.631 9	0.852 64	58.5
25.6	0.432 09	0.479 12	2.087 2	0.901 83	64.4	31.6	0.523 99	0.615 20	1.625 5	0.851 73	58.4
25.7	0.433 66	0.481 27	2.077 8	0.901 08	64.3	31.7	0.525 47	0.617 61	1.619 1	0.850 81	58.3
25.8	0.435 23	0.483 42	2.068 6	0.900 32	64.2	31.8	0.526 96	0.620 03	1.612 8	0.849 89	58.2
25.9	0.436 80	0.485 57	2.059 4	0.899 56	64.1	31.9	0.528 44	0.622 45	1.606 6	0.848 97	58.1
26.0	0.438 37	0.487 73	2.050 3	0.898 79	64.0	32.0	0.529 92	0.624 87	1.600 3	0.848 05	58.0
26.1	0.439 94	0.489 89	2.041 3	0.898 03	63.9	32.1	0.531 40	0.627 30	1.594 1	0.847 12	57.9
26.2	0.441 51	0.492 06	2.032 3	0.897 26	63.8	32.2	0.532 88	0.629 73	1.588 0	0.846 19	57.8
26.3	0.443 07	0.494 23	2.023 3	0.896 49	63.7	32.3	0.534 35	0.632 17	1.581 8	0.845 26	57.7
26.4	0.444 64	0.496 40	2.014 5	0.895 71	63 6	32.4	0.535 83	0.634 62	1.575 7	0.844 33	57.6
26.5	0.446 20	0.498 58	2.005 7	0.894 93	63.5	32.5	0.537 30	0.637 07	1.569 7	0.843 39	57.5
26.6	0.447 76	0.500 76	1.997 0	0.894 15	63.4	32.6	0.538 77	0.639 53	1.563 7	0.842 45	57.4
26.7	0.449 32	0.502 95	1.988 3	0.893 37	63.3	32.7	0.540 24	0.641 99	1.557 7	0.841 51	57.3
26.8	0.450 88	0.505 14	1.979 7	0.892 59	63.2	32.8	0.541 71	0.644 46	1.551 7	0.840 57	57.2
26.9	0.452 43	0.507 33	1.971 1	0.891 80	63.1	32.9	0.543 17	0.646 93	1.545 8	0.839 62	57.1
27.0	0.453 99	0.509 53	1.962 6	0.891 01	63.0	33.0	0.544 64	0.649 41	1.539 9	0.838 67	57.0
27.1	0.455 54	0.511 73	1.954 2	0.890 21	62.9	33.1	0.546 10	0.651 89	1.534 0	0.837 72	56.9
27.2	0.457 10	0.513 93	1.945 8	0.889 42	62.8	33.2	0.547 56	0.654 38	1.528 2	0.836 76	56.8
27.3	0.458 65	0.516 14	1.937 5	0.888 62	62.7	33.3	0.549 02	0.656 88	1.522 4	0.835 81	56.7
27.4	0.460 20	0.518 35	1.929 2	0.887 82	62.6	33.4	0.550 48	0.659 38	1.516 6	0.834 85	56.6
27.5	0.461 75	0.520 57	1.921 0	0.887 01	62.5	33.5	0.551 94	0.661 89	1.510 8	0.833 89	56.5
27.6	0.463 30	0.522 79	1.912 8	0.886 20	62.4	33.6	0.553 39	0.664 40	1.505 1	0.832 92	56.4
27.7	0.464 84	0.525 01	1.904 7	0.885 39	62.3	33.7	0.554 84	0.666 92	1.499 4	0.831 95	56.3
27.8	0.466 39	0.527 24	1.896 7	0.884 58	62.2	33.8	0.556 30	0.669 44	1.493 8	0.830 98	56.2
27.9	0.467 93	0.529 47	1.888 7	0.883 77	62.1	33.9	0.557 75	0.671 97	1.488 2	0.830 01	56.1
28.0	0.469 47	0.531 71	1.880 7	0.882 95	62.0	34.0	0.559 19	0.674 51	1.482 6	0.829 04	56.0
28.1	0.471 01	0.533 95	1.872 8	0.882 13	61.9	34.1	0.560 64	0.677 05	1.477 0	0.828 06	55.9
28.2	0.472 55	0.536 20	1.865 0	0.881 30	61.8	34.2	0.562 08	0.679 60	1.471 5	0.827 08	55.8
28.3	0.474 09	0.538 44	1.857 2	0.880 48	61.7	34.3	0.563 53	0.682 15	1.465 9	0.826 10	55.7
28.4	0.475 62	0.540 70	1.849 5	0.879 65	61.6	34.4	0.564 97	0.684 71	1.460 5	0.825 11	55.6
28.5	0.477 16	0.542 96	1.841 8	0.878 82	61.5	34.5	0.566 41	0.687 28	1.455 0	0.824 13	55.5
28.6	0.478 69	0.545 22	1.834 1	0.877 98	61.4	34.6	0.567 84	0.689 85	1.449 6	0.823 14	55.4
28.7	0.480 22	0.547 48	1.826 5	0.877 15	61.3	34.7	0.569 28	0.692 43	1.444 2	0.822 14	55.3
28.8	0.481 75	0.549 75	1.819 0	0.876 31	61.2	34.8	0.570 71	0.695 02	1.438 8	0.821 15	55.2
28.9	0.483 28	0.552 03	1.811 5	0.875 46	61.1	34.9	0.572 15	0.697 61	1.433 5	0.820 15	55.1
29.0	0.484 81	0.554 31	1.804 0	0.874 62	61.0	35.0	0.573 58	0.700 21	1.428 1	0.819 15	55.0
29.1	0.486 34	0.556 59	1.796 6	0.873 77	60.9	35.1	0.575 01	0.702 81	1.422 9	0.818 15	54.9
29.2	0.487 86	0.558 88	1.789 3	0.872 92	60.8	35.2	0.576 43	0.705 42	1.417 6	0.817 14	54.8
29.3	0.489 38	0.561 17	1.782 0	0.872 07	60.7	35.3	0.577 86	0.708 04	1.412 4	0.816 14	54.7
29.4	0.490 90	0.563 47	1.774 7	0.871 21	60.6	35.4	0.579 28	0.710 66	1.407 1	0.815 13	54.6
29.5	0.492 42	0.565 77	1.767 5	0.870 36	60.5	35.5	0.580 70	0.713 29	1.401 9	0.814 12	54.5
29.6	0.493 94	0.568 08	1.760 3	0.869 49	60.4	35.6	0.582 12	0.715 93	1.396 8	0.813 10	54.4
29.7	0.495 46	0.570 39	1.753 2	0.868 63	60.3	35.7	0.583 54	0.718 57	1.391 6	0.812 08	54.3
29.8	0.496 97	0.572 71	1.746 1	0.867 77	60.2	35.8	0.584 96	0.721 22	1.386 5	0.811 06	54.2
29.9	0.498 49	0.575 03	1.739 1	0.866 90	60.1	35.9	0.586 37	0.723 88	1.381 4	0.810 04	54.1
30.0	0.500 00	0.577 35	1.732 1	0.866 03	60.0	36.0	0.587 79	0.726 54	1.376 4	0.809 02	54.0
	Cos	Cot	Tan	Sin	θ°		Cos	Cot	Tan	Sin	θ°

Figure 9.10
Sample page of Table 5, Appendix

414

Problem Set 9.5

Using Tables 3 and 5 of the Appendix, find all six trigonometric functions for each given angle and list in the following order: sin, cos, tan, cot, sec, csc. For secants and cosecants, either use a handbook containing these values or find the reciprocal on a slide rule.

1. 31°14′	**6.** 0°41′	**11.** 27.4°	**16.** 81.47°
2. 47°46′	**7.** 22°17′12″	**12.** 44.7°	**17.** 77.124°
3. 52°31′	**8.** 37°47′57″	**13.** 68.8°	**18.** 14.077°
4. 67°18′	**9.** 3°42′37.2″	**14.** 79.9°	**19.** 13.798°
5. 89°12′	**10.** 86°33′51.6″	**15.** 12.88°	**20.** 80.122°

9.10 / Use of tables; angle not in first quadrant

If any page of Table 3, such as Figure 9.9, is examined, it will be noted that besides the boldfaced angle in the upper left and lower right corners, two more boldfaced and four angles of conventional type appear. The boldfaced series covers angles from 0° to 180° and the series of conventional type covers angles from 180° to 360°. This location of the angle in degrees indicates which column of minutes to use and which row of headings to use. Referring to Figure 9.9, for a sine of 167°13′, the 13′ are found in the *right* column. Had the given angle been 167°13′42″, the increments are now subtracted, because this minute column is read *upward*. The heading for the sine column would be across the *top*, because the angle in degrees is in the *top* right corner. Exactly the same reasoning (and exactly the same numerical answers) would be found for 347°13′42″, except that the rules for the signs must be followed, since these two angles are not in the same quadrant.

In contrast, for a given angle of 262°27′13″, the given angle is in the *lower left* corner, so the *left*-hand column of minutes would be used, the computed increment for the sine would be *added*, and the *lower* headings would be used.

Example 9.14
Find the sine of 282°27′13″.

SOLUTION
sin 282°27′ is read directly as 0.976 48 (without regard to sign). The change in sin for 1′ is −0.000 06.

$$\frac{13}{60}(0.000\ 06) = -0.000\ 01$$

Thus, sin 282°27′13″ = −0.976 47, since the angle is in quadrant IV.

Note that the addition of the increment in Example 9.14 was an algebraic addition; the actual arithmetic was a subtraction. Rather than regarding this procedure as rules to be memorized, it is better to look at the functional values and see if they are increasing or decreasing as the angle increases. Doing this will always indicate whether the increment is to be added or subtracted.

It may be observed that in Table 5 there are no angles listed larger than 90°. Table 3 does not cover angles greater than 360°. Neither table covers negative angles. Obviously, a method is needed for angles not in available tables. The method used is quite simple and it is based upon finding a reference angle ϕ for any given angle θ.

The **reference angle** ϕ for an angle θ in standard position is the acute angle between the terminal side of the given angle and the x axis.

Figure 9.11 shows the reference angle ϕ for a variety of given angles θ. From the figure it may be noted that the value of a trigonometric function of any angle will have the same numerical value as that for its reference angle and will differ only in sign if it differs at all. In symbols, either

$$f(\theta) = f(\phi) \qquad \text{or} \qquad f(\theta) = -f(\phi)$$

To Find the Correct Functional Value of Any Angle
(1) Sketch the angle given in standard position.
(2) Obtain the numerical value of the function for the reference angle. (Use the methods previously discussed for angles between 0° and 90°.)
(3) Obtain the correct sign by the methods of Section 9.05.

Example 9.15
Find the cosine of 113.12°.

SOLUTION
(1) A sketch (omitted here) shows that the terminal side of the angle is in quadrant II. The reference angle ϕ is $180° - 113.12° = 66.88°$.
(2) Cos 66.8° is read directly from Table 5 as 0.393 94. The change in cos of 0.1° is -0.00160.

$$0.8(-0.001\ 60) = -0.001\ 28$$

Thus, cos 66.88° = 0.392 66.
(3) In quadrant II, x is negative and thus cosine is negative. Therefore, cos 113.12° = $-0.392\ 66$.

Example 9.16
Find the tangent of 712°10′36″.

SOLUTION
(1) A sketch (omitted here) shows that the terminal side of the angle is in quadrant IV. The reference angle ϕ is $720° - 712°10′36″ = 7°49′24″$.

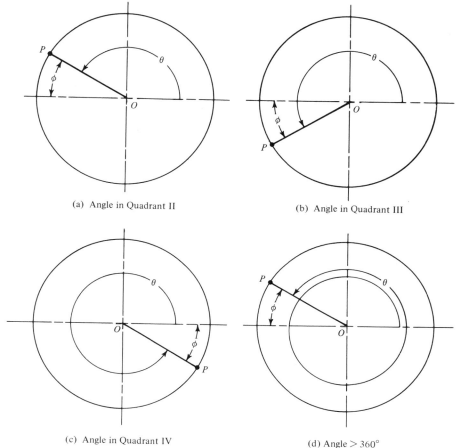

(a) Angle in Quadrant II

(b) Angle in Quadrant III

(c) Angle in Quadrant IV

(d) Angle > 360°

Figure 9.11
The reference angle

(2) tan 7°49′ is read directly as 0.137 28. The change in tan for 1′ is 0.000 30 and 0 4(0.000 30) = 0.000 12. Thus, tan 7°49′24″ = 0.137 40.

(3) In quadrant IV, x is positive and y is negative, so the tangent is negative.
Thus, tan 712°10′36″ = −0.137 40.

9.11 / Negative angles

Figure 9.1 showed that a negative angle was one whose terminal side is rotating clockwise instead of counterclockwise. Section 9.10 stressed that the functions of any angle depend upon the position of the terminal side of the angle, from which a reference angle was found. Thus, if any negative angle is sketched, its trigonometric functions are identical with those for the positive angle having a coterminal side. This is so because both angles have the same reference angle and are in the same quadrant determining the sign. For this reason, detailed examples and a problem set based upon negative angles will not be given. Figure 9.12 illustrates, for each quadrant, the method that would be used for negative angles.

In later problems, particularly those where trigonometric functions are used in equations, it is usually desirable to replace a function of a negative angle by its positive-angle counterpart. For the cosine and the secant, the function of the negative angle is the same as the function of the positive angle.

Figure 9.12
Negative angles and their reference angles

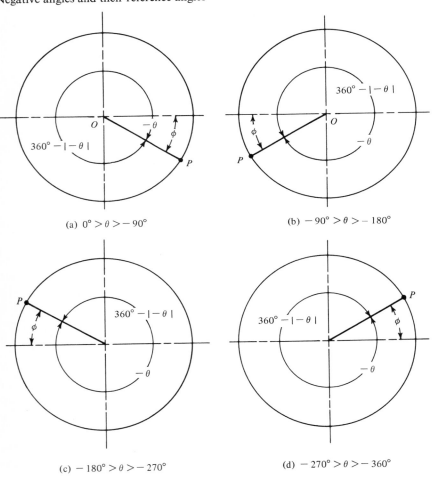

(a) $0° > \theta > -90°$

(b) $-90° > \theta > -180°$

(c) $-180° > \theta > -270°$

(d) $-270° > \theta > -360°$

For the other four functions, the function of the negative angle is replaced by the negative of the function of the positive angle. In tabular form,

$$\sin(-\theta) = -\sin\theta \qquad \cot(-\theta) = -\cot\theta$$

$$\cos(-\theta) = \cos\theta \qquad \sec(-\theta) = \sec\theta$$

$$\tan(-\theta) = -\tan\theta \qquad \csc(-\theta) = -\csc\theta$$

Problem Set 9.6

For each given angle, list the values of the four trigonometric functions in the order given in the tables. For angles given in degrees, minutes, and seconds up to 360°, use Table 3. For all other angles, also state the reference angle and the quadrant in which the angle lies.

1. 119°49′	**9.** 309°10′12″	**17.** 698°12′17″	**24.** −149.66°
2. 232°37′	**10.** 109°49′48″	**18.** 588°37′37″	**25.** −190°4′
3. 258°31′	**11.** 209°32′14″	**19.** 414°58′47.6″	**26.** −213°58′
4. 332°29′	**12.** 315°56′11″	**20.** 399°59′3.3″	**27.** −285.16°
5. 291.9°	**13.** 401.34°	**21.** −56°35′	**28.** −324.65°
6. 158.8°	**14.** 501.56°	**22.** −75°08′	**29.** −400°54′
7. 340.7°	**15.** 601.89°	**23.** −106.79°	**30.** −800°15′
8. 248.6°	**16.** 701.77°		

9.12 / Use of tables; finding angle from function

Inverse functions were defined in Section 7.06. One requirement for an inverse function is that for each value of the original dependent variable there exists only one value for the original independent variable. If the rule for the original function is $f(\theta) = \sin\theta$, then for $\theta = 30°$ there is a single answer, $+\frac{1}{2}$. However, if the inverse of this function is tested by using the rule "Find an angle whose sine is $+\frac{1}{2}$," then there are infinitely many solutions. If $\sin\theta = \frac{1}{2}$, then θ may have any of these values:

$$\ldots, -330°, -210°, 30°, 150°, 390°, 510°, \ldots$$

Because there is not exactly one value for the angle for each value of a trigonometric function, the inverse relation of a trigonometric function is not a function. There is a method to handle this situation and obtain an inverse function by limiting the angles that may be permitted as answers. If the value of the trigonometric function is positive or zero, the angle is limited to the values $0° \leq \theta \leq 90°$. If the value of the function is negative, the angle is limited to either the values $90° \leq \theta \leq 180°$ or $-90° \leq \theta \leq 0°$, whichever permits the trigonometric function to take on all its values without allowing an undefined value in the middle. Values in these designated intervals are called the **principal values** of the angle. In this way, the inverse functions for the sine, cosine, and tangent are obtained and they may be designated either as Arcsin, Arccos, Arctan or as Sin^{-1}, Cos^{-1}, Tan^{-1}, using the inverse notation introduced in Chapter 7. The inverses of the cosecant, secant, and cotangent are usually obtained by restricting the angle to the same values as those for its reciprocal function.

Definitions

$\theta = \text{Sin}^{-1} x$ *if and only if* $\sin \theta = x$ *and* $-90° \leq \theta \leq 90°$
$\theta = \text{Cos}^{-1} x$ *if and only if* $\cos \theta = x$ *and* $\quad 0° \leq \theta \leq 180°$
$\theta = \text{Tan}^{-1} x$ *if and only if* $\tan \theta = x$ *and* $-90° < \theta < 90°$
$\theta = \text{Csc}^{-1} x$ *if and only if* $\csc \theta = x$ *and* $-90° \leq \theta \leq 90°, \theta \neq 0°$
$\theta = \text{Sec}^{-1} x$ *if and only if* $\sec \theta = x$ *and* $\quad 0° \leq \theta \leq 180°, \theta \neq 90°$
$\theta = \text{Cot}^{-1} x$ *if and only if* $\cot \theta = x$ *and* $-90° \leq \theta \leq 90°, \theta \neq 0°$

In a practical problem, the physical conditions of the problem may limit the angle to a single value. Figure 9.13 shows a small hoisting device and an angle θ is desired, such that $\sin \theta = \frac{10}{20} = \frac{1}{2}$. In this case, θ is recorded as 30° and not as 150°, since θ is drawn on the sketch.

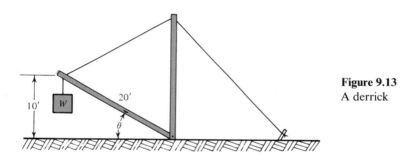

Figure 9.13
A derrick

The preceding discussion has been preparation for the technique of finding an angle from the tables given the value of its trigonometric function. There is a direct analogy between the method to be used and the method previously used to find an antilogarithm. Both methods use an entry value in the table adjacent to the given functional value and by linear interpolation the exact result is obtained. There is one exception; for the sine, tangent, and secant, the entry angle is the nearest listed *smaller* angle; for the cofunctions, the entry angle is the nearest listed *larger* angle.

Example 9.17

Find $\text{Sin}^{-1}\, 0.114\,04$.

SOLUTION

The value appears in Table 3. $\theta = 8°3'$.

Example 9.18

Find the decimal degree value of $\text{Cos}^{-1}\, 0.06\,105$.

SOLUTION

The value appears in Table 5 and $\theta = 86.6°$.

Example 9.19

Find $\text{Sin}^{-1}\, 0.226\,00$ to the nearest second.

SOLUTION (Figure 9.9 can be used.)

The closest *smaller* function is 0.225 80 for an angle of $13°3'$.
The change in sin for $1'$ is 0.000 28.
The difference between the given value and the tabulated value is 0.000 20.

$$\frac{0.000\,20}{0.000\,28}(60'') = 43''$$

Thus, $\theta = 13°3'43''$.

ALTERNATIVE SOLUTION USING A TABULATION

$$\sin 13°3' = 0.225\,80$$
$$\sin \theta = 0.226\,00 \quad \bigg] -0.000\,20$$
$$\sin 13°4' = 0.226\,08 \quad \bigg] -0.000\,28$$

$$\theta = 13°3' + \frac{20}{28}(60'') = 13°3'43''$$

Example 9.20

Find $\text{Cos}^{-1}\, 0.977\,89$ to the nearest tenth of a second.

SOLUTION (Figure 9.9 can be used.)

The tabular method will be used. Remember that for cofunctions, the functional value decreases as the angle increases.

$$\cos 12°4' = 0.977\,91$$
$$\cos \theta = 0.977\,89 \quad \bigg] -0.000\,02$$
$$\cos 12°5' = 0.977\,84 \quad \bigg] -0.000\,07$$

$$\theta = 12°4' + \frac{2}{7}(60'') = 12°4'17.1''$$

(Note that precision has been ignored. The smallest meaningful precision is $\frac{1}{7}$ of 60, or about 9". To give this angle to tenths of seconds is certainly not meaningful. If this calculation occurred in a problem involving three angles of a triangle and if the sum of the three computed angles did not total exactly 180°, this angle θ could be given any value 9" above or below 12°4'17" if that would balance the sum.)

Example 9.21
Find $\text{Tan}^{-1}\frac{1}{2}$ to the nearest 0.01°.

SOLUTION (Figure 9.10 can be used.)

$$\tan 26.5° = 0.4986$$
$$\tan \theta = 0.5000$$
$$-0.0014$$
$$-0.0022$$
$$\tan 26.6° = 0.5008$$

$$\theta = 26.5° + \frac{14}{22}(0.1)° = 26.5 + 0.06 = 26.56°$$

Example 9.22
Find $\text{Cot}^{-1} - \frac{3}{2}$ to the nearest 0.0001°.

SOLUTION

$$\cot 33.7° = 1.4994$$
$$\cot \phi = 1.5000$$
$$-0.0051$$
$$-0.0057$$
$$\cot 33.6° = 1.5051$$

$$\phi = 33.6° + \frac{51}{57}(0.1°) = 33.6 + 0.0895 = 33.6895°$$

$$\theta = -33.6895°$$

(Note that a reference angle was first calculated and then the principal value of the angle was found.)

Example 9.23
Find θ to the nearest 0.001° so that $\csc \theta = \frac{9}{8}$.

SOLUTION
Before solving this problem, notice that two new ideas are included. Since the inverse notation is not used, a general answer rather than the principal value is required. This book does not include a table for cosecants, so the reciprocal function must be found and used.

(1) Find the reciprocal function:

$$\text{If } \csc \theta = \frac{9}{8}, \text{ then } \sin \theta = \frac{8}{9} = 0.8889$$

(2) Find the reference angle ϕ:

$$\sin 62.7° = 0.8886$$
$$\sin \phi = 0.8889$$
$$-0.0003$$
$$-0.0008$$
$$\sin 62.8° = 0.8894$$

$$\phi = 62.7° + \frac{3}{8}(0.1°) = 62.738°$$

(3) Find an algebraic method for writing *all* possible values of θ, which will always be in quadrants I and II, since the given function is positive.

For quadrant I, $\theta = \phi \pm n\,360°$, where n is an integer.

For quadrant II, $\theta = (180° - \phi) \pm n\,360°$.

Therefore, the final answer is written in the form

$$\theta = (62.738° \text{ or } 117.262°) \pm n\,360°, \; n \text{ is an integer.}$$

Example 9.24

Find θ in radian measure to the nearest 0.0001 rad so that $\sec \theta = 4.500\,000$.

SOLUTION

(1) The reciprocal function is $\cos \theta = \dfrac{1}{4.5} = 0.222\,22$.

(2) The reference angle is found using degrees, minutes, and seconds:

$$\cos 77° 10' = 0.222\,12$$
$$\cos \phi = 0.222\,22$$
$$-0.000\,28$$
$$-0.000\,18$$
$$\cos 77°9' = 0.222\,40$$

$$\phi = 77°9' + \frac{18}{28}(60'') = 77°9'38.6''$$

(3) Use Table 2E to convert to radian measure.

$$
\begin{aligned}
70° &= 1.221\,73 \\
7° &= 0.122\,17 \\
9' &= 0.002\,62 \\
30'' &= 0.000\,15 \\
9'' &= 0.000\,04 \\
\hline
\phi &= 1.346\,71 \text{ rad}
\end{aligned}
$$

(4) The secant is positive in quadrants I and IV, so the final answer is

$$\theta = (1.3467 \text{ or } 4.9365) \pm 2\pi n \text{ radians, } n \text{ is an integer.}$$

Problem Set 9.7

1–12
Find θ to the nearest second.

1. $\text{Sin}^{-1} \, 0.997\,44$ 5. $\text{Sec}^{-1} \, \frac{4}{3}$ 9. $\text{Cot}^{-1} \, 9.000\,00$
2. $\text{Cos}^{-1} \, 0.276\,20$ 6. $\text{Csc}^{-1} \, \frac{5}{4}$ 10. $\text{Tan}^{-1} \, 6.000\,00$
3. $\text{Tan}^{-1} \, 9.7048$ 7. $\text{Cos}^{-1} \, 0.905\,90$ 11. $\text{Csc}^{-1} \, \frac{5}{3}$
4. $\text{Cot}^{-1} \, 0.971\,61$ 8. $\text{Sin}^{-1} \, 0.913\,10$ 12. $\text{Sec}^{-1} \, \frac{7}{4}$

13–20
Find θ to the nearest 0.001°.

13. $\text{Sin}^{-1} \, -0.247\,00$ 16. $\text{Cot}^{-1} \, \frac{9}{10}$ 19. $\text{Cot}^{-1} \, -\frac{3}{2}$
14. $\text{Cos}^{-1} \, -0.521\,01$ 17. $\text{Cos}^{-1} \, 0.998\,00$ 20. $\text{Tan}^{-1} \, 5.5000$
15. $\text{Tan}^{-1} \, 0.929\,10$ 18. $\text{Sin}^{-1} \, 0.123\,45$

21–26
Find θ to the nearest 0.0001 rad.

21. $\sin \theta = 0.099\,10$ 23. $\tan \theta = -6.0400$ 25. $\text{Arcsin} \, \frac{1}{11}$
22. $\cos \theta = 0.128\,90$ 24. $\text{Arccos} \, \frac{7}{9}$ 26. $\text{Arctan} \, -\frac{2}{3}$

9.13 / Finding all trigonometric functions from one given function

If any one of the six trigonometric functions is known, a right triangle can be sketched such that the given function is a function of one of its angles in standard position. However, the solution is not unique, because each function has the same sign in two quadrants. If one other condition is given, either about the domain of the angle or the sign of one other function not the reciprocal, there is a single solution to the problem; that is, there is exactly one value for each of the remaining five functions.

Method for Finding All Functions from One Given Function
(1) Determine the quadrant for the angle of the problem.
(2) Sketch the triangle defined by the given function, using the quadrant found in step (1).

(3) Find the third side of the triangle by the Pythagorean theorem.
(4) State the coordinates (x,y) of a point on the terminal side of the angle and state the value of r.
(5) State the values of all the functions, using the values for x, y, and r found in step (4).

Example 9.25
Find the functions of θ if $\sin \theta = \frac{3}{5}$ and $90° < \theta < 180°$.

SOLUTION
(1) The given domain places θ in quadrant II.
(2) The sketch is shown in Figure 9.14.

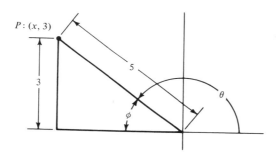

P : (x, 3)

5

3

ϕ

θ

Figure 9.14

$$\sin \theta = \frac{3}{5}$$

(3) The missing side is $\sqrt{5^2 - 3^2} = \sqrt{16} = 4$.
(4) $x = -4$, $y = 3$, and $r = 5$.
(5) The values of the six functions are:

$$\sin \theta = \frac{y}{r} = \frac{3}{5} \qquad \cos \theta = \frac{x}{r} = -\frac{4}{5} \qquad \tan \theta = \frac{y}{x} = -\frac{3}{4}$$

$$\csc \theta = \frac{r}{y} = \frac{5}{3} \qquad \sec \theta = \frac{r}{x} = -\frac{5}{4} \qquad \cot \theta = \frac{x}{y} = -\frac{4}{3}$$

Example 9.26
Find the functions of θ if $\cot \theta = \frac{12}{5}$ and $\sin \theta$ is negative.

SOLUTION

(1) cotangent $= \dfrac{x}{y}$ is positive in quadrants I and III.

sine $= \dfrac{y}{r}$ is negative in quadrants III and IV.

Therefore, θ lies in quadrant III.
(2) The sketch is shown in Figure 9.15.

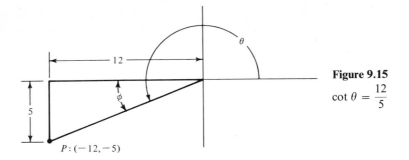

Figure 9.15

$$\cot \theta = \frac{12}{5}$$

$P:(-12,-5)$

(3) $r = \sqrt{12^2 + 5^2} = \sqrt{169} = 13.$
(4) $x = -12,\ y = -5,$ and $r = 13.$
(5) Values of the six functions:

$$\sin \theta = -\frac{5}{13} \qquad \cos \theta = -\frac{12}{13} \qquad \tan \theta = \frac{5}{12}$$

$$\csc \theta = -\frac{13}{5} \qquad \sec \theta = -\frac{13}{12} \qquad \cot \theta = \frac{12}{5}$$

Problem Set 9.8

1–12
Find the values of the six trigonometric functions of θ, leaving all answers in fractional form, using radicals if they occur.

1. $\sin \theta = \frac{2}{3}$ and θ is in quadrant I
2. $\sin \theta = \frac{3}{4}$ and θ is in quadrant II
3. $\cos \theta = \frac{24}{25}$ and θ is in quadrant IV
4. $\cos \theta = -\frac{15}{17}$ and θ is in quadrant III
5. $\tan \theta = 2$ and θ is in quadrant III
6. $\tan \theta = 3$ and θ is in quadrant I
7. $\cot \theta = -\frac{12}{13}$ and $90° < \theta < 180°$
8. $\cot \theta = -\frac{3}{7}$ and $270° < \theta < 360°$

9. $\sin \theta = 0.3$ and $\dfrac{\pi}{2} < \theta < \pi$

10. $\cos \theta = 0.375$ and $\dfrac{3\pi}{2} < \theta < 2\pi$

11. $\tan \theta = 0.125$ and $180° < \theta < 270°$
12. $\cot \theta = -2.75$ and $90° < \theta < 180°$

13–20

Find the values of the six trigonometric functions of θ, leaving all answers in fractional form.

13. $\csc \theta = 4$ and $\tan \theta$ is negative.
14. $\cos \theta = 0.5625$ and $\sin \theta$ is negative.
15. $\sin \theta = -\frac{2}{5}$ and $\tan \theta$ is positive
16. $\csc \theta = 8$ and $\cos \theta$ is positive
17. $\cot \theta = -3$ and $\sin \theta$ is positive
18. $\sec \theta = 5$ and $\tan \theta$ is negative
19. $\tan \theta = 0.3125$ and $\cos \theta$ is positive
20. $\tan \theta = 0$ and $\sec \theta$ is negative

9.14 / Trigonometric functions on the slide rule

The slide rule may be used to find trigonometric functions when no trigonometric tables are available or the calculations to be made are quite approximate, as in hasty estimates. For most calculations, the slide rule is less desirable than tables for finding the values of the trigonometric functions, for these reasons:

(1) The subdivisions of degrees are quite large, covering 5 to 10′ on ordinary scales and 0.05 to 0.10° on the decitrig.
(2) Values for the sine are difficult to read above 60° and impossible to read between 80° and 90°.
(3) The method of reading values of the functions differs with the various manufacturers, making it awkward if the slide rule of another person must be used.

In contrast, if the function itself is found in a table, the slide rule is quite adequate for any subsequent arithmetic operations, provided that three significant figures in the final answer are adequate. Countless engineering formulas involve the product of one or two variables and a trigonometric function, with the given data justifying only three significant figures.

Constant use of trigonometric tables may result in forgetting how to read trigonometric functions on one's own slide rule. When such an emergency arises, first find a known functional value such as sin 30°, tan 30°, sin 45°, or tan 45°.

Example 9.27a
Find sin 30° on the AcuMath type of slide rule.

SOLUTION
(If this slide rule is not available, use Figure 9.16.)
On this rule, sines are keyed to the A scale, the left index representing

0.01, the middle index 0.10, and the right index 1.0. The S scale is graduated in degrees and minutes.
Set the hairline to 30° on S.
Read the answer, 0.5, on A.

Example 9.27b
Find sin 30° using a slide rule of the Keuffel & Esser GP-12 type.

SOLUTION
(If this slide rule is not available, use Figure 2.1.)
On this rule, sines are keyed to the C scale, the left index representing 0.1 and the right index 1.0. The S scale is graduated in the decitrig system and the smallest angle that can be read is 5.7°. Finding the functions of small angles will be discussed in Section 9.15.
Set the hairline to 30.0° on S.
Read the answer, 0.5, on C.

Example 9.28a
Find cos 30° on the AcuMath type of rule.

SOLUTION
As shown in Section 9.08, the cosine of 30° is the sine of 60°, the complementary angle, so sin 60° will be found.
Set the hairline to 60° on S.
Read the answer, 0.86(?), on A.

The ? indicates the difficulty of estimating the third digit. One method to avoid this difficulty is to avoid reading the value if any subsequent arithmetic operation is to be performed. Merely set the proper index of the slide for a multiplication and the divisor for a division to the hairline. Figure 9.16 illustrates finding $\dfrac{\cos 65°}{75}$, for which the answer shown is 0.005 63.

Figure 9.16
Trigonometric functions, AcuMath rule

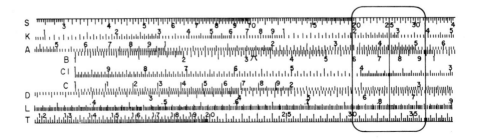

Example 9.28b

Find cos 30° using the K & E GP-12 type of rule.

SOLUTION

Set the hairline to 60° on S (sin 60° is being found).
Read the answer, 0.865, on C.

On the K & E GP-12 slide rule and other more expensive types, cofunctions are found by using the left-sloping numerals printed on the left side of the vertical mark. On most rules of this type, they are also printed in red, with the regular function printed in dark blue or black. The instructions in Example 9.28b therefore could have been written as follows:

Set the hairline to red, left-sloping 30° on S.
Read the answer, 0.865, on C.

Example 9.29a

Find tan 50° on the AcuMath type of rule.

SOLUTION

On this rule, tangents are keyed to the D scale, the left index representing 0.1 and the right index 1.0. Tangents for angles smaller than 5°45' or cotangents for angles larger than 84°15' cannot be read. The T scale is graduated in degrees and minutes to 45°. For angles in this range, the hairline is set to the angle and the value of the tangent read on D.

For angles greater than 45°, as in this example, the complementary angle is used, here 40°. If the indexes of the C and D scales are aligned, the value of tan 40° is not read on D, but the value of tan 50° (= cot 40°) is read directly on the CI scale, the right index of CI representing 1.0 and the left index 10.0.

Set the hairline to 40° on *T*.
Read the answer, 1.19, on CI.

Example 9.29b

Find tan 50° using the K & E GP-12 type of rule.

SOLUTION

On this rule, the T scale, like the S scale, is keyed to the C scale. The complementary angles are identical to the S scale; left-sloping and in red. Since T and CI are both on the slide, no alignment of indexes is required.

Set the hairline to the red, left-sloping 50° on T.
Read the answer, 1.19, on CI.

The tangents of small angles will be covered in Section 9.15.

Example 9.30a

Find sec 30°30′ on the AcuMath type of rule.

SOLUTION

(1) $\sec 30°30' = \dfrac{1}{\cos 30°30'} = \dfrac{1}{\sin 59°30'}$.

(2) Set the hairline to 59°30′ on S.
(3) Read 862 on B.
(4) Set the hairline to 862 on C.
(5) Read the answer, 1.16, on CI. sec 30°30′ = 1.16.

Example 9.30b

Find sec 30°30′ using the K & E GP-12 rule.

SOLUTION

(1) $\sec 30°30' = \dfrac{1}{\cos 30.5°}$.

(2) Set the hairline to red, left-sloping 30.5° on S.
(3) Read the secant on CI as 1.16.

Problem Set 9.9

Find the stated functional value to three significant figures. (Since some students may have decitrig scales and others the degree and minute scales, the problems are given in both types of units. Angles smaller than 6° or larger than 70° have been intentionally omitted to permit solutions on either type of slide rule.)

1. sin 6°30′ (6.5°)
2. sin 6°42′ (6.7°)
3. tan 7°45′ (7.75°)
4. tan 8°15′ (8.25°)
5. cos 50°30′ (50.5°)
6. cos 52°30′ (52.5°)
7. cot 55°10′ (55.17°)
8. cot 54°40′ (54.67°)
9. sec 75°36′ (75.6°)
10. sec 72°48′ (72.8°)

11. csc 12°39′ (12.65°)
12. csc 11°51′ (11.85°)
13. sin 62°
14. sin 64°
15. cos 21°
16. cos 22°
17. tan 55°45′ (55.75°)
18. tan 58°24′ (58.4°)
19. cot 25°36′ (25.6°)
20. cot 22°18′ (22.3°)

9.15 / Functions of small angles

This section covers the sine and tangent of small angles and the cosine and cotangent of angles near 90°. There are three separate problems:
(1) Finding functions using tables.

(2) Finding functions using the slide rule.

(3) Finding logarithmic values for these functions. (This topic will be covered in Chapter 10.)

In precise surveying, night observations to eliminate thermal distortion are made on two target light slits, usually spaced 1 m apart. This method, called the *subtense bar method*, requires reading very small angles and calculations using one half of the measured angle. By using the best types of instruments and making multiple observations of the same angle, accurate readings to tenths of seconds are found. In physics laboratories, a light beam is used to measure small angular rotations and, again, computations involving very small angles will be involved. However, the smallest increment in the average trigonometric tables is 1'.

The U.S. Coast and Geodetic Survey *Special Publication 231* contains sines and cosines to eight decimal places by increments of 1". Since this publication may not be readily available, the obvious question is what can be done without using it. Fortunately, it can be proved that for very small angles, with the angle measured in radians,

$$\theta \text{ (in radians)} = \sin \theta = \tan \theta$$

Checking this equation for an angle of 1':

$$\theta = 0.000\ 290\ 89 \qquad \text{(Table 2E of Appendix)}$$

$$\sin \theta = 0.000\ 290\ 89 \qquad \text{(SP 231)}$$

$$\tan \theta = 0.000\ 290\ 89 \qquad \text{(computed from SP 231)}$$

Therefore, to the maximum angle for which linear interpolation is accurate, the sine or a tangent of a very small angle can be found by knowing an accurate value for the sine of 1 minute and multiplying this value by the desired angle expressed in minutes.

Table 9.2 lists the largest angle for which there will be no error for the stated number of decimal places. The examples that follow are calculated to eight decimal places to show that outside these limits the error is still fairly small. Calculations of this type must be made using a desk calculator or laborious long multiplication.

Table 9.2
Limiting angles for no error*

	Eight decimal places	Seven decimal places	Six decimal places	Five decimal places
sin θ, θ in minutes	8	29	52	110
tan θ, θ in minutes	7	12	37	59

* Based upon $\theta = 0.000\ 290\ 886$ rad for 1'.

Example 9.31

Find the sine of $0°12'32''$.

SOLUTION

(1) Express the angle in minutes: $\frac{32}{60} = 0.5333$ and $\theta = 12.5333'$.

(2) Find the sine by multiplication:

$$12.5333(0.000\ 290\ 886) = 0.003\ 645\ 76$$

The true value from SP 231 $= 0.003\ 645\ 79$.

The answer is correct to seven decimal places.

Example 9.32

Find the cosine of $88°28'48''$.

SOLUTION

(1) Change to sine function by subtracting angle from $90°$:

$$\cos 88°28'48'' = \sin 1°31'12''$$

(2) Express the angle in minutes:

$$\theta = 60 + 31 + 0.2 = 91.2'$$

(3) Multiplying: $\sin \theta = 91.2(0.000\ 290\ 886) = 0.026\ 528\ 80$

From SP 231: $\sin \theta$ $= 0.026\ 525\ 89$

The answer is correct to five decimal places.

(Note that the percentage error for eight decimal places is only 0.01 per cent.)

The tangent of a small angle or the cotangent of an angle near $90°$ is found in a similar manner to that shown in Example 9.31 for the tangent and in Example 9.32 for the cotangent.

Table 9.3 was prepared to show the small error that would exist if linear interpolation is used for a five-place table with increments of $1'$. A purely arbitrary amount of $14''$ was picked to require interpolation.

If a similar tabulation is made for the accuracy of interpolated values using a decitrig table with increments of $0.1°$, the error for an interpolation to hundredths is equal to or less than 0.00001 for angles below $1.5°$.

Table 9.3

Error in interpolation in five-place tables

	Value by interpolation	Value by six-place table	Error
$0°10'14''$	0.002 98	0.002 977	None
$20'14''$	0.005 91	0.005 886	0.00002
$30'14''$	0.008 80	0.008 794	0.00001
$40'14''$	0.011 71	0.011 703	0.00001
$50'14''$	0.014 61	0.014 612	None
$1°0'14''$	0.017 52	0.017 520	None

In summary, linear interpolation in five-place tables can be used for small angles larger than 1° unless the function is multiplied by a relatively large number. In a routine survey, a distance would average 500 ft and the error of 500(0.00001) is 0.005 ft, a distance smaller than a surveyor actually measures, his distances being recorded to the nearest hundredth of a foot.

Methods shown in Chapter 10 do not use a linear interpolation and, therefore, cover angles smaller than 3°. Although these values are correct, they are still five-place logarithms, yielding five significant figures, so the methods shown in this section are best if more significant figures are needed.

Slide-rule calculation

On the AcuMath type of slide rule, sines are read on the A scale, so sines of small angles down to 0°34′ can be read to three significant figures but only in increments of about 30″, because each graduation on the S scale at this end is 2′. Tangents for angles smaller than the left end of the T scale, 5°45′, cannot be read directly. However, a method to be described for the other type of rule can readily be adapted to the AcuMath, so that in reality very small sines and tangents corresponding to very small angles can be found. This method is not described in the manufacturer's manual.

On most slide rules except the AcuMath, there is a scale marked SRT, as seen in Figure 2.1. This scale is based upon the equality of sines, radians, and tangents for small angles and permits finding by direct reading on C this common value, correct to three significant figures. The SRT scale covers values from 0.01 to 0.10 rad but is graduated in decitrig values, which are therefore 0.57° to 5.7°.

On some slide rules, including the K & E GP-12, the numerical values for a sine of 1′ and a sine of 1″ are marked. The 1′ constant used with Table 9.2, reduced to three significant figures, is 0.000291 and on the D scale an extra graduation at that value is marked ′. The value for the sine of 1″ is 0.000 004 85 and at 485 on D, an additional graduation is marked ″. Thus, for three significant figures, the sine, tangent, or radian measure of angles smaller than 0.57° can be found on the C and D scales. This method is the one that can be used on the AcuMath type of rule. It is recommended that the two constants be pasted on the back side of the rule. Table 9.2 indicates that there will be a very small error in the tangents between 1° and 6°, but if working to three significant figures, there is no discernible error.

Example 9.33a
Find the sine of 1°12′ on the AcuMath type of rule.

SOLUTION
(1) Set the hairline to 1°12′ on S.
(2) Read the answer, 0.0209, on A.

Example 9.33b

Find the sine of 1°12′ using the K & E GP-12 type of rule.

SOLUTION

(1) Convert the angle to decitrig form: 1°12′ = 1.2°.
(2) Set the hairline to 1.2 on SRT.
(3) Read the answer, 0.020 95, on C.

Example 9.33c

Find the sine of 1°12′ using the ′ setting on the K & E GP-12 rule, or 291 on D using the AcuMath.

SOLUTION

(1) Convert the angle to minutes: 1°12′ = 72′.
(2) Set the right index of the slide to the ′ mark (or to 291).
(3) Move the hairline to 72 on C.
(4) Read the answer, 0.020 95, on D.

Example 9.33d

Find the tangent of 0°0′36.8″.

SOLUTION

(1) Set the right index of the slide to the ″ mark (or to 485).
(2) Move the hairline to 368 on C.
(3) Read the answer, 0.000 179, on D.

Problem Set 9.10

1–10

Find the indicated functional value correct to six decimal places, using a desk calculator if available. Check your result by interpolation in a five-place table.

1. sin 0°0′42″

2. sin 0°0′27″

3. sin 0°0′21.2″

4. sin 0°0′18.7″

5. tan 0°57′11″

6. tan 0°47′31″

7. sin 0.123°

8. tan 0.189°

9. cos 89°47′12.2″

10. cot 89°53′31.8″

11–20

Use the slide rule and find to three significant figures (except where four can be readily estimated) the stated functional value. Do all problems using the given constants for 1′ and 1″. If your slide rule has the SRT scale, check your result with this scale.

11. sin 0°0′11″

12. tan 0°0′13″

13. tan 0°12′12″

14. sin 0°31′57″

15. sin 0.118°

16. sin 0.246°

17. cos 88°42′12″

18. cot 87°39′35″

19. cot 86°1′58″

20. sin 0.000 147 rad

9.16 / Graphs of the trigonometric functions

Graphing a trigonometric function is analogous to plotting an algebraic function. The ordered pairs $(\theta, f(\theta))$ are used where θ is the independent variable plotted along the horizontal axis. The units on this axis can be ordinary real numbers if θ is measured in radians. Usually, for the ease of finding $f(\theta)$, the scale is in degrees or fractions of π radians. For mechanical devices, the degree is preferred; mathematically, the radian is preferred. In Figure 9.19 both types of units are shown along the horizontal axis. Incre-

Figure 9.17
Trigonometric functions as line segments, quadrant I

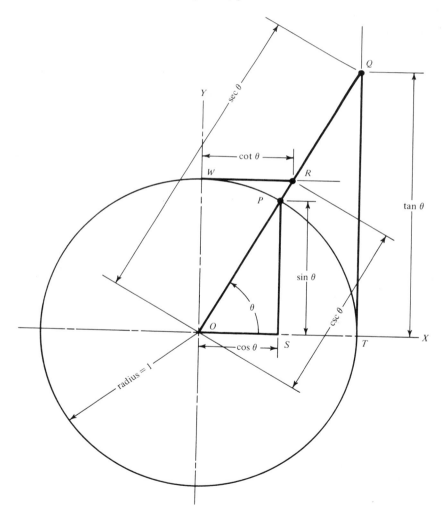

ments of 15° ($\frac{\pi}{12}$ rad) often prove convenient, but the actual scale chosen depends upon the problem and the intended use of the graph. Increments of 30° ($\frac{\pi}{6}$ rad) are used for the graphs in this chapter since only the general shape of the functional plot is desired.

A very powerful method for visualizing all trigonometric functions is provided by the unit circle. The unit circle shows at a glance the maximum and minimum values of any function, the sign of the function in any quadrant, and whether the functional value is increasing or decreasing as the angle increases. In Figure 9.17, using an angle θ in the first quadrant, each of the six functions is shown as a line segment with respect to the unit circle. Because this figure tells so much about the functions, it is suggested that the student sketch it a few times from memory, using different values for θ.

Figure 9.18 illustrates the six trigonometric functions as directed line segments with respect to the unit circle for an angle θ in quadrant II. The same identifying letters are used for the key points in the two figures. Note that the tangent is drawn through point T and the cotangent through point W no matter what quadrant the given angle may occupy. The signs of the functions are determined by noting that a directed line segment is positive if it points to the right or upward and is negative if it points to the left or downward. The signs for the secant and cosecant are best determined from the signs of their reciprocals.

Figure 9.18
Trigonometric functions as line segments, quadrant II

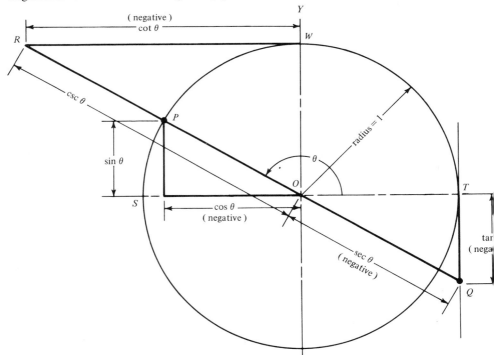

Since each function with its cofunction has been allocated a separate section, the observations to be drawn from the unit circle for each function will be discussed in these sections. However, note in Figures 9.17 and 9.18:

(1) Each cofunction is at right angles to the function, except for the secant and cosecant.
(2) The names tangent, cotangent, secant, and cosecant are given to lines that are actually tangents or secants of the unit circle.

As will be shown in the following section, the graph of any trigonometric function can be plotted by drawing the appropriate angle in the unit circle and transferring the measurement for the value of the function with a pair of dividers or by orthographic projection to the graph. This method will be done only for the sine and cosine graphs, because it is quicker to look up values in a table and plot directly. No data points are shown since this is not done for continuous mathematical functions.

9.17 / Graphs of sine and cosine

In Figures 9.17 and 9.18, the vertical directed line segment PS, marked $\sin \theta$, is actually the y coordinate of P. In quadrants I and II, for angles between $0°$ and $180°$, PS is always above the x axis and therefore positive. In quadrants III and IV, for angles between $180°$ and $360°$, PS is below the x axis and therefore negative. Figure 9.17 indicates that the sine varies in absolute value from 0 to 1, the radius of the unit circle. It further indicates that the maximum value, 1, for the sine occurs when $\theta = 90°$. Figure 9.18 shows that the sine decreases in the second quadrant from 1 back to 0 at $180°$.

For values of θ larger than $360°$, the sine function repeats its values. Each trigonometric function is a **periodic function**; that is, beginning at any arbitrary point there is some fixed interval of θ, called the **period**, after which the graph repeats itself. The period for the sine and cosine functions is $360°$ (2π radians). The measure of θ to cover one repetition is called one **cycle**. The number of cycles per second is called the **frequency**, given in cycles per second (cps). For radio and television, the unit of frequency has been renamed the hertz, which is still 1 cps.

In Figure 9.19 a domain larger than $360°(2\pi)$ was chosen to emphasize the periodicity. Note in this figure that if $360°$ is added to the first value of θ plotted, $-60°$, the value of y at $\theta = -60°$ is identical to the value of y at $-60° + 360° = 300°$.

The fact that $\sin \theta = \cos(90° - \theta)$, found in studying the tables of functions, indicates that the graphs of $\sin \theta$ and $\cos \theta$ should be identical in shape but differ in position by $90°$. The cosine curve is said to be **displaced** to the left of the sine curve or **out of phase**. The **phase angle** is the angle that measures the displacement.

Figure 9.19

Graphs of sine θ and cosine θ, $-\dfrac{\pi}{3} \leq \theta \leq \dfrac{7\pi}{3}$

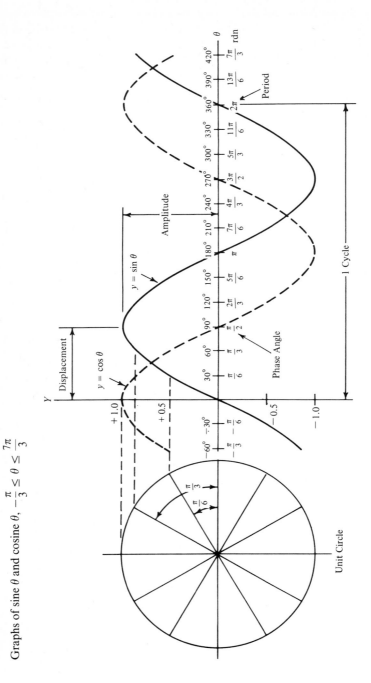

The graphical plot in Figure 9.19 gives the user the same information as any graphical plot of any function does. At a glance the user can see the location and the value of the maximum and minimum values of the function, the zeros of the function, and in Figure 9.19 one can see the places where $\sin \theta = \cos \theta$, which occur at 45° and 225° for θ between 0° and 360°. The absolute value of the maximum or the minimum of a periodic function is called its **amplitude**. The amplitude is 1 for both the sine and cosine functions.

9.18 / Graphs of tangent and cotangent

The concepts positive infinity and negative infinity were introduced in the discussion of quadrantal angles. Figure 9.20 reveals why these terms are so useful.

The tangent and the sine of small angles are almost identical, so the graphs of these two functions appear similar at the start and are almost linear. However, as soon as the curvature becomes apparent, it is seen that the tangent graph is concave upward and the sine curve downward. Whereas 1 is the maximum of the sine curve at 90°, the tangent reaches a value of 1 at 45° and it is still increasing. What is the maximum value of the tangent curve? On Figure 9.20 there is an arrowhead on the curve near $\theta = 90°$, meaning

Figure 9.20
Graphs of tangent and cotangent $0 \le \theta \le 2\pi$

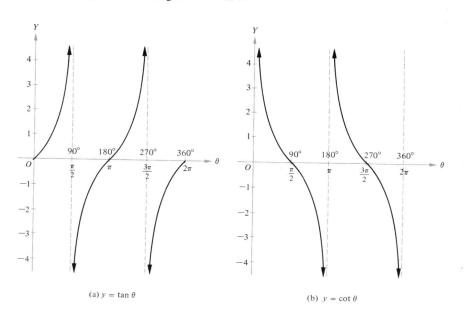

(a) $y = \tan \theta$

(b) $y = \cot \theta$

that the graph continues upward indefinitely. There is a vertical dashed line through $\theta = 90°$. The graph of tan θ approaches this line but never reaches it. Figure 9.20 stops at $y = 4$, the tangent of 76°. At 89° the tangent has reached 57, at 89°59′ it has reached 3438, and at 89°59′59″ the value is 2.06×10^7. As θ approaches 90° closer and closer, the tangent value becomes fantastically larger and larger. The graph of tan θ is said to be **asymptotic** to the vertical line through 90°($\frac{\pi}{2}$). An asymptote is a line that a curve approaches coming closer and closer to it but never reaching it. Tan 90° is not a real number, but it is undefined. Because tan θ is so tremendously large just before 90°, tan θ is said to approach positive infinity from the left. Referring to Figure 9.20, it is also apparent that for an angle of 90°0′1″, the value of the tangent is -2.06×10^7, a negative number whose absolute value is very large. Thus, as 90° is approached from the right, the value of tan θ approaches negative infinity. These two statements can be written in symbols as follows:

$$\tan \theta \to +\infty \quad \text{and} \quad \tan \theta \to -\infty$$
$$\theta \to \frac{\pi}{2}^- \qquad\qquad\qquad \theta \to \frac{\pi}{2}^+$$

Figure 9.20 reveals that, wherever they are defined, the tangent function is always increasing and the cotangent function is always decreasing. The tangent increases from 0 to positive infinity and from negative infinity to 0. The *period* for tan θ and for cot θ is 180° (π).

Unlike the sine–cosine relationship, the two plots for the tangent and cotangent do not involve a simple displacement but a 90° displacement of their **mirror images**. To visualize this concept, the two portions of the cotangent graph can be thought of as rotated 180° in space about the asymptote at π and then they form the tangent graph displaced 90°.

9.19 / Graphs of secant and cosecant

Referring to Figures 9.17 and 9.18, point Q, where the secant line intersects the tangent line, determines the magnitude of both the tangent and the secant. Initially, for $\theta = 0$, point Q coincides with point T, which is at a unit radius from point O. Thus, the secant can never be smaller than 1. As θ nears 90°, OQ is approaching a position through point W which would make it parallel to the vertical tangent line through T, a position it can never reach and still form a triangle. The secant graph, shown in Figure 9.21, near 90° and 270° is very much like the tangent graph; it is approaching positive infinity from one side of the angle and negative infinity from the other side. The graph is asymptotic to the vertical lines through 0°, 180°, 360°, and any multiple of 180°. Since the secant and cosecant are reciprocals of the cosine and the sine, respectively, Figure 9.21 verifies that, similarly, their graphs are displaced 90°. The period for both sec θ and csc θ is 360° (2π).

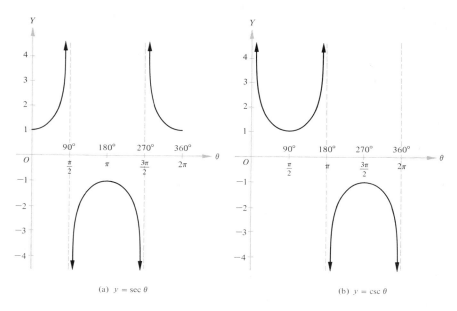

(a) $y = \sec \theta$ (b) $y = \csc \theta$

Figure 9.21
Graphs of secant and cosecant $0 \leq \theta \leq 2\pi$

Problem Set 9.11

(This is a very limited problem set with no solutions given for the odd-numbered problems.)

1. Plot $\cos \theta$ and $\tan \theta$ on the same axes and graphically find the smallest positive value for θ such that $\cos \theta = \tan \theta$. ($\theta$ will be smaller than $45°$ so use a fairly large scale for θ.)

2. Plot $\frac{5}{4} \tan \theta$ and $\sec \theta$ on the same axes and graphically find the smallest positive value for θ such that $\frac{5}{4} \tan \theta = \sec \theta$. Use $45° \leq \theta \leq 55°$ as the domain.

3. Plot $\sin \theta$ between $\frac{\pi}{4}$ and $\frac{\pi}{3}$ and graphically scale the value of $\sin 1$ to two decimal places.

4. Plot $\cos \theta$ between $\frac{\pi}{2}$ and $\frac{2\pi}{3}$ and graphically find $\cos 2$ to two decimal places.

5. Plot $\tan \theta$ between $\frac{5\pi}{6}$ and π and graphically find the value of $\tan 3$ to two decimal places.

6. Plot $\sec \theta$ and $y = 2\theta$ on the same axes. Determine if they intersect and, if so, give the coordinates of the point of intersection.

7. Plot $\tan \theta$ and $y = 2\theta$ on the same axes. Determine if they intersect and, if so, give the coordinates of the point of intersection.

9.20 / Special trigonometric functions

There are four additional trigonometric functions not mentioned in some texts but which are used in engineering and science. Tables exist for three of these functions.

The **versed sine**, shown in Figure 9.22, is defined as versin $\theta = 1 - \cos \theta$. This function is used in simple surveying where the true distance between two points is the horizontal projection of a measured distance on a slope.

Figure 9.22
Special trigonometric functions

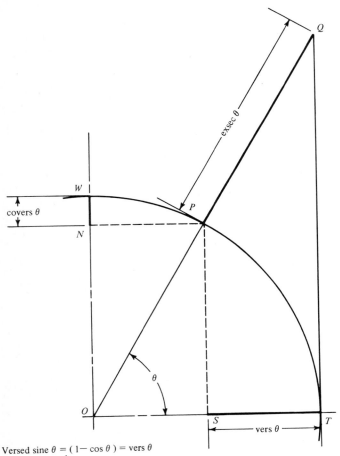

Versed sine $\theta = (1 - \cos \theta) = $ vers θ

Haversine $\theta = \frac{1}{2}(1 - \cos \theta) = $ havers θ

Coversed sine $\theta = (1 - \sin \theta) = $ covers θ

Exsecant $\theta = $ secant $\theta - 1 = $ exsec θ

For appreciable slopes, the true length L is found by multiplying the measured length M by the cosine of the angle of the slope; $L = M \cos \theta$. For lengthy baselines, as can be found by electronic surveying devices, and for very small angles of slope, the computations are awkward. Use of the versed sine permits easy calculations, often possible by inspection. The difference $M - L$ between the measured length and the true length is found, using

$$M - L = M - M \cos \theta = M(1 - \cos \theta) = M \text{ versin } \theta$$

For example, if a baseline of approximately 10,000 ft were used (nearly 2 miles) and the angle of slope was only 4′, the versed sine to seven decimal places for 0°4′ is 0.000 0007, which would make a difference in the baseline of only 0.01 ft. The versed sine of 0°11′ is 0.000 0051, which would affect a 10,000-ft baseline by 0.1 ft. Linear interpolation is theoretically incorrect for versed sines, but the error is small and tables do not exist for increments smaller than 1′.

The **haversine** is a contraction of the phrase "half of the versed sine" and havers $\theta = \frac{1}{2}(1 - \cos \theta)$. It appears in a number of navigational formulas used for finding a geographic location by a method known as the "Sumner Line." Using the haversine permits logarithmic computations since it

Figure 9.23
A typical circular curve

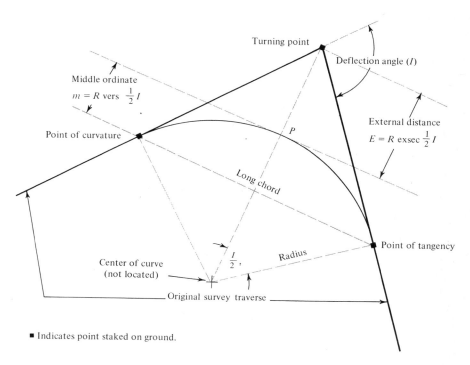

■ Indicates point staked on ground.

eliminates a subtraction. Most published tables of haversines are in logarithmic form. The use of the haversine and tables for it can be found in the U.S. Government Manual, *The American Practical Navigator*. Obviously, the same methods can be used to determine a location on land.

The **coversed sine** is $(1 - \sin \theta)$. No tables have been seen for this function nor is there any known use for it. It continues to be listed in handbooks.

The **exsecant** is $(\sec \theta - 1)$. The exsecant and the versed sine both appear in computations dealing with the circular curves used in highway and railway layouts. Figure 9.23 shows a simple curve and identifies the lines used. The center of the curve is almost never found, the radius being computed by tables based upon the sharpness of the desired curve, the deflection angle, and the desired tangent distance. Point P in Figure 9.23 is of particular interest, as it may determine if a planned curve will clear existing structures or other obstacles. It can be found from the turning point by the exsecant function, or from the long chord, using the versed sine. Tables for both natural and logarithmic values of these two special functions can be found in texts and tables on "Route Surveying." Since these tables are not available to the average student, no problem set is given, but a problem involving these functions will be included in the review problems.

9.21 / Chapter Review

1. A trigonometric function is a true mathematical function of a real number, often interpreted as an angle. The six trigonometric functions are defined as ratios. All trigonometric functions are periodic with a period of π or 2π radians.

2. The unit circle, a circle with a radius of 1 unit, permits visualization of the magnitude and sign of each function and is the basis for the mathematical unit of measure for angles, the radian.

3. Angles are measured primarily in degrees or radians. The degree system using minutes and seconds is the older one and is used in surveying, navigation, astronomy, and allied fields where the actual measurement of an angle is involved. The decimal degree system is a more modern innovation used to simplify calculations, particularly where the angle is found by calculations.

4. Most problems involving negative angles or angles falling outside quadrant I are simplified if sketched approximately to scale from the given data.

5. The best method for finding the value of a trigonometric function is by use of tables. Certain values can be found on a slide rule to three significant figures, but there are many limitations.

6. In problems involving three-, four-, and five-place values, linear interpolation is adequate for angles not closer than 1° to a quadrantal angle.

7. Depending upon the precision desired, special methods may be required for finding the functional values of small angles. Each method and its proper use is covered in this book.

8. Finding an angle from a given trigonometric functional value is not a true inverse function operation unless limiting rules, such as requiring principal values, are used so that a single answer is obtained.

A periodic function has infinitely many values of the independent variable for each value of the function.

9. If the value of one trigonometric function is given and if the quadrant for the angle is specified, the values of the other five trigonometric functions can be found by sketching the angle and determining the ratios from the values for x, y, and r.

10. Values of the six natural trigonometric functions for 0°, 30°, 45°, 60°, and 90° should be memorized in both radical and decimal form.

11. Graphs of the functions give an excellent indication of the maximum, minimum, and zero values, or where the function is positive or negative, and of where the function is increasing or decreasing.

12. Special trigonometric functions exist for use in surveying and navigation.

Problem Set 9.12 (Chapter Review)

1. Using five-place tables, find the functional values to five significant figures.
   (a) sin 12°13′14″
   (b) cos 68°58′47″
   (c) tan 47°37′27″
   (d) cot 42°24′9″
   (e) sec 52°45′
   (f) csc 39°52′
   (g) cos 37.146°
   (h) sin 72.847°
   (j) cot 10.021°
   (k) tan 77.765°
   (l) csc 21.1°
   (m) sec 81.9°

2. Find the radian measure of the given angle to six decimal places.
   (a) 121°14′11.2″
   (b) 237°47′23.3″
   (c) 416.152°
   (d) 522.814°
   (e) 896.756°
   (f) 939.726°
   (g) 14 mils
   (h) 212 grades 10′12″

3. Find the equivalent angle in (1) degrees, minutes, and seconds and (2) in the decitrig notation.
   (a) 0.0259 rad
   (b) 1.2467 rad
   (c) 3.7522 rad
   (d) 6.4888 rad
   (e) 7.1628 rad
   (f) 9.753 rad

4. Find the indicated angle in the decitrig notation.
   (a) Sin⁻¹ 0.986 42
   (b) Cos⁻¹ 0.010 25
   (c) Tan⁻¹ −4.7500
   (d) Cot⁻¹ −5.5000
   (e) Arcsec 0.1875
   (f) Arccsc 5.625

5. Find to six decimal places.
   (a) sin 0°0′1.35″
   (b) cos 89°59′7.7″
   (c) tan 0°5′12″
   (d) sin 0.0002°
   (e) cos 89.999 35°
   (f) cot 1.570 796 rad

6. (Recommended only for civil technology students.) Use Figure 9.23. A survey traverse has a deflection angle of 36°48′ at a place where a

circular curve having 600.00 ft tangents is desired. Compute the external distance and the middle ordinate if the versed sine of 18°24′ is 0.051 1240 and the exsecant is 0.053 8785. All answers should be to the nearest 0.01 ft.

7. Graph the set of ordered pairs (x, y) defined by the parametric equations $x = \theta - \sin \theta$ and $y = 1 - \cos \theta$ for the domain $-\pi \le \theta \le 4\pi$. [This graph, called a *cycloid*, is the locus (path) of a point on a circle as it rolls on a straight line.]

Right triangles, vectors, and trigonometric applications

10.01 / Logarithms of trigonometric functions

Table 4 of the Appendix gives the logarithm of the four functions of angles in degrees and minutes. A page from that table is shown in Figure 10.1. The placement of the angles, the location of the minutes, and the use of the functional headings are the same as those for Table 3, which gives the natural functions.

There are two minor differences between Table 7, the logarithms of numbers, and this table. Table 4 shows the mantissa and the characteristic increased by 10. In other words, 10 must be subtracted from each tabular entry. For example, a reading of 9.87654 is recorded as 9.87654 − 10. After the logarithm of a function for any angle there is an additional number in a column headed either d or cd. Each column is the arithmetic differences of the logarithms for a $1'$ change of angle. The d or cd number indicates the column to be used in the proportional parts section of the table. The heading cd means *common difference* and it is placed between the tangent and cotangent, which do have the same value for the difference, since they are reciprocals. For sines of angles greater than 80° or cosines of angles less than 10°, d is omitted since the difference is either 1 or 2. For angles less than 3°, there is a warning that linear interpolation should not be used for sines and tangents, and a reference is given in Table 4 as to the method that should be used. This applies similarly for cosines and cotangents of angles greater than 87°.

′	L Sin	d	L Tan	cd	L Cot	L Cos	′		″	121	120	119	118
0	9.019 23	120	9.021 62	121	10.978 38	9.997 61	60			121	120	119	118
1	9.020 43	120	9.022 83	121	10.977 17	9.997 60	59		1	2.0	2.0	2.0	2.0
2	9.021 63	120	9.024 04	121	10.975 96	9.997 59	58		2	4.0	4.0	4.0	3.9
3	9.022 83	119	9.025 25	121	10.974 75	9.997 57	57		3	6.0	6.0	6.0	5.9
4	9.024 02	118	9.026 45	120	10.973 55	9.997 56	56		4	8.1	8.0	7.9	7.9
5	9.025 20	119	9.027 66	121	10.972 34	9.997 55	55		5	10.1	10.0	9.9	9.8
6	9.026 39	118	9.028 85	119	10.971 15	9.997 53	54		6	12.1	12.0	11.9	11.8
7	9.027 57	117	9.030 05	120	10.969 95	9.997 52	53		7	14.1	14.0	13.9	13.8
8	9.028 74	118	9.031 24	119	10.968 76	9.997 51	52		8	16.1	16.0	15.9	15.7
9	9.029 92	117	9.032 42	118	10.967 58	9.997 49	51		9	18.2	18.0	17.8	17.7
10	9.031 09	117	9.033 61	119	10.966 39	9.997 48	50		10	20.2	20.0	19.8	19.7
11	9.032 26	116	9.034 79	118	10.965 21	9.997 47	49		20	40.3	40.0	39.7	39.3
12	9.033 42	116	9.035 97	118	10.964 03	9.997 45	48		30	60.5	60.0	59.5	59.0
13	9.034 58	116	9.037 14	117	10.962 86	9.997 44	47		40	80.7	80.0	79.3	78.7
14	9.035 74	116	9.038 32	118	10.961 68	9.997 42	46		50	100.8	100.0	99.2	98.3
15	9.036 90	115	9.039 48	117	10.960 52	9.997 41	45		″	117	116	115	114
16	9.038 05	115	9.040 65	116	10.959 35	9.997 40	44		1	2.0	1.9	1.9	1.9
17	9.039 20	114	9.041 81	116	10.958 19	9.997 38	43		2	3.9	3.9	3.8	3.8
18	9.040 34	115	9.042 97	116	10.957 03	9.997 37	42		3	5.8	5.8	5.8	5.7
19	9.041 49	113	9.044 13	115	10.955 87	9.997 36	41		4	7.8	7.7	7.7	7.6
20	9.042 62	114	9.045 28	115	10.954 72	9.997 34	40		5	9.8	9.7	9.6	9.5
21	9.043 76	114	9.046 43	115	10.953 57	9.997 33	39		6	11.7	11.5	11.5	11.4
22	9.044 90	113	9.047 58	115	10.952 42	9.997 31	38		7	13.6	13.5	13.4	13.3
23	9.046 03	112	9.048 73	114	10.951 27	9.997 30	37		8	15.6	15.5	15.3	15.2
24	9.047 15	113	9.049 87	114	10.950 13	9.997 28	36		9	17.6	17.4	17.2	17.1
25	9.048 28	112	9.051 01	113	10.948 99	9.997 27	35		10	19.5	19.3	19.2	19.0
26	9.049 40	112	9.052 14	114	10.947 86	9.997 26	34		20	39.0	38.7	38.3	38.0
27	9.050 52	112	9.053 28	113	10.946 72	9.997 24	33		30	58.5	58.0	57.5	57.0
28	9.051 64	111	9.054 41	112	10.945 59	9.997 23	32		40	78.0	77.3	76.7	76.0
29	9.052 75	111	9.055 53	113	10.944 47	9.997 21	31		50	97.5	96.7	95.8	95.0
30	9.053 86	111	9.056 66	112	10.943 34	9.997 20	30		″	113	112	111	110
31	9.054 97	110	9.057 78	112	10.942 22	9.997 18	29		1	1.9	1.9	1.8	1.8
32	9.056 07	110	9.058 90	112	10.941 10	9.997 17	28		2	3.8	3.7	3.7	3.7
33	9.057 17	110	9.060 02	111	10.939 98	9.997 16	27		3	5.6	5.6	5.6	5.5
34	9.058 27	110	9.061 13	111	10.938 87	9.997 14	26		4	7.5	7.5	7.4	7.3
35	9.059 37	109	9.062 24	111	10.937 76	9.997 13	25		5	9.4	9.3	9.2	9.2
36	9.060 46	109	9.063 35	110	10.936 65	9.997 11	24		6	11.3	11.2	11.1	11.0
37	9.061 55	109	9.064 45	111	10.935 55	9.997 10	23		7	13.2	13.1	13.0	12.8
38	9.062 64	108	9.065 56	110	10.934 44	9.997 08	22		8	15.1	14.9	14.8	14.7
39	9.063 72	109	9.066 66	109	10.933 34	9.997 07	21		9	17.0	16.8	16.6	16.5
40	9.064 81	108	9.067 75	110	10.932 25	9.997 05	20		10	18.8	18.7	18.5	18.3
41	9.065 89	107	9.068 85	109	10.931 15	9.997 04	19		20	37.7	37.3	37.0	36.7
42	9.066 96	108	9.069 94	109	10.930 06	9.997 02	18		30	56.5	56.0	55.5	55.0
43	9.068 04	107	9.071 03	108	10.928 97	9.997 01	17		40	75.3	74.7	74.0	73.3
44	9.069 11	107	9.072 11	109	10.927 89	9.996 99	16		50	94.2	93.3	92.5	91.7
45	9.070 18	106	9.073 20	108	10.926 80	9.996 98	15		″	109	108	107	106
46	9.071 24	107	9.074 28	108	10.925 72	9.996 96	14		1	1.8	1.8	1.8	1.8
47	9.072 31	106	9.075 36	107	10.924 64	9.996 95	13		2	3.6	3.6	3.6	3.5
48	9.073 37	105	9.076 43	108	10.923 57	9.996 93	12		3	5.4	5.4	5.4	5.3
49	9.074 42	106	9.077 51	107	10.922 49	9.996 92	11		4	7.3	7.2	7.1	7.1
50	9.075 48	105	9.078 58	106	10.921 42	9.996 90	10		5	9.1	9.0	8.9	8.8
51	9.076 53	105	9.079 64	107	10.920 36	9.996 89	9		6	10.9	10.8	10.7	10.6
52	9.077 58	105	9.080 71	106	10.919 29	9.996 87	8		7	12.7	12.6	12.5	12.4
53	9.078 63	105	9.081 77	106	10.918 23	9.996 86	7		8	14.5	14.4	14.3	14.1
54	9.079 68	104	9.082 83	106	10.917 17	9.996 84	6		9	16.4	16.2	16.0	15.9
55	9.080 72	104	9.083 89	106	10.916 11	9.996 83	5		10	18.2	18.0	17.8	17.7
56	9.081 76	104	9.084 95	105	10.915 05	9.996 81	4		20	36.3	36.0	35.7	35.3
57	9.082 80	103	9.086 00	105	10.914 00	9.996 80	3		30	54.5	54.0	53.5	53.0
58	9.083 83	103	9.087 05	105	10.912 95	9.996 78	2		40	72.7	72.0	71.3	70.7
59	9.084 86	103	9.088 10	104	10.911 90	9.996 77	1		50	90.8	90.0	89.2	88.3
60	9.085 89		9.089 14		0.910 86	9.996 75	0						

′	L Cos	d	L Cot	cd	L Tan	L Sin	′	Prop. Pts.

Figure 10.1
Sample page from Table 4, Appendix

Table 6 of the Appendix is similar to Table 4 but uses the decitrig values for the angles. Figure 10.2 is a sample page from that table. No column of differences is shown. Proportional parts are not listed, since in the decitrig system only a movement of the decimal point is involved when the difference for 0.1° is known. There is a warning about interpolation for small angles, but no auxiliary table is provided as is done for Table 4. For angles under 3°, convert the given angle to minutes and seconds using Table 2B.

Example 10.1
Find log sin 83°13′.

SOLUTION
83° appears in the *lower right* corner of the page from Table 4. Using the *lower* headings and the *right* column of minutes, reading *upward*, the value of log sin 83°13′ is read directly as 9.99695 − 10.

Example 10.2
Find log tan 6°32′14″.

SOLUTION (Use Figure 10.1.)
(1) 6° appears in the *upper left* corner. Using the *upper* headings and the *left*-hand column of minutes reading *down*, record log tan 6°32′ and the difference shown in the cd column:

$$\text{log tan } 6°32′ = 9.05890 - 10 \text{ and cd} = 112$$

(2) Under proportional parts for 112, find

$$\left.\begin{array}{ll} 10″ & 18.7 \\ 4″ & 7.5 \end{array}\right\} 14″ = 26.2$$

(3) log tan 6°32′14″ = 9.05890 − 10 + 0.00026 = 9.05916 − 10.

Example 10.3
Find log cos 57°12′57″.

SOLUTION
(1) The tabular value of log cos 57°12′ = 9.73377 − 10.
(2) d = 19.

For 57″ *subtract*	18
log cos 57°12′57″	= 9.73359 − 10

(Note that rather than add the values for 50″ plus the value for 7″, subtract mentally 3″ from 60″, and thus 1 from 19.)

θ°	L Sin	L Tan	L Cot	L Cos	θ°		θ°	L Sin	L Tan	L Cot	L Cos	θ°
24.0	9.609 31	9.648 58	0.351 42	9.960 73	66.0		30.0	9.698 97	9.761 44	0.238 56	9.937 53	60.0
24.1	9.611 01	9.650 62	0.349 38	9.960 39	65.9		30.1	9.700 28	9.763 19	0.236 81	9.937 09	59.9
24.2	9.612 70	9.652 65	0.347 35	9.960 05	65.8		30.2	9.701 59	9.764 93	0.235 07	9.936 65	59.8
24.3	9.614 38	9.654 67	0.345 33	9.959 71	65.7		30.3	9.702 88	9.766 68	0.233 32	9.936 21	59.7
24.4	9.616 06	9.656 69	0.343 31	9.959 37	65.6		30.4	9.704 18	9.768 41	0.231 59	9.935 77	59.6
24.5	9.617 73	9.658 70	0.341 30	9.959 02	65.5		30.5	9.705 47	9.770 15	0.229 85	9.935 32	59.5
24.6	9.619 39	9.660 71	0.339 29	9.958 68	65.4		30.6	9.706 75	9.771 88	0.228 12	9.934 87	59.4
24.7	9.621 04	9.662 71	0.337 29	9.948 33	65.3		30.7	9.708 03	9.773 61	0.226 39	9.934 42	59.3
24.8	9.622 68	9.664 70	0.335 30	9.957 98	65.2		30.8	9.709 31	9.775 33	0.224 67	9.933 97	59.2
24.9	9.624 32	9.666 69	0.333 31	9.957 63	65.1		30.9	9.710 57	9.777 06	0.222 94	9.933 52	59.1
25.0	9.625 95	9.668 67	0.331 33	9.957 28	65.0		31.0	9.711 84	9.778 77	0.221 23	9.933 07	59.0
25.1	9.627 57	9.670 65	0.329 35	9.956 92	64.9		31.1	9.713 10	9.780 49	0.219 51	9.932 61	58.9
25.2	9.629 18	9.672 62	0.327 38	9.956 57	64.8		31.2	9.714 35	9.782 20	0.217 80	9.932 15	58.8
25.3	9.630 79	9.674 58	0.325 42	9.956 21	64.7		31.3	9.715 60	9.783 91	0.216 09	9.931 69	58.7
25.4	9.632 39	9.676 54	0.323 46	9.955 85	64.6		31.4	9.716 85	9.785 62	0.214 38	9.931 23	58.6
25.5	9.633 98	9.678 50	0.321 50	9.955 49	64.5		31.5	9.718 09	9.787 32	0.212 68	9.930 77	58.5
25.6	9.635 57	9.680 44	0.319 56	9.955 13	64.4		31.6	9.719 32	9.789 02	0.210 98	9.930 30	58.4
25.7	9.637 15	0.682 39	0.317 61	9.954 76	64.3		31.7	9.720 55	9.790 72	0.209 28	9.929 83	58.3
25.8	9.638 72	9.684 32	0.315 68	9.954 40	64.2		31.8	9.721 77	9.792 41	0.207 59	9.929 36	58.2
25.9	9.640 28	9.686 26	0.313 74	9.954 03	64.1		31.9	9.722 99	9.794 10	0.205 90	9.928 89	58.1
26.0	9.641 84	9.688 18	0.311 82	9.953 66	64.0		32.0	9.724 21	9.795 79	0.204 21	9.928 42	58.0
26.1	9.643 39	9.690 10	0.309 90	9.953 29	63.9		32.1	9.725 42	9.797 47	0.202 53	9.927 95	57.9
26.2	9.644 94	9.692 02	0.307 98	9.952 92	63.8		32.2	9.726 63	9.799 16	0.200 84	9.927 47	57.8
26.3	9.646 47	9.693 92	0.306 07	9.952 54	63.7		32.3	9.727 83	9.800 84	0.199 16	9.926 99	57.7
26.4	9.648 00	9.695 84	0.304 16	9.952 17	63.6		32.4	9.729 02	9.802 51	0.197 49	9.926 51	57.6
26.5	9.649 53	9.697 74	0.302 26	9.951 79	63.5		32.5	9.730 22	9.804 19	0.195 81	9.926 03	57.5
26.6	9.651 04	9.699 63	0.300 37	9.951 41	63.4		32.6	9.731 40	9.805 86	0.194 14	9.925 55	57.4
26.7	9.652 55	9.701 52	0.298 48	9.951 03	63.3		32.7	9.732 59	9.807 53	0.192 47	9.925 06	57.3
26.8	9.654 06	9.703 41	0.296 59	9.950 65	63.2		32.8	9.733 76	9.809 19	0.190 81	9.924 57	57.2
26.9	9.655 56	0.705 29	0.294 71	9.950 27	63.1		32.9	9.734 94	9.810 86	0.189 14	9.924 08	57.1
27.0	9.657 05	9.707 17	0.292 83	9.949 88	63.0		33.0	9.736 11	9.812 52	0.187 48	9.923 59	57.0
27.1	9.658 53	9.709 04	0.290 96	9.949 49	62.9		33.1	9.737 27	9.814 18	0.185 82	9.923 10	56.9
27.2	9.660 01	9.710 90	0.289 10	9.949 11	62.8		33.2	9.738 43	9.815 83	0.184 17	9.922 60	56.8
27.3	9.661 48	9.712 77	0.287 23	9.948 71	62.7		33.3	9.739 59	9.817 48	0.182 52	9.922 11	56.7
27.4	9.662 95	9.714 62	0.285 38	9.948 32	62.6		33.4	9.740 74	9.819 13	0.180 87	9.921 61	56.6
27.5	9.664 41	9.716 48	0.283 52	9.947 93	62.5		33.5	9.741 89	9.820 78	0.179 22	9.921 11	56.5
27.6	9.665 86	9.718 33	0.281 67	9.947 53	62.4		33.6	9.743 03	9.822 43	0.177 57	9.920 60	56.4
27.7	9.667 31	9.720 17	0.279 83	9.947 14	62.3		33.7	9.744 17	9.824 07	0.175 93	9.920 10	56.3
27.8	9.668 75	9.722 01	0.277 99	9.946 74	62.2		33.8	9.745 31	9.825 71	0.174 29	9.919 59	56.2
27.9	9.670 18	9.723 84	0.276 16	9.946 34	62.1		33.9	9.746 44	9.827 35	0.172 65	9.919 08	56.1
28.0	9.671 61	9.725 67	0.274 33,	9.945 93	62.0		34.0	9.747 56	9.828 99	0.171 01	9.918 57	56.0
28.1	9.673 03	9.727 50	0.272 50	9.945 53	61.9		34.1	9.748 68	9.830 62	0.169 38	9.918 06	55.9
28.2	9.674 45	9.729 32	0.270 68	9.945 13	61.8		34.2	9.749 80	9.832 25	0.167 75	9.917 55	55.8
28.3	9.675 86	9.731 14	0.268 86	9.944 72	61.7		34.3	9.740 91	9.833 88	0.166 12	9.917 03	55.7
28.4	9.677 26	9.732 95	0.267 05	9.944 31	61.6		34.4	9.752 02	9.835 51	0.164 49	9.916 51	55.6
28.5	9.678 66	9.734 76	0.265 24	9.943 90	61.5		34.5	9.753 13	9.837 13	0.162 87	9.915 99	55.5
28.6	9.680 06	9.736 57	0.263 43	9.943 49	61.4		34.6	9.753 23	9.838 76	0.161 24	9.915 47	55.4
28.7	9.681 44	9.738 37	0.261 63	9.943 07	61.3		34.7	9.755 33	9.840 38	0.159 62	9.914 95	55.3
28.8	9.682 83	9.740 17	0.259 83	9.942 66	61.2		34.8	9.756 42	9.842 00	0.158 00	9.914 42	55.2
28.9	9.684 20	9.741 96	0.258 04	9.942 24	61.1		34.9	9.757 51	9.843 61	0.156 39	9.913 89	55.1
29.0	9.685 57	9.743 75	0.256 25	9.941 82	61.0		35.0	9.758 89	9.845 23	0.154 77	9.913 36	55.0
29.1	9.686 94	9.745 54	0.254 46	9.941 40	60.9		35.1	9.759 67	9.846 84	0.153 16	9.912 83	54.9
29.2	9.688 29	9.747 32	0.252 68	9.940 98	60.8		35.2	9.760 75	9.848 45	0.151 55	9.912 30	54.8
29.3	9.689 65	9.749 10	0.250 90	9.940 55	60.7		35.3	9.761 82	9.850 06	0.149 94	9.911 76	54.7
29.4	9.691 00	9.740 87	0.249 13	9.940 12	60.6		35.4	9.762 89	9.851 66	0.148 34	9.911 23	54.6
29.5	9.692 34	9.752 64	0.247 36	9.939 70	60.5		35.5	9.763 95	9.853 27	0.146 73	9.910 69	54.5
29.6	9.693 68	9.754 41	0.245 59	9.939 27	60.4		35.6	9.765 01	9.854 87	0.145 13	9.910 14	54.4
29.7	9.695 01	9.756 17	0.243 83	9.938 84	60.3		35.7	9.766 07	9.856 47	0.143 53	9.909 60	54.3
29.8	9.696 33	9.757 93	0.242 07	9.938 40	60.2		35.8	9.767 12	9.858 07	0.141 93	9.909 06	54.2
29.9	9.697 65	9.759 69	0.240 31	9.937 97	60.1		35.9	9.768 17	9.859 67	0.140 33	9.908 51	54.1
30.0	9.698 97	9.761 44	0.238 56	9.937 53	69.0		36.0	9.769 22	9.861 26	0.138 74	9.907 96	54.0
θ°	L Cos	L Cot	L Tan	L Sin	θ°		θ°	L Cos	L Cot	L Tan	L Sin	θ°

Figure 10.2
Sample page from Table 6, Appendix

450

Example 10.4

Find log cot 167°42′43″.

SOLUTION

(1) The reference angle = 180° − 167°42′43″ = 12°17′17″.
(2) From the table, log cot 12°17′ = 10.66208 − 10.
(3) d = 61; d for 17″ = d for 10″ + d for 7″ = 10.2 + 7.1 = 17.3.
(4) log cot 12°17′17″ = 0.66208 − 0.00017 = 0.66191.
(5) log cot 167°42′43″ = [−] 0.66191.

Example 10.5

Find log sin 0°37′14.2″.

SOLUTION

Noting that the angle is less than 3°, use the method outlined in Table 4.

(1) Convert angle to seconds:

$$37(60) = 2220$$
$$14.2$$
$$\overline{}$$
$$2234.2″$$

(2)

log 2234.2	= 3.34912
log S for 37′	= 4.68557 − 10 (see Table 4A)

log sin 0°37′14.2″ = 8.03469 − 10

For this example only, linear interpolation will be used for comparison.

log sin 0°37′   = 8.03192 − 10 and d = 1158

$$\frac{14.2}{60} = 0.2367$$

0.2367(1158)   =   274

log sin 37′14.2″ = 8.03466 − 10

(The smaller the angle, the greater the error. Here the difference is only 0.00003. In a well-known seven-place table by Baron Von Vega, values of S and T are given in increments of 100″ up to 100,000″. However, the electronic computer can compute the sine or tangent of any angle to whatever degree of precision is warranted and such tables as Vega's are fast disappearing.)

Example 10.6
Find log cot 88°1′37″.

SOLUTION
Noting that the angle is greater than 87°, the method outlined in Table 4 is used.
(1) Find the complementary angle as 1°58′23″.
(2) Convert 1°58′ to minutes: 60′ + 58′ = 118′.
(3) Convert the angle to seconds: 118(60) + 23 = 7103″.
(4)

$$
\begin{aligned}
\log 7103 &= 3.85144 \\
\log T \text{ for } 118' &= 4.68575 - 10 \\
\hline
\log \cot 88°1'37'' &= 8.53719 - 10
\end{aligned}
$$

Example 10.7
Find log sin 25.4267°.

SOLUTION (Use Figure 10.2.)
(1) Tabular value for 25.4° = 9.63239 − 10   d for 0.1° = 0.00159
(2) Increment for 0.02°   =   32   d for 0.01° = 0.00016
(3) Increment for 0.0067°   =   11

(4) log sin 25.4267°   = 9.63282 − 10

Example 10.8
Find log tan 0.0052°.

SOLUTION
(1) From Table 2B,

$$
\begin{aligned}
0.005° &= 18.0'' \\
0.0002° &= 0.7'' \\
\hline
0.0052° &= 18.7''
\end{aligned}
$$

(2)

$$
\begin{aligned}
\log 18.7 &= 1.27184 \\
\log T \text{ for } 0.3' &= 4.68557 - 10 \\
\hline
\log \tan 0.0052° &= 5.95741 - 10
\end{aligned}
$$

Problem Set 10.1

1–18

Find the five-place logarithm of the given function.

1. sin 28°39′42″
2. cos 59°58′57″
3. tan 65°7′20.6″
4. cot 34°58′19.3″
5. sec 75°45′13.3″
6. csc 15°2′46.6″

7. cos 12.21°
8. sin 17.345°
9. cot 72.426°
10. tan 88.214°
11. csc 58.1337°
12. sec 45.2462°

13. sin 44°57′56″
14. cot 89°49′11.7″
15. tan 0°15′12.8″
16. sin 0.00123°
17. cot 89.975°
18. tan 0.4576°

19–28

Do the indicated arithmetic operation using logarithmic methods. Give the answer to an appropriate number of significant figures.

19. 789 sin 21.427°

20. 0.867 cos 10°12′47″

21. 2.984 cot 85°32′46″

22. 68,970 tan 85.178°

23. 910,000 cos 10.758°

24. 31.758 sin 4.184°

25. $\dfrac{398.53}{\cot 71°32′57″}$

26. $\dfrac{478.69}{\tan 31°49′24″}$

27. $\dfrac{845.25}{\sin 14.916°}$

28. $\dfrac{1650.5}{\cos 82.456°}$

10.02 / Applications of trigonometric functions

Many formulas exist in which one or more factors are indicated trigonometric values. Once the indicated trigonometric value has been changed to its numerical value, the problem is arithmetical. The rules for precision apply and may save the use of unwarranted precision in finding the trigonometric values if the other factors do not warrant it. Slide-rule calculations should always be used for the arithmetic operations if the data justify the use of only three significant figures.

Powers of functions are written with the exponent immediately following the abbreviation. Thus the square of the sine of an angle is written $\sin^2 \theta$ and not $(\sin \theta)^2$.

Example 10.9

The length L of a skewed culvert under a highway is the distance d measured perpendicularly to the highway centerline from headwall to headwall divided by the cosine of the angle of skew θ_s:

$$L = \frac{d}{\cos \theta_s}$$

Find the culvert length required if the perpendicular distance is 67.82 ft and the angle of skew is 12°31'.

SOLUTION

(1) Determine precision. Data are given to four significant figures, so calculations will be made to five significant figures using a five-place table and the result rounded to four figures.

(2) Substitute into formula:

$$L = \frac{d}{\cos \theta_s} = \frac{67.82}{\cos 12°31'}$$

(3) Calculate using logarithms:

$$
\begin{aligned}
\log 67.82 &= 11.83136 - 10 \\
\log \cos 12°31' &= 9.98955 - 10 \\
\text{difference} = \log L &= 1.84181 \\
L &= 69.47 \text{ ft}
\end{aligned}
$$

(*Note:* Look up the log of the trigonometric function first. Then the next two operations are both in Table 7.)

Example 10.10

In designing sprocket gears, the maximum guide groove diameter G is

$$G = P\left(\cot \frac{180°}{N} - 1.16\right)$$

where P = chain pitch, in.
N = number of teeth in sprocket
Find G if $P = 1\frac{1}{2}$ in. and $N = 37$.

SOLUTION

(1) Use of the slide rule is indicated because only three significant figures are given.

(2) $G = 1.50\left(\cot \dfrac{180°}{37} - 1.16\right)$ $\quad$ and $\quad$ $\dfrac{180°}{37} = 4.86°$

(3) Using Table 5,

$$\cot 4.8° \ = 11.909$$

$$\cot 4.9° \ = 11.664$$

$$\text{difference} = \ 0.245$$

$$0.4(0.245) = 0.098$$

$$\cot 4.86° = 11.664 + 0.098 = 11.762$$

$$G = 1.50(11.762 - 1.16) = 1.50(10.60) = 15.90 \text{ in.}$$

In some situations the argument used with a trigonometric function may not be given as an angle measured in degrees. Figure 10.3 shows a crank revolving about an axle at point O and traveling with an angular velocity ω often expressed in radians per second. If the crank is assumed to be horizontal initially when $t = 0$, then at some later time t_1 the handle has reached the position P. The handle has traveled a distance $S–P$ along the arc of the

Figure 10.3
Simple harmonic motion: Rotation of a crank

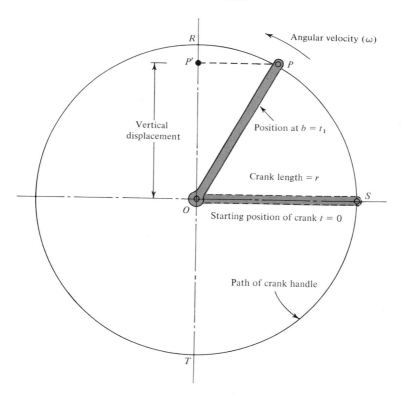

circle. This arc has a measure of $r\omega t_1$, where r is the length of the crank and thus the radius of the circle that is the path of the handle.

Point P' is the projection of point P on the vertical axis through the axle, which is the center of rotation. The distance that point P' is above or below the horizontal axis is called the **vertical displacement** and reaches the positive maximum position at R and the maximum negative position at T.

When the angular velocity is constant, the motion of point P' is called **simple harmonic motion.** The value of the vertical displacement at any instant of time t is

$$S_v = r \sin \omega t$$

The horizontal displacement of the handle may be desired and it is

$\quad S_h = r(1 - \cos \omega t) \qquad$ if measured from the point on the circle

or $\quad S_h = r \cos \omega t \qquad\qquad$ if measured from the center of the circle

It can be shown that a limber spring supporting a weight has a very small damping factor, so initially the motion of the weight is a simple harmonic motion. The circular path of point P is called the reference circle.

Example 10.11
A crank 10 in. long is rotating at 2 rad/sec in a CCW direction, starting from a horizontal position.
(a) What is the vertical displacement at the end of 0.1 sec?
(b) What is the location of the handle, given in inches of arc length, at the end of 2.4 sec?
(c) What is the horizontal displacement of the handle measured from the point on the circle at the end of 0.04 sec?

SOLUTION
(a) $S_v = 10 \sin(2 \cdot 0.1) = 10 \sin 0.2$ rad. Although many handbooks contain values of the trigonometric functions for arguments in radians, this book does not have this table. Using Table 2,

$$0.2 \text{ rad} = 11°27'33''$$

$$S_v = 10 \sin 11°27'33'' = 10(0.19867) = 1.987 \text{ in.}$$

(b) arc $= r\omega t = 10(2)(2.4) = 48$ in.

(c) $\qquad\qquad\qquad S_h = 10(1 - \cos 0.08 \text{ rad})$

$$= 10(1 - \cos 4°35'1.2'')$$

$$= 10(1 - 0.9968)$$

$$= 0.032 \text{ in.}$$

Problem Set 10.2

1. The adhesive force A is the attraction between a liquid and the wall of its container and is given by

$$A = S \sin \theta$$

where S = surface tension, dynes/cm
θ = contact angle between liquid and wall of container

Find A for each of the following:
   (a) Water in a container of paraffin; $S = 72.8$ dynes/cm and $\theta = 107°$.
   (b) Mercury in a soda-lime glass container; $S = 475$ dynes/cm, $\theta = 140°$.
   (c) Bromonaphthalene in a Pyrex container; $S = 27.2$ dynes/cm, $\theta = 20°30'$.
   (d) Methylene iodide in a fused quartz container; $S = 25.7$ dynes/cm, $\theta = 33°$.

2. Jurin's law for the height h to which a liquid will rise or be depressed in a capillary tube inserted in the liquid is

$$h = \frac{2S \cos \theta}{dgr} \quad \text{cm}$$

where S = surface tension, dynes/cm
θ = contact angle between liquid and wall of tube
d = density of liquid, g/cc
g = 980 cm/sec^2
r = radius of tube, cm

Find the height or depression for each of the following and state whether the liquid rises or is depressed.
   (a) Mercury in a soda-lime glass tube 0.5 mm in diameter if $S = 475$ dynes/cm, $\theta = 140°$, and $d = 13.6$ gm/cc.
   (b) Water in a lead glass tube 1 mm in diameter if $S = 72.8$ dynes/cm, $\theta = 0.005°$, and $d = 1.00$ g/cc.
   (c) Methylene iodide in a Pyrex tube 2 mm in diameter if $S = 26.8$ dynes/cm, $\theta = 29°$, and $d = 3.325$ g/ml.
   (d) Water in a paraffin tube 5 mm in diameter if $S = 72.76$ dynes/cm, $\theta = 107°$, and $d = 1.00$ g/cc.

3. Neglecting air resistance, the time of flight of a projectile is

$$T = \frac{2v_0 \sin \theta}{g} \quad \text{sec}$$

Find T if the initial velocity v_0 is 2716 fps, the angular inclination θ of the launcher is $37°22'10''$, and $g = 32.158$ ft/sec^2 (for latitude 40° N).

4. The area A of a triangle having an angle θ between two adjacent sides of lengths a and b, respectively, is given by

$$A = \tfrac{1}{2}ab \sin \theta$$

Find the area of a triangle if
(a) $a = 12''$, $b = 18''$, $\theta = 30°$
(b) $a = 12''$, $b = 18''$, $\theta = 45°$
(c) $a = 12''$, $b = 18''$, $\theta = 60°$
(d) $a = 12''$, $b = 18''$, $\theta = 90°$

5. The area of a circular segment is given by

$$A = \frac{r^2}{2}(\theta - \sin \theta) \qquad \text{where } \theta \text{ is in radians}$$

Find the area of a segment for a circle 6.478 in. in diameter intercepted by two radii 47.168° apart.

6. Find the torque T to turn a conical point bearing of a vertical shaft if

$$T = \frac{2f\,Wr}{3 \sin \theta} \qquad \text{in.-lb}$$

where f = coefficient of friction = 0.156
   W = weight on shaft = 479 lb
   r = radius of shaft in inches = $1\frac{7}{8}$ in.
   θ = half-angle of cone = 58°30'

7. The heating effect E of the sun is the product of a constant K and the normal direct radiation. K is a product defined by

$$K = \cos B \cos C$$

where B = solar altitude, deg
   C = solar azimuth angle of a vertical surface, deg
(a) Find K for a wall facing 24° east of south at 11 A.M. on August 1 in latitude 40°N. For this latitude on August 1, the solar altitude is 64.5° at 11 A.M. The value of angle C under these conditions is 35° − (angle from the south) = 11°.
(b) Find E, the heating effect, in Btu/sq ft/hr if the normal direct radiation in clear air is 286 Btu/sq ft/hr. (Adapted from the ASHRAE Guide.)

8. Find the coefficient of lift C_L for a sweptback airfoil at supersonic speeds if

$$C_L = \frac{4 \cos \lambda}{\sqrt{M^2 \cos^2 \lambda - 1}}\theta \qquad \text{where } \theta \text{ is in radians}$$

where λ = angle of sweepback = 35°
   M = Mach number = 1.87
   θ = angle of attack = 5.72°

9. Polarized light is rotated through a small angle when passing through a strong magnetic field. The rotation θ, in minutes, is given by

$$\theta = rLH \cos \lambda$$

where $r =$ Verdet's constant $= 13.00 \times 10^{-6}$ for carbon dioxide
$L =$ length of the path of light, cm $= 10.42$ cm
$H =$ intensity of magnetic field, oersteds, $= 127.2$
$\lambda =$ angle H makes with the ray of light $= 79.416°$

Find θ.

10. When a compressive force acts on wood at an angle θ to the direction of the grain, the allowable working stress in psi, (s_{allow}) is given by

$$s_{allow} = \frac{s_p s_\perp}{s_p \sin^2 \theta + s_\perp \cos^2 \theta}$$

where $s_p =$ allowable unit stress parallel to the grain
$s_\perp =$ allowable unit stress perpendicular to the grain

Find the allowable stress if the load is acting at an angle of 30° to the grain on Douglas fir, structural grade, for which s_p is 1400 psi and $s_\perp$ is 400 psi.

11. A 10-in. crank is revolving in a CCW direction, starting from a horizontal position, at 10 revolutions per second (rps). Find the requested data at the end of 2, 0.2, and 0.02 sec.
    (a) The vertical displacements.
    (b) The horizontal displacements, given as distances from the axle.
    (c) The *total* movement of the handle measured in distances along the path described by the handle.

12. A 12-in. crank is revolving in a CCW direction at 90 rpm starting from a horizontal position. Find the number of seconds that elapse until
    (a) the handle has completed three full revolutions.
    (b) the handle has traveled 1.5 rad.
    (c) the handle has traveled 36 in. along its path.
    (d) the vertical displacement is 9 in.

13. An oscillating spring has an amplitude of 20 cm and a frequency of 4 vibrations per second.
    (a) Find the position of the mass at the end of the spring after 10, $10\frac{1}{16}$, $10\frac{1}{8}$, and $10\frac{1}{4}$ sec.
    (b) Find the time it takes for the mass to move 5, 10, 15, and 20 cm from the rest position.

    For an oscillating spring, the distance x of a mass at the end of the spring from its rest position is given by

$$x = A \cos 2\pi f t$$

where $x =$ distance of mass from its rest position, cm
$A =$ amplitude, cm
$f =$ frequency, vibrations/sec
$t =$ time, sec, to move from position $x = +A$

14. The motion of the piston of an automobile engine can be approximated by the equations

$$x = A - A \cos 2\pi\omega t = \text{distance of piston from one end}$$

$$v = 2\pi\omega A \sin 2\pi\omega t = \text{velocity of piston}$$

$$a = (2\pi\omega)^2 A \cos 2\pi\omega t = \text{acceleration of piston}$$

$$2A = \text{stroke of engine}$$

$$\omega = \text{angular velocity, rpm}$$

$$t = \text{time}$$

(a) Find the velocity of the piston in mph at the midpoint of its stroke if the stroke is 5 in. and the angular velocity is 3600 rpm. (*Hint :* Find t when $x = A$ and remember that $2\pi\omega t$ is measured in radians.)

(b) Find the acceleration of the piston at the end of its stroke, that is, when $x = 2A$.

15. The approximate time of the swing of a pendulum of length L is

$$T = 2\pi\sqrt{\frac{L}{g}}\left(1 + \tfrac{1}{4}\sin^2\frac{\theta}{2}\right)$$

Find T if $L = 18$ in., $g = 32.2$ ft/sec^2, $\theta = 25°$.

16. The force F at an angle of θ from the horizontal required to pull a weight W along a horizontal path is given by

$$F = \frac{fW}{\cos\theta + f\sin\theta}$$

where f = coefficient of friction. Find the force at an angle of 30° above the horizontal required to pull a 50-lb object along a horizontal road if the coefficient of friction is 0.24.

17. The length L in statute miles of 1 degree of arc of latitude at a latitude θ is given by

$$L = 69.0543 - 0.3517\cos 2\theta + 0.0007\cos 4\theta$$

Make a table of values of L and θ for $\theta = 0°, 10°, 20°, 30°, 40°, 50°, 60°, 70°, 80°,$ and $90°$.

18. Find the power P in watts for an alternating current if

$$P = EI\cos\phi$$

where $E = 220$ volt, $I = 18$ amp, and ϕ = phase angle = 22.5°.

19. To find the position of a planet or satellite in its orbit t days after the planet or satellite is at its greatest distance from the sun or earth, it is necessary to solve Kepler's equation:

$$\frac{2\pi t}{P} = E - e\sin E$$

where P = period of revolution of the planet, days
E = the eccentric anomaly, in radians
e = eccentricity of the orbit of the planet or satellite

Find the time for each of the following to travel the first eighth of its orbit $\left(\text{from } E = 0 \text{ to } E = \dfrac{\pi}{4}\right)$ and the second eighth of its orbit $\left(\text{from } E = \dfrac{\pi}{4} \text{ to } E = \dfrac{\pi}{2}\right)$.

(a) Earth about sun; P = 365.256 days, e = 0.016 750
(b) Moon about earth; P = 27.321 661 days, e = 0.0549.

20. (a) Referring to Problem 19, solve Kepler's equation (find E) for the earth at the end of 779.94 days by using the following process:

Step 1. Let $E_0 = M_0 = \dfrac{2\pi t}{P}$ where t = 779.94 − 2(365.256).

Step 2. Find $M_1 = E_0 - e \sin E_0$.

Step 3. Find $E_1 = \dfrac{-(M_1 - M_0)}{1 - e \cos E_0} + E_0$.

Step 4. Find $M_2 = E_1 - e \sin E_1$.

Step 5. Find $E_2 = \dfrac{-(M_2 - M_0)}{1 - e \cos E_1} + E_1$.

Continue until $M_n = M_0$ to five significant figures.
(b) Using the value for E found in part (a), find the position of the earth in its orbit by calculating its x and y coordinates using the equations
$$x = a \cos E \qquad \text{and} \qquad y = a\sqrt{1 - e^2} \sin E$$
given a = 149.60 × 10^6 km and e = 0.016 750.

21. The total surface area of an oblate ellipsoid, formed by rotating an ellipse about its major axis, is given by
$$A_t = 2\pi a^2 + 2.303\frac{\pi b^2}{e} \log \frac{1 + e}{1 - e} \qquad \text{where } e = \frac{\sqrt{a^2 - b^2}}{a}$$
Find the total surface area of an oblate ellipsoid whose ellipse has a semimajor axis (a) of 3 units and a semiminor axis (b) of 2 units. (Use Table 1 to simplify calculations where possible.)

22. The total surface area of a prolate ellipsoid, formed by rotating an ellipse about its minor axis, is given by
$$A_t = 2\pi b^2 + 2\pi ab \frac{\text{Sin}^{-1} e}{e} \qquad \text{where } e = \frac{\sqrt{a^2 - b^2}}{a}$$
Find the total surface area of a prolate ellipsoid whose ellipse has a semimajor axis (a) of 3 units and a semiminor axis (b) of 2 units. ($\text{Sin}^{-1} e$ must be expressed in radians.)

10.03 / The right triangle; notation

To explain the methods for solving a right triangle, it is convenient to use a simple notation to identify the sides and angles. One of the simplest designates the hypotenuse as c and the right angle as C. If the triangle is sketched so that one leg coincides with the positive x axis, the acute angle in the standard position is designated as A and the side opposite this angle is designated as a. The other acute angle is designated as B and the side opposite it as b. Figure 10.4 shows this notation, the notation used in the previous chapter based upon coordinates, and the system using names of the sides of the right triangle.

This text will continue to use a single capital letter for angles of a geometric configuration in which the intersections are lettered, unless ambiguity requires the use of three letters, as explained in Chapter 4.

The values of the trigonometric functions, being ratios, can be identified in the three systems listed above. This is shown in Table 10.1. The first system is based upon $P:(x,y)$ and $P:(r,\theta)$, the rectangular and polar coordinates. The second system is a simple, widely used notation. The third system using names may serve as a helpful learning device, but it is seldom used by technically trained personnel.

Figure 10.4
Triangle notation systems

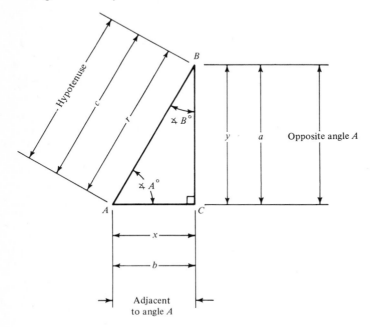

Table 10.1
Definition of trigonometric functions

Trigonometric function	Basis		
	Coordinates	Standard triangle	Names
Sine A	$\dfrac{y}{r}$	$\dfrac{a}{c}$	$\dfrac{\text{opposite}}{\text{hypotenuse}}$
Cosine A	$\dfrac{x}{r}$	$\dfrac{b}{c}$	$\dfrac{\text{adjacent}}{\text{hypotenuse}}$
Tangent A	$\dfrac{y}{x}$	$\dfrac{a}{b}$	$\dfrac{\text{opposite}}{\text{adjacent}}$
Cotangent A	$\dfrac{x}{y}$	$\dfrac{b}{a}$	$\dfrac{\text{adjacent}}{\text{opposite}}$
Secant A	$\dfrac{r}{x}$	$\dfrac{c}{b}$	$\dfrac{\text{hypotenuse}}{\text{adjacent}}$
Cosecant A	$\dfrac{r}{y}$	$\dfrac{c}{a}$	$\dfrac{\text{hypotenuse}}{\text{opposite}}$

10.04 / Solving the right triangle

To solve a right triangle means to find and list the measures of the three angles and the three sides of the triangle. If two sides, or one acute angle and one side, are known, exactly one right triangle is determined. If two acute angles and no sides are known, an infinite number of similar triangles are possible.

In Section 1.12 the precision of the measure of the angle and the matching number of significant figures in distances were listed. These results are repeated here as Table 10.2, which has a slightly different arrangement.

Remember that this table is slightly artificial in that the precision measure does vary with the size of the angle and the particular function. Moreover,

Table 10.2
Precision of calculations

Significant figures used	Unit of measure of angle		
	° ′ ″	Decimal	Radian
2	10′	0.1°	0.01
3	1′	0.01°	0.001
4	10″	0.001°	0.0001
5	1″	0.0001°	0.00001

the table has been prepared to use convenient decimal increments of the unit of angular measure. These values may vary from book to book, but the important idea is to use no more accuracy in actual measurement than justified. If slide-rule computations are to be used, yielding three significant figures, the cosine of small angles can be read only to the nearest 2° and sines to the nearest 1'. Near 45°, both of these functions can be read to the nearest 5'. Thus, the assignment of 1' increments for three significant figures is a very broad value.

When any two sides of a right triangle are known, the third side can be calculated by the Pythagorean theorem, $c^2 = a^2 + b^2$. (Refer to Section 1.16 for a review.) The angles can then be computed by using the trigonometric functions involving the given sides.

Figure 10.5
Finding parts of a right triangle

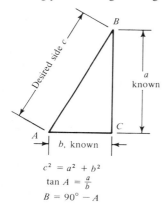

$c^2 = a^2 + b^2$
$\tan A = \frac{a}{b}$
$B = 90° - A$

(a) Given: 2 legs

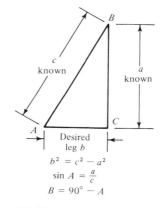

$b^2 = c^2 - a^2$
$\sin A = \frac{a}{c}$
$B = 90° - A$

(b) Given: hypotenuse and 1 leg

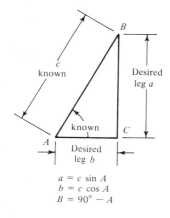

$a = c \sin A$
$b = c \cos A$
$B = 90° - A$

(c) Given: hypotenuse and 1 angle

$a = b \tan A$
$c = \frac{b}{\cos A}$
$B = 90° - A$

(d) Given: 1 leg and 1 angle

When one angle and one side are known, the trigonometric function involving the known side and the side to be found is used to find the measure of this desired side. Since two sides are to be found, it is always better to use the known side twice rather than one of the calculated sides, to avoid an error being carried forward.

Although Table 10.1 can always be used to find the functions relating the given side to the desired side, it may be easier to use the scheme shown in Figure 10.5, where the relationships can be seen readily.

In a right triangle, knowing one acute angle means that the other is known, since the acute angles are complementary (their sum is 90°). Thus, the angle opposite the desired leg is always known. The desired leg is named a and its opposite angle A is placed in standard position. Figure 10.5 shows that the side a is then found by

$$a = c \sin A, \text{ if the hypotenuse } c \text{ is known}$$

or $\qquad a = b \tan A, \text{ if the other leg } b \text{ is known}$

When the given side is not the hypotenuse, the hypotenuse is best found by the division

$$c = \frac{b}{\cos A}$$

Whether a slide rule, logarithms, or a desk calculator is used, division is no more difficult than multiplication and is preferable to using the Pythagorean theorem, which is recommended as a check calculation.

Method for Solving a Right Triangle
Step 1. Prepare format and make a scaled sketch, as shown below

$$a = \qquad A =$$
$$b = \qquad B =$$
$$c = \qquad C = 90°$$

$$\text{sum} = \qquad \text{(adjust if } 1' \text{ or } 0.01° \text{ off } 180°\text{)}$$

Figure 10.6
Standard notation: A scaled sketch

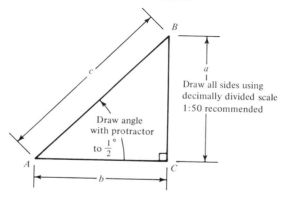

Step 2. Record the given information on format and on sketch.
Step 3. Find the missing parts as follows:

Given (a) two legs	(b) hypotenuse and leg	(c) hypotenuse and angle	(d) leg and angle
1. $c^2 = a^2 + b^2$	$b^2 = c^2 - a^2$	$B = 90° - A$	$B = 90° - A$
2. $\tan A = \dfrac{a}{b}$	$\sin A = \dfrac{a}{c}$	$a = c \sin A$	$a = b \tan A$
3. $B = 90° - A$	$B = 90° - A$	$b = c \cos A$	$c = \dfrac{b}{\cos A}$

Step 4.
Check:

$\sin B = \dfrac{b}{c}$	$\cos B = \dfrac{b}{c}$	$c^2 = a^2 + b^2$	$c^2 = a^2 + b^2$

Step 5. Record the calculated information on format.

Example 10.12
Solve the right triangle whose two legs are given as 127 and 478.

SOLUTION
Steps 1 and 2

$a = 127$ $A =$
$b = 478$ $B =$
$c =$ $C = 90°$
$\overline{}$
             sum =

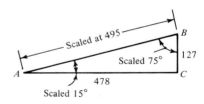

Figure 10.7

Step 3. Using Table 1 of the Appendix,

$a^2 = (127)^2 = 16{,}129$
$b^2 = (478)^2 = 228{,}484$
$\overline{}$

$c^2 = 244{,}613 = (495)^2$ (to three significant figures)

Since c is a calculated distance, only the given sides a and b are used to find the angles. Using the sketch,

$$\tan A = \frac{a}{b} = \frac{127}{478} = 0.266 \qquad \text{and} \qquad A = 14°54'$$
$$B = 90° - A = 75°06'$$

Step 4. Check:

$$\sin B = \frac{478}{495} = 0.966 \quad \text{and} \quad 74°55' \leq B \leq 75°7'$$

Step 5. Completing the format,

$$
\begin{array}{ll}
a = 127 & A = 14°54' \\
b = 478 & B = 75°06' \\
c = 495 & C = 90°
\end{array}
$$

$$\text{sum} = 180°$$

Example 10.13

Find the six parts of a right triangle if its hypotenuse is 3.47 and one acute angle = 34°37'.

SOLUTION

(1) Prepare the format and sketch:

(2)

$$
\begin{array}{ll}
a = & A = 34°37' \\
b = & B = \\
c = 3.47 & C = 90°
\end{array}
$$

$$\text{sum} =$$

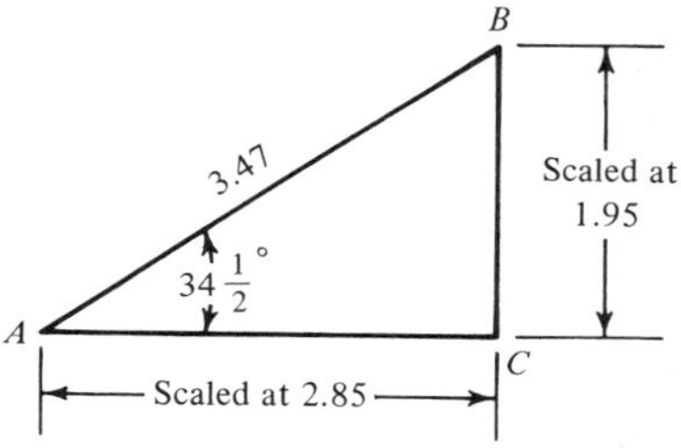

Figure 10.8

(3) $B = 90° - 34°37' = 55°23'$

$a = 3.47(\sin 34°37') = 3.47(0.568) = 1.97$

$b = 3.47(\cos 34°37') = 3.47(0.823) = 2.86$

(4) Check:

$$
\begin{array}{ll}
a^2 = & 3.88 \\
b^2 = & 8.18
\end{array}
$$

$$a^2 + b^2 = 12.06 = (3.47)^2 = c^2$$

(5) Completing the format,

$$
\begin{array}{ll}
a = 1.97 & A = \quad 34°37' \\
b = 2.86 & B = \quad 55°23' \\
c = 3.47 & C = \quad 90°
\end{array}
$$

$$\text{sum} = 180°$$

Note that the scaled sketch can also be used as a final check. Although Table 1 provides a rapid check for three significant figures, this is a laborious procedure for five significant figures, whereas the use of the scaled sketch remains simple. Later, when other triangles are solved, the scaled-sketch method still works efficiently. Therefore, it is stressed at this time as the best method for checking, even though it will not detect a minor error in calculating parts of a degree.

Example 10.14

Find the six parts of a right triangle, given one leg $= 0.872$ and the acute angle adjacent to this leg $= 40°12'$.

SOLUTION

(1) and (2) Prepare the format and sketch:

$a =$
$b = 0.872$
$c =$

$A = 40°12'$
$B =$
$C = 90°$

sum $=$

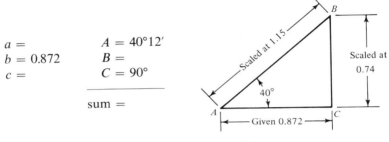

Figure 10.9

(3)

$$B = 90° - 40°12' = 49°48'$$

$$a = 0.872(\tan 40°12') = 0.872(0.845) = 0.737$$

$$c = \frac{0.872}{\cos 40°12'} = \frac{0.872}{0.764} = 1.14$$

(4) Check:

$$a^2 = (0.737)^2 = 0.543$$
$$b^2 = (0.872)^2 = 0.760$$

$$a^2 + b^2 = \quad\quad 1.303 = (1.14)^2 = c^2$$

(5) Completing the format,

$a = 0.737$
$b = 0.872$
$c = 1.14$

$A = 40°12'$
$B = 49°48'$
$C = 90°$

sum $= 180°$

Problem Set 10.3

From the given data, solve the right triangle, using the method outlined in the text.

1. The two legs are 23 and 43, respectively.
2. The hypotenuse = 72 and one leg = 47.
3. The hypotenuse is 651 and one leg is 317.
4. The two legs are 372 and 525, respectively.
5. One leg = 0.22 and its opposite angle = 22°10′.
6. One leg = 0.71 and its opposite angle = 44°42′.
7. The hypotenuse = 0.0711 and one angle = 62°38′.
8. The hypotenuse = 0.0985 and one angle = 71°37′.
9. One leg = 524 and its adjacent acute angle = 18.8°.
10. One leg = 644 and its adjacent acute angle = 22.2°.
11. The hypotenuse = 41.7 and one angle = 62°38′.
12. The hypotenuse = 82.2 and one angle = 42.2°.
13. The hypotenuse = 2.568 and one leg = 1.473.
14. The two legs are 684.9 and 593.4, respectively.
15. The two legs are 1.3582 and 1.8976, respectively.
16. The hypotenuse = 32.964 and one leg = 24.758.
17. One leg = 4572 and its opposite angle = 36°28′49″.
18. One leg = 5.493 and its adjacent acute angle = 57°18′35″.
19. The hypotenuse = 15,895 and one angle = 46.3956°.
20. The hypotenuse = 46.453 and one angle = 44.4343°.
    (*Note:* Problems 13–20 require the use of five-place tables and logarithms or a desk calculator.)

10.05 / Applications of the right triangle

In applied problems, the vertices of the right triangle are not always given as *A*, *B*, and *C*, nor is the right triangle given in an appropriate standard position as shown in Figure 10.5. The basic techniques, however, remain the same; Table 10.1 is still appropriate and the student could relabel the vertices as *A*, *B*, and *C*, if this should be necessary.

Examples are presented below from four areas of application. Although this does not cover all kinds of applications, it should be sufficient to indicate the wide use of the right triangle.

Geometric configurations

Example 10.15
A 20-ft ladder leans from the ground to a point on a wall that is 15 ft above the ground. Find the distance along the ground from the end of the ladder to the wall.

(1) Make a sketch. (See Figure 10.10.)

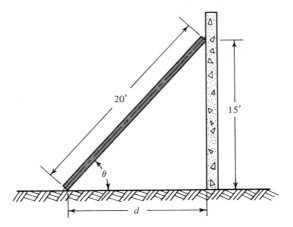

Figure 10.10
Ladder and wall

(2) The hypotenuse and one leg of a right triangle are given and the other leg is desired.

$$d = \sqrt{(20)^2 - (15)^2}$$

$$= \sqrt{175}$$

$$= 13.2 \text{ ft to the nearest tenth of a foot}$$

Example 10.16
The pitch of the roof of a building is specified as 4 to 12. (This means that for every 12-in. horizontal run, there is a 4-in. vertical rise.) Find the length of lumber a carpenter must cut for the roof line if there is to be a 2-ft overhang and if he allows 1 in. at each end for nailing purposes. The span is 20 ft.

SOLUTION
(1) Make a sketch. (See Figure 10.11.)

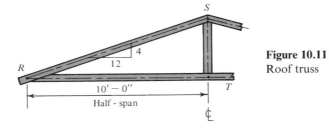

Figure 10.11
Roof truss

(2) One leg and an acute angle of a right triangle are given and the hypotenuse is desired.

$$\tan R = \frac{4}{12} = \frac{1}{3} = 0.333\,33 \qquad \text{and} \qquad R = 18°26'$$

$$RS = c = \frac{10}{\cos 18°26'} = \frac{10}{0.9478}$$

$$= 10.5 \text{ ft} = 10 \text{ ft } 6 \text{ in. to the nearest inch}$$

length to be cut $= 10$ ft 6 in. $+ 2$ ft $+ 1$ in. $+ 1$ in. $= 12$ ft 8 in.

Physics

Figure 10.12 shows a force triangle. F is the given force in magnitude and direction. The magnitude is often given in kips, ^{K}, an abbreviated form of a kilopound, 1000 lb. Direction is usually given as the acute angle from the X axis. F_x and F_y are called the x and y components of the force. Signs for these components agree with the standard quadrant sign conventions for x and y.

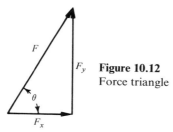

Figure 10.12
Force triangle

Example 10.17
Find the x and y components of a 2.75^{K} force from the origin passing through the point $P : (-2, 5)$.

SOLUTION
(1) Sketch the force triangle as shown in Figure 10.13.
(2) Find the reference angle ϕ:

$$\phi = \tan^{-1} \frac{5}{2} = \tan^{-1} 2.5 = 68°12'$$

(3) Find the components:
$$F_x = -2.75 \cos 68°12' = -2.75\,(0.371) = -1.02^{K}$$
$$F_y = 2.75 \sin 68°12' = 2.75\,(0.928) = 2.55^{K}$$

Note that the sign for the components is obtained from the sketch, which indicates that the x component is to the left, or negative, and the y component is upward, or positive. The magnitude of the force is always a positive quantity.

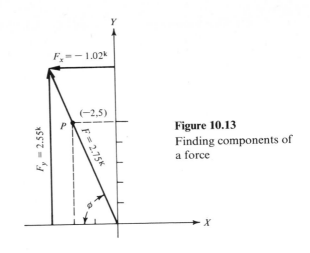

$F_x = -1.02^k$

$(-2,5)$

P

$F = 2.75^k$

$F_y = 2.55^k$

Scale of distances
1″ = 3 units
Scale of forces
1″ = 1^k

ϕ

Figure 10.13
Finding components of
a force

Example 10.18
An airplane is flying due east in still air with a speed of 180 mph
when a 40-mph wind from the north forces him off his course.
Find his resulting speed and direction.

SOLUTION
(1) Sketch the velocity triangle as shown in Figure 10.14.

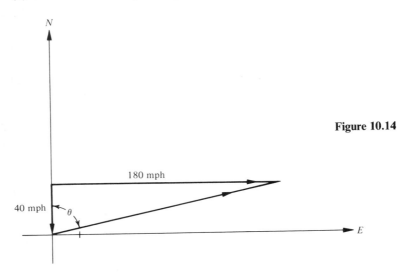

180 mph

40 mph

θ

Figure 10.14

(2) The resulting speed is the hypotenuse c:

$$c = \sqrt{(40)^2 + (180)^2} = \sqrt{33,844}$$

$$= 184 \text{ mph to the nearest mph}$$

(3) Find angle θ:

$$\tan \theta = \frac{180}{40} = 4.5 \qquad \text{and} \qquad \theta = 77°28' \text{ to the nearest minute}$$

The resulting direction is 77°28' from the north toward the east, or N77°28'E.

Surveying

A surveying transit that can measure vertical angles usually reads to the nearest minute. A level bubble tube that indicates when the telescope is horizontal and the 0° marking on the vertical scale are made to agree by adjustments prior to use. An angle read to a point higher than the horizontal is called an **angle of elevation.** An angle read to a point lower than the horizontal is called an **angle of depression.** The computed rise or fall is algebraically added to the elevation of the horizontal line of sight found by adding the height of the line of sight to a known elevation. The amount added is called the **height of instrument** (HI) and the known elevation is called a **bench mark** (BM). Bench marks are usually set by state or federal agencies.

Example 10.19

A calibrated transit is set up over a bench mark at 98.71 ft above sea level. The HI is measured as 5.08 ft. The angle of elevation to a lighthouse balcony rail, known to be at 162.78 ft above sea level is read as 17°14'. A certain post on a pier jutting into the ocean has been located by a previous survey as 514.78 ft from the bench mark.* The angle of depression to it is read as 3°48'. Find (a) the (horizontal) distance to the lighthouse from the bench mark and (b) the elevation of the post on the pier. (Assume that the angles are correct, warranting the use of five significant figures. This is a common practice in surveying, and distances are adjusted later if a closed polygon can be formed and the error of closure can be computed. The corrections needed are usually very small, one to three hundredths of a foot.)

SOLUTION
Part (a)
(1) Referring to Figure 10.15, the vertical side of the right triangle determined by the angle of elevation is the known side since it is the difference in elevations. Calling this vertical side a,

$a =$ (elevation of lighthouse) $-$ (elevation of horizontal line of sight)

$= 162.78 - (98.71 + 5.08) = 58.99 \text{ ft}$

*Recorded survey distances are always horizontal distances.

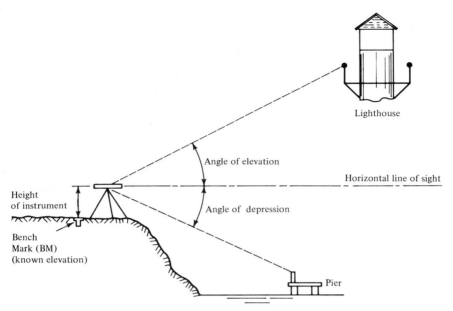

Figure 10.15
Surveying terminology

    (2) The distance desired is the horizontal side, b, and
$b = a\,\cot(\text{angle of elevation}) = 58.99\cot 17°14'$:

$$\begin{aligned}\log 58.99 &= 1.77078\\ \log\cot 17°14' &= 0.50837\end{aligned}$$

$$\begin{aligned}\text{sum} = \log a &= 2.27915\\ a &= 190.17 \text{ ft, the distance to the lighthouse}\end{aligned}$$

Part (b)

    (1) Referring to Figure 10.15, the horizontal leg of the right triangle determined by the angle of depression is given as 514.78 ft. Calling this side b, the side desired is the vertical side a, the change in elevation:

$$a = b\,\tan(\text{angle of depression}) = 514.78\tan 3°48'$$

$$\begin{aligned}\log 514.78 &= 2.71162\\ \log\tan 3°48' &= 8.82230 - 10\end{aligned}$$

$$\begin{aligned}\text{sum} = \log a &= 11.53392 - 10\\ a &= 34.92 \text{ ft}\end{aligned}$$

    (2) Elevation of post = elevation of horizontal line of sight $- a$

$$= (98.71 + 5.08) - 34.92 = 68.87 \text{ ft}$$

In discussing a line on the ground, its direction is called a **bearing,** an acute angle measured from a north–south meridian. In some work an **azimuth** is used; this is the clockwise angle from the north as used for routine surveying. In geodetic and other precision surveys, the angle is measured from the south. As a result, the reference system must always be checked.

In Figure 10.16, the bearing angle from R to T is S 60°7′ W, the S meaning from the south end of the meridian and the W meaning that the angle is toward the west. The azimuth for line R–T from the north is 240°7′ (180° + 60°7′). If the bearing was wanted for line T–R (from T to R), it would be N 60°7′ E.

The two perpendicular offsets from the initial point, corresponding to the x and y coordinates, are usually given in the reverse of the order used for coordinates. The y coordinate is called a **northing** (a *positive latitude*) or a **southing** (a *negative latitude*). The x coordinate is called an **easting** (a *positive departure*) or a **westing** (a *negative departure*).

Example 10.20

Find the latitude and departure for a line 367.18 ft long at an azimuth from the north of 162°13′20″.

SOLUTION

(1) Make a sketch. (See Figure 10.17.)

(2) Find the bearing angle, θ:

$$\theta = 180° - 162°13'20'' = 17°46'40''$$

The bearing is S17°46′40″E.

Figure 10.16
Direction and offsets

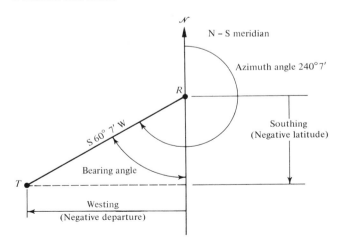

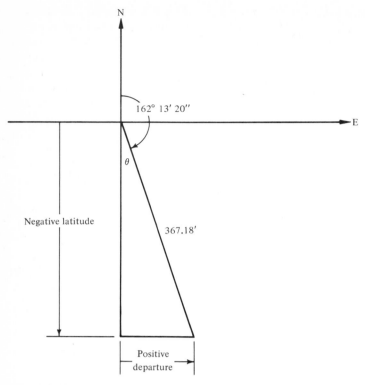

Figure 10.17

(3) The magnitude a of the departure and the magnitude b of the latitude correspond to the legs of a right triangle whose hypotenuse c is known as 367.18.

Thus, $a = c \sin \theta = 367.18 \sin 17°46'40''$

and $b = c \cos \theta = 367.18 \cos 17°46'40''$

(4) Calculate, using the compact form for logarithmic computations recommended in Section 8.07.

	(Complete all headings first)	(Find values in sequence shown)	
(Sequence)			
Step 6	$a = $ antilog	$= \;\;112.11$	
Step 4	$\log a = $ sum	$= 2.04965$	Working
Step 1	$\log \sin 17°46'40'' = \overline{9.48477 - 10}$		upward
Step 3	$\log 367.18$	$= 2.56488$	Start here
Step 2	$\log \cos 17°46'40'' = 9.97877 - 10$		Working
Step 5	$\log b = $ sum	$= \overline{2.54365}$	downward
Step 7	$b = $ antilog	349.66	

(5) From the sketch,

$$\text{departure} = +a = 112.11 \text{ ft}$$
$$\text{latitude} = -b = -349.66 \text{ ft}$$

Navigation

For short trips, navigators use "dead reckoning," which assumes that the portion of the earth's surface involved is a flat plane.

Example 10.21

A ferry is to cross a wide river from a dock at *A*, as shown in Figure 10.18, to a point directly across the river marked *B*. Point *B* is at a bearing of S 44°31′E and 12,840 ft distant. If the ferry has a speed of 4 mph and the river current is $1\frac{1}{2}$ mph, find (a) the actual

Figure 10.18
Navigation

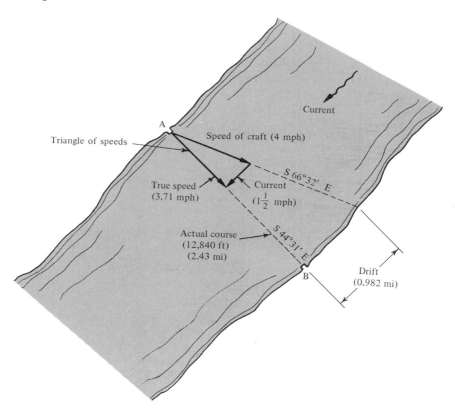

length of the trip in miles; (b) the magnetic heading the pilot should hold; (c) the trip time for a single crossing; (d) the drift in miles.

SOLUTION

(a) Length of trip in miles $= \dfrac{12,840}{5,280} = 2.43$ miles.

(b) Find angle A:

$$A = \sin^{-1}\dfrac{1.5}{4} = \sin^{-1} 0.375 = 22°01'$$

Find heading:

$$\begin{array}{l} \text{bearing is S } 44°31'\text{E} \\ \text{angle } A = \ \ 22°01' \\ \hline \text{heading is S } 66°32'\text{E} \end{array}$$

(c) From the triangle of speeds,
speed along actual course is $4 \cos 22°01' = 4(0.927) = 3.71$ mph

$$\text{time to cross} = \dfrac{2.43}{3.71}(60) = 39.3 \text{ min, or 40 min, approx.}$$

(d) Drift $= 2.43 \tan 22°1' = 2.43(0.404) = 0.982$ mile.
Since the drift is the product of the current by the time of crossing, it can be used as a check calculation:

$$\text{drift} = 1.5\left(\dfrac{39.3}{60.0}\right) = 0.982 \text{ mile, check.}$$

Problem Set 10.4

1. A contractor in laying out the plot plan of a house measures two points P and Q that are 50 ft apart. He then locates point R, 30 ft from P, so that angle RPQ is a right angle. He checks his work by calculating the hypotenuse RQ and by measuring RQ along the ground. Calculate the length of RQ.
2. Working lines are usually the lines that describe the shape of a structure and ignore the actual dimensions of the materials used. These refinements are added later by either more detailed calculations or by the builder using a carpenter's square. For a triangular roof with an overhang of $2\frac{1}{2}$ ft on each side of a 40-ft-wide house, and with a pitch of 3 on 12, find the length of the working line for the sloping member.

3. Find the length s of a side of a regular polygon of n sides inscribed in a circle of radius r. $\left(\text{The central angle } \theta \text{ subtended by the side } = \dfrac{360°}{n}\right)$. Consider r as exact.
   (a) $r = 10$ in. and $n = 8$
   (b) $r = 10$ in. and $n = 16$
   (c) $r = 10$ in. and $n = 32$
   (d) $r = 10$ in. and $n = 64$

4. The diagonals of a rhombus (a parallelogram with four equal sides) are exactly 16 and 20 in. respectively. The diagonals of a rhombus are perpendicular and they bisect each other.
   (a) Find the length of one side of the rhombus.
   (b) Find the measure of an acute angle of the rhombus.

5. Find to the nearest tenth the area of an isosceles trapezoid if the sides are 12, 15, 12, and 20 in., respectively.

6. A guy wire is to just pass over a 6-ft-high wall and be attached to a point 14 ft high on a telephone pole. Find the length of wire to be used if the wall is 8 ft from the telephone pole.

7. Find the angle through which a pendulum swings if its length is 32 in. and the horizontal distance between its two extreme positions is 18.5 in.

8. Find the distance that the bob of a pendulum 5.2 in. in length rises above its lowest position if the angle of the swing is 32°.

9. The perpendicular distance of a chord from the center of a 5-cm circle is 1.5 cm. Find the length of the chord.

10. Find the diameter of a circle if a 48-in. chord is 10 in. from the center of the circle.

11. An approximate rule for the length of an uncrossed belt connecting two pulleys a distance d apart center to center is

$$L \approx 2d + \pi(r_1 + r_2)$$

   (a) Find L using this rule for an 8 in. and a 12-in. pulley 8 ft apart.
   (b) Develop an exact formula for L and then substitute the values given in part (a) and compute L. Using the solution in the text for part (a), compute the percentage of error of the approximation.

12. Calculate the length of the arc subtended by the stated angles and the length of a long chord, using a unit circle.
   (a) $10°$ (b) $1°$ (c) $1'$ (d) $10''$ (e) $1''$
   Make a general statement about the effect of the angle on the length of the chord and arc as the angle becomes progressively smaller. Use seven decimal places for arcs; use the method of Section 9.15 for angles $1°$ or smaller for chords to obtain seven places.

13. At what angle with the horizontal must a disabled airplane glide to reach an airport 12 miles away from the point he is 10,500 ft above?

14. Find the resultant force and the angle of its line of action for the given horizontal and vertical forces.
    (a) 45 lb downward, 38 lb to the right
    (b) 220 lb upward, 54 lb to the left.
15. Considering the given values as exact, find the direction and true airspeed of an airplane if
    (a) its speed in still air is 450 mph, its heading is due east, and the wind blows 28 mph from the north.
    (b) its speed in still air is 250 mph, its heading is due north, and the wind blows 17 mph from the east.
16. Find to the nearest minute the heading an airplane must have to reach a point due north if
    (a) its speed in still air is 190 mph and the wind blows 32 mph from the west.
    (b) its speed in still air is 550 mph and the wind blows 45 mph from the east.

17–20

The force F that is just sufficient to keep a weight W from sliding down a smooth plane inclined at an angle θ from the horizontal is determined from the illustration.

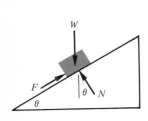

(a) Free Body Diagram

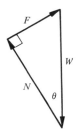

(b) Force Triangle

17. What braking force is necessary to hold a 2000-lb car on a hill inclined at an angle of 8°24′ from the horizontal?
18. What is the maximum weight that a force of 500 lb can drag up a smooth plane inclined at an angle of 16°30′?
19. Find the angle at which a smooth plane is inclined if a 300-lb weight requires a force of 178 lb to pull it upward.
20. Find the shortest length that can be used for an inclined plane so that a man whose pulling strength is 145 lb can raise a 250-lb weight to the top of a hill 18 ft high.

21. Find the speed in mph of a point that is on the 40°N parallel of latitude. Assume that the earth is a perfect sphere, its radius is 3960 miles, and it rotates once every 24 hr.

22. The tension T in a suspension cable carrying a pipeline across a gorge is maximum at the point of support, and can be determined from the figure, where $W = \frac{1}{2}wL$, L is the distance between supports in feet, and w is the weight per foot of the load supported. Find this tension T for a cable 200 ft between supports, carrying a load of 80 lb/ft, with a sag s of 18 ft and $\tan\theta = \dfrac{4s}{L}$.

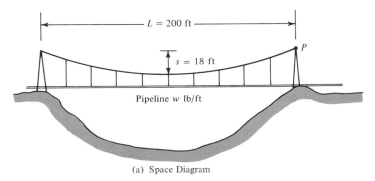

(a) Space Diagram

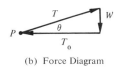

(b) Force Diagram

23. In the figure below find an expression for the distance d to the point of intersection if the height h and the angles θ and ϕ are given.

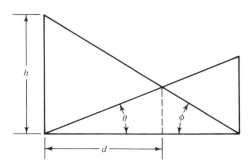

24. In the diagram, use the given dimensions to calculate the distance AB.

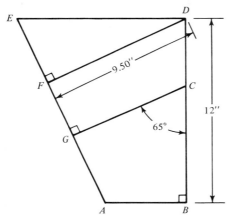

25. From a transit on a hilltop, a flagpole atop a school is observed. The angle of elevation to the top of the flagpole is $1°11'$ and the angle of depression to the base is $0°58'$. By scaling on a map the flagpole is about 250 ft distant. How high is the flagpole?

26. Find the solar altitude (angle of elevation of the sun) in decimals of a degree to the nearest thousandth of a degree if a flagpole 87.42 ft high casts a shadow on level ground 109.19 ft long.

27. A highway has a stretch at a uniform grade of $+1.2\%$. (A percentage grade expresses the vertical change in elevation per 100 ft of horizontal run.) Two points on the pavement are measured with a steel tape resting upon the pavement and found to be 517.86 ft apart.
(a) What is the true horizontal distance between these points?
(b) What is the difference in elevation of these two points?

28. A survey party has their transit set up at Station $10 + 00$. The transitman

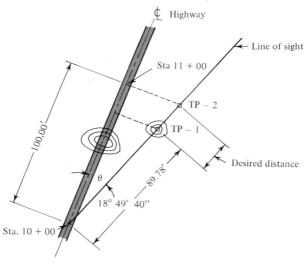

cannot see the rodman much past the crest of the hill, so the rodman moves to a small hill to the northeast and drives a stake for a temporary station, TP-1. By using the stadia method the distance to TP-1 is read as 89.78 ft, and angle θ measured as 18°49′40″. Calculate how far beyond TP-1, a second point TP-2 should be located on the same line of sight if the distance along the highway centerline to Station 11 + 00 is to be exactly 100.00 ft. All offsets are perpendicular to the centerline.

29. A clinometer is a crude device for measuring angles to the nearest $\frac{1}{2}°$ vertically. From his office on the tenth floor of a building, an observer reads the angle to the flagpole topping a new skyscraper at $67\frac{1}{2}°$. Knowing his own eye height (5 ft) and the floor elevation of his office, he knows that his eye was at elevation 110.24 ft above street grade. From street level, standing directly below his office window, he now reads the angle to the flagpole as $73\frac{1}{2}°$. What is the elevation above the street of the top of the new pole?

30. From the balcony of a lighthouse, a surveyor measures the angle of depression to two channel marking buoys as 19°47′13″ and 24°19′18″, each reading being the average of six observations. If the balcony is 92.46 ft above the water, what is the distance between the two buoys, which are on the same line of sight?

31. The base of a water tower is inaccessible because of a security fence. A transit is set up at a random distance from the tower on level ground, and an observation on the top of the tower gave an angle of elevation of 31°55′. A stake was set on the ground exactly 100.00 ft farther away on the line of sight, and the new angle of elevation read as 27°28′. How high is the tower?

32. A measurement of the exact height of the Washington Monument in Washington, D.C., was directed. A location due west of the monument and accurately measured to be 500.00 ft from the center of the structure was staked, but when attempts were made to read the angle of elevation,

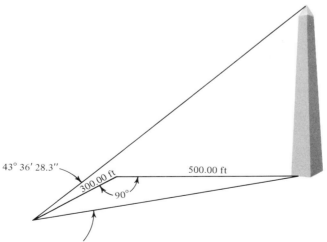

the morning sun blinded the observer. So a right angle toward the south side of the Mall was turned and a new location established exactly 300.00 ft due south. Here the angle of elevation was read as 43°36′28.3″ by repeating the observation six times. What is the height of the monument expressed in feet and inches to the nearest $\frac{1}{8}$ in.?

33. A subtense bar with targets exactly 5 ft apart was observed by a theodolite reading to 10 sec, and the use of multiple observations gave an angular measurement of 1°31′33.7″. How far away was the subtense bar? Remember to use the right triangle formed by the bisector of the measured angle.

34. Find the distance in feet to a European-made subtense bar with exactly 1 m between target lamps and with an observed angle of 0°49′37.3″. Use Table 10 if needed.

35. A ship sails on a course of N42°41′E from New York at an average speed of 18 knots. Locate the position of the ship in nautical miles north and east of New York at the end of 4 hr 32 min.

36. If a ferry crosses the Mississippi River at a point where it is $2\frac{1}{4}$ miles wide, if the river is flowing at $7\frac{1}{2}$ fps, and if the ferry averages 12 mph in still water,
    (a) how far downstream does it drift if the heading is perpendicular to the channel?
    (b) how long in minutes does this trip take?

37. A ferry with a still water speed of 12.5 mph crosses a river in 5 min. If the dock on the far, downstream bank is $\frac{1}{2}$ mile below the dock on the near bank and the river current is $2\frac{1}{4}$ mph, what heading was used?

38. An airliner whose course is due west between two cities 720 miles apart has a speed in still air of 360 mph. The heading is calculated to take account of a wind blowing 40 mph from the south. After 20 min on the calculated heading, ground objects appear unfamiliar. The navigator checks and finds an error of 5° counterclockwise in the automatic pilot. Thus, the plane has been traveling south of the desired course. This checking and readjustment took another 10 min. At the end of this time, the weather reports showed the winds aloft at a negligible velocity. Find the heading to complete the trip.

39. The pilot of a fighter plane wants to intercept a bomber that is 285 miles south of him and flying due west at 320 mph.
    (a) What course should the fighter plane take to intercept the bomber in the least time if his speed is 640 mph?
    (b) How long does it take the fighter pilot to intercept the bomber?

40. Assume that the figure on the next page represents the earth as a perfect sphere, with OA and OB radii of 3965 miles. Let PA represent the height of an observer above the surface of the earth. PB is the distance to the horizon. Let $PA = h$, $PB = d$, and in triangle POB, $(r + h)^2 = r^2 + d^2$. Expanding and simplifying gives $2rh + h^2 = d^2$, or $d = \sqrt{2rh + h^2} \approx \sqrt{2rh}$,

since h^2 for a terrestrial man is very small compared to $2rh$. Angle θ is called the *dip* of the horizon.

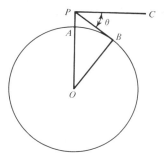

(a) Find the constant c, correct to one decimal place, so that $d \approx \sqrt{ch}$, where d is in miles and h is in feet.
(b) Find the angle of dip for an observer 102.65 ft above sea level.
(c) If the balcony of a lighthouse is 94.75 ft above the water and the focal point of the lens of the light is 7.84 ft above the balcony, how far away in miles can the lighthouse be seen from the bridge of a ship that is 37.75 ft above the waterline?

10.06 / Scalars and vectors

A **vector** is a quantity that has both magnitude and direction. A **scalar** is a quantity that has magnitude only. Some common examples of these two concepts are cited in Table 10.3. Care must be taken to recognize that although most descriptions of vector quantities include both a measure of the magnitude and a measure of the direction involved, in some cases the direction is so well known that it is not listed. For example, a force due to a weight or a mass always acts toward the center of the earth. Thus, given the magnitude or weight, the force is represented by a vertical arrow pointing downward. Similarly, lift on an airfoil or the effect of buoyancy is always upward and a frictional force acts along a tangent to a curved surface at a point of contact. Figure 10.19 illustrates vectors and allied notation.

Table 10.3

Subject Area	Scalar	Vector
Measurement	Height (6 ft 1 in.)	Directed distance (30 miles NE of city)
Motion	Time (3 hr)	Velocity (30 mph north)
Air	Pressure of 1 atmosphere (14.7 psi)	Wind force (30 lb/sq ft from SW)
Electricity	D.C. resistance (12 Ω)	A.C. impedance (18 Ω, phase angle $-53.3°$)

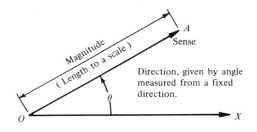

(a) Geometric Notation for a General Vector $\mathbf{A} = \overrightarrow{OA}$

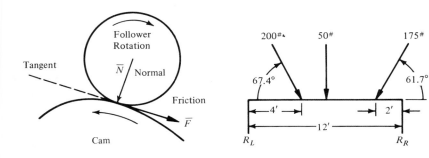

(b) Cam with Friction

(c) A 50-lb Beam Carrying Two Given Loads

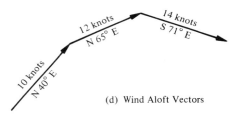

(d) Wind Aloft Vectors

Figure 10.19
Vector notations

Vectors are classified as **fixed, sliding,** or **free.** Examples of these three types of vectors are

1. Free vector: a car moving 30 mph north.
2. Sliding vector: a car moving 30 mph north along 16th Street.
3. Fixed vector: a car moving 30 mph north along 16th Street at the intersection of 16th and K Streets.

A fixed vector has a known point of application, such as a force acting upon a particle. A sliding vector has a known line of action, for example an automobile either pushed on its rear bumper or towed by a force of the same magnitude and direction on its front bumper, since the force moving the car acts upon the car without regard to the point of application. A large plate acted upon by a wind pressure of 20 psf can be considered to have a free vector acting perpendicularly to the plate on any area of the plate selected. Another common example of a free vector is a twist applied by a plumber to a long length of pipe by a pipe wrench; this twist is acting anywhere along the entire length of the pipe.

Vectors can be one-dimensional acting on a line, two-dimensional acting in a plane, three-dimensional acting in space, or n-dimensional.

Scalar quantities are written or printed in the same way as any other numerical value. Vectors are usually indicated in textbooks by boldface type. However, since this cannot be done for handwritten work, a common convention is to place a line over the letter designation of the vector. Some textbooks use an arrow, but this is time consuming and is not necessary. As an example, vector A would appear in printed form as **A** and in hand-written work as $\overline{A}$ or $\vec{A}$. There is no mathematical significance as to capital letters versus lowercase letters, but often in problems involving force, a force is designated by a capital letter and a distance locating that force by a lowercase letter.

The numerical values for the magnitude and direction of a vector may be given in either of the two forms for polar coordinates, (r, θ) or $r \underline{/\theta}$, or by a convention used in the study of forces, where the angle is always given without sign, measured from the X axis, and its quadrant indicated by a sketched symbol. The sketched angle is not shown to scale but is usually drawn about 45°. Figure 10.20 shows this system of notation in the four quadrants. The advantage of this method is that the angle and the reference angle are always alike and no signs are required.

Figure 10.20
Vector notation used for solutions to problems

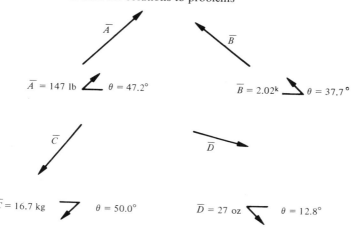

10.07 / Vector algebra

The negative of a vector **A** is a vector −**A** having the same magnitude as **A** but a direction opposite to that of **A**. The negative of a vector is illustrated in Figure 10.21(a).

Figure 10.21
Vector algebra

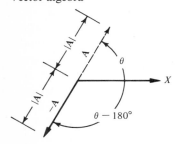

(a) Negative of a Vector

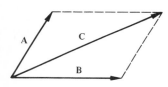

Parallelogram   Head to Tail

(b) Addition of Two Vectors   **C** = **A** + **B**

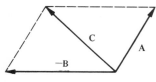
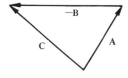

Parallelogram   Head to Tail

(c) Subtraction of Two Vectors   **C** = **A** − **B** = **A** + (−**B**)

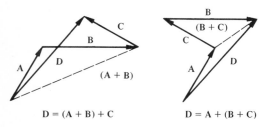

D = (**A** + **B**) + **C**   **D** = **A** + (**B** + **C**)

(d) Associative Quality of Vector Addition

If two vectors are acting upon a given particle or a point, a graphical representation would be two vectors, each drawn to a proper scale for its magnitude and at the given angle for its direction. Their combined effect is a vector, indicated as the sum of the two vectors. This vector sum may be obtained by a geometric process. The diagonal of the parallelogram formed by using the two given vectors as the sides yields this sum, called the **resultant vector**. In Figure 10.21(b), vector **C** is the sum of vectors **A** and **B**, **C** = **A** + **B**. The full parallelogram need not be drawn. Vector **B** can be drawn with its tail at the head of vector **A** and the same value will be obtained for vector **C**, because this is merely the upper half of the same parallelogram. The same result would occur if vector **A** was drawn from the head of vector **B**. This indicates that vector addition is commutative; that is, **A** + **B** = **B** + **A**.

The use of the parallelogram is preferred only when the work is being done by drafting methods, where it is slightly quicker to draw the parallel lines than to repeat the second vector length to scale. The head-to-tail method is preferred in most cases, because it can be used for the sum of three or more vectors without the need to find the resultant of each successive pair. The resultant vector is always that vector whose tail is the tail of the first vector and whose head is the head of the last vector. This is shown in Figure 10.21(d).

For vector subtraction, the subtrahend is drawn with the direction opposite to that of the given vector. As shown in Figure 10.21(c), **A** − **B** = **A** + (−**B**). In the parallelogram method, the difference is the vector from the head of the subtrahend instead of the common point. The head-to-tail method is clearer since the subtrahend is replaced by its negative and the addition is readily observed.

Addition of vectors is also associative; that is, (**A** + **B**) + **C** gives the same resultant vector as **A** + (**B** + **C**). [See Figure 10.21(d).] Since addition is both associative and commutative, the terms of a sum can be rearranged in any convenient way; for example, (**A** + **B**) + **C** = **C** + (**A** + **B**).

In this book vector multiplication will be limited to the multiplication of a vector by a scalar. If k is a scalar, k**A** is defined as a vector whose direction is the same as that for **A** but whose magnitude is k times as large. If **n** is used to represent any *unit vector* (a vector whose magnitude is 1), a given vector **A** may be written as | **A** | **n**, where | **A** | is used to represent the scalar magnitude of **A**. When no ambiguity will result, this statement is often written **A** = A**n**.

Problem Set 10.5

1–20

*Given the vectors **A** through **H** shown, find graphically the resultant vector of the indicated algebraic operations. Use paper ruled five squares to the inch, a decimally graduated scale, and a protractor. Each square is 1 unit.*

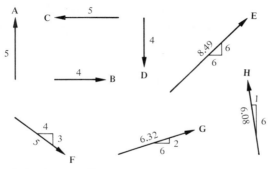

For ease in drawing, true offset distances are shown for each inclined vector.

1. **A + B**	11. **4(A − B)**
2. **C + D**	12. **3(B − C − D)**
3. **A − E**	13. **(B + G) − (D − C)**
4. **B − F**	14. **(E + F) − (B + G)**
5. **2A + 3F**	15. **A + C − B − E**
6. **3C − 2G**	16. **B + E − G + A**
7. **A + E + F**	17. **(E − F) + (H − G)**
8. **B + G + H**	18. **(F − G) + (C − F − G)**
9. **A − B + G**	19. **(A − C + E − F + G)**
10. **C − B + F**	20. **(B + D − E − H + F + G)**

21. Given **J** as the wind vector for a wind of 25 mph blowing from the northeast, write 3**J** in polar coordinates.

22. A ship is on a heading of N15°12′W and traveling at 23.2 knots. Express its velocity in vector notation, using the angle symbol form of polar coordinates. Give its magnitude in miles per hour. Use Table 10 of the Appendix.

10.08 / Graphical resolution of vectors

In the preceding section the sum of two vectors was defined as a single vector called the resultant vector. If any single given vector is considered the resultant of two other vectors, the finding of the magnitude and direction of these two vectors is called **resolving the given vector into components**.

For most practical problems vectors are resolved into components parallel to the X and Y axes. In problems involving an inclined plane, it is often more useful to resolve a given force vector into components parallel and perpendicular to the given plane. Components do not have to be mutually perpendicular and occasional problems may arise where angles other than right angles are used between components. Figure 10.22 illustrates the graphical construction for finding the vector components of a given vector for the first two cases stated. An example is also given showing the resolution of two vectors into components that are not perpendicular but instead pass through a common point O. For rectangular components, the given vector is used as the hypotenuse of a right triangle and the legs of this right triangle determine the component vectors.

Figure 10.22
Types of vector components

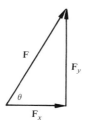

(a) Rectangular Components Parallel to Axes

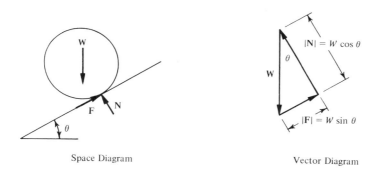

Space Diagram

Vector Diagram

(b) Rectangular Components, One Parallel to Plane

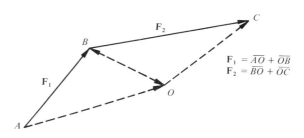

(c) Nonrectangular Components (as used in proof of a Maxwell diagram in mechanics)

10.08 / Graphical resolution of vectors □ **491**

10.09 / Algebraic resolution of vectors

Although the graphical procedure is rapid, in most cases drafting equipment is not at hand and greater precision is usually desired. The value of the components that are mutually perpendicular can be found readily by solving the right triangle that is formed. For any vector **F** whose magnitude and direction are known, the magnitudes of the x and y components are

$$|\mathbf{F}_x| = |\mathbf{F}| \cos \theta \qquad \text{and} \qquad |\mathbf{F}_y| = |\mathbf{F}| \sin \theta$$

If, at the origin of a two-dimensional coordinate system, two unit vectors are drawn, one parallel to the X axis and one parallel to the Y axis, the notation for these has been standardized. The unit vector along the X axis is designated **i** and the unit vector along the Y axis is designated **j**. Using the concepts from Section 10.07, the vector components can now be written as follows:

$$\mathbf{F}_x = F_x \mathbf{i} = |\mathbf{F}| \cos \theta \, \mathbf{i}$$

$$\mathbf{F}_y = F_y \mathbf{j} = |\mathbf{F}| \sin \theta \, \mathbf{j}$$

where F_x is the magnitude of $\mathbf{F}_x$ and F_y is the magnitude of $\mathbf{F}_y$. However, it is customary to write the scalar components (F_x and F_y) unless vector components are specified.

Figure 10.23 shows a two-dimensional vector that does not originate at the origin. Polar coordinates do not properly describe it, since the r coordinate of the ordered pair (r,θ) must refer to a known origin. The vector **F** shown in the figure can be defined uniquely in any one of the following four ways.

Figure 10.23
Vector components

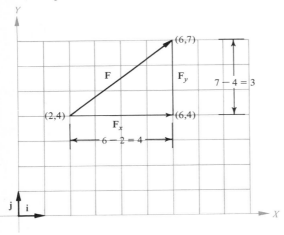

(1) By stating its terminal points, as the vector from (2,4) to (6,7).

(2) By giving its magnitude, direction, and one terminal point, as the vector $5\underline{/36.9°}$ terminating at (6,7).

(3) By giving the magnitudes of its components and one terminal point, as the vector with $F_x = 4$, $F_y = 3$, and terminating at (6,7).

(4) By using unit vector notation and stating one terminal point, as $\mathbf{F} = 4\mathbf{i} + 3\mathbf{j}$, terminating at (6,7).

Note that a vector can be found if its components are known. This is illustrated in Example 10.25. All the vectors described above are fixed vectors. For a sliding vector, a terminal point is not needed and any point on its line of action adequately describes it. For free vectors, no point or line is needed since the vector is not located uniquely.

Example 10.22
Given a radius vector $\mathbf{F} = 7\underline{/36°}$, find its x and y components.

SOLUTION

$$F_x = 7 \cos 36° = 7(0.809) = +5.66$$
$$F_y = 7 \sin 36° = 7(0.588) = +4.12$$

Example 10.23
Given a radius vector $\mathbf{Q}$ with a terminal point at $Q:(7,3)$, find its notation in unit vector form.

SOLUTION

By inspection, $\mathbf{Q} = 7\mathbf{i} + 3\mathbf{j}$. (If this is not obvious, a sketch should be made.)

Example 10.24
Given a vector $\mathbf{R}$ originating at $(-2,-4)$ and terminating at $(5, 2)$. Find its x and y components.

SOLUTION

$$R_x = \text{difference in } x \text{ components} = x_2 - x_1 = 5 - (-2) = 7$$
$$R_y = \text{difference in } y \text{ components} = y_2 - y_1 = 2 - (-4) = 6$$

Example 10.25
Given vector $\mathbf{S} = 5\mathbf{i} - 6\mathbf{j}$, find its magnitude and direction.

SOLUTION

$$\text{magnitude, } S = \sqrt{F_x^2 + F_y^2} = \sqrt{5^2 + 6^2} = \sqrt{61} = 7.81$$

$$\text{direction, } \theta = \tan^{-1}\frac{F_y}{F_x} = \tan^{-1}\frac{-6}{5} = \tan^{-1}(-1.2)$$

The reference angle $= 50.2°$ and the sketch in the first form of the final answer shows the quadrant:

$$\mathbf{S} = 7.81\angle\;\theta = 50.2° \quad \text{or} \quad (7.81, 309.8°)$$

Probably the most important use of vector components is in finding the resultant vector of two or more vectors. The algebraic sum of the x components is the x component of the resultant vector, and the algebraic sum of the y components is the y component of the resultant vector. In symbols,

$$R_x = F_{1_x} + F_{2_x} + F_{3_x} + \cdots + F_{n_x}$$

$$R_y = F_{1_y} + F_{2_y} + F_{3_y} + \cdots + F_{n_y}$$

This use of vector components will be shown in the next section, which is devoted to applications of vectors.

Problem Set 10.6

1–8
Given the initial and terminal coordinates, express each of the following vectors (a) using the unit vectors $\mathbf{i}$ and $\mathbf{j}$ and (b) using polar coordinates.

1. $P : (3, 4)$ to $Q : (7, 8)$
2. $R : (2, 2)$ to $S : (7, 16)$
3. $T : (-2, 5)$ to $U : (3, -4)$
4. $V : (-3, 4)$ to $W : (4, -3)$

5. $L : (3, 5)$ to $M : (-4, -6)$
6. $G : (-2, 2)$ to $H : (-6, -5)$
7. $C : (5, -8)$ to $D : (-5, 16)$
8. $E : (-1, -2)$ to $F : (-7, 6)$

9–12
Find the magnitude and direction of the given vector, using the notation shown in Figure 10.20.

9. $\mathbf{A} = 4\mathbf{i} + 5\mathbf{j}$
10. $\mathbf{B} = 5\mathbf{i} - 4\mathbf{j}$

11. $\mathbf{C} = -6\mathbf{i} + 3\mathbf{j}$
12. $\mathbf{D} = -5\mathbf{i} - 7\mathbf{j}$

13–20
Find the x and y components for each of the following vectors.

13. $\mathbf{E} = 72/30°$
14. $\mathbf{F} = 32/105°$
15. $\mathbf{G} = 8/200°$
16. $\mathbf{H} = 12/350°$

17. $\mathbf{W} = 1500/315°$
18. $\mathbf{V} = 5600/240°$
19. $\mathbf{R} = 0.45/165°$
20. $\mathbf{T} = 0.225/50°$

10.10 / Applications of vectors

The examples and problems of this section illustrate some of the many fields in which two-dimensional vectors are used.

Example 10.26
Figure 10.24 shows a horizontal wooden strut AC supported by a cable, located by the given dimensions, and carrying a vertical load of 800 lb. Find the magnitude and direction of the force in the cable AB acting at A and find the magnitude of the force in the strut AC.

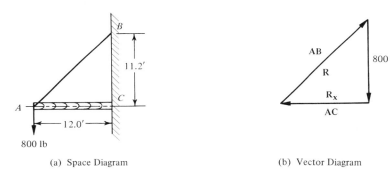

(a) Space Diagram   (b) Vector Diagram

Figure 10.24
Two-dimensional forces

SOLUTION
The downward force of 800 lb is completely known. The horizontal force acting at A along AC is known to be directed to the left in order to balance the force exerted by the wall at C, this force being directed to the right.

The direction of the force at A acting along the cable AB is now known since angle A is known:

$$A = \text{Tan}^{-1}\frac{11.2}{12.0} = \text{Tan}^{-1}\, 0.9333 = 43°1', \text{ using Table 3}$$

The value of the sine is recorded at this time for later use:

$$\sin A = 0.682$$

Letting $\mathbf{R}$ = the force in the cable AB acting at A,

$$R_y = 800$$

$$R_x = \frac{800}{\tan A} = \frac{800}{0.933} = 857\,\text{lb, magnitude of force in strut } AC$$

$$R = \frac{800}{\sin A} = \frac{800}{0.682} = 1173\,\text{lb, magnitude of force in cable } AB$$

As a check calculation,

$$R_x^2 + R_y^2 = (857)^2 + (800)^2 = 734{,}449 + 640{,}000 = 1{,}374{,}449$$

$$R^2 = (1173)^2 = 1{,}375{,}929, \text{ checking to three significant figures}$$

Example 10.27
Two cables support a 1000-lb load, as shown in Figure 10.25. Find the magnitude of the force in each cable.

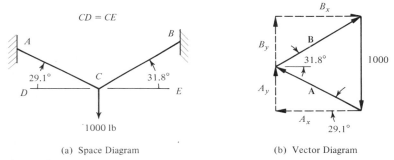

(a) Space Diagram

(b) Vector Diagram

Figure 10.25
Addition of vectors

SOLUTION
Since the force due to the 1000-lb load acts downward and since the forces in the cables acting at point C are directed toward the supporting walls, the directions of the forces are known. Letting

$$\mathbf{A} = \text{the force acting along } CA$$

$$\mathbf{B} = \text{the force acting along } CB$$

then

$$A_x = A \cos 29.1° = 0.874A$$

$$B_x = B \cos 31.8° = 0.845B$$

Using the vector diagram, $A_x = B_x$ and

$$0.874A = 0.845B \qquad \text{and thus} \qquad B = \frac{0.874A}{0.845} = 1.034A$$

$$A_y = A \sin 29.1° = 0.486A$$

$$B_y = B \sin 31.8° = 0.512B$$

Using the vector diagram, $A_y + B_y = 1000$:

$$0.486A + 0.512B = 1000$$

Substituting the value for B found from the x components,

$$0.486A + 0.512 (1.034A) = 1000$$

$$0.486A + 0.529A = 1000$$

$$1.015A = 1000 \quad \text{and} \quad A = \frac{1000}{1.015} = 985 \text{ lb}$$

$$B = 1.034 (985) = 1018 \text{ lb}$$

This problem can be checked either by an accurately drawn sketch or by finding the numerical values of the components. However, if an error has been made in looking up the trigonometric functions, an error may be found if the error lies in just one function, but a false check may result if the wrong angle is used to enter the tables.

Example 10.28
Given the measured wind velocities and their directions, as shown in Figure 10.26, which are based upon radiosonde observations every 2000 ft, find the resultant wind-velocity vector. (This is a rapid method used to determine fallout danger zones.)

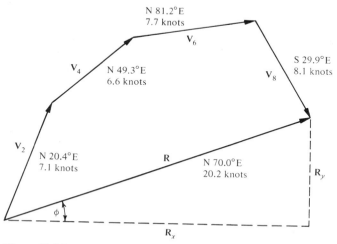

Figure 10.26
Combining wind vectors

SOLUTION

A tabular arrangement is recommended. Bearing angles are measured from the north–south meridian line; therefore $V_x = V \sin \theta$ and $V_y = V \cos \theta$:

Elevation, ft	Velocity, knots	Direction	$\sin \theta$	V_x	$\cos \theta$	V_y
2000	8.1	N 20.4°E	0.349	+2.83	0.937	+7.59
4000	6.6	N 49.3°E	0.758	+5.00	0.758	+4.30
6000	7.7	N 81.2°E	0.988	+7.61	0.153	+1.18
8000	7.1	S 29.9°E	0.498	+3.54	0.867	−6.16
				$R_x = +18.98$		$R_y = +6.91$

$$\tan \phi = \frac{6.91}{18.98} = 0.364 \quad \text{and} \quad \phi = 20.0°$$

$$R = \sqrt{(18.98)^2 + (6.91)^2} = \sqrt{409} = 20.2 \text{ knots}$$

Checking, $$R = \frac{6.91}{\sin 20.0°} = \frac{6.91}{0.342} = 20.2 \text{ knots}$$

Problem Set 10.7

1. A ship heading N5°W has a forward velocity of 9 fps and meets a strong littoral (along the shore) current of 5 fps flowing N15°E. What is the heading that the ship will actually follow and what will be the speed along this course?

2. Find the speed and the direction of the course of an airplane flying at 245 knots with a heading of N38°E if it meets a 35-knot wind blowing from the direction S27°E.

3. If the lower left vertex of a horizontal side of a regular hexagon with 3-in. sides has coordinates $A : (2, 2)$, find the coordinates of all remaining vertices. Identify them in alphabetical order, moving clockwise.

4. Find the resultant force vector due to the following forces all acting at the same point: (8 kg, 22°), (12 kg, 79°), (15 kg, 125°).

5. Find the resultant displacement vector for the following displacements: 25 miles N 20°E, 46 miles S 15°E, 32 miles S 44°W.

6. Two steel bars are supporting a weight of 1200 lb as shown on the next page. Find the forces acting along RQ and RP, by stating their magnitudes and directions.

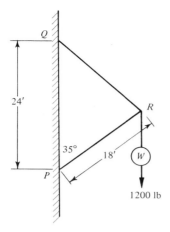

7. Draw the force triangles at points R and S of the King Post truss shown in the figure and find the unknown vectors at these points. The vector force in SP is a tension equal to the load at P. An arrow indicates the direction of each vector force at the point indicated.

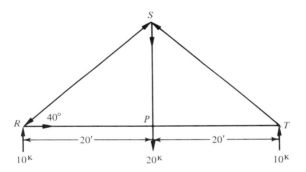

8. An inclined ramp makes an angle of 20° with the horizontal. A cubical weight of 144 lb is resting upon it. Find the force tending to slide the weight down the plank (the force parallel to the plank) and the force normal to the plank.

9. At the end of each minute an object changes its course 5° in a clockwise direction, maintaining a constant velocity. If it is originally at the origin of coordinates, and its first movement is along the Y axis in a positive direction at a velocity of 5 units per minute, give its location as a radius vector at the end of the fifth minute. Show a graphical check of your computed solution.

10. A 1200-lb sign 8 ft wide and 6 ft high is hung by three chains. One is fastened to the middle of the upper edge and is vertical. The other two chains are fastened to the upper corners and make an angle of 25°

with the vertical. A turnbuckle is introduced into the middle chain and adjusted so that the chain will carry exactly 215 lb, its safe working load. Find the load in the individual chains at each corner. These are stronger chains and do not have the same load limitation as the middle chain.

10.11 / Chapter Review

1. A unique right triangle is determined by two given sides or by one given acute angle and one given side.
2. Missing parts of a right triangle can be found using the basic definitions of the trigonometric functions. When only one side is given originally, the Pythagorean theorem provides a good check of a solution. In all cases a reasonably large scaled sketch provides a good check.
3. When the data warrant it, more than three significant figures can be obtained using a desk calculator or logarithms. Special procedures are needed for logarithms of angles less than 3°.
4. Scalar quantities have magnitude only. Vector quantities have both magnitude and direction.
5. Vector addition is commutative and associative. Vector subtraction is defined as the addition of the negative of the subtrahend vector. Vectors are readily combined graphically by drawing them to scale in a head-to-tail sequence. A negative vector has the same magnitude but the opposite direction of its corresponding positive vector.
6. Any vector can be resolved into components that are perpendicular to each other. In most problems, components parallel to the coordinate axes are used, and treated as scalars.
7. The resultant vector of a combination of vectors originates with the tail of the first vector and terminates at the head of the last vector of the given system.
8. After resolving all vectors of a system into rectangular components, a component of the resultant vector is the algebraic sum of all components having the same direction.
9. All solutions should be checked. A graphical check is quick and can be used for any number of vectors in a system.

Problem Set 10.8 (Chapter Review)

1. An existing highway with 1 : 4 side slopes is to be widened by one lane, requiring 11 ft of additional width on each side. The ground is quite cohesive and can accept a steeper slope up to 1 : 2. The sketch below shows the proposed scheme. Find (a) the slope of the proposed scheme,

giving the answer in the form $1 : x$ to see if it meets the limiting specification. If it does, (b) calculate the volume of earth in cubic yards to be removed for a 100-ft length of road. (Remember to include the other side which is identical.)

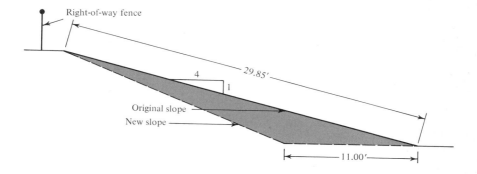

2. Using the vectors shown in the figure, find the resultant vector of $\mathbf{A} + 2\mathbf{D} + \mathbf{C} - \mathbf{E}$. Then find the resultant vector of each of the following and state whether each is identical to or different from $\mathbf{A} + 2\mathbf{D} + \mathbf{C} - \mathbf{E}$.

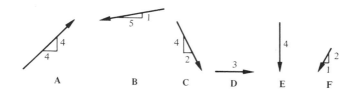

(a) $\frac{1}{2}\mathbf{A} - 2\mathbf{B}$
(b) $5\mathbf{D} - \frac{1}{2}\mathbf{C} - 1\frac{1}{2}\mathbf{E} + 2\mathbf{F}$
(c) $2\mathbf{A} + \mathbf{C} + \mathbf{D}$
(d) $\mathbf{C} + 2\mathbf{D} - 4\mathbf{F}$

3. A plane leaves Atlantic City, NJ bound for Wilmington, DE which lies on a course of N22°30′W. If a crosswind from the southwest is exactly at right angles to this direction and is blowing with an average velocity of 15 mph and if the average speed of the airplane in still air is 335 mph, what heading should the pilot take?

4. The degree of a highway curve is defined as the angle in degrees subtended by a chord of 100 ft. The degree D is therefore a function of the radius R. An approximation for R is $R \approx \dfrac{5730}{D}$

(a) Find the percentage of error in this approximation for a 4° curve. (Work to five significant figures but record your answer to two significant figures.)

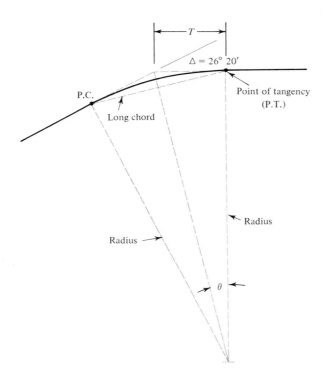

(b) Using the radius calculated, calculate the tangent distance shown as T and calculate the long chord. (Recall the geometric relations for finding angle θ.)

5. Grades on railroads are the rise or fall in feet per 100 ft horizontally, expressed as a percentage. On the Midwestern plains the grade is often very small. Find the grade for a stretch where the track falls 24 ft in 1 mile. At what angle is the roadbed sloping, expressed as a decimal?

6. If an isosceles triangle has sides of 15.76″, 8.48″, and 15.76″, find the three angles of the triangle to the nearest 0.01°.

7. For any right triangle positioned with its hypotenuse horizontal, find the altitude upon the hypotenuse in terms of the hypotenuse and the angles of the triangle.

8. A carpenter is making a redwood planter in the shape of a regular pentagon as shown in the figure. He must lay off angle θ using his carpenter's square, which is graduated in $\frac{1}{16}$-in. increments. Carpenters always use 12 in. as one leg of their triangle. What should he use for the other side, shown as d? He can estimate to the nearest $\frac{1}{32}$ in.

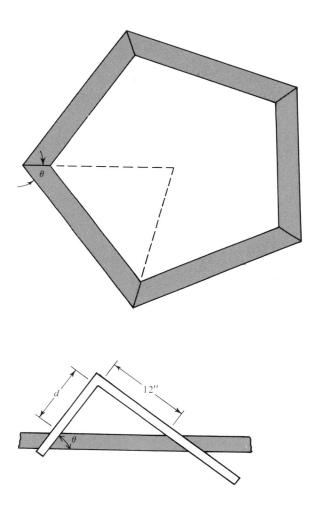

9. A hunter fires a rifle held 10° above the horizontal. The initial velocity of the bullet is 2700 fps and the bullet hits the ground in 29.2 sec, having missed its target. How many miles did it travel, neglecting air resistance and other minor corrections? (The distance is the horizontal component of the velocity times the time of flight.)

10. Particle P will not move if the resultant vector of the forces $\mathbf{F}_1$, $\mathbf{F}_2$, $\mathbf{F}_3$, and $\mathbf{F}_4$ shown in the figure is zero. Find the magnitude and direction of vector $\mathbf{F}_3$ to produce no movement. ($\mathbf{F}_3$ may be in any quadrant.)

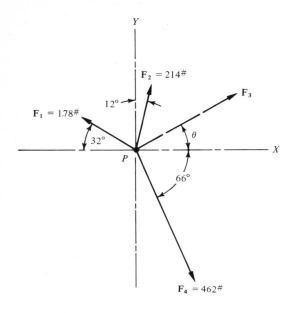

Radicals, exponents, and theory of logarithms

11.01 / Review of previous concepts

Exponents were first met in Chapter 1 as positive, integral numbers used as a mathematical shorthand to indicate repeated multiplication of the base number. Scientific notation showed that powers of 10 in a denominator could be expressed by using a negative exponent. In Chapter 2 numbers written in scientific notation were used in the arithmetic operations of multiplication, division, raising a number to a power, and extracting a root. The matching operations on the exponents of 10 were addition, subtraction, multiplication, and division, respectively. The following results are restatements of these concepts in algebraic symbols.

For any real number x and for any natural numbers n and m,

$$x^1 = x \qquad \text{and} \qquad x^n = x \cdot x \cdots x \ (n \text{ factors})$$

$$\frac{1}{x^n} = x^{-n} \qquad \text{for } x \neq 0$$

$$x^m x^n = x^{m+n}$$

$$\frac{x^m}{x^n} = \begin{cases} x^{m-n} & \text{if } m > n \text{ and } x \neq 0 \\ \dfrac{1}{x^{n-m}} & \text{if } m < n \text{ and } x \neq 0 \end{cases}$$

$$(x^m)^n = x^{mn}$$

$$\sqrt[n]{10^m} = 10^{m/n}$$

These concepts will be reexamined in greater depth in the sections that follow, with the important goal of showing that these basic concepts hold if x, m, and n are real numbers. Note that imaginary numbers are excluded.

11.02 / Radicals

The radicals met in Chapters 1 and 2 were limited to square, cube, fourth, and sixth roots. The symbol $\sqrt[n]{x}$, called a **radical**, is read "the principal nth root of x." The real number x is called the **radicand** and the natural number n is called the **index.**

An nth root of a number x is a number which when used as a factor n times produces the radicand x as the product.

The **principal nth root** of a *positive* real number is the *positive* nth root.

For example, 9 has two square roots, $+3$ and -3, since $(+3)^2 = 9$ and $(-3)^2 = 9$. However, the symbol $\sqrt{9}$ is reserved for the principal square root; in this case, the positive root $+3$. In symbols, $\sqrt{9} = 3$. The other square root is indicated symbolically as $-\sqrt{9}$; that is, $-\sqrt{9} = -3$.

The principal fifth root of 32 is the positive real number which if multiplied by itself 5 times produces the product 32. In symbols,

$$\sqrt[5]{32} = 2 \qquad \text{since } 2^5 = 2 \cdot 2 \cdot 2 \cdot 2 \cdot 2 = 32$$

Note also that $\qquad (\sqrt[5]{32})^5 = (\sqrt[5]{32})(\sqrt[5]{32})(\sqrt[5]{32})(\sqrt[5]{32})(\sqrt[5]{32}) = 32$

and that $\qquad \sqrt[5]{2^5} = 2$

In general, if $x \geq 0$, then $\sqrt[n]{x^n} = x$.
As special cases, if x is any real number,

$$\sqrt{x^2} = |x| \qquad \text{and} \qquad \sqrt[3]{x^3} = x$$

Two radicals are said to be of the **same order** if they have the same index. Two radicals of the same order have a product equal to that obtained by multiplying their radicands. For example,

$$\sqrt{5x}\,\sqrt{2y} = \sqrt{10xy}$$

and $\qquad \sqrt[3]{7a}\,\sqrt[3]{4ab} = \sqrt[3]{28a^2b}$

but $\sqrt{5x}\sqrt[3]{2y}$ cannot be so combined.

In general, if x and y are not negative,

$$\sqrt{x}\,\sqrt{y} = \sqrt{xy} \qquad \text{and} \qquad \sqrt[3]{x}\,\sqrt[3]{y} = \sqrt[3]{xy}$$

A radical whose radicand is a product of integral factors is said to be *simplified* when no prime factor of the radicand has an exponent greater than or equal to the index.

Example 11.1

Simplify: $\sqrt{48y^5}$, where $y \geq 0$.

SOLUTION

(1) Write the radicand as a product of powers of primes:

$\sqrt{3(2^4)y^5}$

(2) Write the radicand as a product of a perfect square and a factor free of squares:

$\sqrt{(2^2y^2)^2 3y}$

(3) Write the radical as product of two radicals:

$\sqrt{(4y^2)^2}\sqrt{3y}$

(4) Use the definition $\sqrt{x^2} = x$ for $x \geq 0$:

$4y^2\sqrt{3y}$

Example 11.2

Simplify: $\sqrt[3]{16y^5}$.

SOLUTION

(1) Factoring:

$\sqrt[3]{2^4y^5}$

(2) Isolating perfect cube:

$\sqrt[3]{(2y)^3 2y^2}$

(3) Writing as a product of radicals:

$\sqrt[3]{(2y)^3}\sqrt[3]{2y^2}$

(4) Using $\sqrt[3]{x^3} = x$:

$2y\sqrt[3]{2y^2}$

Example 11.3

Multiply and simplify: $\sqrt{12}\sqrt[3]{54}\sqrt{18}\sqrt[3]{72}$.

SOLUTION

(1) Multiply radicands of same order:

$\sqrt{12(18)}\sqrt[3]{54(72)}$

(2) Factor:

$\sqrt{2^2(3)(2)(3^2)}\sqrt[3]{2(3^3)(2^3)(3^2)}$

(3) Multiply like powers:

$\sqrt{2^3 3^3}\sqrt[3]{2^4 3^5}$

(4) Simplify:

$6\sqrt{6} \cdot 6\sqrt[3]{18} = 36\sqrt{6}\sqrt[3]{18}$

Two radicals are said to be **like radicals** whenever their radicands are identical *and* their indices are identical. An indicated addition or subtraction of two radicals can be rewritten in a simpler form by applying the distributive law to like radicals.

Example 11.4

Add: $\sqrt{27x} + \sqrt{48x}$, where $x \geq 0$.

SOLUTION

(1) Simplify each radical:

$3\sqrt{3x} + 4\sqrt{3x}$

(2) Use the distributive law:

$(3 + 4)\sqrt{3x} = 7\sqrt{3x}$

Example 11.5

Simplify: $\sqrt[3]{32y} - \sqrt[3]{500y} + \sqrt[3]{108y}$.

SOLUTION

(1) Simplify each radical: $2\sqrt[3]{4y} - 5\sqrt[3]{4y} + 3\sqrt[3]{4y}$

(2) Add coefficients of like radicals: $(2 - 5 + 3)\sqrt[3]{4y} = 0$

Example 11.6

Multiply: $(2 + \sqrt{3})(\sqrt{2} + \sqrt{6})$.

SOLUTION

(1) Using the distributive law:

$$2\sqrt{2} + 2\sqrt{6} + \sqrt{3}\sqrt{2} + \sqrt{3}\sqrt{6}$$
$$= 2\sqrt{2} + 2\sqrt{6} + \sqrt{6} + 3\sqrt{2}$$

(2) Collecting like terms:

$$5\sqrt{2} + 3\sqrt{6}$$

The quotient of two radicals of the same order may be rewritten as one radical by dividing the radicands. In general, for $x \geq 0$ and $y > 0$,

$$\frac{\sqrt{x}}{\sqrt{y}} = \sqrt{\frac{x}{y}} \quad \text{and} \quad \frac{\sqrt[n]{x}}{\sqrt[n]{y}} = \sqrt[n]{\frac{x}{y}}$$

Example 11.7

Simplify: $\dfrac{\sqrt{147y^5}}{\sqrt{108y^3}}$, where $y > 0$.

SOLUTION

(1) Dividing radicands: $\sqrt{\dfrac{147y^5}{108y^3}}$

(2) Simplifying radicand: $\sqrt{\dfrac{49y^2}{36}}$

(3) Using the definition of a radical: $\dfrac{7y}{6}$

A quotient involving radicals is in **simplified form** if no radical appears in a denominator and if no denominator appears in a radicand. The denominator is then said to be **rationalized.** To rationalize a denominator that is an indicated square root, the denominator is multiplied by a number so that the resulting radicand in the denominator is a perfect square. The numerator of the fraction must also be multiplied by this number so that the value of the fraction is not changed. In reality, the fraction itself is multiplied by 1.

Example 11.8

Simplify: $\dfrac{\sqrt{50x^3}}{\sqrt{80x^2}}$, where $x > 0$.

SOLUTION

(1) Combine under one radical: $\qquad\qquad\qquad \sqrt{\dfrac{50x^3}{80x^2}} = \sqrt{\dfrac{5x}{8}}$

(2) Rewrite as quotient of two radicals: $\qquad\qquad \dfrac{\sqrt{5x}}{\sqrt{8}}$

(3) Simplify each radical: $\qquad\qquad\qquad\qquad \dfrac{\sqrt{5x}}{2\sqrt{2}}$

(4) Rationalize denominator
    (multiply by $\sqrt{2}$): $\qquad\qquad\qquad \dfrac{\sqrt{5x}}{2\sqrt{2}}\dfrac{\sqrt{2}}{\sqrt{2}} = \dfrac{\sqrt{10x}}{4}$

Note that $\dfrac{\sqrt{5}}{2\sqrt{2}}$ would be difficult to change to an equivalent decimal, whereas the numerical result $\dfrac{\sqrt{10}}{4}$ is one fourth of the value for $\sqrt{10}$ found in Table 1; that is, $\frac{1}{4}(3.1622) = 0.7906$.

If the denominator has the form $A + \sqrt{B}$, where B is rational and $\sqrt{B}$ is irrational, $A + \sqrt{B}$ is called a **quadratic surd** and $A - \sqrt{B}$ is called its **conjugate** ("married number"). Also, $A + \sqrt{B}$ is the conjugate of $A - \sqrt{B}$.

To simplify a quotient having a quadratic surd in its denominator, both numerator and denominator of the fraction are multiplied by the conjugate surd.

Example 11.9

Simplify: $\dfrac{4 + \sqrt{2}}{4 - \sqrt{2}}$.

SOLUTION

$$\dfrac{4 + \sqrt{2}}{4 - \sqrt{2}} \cdot \dfrac{4 + \sqrt{2}}{4 + \sqrt{2}} = \dfrac{16 + 8\sqrt{2} + 2}{16 - 2}$$

$$= \dfrac{18 + 8\sqrt{2}}{14}$$

$$= \dfrac{2(9 + 4\sqrt{2})}{2(7)}$$

$$= \dfrac{9 + 4\sqrt{2}}{7}$$

Example 11.10

Rationalize the denominator: $\dfrac{1}{\sqrt{x} + \sqrt{75y^3}}$, where x and y are positive.

SOLUTION

(1) Simplify each radical:

$$\frac{1}{\sqrt{x} + 5y\sqrt{3y}}$$

(2) Multiply by conjugate:

$$\frac{1}{\sqrt{x} + 5y\sqrt{3y}} \cdot \frac{\sqrt{x} - 5y\sqrt{3y}}{\sqrt{x} - 5y\sqrt{3y}} = \frac{\sqrt{x} - 5y\sqrt{3y}}{x - 25y^2(3y)}$$

$$= \frac{\sqrt{x} - 5y\sqrt{3y}}{x - 75y^3}$$

Problem Set 11.1

Simplify. This requires that
(a) *The radicand does not have a factor that is a power with exponent greater or equal to the index.*
(b) *The radicand does not contain a fraction.*
(c) *No denominator contains any radical.*
Assume all variables to be positive real numbers.

1. $\sqrt{216}$
2. $\sqrt{1620}$
3. $\sqrt[3]{6750}$
4. $\sqrt[3]{24{,}000}$
5. $\sqrt{6}\sqrt{14}\sqrt{15}$
6. $\sqrt{35}\sqrt{21}\sqrt{45}$
7. $\sqrt{12} + \sqrt{28} - \sqrt{7} - \sqrt{27}$
8. $\sqrt{20} - \sqrt{48} - \sqrt{75} + \sqrt{45}$
9. $\sqrt[3]{250} - \sqrt[3]{192} + \sqrt[3]{16} + \sqrt[3]{81}$
10. $\sqrt[3]{24} + \sqrt[3]{135} + \sqrt[3]{375} - \sqrt[3]{320}$
11. $(2 - \sqrt{5})(\sqrt{20} - 2)$
12. $(\sqrt{3} + \sqrt{12})(\sqrt{12} + \sqrt{18})$

13. $\dfrac{\sqrt{294}}{\sqrt{96}}$

14. $\dfrac{\sqrt{320}}{\sqrt{605}}$

15. $\dfrac{\sqrt{242}}{\sqrt{405}}$

16. $\dfrac{\sqrt{252}}{\sqrt{350}}$

17. $\dfrac{2 + \sqrt{5}}{2 - \sqrt{5}}$

18. $\dfrac{5 - \sqrt{7}}{5 + \sqrt{7}}$

19. $\dfrac{16}{\sqrt{3} + \sqrt{5}}$

20. $\dfrac{2\sqrt{7}}{\sqrt{20} - \sqrt{28}}$

21. $(\sqrt{3} + \sqrt{12})(\sqrt{6} - 2\sqrt{2})$

22. $(\sqrt{5} - \sqrt{10})(\sqrt{20} - \sqrt{90})$

23. $(1 + \sqrt{3})(\sqrt{2} - \sqrt{6})$

24. $(2 - \sqrt{5})(3 - \sqrt{20})$

25. $\left|\sqrt{2} - \sqrt{3}\right|^2$

26. $\left|\sqrt{2} + \sqrt{32}\right|^2$

27. $\dfrac{2 - \sqrt{2}}{2 + \sqrt{2}}$

28. $\dfrac{4\sqrt{5}}{3 - \sqrt{5}}$

29. $\sqrt{32x^2} + \sqrt{98x^2} + \sqrt{72x^2}$

30. $\sqrt{192x^4} + \sqrt{75x^4} + \sqrt{108x^4}$

31. $\sqrt{117x^3} - \sqrt{13x^3} + \sqrt{52x^3}$

32. $\sqrt{68r^5} + \sqrt{153r^5} - \sqrt{272r^5}$

33. $\sqrt{50x^4} - \sqrt{72x^5} - \sqrt{98x^4} + \sqrt{128x^5}$

34. $\sqrt[3]{16x^5} - \sqrt[3]{250x^7} + \sqrt[3]{128x^5} - \sqrt[3]{54x^7}$

35. $(5 - \sqrt{243y^7}) - (6 - \sqrt{363y^7})$

36. $(11 + \sqrt{196s^3}) - (17 - \sqrt{324s^3})$

37. $\sqrt[3]{2197t^5} - 12\frac{1}{2} - 13\frac{1}{4} - \sqrt[3]{9261t^5}$

38. $\sqrt[3]{6859v} - \sqrt[3]{4913v} - 22.631$

39. $\sqrt{18w^2}(\sqrt{8w^2})(\sqrt{32w^2})(\sqrt{648w^2})$

40. $\sqrt{125x^2}(\sqrt{128x^2})(\sqrt{245x^4})(\sqrt{363x^4})$

41. $\sqrt[3]{81y^6}(\sqrt{75y^4})(\sqrt[3]{192y^3})(\sqrt[3]{375y^3})$

42. $\sqrt{441z^3}(\sqrt[3]{3375z^4})(\frac{2}{15}\sqrt[3]{z^7})(\sqrt{400z^5})$

43. $\dfrac{\sqrt{121r^5}}{\sqrt{128r^3}}$

44. $\dfrac{\sqrt{128r^3}}{\sqrt{121r^5}}$

45. $\dfrac{\sqrt{196r^2s^4t^6}}{\sqrt{225r^6s^4t^2}}$

46. $\dfrac{\sqrt[3]{54r^5t^8}}{\sqrt[3]{64r^8s^6t^2}}$

47. $\dfrac{2x - 2\sqrt{3}}{3x - 6\sqrt{3}}$

48. $\dfrac{y - \sqrt{5x}}{y + \sqrt{5x}}$

49. $\dfrac{\sqrt{x}}{\sqrt{x} + \sqrt{y}}$

50. $\dfrac{\sqrt{x} + \sqrt{y}}{\sqrt{x} - \sqrt{y}}$

51 and **52**

Write each answer as a number correct to three decimal places.

51. $\dfrac{1}{\sqrt{3} - \sqrt{2}}$

52. $\dfrac{\sqrt{8}}{\sqrt{12} + \sqrt{10}}$

11.03 / Integral exponents

If $\dfrac{x^n}{x^n}$ is to be equal to $x^{n-n} = x^0$, x^0 must equal 1, since for all $x \neq 0$, $\dfrac{x^n}{x^n} = 1$. (Any number divided by itself is 1.)

By *definition* $x^0 = 1$ for all real numbers x except $x = 0$. For example, $(10)^0 = 1$, $2^0 = 1$, $\pi^0 = 1$, and $(3 + \sqrt{2})^0 = 1$.

If $x^{-n}x^n$ is to be equal to $x^{-n+n} = x^0 = 1$, x^{-n} must equal $1/x^n$ for all real x except $x = 0$.

By *definition* $x^{-n} = \dfrac{1}{x^n}$ for all real numbers x except $x = 0$.

Negative exponents are usually eliminated from final solutions. They will appear in some handbooks to permit printing a formula on a single line of type.

It may be shown that the statements below, called the basic exponent theorems, are valid if x and y are any nonzero real numbers and if a and b are any integers (positive, zero, or negative).

The Basic Exponent Theorems

1. $x^a x^b = x^{a+b}$

2. $\dfrac{x^a}{x^b} = x^{a-b}$

3. $(x^a)^b = x^{ab}$

4. $(xy)^a = x^a y^a$

5. $\left(\dfrac{x}{y}\right)^a = \dfrac{x^a}{y^a}$

Example 11.11

Simplify: $\dfrac{(2^{-3}x^2)^{-3}}{(2^2x^{-3})^2}$.

SOLUTION

(1) Using theorem 4: $\dfrac{(2^{-3})^{-3}(x^2)^{-3}}{(2^2)^2(x^{-3})^2}$

(2) Using theorem 3: $\dfrac{2^9 x^{-6}}{2^4 x^{-6}}$

(3) Using theorem 2: $2^{9-4}x^{-6-(-6)} = 2^5 x^0$

(4) Using the definition of x^0: $2^5 x^0 = 2^5(1) = 2^5 = 32$

Problem Set 11.2

By using the definitions and the basic exponent theorems, rewrite each of the following so that a variable base occurs once with a positive exponent. (Assume that each denominator is not zero.)

1. 5^{-2}

2. 2^{-4}

3. $\left(\frac{5}{3}\right)^{-3}$

4. $\left(\frac{5}{4}\right)^{-3}$

5. $(0.125)^{-1}$

6. $(0.625)^{-2}$

7. $\left(-\frac{1}{2}\right)^{-5}$

8. $\left(-\frac{1}{3}\right)^{-4}$

9. $(\sqrt{2})^{-4}$

10. $\left(-\sqrt{3}\right)^{-2}$

11. $x^{-3}(x^3 x^{-5})$

12. $y^{-1}(y^{-2}y^{-3})$

13. $p^{-5}p^{-2}p^7$

14. $q^{-4}q^{-3}q^{-2}q^9$

15. $\dfrac{3^{-5}r^4}{3^{-3}r^{-2}}$

16. $\dfrac{2^{-3}s^{-6}}{2^{-1}s^{-3}}$

17. $(3^{-2}t^3)^{-2}$

18. $(2^{-2}w^{-4})^{-3}$

19. $\left(\dfrac{5^{-2}z^{-1}}{5^{-1}z^{-2}}\right)^{-2}$

20. $\left(\dfrac{2^3v^{-3}}{5^2u^{-2}}\right)^{-3}$

21. $\left(\dfrac{x^{-2}+y^{-2}}{x^2y^2}\right)^0$

22. $x^{-2}(2x^{-2}+x^2)$

23. $\dfrac{(x-1)^2\ (x-1)^3\ (x-1)^4}{(x-1)^{-2}(x-1)^{-3}(x+2)}$

24. $\dfrac{(x-2)^{-2}(x-3)^2\ (x-4)^{-2}}{(x-4)^{-4}(x-3)^{-2}(x-2)^2}$

25. $\dfrac{2x(2^{-1}-x^{-1})}{2x(x-4x^{-1})}$

26. $(R_1^{-1}+R_2^{-1})^{-1}$

27. $(v_1^{-2}+v_2^{-2})^{-2}$

28. $(x^2y^2)^{-3}(x^{-3}y^{-3})^{-2}$

29. $\sqrt[3]{\dfrac{r^4s^{-2}t^5}{r^{-2}s^{-5}t^2}}$

30. $\sqrt{\dfrac{12x^2y^{-5}z^{-7}}{75x^6y^{-9}z^{-3}}}$

11.04 / Rational exponents

If n is a natural number and if $(x^{1/n})^n$ is to equal $x^{(1/n)n} = x$, then, since $(\sqrt[n]{x})^n = x$ for x nonnegative, it follows that

$$x^{1/n} = \sqrt[n]{x} \qquad \text{for } x \geq 0 \qquad \text{(Definition)}$$

In particular, $x^{1/2} = \sqrt{x}$ and $x^{1/3} = \sqrt[3]{x}$ for $x \geq 0$. As specific examples, $9^{1/2} = \sqrt{9} = 3$ and $8^{1/3} = \sqrt[3]{8} = 2$. Since $(x^{1/n})^m = x^{m/n} = (x^m)^{1/n}$,

$$x^{m/n} = \left|\sqrt[n]{x}\right|^m = \sqrt[n]{x^m} \qquad \text{for } x \geq 0.$$

With these meanings for fractional exponents, it may be shown that the basic exponent theorems are valid if the exponents are any rational numbers.

If x is not negative, the order of operations in finding the value of $x^{m/n}$ does not make a difference. If the arithmetic values for an integer are found by using a table, it is usually better to find the power first and then round off that result to permit finding the root. The seventeenth and later editions of the CRC tables contain tables of fifth roots.

Example 11.12

Find the value of $(12.7)^{4/3}$.

SOLUTION

(This means find the cube root of the fourth power of 12.7.) Using Table 1,

$$(12.7)^2 = 161.3$$

$$(161.3)^2 \approx 26,000$$

$$(26'000)^{1/3} \approx 29.6$$

(The same result, with identical precision, can be obtained on the slide rule.)

Example 11.13

See if $[(-3)^2]^{1/2}$ is equal to $[(-3)^{1/2}]^2$.

SOLUTION

The number on the left involves the square root of the square of a negative number:

$$[(-3)^2]^{1/2} = 9^{1/2} = +3$$

The number on the right involves the square root of a negative number and there is no real number whose square is -3.

$$(-3)^{1/2} = \sqrt{-3} \quad \text{and} \quad \sqrt{-3} \quad \text{is not a real number}$$

However, $(\sqrt{-3})^2 = \sqrt{-3}\sqrt{-3} = -3$. Since $+3 \neq -3$, the two expressions are *not* equal.

It follows from Example 11.13 that the order of the operations of raising to a power and root extraction does make a difference when the base number is negative and an even root is involved.

In general, if x is a *positive* real number and n is a natural number,

$$x^{1/n} = \sqrt[n]{x} \qquad \text{a positive real number}$$

$$(-x)^{1/n} = \sqrt[n]{-x} = -\sqrt[n]{x} \qquad \text{if } n \text{ is odd}$$

$$(-x)^{1/n} = \sqrt[n]{-x} \qquad \text{not a real number if } n \text{ is even}$$

If n is odd, $(-x)^{m/n} = \sqrt[n]{(-x)^m} = \left(\sqrt[n]{-x}\right)^m$.

If n is even, $(-x)^{m/n} = \left(\sqrt[n]{-x}\right)^m \neq \sqrt[n]{(-x)^m}$ in general.

Example 11.14

Express each of the following in radical form and find the real value, if it exists: (a) $8^{2/3}$; (b) $(-27)^{5/3}$; (c) $[(-5)^4]^{1/2}$; (d) $(-4)^{3/2}$.

SOLUTION

(a) $\sqrt[3]{8^2} = \left(\sqrt[3]{8}\right)^2 = 2^2 = 4$.

(b) $\sqrt[3]{(-27)^5} = \left(\sqrt[3]{-27}\right)^5 = (-3)^5 = -243$.

(c) $\sqrt{(-5)^4} = \sqrt{625} = 25$.

(d) $\left(\sqrt{-4}\right)^3$ is not a real number.

When a term contains a fractional exponent in the denominator, it is desirable to operate on the term to produce only integral exponents in the denominator. This is done by multiplying both the numerator and denominator of the term by the same fractional power of the base that will make the sum of the exponents in the denominator an integer. This process is called rationalizing the denominator.

Example 11.15

Rationalize the denominator: $\dfrac{1}{x^{3/4}}$, where $x > 0$.

SOLUTION

$$\frac{1}{x^{3/4}} \cdot \frac{x^{1/4}}{x^{1/4}} = \frac{x^{1/4}}{x^{3/4 + 1/4}} = \frac{x^{1/4}}{x}$$

Example 11.16

Rationalize the denominator: $\dfrac{x + 3}{x^{4/3}}$, where $x \neq 0$.

SOLUTION

$$\frac{x + 3}{x^{4/3}} \cdot \frac{x^{2/3}}{x^{2/3}} = \frac{x^{2/3}(x + 3)}{x^2}$$

In Problem Set 11.1, no exercises were included with cube roots in the denominator. This omission was intentional, for there is an erroneous tendency to treat cube roots and square roots alike. Using fractional exponents, it is readily seen that

$$\frac{1}{\sqrt[3]{x}} = \frac{1}{x^{1/3}} = \frac{1}{x^{1/3}} \cdot \frac{x^{2/3}}{x^{2/3}} = \frac{x^{2/3}}{x} = \frac{\sqrt[3]{x^2}}{x} \qquad \text{if } x \neq 0$$

Example 11.17

Simplify: $\dfrac{\sqrt{2}}{\sqrt[3]{32}}$.

SOLUTION

$$\frac{\sqrt{2}}{\sqrt[3]{32}} = \frac{\sqrt{2}}{\sqrt[3]{2^5}} = \frac{2^{1/2}}{2^{5/3}} \cdot \frac{2^{1/3}}{2^{1/3}}$$

$$= \frac{2^{(3 + 2)/6}}{2^{(5 + 1)/3}} = \frac{2^{5/6}}{2^2} = \frac{\sqrt[6]{32}}{4}$$

Decimal exponents that terminate are handled exactly as fractional ones when being rationalized. The decimal needed to raise the given decimal exponent to the next higher integer is the exponent of the rationalizing multiplier.

Example 11.18

Simplify: $\dfrac{x^{0.702} y^{1.317}}{y^{1.889} z^{0.213}}$, where x, y, and z are positive.

SOLUTION

(1) Combine variables to yield positive exponents:

$$\frac{x^{0.702}}{y^{0.572}z^{0.213}}$$

(2) Rationalize:

$$\frac{x^{0.702}}{y^{0.572}z^{0.213}} \cdot \frac{y^{0.428}z^{0.787}}{y^{0.428}z^{0.787}} = \frac{x^{0.702}y^{0.428}z^{0.787}}{yz}$$

Numerical evaluation of a number raised to a fractional or decimal exponent will be illustrated in Section 11.08.

11.05 / Irrational exponents

There is no simple way to explain 2^{π} or any other power having an irrational exponent by using powers or roots with integral values, as was done for rational exponents. However, the technique developed in Section 1.06 and Figure 1.3 can be applied.

In Chapter 1 it was shown that π can be approximated by 3.14, 3.142, 3.1416, 3.14159, or any desired number of decimal places, and, by choice of a suitable scale, plotted upon a number line. Similarly, any degree of precision can be attained for a power having an irrational exponent by approximations using rational exponents. In Section 11.08 the value of a number raised to the πth power will be calculated.

It may be shown that the basic exponent theorems given for rational exponents can be extended to include irrational exponents. In other words, the basic exponent theorems are valid if the exponent is any real number and the base is any positive real number. The definitions and theorems for exponents are conveniently tabulated in the chapter review, Section 11.21.

Problem Set 11.3

1–14

Find the value of each of the following, if the value is a real number. If the value is not a real number, write "not real."

1. $(16)^{3/4}$ **5.** $[(-2)^4]^{1/2}$ **9.** $(\frac{8}{27})^{-2/3}$ **12.** $(7.92)^{3/4}$

2. $(125)^{4/3}$ **6.** $(-25)^{3/2}$ **10.** $(-\frac{125}{343})^{-5/3}$ **13.** $(8.06)^{-2/3}$

3. $(-27)^{2/3}$ **7.** $(-3)^{5/4}$ **11.** $(35.8)^{4/3}$ **14.** $(-24.1)^{-2/3}$

4. $(-64)^{3/2}$ **8.** $(-32)^{4/5}$

15–40
Simplify. (*See the instructions for Problem Set 11.1.*) *Assume all variables to be positive.*

15–36
Do not evaluate numerical constants after simplification.

15. $\dfrac{1}{\sqrt[3]{25}}$

16. $\dfrac{1}{\sqrt[3]{49}}$

17. $\dfrac{2^{1/3}x^{1/4}}{2^{2/3}x^{3/4}}$

18. $\dfrac{5^{2/3}y^{3/4}}{5^{4/3}y^{5/4}}$

19. $\dfrac{s^{4/3}t^{5/4}}{s^{2/3}t^{3/4}}$

20. $\dfrac{p^{2/3}r^{5/4}}{p^{4/3}r^{7/4}}$

21. $\dfrac{t^{1.23}u^{2.34}}{t^{0.88}u^{0.34}}$

22. $\dfrac{r^{4.23}s^{0.19}}{r^{3.74}s^{-0.20}}$

23. $\left(\dfrac{r^{1.11}s^{0.12}t^{2.16}}{r^{4.18}s^{0.12}t^{3.78}}\right)^{0}$

24. $\left(\dfrac{x^{2.12}y^{2.84}z^{2.67}}{x^{3.24}(y^{0.717}-z^{3.5})}\right)^{0}$

25. $\left(\dfrac{p^{2}r^{3}s^{4}}{p^{1.8}r^{3.2}s^{2.8}}\right)^{-1}$

26. $\left(\dfrac{x^{3.78}y^{0.414}z^{2.02}}{x^{5.68}y^{0.237}z^{1.72}}\right)^{-2}$

27. $\sqrt{\dfrac{s^{0.78}t^{2.52}}{s^{1.54}t^{3.46}}}$

28. $\sqrt[3]{\dfrac{u^{4.16}v^{0.240}}{u^{1.01}v^{0.573}}}$

29. $\dfrac{1}{x^{1/2}y^{7/8}}$

30. $\dfrac{1}{x^{2/3}y^{2/9}}$

31. $(3^{\sqrt{2}})^{-\sqrt{8}}$

32. $(5^{-\sqrt[3]{2}})^{\sqrt[3]{4}}$

33. $r^{\pi}(r^{-2}+r^{-\pi})$

34. $s^{\sqrt{2}}\left(s^{\sqrt{2}}+s^{-\sqrt{2}}\right)$

35. $\left(5^{\sqrt{2}}\cdot t^{-\sqrt{2}}\right)^{2\sqrt{2}}$

36. $\left(5^{\sqrt{3}}\cdot t^{-\sqrt{3}}\right)^{2\sqrt{3}}$

37–40
Express the exponent of the answer as a decimal correct to three decimal places.

37. $\dfrac{u^{\pi}}{u^{2/3}}$

38. $\dfrac{v^{\sqrt{2}}}{v^{3/5}}$

39. $\dfrac{w^{\sqrt{2}}}{w^{1.220}}$

40. $\dfrac{w^{(\pi-1)}}{w^{0.880}}$

11.06 / Definition of a logarithm

A logarithm is an exponent. A positive real number b, different from 1, is selected as the base and the exponent y that yields a positive number x is called the logarithm of x to the base b.

Definition

For all positive real numbers x and for all positive real numbers b different from 1,

$$\log_b x = y \qquad \textit{if and only if } x = b^y$$

Example 11.19

Express each of the following as a logarithmic statement. (a) $2^2 = 4$; (b) $4^1 = 4$; (c) $16^{0.5} = 4$; (d) $10^{-3} = 0.001$.

SOLUTION

Using the definition,
(a) $\log_2 4 = 2$ since $2^2 = 4$
(b) $\log_4 4 = 1$ since $4^1 = 4$
(c) $\log_{16} 4 = 0.5$ since $(16)^{0.5} = 4$
(d) $\log_{10} 0.001 = -3$ since $(10)^{-3} = 0.001$

It should be noted that the logarithm of a number equal to the base is 1; $\log_b b = 1$ since $b^1 = b$. Also, the logarithm of 1 to any base b is 0; $\log_b 1 = 0$ since $b^0 = 1$. If $b > 1$, any number greater than 1 but smaller than the base has a decimal value between 0 and 1 for its logarithm, and a positive number smaller than 1 has a negative logarithm. Negative numbers and 0 do not have logarithms.

Example 11.20

Find the logarithm to the base 2 and to the base 10 of each of the following numbers: 32, 8, 2, 1, 0.5.

SOLUTION

From Table 7,

$$\log_{10} 32 = \quad 1.50515 \text{ and } \log_2 32 = 5 \quad \text{since } 2^5 = 32$$

$$\log_{10} 8 = \quad 0.90309 \text{ and } \log_2 8 = 3 \quad \text{since } 2^3 = 8$$

$$\log_{10} 2 = \quad 0.30103 \text{ and } \log_2 2 = 1 \quad \text{since } 2^1 = 2$$

$$\log_{10} 1 = \quad 0.00000 \text{ and } \log_2 1 = 0 \quad \text{since } 2^0 = 1$$

$$\log_{10} 0.5 = -0.30103 \text{ and } \log_2 0.5 = -1 \text{ since } 2^{-1} = \tfrac{1}{2} = 0.5$$

The definition preceding Example 11.19 permits the following statements:

$$\log_b b^x = x \qquad (\text{since } \log_b b^y = \log_b x = y \text{ and replacing } y \text{ by } x)$$

$$b^{\log_b x} = x \qquad (\text{since } b^{\log_b x} = b^y = x)$$

11.07 / Systems of logarithms

Although there can be an infinite number of logarithmic systems, since the base b can be any positive real number different from 1, two systems meet the practical requirements for computations and advanced mathematical topics.

As seen in the many calculations performed in Chapter 8, the system using the base 10, called the common or Briggs system, is extremely convenient since the number notation system is also based upon exponents of 10. Characteristics of logarithms were obtained by inspection and only the mantissa required a table.

In the study of mathematical series, in the calculus, and in many laws of physics, it is found that a logarithm is needed to the base e, an irrational number approximately 2.71828.... This system is called the **natural logarithm,** or **Naperian logarithm, system,** after John Napier, one of the founders of the theory of logarithms. Although this book does not contain a table of natural logarithms, a simple method for computing them will be shown in Section 11.09. Many problems appearing in Chapter 8 were originally stated in the source material in terms of natural logarithms but converted to common logarithms for ease of use. To simplify written work, natural logarithms are written as ln x, common logarithms are written as log x, and logarithms to any other base are written as $\log_b x$.

Problem Set 11.4

1–10
Using the definition and the notation described, write each of the following statements in logarithmic form.

1. $10^3 = 1000$	**5.** $2^3 = 8$	**9.** $7^0 = 1$
2. $10^5 = 100{,}000$	**6.** $3^4 = 81$	**10.** $\pi^0 = 1$
3. $10^{-1} = \frac{1}{10}$	**7.** $4^{1/2} = 2$	
4. $10^{-2} = 0.01$	**8.** $(32)^{1/5} = 2$	

11–20

Using the definition, write each of the following statements in exponential form.

11. $\log 0.001 = -3$ **15.** $\log_{49} 7 = \frac{1}{2}$ **19.** $\ln 54.6 = 4$

12. $\log 100 = 2$ **16.** $\log_{27} 3 = \frac{1}{3}$ **20.** $\ln 0.687 = -\frac{3}{8}$

13. $\log 10{,}000 = 4$ **17.** $\log_{32} 4 = \frac{2}{5}$

14. $\log 0.000\,000\,1 = -7$ **18.** $\log_{81} \frac{1}{27} = -\frac{3}{4}$

21–30

Replace the given logarithm with a number equivalent.

21. $\log 100{,}000{,}000$ **25.** $\ln 1$ **29.** $2.62^{\log_{2.62} 0.147}$

22. $\log 1{,}000{,}000{,}000$ **26.** $\ln 2.718\,28$ **30.** $\log_{9.684} 9.684^{7.153}$

23. $\log 0.0001$ **27.** $\log_4 \frac{1}{64}$

24. $\log 0.000\,01$ **28.** $\log_5 125$

11.08 / Theory of logarithmic and slide-rule computations

In Chapters 2 and 8, the operations of arithmetic were performed by a simpler method, retabulated below as Table 11.1.

In Chapter 2 it was stated that the scales of the slide rule were logarithmically graduated. Although not explained there, this meant that the common logarithms studied in Chapter 8 were used to construct a **functional scale.** Any functional scale is one where the graduations are marked in values of the variable x and the actual location of the graduation mark is found by computing the functional value $f(x)$. Thus, the line marked 2 on a 10-in. slide rule was measured as $10 \log 2$ or 3.0103 in. from the left index. As a result, the slide rule mechanically performs the calculations by the same method as that of logarithms.

The validity of Table 11.1 can be seen by examining the statements in terms of logarithms. For multiplication, the logarithm of the product mn

Table 11.1
Computational methods

Arithmetic	Exponents in scientific-notation Logarithms
Multiplication	Addition
Division	Subtraction
Raising to a power	Multiplication
Extracting the nth root	Division

can be written as

$$\log mn = \log(10^{\log m}\, 10^{\log n}) = \log(10^{\log m + \log n}) = \log m + \log n$$

Since division is multiplication by the reciprocal of the divisor,

$$\log \frac{m}{n} = \log m\left(\frac{1}{n}\right) = \log mn^{-1} = \log m - \log n$$

Since powers and roots can be indicated by fractional exponents,

$$\log x^{m/n} = \log(10^{\log x})^{m/n} = \log(10^{(m/n)\log x}) = \frac{m}{n}\log x$$

All the above concepts were used in Chapter 8. The above discussion shows that the methods of computation used in that chapter are in agreement with the theories developed in this chapter.

If a nonterminating decimal appears as an exponent, two possibilities exist. If it is a repeating decimal, it may be a relatively simple fraction that can be used as the multiplier of a logarithm of the given base to find the numerical value desired. If the exponent is nonrepeating and thus irrational, a decision is made as to the precision warranted. Generally no more significant figures should be used for the multiplier than the places in the table of logarithms to be used. Both types of problems are illustrated below.

Example 11.21
Find the numerical value of $2.745^{0.\overline{142857}}$. (The bar over the digits 142857 means that this set of digits repeats.)

SOLUTION
(1) Let $n = 0.\overline{142857}$.
(2) Multiply n by the power of 10 required to move the decimal point to the right of the last digit of the set of repeating digits.
(3) Subtract n:

$$
\begin{aligned}
1{,}000{,}000n &= 142{,}857.\overline{142857} \\
n &= \phantom{142{,}857.}0.\overline{142857} \\
\hline
999{,}999n &= 142{,}857
\end{aligned}
$$

(4) Solve for n by division. Either divide out common factors or use a desk calculator. For the first method,

$$\frac{142{,}857}{999{,}999} = \frac{15{,}873}{111{,}111} = \frac{1443}{10{,}101} = \frac{481}{3367}$$

At this stage, if no division can be seen readily, set the inverted fraction on a slide rule as $\dfrac{3367}{481}$ and read 7. Check by finding that $7(481) = 3367$. Therefore, $n = \frac{1}{7}$. If a desk calculator is available, immediately divide $\dfrac{999{,}999}{142{,}857}$ and obtain 7.

(5) Using five-place logarithms,

$$\log 2.745^{0.\overline{142857}} = \log 2.745^{1/7} = \tfrac{1}{7} \log 2.745$$

$$\log 2.745 = 0.43854$$

$$\tfrac{1}{7} \log 2.745 = 0.06265$$

$$\text{antilog} = 1.1552$$

Example 11.22
Find the numerical value of $(0.078\,62)^{\pi}$.

SOLUTION
Using logarithms only, $\log(0.078\,62)^{\pi} = \pi \log 0.078\,62$:

$$
\begin{array}{rr}
\pi \log 0.078\,62 = \pi(8.89553 - 10) = \pi(8.89553) - 10\pi & \\
\log 8.895\,53 = & 0.94917 \\
\log \pi = & 0.49715 \\ \hline
\log \text{product} = & 1.44632 \\
\text{antilog} = & 27.946 \\
\pi \log 0.078\,62 = & 27.946 - 31.416 \\
& -21.416 + 21.416 \\ \hline
\log(0.078\,62)^{\pi} = & 6.530 - 10 \\
(0.078\,62)^{\pi} = & 0.000\,339
\end{array}
$$

ALTERNATIVE SOLUTION
Using a desk calculator,

$$3.1416(\log 0.078\,62) = 3.1416\,(-1.10447)$$

$$\log \text{power} = -3.46980$$

$$= 6.53020 - 10$$

$$\text{power} = 0.000\,339\,00$$

11.09 / Change of base

Since a logarithm has been defined as an exponent of a chosen base, any positive real number x can be expressed as a power of any base b, $b > 1$. Limiting this statement to the two commonly used bases, 10 and e, for some real number z,

$$x = e^{z} \qquad \text{and thus} \qquad z = \ln x$$

$$\log x = z \log e \qquad \text{and} \qquad z = \frac{\log x}{\log e}$$

Therefore,

$$\ln x = \frac{\log x}{\log e}$$

Expressing the above statement in words, the natural logarithm of a number is obtained by dividing the common logarithm of the number by the constant $\log e = 0.43429$ approximately. It may be more convenient to use the reciprocal of the constant as a multiplier.

$$\ln x = \frac{\log x}{0.434\ 29} = 2.302\ 59 \log x$$

There were several problems in Chapters 2 and 8 in which a coefficient of 2.30 appeared. It is now apparent that the original formula contained a natural logarithm and the multiplier 2.30 converted this logarithm to a common logarithm.

It is important to remember that the logarithm of a number between 0 and 1 (both of these values excluded) is negative. To convert the common logarithm of such a number to a natural logarithm, the common logarithm must be written as a completely negative logarithm.

Example 11.23
Find $\ln \frac{1}{2}$.

SOLUTION

$$\log \tfrac{1}{2} = \log 0.5 = 9.69897 - 10 = -0.30103$$

$$\ln \tfrac{1}{2} = 2.30259\,(-0.30103) = -0.693\ 149$$

If the above calculations are done on a slide rule, $2.30\,(-0.301) = -0.692$. From a standard handbook containing tables of natural logarithms, $\ln \frac{1}{2} = -0.69315$.

If several natural logarithms are needed and if they must be calculated from common logarithms, it is recommended that all the multiplications be done at one time by using the constant multiplier. Use of a constant multiplier on a slide rule has been explained in Chapter 2. On the rotary desk calculator, a constant multiplier can be locked into the dials. The $5000 class of electronic desk calculators are programmed to find natural logarithms and antilogarithms each by the touch of a single key.

Example 11.24
Find the antilogarithm of 3.45890, given that 3.45890 is a natural logarithm.

SOLUTION

$$\ln x = 3.45890$$

$$\log x = 0.43429\,(3.45890) = 1.50217$$

$$\text{antilog} = x = 31.782$$

11.10 / Logarithmic graphing

In Figures 8.1 and 8.2, the graph of log x was plotted for a small domain. For $b > 1$, all plots of $\log_b x$ are similar. Each of these graphs is asymptotic to the Y axis at $x = 0$ since $\log_b 0$ does not exist. Between $x = 0$ and $x = 1$, the plotted values are negative and at $x = 1$, each graph crosses the X axis since $b^0 = 1$ for all $b > 1$. For all x greater than 1, the values of the logarithm are positive and continually increase as x increases.

Special graph paper, called semilogarithmic graph paper, on which the Y axis is a functional scale of log y, is especially useful. Conventionally, the X axis is uniformly graduated. The X axis may be used to represent several different things, and a series of vertical bar charts drawn so that the vertical heights are recorded in values of the variable y, although actually drawn to the scale of log y. This technique permits the plotting of an extremely wide range of data without the loss of identity of the smaller observations.

Example 11.25
Plot the enrollment of the XYZ University by departments for 1970 and for 1971 using the following tabulated data.

Enrollment	1970	1971
Liberal Arts	5400	5500
Fine Arts	2700	2950
Life Science	1250	1400
Natural Science	1450	1600
Engineering	880	920
Bioengineering	60	85

SOLUTION
Three-cycle semilogarithmic graph paper was selected to cover the range of the given enrollments. Figure 11.1 shows the completed graph.

Growth curves, when plotted on semilogarithmic paper, have the property of indicating, by the slope of the plot, the rate of change of the growth rate. The steeper the slope, the greater the change in the growth rate. A straight-line plot indicates no change in the growth rate, that is, a uniform growth rate. A decreasing slope indicates a falling growth rate even though there is growth occurring. Figure 11.2(a) shows the growth of four states on a conventional rectangular plot and Figure 11.2(b) shows the same data on semilogarithmic paper. Time is always plotted on the X axis.

The use of logarithmically ruled paper is not affected by the base selected since a logarithm to an arbitrary base b is related to the common logarithm by the constant $1/\log b$.

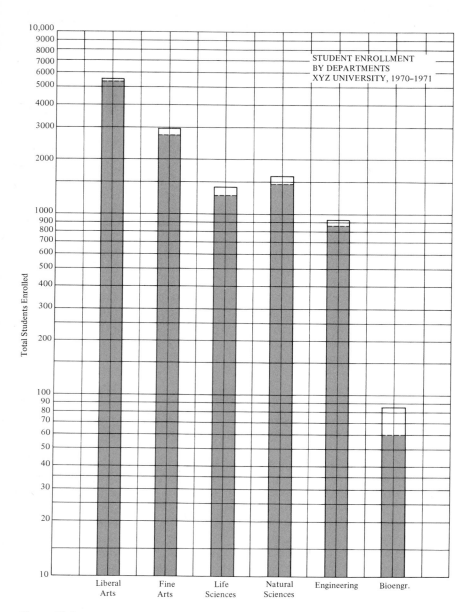

Figure 11.1
Use of semilogarithmic paper for large ranges of data

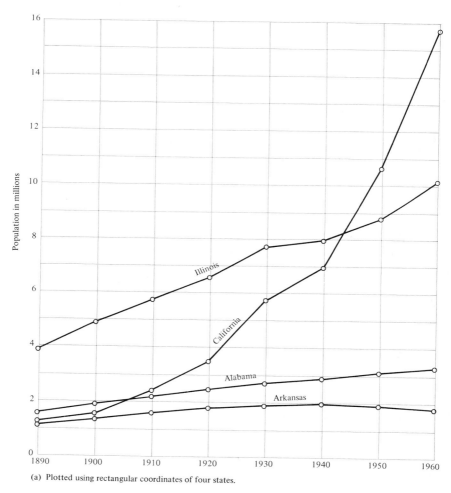

(a) Plotted using rectangular coordinates of four states.

Figure 11.2(a)
Population growth curves

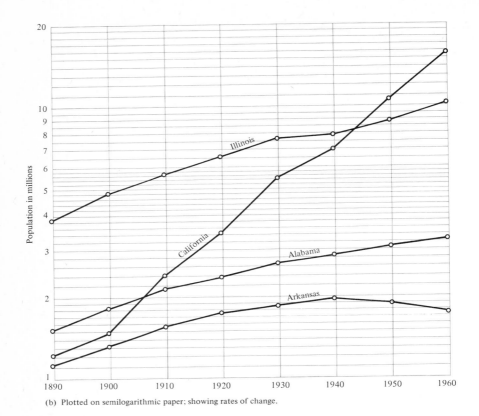

(b) Plotted on semilogarithmic paper; showing rates of change.

Figure 11.2(b)

Problem Set 11.5

1–4
Plot on semilogarithmic graph paper, using three-cycle paper for Problems 1 and 2 and two-cycle paper for Problems 3 and 4. (No answers to these four problems are given in the text.)

1. Plot the following information giving the number of driver's licenses in force in certain states.

California	10,356,000	New York	7,609,000
Illinois	5,820,000	Rhode Island	434,000
Nevada	901,000	Vermont	213,000

2. Plot the following information showing the total highway gasoline consumption for selected states. All data is in millions of gallons per year.

Alaska	69.6	Michigan	3423
Arkansas	822	Oregon	903
Hawaii	180	Texas	4928

3. Plot the following data, which represent the value of $1 at the end of *n* years when invested at 8 per cent compound interest (the highest rate in recent years). From your plot, determine in how many years the original investment will increase fivefold.

Years	5	10	15	20	25	30
Value	$1.47	2.16	3.17	4.66	6.85	10.06

4. Plot the following data, which represent the accumulated value when $1 is invested every year at 6 per cent compound interest. From your plot, determine in how many years a man, who invested $1000 every year, could stop investing his own funds, withdraw $2000 every year, and not reduce the total value of his investment at that time.

Years	5	10	15	20	25	30
Value	$5.64	13.18	23.28	36.79	54.86	79.06

5–14

Each of the following statements is a fairly simple arithmetic operation. Do each given operation (a) manually, (b) by the slide rule, (c) using common logarithms, and (d) using natural logarithms obtained by the change of base method. Do not simplify any problem when solving manually.

5. 24(12)

6. 15(36)

7. $\dfrac{72}{36}$

8. $\dfrac{156}{12}$

9. 0.75(6)

10. $0.625\left(\dfrac{12}{25}\right)$

11. $(169)^{3/2}$

12. $(3.24)^{3/2}$

13. $\left(\dfrac{119}{343}\right)^{2/3}$

14. $\left(\dfrac{0.000\ 004\ 8}{0.001\ 728}\right)^{2/3}$

15–20
Evaluate to at least three significant figures, and to five if feasible.

15. $(62.88)^{0.076923076923...}$

16. $(818.1)^{0.42857142857...}$

17. $(0.9542)^{0.03333...}$

18. $(0.007\,617)^{1.272727...}$

19. $(475.8)^{2\pi}$

20. $(0.096\,12)^{\pi/2}$

11.11 / Simplification of exponential terms

In Section 11.02 the simplification of radicals was limited to square roots and simple cube roots because operations on radicals of a higher order are handled with greater ease if fractional exponents are used. The conditions for a simplified exponential term involving a fractional exponent correspond to the conditions for a simplified radical.

A **simplified exponential term** is defined as one in which

(1a) The fractional exponent of each prime integral factor has been reduced to lowest terms, or, alternatively,

(1b) No integral base with a fractional exponent can be written as a power whose exponent divides the denominator of the fractional exponent.

(2) No fractional base has a fractional exponent.

(3) The denominator of any fraction does not contain a fractional exponent.

Example 11.26
[Illustrating Condition (1).] Simplify $(3^{12}x^8)^{1/24}$.

SOLUTION

For (a): $(3^{12}x^8)^{1/24} = (3^{12})^{1/24}(x^8)^{1/24}$

$$= 3^{12/24}x^{8/24} = 3^{1/2}x^{1/3}$$

For (b): $(3^{12}x^8)^{1/24} = [(3^3x^2)^4]^{1/24}$

$$= (3^3x^2)^{4/24} = (27x^2)^{1/6}$$

Example 11.27
[Illustrating Condition (2).] Simplify $(\frac{3}{16})^{1/4}$.

SOLUTION

$$\left(\frac{3}{16}\right)^{1/4} = \frac{3^{1/4}}{(2^4)^{1/4}} = \frac{3^{1/4}}{2}$$

Example 11.28

[Illustrating Condition (3).] Simplify $\dfrac{2xy}{3z^{2/5}}$, where $z \neq 0$.

SOLUTION

$$\frac{2xy}{3z^{2/5}} = \frac{2xyz^{3/5}}{3z^{2/5}z^{3/5}} = \frac{2xyz^{3/5}}{3z}$$

Problem Set 11.6

1–12

Simplify by first changing any radical into an exponential term and by writing the answer to conform to (1a), (2), and (3) of this section. (Assume all variables to be > 0.)

1. $(27x^3)^{1/6}$

2. $(625y^4)^{1/8}$

3. $\sqrt[6]{\dfrac{4x^4}{9}}$

4. $\sqrt[5]{\dfrac{3x^7}{128}}$

5. $\sqrt[8]{49x^6y^{12}}$

6. $\sqrt[12]{16r^3s^6}$

7. $(p^{10/7}v^{3/5})p^{-5/14}$

8. $(a^{7/8}b^{5/8})a^{-7/4}b^{-3/2}$

9. $\dfrac{1}{\sqrt[3]{9xy^2}}$

10. $\dfrac{1}{\sqrt[5]{125xy^2}}$

11. $\dfrac{2vxz}{3v^{1/2}x^{1/3}z^{5/4}}$

12. $\dfrac{3r^2s^3t^4}{81r^{5/4}s^{4/3}t^{9/2}}$

13–18

Simplify, writing the final answer using only one fractional exponent.

13. $r^{1/2}s^{1/3}t^{1/4}$

14. $\frac{2}{3}s^{1/4}t^{1/5}u^{1/6}$

15. $v^{-1/3}w^{-1/4}x^{2/3}$

16. $\frac{7}{35}w^{7/8}x^{-1/8}y^{-5/24}$

17. $10t^{1/4}u^{2/3}v^{3/5}$

18. $\frac{21}{14}u^{2/3}v^{4/7}w^{5/14}$

19–26

Using Table 1 of the Appendix, as needed, find the numerical value of each of the following to five significant figures.

19. $\sqrt[3]{\frac{3}{4}}$

20. $\sqrt[3]{\frac{7}{8}}$

21. $\dfrac{5}{3^{1/4}}$

22. $\dfrac{7}{5^{1/4}}$

23. $2(10^{-8/3})$

24. $8(32^{-19/10})$

25. $\dfrac{50}{(81)^{13/12}}$

26. $\dfrac{200}{(343)^{11/9}}$

11.12 / Addition and subtraction of exponential terms

Radicals can be combined by addition or subtraction only when the indices are the same and the radicands are identical. The conditions for exponential terms are similar; the exponents must be the same and the bases must be identical. Although an initial glance may seem to indicate no like terms, proper simplification may prove otherwise.

Example 11.29

Simplify $(8xy)^{1/3} + (x^{1/2}y^{1/2})^{2/3}$, where $x > 0$ and $y > 0$.

SOLUTION

First simplifying each term,

$$2(xy)^{1/3} + [(xy)^{1/2}]^{2/3} = 2(xy)^{1/3} + (xy)^{1/3} = 3(xy)^{1/3}$$

Example 11.30

Simplify $r^{-1/3}s^{-1/3} - 2r^{2/3}s^{2/3}$, where $rs \neq 0$.

SOLUTION

Eliminating negative exponents:

$$r^{-1/3}s^{-1/3} = \frac{1}{r^{1/3}s^{1/3}} = \frac{r^{2/3}s^{2/3}}{rs}$$

Combining like terms:

$$\frac{r^{2/3}s^{2/3}}{rs} - 2r^{2/3}s^{2/3} = \frac{(rs)^{2/3}}{rs} - 2(rs)^{2/3}$$

$$= \left(\frac{1}{rs} - 2\right)(rs)^{2/3}$$

$$= \frac{1 - 2rs}{rs}(rs)^{2/3}$$

Problem Set 11.7

Simplify. (Write as one term.) Assume all variables to be positive. Express each nonintegral numerical coefficient as a decimal correct to three decimal places.

1. $3x^{2/3} + 7x^{-1/3} - (27x^4)^{1/6}$
2. $4y^{2/5} - 3y^{-3/5} + (32y^2)^{1/5}$
3. $(625x^{3/2})^{1/4} + (81x^3)^{1/8} - (4^8x^6)^{1/16}$
4. $(b^{12}y^4)^{1/6} - (b^9y^6)^{1/9} - (9^6y^8)^{1/12}$
5. $2(r^2s^2)^{1/4} + 3(r^2s^3)^{1/6} - 4[(rs)^{9/8}]^{4/3}$
6. $7(s^{2/3}t^{4/5})^{3/2} - 6(s^{10/3}t^4)^{3/10} - 12(s^{3/36}t^{1/10})^{12}$
7. $\sqrt{169u^3v^5} + \sqrt[4]{u^6v^{10}} - 7\sqrt[8]{u^{12}v^{20}}$
8. $\sqrt{2t}\sqrt[3]{u^2} - \sqrt[6]{64t^3u^4} - \sqrt[8]{256t^4}\sqrt[5]{u^{10/3}}$
9. $x^{-1/4}y^{-3/4} + 2(x^3y)^{1/4} - 5(x^6y^2)^{1/8}$
10. $y^{-2/3}z^{-7/6} - y^{1/3}z^{5/6} - 2(y^2z^5)^{1/6}$
11. $8^{1/4}x^2 - (128)^{1/4}x^2 - 3(2048)^{1/4}x^2$
12. $(2187)^{1/3}y^5 + (81)^{1/3}y^5 + 3^{-2/3}y^5$

11.13 / Multiplication of exponential terms

It is sometimes desirable to rewrite a product such as $\sqrt{x^3}\sqrt[3]{x^2}\sqrt[4]{x}$ as a single power of the base x. The use of fractional exponents makes such a problem relatively easy by reducing it to the addition of arithmetic fractions. For example, the product cited above becomes $x^{3/2}x^{2/3}x^{1/4}$ and then by the addition of exponents:

$$x^{3/2}x^{2/3}x^{1/4} = x^{18/12 + 8/12 + 3/12} = x^{29/12} \qquad \text{or} \qquad x^2 x^{5/12} \text{ if desired}$$

The product of several variables is handled with equal facility.

Example 11.31

Express as the product of a single power of x and a single power of y: $\sqrt[5]{x^2 y^3}\,\sqrt[6]{y^7}\,\sqrt[3]{xy^2}$.

SOLUTION

$$x^{2/3}y^{3/5}(y^{7/6})(x^{1/3}y^{2/3}) = (x^{2/5 + 1/3})(y^{3/5 + 7/6 + 2/3})$$

$$= x^{11/15}y^{73/30}$$

If desired, this product may be written $y^2(x^{11/15}y^{13/30})$ or, using radicals, as $y^2\sqrt[30]{x^{22}y^{13}}$.

One operation not yet covered is the raising of a binomial to a given integral power. This will be shown first for a binomial without internal exponents and then for a binomial that does contain fractional exponents.

The tabulation that follows shows the values of $(a + b)^n$ for $n = 1, 2, 3$, and 4. To the right of the algebraic result the numerical coefficients of the terms of the expansion are displayed in an array known as **Pascal's triangle.**

$(a + b)^1 = \qquad\qquad a + b \qquad\qquad\qquad\qquad\quad 1 \quad 1$

$(a + b)^2 = \qquad\qquad a^2 + 2ab + b^2 \qquad\qquad\quad 1 \quad 2 \quad 1$

$(a + b)^3 = \qquad a^3 + 3a^2b + 3ab^2 + b^3 \qquad 1 \quad 3 \quad 3 \quad 1$

$(a + b)^4 = a^4 + 4a^3b + 6a^2b^2 + 4ab^3 + b^4 \quad 1 \quad 4 \quad 6 \quad 4 \quad 1$

The following observations can be made:

(1) The first and last terms are nth powers.
(2) From left to right, the exponent of a decreases by 1 and the exponent of b increases by 1.
(3) The sum of the exponents in any term is n.
(4) The numerical coefficients can be found by using Pascal's triangle. The first is always 1, the last is always 1, and any other is the sum of the two numbers immediately above it in the array.

It can be shown that the observations stated above are valid for any positive integer n.

Example 11.32
Expand $(3x - 2y)^5$.

SOLUTION
(1) Extend Pascal's triangle one more line to obtain:

$$1 \quad 5 \quad 10 \quad 10 \quad 5 \quad 1$$

(2) Write the expansion for $(a + b)^5$:

$$a^5 + 5a^4b + 10a^3b^2 + 10a^2b^3 + 5ab^4 + b^5$$

(3) Replace a by $3x$ and b by $-2y$:

$$(3x)^5 + 5(3x)^4(-2y) + 10(3x)^3(-2y)^2 + 10(3x)^2(-2y)^3$$
$$+ 5(3x)(-2y)^4 + (-2y)^5$$

(4) Simplify each term:

$$243x^5 - 810x^4y + 1080x^3y^2 - 720x^2y^3 + 240xy^4 - 32y^5$$

Example 11.33
Expand $(2x^{2/3} - y^{3/4})^4$.

SOLUTION

$$(2x^{2/3})^4 + 4(2x^{2/3})^3(-y^{3/4}) + 6(2x^{2/3})^2(-y^{3/4})^2$$
$$+ 4(2x^{2/3})(-y^{3/4})^3 + (-y^{3/4})^4$$
$$16x^{8/3} - 32x^2y^{3/4} + 24x^{4/3}y^{3/2} - 8x^{2/3}y^{9/4} + y^3$$

11.14 / Division of exponential terms

Since division by a monomial has already been discussed in previous sections, this section will be devoted to more complicated problems. It has been shown that a quotient having a binomial denominator involving square roots is simplified by multiplying numerator and denominator by the conjugate of the denominator. If this problem is restated using fractional exponents instead of radicals, the simplification process is similar.

Example 11.34
Using fractional exponents, rationalize the denominator of the quotient $\sqrt{3x}$ divided by $\sqrt{x} - \sqrt{3}$.

SOLUTION

$$\frac{\sqrt{3x}}{\sqrt{x} - \sqrt{3}} = \frac{3^{1/2}x^{1/2}}{x^{1/2} - 3^{1/2}} \cdot \frac{x^{1/2} + 3^{1/2}}{x^{1/2} + 3^{1/2}}$$

$$= \frac{3^{1/2}x + 3x^{1/2}}{x - 3} = \frac{x\sqrt{3} + 3\sqrt{x}}{x - 3}$$

The next sample shows how certain denominators involving three terms can be rationalized by two multiplications by a conjugate.

Example 11.35

Rationalize: $\dfrac{1}{1 + \sqrt{2} + \sqrt{3}}$.

SOLUTION

$$\frac{1}{(1 + 2^{1/2}) + 3^{1/2}} \cdot \frac{(1 + 2^{1/2}) - 3^{1/2}}{(1 + 2^{1/2}) - 3^{1/2}} = \frac{(1 + 2^{1/2}) - 3^{1/2}}{(1 + 2 \cdot 2^{1/2} + 2) - 3}$$

$$= \frac{(1 + 2^{1/2}) - 3^{1/2}}{2(2^{1/2})} \cdot \frac{2^{1/2}}{2^{1/2}}$$

$$= \frac{2^{1/2} + 2 - 6^{1/2}}{4}$$

$$= \frac{2 + \sqrt{2} - \sqrt{6}}{4}$$

A binomial denominator involving a cube root can be rationalized by applying the special product that yields the sum or difference of cubes.

Example 11.36

Rationalize: $\dfrac{1}{\sqrt[3]{5} + 2}$.

SOLUTION

$$\frac{1}{\sqrt[3]{5} + 2} = \frac{1}{5^{1/3} + 2} \cdot \frac{5^{2/3} - (5^{1/3})(2) + 2^2}{5^{2/3} - (5^{1/3})(2) + 2^2} = \frac{5^{2/3} - 2(5^{1/3}) + 4}{5 + 8}$$

$$(A \quad + B)(A^2 \quad - \quad A \quad B + B^2) = \quad A^3 + B^3$$

$$= \frac{5^{2/3} - 2(5^{1/3}) + 4}{13}$$

$$= \frac{\sqrt[3]{25} - 2\sqrt[3]{5} + 4}{13}$$

Example 11.37

Simplify: $\dfrac{x - y}{\sqrt[3]{x} - \sqrt[3]{y}}$.

SOLUTION

$$\frac{x - y}{x^{1/3} - y^{1/3}} \cdot \frac{x^{2/3} + x^{1/3}y^{1/3} + y^{2/3}}{x^{2/3} + x^{1/3}y^{1/3} + y^{2/3}}$$

$$= \frac{(x - y)(x^{2/3} + x^{1/3}y^{1/3} + y^{2/3})}{x - y}$$

$$= x^{2/3} + x^{1/3}y^{1/3} + y^{2/3}$$

$$= \sqrt[3]{x^2} + \sqrt[3]{xy} + \sqrt[3]{y^2}$$

Problem Set 11.8

Do the indicated operations and simplify the results, accepting improper fractions as exponents. Assume all variables to be positive. Leave all answers in exact form; do not convert to decimals.

1. $(2p^{1/2} - 3r^{1/3})(3p^{1/2} - 4r^{1/3})$

2. $(3r^{1/3} - 4s^{1/2})^2$

3. $(2x^{1/2})(3x^{1/3})(4x^{1/4})$

4. $(32y)^{3/5}(2y)^{1/2}(32y)^{1/10}$

5. $(t^{1/3} - 3)(t^{2/3} + 3t^{1/3} + 9)$

6. $(s^{2/3} + 5)(s^{4/3} - 5s^{2/3} + 25)$

7. $(4 + x^{2/3})^3$

8. $(3 + y^{3/4})^4$

9. $(2 - z^{4/5})^5$

10. $(r^{1/2} - s^{1/4})^5$

11. $\left(\sqrt[3]{4} - \sqrt[4]{32}\right)^4$

12. $\left(3\sqrt[5]{r^2} - 2\sqrt[5]{s^4}\right)^4$

13. $\dfrac{(st)^{1/2}}{3s^{1/2} - 4t^{1/2}}$

14. $\dfrac{(2s)^{1/2} - (3t)^{1/2}}{(2s)^{1/2} + (3t)^{1/2}}$

15. $\dfrac{1}{\sqrt{3} + \sqrt{4} + \sqrt{5}}$

16. $\dfrac{2}{\sqrt{2} - \sqrt{4} - \sqrt{6}}$

17. $\dfrac{x + 8}{x^{1/3} + 2}$

18. $\dfrac{y - 27}{y^{1/3} - 3}$

19. $\dfrac{1 + r}{1 + r^{1/3}}$

20. $\dfrac{1 - s^2}{1 - s^{1/3}}$

21. $\dfrac{27x^2 - 62xy + 16y^2}{3x^{1/3} - 2y^{1/3}}$

22. $\dfrac{3x + 1}{(9x^2)^{1/3} + (3x)^{1/3}}$

11.15 / Operations with pure imaginary numbers

Imaginary numbers were briefly discussed, both historically and as to their mathematical meaning, in Section 1.07. The engineering symbol for the basic imaginary number, $\sqrt{-1}$, is j, named in Chapter 1 as the jay operator. Its properties are the subject of this section.

Since imaginary numbers are not part of the set of real numbers, the laws for real numbers do not always apply.

Example 11.38

Find the error in the following "proof" that $-2 = +2$:

$$-2 = \sqrt{-2}\sqrt{-2} = \sqrt{(-2)(-2)} = \sqrt{4} = +2$$

SOLUTION

The error lies in the statement that $\sqrt{-2}\sqrt{-2} = \sqrt{(-2)(-2)}$. The statement $\sqrt{a}\sqrt{b} = \sqrt{ab}$ is *not* true when a and b are negative. This error and similar ones can be avoided if the square root of any negative number is first written in the jay-operator form. Then the laws of real numbers may be applied if the powers of j are replaced by the values

$$j = \sqrt{-1}$$
$$j^2 = -1$$
$$j^3 = j^2 j = -j$$
$$j^4 = (j^2)^2 = +1$$

For powers of j greater than 4, write the power as a product of a power divisible by 4 and a power less than 4. Then replace the power divisible by 4 by the value 1 and the other power by the value obtained from the values above. For example, $j^{103} = j^{100} \cdot j^3 = (1) \cdot (-j) = -j$.

The square root of a negative number may now be defined in terms of the jay operator.

Definition

If x is a positive real number, $\sqrt{-x} = \sqrt{(-1)x} = j\sqrt{x}$.

Example 11.39

Write each of the following in terms of the jay operator: $\sqrt{-25}$, $\sqrt{-5}$, $\sqrt{-75}$.

SOLUTION

$$\sqrt{-25} = \sqrt{(-1)25} = \sqrt{-1}\sqrt{25} = j \cdot 5 = 5j$$

$$\sqrt{-5} = \sqrt{(-1)5} = \sqrt{-1}\sqrt{5} = j\sqrt{5}$$

$$\sqrt{-75} = \sqrt{-1}\sqrt{75} = \sqrt{-1}\,5\sqrt{3} = j5\sqrt{3} = 5j\sqrt{3}$$

Note in the above example that $jb = bj$. In the field of electricity, the preferred form is jb. The j operator should precede any radical for clarity of reading.

Example 11.40

Given $\sqrt{-18}$ and $\sqrt{-2}$, find their sum, difference, product, and quotient.

SOLUTION

First rewrite these numbers in terms of the jay operator.

$$\sqrt{-18} = j\sqrt{18} = j(3\sqrt{2})$$

$$\sqrt{-2} = j\sqrt{2}$$

Sum: $\quad \sqrt{-18} + \sqrt{-2} = j3\sqrt{2} + j\sqrt{2} = (3\sqrt{2} + \sqrt{2})j = j4\sqrt{2}$

Difference: $\quad j3\sqrt{2} - j\sqrt{2} = (3\sqrt{2} - \sqrt{2})j = j2\sqrt{2}$

Product: $\quad (3\sqrt{2}j)(\sqrt{2}j) = 3(2)j^2 = -6$

Quotient: $\quad \dfrac{j3\sqrt{2}}{j\sqrt{2}} = 3$

11.16 / Operations with complex numbers

A complex number is a number having the form $a + bj$, where a and b are real numbers and $j = \sqrt{-1}$. For the nonelectronics technician, complex numbers will be found in the solution of some equations. Complex numbers must be accepted so that every polynomial equation with either real or imaginary coefficients will have at least one solution. The fact that imaginary solutions are rejected when the conditions of a problem require the admissible values to be real numbers does not invalidate the existence of imaginary roots.

Nonelectronic technicians should be able to solve simple problems in industrial electricity since most modern powered devices use electric motors, fluorescent lighting, and other electrical components. Since about 99 per cent of the United States uses alternating current, calculations involving power requirements may be needed and these require at least the rudiments of complex numbers.

Two complex numbers are equal, $a + bj = c + dj$, if and only if $a = c$ and $b = d$. The **real part** of $a + bj$ is the real number a and the **imaginary part** of $a + bj$ is the real number b, the number that multiplies the jay operator.

The ordinary arithmetic operations of addition, subtraction, multiplication, and division are done by treating the complex number as an algebraic binomial. However, the properties of the jay operator given in the previous section must be used. Powers and roots are more complicated operations and will not be covered in this text. These computations can be found in most texts for electronic technicians. The square of a complex number can be found by multiplication and this is the power most frequently used.

Example 11.41
Find the sum of $2 + j\sqrt{3}$ and $4\sqrt{2} - 2j$.

SOLUTION
(1) Add the real parts: $2 + 4\sqrt{2} \approx 7.657$

(2) Add the imaginary parts: $\sqrt{3} - 2 \approx -0.268$

(3) Exact sum: $(2 + 4\sqrt{2}) + (\sqrt{3} - 2)j$

(4) Approximate sum: $7.657 - 0.268j$

Example 11.42
Find the difference when $4\sqrt{2} - 2j$ is subtracted from $2 + j\sqrt{3}$.

SOLUTION
(1) The difference is $(2 + j\sqrt{3}) - (4\sqrt{2} - 2j)$.

(2) Subtract the real parts: $2 - 4\sqrt{2} \approx -3.565$

(3) Subtract the imaginary parts: $\sqrt{3} + 2 \approx 3.732$

(4) Exact difference: $(2 - 4\sqrt{2}) + (\sqrt{3} + 2)j$

(5) Approximate difference: $-3.565 + 3.732j$

Example 11.43
Find the product of $2 + j\sqrt{3}$ and $4\sqrt{2} - 2j$.

SOLUTION

$$(2 + j\sqrt{3})(4\sqrt{2} - 2j) = 8\sqrt{2} + j4\sqrt{6} - 4j - 2\sqrt{3}\,j^2$$
$$= 8\sqrt{2} + (4\sqrt{6} - 4)j - 2\sqrt{3}(-1)$$
$$= (8\sqrt{2} + 2\sqrt{3}) + (4\sqrt{6} - 4)j$$
$$\approx 14.778 + 5.798j$$

Example 11.44

Find the quotient: $\dfrac{2 + j\sqrt{3}}{4\sqrt{2} - 2j}$.

SOLUTION

$$\frac{2 + j\sqrt{3}}{4\sqrt{2} - 2j} \cdot \frac{4\sqrt{2} + 2j}{4\sqrt{2} + 2j} = \frac{8\sqrt{2} + (4 + 4\sqrt{6})j + 2\sqrt{3}\,j^2}{16(2) - 4j^2}$$
$$= \frac{8\sqrt{2} + (4 + 4\sqrt{6})j + 2\sqrt{3}(-1)}{16(2) - 4(-1)}$$
$$= \frac{(8\sqrt{2} - 2\sqrt{3}) + (4 + 4\sqrt{6})j}{36}$$
$$= \frac{2(4\sqrt{2} - \sqrt{3}) + j4(1 + \sqrt{6})}{36}$$
$$= \frac{4\sqrt{2} - \sqrt{3}}{18} + j\frac{1 + \sqrt{6}}{9}$$
$$\approx 0.2181 + j0.3833$$

It is possible to plot complex numbers, although not on the conventional number line which represents all real numbers. The value of a in $a + bj$ is plotted on this real-number axis. Obviously a new line is needed to plot the b values. This line is named the axis of imaginaries and it is drawn perpendicular to and through the zero point of the axis of reals. The intersection of the two axes has the coordinate $0 + 0j$. Positive values of b are located on the axis of imaginaries above the real axis and negative values below.

Example 11.45

Graph (a) $2j$; (b) $-3j$; (c) $2 + 3j$; (d) $3 - 2j$; (e) $-3 + 3j$; (f) $-4 - 5j$.

SOLUTION
See Figure 11.3(a).

In Chapter 3 it was shown that multiplication by -1 could be interpreted as a rotation of a point on the number line through an angle of $180°$.

Figure 11.3(b) shows that multiplication by the jay operator can be interpreted as the rotation of a point through an angle of 90°. Since $j^2 = -1$, two multiplications by the jay operator produce a rotation through 180°.

The plot of an imaginary number by its real and imaginary parts corresponds to the plot of a radius vector by its x and y components. The methods shown in Chapter 10 for operations on vectors are similar to those used for complex numbers.

Figure 11.4 shows a plot of an alternating current where the voltage E and the current I are out of phase with the current lagging or leading the voltage by an angle ϕ. This occurs when the circuit contains conductance or inductance in addition to resistance. A commercial fluorescent light fixture has a large ballast coil that produces an inductive reactance X_L with a lagging current. The impedance Z is plotted as $R + jX_L$. The impedance of devices with a capacitive reactance X_C is plotted as $R - jX_C$, which indicates a leading current. For industrial electrical installations, it is desirable to try and balance these reactances so that the power factor, the ratio of the apparent power ($EI \cos \phi$) to the source power (EI), approaches unity. The smaller the power factor, the more expensive the cost of electricity to produce a given amount of power at the point of use. All technicians, using manufacturer's data, should be able to calculate power factors.

Figure 11.3(a)
Plot of complex numbers

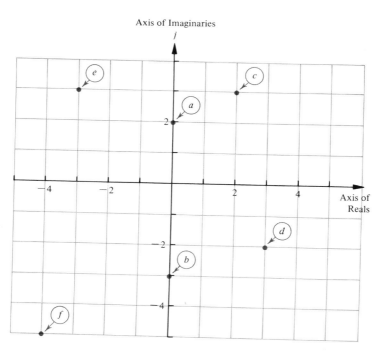

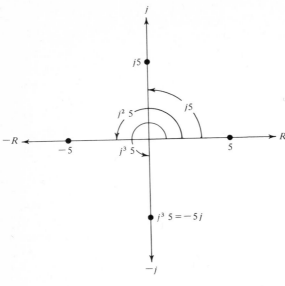

Figure 11.3(b)
Rotational effect of jay operator

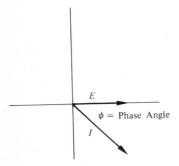

ϕ = Phase Angle

Lagging Current

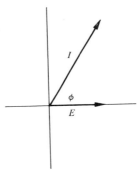

Leading Current

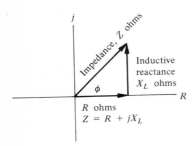

(a) Circuit with resistance and inductance

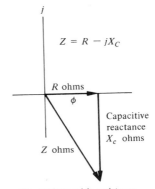

(b) Circuit with resistance and capacitance

Figure 11.4
Alternating current

542

Example 11.46

A fluorescent lamp is listed as a 60-watt lamp drawing 1.0 amperes from a 120-volt, 60-Hz source. Find (a) the power factor for this lamp and (b) the reactive power of its ballast.

SOLUTION

(a)   Power at source $= P_s = EI = 120(1) = 120$ va (volt-amperes)

Apparent power $= P_a =$ power available at the lamp given as 60 watts $= 60$ va

$$\text{Power factor} = \frac{P_a}{P_s} = \frac{60}{120} = 0.5, \text{ or } 50\%, \text{ lagging}$$

(b) To find the reactive power of the ballast (P_q), the vector power diagram is drawn using complex numbers, where $P_a + jP_q = \mathbf{P}_s$. This is shown in Figure 11.5. Using the Pythagorean theorem,

$$P_q = \sqrt{(120)^2 - (60)^2} \approx 104 \text{ vars}$$

The unit for reactances is vars, a volt-ampere reactance.

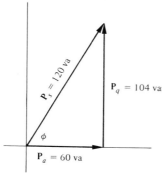

$P_q = 104$ vars

Figure 11.5
Reactive power

$P_a = 60$ va

$P_q = \sqrt{P_s^2 - P_a^2}$

Power Factor $= \dfrac{P_a}{P_s} = \cos \phi$

Example 11.47

Using data from Example 11.46, find the inductive reactance X_L of the ballast and express the total impedance Z in complex co-ordinates.

SOLUTION

From electrical handbooks, P_q (in vars) $= I^2 X_L$. Thus,

$$X_L = \frac{P_q}{I^2} = \frac{104}{1^2} = 104 \ \Omega$$

$$R = \frac{E^2}{P_s} = \frac{(120)^2}{120} = 120 \ \Omega$$

$$Z = 120 + j104 \qquad \text{with the magnitude of } Z \text{ in ohms}$$

(*Note:* In alternating-current circuits, the total impedance **Z** is the vector sum of the pure resistance **R**, drawn on the axis of the reals, and the reactance **X** drawn on the axis of imaginaries; that is, $\mathbf{Z} = \mathbf{R} + j\mathbf{X}_L$.)

The next example does not involve any complex numbers but is included here to show the industrial application of power factors, as well as to review other concepts previously studied.

Example 11.48
An electric motor produces 11.2 actual mechanical horsepower. It has a rated efficiency of 92 per cent, operating on a 440 volt line. The motor has a power factor of 84.7 per cent. Find (a) the kilowatt (kw) input to the motor and (b) the current that must be supplied at the source.

SOLUTION
Using Table 10,

$$1\ \text{hp} = 0.746\ \text{kw}$$

$$11.2\ \text{hp} = 8.36\ \text{kw output}$$

(a) $$\text{kw input} = \frac{\text{kw output}}{\text{efficiency}} = \frac{8.36}{0.92} = 9.09\ \text{kw}$$

(b) $$\text{kva at source} = \frac{\text{kw input}}{\text{power factor}} = \frac{9.09}{0.847} = 10.73\ \text{kva}$$

$$\text{current required} = \frac{\text{power at source in kva}}{\text{voltage}} \times 1000$$

$$= \frac{10.73}{440}(1000) = 24.4\ \text{amp}$$

Problem Set 11.9

1–6
Evaluate numerically.

1. $\left(\sqrt{-2}\right) j^{63}$ 3. $\left(\sqrt[3]{-54}\right)^2 j^{17}$ 5. $\left(\sqrt{\dfrac{-2}{3}}\right) j^{40}$ 6. $\left(\sqrt{-\dfrac{16}{125}}\right) j^{79}$

2. $\left(\sqrt{-48}\right)^3 j^{13}$ 4. $\left(\sqrt{-75}\right)^4 j^{101}$

7–10.
Simplify

7. $\sqrt{-125} + \sqrt{-80} - \sqrt{-405}$

9. $\dfrac{\sqrt{-3} - \sqrt{2}}{\sqrt{-3} + \sqrt{-2}}$

8. $\sqrt{-112} - \sqrt{-252} + \sqrt{-175}$

10. $\dfrac{\sqrt{-3} + \sqrt{4}}{\sqrt{-4} - \sqrt{-3}}$

11–20
Perform the indicated operations and express the results in the form a + jb.

11. $(6 - j\sqrt{8}) - (7 - j\sqrt{2}) - (2 - j\sqrt{18})$

12. $(2 + j\sqrt{3}) + (7 - j\sqrt{12}) - (5 - j\sqrt{75})$

13. $(2 - j\sqrt{5})(3 + j\sqrt{5})$
    14. $(\sqrt{3} - 2j\sqrt{3})(3 - 2j\sqrt{27})$

15. $\dfrac{2 + j\sqrt{2}}{3 + j\sqrt{3}}$
    17. $\dfrac{\sqrt{2} - j\sqrt{3}}{\sqrt{3} + j\sqrt{2}}$
    19. $\dfrac{\left|\sqrt{2} + j\sqrt{3}\right|^2}{\left|\sqrt{2} - j\sqrt{3}\right|^2}$

16. $\dfrac{3 - j\sqrt{2}}{2 - j\sqrt{3}}$
    18. $\dfrac{\sqrt{3} + j\sqrt{5}}{\sqrt{2} - j\sqrt{5}}$
    20. $\dfrac{\left|\sqrt{3} - j\sqrt{2}\right|^2}{\left|\sqrt{2} - j\sqrt{3}\right|^2}$

21–26
Find the values for x and y that make the two given complex numbers equal.

21. $(x + 7) + 2j(y + 1) = 2(x + 1) + 8j$

22. $(2x - 1) + jy = (x + 1) + j\dfrac{2y + 7}{3}$

23. $(2 + 3j)(4 - 5j) = (x - 2) + yj$

24. $(3 - 4j)(4 - 5j) = \tfrac{1}{2}x + (4y - 1)j - 4$

25. $\dfrac{3 + j}{2 - j} = 5(2x - j3y)$

26. $\dfrac{1 - j\sqrt{2}}{1 + j\sqrt{2}} = 3(x - j\sqrt{18}\,y)$

27–30
Using graph paper ruled five squares to the inch, plot the impedance for each of the following electrical conditions. Mark appropriate intervals with a numerical scale value for ease of reading.

27. $R = 12\,\Omega,\; X_L = 7\,\Omega$
    29. $R = 100\,\Omega,\; X_C = 120\,\Omega$

28. $R = 35\,\Omega,\; X_L = 5\,\Omega$
    30. $R = 1.50\,\Omega,\; X_C = 3.75\,\Omega$

31. Fluorescent lights can be obtained with either a capacitive or an inductive characteristic, which permits design of a two-lamp fixture that contains one circuit of each type. A certain lighting fixture has a capacitive reactance X_c of $210\,\Omega$, and its other circuit an inductive reactance X_L of $324\,\Omega$. The pure resistance of the circuit containing the two lamps is $40\,\Omega$.

(a) Plot the net reactance, $|X_L| - |X_C|$, the resistance, R, and draw the impedance vector, Z. Compute its value.

(b) Is the effective current leading or lagging?

(c) Write the impedance Z as a complex number.

(d) Find the phase angle (ϕ) by scaling the plot in part (a).

(e) Compute the phase angle (ϕ).

(f) The power factor PF as a percentage is $100\cos\phi$. Find the power factor for just the capacitive loaded lamp, for just the inductive loaded lamp, and for the complete fixture containing both lamps.

(g) If the complete fixture is used on a 220 volt system, the current is
$$I = \frac{E}{Z},$$
E being the line voltage and Z the impedance found in part (a).

Find the power used if the power is $EI\cos\phi$.

(h) Recompute the power using $P = I^2 R$, where the values are as given.

11.17 / Equations containing radicals

If an equation contains one radical of the second order, the method of solution is as follows:

(1) Rearrange the given equation so the radical alone forms the left side.

(2) Square both sides, obtaining an equation free of radicals.

(3) Solve the resulting equation. If not linear, collect all nonzero terms on the left side, factor, and set each nonconstant factor equal to zero. (See Example 11.49.)

(4) Check the solutions of the resulting equation in the original equation.

(5) State the solutions of the original equation.

It is *mandatory* that any solution obtained by squaring an equation be checked by substitution in the original equation, since a solution of the equation free of radicals may not be a root of the original equation. In other words, if r is a root of $f(x) = g(x)$, r is also a root of $[f(x)]^2 = [g(x)]^2$. However, a root of $[f(x)]^2 = [g(x)]^2$ is not necessarily a root of $f(x) = g(x)$.

If the given equation has only two terms and both are radicals, one radical is placed on each side of the equality symbol and the same general procedure is followed.

To eliminate the possibility of improperly rejecting a root due to an error in checking, examine the last two lines of the check. If the left side of the equation differs from the right side by only a change of sign in any one term, probably there was no error in the checking process and the root is correctly rejected. This will be illustrated in Example 11.49.

Example 11.49

Solve $2x - 3 = \sqrt{4x - 3}$.

SOLUTION

(1) Rearranging: $\qquad\qquad\qquad\qquad\qquad \sqrt{4x - 3} = 2x - 3$

(2) Squaring both sides: $\qquad\qquad\qquad 4x - 3 = 4x^2 - 12x + 9$

(3) Solving:

    (a) Since there is an x^2 term, collect all nonzero terms on the left: $\qquad 4x^2 - 16x + 12 = 0$

    (b) Factoring left side: $\qquad\qquad\quad 4(x^2 - 4x + 3) = 0$

$$4(x - 3)(x - 1) = 0$$

    (c) Setting each nonconstant factor $= 0$: $\qquad\qquad x - 3 = 0 \text{ or } x - 1 = 0$

    (d) Solving the linear equations: $\qquad x = 3 \text{ or } x = 1$

    Possible solutions: $x = 3$ or $x = 1$

(4) Checking $x = 3$: $\qquad 2(3) - 3 = \sqrt{4(3) - 3}$

$$6 - 3 = \sqrt{9}$$

$$3 = 3, \text{ true; accept root}$$

    Checking $x = 1$: $\qquad 2(1) - 3 = \sqrt{4(1) - 3}$

$$2 - 3 = \sqrt{1}$$

$$-1 = +1, \text{ false; reject root}$$

(5) The solution is 3.

Note that in the last line of the checking process for $x = 1$; that is, $-1 = +1$, the left and right sides differ by sign only, thus giving assurance that probably no error was made and the root is properly rejected.

Example 11.50

Solve $\sqrt{x^2 - 2} - \sqrt{3x + 2} = 0$.

SOLUTION

(1) Isolating radicals: $\qquad \sqrt{x^2 - 2} = \sqrt{3x + 2}$

(2) Squaring both sides: $\qquad x^2 - 2 = 3x + 2$

(3) Collecting terms: $x^2 - 3x - 4 = 0$

(4) Factoring: $(x - 4)(x + 1) = 0$

(5) Possible solutions are: $x = 4$ or $x = -1$

(6) Checking: For $x = 4$: $\sqrt{4^2 - 2} - \sqrt{3(4) + 2} = 0$

$$\sqrt{14} - \sqrt{14} = 0, \text{true; accept root}$$

For $x = -1$: $\sqrt{(-1)^2 - 2} - \sqrt{3(-1) + 2} = 0$

$$\sqrt{-1} - \sqrt{-1} = 0, \text{true; accept root}$$

The solutions are 4 and -1.

When the original equation contains three or more terms of which at least two contain radicals, it will be necessary to square both sides more than once. The general process remains the same but is repeated as many times as needed to obtain an equation free of radicals.

Example 11.51

Solve $\sqrt{x^2 - 2x + 1} - \sqrt{x^2 - 3x - 1} = 1$.

SOLUTION

(1) Separating radicals: $\sqrt{x^2 - 2x + 1} = 1 + \sqrt{x^2 - 3x - 1}$

(2) Squaring both sides: $x^2 - 2x + 1 = 1 + x^2 - 3x - 1$

$$+ 2\sqrt{x^2 - 3x - 1}$$

(3) Collecting: $2\sqrt{x^2 - 3x - 1} = 1 + x$

(4) Squaring: $4(x^2 - 3x - 1) = 1 + 2x + x^2$

(5) Expanding: $4x^2 - 12x - 4 = 1 + 2x + x^2$

(6) Collecting: $3x^2 - 14x - 5 = 0$

(7) Factoring: $(3x + 1)(x - 5) = 0$

(8) Solving: $x = -\frac{1}{3}$ or $x = 5$

(9) Checking: For $x = -\frac{1}{3}$:

$$\sqrt{(-\tfrac{1}{3})^2 - 2(-\tfrac{1}{3}) + 1} - \sqrt{(-\tfrac{1}{3})^2 - 3(-\tfrac{1}{3}) - 1} = 1$$

$$\sqrt{\tfrac{16}{9}} - \sqrt{\tfrac{1}{9}} = 1$$

$$\tfrac{4}{3} - \tfrac{1}{3} = 1, \text{true; accept } x = -\tfrac{1}{3}$$

for $x = 5$:

$$\sqrt{5^2 - 2(5) + 1} - \sqrt{5^2 - 3(5) - 1} = 1$$

$$\sqrt{16} - \sqrt{9} = 4 - 3 = 1, \text{ true; accept } x = 5$$

The solutions are $-\frac{1}{3}$ and 5.

Occasionally a problem may arise with a radical contained in a radical. The same concept of repeated squarings is used.

Example 11.52

Solve $\sqrt{x - \sqrt{2x}} = 2$.

SOLUTION

(1) Squaring both sides: $\quad x - \sqrt{2x} = 4$

(2) Isolating the radical: $\quad \sqrt{2x} = x - 4$

(3) Squaring both sides: $\quad 2x = x^2 - 8x + 16$

(4) Collecting: $\quad x^2 - 10x + 16 = 0$

(5) Factoring: $\quad (x - 8)(x - 2) = 0$

(6) Solving: $\quad x = 8 \text{ or } x = 2$

(7) Checking: For $x = 8$: $\quad \sqrt{8 - \sqrt{2(8)}} = \sqrt{8 - 4} = 2, \text{ true;}$

accept $x = 8$

For $x = 2$: $\quad \sqrt{2 - \sqrt{2(2)}} = \sqrt{2 - 2} = 0 \neq 2;$

reject $x = 2$

The solution is $x = 8$.

Example 11.53

Solve $\sqrt{x} + 5 = 0$.

SOLUTION

By observation, there can be no root. The radical symbol always indicates the principal square root, which is positive. Thus, it is impossible for $\sqrt{x} = -5$, that is, for a principle square root to be negative. If both sides are squared, one obtains $x = 25$. However, upon checking, $\sqrt{25} + 5 = 5 + 5 = 10 \neq 0$ and 25 is rejected.

Problem Set 11.10

Solve. The required checking should be as neat and legible as the solution process.

1. $\sqrt{x-1} = 3$

2. $\sqrt{x-2} = \sqrt{2}$

3. $y - 2 = \sqrt{y-2}$

4. $y - 3 = \sqrt{7y-3}$

5. $z = \sqrt{z+12}$

6. $2z = \sqrt{5z+6}$

7. $\sqrt{2x^2+7x} = \sqrt{15}$

8. $\sqrt{3x^2-22x} - 4 = 0$

9. $\sqrt{p+2} - \sqrt{3p-2} = 2$

10. $\sqrt{3r+2} + \sqrt{8r+1} = 4$

11. $\sqrt{\sqrt{2} + 7\sqrt{2s}} = 2$

12. $\sqrt{2(t + \sqrt{4t+9})} - 9 = 3$

13. $3 + \sqrt{u} = \sqrt{6u+1}$

14. $3 + \sqrt{3v-2} = \sqrt{8v+1}$

15. $3 + \sqrt{4w^2+125} = \sqrt{4w^2+18w+134}$

16. $7 - \sqrt{3x^2-2} = \sqrt{3x^2-2x-1} - 4$

17. $\sqrt{2x+13} - \sqrt{10-3x} + \sqrt{4x+9} = 0$

18. $\sqrt{5y-4} - \sqrt{2(y-2)} = \sqrt{3y-8}$

11.18 / Equations involving rational exponents

If an equation contains expressions with rational exponents, it can often be solved by extending the concept used to solve equations involving radicals. By raising both sides of the equation to a proper power, one or more times, an equation free of fractional exponents may be obtained. Again, all solutions of this resulting equation *must* be checked in the original equation.

Example 11.54
Solve: $(x^2 - x + 26)^{1/5} = 2$.

SOLUTION
(1) Raising both sides to the fifth power,

$$[(x^2 - x + 26)^{1/5}]^5 = 2^5$$

$$x^2 - x + 26 = 32$$

$$x^2 - x - 6 = 0$$
$$(x - 3)(x + 2) = 0$$
$$x = 3 \text{ or } x = -2$$

(2) Checking: For $x = 3$:
$$(3^2 - 3 + 26)^{1/5} = (32)^{1/5} = 2, \text{ check}$$

For $x = -2$:
$$[(-2)^2 - (-2) + 26]^{1/5} = (32)^{1/5} = 2; \text{ check}$$

The solutions are 3 and -2.

Example 11.55
Solve: $(x^6 - 2x + 7)^{1/3} = x^2$.

SOLUTION

(1) Cubing both sides: $\qquad x^6 - 2x + 7 = x^6$
$$2x = 7 \text{ and } x = \tfrac{7}{2}$$

(2) Checking: $\qquad [(\tfrac{7}{2})^6 - 2(\tfrac{7}{2}) + 7]^{1/3} = (\tfrac{7}{2})^2$
$$[(\tfrac{7}{2})^6]^{1/3} = (\tfrac{7}{2})^2, \text{ true}$$

The solution is $\tfrac{7}{2}$.

Example 11.56
Solve: $(x^4 + 4x^3 + 7x^2 + 2x - 7)^{1/4} = x + 1$.

SOLUTION

(1) Raising both sides to the fourth power,
$$x^4 + 4x^3 + 7x^2 + 2x - 7 = x^4 + 4x^3 + 6x^2 + 4x + 1$$

(2) Collecting: $\qquad x^2 - 2x - 8 = 0$
$$(x - 4)(x + 2) = 0$$
$$x = 4 \text{ or } x = -2$$

(3) Checking: For $x = 4$:
$$[4^4 + 4(4)^3 + 7(4)^2 + 2(4) - 7]^{1/4} = 4 + 1$$
$$(625)^{1/4} = 5, \text{ true}$$

For $x = -2$:
$$[(-2)^4 + 4(-2)^3 + 7(-2)^2 + 2(-2) - 7]^{1/4} = -2 + 1$$
$$(1)^{1/4} = 1 \neq -1; \text{ reject}$$

The solution is 4.

11.19 / Exponential equations

An equation in which the variable appears in an exponent is called an **exponential equation.** Such equations are found both in the natural and life sciences, particularly in the studies of growth and decay.

Two types of exponential equations are found. In the first and simplest form, but also the one rarely met in real problems, both sides of the equation can be expressed in terms of a common base and the exponents can be equated. The type more commonly met requires the use of logarithms to obtain a solution.

Example 11.57
Solve: $2^{0.417x} = 0.0625$.

SOLUTION
(1) Expressing both sides to the base 2,

$$2^{0.417x} = \frac{1}{16} = \frac{1}{2^4} = 2^{-4}$$

(2) Equating exponents: $\quad 0.417x = -4$

$$x = \frac{-4}{0.417} = -9.59$$

Example 11.58
Solve: $2^{0.417x} = 3^{0.417}$.

SOLUTION
(The similarity of exponents is used to show that this does not affect the method of solution.) Taking the common logarithm of both sides,

$$0.417x \log 2 = 0.417 \log 3$$

$$x = \frac{0.417 \log 3}{0.417 \log 2} = \frac{0.477}{0.301} = 1.58$$

Example 11.59
Solve: $2^{1.67x+3} = 3^{0.892x+1}$.

SOLUTION
Taking the common logarithm of both sides:

$$(1.67x + 3) \log 2 = (0.892x + 1) \log 3$$

$$(1.67x + 3)(0.301) = (0.892x + 1)(0.477)$$

$$0.503x + 0.903 = 0.425x + 0.477$$

$$0.078x = -0.426$$

$$x = -\frac{0.426}{0.078} = -5.46$$

11.20 / Logarithmic equations

Again, as for exponential equations, two distinct types of logarithmic equations can be found. The first type contains a single logarithmic term and a direct solution can be obtained by ordinary algebraic operations. Some problems in Chapter 8 were of this type.

For the second type, the equation contains several terms involving the logarithm of a variable. In general, by using the basic laws of logarithms, these terms are combined until a single logarithm results. If one side contains a logarithm and the other side a known real number, the solution can be obtained by changing the statement to the exponential form.

Example 11.60

In a study of the reverberations in a large auditorium, the time T in seconds that it took for a sound of standard intensity to become inaudible was

$$T = -\frac{0.05V}{S \log(1 - a)}$$

where V = volume of the auditorium, cu ft
S = total surface area of the auditorium, sq ft
a = average absorption coefficient

To find some experimental values for a, an auditorium of 200,000 cu ft with a total effective surface of 30,000 sq ft was used. If, in this test, T averaged 2 sec, find the absorption coefficient a.

SOLUTION

(1) Rearranging: $\quad \log(1 - a) = -\dfrac{0.05V}{ST}$

(2) Substituting: $\quad \log(1 - a) = -\dfrac{0.05(200,000)}{(30,000)(2)}$

$$= -0.167 = 9.833 - 10$$

(3) Taking the antilogarithm:

$$1 - a = 0.68$$

(4) Solving: $\quad a = 1 - 0.68 = 0.32$

Example 11.61

Solve: $\log(x - 3) + \log(x + 17) - \log(x + 3) = 4 \log 2$.

SOLUTION

(1) Using the basic laws of logarithms:

$$\log \frac{(x - 3)(x + 17)}{x + 3} = \log 2^4 = \log 16$$

(2) Equating antilogarithms:

$$\frac{(x - 3)(x + 17)}{x + 3} = 16$$

(3) Solving:

$$(x - 3)(x + 17) = 16(x + 3)$$

$$x^2 + 14x - 51 = 16x + 48$$

$$x^2 - 2x - 99 = 0$$

$$(x - 11)(x + 9) = 0$$

$$x = 11 \text{ or } x = -9$$

(4) Checking: For $x = 11$:

$$\log 8 + \log 28 - \log 14 = \log \frac{8(28)}{14} = \log 16 = 4 \log 2$$

For $x = -9$: $\log(x - 3) = \log(-12)$ which is undefined. Therefore, $x = -9$ is rejected. The solution is 11.

Example 11.62
Solve: $\log(x + 1.2) - \log(x + 4) + \log(x - 0.8) = -0.3979$.

SOLUTION

(1) Combining:

$$\log \frac{(x + 1.2)(x - 0.8)}{x + 4} = -0.3979$$

(2) Taking the antilogarithms:

$$\frac{(x + 1.2)(x - 0.8)}{x + 4} = \text{antilog}(-0.3979) = \text{antilog}(9.6021 - 10)$$

$$\frac{(x + 1.2)(x - 0.8)}{x + 4} = 0.4$$

(3) Solving:

$$(x + 1.2)(x - 0.8) = 0.4(x + 4)$$

$$x^2 + 0.4x - 0.96 = 0.4x + 1.6$$

$$x^2 = 2.56$$

$$x = \pm 1.60$$

(4) Checking: For $x = 1.60$:

$$\log \frac{2.8(0.8)}{5.6} = \log 0.4 = -0.3979, \text{ check}$$

For $x = -1.60$: $\log(x + 1.2) = \log(-0.4)$ which is undefined. The solution is 1.60.

Problem Set 11.11

1–10

Solve and check each real root found. Do not use more than one decimal place in the results of intermediate calculations.

1. $(8x^6 + 12x^2 - 25x + 12)^{1/3} = 2x^2$
2. $(52x^4 + 19x^2 - 225)^{1/4} = -2x$
3. $(2x^2 - 5x + 24)^{1/3} = 3$
4. $(6x^2 - 5x + 10)^{1/4} = -2$
5. $(2x^2 - 3x - 26)^{1/3} = 2.08$
6. $(20x^2 - 83x + 1)^{1/5} = -2.42$
7. $(x^3 - 2x^2 + 7x - 22)^{1/3} = x - 1$
8. $(8x^3 - 30x^2 + 29x - 2)^{1/3} = 2x - 3$
9. $(x + 2)^{2/3} = 2.52$
10. $(2x - 1)^{2/5} = 1.90$

11. A transmission line is to be erected using No. 2 AWG copper wire, with a diameter of 258 mils. The characteristic impedance desired Z in ohms is $Z = 276 \log \dfrac{d}{r}$. Find the spacing d of the conductors for $Z = 543$ ohms.

    The value for r, the radius of the wire, must be in the same units as d.
12. Computing the characteristic impedance of a concentric line, Z, in ohms, one uses

$$Z = 138 \log \frac{d_1}{d_2}$$

where d_1 = inside diameter of the outer conductor

$\quad\quad d_2$ = outside diameter of the inner conductor

Find the outside diameter of the outer conductor if the outer conductor is $\frac{1}{16}$ in. thick, the inner conductor is No. 0 AWG copper wire, $d_2 = 325$ mils, and the desired Z is 67.5 Ω. The space between the two conductors is an insulator which does not affect these calculations.
13. A jet stream of air has varying velocities, depending on where the velocity is measured. The relationship is

$$\left(\frac{r}{r_1}\right)^2 = 3.3 \log \frac{V_{CL}}{V}$$

where r = radial distance to a point P measured from the centerline of the jet

$\quad\quad r_1$ = radial distance to some point where the velocity is one half of the centerline velocity

$\quad\quad V_{CL}$ = centerline velocity, fpm

$\quad\quad V$ = velocity at point P

If $\dfrac{r}{r_1}$ is 0.6, find V if the centerline velocity is 60 ft/min. (Adapted from ASHRAE Guide and Data Book.)

14. Referring to Problem 13, find V if $\dfrac{r}{r_1}$ is 1.5 and V_{CL} is 80 fpm.

15–22
Solve for all positive real values that satisfy the given equation.

15. $2^{3x-1} = 0.125$ 17. $3^{1.25x} = 4^{1/3}$
16. $11^{y(y+2)} = 0.090909\ldots$ 18. $6^{0.895y} = 26.123$
19. If the salvage value S of a machine after y years, based upon an original cost C, is $S = C(1 - r)^y$, where r is the rate of depreciation, find the economic life y for a $5000 machine if the depreciation rate is assumed constant at 12 per cent per year and the lower limit of the salvage value has been set at $1000.
20. If $2500 is to be charged off annually as depreciation at 6 per cent interest, in how many years will a $100,000 machine be fully depreciated using the sinking-fund method? In this method, the factor S is the annual depreciation divided by the original cost and is equal to

$$S = \frac{i}{(1 + i)^n - 1}$$

where i is the interest rate and n is the number of years.
21. For adiabatic conditions (no change in total heat), the changes in pressure corresponding to changes in heat are given by

$$P_2 = P_1\left(\frac{T_2}{T_1}\right)^{k/(k-1)}$$

Find k if P_2 is 308 psia, P_1 is 50 psia, T_2 is 1000°R, and T_1 is 600°R, all data being for ordinary air.
22. If a related test as described in Problem 21 is run for ammonia, the results are $P_2 = 1750$ psia, $P_1 = 100$ psia, $T_2 = 1600°$R, and $T_1 = 800°$R. Find k for ammonia.

23–30
Solve, using four-place logarithms.

23. $2^{x+1} = 0.031\,25$
24. $5^{(3/2)x - (2/3)} = 0.008$
25. $3^{(3/4)x - 2} = 5.196$
26. $6^{(2/3)x + 2} = 2.4495$
27. $\log(x + 2) - \log(x + 5) + \log(x + 3) = \log(x^2 - 2) - \log(x - 1)$

28. $\log(x - 1.5) - \log 2x + \log(x + 2.5) = -0.3010$

29. $2 \log 5 + \log 15 - \log 3 + 3 \log x = 0$

30. $6 \log x = \log 21 - \log 1344$

11.21 / Chapter Review

1. The definitions and basic laws of exponents are listed in Table 11.2, where m and n are natural numbers, x and y are positive real numbers, and a and b are any real numbers.

2. Exponents may be positive or negative integers, rational numbers, decimals, or irrational numbers. For practical use, an irrational exponent is approximated by a rational number selected according to the desired degree of precision.

3. The use of the radical symbol $\sqrt{}$ is common for square roots because it is a highly visible symbol. Cube roots are often indicated by $\sqrt[3]{}$, but modern science and engineering tend toward the use of fractional or decimal exponents.

4. The number under a radical symbol is called the radicand. The small number on the symbol is called the index and it indicates the order of the radical. For square roots, the index number is omitted. The result of the operation indicated by the radical symbol is called the principal root, which is the positive root for all positive radicands. Negative numbers do not have real numbers for their square roots.

Table 11.2
Exponential Operations

Definitions	Operation	Law
$x^1 = x$	Multiplication	$x^a x^b = x^{a+b}$
$x^n = x \cdot x \cdots x \ (n \text{ factors})$	Division	$\dfrac{x^a}{x^b} = x^{a-b}$
$x^0 = 1$		
$x^{-n} = \dfrac{1}{x^n}$	Power	$(x^a)^b = x^{ab}$
$x^{1/n} = \sqrt[n]{x}$		$(xy)^a = x^a y^a$
$x^{m/n} = \sqrt[n]{x^m} = \left(\sqrt[n]{x}\right)^m$		$\left(\dfrac{x}{y}\right)^a = \dfrac{x^a}{y^a}$
$x^{-m/n} = \dfrac{1}{x^{m/n}}$		
$0^a = 0 \text{ if } a \neq 0$		

5. If x is a positive real number and if n is a natural number, then

$$x^{1/n} = \sqrt[n]{x}$$ is a positive real number

$$(-x)^{1/n} = \sqrt[n]{-x} = -\sqrt[n]{x}$$ is a negative real number if n is odd

$$(-x)^{1/n} = \sqrt[n]{-x}$$ is not a real number if n is even

6. A properly simplified term having a rational exponent contains no internal fraction, no negative exponents, and, if fractional, only integral exponents in its denominator.

7. Terms with rational exponents can be combined by addition or subtraction only if the bases are identical and the exponents are identical.

8. Fractional terms containing nonintegral exponents in their denominators are rationalized by multiplying numerator and denominator by a term whose exponent for each variable added to the original exponent of that variable in the denominator results in the next sequential integer.

9. Fractions containing binomials to the $\frac{1}{2}$ or $\frac{1}{3}$ power are rationalized using the special product factor that yields the difference of two squares, or the sum or difference of two cubes, respectively.

10. Imaginary numbers do not obey all laws for real numbers. If the jay operator, $j = \sqrt{-1}$ and $j^2 = -1$, is introduced as the first step, the complex numbers may be treated as binomials and the usual laws for real numbers may be used if the special powers of the jay operator are used in conjunction.

11. Except for industrial electricity, other fields of technology seldom find a meaning for imaginary answers to practical problems. Complex numbers do have a useful meaning in making mathematical concepts complete.

12. Equations containing terms or expressions with a rational exponent can usually be solved by isolating such a quantity and raising it to an appropriate power to produce an integral exponent. In some cases, this operation may have to be repeated to eliminate all nonintegral exponents from the equation.

13. If the variable appears in an exponent, the equation is said to be an exponential equation. The solution can be found by equating the exponents of identical bases or by taking the logarithm of each side.

14. If an equation involves the logarithm of a variable, it may be possible to obtain a solution by restating the relationship in exponential form.

15. It is always possible to change a repeating decimal to a quotient of two integers. If this quotient is a simple fraction, it permits a rapid solution to a problem with decimal exponents.

16. Pascal's triangle can be used for the expansion of binomial expressions raised to a positive integral exponent. This has been useful for problems in this chapter and is also useful for many algebraic problems involving such powers.

Problem Set 11.12 (Chapter Review)

1. The IBM Company has a machine language called FFT for certain problems involving series. The time T required by this new language is given by

$$T = \frac{\log_2 N}{N} t$$

where N = number of terms in the series
   t = old time
   If it formerly took 3 sec to solve a problem for a series with 512 terms, compute the time using FFT.

2. Find and check the solution of

$$\sqrt{\sqrt[3]{x^{4/5 - \pi/11}}} - \frac{17}{13} = 0$$

3. The approximate pressure in mm of mercury for an altitude h in thousands of feet above sea level is given by

$$P = 760e^{-0.04724h}$$

At what altitude, to the nearest hundred feet, has the pressure dropped to one half of the value at sea level?

4. Find the length L of a side weir in a sewer line to produce a flow Q of 4 cfs if the depth of flow h over the downstream end of the weir is 10 in. and

$$Q = 3.32L^{0.83}h^{1.6}$$

(All units must be compatible.)

5. Solve: $\sqrt{x - 3.44} + \sqrt{x + 0.82} = \sqrt{x + 2.62}$.

6. If a pipe is suddenly enlarged, the velocity drops from V_0 to V_1. The head lost h is given by

$$h = 1.098 \frac{(V_0 - V_1)^{1.919}}{2g}$$

Find the final velocity V_1 if the initial velocity is 5 fps, h is 0.184 ft, and g is 32.2 ft/sec^2.

7. Solve: $(x^6 - 11x^4 + 42x^2 - 136)^{1/3} = x^2 - 4$.

8. A certain impedance is given as $240 - j60 \, \Omega$. Find the resistance and capacitive reactance in this circuit, the value of the impedance in ohms, and the phase angle.

9. Solve: $3 \log x = \log(x + 3) + \log(x - 3) + \log(x + 2)$.

10. Find the number different from 10 so that its common logarithm is equal to the number divided by 10; that is, $\log x = \frac{1}{10}x$. (Hint: Using

small integers, find the interval where $\log x < \frac{1}{10}x$ changes to $\log x > \frac{1}{10}x$. Plot the graphs of $\log x$ and of $\frac{1}{10}x$ between these two limiting values and obtain an approximate solution. Enlarge the scale and decrease the domain and replot. Repeat this process until an answer correct to five significant figures is obtained. This is an excellent method for solving equations for which a direct solution cannot be found.)

Second-degree equations and inequalities

12.01 / Forms of second-degree equations

An expression having the form $ax^2 + bx + c$, where $a \neq 0$ is called a **second-degree,** or **quadratic, polynomial** in the variable x. An equation that can be reduced to the form

$$ax^2 + bx + c = 0 \qquad \text{where } a \neq 0$$

is called a **second-degree,** or **quadratic, equation** in the variable x.

Whenever $b = 0$ or $c = 0$, the quadratic equation becomes

$$ax^2 + c = 0 \qquad \text{or} \qquad ax^2 + bx = 0$$

and either of these is called an *incomplete quadratic equation.*

The incomplete quadratic equations can be easily solved by factoring and by using the fact that a product that is zero must have a factor that is zero.

Example 12.1
Solve: $2x^2 = 5x$.

SOLUTION

(1) Rewrite so the right side is 0: $2x^2 - 5x = 0$

(2) Factor the left side: $x(2x - 5) = 0$

(3) Set each factor equal to 0: $x = 0$ or $2x - 5 = 0$

(4) Solve each linear equation: $x = 0$ or $x = \frac{5}{2}$

Thus, the solutions are 0 and $\frac{5}{2}$.

Example 12.2
Solve: $9x^2 - 4 = 0$.

SOLUTION
(1) Factor the left side: $(3x - 2)(3x + 2) = 0$
(2) Set each factor equal to 0: $3x - 2 = 0$ or $3x + 2 = 0$
(3) Solve the linear equations: $x = \frac{2}{3}$ or $x = -\frac{2}{3}$

Thus, the solutions are $\frac{2}{3}$ and $-\frac{2}{3}$.

Another convenient technique for solving the equation of Example 12.2 is shown in Example 12.3.

Example 12.3
Solve: $9x^2 - 4 = 0$.

SOLUTION
(1) Solve for x^2: $9x^2 = 4$

$$x^2 = \frac{4}{9}$$

(2) Take the square roots of both sides:

$$x = \pm\frac{2}{3}$$

Note that in Example 12.3, one could have written $\pm x = \pm\frac{2}{3}$. However, this does not give any additional roots, so the $\pm$ symbol is used *only* on the right side of the equation.

Example 12.4
Solve: $2x^2 + 50 = 0$.

SOLUTION
(1) Solving for x^2: $x^2 = -25$
(2) Taking square roots: $x = \pm\sqrt{-25}$

$x = \pm 5j$ (imaginary roots)

The equation $ax^2 + c = 0$ is called a *pure quadratic equation*. Its solution is obtained by generalizing the method used in Example 12.3.

The general solution of $ax^2 + c = 0$ is $x = \pm\sqrt{-\dfrac{c}{a}}$

Note that two real roots are obtained only when the constants a and c are opposite in sign. If a and c have the same sign, the solutions are imaginary numbers.

12.02 / Graphing the quadratic function

An expression of the form $ax^2 + bx + c$ with $a \neq 0$ determines a **quadratic function** of the variable x. The **graph of a quadratic function** is obtained by graphing the set of ordered pairs (x,y) for which $y = ax^2 + bx + c$.

The *zeros* of this function are the values of x for which $y = 0$ and thus for which $ax^2 + bx + c = 0$, that is, the *roots* or *solutions* of the quadratic equation. Since $y = 0$ on the x axis, the real solutions of a quadratic equation can be approximated from the graph of the quadratic function by reading the values of x at the points where the graph crosses the x axis, that is, the values of the x intercepts. Imaginary roots cannot be read directly from the graph although techniques are available to approximate such roots graphically.

The graph of $y = ax^2 + bx + c$ may be obtained by plotting selected points on the graph and then drawing a smooth curve through these points in order of increasing values of x. Since the squared values increase so rapidly, it is often necessary to use two different scales for the X and Y axes. However, a single scale must be maintained on each axis.

Example 12.5

Graph $y = 2x^2 + 4x - 5$.

SOLUTION

(1) Make a table of values for x and y using integers for x.

x	y	
-4	11	$y = 2(-4)^2 + 4(-4) - 5 = 32 - 16 - 5 = 11$
-3	1	$y = 2(-3)^2 + 4(-3) - 5 = 18 - 12 - 5 = 1$
-2	-5	$y = 2(-2)^2 + 4(-2) - 5 = 8 - 8 - 5 = -5$
-1	-7	$y = 2(-1)^2 + 4(-1) - 5 = 2 - 4 - 5 = -7$
0	-5	$y = 2(0)^2 + 4(0) - 5 = 0 + 0 - 5 = -5$
1	1	$y = 2(1)^2 + 4(1) - 5 = 2 + 4 - 5 = 1$
2	11	$y = 2(2)^2 + 4(2) - 5 = 8 + 8 - 5 = 11$
3	25	$y = 2(3)^2 + 4(3) - 5 = 18 + 12 - 5 = 25$
4	43	$y = 2(4)^2 + 4(4) - 5 = 32 + 16 - 5 = 43$

(2) Plot the points obtained and join with a smooth curve. The graph is shown in Figure 12.1, where the domain $-4 \leq x \leq 2$ is used for convenience. The arrows at each end of the graph indicate that the graph continues indefinitely upward.

Example 12.6

Solve $2x^2 + 4x - 5 = 0$ graphically.

SOLUTION

(1) Graph $y = 2x^2 + 4x - 5$. (See Figure 12.1.)

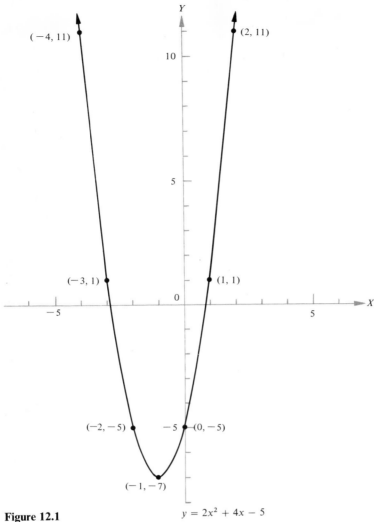

Figure 12.1
Graph of a quadratic function

$$y = 2x^2 + 4x - 5$$

(2) From the graph, read the values of x for the points where the graph crosses the x axis.

Approximately, $x = 0.9$ and $x = -2.9$.

(*Note:* Later techniques will show that $x = -1 \pm \sqrt{3.5}$ exactly, and that $x = 0.8708$ and $x = -2.8708$ are better approximations.)

Example 12.7

Graph $s = -16t^2 + 80t$, where t is the time in seconds and s is the distance in feet of an object tossed vertically upward at $t = 0$ with an initial velocity of 80 ft/sec.

SOLUTION

(1) Make a table of values for nonnegative integral values of t.

t	0	1	2	3	4	5
s	0	64	96	96	64	0

(2) Plot the tabled values using a scale for s 10 times that for t. Different scales are chosen for the horizontal and vertical axes whenever this is convenient for graphing.

(3) Find the highest point on the graph.

For this graph, the highest point on the graph does not appear in the table of values. However, the table does reveal that the same values of s are obtained at equally spaced intervals. Noting that $s = 96$ for $t = 2$ and for $t = 3$, and that $s = 64$ for $t = 1$ and $t = 4$, it may be concluded that the highest point corresponds to t halfway between 2 and 3 (or halfway between 1 and 4); that is,

$$t = \frac{2 + 3}{2} = \frac{1 + 4}{2} = 2.5$$

$$s = -16(2.5)^2 + 80(2.5) = 100$$

Plot (2.5, 100).

Join the plotted points with a smooth curve. (See Figure 12.2.)

The graph of a quadratic function in one variable is called a **parabola,** having the general shape illustrated in Figures 12.1 and 12.2. Note that if the coefficient of the square term is positive, the parabola opens upward and it has a lowest point, called a **minimum point.** If the coefficient of the square term is negative, the parabola opens downward and it has a highest point, called a **maximum point.** The minimum point or the maximum point is called the **vertex** of the parabola.

Not only is the vertex of the parabola an important feature of its graph, but also the coordinates of the vertex provide useful information for practical applications of the quadratic function. In Example 12.7, the coordinates of the vertex of the parabola give the maximum height the object reaches and the time it takes to reach that height.

An *axis of symmetry* exists through the vertex parallel to the Y axis. Therefore, if the values of y for selected values of the independent variable x are computed on one side of the axis of symmetry, matching points can be drawn on the other side without further calculations.

It may be shown that for $y = ax^2 + bx + c$, the **vertex of the parabola has coordinates**

$$x = -\frac{b}{2a} \quad \text{and} \quad y = -\frac{b^2 - 4ac}{4a}$$

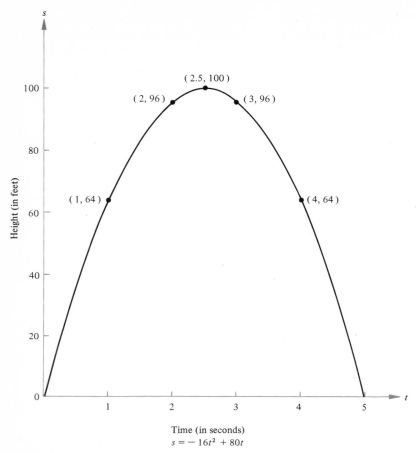

Figure 12.2
Plotting a quadratic equation for peak value

Example 12.8
Using the formulas for the vertex, find the maximum point of the graph of $s = -16t^2 + 80t$.

SOLUTION

$$a = -16, b = 80, c = 0:$$

$$x = -\frac{b}{2a} = -\frac{80}{-32} = 2.5$$

$$y = -\frac{b^2 - 4ac}{4a} = -\frac{(80)^2 - 0}{-64} = 100$$

From the formulas for the coordinates of the vertex, it may be seen that if a is positive, the lowest point of the parabola will be below the x axis if $b^2 - 4ac$ is positive, on the x axis if $b^2 - 4ac = 0$, and above the x axis if $b^2 - 4ac$ is negative. Accordingly, since the roots of $ax^2 + bx + c = 0$ are the x values of $y = ax^2 + bx + c$ when $y = 0$, the quadratic equation has two real solutions when $b^2 - 4ac$ is positive, one real solution when $b^2 - 4ac = 0$, and no real solutions (or two imaginary solutions) when $b^2 - 4ac$ is negative. (See Figure 12.3.)

Problem Set 12.1

1–20
Solve by factoring.

1. $x^2 + 3x = 0$

2. $x^2 - 7x = 0$

3. $5x^2 - 4x = 0$

4. $4x^2 - 9x = 0$

5. $2x^2 = 7x$

6. $x = 16x^2$

7. $25x^2 - 1 = 0$

8. $49x^2 - 64 = 0$

9. $3x^2 - 8 = 0$

10. $25 - 2x^2 = 0$

11. $4x^2 + 4 = 0$

12. $16x^2 + 25 = 0$

13. $5x^2 + 3x = 3x - 7$

14. $9x - 12 = 2x^2 + 9x$

15. $6x^2 - 8x = 5x^2 - 8x$

16. $2x^2 - 5x + 3 = 3x^2 - 5x + 4$

17. $(x - 3)(x - 4) = 12$

18. $(x + 2)(x + 5) = 10$

19. $\dfrac{0.25}{x} = \dfrac{x}{0.01}$

20. $\dfrac{x}{100} = \dfrac{30}{x}$

Figure 12.3
Possible roots of a quadratic equation

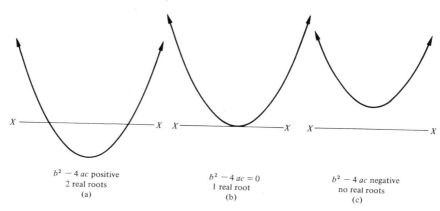

$b^2 - 4\,ac$ positive
2 real roots
(a)

$b^2 - 4\,ac = 0$
1 real root
(b)

$b^2 - 4\,ac$ negative
no real roots
(c)

21. Graph each of the following on the same set of coordinate axes. By comparing the graphs, state what effect the coefficient of x^2 has on the graph. $y = \frac{1}{2}x^2 - 1$, $y = x^2 - 1$, $y = 2x^2 - 1$.
22. Graph each of the following on the same set of coordinate axes. By comparing the graphs, state what effect the linear term (x term) has on the graph. $y = x^2 - 2x$, $y = x^2$, $y = x^2 + 4x$.
23. Graph each of the following on the same set of coordinate axes. By comparing the graphs, state what effect the constant term has on the graph. $y = x^2 - 4$, $y = x^2$, $y = x^2 + 5$.
24. Graph each of the following on the same set of coordinate axes. By comparing the graphs, state how each graph is related to the graph of $y = x^2$. (a) $y = -x^2 - x$; (b) $y = -x^2$; (c) $y = -x^2 + 2$; (d) $y = -x^2 + 2x - 3$.

25–40

(a) *Graph each of the following.*
(b) *Write the coordinates of the vertex of each graph.*
(c) *Estimate the x intercepts of each graph, if they are real numbers.*

25. $y = x^2 - 4x - 1$
26. $y = x^2 + 6x + 7$
27. $y = 3 - 2x - x^2$
28. $y = 8x - 10 - x^2$
29. $y = 2x^2 - x - 3$
30. $y = 6x^2 - 5x - 4$
31. $y = -4x^2 + 4x - 1$
32. $y = -4 - 6x - 3x^2$

33. $y = 3x^2 - 2x + 1$
34. $y = 9x^2 - 6x + 1$
35. $s = -16t^2 + 200t$
36. $s = 120t - 16t^2$
37. $s = 480t + 16t^2$
38. $s = 16t^2 + 520t$
39. $h = 400 - 5d^2$
40. $h = 100 - 3d^2$

12.03 / Algebraic solution by factoring

Four methods are used for solving a quadratic equation:
1. Graphing the quadratic function.
2. Factoring the quadratic equation.
3. Completing the square.
4. Using the quadratic formula.

The graphical solution was illustrated in the previous section, where it was seen that the graph yields approximations only and approximations for the real solutions only. The remaining three algebraic methods produce both real and imaginary solutions in exact form. The factoring method, introduced earlier in Chapter 11, is the quickest whenever it is possible to identify easily the factors of a special product. The quadratic formula method is a generalization of the solution by completing the square. These last two methods are used primarily for literal equations and for equations whose factors cannot be recognized immediately.

Example 12.9

Solve $x^2 = 11x - 18$ by factoring.

SOLUTION

(1) Rewrite the equation so the right side is 0:

$$x^2 - 11x + 18 = 0$$

(2) Factor the left side:

$$(x - 2)(x - 9) = 0$$

(3) Set each linear factor $= 0$:

$$x - 2 = 0 \text{ or } x - 9 = 0$$

(4) Solve each linear equation:

$$x = 2 \text{ or } x = 9$$

(5) Check each solution:

If $x = 2$, then $x^2 - 11x + 18 = 2^2 - 11(2) + 18 = 22 - 22 = 0$

If $x = 9$, then $x^2 - 11x + 18 = 9^2 - 11(9) + 18 = 99 - 99 = 0$

Example 12.10

By factoring, solve $42x^2 + 7x - 105 = 0$.

SOLUTION

(1) Remove the common monomial factor:

$$7(6x^2 + x - 15) = 0$$

(2) Factor the general trinomial:

$$7(2x - 3)(3x + 5) = 0$$

(3) Set the nonconstant factors $= 0$:

$$2x - 3 = 0 \text{ or } 3x + 5 = 0$$

(4) Solve the linear equations:

$$x = \frac{3}{2} \text{ or } x = -\frac{5}{3}$$

(5) Check each solution:

If $x = \frac{3}{2}$, then $42x^2 + 7x - 105 = 42\left(\frac{3}{2}\right)^2 + 7\left(\frac{3}{2}\right) - 105$

$$= \frac{189}{2} + \frac{21}{2} - 105$$

$$= 105 - 105 = 0$$

$$\text{If } x = -\frac{5}{3}, \text{ then } 42x^2 + 7x - 105 = 42\left(-\frac{5}{3}\right)^2 + 7\left(-\frac{5}{3}\right) - 105$$

$$= \frac{350}{3} - \frac{35}{3} - 105$$

$$= 105 - 105 = 0$$

Note that the solutions were checked in the original equation. If the easier reduced equation had been used and if an arithmetic error in dividing by the common factor 7 had been made, a false check would probably result.

Problem Set 12.2

Solve each equation by factoring and check the solutions.

1. $3x^2 = 48$
2. $5x^2 = 25x$
3. $4x = 64x^2$
4. $6x^2 = 42$
5. $x^2 - 8x + 15 = 0$
6. $x^2 - 9x + 18 = 0$
7. $7y^2 - 7y - 14 = 0$
8. $8y^2 + 8y - 16 = 0$
9. $(x - 3)(x + 2) = 6$
10. $(x + 5)(x - 4) = 10$
11. $9x^2 = 45x + 54$
12. $25x^2 = 50x + 2000$
13. $-16t^2 + 48t + 448 = 0$
14. $-16t^2 + 80t + 800 = 0$
15. $2x^2 - 5x + 2 = 0$

16. $3x^2 - 10x + 3 = 0$
17. $10x^2 + 34x - 24 = 0$
18. $20x^2 + 5x - 25 = 0$
19. $(2r + 3)^2 = 20r + 30$
20. $(3r + 1)^2 = 17r - 1$
21. $(r + 5)(r - 5) = 4r^2 - 11r - 15$
22. $3r(r - 1) = (r - 1)(r + 3)$
23. $w^2 = 2(5w - 12)$
24. $v^2 = 9(v - 2)$
25. $(2R - 1)(2R - 3) = 4(2R - 3)(R - 2)$
26. $(3T - 2)(3T - 5) = 2(3T - 5)(3T - 8)$
27. $8M^2 + 0.14M - 0.0015 = 0$
28. $6E^2 - 2.5E + 0.14 = 0$
29. $2.56V^2 - 1.76V + 0.30 = 0$
30. $10.24K^2 + 6.08K - 1.20 = 0$

12.04 / Completing the square

When the linear factors of the quadratic function cannot be recognized easily, the quadratic equation can be solved by *completing the square*. This method involves the special product known as the perfect-square trinomial:

$$x^2 + 2ax + a^2 = (x + a)^2$$

Example 12.11
Find the term that must be added to $x^2 + 10x$ so that the resulting expression is a perfect-square trinomial.

SOLUTION

Comparing $x^2 + 2ax + a^2$ with $x^2 + 10x$, it may be seen that $2a = 10$ and thus $a = 5$ and $a^2 = 25$. Therefore, $x^2 + 10x + 25$ is a perfect-square trinomial.

Example 12.12

Solve $x^2 + 6x - 4 = 0$ by completing the square.

SOLUTION

(1) Rewrite the equation so only the x terms are on the left side:

$$x^2 + 6x = 4$$

(2) Complete the square by adding the square of one half the coefficient of x to both sides[1] : $(\frac{6}{2})^2 = 3^2 = 9$

$$x^2 + 6x + 3^2 = 4 + 9$$

(3) Factor the left side and simplify the right side:

$$(x + 3)^2 = 13$$

(4) Take square roots of both sides:

$$x + 3 = \pm\sqrt{13}$$

(5) Solve for x:

$$x = -3 \pm \sqrt{13}$$

Thus, $x = -3 + \sqrt{13}$ or $x = -3 - \sqrt{13}$

$$x \approx 0.6056 \quad \text{or} \quad x \approx -6.6056$$

(6) Check by substituting the *exact* values into the original quadratic equation. The check is shown for $x = -3 + \sqrt{13}$:

$$x^2 = (-3 + \sqrt{13})^2 = 9 - 6\sqrt{13} + 13 = 22 - 6\sqrt{13}$$
$$6x = 6(-3 + \sqrt{13}) \qquad\qquad = -18 + 6\sqrt{13}$$
$$-4 \qquad\qquad\qquad\qquad\qquad = -4$$
$$\overline{}$$
$$x^2 + 6x - 4 \qquad\qquad\qquad = 0 + 0 = 0$$

Example 12.13

Solve $3x^2 - 5x + 2 = 0$ by completing the square.

SOLUTION

(1) Rewrite, so the x terms are on the left:

$$3x^2 - 5x = -2$$

[1] Note that the indicated square (3^2) was added to the left side and the numerical value of the square (9) was added to the right side. This permits the next step to be done more easily.

(2) Divide by the coefficient of x^2:

$$x^2 - \frac{5}{3}x = -\frac{2}{3}$$

(3) Add the square of $\frac{1}{2}(\frac{5}{3})$ to both sides:

$$x^2 - \frac{5}{3}x + \left(\frac{5}{6}\right)^2 = -\frac{2}{3} + \frac{25}{36}$$

(4) Factor the left side, simplify right:

$$\left(x - \frac{5}{6}\right)^2 = \frac{1}{36}$$

(5) Take the square root of each side:

$$x - \frac{5}{6} = \pm\frac{1}{6}$$

(6) Solve for x: $x - \frac{5}{6} = \frac{1}{6}$ or $x - \frac{5}{6} = -\frac{1}{6}$

$$x = 1 \quad \text{or} \quad x = \frac{2}{3}$$

(7) Check by substitution (left for student.)

As the above examples illustrate, this method is most convenient when the coefficient of x^2 is 1 or a perfect square and when the coefficient of x is an even number. The technique of completing the square is also extremely useful in more advanced topics such as quadratic equations in *two* variables. Example 12.14 shows how the vertex of a parabola may be found by completing the square.

Example 12.14
Find the vertex of the parabola $y = 4x^2 - 24x + 43$ by completing the square.

SOLUTION
(1) Writing the x terms on the left side:

$$4x^2 - 24x = y - 43$$

(2) Removing the coefficient of x^2 as a factor:

$$4(x^2 - 6x) = y - 43$$

(3) Completing the square[1]:

$$4(x^2 - 6x + 9) = y - 43 + 36$$

[1] Note that $4 \cdot 9 = 36$ must be added to *each* side of the equation.

(4) Writing as a perfect square and simplifying:

$$4(x - 3)^2 = y - 7$$

(5) Setting each side $= 0$ and solving:

$$x - 3 = 0 \text{ and } y - 7 = 0$$
$$x = 3 \text{ and } y = 7$$

Thus, the vertex is $(3, 7)$.

This result may be checked by using the symmetry of the parabola; for example, the y value for $x = 2$ should equal the y value for $x = 4$.

Problem Set 12.3

1–20

Solve by completing the square. Check by substitution.

1. $x^2 + 8x - 3 = 0$

2. $x^2 + 2x - 1 = 0$

3. $y^2 - 3y + 1 = 0$

4. $y^2 - 5y + 5 = 0$

5. $2x^2 + 4x + 1 = 0$

6. $3x^2 + 12x + 5 = 0$

7. $5t^2 - 5t - 2 = 0$

8. $4t^2 - 2t - 3 = 0$

9. $x^2 + 6x + 10 = 0$

10. $x^2 - 10x + 4 = 0$

11. $9v^2 = 6v - 1$

12. $25w^2 = 10w - 1$

13. $x^2 + x + 1 = 0$

14. $x^2 + x - 1 = 0$

15. $2y^2 + y = 1$

16. $2y^2 - 2y = 1$

17. $3.00z^2 = 3.60z - 1.05$

18. $5.00z^2 = 1.80 - 2.50z$

19. $R^2 = 1600R + 800,000$

20. $T^2 + 4700T - 1,500,000 = 0$

21–26

By completing the square, find the coordinates of the vertex of each of the following parabolas.

21. $y = x^2 - 4x + 9$

22. $y = x^2 + 6x + 2$

23. $y = -x^2 - 8x - 13$

24. $y = -x^2 + 10x - 24$

25. $y = 4x^2 - 8x + 10$

26. $y = -9x^2 + 126x - 441$

12.05 / The quadratic formula

By applying the method of completing the square to the general quadratic equation, the *quadratic formula* can be obtained. The solutions of any special quadratic equation can then be found by substituting the values of the coefficients into this formula.

Example 12.15

Solve $ax^2 + bx + c = 0$ by completing the square.

SOLUTION

(1) Write the x terms on the left:

$$ax^2 + bx = -c$$

(2) Divide by the coefficient of x^2:

$$x^2 + \frac{b}{a}x = -\frac{c}{a}$$

(3) Add $\left(\frac{1}{2}\frac{b}{a}\right)^2 = \left(\frac{b}{2a}\right)^2$ to both sides:

$$x^2 + \frac{b}{a}x + \left(\frac{b}{2a}\right)^2 = -\frac{c}{a} + \frac{b^2}{4a^2}$$

(4) Factor the left side; simplify:

$$\left(x + \frac{b}{2a}\right)^2 = \frac{b^2 - 4ac}{4a^2}$$

(5) Take square roots:

$$x + \frac{b}{2a} = \pm\frac{\sqrt{b^2 - 4ac}}{2a}$$

(6) Solve for x:

$$x = -\frac{b}{2a} \pm \frac{\sqrt{b^2 - 4ac}}{2a}$$

By combining the fractions on the right side, one obtains

The Quadratic Formula

If $ax^2 + bx + c = 0$, then $x = \dfrac{-b \pm \sqrt{b^2 - 4ac}}{2a}$

The quadratic formula is so widely used in the solution of quadratic equations that its form should be memorized.

Example 12.16

Solve $3x^2 + x - 4 = 0$ by using the quadratic formula.

SOLUTION

(1) Write the values of a, b, and c:

$$ax^2 + bx + c = 0$$
$$3x^2 + x - 4 = 0$$

Thus, $a = 3$, $b = 1$, and $c = -4$.

(2) Substitute these values into the formula:

$$x = \frac{-b \pm \sqrt{b^2 - 4ac}}{2a}$$

$$x = \frac{-1 \pm \sqrt{1^2 - 4(3)(-4)}}{2(3)}$$

(3) Simplify:

$$x = \frac{-1 \pm \sqrt{1 + 48}}{6} = \frac{-1 \pm 7}{6}$$

$$x = \frac{-1 + 7}{6} \quad \text{or} \quad x = \frac{-1 - 7}{6}$$

Thus, $x = 1$ or $x = -\frac{4}{3}$.

Each example should be checked by substitution, but that step is omitted here and in subsequent examples for brevity.

Example 12.17
Solve $2x^2 - 5x + 1 = 0$ by using the quadratic formula.

SOLUTION

(1) $\qquad a = 2, b = -5, c = 1.$

(2) $$x = \frac{-(-5) \pm \sqrt{(-5)^2 - 4(2)(1)}}{2(2)}$$

(3) $$x = \frac{5 \pm \sqrt{17}}{4} \approx \frac{5 \pm 4.1231}{4}$$

To three decimal places, $x = 2.281$ or $x = 0.219$

Example 12.18
Solve $x^2 - 2x + 5 = 0$ by using the quadratic formula.

SOLUTION

(1) $a = 1, b = -2, c = 5.$

(2) $$x = \frac{-(-2) \pm \sqrt{4 - 4(1)(5)}}{2(1)}$$

(3) $$x = \frac{2 \pm \sqrt{-16}}{2}$$

$$x = \frac{2 \pm j4}{2} = \frac{2(1 \pm j2)}{2} = 1 \pm j2$$

The solutions are $1 + j2$ and $1 - j2$.

The expression $b^2 - 4ac$ is called the **discriminant** of the quadratic equation because it determines the types of roots the equation has. Letting $D = b^2 - 4ac$, the quadratic formula can be written as

$$x = \frac{-b \pm \sqrt{D}}{2a}$$

Note that if a, b, and c are integers,

for $D = 0$, there is one real root
for $D = k^2$, there are two rational real roots for k a positive integer
for $D > 0$, there are two real roots
for $D < 0$, there are two imaginary roots

The formula also reveals that if a, b, and c are rational numbers,

irrational roots occur in pairs, such as $m + \sqrt{n}$ and $m - \sqrt{n}$
imaginary roots occur in pairs, such as $m + jn$ and $m - jn$

For practical applications, unless otherwise instructed, all real roots should be reduced to a numerical solution in decimals, as shown in Example 12.17.

12.06 / Sum and product of roots

Formulas for the sum and product of the roots of a quadratic equation can be obtained from the quadratic formula. The roots of $ax^2 + bx + c = 0$ are

$$x_1 = \frac{-b + \sqrt{b^2 - 4ac}}{2a}$$

and

$$x_2 = \frac{-b - \sqrt{b^2 - 4ac}}{2a}$$

Adding the roots,

$$x_1 + x_2 = \frac{-b + (-b)}{2a} = \frac{-2b}{2a} = -\frac{b}{a}$$

Multiplying,

$$x_1 x_2 = \frac{(-b)^2 - \left|\sqrt{b^2 - 4ac}\right|^2}{4a^2}$$

$$= \frac{b^2 - (b^2 - 4ac)}{4a^2} = \frac{4ac}{4a^2} = \frac{c}{a}$$

Now, by dividing $ax^2 + bx + c = 0$ by a,

$$x^2 + \frac{b}{a}x + \frac{c}{a} = 0$$

Since the sum of the roots $x_1 + x_2 = -\dfrac{b}{a}$ and the product of the roots

$x_1 x_2 = \dfrac{c}{a}$, it is noted that *when the coefficient of $x^2 = 1$,*

the sum of the roots is the negative of the coefficient of x
the product of the roots is the constant term.

Note that these two concepts were used in factoring the general trinomial.

Example 12.19
Without solving the equation, find the sum and the product of the roots of $3x^2 + 5x + 8 = 0$.

SOLUTION
(1) Divide by 3, the coefficient of x^2:

$$x^2 + \frac{5}{3}x + \frac{8}{3} = 0$$

(2) Sum $= -$ coefficient of x:

$$\text{sum} = -\frac{5}{3}$$

(3) Product $=$ constant term:

$$\text{product} = \frac{8}{3}$$

The formulas for the sum and product of the roots furnish a very easy check for the solutions of the quadratic equation. This is illustrated in Example 12.20.

Example 12.20
By using the formulas for the sum and product of roots, check that $\dfrac{3 + \sqrt{7}}{2}$ and $\dfrac{3 - \sqrt{7}}{2}$ are the solutions of $2x^2 - 6x + 1 = 0$.

SOLUTION
Adding:

$$\text{sum of roots} = \left(\frac{3 + \sqrt{7}}{2}\right) + \left(\frac{3 - \sqrt{7}}{2}\right) = 3$$

Multiplying:

$$\text{product of roots} = \left(\frac{3 + \sqrt{7}}{2}\right) \cdot \left(\frac{3 - \sqrt{7}}{2}\right) = \frac{9 - 7}{4} = \frac{1}{2}$$

Dividing the equation by 2:

$$x^2 - 3x + \frac{1}{2} = 0$$

Using the formulas:

$$\text{sum of roots} = -(-3) = 3$$

$$\text{product of roots} = \frac{1}{2}$$

If the sum and product of the roots of a quadratic equation are known, the sum and product formulas can be used to find the quadratic equation. This is shown in Example 12.21.

Example 12.21
Find the quadratic equation such that the sum of its roots is $\frac{2}{5}$ and the product of its roots is 3.

SOLUTION
(1) Write the formula: $\qquad x^2 - (\text{sum})x + \text{product} = 0$

(2) Substitute: $\qquad\qquad x^2 - \frac{2}{5}x + 3 \qquad\qquad = 0$

(3) Simplify: $\qquad\qquad 5x^2 - 2x + 15 = 0$

Problem Set 12.4

1–20
Solve each equation by using the quadratic formula. Check the solutions by using the sum and product of roots formulas. Express all irrational real roots in decimal form to three places.

1. $2x^2 + 3x - 4 = 0$
2. $3x^2 - 5x - 6 = 0$
3. $5x^2 - 2x - 3 = 0$
4. $4x^2 + 4x - 5 = 0$
5. $6y^2 + 7y + 7 = 0$
6. $10y^2 - 9y + 2 = 0$
7. $y^2 - 4y = 3$
8. $y^2 - 6y = 3$
9. $4r^2 = 12r - 25$
10. $9r^2 = 6r - 10$

11. $-13t^2 = 12t + 13$
12. $-16t^2 = 7t - 9$
13. $R(R + 10) = R - 10$
14. $10V - V^2 = 2(V + 10)$
15. $E + 4 = 5E^2$
16. $2 - T = 7T^2$
17. $0.8y^2 + 0.3y + 0.1 = 0$
18. $0.15x^2 + 0.02x - 0.01 = 0$
19. $5(2x - 7) = 2(5x - x^2)$
20. $4(5x - 48) = 5x(4 - x)$

21–30

Find the quadratic equation for the given sum and product of its roots. Then solve the equation.

21. sum $= 5$, product $= 6$

22. sum $= 7$, product $= 12$

23. sum $= -3$, product $= \frac{1}{4}$

24. sum $= -2$, product $= -\frac{1}{2}$

25. sum $= -0.40$, product $= 0.04$

26. sum $= 3.00$, product $= 2.25$

27. sum $= 70$, product $= 1325$

28. sum $= 100$, product $= 3400$

29. sum $= \frac{4}{3}$, product $= -\frac{1}{3}$

30. sum $= -\frac{1}{2}$, product $= -\frac{19}{16}$

12.07 / Equations in quadratic form

For certain equations, the substitution $y = f(x)$ may change the equation into a quadratic equation in y. The resulting equation may then be solved for y by any of the methods previously discussed, and, finally, $f(x) = y$ is solved for x.

Example 12.22
Solve $x^4 - 3x^2 - 4 = 0$.

SOLUTION

(1) Let $y = x^2$. Then $y^2 = x^4$.

(2) Substituting: $\qquad\qquad y^2 - 3y - 4 = 0$

(3) Factoring: $\qquad\qquad (y - 4)(y + 1) = 0$

(4) Solve for y: $\qquad\qquad y = 4$ or $y = -1$

(5) Replace y by x^2: $\qquad x^2 = 4$ or $x^2 = -1$

(6) Solve for x: $\qquad\qquad x = \pm 2$ or $x = \pm j$

The solutions are $2, -2, j, -j$.

Checking:

$x = 2, \quad x^4 - 3x^2 - 4 = 16 - 12 - 4 = 0$

$x = -2, x^4 - 3x^2 - 4 = 16 - 12 - 4 = 0$

$x = j, \quad x^4 - 3x^2 - 4 = j^4 - 3j^2 - 4 = 1 + 3 - 4 = 0$

$x = -j, x^4 - 3x^2 - 4 = j^4 - 3j^2 - 4 = 0$

From this point on, no further checks are supplied but they are left for the student.

Example 12.23

Solve $\sqrt[3]{x^2} + 7\sqrt[3]{x} - 8 = 0$.

SOLUTION

(1) Let $y = \sqrt[3]{x} = x^{1/3}$. Then $y^2 = (x^{1/3})^2 = x^{2/3} = \sqrt[3]{x^2}$.

(2) Substituting: $\quad\quad\quad\quad\quad y^2 + 7y - 8 = 0$

(3) Factoring: $\quad\quad\quad\quad\quad\quad (y + 8)(y - 1) = 0$

(4) Solving: $\quad\quad\quad\quad\quad\quad\quad y = -8 \text{ or } y = 1$

(5) Replacing y by $\sqrt[3]{x}$: $\quad\quad \sqrt[3]{x} = -8 \text{ or } \sqrt[3]{x} = 1$

(6) Cubing both sides: $\quad\quad (\sqrt[3]{x})^3 = (-8)^3 \text{ or } (\sqrt[3]{x})^3 = 1^3$

$$x = -512 \text{ or } x = 1$$

Problem Set 12.5

Solve, expressing all real irrational solutions in decimal form correct to three significant digits.

1. $x^4 - 29x^2 + 100 = 0$
2. $x^4 + 4x^2 - 45 = 0$
3. $x - 2\sqrt{x} - 48 = 0$
4. $\sqrt{x} - 5\sqrt[4]{x} + 6 = 0$
5. $t^{-2} - 16t^{-1} + 63 = 0$
6. $12t^{-4} - 7t^{-2} + 1 = 0$
7. $16r^8 - 17r^4 + 1 = 0$
8. $r^6 + 117r^3 - 1000 = 0$

9. $y^{2/3} - 4y^{1/3} + 1 = 0$

10. $y^{4/3} - 6y^{2/3} + 4 = 0$

11. $(2R - 1)^2 - 10(2R - 1) + 23 = 0$
12. $(T^2 - 2T)^2 - 3(T^2 - 2T) - 4 = 0$
13. $2\sin^2 x + \sin x = 1$
14. $2\cos^2 x - \cos x = 1$
15. $3\tan^2 x - 2\sqrt{3}\tan x = -1$
16. $\cot^2 x - 1.56\cot x - 2.56 = 0$
17. $10^{2x} - 5(10^x) - 14 = 0$
18. $2^x - 24(2^{-x}) = 5$

19. $\left(v + \dfrac{1}{v}\right)^2 + 4\left(v + \dfrac{1}{v}\right) = 77$

20. $2\left(v^2 + \dfrac{1}{v^2}\right)^2 - 5\left(v^2 + \dfrac{1}{v^2}\right) + 2 = 0$

12.08 / Literal quadratic equations

Many formulas used in engineering and science are quadratic in form. For certain problems it is convenient to solve the formula for a variable other than the one explicitly given. This can be done by using the methods developed in this chapter.

Example 12.24
Solve $s = \frac{1}{2}gt^2 + v_0t$ for t. (s is the distance an object falls in t time given an initial velocity of v_0, and g is the acceleration due to gravity.)

SOLUTION

(1) Rewrite all terms on the left side of the equal sign in order of decreasing powers of t:

$$\tfrac{1}{2}gt^2 + v_0t - s = 0$$

(2) Use the quadratic formula:

$$a = \tfrac{1}{2}g \qquad b = v_0 \qquad c = -s$$

$$t = \frac{-v_0 \pm \sqrt{v_0^2 - 4(\tfrac{1}{2}g)(-s)}}{2(\tfrac{1}{2}g)}$$

(3) Simplify:

$$t = \frac{-v_0 \pm \sqrt{v_0^2 + 2gs}}{g}$$

Example 12.25

Solve $S = \pi r\sqrt{r^2 + h^2}$ for r. (S is the surface area of a right circular cone having radius r and height h.)

SOLUTION

(1) Squaring both sides:

$$S^2 = \pi^2 r^2(r^2 + h^2)$$

(2) Simplifying:

$$S^2 = \pi^2 r^4 + \pi^2 h^2 r^2$$

(3) Rewriting as a quadratic in r^2:

$$\pi^2(r^2)^2 + \pi^2 h^2(r^2) - S^2 = 0$$

(4) Using the quadratic formula:

$$r^2 = \frac{-\pi^2 h^2 \pm \sqrt{\pi^4 h^4 + 4\pi^2 S^2}}{2\pi^2}$$

(5) Simplifying:

$$r^2 = \frac{-\pi h^2 \pm \sqrt{\pi^2 h^4 + 4S^2}}{2\pi}$$

(6) Selecting positive root since r^2 must be positive:

$$r^2 = \frac{-\pi h^2 + \sqrt{\pi^2 h^4 + 4S^2}}{2\pi}$$

(7) Solving for r:

$$r = \sqrt{\frac{-\pi h^2 + \sqrt{\pi^2 h^4 + 4S^2}}{2\pi}}$$

(Note again that only the positive root was accepted since r must be positive.)

Problem Set 12.6

Solve each formula for the variable stated at the right of the formula.

1. Gravitational force: $\qquad$ $F = \dfrac{GMm}{R^2}$; R

2. Kinetic energy: $\qquad$ $E = \frac{1}{2}mv^2$; v

3. Range of projectile: $\qquad$ $R = \dfrac{v_0{}^2 \sin 2\theta}{g}$; v_0

4. Hypotenuse of right triangle: $\qquad$ $c^2 = a^2 + b^2$; a

5. Light intensity: $\qquad$ $\dfrac{c_1}{r_1{}^2} = \dfrac{c_2}{r_2{}^2}$; r_1

6. Black-body radiation: $\qquad$ $W = SA(T_1{}^4 - T_2{}^4)$; T_2

7. Total area, right circular cone: $\qquad$ $T = \pi r(r + s)$; r

8. Total area, right circular cylinder: $\quad$ $T = 2\pi r(r + h)$; r

9. Motion of projectile: $\qquad$ $y = (\tan \theta)x - \left(\dfrac{g}{2v_0{}^2} \sec^2 \theta\right)x^2$; x

10. Rotational motion: $\qquad$ $\theta = \frac{1}{2}\alpha t^2 + w_0 t$; t

11. Moment of inertia, circular ring: $\qquad$ $I = \dfrac{\pi(r_2{}^4 - r_1{}^4)}{4}$; r_1

12. Law of cosines: $\qquad$ $c^2 = a^2 + b^2 - 2ab \cos C$; a

13. Resultant vector magnitude: $\qquad$ $v^2 = v_x{}^2 + v_y{}^2 + v_z{}^2$; v_z

14. Work–energy relation: $\qquad$ $W = \frac{1}{2}mv^2 - \frac{1}{2}mv_0{}^2$; v_0

15. Potential energy between two atoms in a molecule $\qquad$ $P = \dfrac{a}{x^{12}} - \dfrac{b}{x^6}$; x

16. Reactance for alternating current: $\quad$ $X = wL - \dfrac{1}{wC}$; w

17. Flow rate of liquid:
$$Q = A_1 \sqrt{\frac{kh}{A_2{}^2 - A_1{}^2}} \; ; A_1$$

18. Doppler effect (sound):
$$f' = f\left(1 + \frac{v_0}{v} + \frac{v_0{}^2}{v^2}\right) \; ; v$$

19. Resistance–temperature:
$$R = R_0(1 + AT + BT^2) \; ; T$$

20. Specific heat:
$$c = A + BT + CT^2 \; ; T$$

21. Electric power:
$$W = Ei - Ri^2 \; ; i$$

22. Efficiency of a screw:
$$E = \frac{x - ux^2}{x + u} \; ; x$$

23. Frequency of damped oscillations:
$$f = \frac{1}{2\pi}\sqrt{\frac{k}{m} - \frac{r^2}{4m^2}} \; ; m$$

24. Reflectance of boundary between two dielectrics:
$$R = \left(\frac{n_1 - n_2}{n_1 + n_2}\right)^2 \; ; n_1$$

25. Gain-in-amplitude factor of vibrating system:
$$G = \frac{a^2}{2b\sqrt{a^2 - b^2}} \; ; a$$

26. Ionization constant of acids:
$$K = \frac{a^2}{(1 - a)V} \; ; a$$

27. Suspended catenary cable:
$$y = \sqrt{s^2 - \left(\frac{H}{w}\right)^2} - \frac{H}{w} \; ; \frac{H}{w}$$

28. Mean free path of molecules in turbulent flow
$$\lambda^2 = a(t - t_0)[1 + b(t - t_0)] \; ; t$$

12.09 / Stated problems in quadratics

Many stated problems require the solution of a quadratic equation. The required quadratic equation may be obtained by applying the same principles developed for linear equations in Section 6.05.

Example 12.26
A power station supplies 60 kw to a load using 5000 ft of No. 000 copper feeder whose resistance is 0.078 Ω/1000 ft. The input voltage is maintained constant at 650 V. Find (a) the current I; (b) the voltage E_2 at the load; (c) the efficiency, $(E_2 \times 100)/E_1$; (d) the maximum power.

SOLUTION

First, supply the formulae that are needed. Power in watts, $P = EI$, where E is in volts and I in amperes. Voltage, $E = IR$, where I is in amperes and R is in ohms.

(a) $\qquad\qquad R = 5(0.078) = 0.39\ \Omega$

$\qquad\qquad$ Voltage drop, $E = 650 - 0.39I$

$\qquad\qquad$ Power, $60,000 = (650 - 0.39I)I$

Thus, $\qquad 0.39I^2 - 650I + 60,000 = 0$

Solving:

$$I = \frac{650 \pm \sqrt{(650)^2 - 4(0.39)(60,000)}}{2(0.39)}$$

$$= \frac{650 \pm 573.5}{0.78}$$

$$= 1569 \text{ amp or } 98.1 \text{ amp}$$

Checking by the sum and the product of roots test,

$$\text{sum} = 1569 + 98 = 1667 \text{ and sum} = \frac{650}{0.39} = 1667$$

$$\text{product} = (1569)(98.1) = 153,800 \text{ and product} = \frac{60,000}{0.39} = 153,800$$

(b) For $I = 1569$, the voltage at the load $E_2 = \dfrac{P}{I} = \dfrac{60,000}{1569} = 38$ V which is too small to be practical.

For $I = 98.1$, $E_2 = \dfrac{60,000}{98.1} = 612$ volts which is acceptable.

Thus, $I = 1569$ amp is rejected as a solution and $I = 98.1$ amp is accepted.

(c) Efficiency $= \dfrac{612}{650} \times 100 = 94\%$.

(d) Since $P = -0.391I^2 + 650I$, the maximum value of P corresponds to the vertex of the parabolic graph. This may be obtained by symmetry. Finding the average of the zeros,

$$\frac{1569 + 98.1}{2} = 833.5$$

Thus, the maximum value of P occurs for $I = 833.5$ amp.

$$P_{max} = 270,900 \text{ watts} = 270.9 \text{ kw}$$

(This value may be checked by graphing.)

Example 12.27

Two light sources having illuminations of 100 and 40 candlepower (cp), respectively, are placed 25 ft apart. Find the distance from the 100-cp source so that an object placed in this location will be equally illuminated by both sources.

SOLUTION

Formula: intensity in foot candles $= \dfrac{\text{candlepower}}{(\text{distance})^2}$

$$I = \frac{c}{d^2}$$

Sketch:

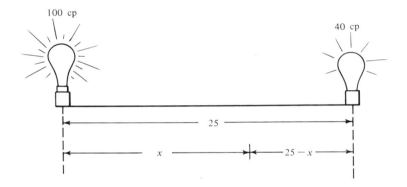

Figure 12.4
Illumination

Equation: $\dfrac{100}{x^2} = \dfrac{40}{(25 - x)^2}$

Solution: $100(625 - 50x + x^2) = 40x^2$

$60x^2 - 5000x + 62{,}500 = 0$

$3x^2 - 250x + 3125 = 0$

$x = \dfrac{125 \pm \sqrt{6250}}{3}$

Approximately, $x = 68$ ft or 15.3 ft.

Both of these answers are acceptable; the 15.3-ft point is between the two light sources and the 68-ft point is $68 - 25 = 33$ ft to the right of the 40-cp source in Figure 12.4.

Example 12.28

Find the range and the maximum height of a projectile fired at an angle of 45° with the horizontal, with an initial velocity of 3200 ft/sec from a hill 300 ft above the ground. ·

SOLUTION

Formula: Neglecting air resistance, the equation of the path of the projectile is

$$y = -\left(\frac{g}{2v_0{}^2}\sec^2\theta\right)x^2 + (\tan\theta)x + h$$

where x = horizontal distance on the ground
$\quad\quad y$ = vertical height

Substituting into the formula:

$$y = -\left(\frac{32}{2(3200)^2}\sec^2 45°\right)x^2 + (\tan 45°)x + 300$$

$$= -\frac{1}{640,000}x^2 + x + 300$$

To find the range, set $y = 0$:

$$-\frac{1}{640,000}x^2 + x + 300 = 0$$

$$x^2 - 640,000x - 192,000,000 = 0$$

$$x = 320,000 \pm \sqrt{1025.92 \times 10^8}$$

To four significant figures, $x = 640,300$ or $x = -300$. The negative answer is rejected.

Thus, the range is 640,300 ft.

To find the maximum height, first average the zeros,

$$x_{max} = \frac{640,300 - 300}{2} = 320,000$$

Thus, $$y_{max} = -\frac{1}{640,000}(320,000)^2 + 320,000 + 300 = 160,300$$

Thus, the maximum height is 160,300 ft.

Problem Set 12.7

1. Find the width that must be turned up on each side of a rectangular sheet of metal of width 25 in. to form a rectangular trough having a cross-sectional area of 75 sq in.

2. An open box is to be made from a rectangular sheet of metal twice as long as it is wide by cutting a square of side 2.5 in. from each corner. Find the dimensions of the rectangular sheet needed to obtain a box having a volume of 180 cu in.
3. A path of uniform width is to be made around a rectangular garden having dimensions 6 by 10 ft. Find the width of the path if the area of the path is $1\frac{1}{2}$ times the area of the garden.
4. How much should the radius of a circular hole, 12 in. in diameter, be enlarged so that the resulting area is twice as large as the original area?
5. Find the width x of the 6- by 8-in. angle if its area is 18.75 sq in.

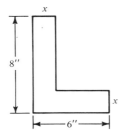

6. A window is in the form of a rectangle surmounted by a semicircle.

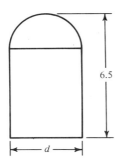

(a) If the total area is 26 sq ft and the total height is 6.5 ft, find the diameter of the semicircle.
(b) For what value of the diameter would the total area be a maximum?
7. Find the height h of a circular arch if its span s is 50 ft and its radius r is 40 ft. (Use $s^2 = 8rh - 4h^2$.)
8. Find the height of an elliptic arch if its span s is 50 ft, its semimajor axis a is 40 ft, and its semiminor axis b is 30 ft [Use $s^2 = \dfrac{4a^2}{b^2}(2bh - h^2)$.]

9. Find the vertical clearance (y) at 10-ft intervals for a parabolic arch having a span s of 100 ft and a maximum height h of 20 ft. [*Hint:* Show that $y = h - \dfrac{4h}{s^2}x^2$, if the vertex is at the origin.]

10. A baseball diamond is a square with each side 90 ft. The pitcher's mound is 60.5 ft from homeplate on the line from homeplate to second base.

   (a) Find the distance from homeplate to second base.

   (b) Find the distance from the pitcher's mound to first base.

11. A 3- by 6-in. timber, which actually measures $2\frac{5}{8}$ by $5\frac{1}{2}$ in., is used as a bumper in a parking area. If the tire is in the position shown in the figure, compute the radius of the tire to the nearest $\frac{1}{32}$ in.

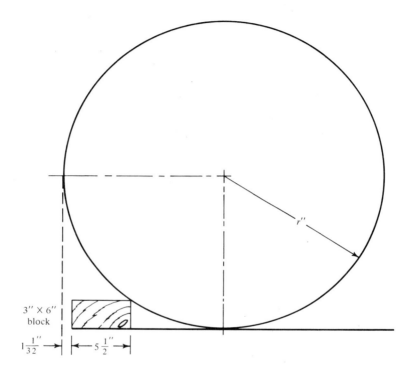

3″ × 6″ block

$1\frac{1}{32}″$

$5\frac{1}{2}″$

$r″$

12. For carrying a heavy gasoline pipeline across a deep ravine, it is hung from a light steel wire cable, which will take the shape of a parabola. If the distance between the two posts used to support the cable is called the span, L, and the distance from the top of the posts to the lowest point on the cable is called the sag, h, the actual length S of wire cable needed between the tops of the posts is given with proper precision by the approximate formula:

$$S = L\left[1 + \frac{8}{3}\left(\frac{h}{L}\right)^2 - \frac{32}{5}\left(\frac{h}{L}\right)^4\right]$$

If a certain crossing is planned for $L = 100$ ft and $S = 104$ ft, find the sag.

13. Find the radii of the two inner circles in the figure if the shaded area is 20 per cent of the area of the boundary circle. [*Hint:* Express the radius of the larger inner circle, r_2, in terms of the radius of the boundary circle and the radius of the smaller inner circle, r_1.]

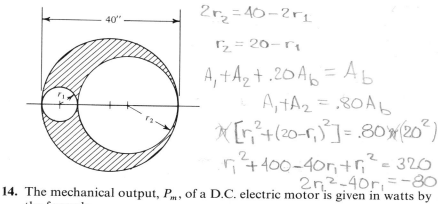

40″

$2r_2 = 40 - 2r_1$

$r_2 = 20 - r_1$

$A_1 + A_2 + .20A_b = A_b$

$A_1 + A_2 = .80A_b$

$\pi[r_1^2 + (20 - r_1)^2] = .80\pi(20^2)$

$r_1^2 + 400 - 40r_1 + r_1^2 = 320$

$2r_1^2 - 40r_1 = -80$

14. The mechanical output, P_m, of a D.C. electric motor is given in watts by the formula

$$P_m = VI_a - I_a^2 R_a$$

where I_a = armature current, amp
V = line voltage
R_a = armature resistance, Ω

For a certain motor the armature resistance is 0.05 Ω, the input line voltage is 110 volts, and the output is 12.73 hp. Find the armature current in amperes. Use Table 10 to change horsepower to watts.

15. Find the hydrogen–ion concentration x in a 0.0500 molar (M) solution of acetic acid if the ionization constant K of acetic acid is 1.721×10^{-5}.

Use $\dfrac{x^2}{M - x} = K$.

16. Find the number of grams (x) of barium sulfate that is dissolved when 200 ml (V) of 0.002 M ammonium sulfate is mixed with an excess of solid barium sulfate. The solubility product S of barium sulfate is 1.00×10^{-10} and the molecular weight W of barium sulfate is 233.

Use $\dfrac{1000x}{VW}\left[M + \dfrac{1000x}{VW}\right] = S$.

17. When two resistors are connected in series, the total resistance, R_s, is 9 Ω.

(a) If the total resistance, R_p, is 2 Ω when these two resistors are connected in parallel, find the number of ohms for each resistor.

(b) Find the number of ohms in each resistor that would produce the maximum total resistance when connected in parallel.

Use $R_s = R_1 + R_2$ and $\dfrac{1}{R_p} = \dfrac{1}{R_1} + \dfrac{1}{R_2}$.

18. (a) Find the inductance L in henrys needed to obtain a frequency (f) of 5 Hz if the capacitance $C = 0.0005$ F and the resistance $R = 40\,\Omega$. Use $(2\pi f)^2 = \dfrac{1}{LC} - \dfrac{R^2}{4L^2}$.

(b) For the same resistance and capacitance as in part (a), what inductance L would produce a maximum value for f?

19. Find the height in feet, s, of a tower if a stone dropped from the top is heard hitting the ground 2 sec later. Use $s = 16\left[2 - \dfrac{s}{1120}\right]^2$, where 1120 fps is used as the velocity of sound.

20. Find the length of time, t, it takes for a weight to slide down a plane 5 ft long, s, inclined at an angle, θ, of 30° with the horizontal if the coefficient of friction, f, is 0.06 and the initial velocity, v_0, is 2 ft/sec. Use $s = 16(\sin\theta - f\cos\theta)t^2 + v_0 t$.

21. For a beam fixed at both ends with a uniformly distributed load of w pounds per foot, and a clear span of L feet, the bending moment is given by

$$M = -\frac{w}{12}(6x^2 - 6Lx + L^2)$$

where x is the distance from one fixed end to the point being investigated.

(a) Find the distance x where the bending moment of a beam with a 12 ft clear span carrying 100 lb/ft is 200 ft-lb.

(b) At what position on the beam is the bending moment a maximum?

(c) At what position on the beam is the absolute value of the bending moment a maximum?

22. The bending moment of a beam of length L in feet, and carrying a uniformly distributed load of w lb/ft when fixed at one end and simply supported at the other, is given for a point located x feet from the fixed end by

$$M = -\frac{w}{8}(4x^2 - 5Lx + L^2)$$

(a) Find the distance x for the maximum bending moment.

(b) If the beam has a span L of 18 ft and is carrying 150 lb/ft, find the value of x for which the bending moment is zero.

23. The Lennard-Jones potential-energy function for nonpolar molecules is given by

$$P = 4e\left[\left(\frac{k}{r}\right)^{12} - \left(\frac{k}{r}\right)^{6}\right]$$

where e = maximum energy of attraction

k = value of r for which $P = 0$

r = intermolecular distance, in angstroms,

Find the distance r between molecules of helium gas for which $P = \frac{1}{2}e$ (half the maximum energy) if $k = 2.566$ angstroms for helium.

24. The international gravity formula

$$g = 978.049(1 + 0.005\,288\,4 \sin^2 \theta - 0.000\,005\,9 \sin^2 2\theta)\,\text{cm/sec}^2$$

gives the acceleration due to gravity for different latitudes with $\theta = 0$ at the equator.

(a) Determine the latitude at which $g = 980.000$.

(b) At what latitude is g a maximum?

(c) At what latitude is g a minimum?

[*Hint*: $\sin^2 2\theta = 4 \sin^2 \theta(1 - \sin^2 \theta)$.]

25. Machine XA can process certain data in 2 hr less time than Machine XB. For a certain rush order, three XA machines and five XB machines were used and the same amount of data was processed in 30 min. Find the time it takes machine XA to process this data alone.

26. One large inlet pipe can fill a tank in 30 min less time than each of the two smaller inlet pipes. When all three pipes are open, the tank is filled in 15 min. Each of the two outlet pipes takes twice as long to drain the tank as the large inlet pipe does to fill it. If all five pipes are left open, will the tank be eventually filled or drained? How long will this take?

27. The owner of an apartment house notes that for every $5 reduction in the monthly rental, he can rent five more apartments.

(a) If he is now renting 20 units at $170 each, find what monthly rental per unit will provide him with a gross income of $6000/month.

(b) Find the maximum income he can hope to obtain by this method.

28. Two hundred feet of fencing is to be used to fence three sides of a rectangular area bordering on a river.

(a) Find the dimensions of the rectangle so that the area is 4800 sq ft.

(b) Find the dimensions of the rectangle so that the area is a maximum.

29. For an optical lens of focal length f,

$$\frac{1}{f} = \frac{1}{d_o} + \frac{1}{d_i}$$

where d_o = distance of the object from the lens

d_i = distance of the image from the lens

Find d_o and d_i if $d_o + d_i = 62.5$ cm and $f = 10$ cm.

30. If the radius of a unit circle is divided into two parts, x and $1 - x$ such that $\dfrac{1 - x}{x} = \dfrac{x}{1}$, x is the length of one side of a regular inscribed decagon. Verify this by solving for x and then showing that $x/2 = \sin 18°$, and thus the central angle subtended by a chord of length x is $36° = \frac{1}{10}(360°)$.

12.10 / Second-degree inequalities

A **second-degree**, or **quadratic, inequality** in the variable x is a statement that can be put into one of the following forms, where $a \neq 0$:

$$ax^2 + bx + c < 0 \qquad ax^2 + bx + c > 0$$

$$ax^2 + bx + c \leq 0 \qquad ax^2 + bx + c \geq 0$$

To solve a quadratic inequality in one variable x means to find those *real* values of x for which the statement is true, since only real numbers possess order.

The technique for solving a quadratic inequality is based upon the fact that a product of two numbers is positive if and only if both factors are positive or both factors are negative; and a product of two numbers is negative if and only if one factor is positive and one factor is negative. In Section 12.06, the two roots of any general quadratic equation were named as x_1 and x_2. Stating this technique in symbols:

$(x - x_1)(x - x_2) > 0$ if both factors have like signs

$(x - x_1)(x - x_2) < 0$ if the two factors have unlike signs

Method for Solving a Quadratic Inequality:
(1) Rewrite the statement so 0 is on the right side, and the coefficient of x^2 is positive.
(2) Find the values $x = x_1$ and $x = x_2$ for which $ax^2 + bx + c = 0$.
(3) Rewrite the left side in factored form as $(x - x_1)(x - x_2)$.
(4) Solve each of the two cases as follows:
    (a) If $(x - x_1)(x - x_2) > 0$, solve:

$$\text{Case 1. } x - x_1 > 0 \text{ and } x - x_2 > 0$$

$$\text{Case 2. } x - x_1 < 0 \text{ and } x - x_2 < 0$$

    (b) If $(x - x_1)(x - x_2) < 0$ solve:

$$\text{Case 1. } x - x_1 > 0 \text{ and } x - x_2 < 0$$

$$\text{Case 2. } x - x_1 < 0 \text{ and } x - x_2 > 0$$

(5) State the solution set, the combination of the solution sets for the two cases.

Example 12.29
Solve $9x - 2x^2 < 30 - 7x$ and graph the solution set on the number line.

SOLUTION

(1) Add $-30 + 7x$ to both sides: $\qquad -2x^2 + 16x - 30 < 0$

Multiply both sides by $-\frac{1}{2}$: $\quad x^2 - 8x + 15 > 0$

(Recall that the inequality sign is changed when both sides are multiplied by a negative number.)

(2)
(3) $\Big\}$ Factor the left side: $\qquad (x - 3)(x - 5) > 0$

(4) Solve the two cases:

Case 1: $x - 3 > 0$ and $x - 5 > 0$

$x > 3 \qquad$ and $x > 5$

To meet both conditions,

$x > 5$

Case 2: $x - 3 < 0$ and $x - 5 < 0$

$x < 3$ and $\quad x < 5$

To meet both conditions,

$x < 3$

(5) The solution set $= \{x \mid x > 5 \text{ or } x < 3\}$.

The graph on the number line is shown in Figure 12.5.

Figure 12.5

Example 12.30

Solve $12x(x - 2) \le 5(4x + 5)$ and graph the solution set on the number line.

SOLUTION

(1) Simplify each side:

$$12x^2 - 24x \le 20x + 25$$

Rewriting:

$$12x^2 - 44x - 25 \le 0$$

(2) Solve the equality:

$$x = \frac{44 \pm \sqrt{(44)^2 - 4(12)(-25)}}{24}$$

$$x_1 = -\tfrac{1}{2} \text{ and } x_2 = \frac{25}{6}$$

(3) Factor left side of inequality:

$$12\left(x + \tfrac{1}{2}\right)\left(x - \frac{25}{6}\right) \leq 0$$

(4) Solve the two cases:

Case 1: $x + \tfrac{1}{2} \geq 0$ and $x - \dfrac{25}{6} \leq 0$

$$x \geq -\tfrac{1}{2} \text{ and } x \leq \frac{25}{6}$$

To meet both conditions;

$$-\tfrac{1}{2} \leq x \leq \frac{25}{6}$$

Case 2: $x + \tfrac{1}{2} \leq 0$ and $x - \dfrac{25}{6} \geq 0$

$$x \leq -\tfrac{1}{2} \text{ and } x \geq \frac{25}{6}$$

There is no value that meets both these conditions.

(5) The solution set is $\{x \mid -\tfrac{1}{2} \leq x \leq \tfrac{25}{6}\}$.
The graph on the number line is shown in Figure 12.6.

Figure 12.6

Example 12.31
Solve: $4x^2 + 25 \geq 20x$.

SOLUTION
Rewriting: $\qquad\qquad 4x^2 - 20x + 25 \geq 0$

Factoring: $\qquad\qquad (2x - 5)^2 \geq 0$
Since the square of a real number is never negative, this statement is true for all real numbers x.
The solution set is R, the set of real numbers.

Example 12.32
Solve: $(10 - 3x)^2 < 0$.

SOLUTION
Since the square of a real number is never negative, this statement is false for all real numbers.
The solution set is $\varnothing$, the empty set.

Problem Set 12.8

1–18
Solve to three significant figures and graph the solution set on the number line.

1. $x^2 - 3x < 4$
2. $x^2 + 4x > 12$
3. $4x^2 \geq 9$
4. $25x^2 \leq 36$
5. $y < 5y^2$
6. $y > 4y^2$
7. $r + 3 \leq 2r^2$
8. $4 - 15r \geq 4r^2$
9. $9v(1 - v) > 4 - 3v$

10. $3x(x - 1) < x^2 + 3x - 10$
11. $4x^2 + 4 > 3x^2 + 4x$
12. $36v(2 - v) < 49 - 12v$
13. $4x^2 - 4x - 5 \leq 0$
14. $9x^2 - 12x - 1 \geq 0$
15. $0.30 - \dfrac{0.15}{y} < \dfrac{0.75}{y^2}$
16. $0.46 + \dfrac{0.23}{y} > \dfrac{0.69}{y^2}$
17. $1.6 \times 10^{-6}R^2 - 4.3 \times 10^{-3}R > 5.0$
18. $6.2 \times 10^{-8}t^2 + 3.5 \times 10^{-4}t < 2.5$

19. The temperature reading T in °F on a thermometer taken from a room temperature of 70°F to an outdoor temperature of 45°F may be approximated by $T - 45 = 25(1 - 0.08t + 0.0016t^2)$ for $0 \leq t < 25$, where t is measured in minutes. During what interval of time will the temperature reading be less than 46°F? Less than 45.01°F?

20. A traffic flow study gave for the capacity C in vehicles per hour of a certain tunnel the empirical relation

$$C = 6.4(50.4S - S^2)$$

where S is the average speed in mph maintained in the tunnel. Find the upper and lower limits of the speed to guarantee at least 3200 vehicles per hour.

21. If the input voltage to a power station over a line having a resistance $R = 0.45\,\Omega$ is maintained constant at 680 volts, what values will the current I have for a power between 50 and 100 kw? (Use $P = EI - RI^2$.)

22. What are the possible values for the diameter of a circular disk if its area must be 10 ± 0.05 in.? (*Hint:* $9.95 \leq$ area ≤ 10.05.)

23. For a car braked at a constant deceleration of 22 ft/sec² the distance and the time the car travels before it stops are given by $s = -11t^2 + v_0t$ and $t = v_0/22$. What are the possible initial velocities v_0 in mph the car may have in order to stop in 99 ft or less?

24. The total force in pounds on the surface of a rectangular plate submerged vertically 3 ft below the water level is given by

$$F = 31.2bh(h + 6)$$

where b is the horizontal width of the plate and h is its vertical height. What values are possible for the height of a plate 4 ft wide if the force is to be kept less than 6864 lb?

12.11 / Chapter Review

1. A *quadratic*, or *second-degree, equation* in the variable x is an equation of the form $ax^2 + bx + c = 0$, where $a \neq 0$.
2. The *algebraic methods* for solving a quadratic equation are
   (a) *Factoring* (useful when the factors are readily observed)
   (b) *Completing the square* (useful when $a = 1$ and b is a multiple of 2)
   (c) *Quadratic formula* (can be used in all cases)

$$x = \frac{-b \pm \sqrt{b^2 - 4ac}}{2a}$$

3. The *discriminant D* of a quadratic equation is the expression under the radical sign in the quadratic formula: $D = b^2 - 4ac$.

   If $D > 0$, the quadratic equation has two real roots

   If $D = 0$, the quadratic equation has one real root

   If $D < 0$, the quadratic equation has two imaginary roots

4. The *sum and the product of the roots* of $ax^2 + bx + c = 0$ are

$$\text{sum} = -\frac{b}{a} \qquad \text{and} \qquad \text{product} = \frac{c}{a}$$

   The formulas for the sum and the product of the roots furnish an easy way to check the solutions of a quadratic equation.
5. The graph of a quadratic function is called a *parabola*.

   For $y = ax^2 + bx + c$

$$\begin{cases} \text{if } a \text{ is positive, the parabola opens upward} \\ \text{if } a \text{ is negative, the parabola opens downward} \end{cases}$$

6. *The vertex of a parabola* has coordinates

$$x = -\frac{b}{2a} \qquad y = -\frac{b^2 - 4ac}{4a}$$

   The vertex of a parabola may also be found by using symmetry.
7. A *quadratic inequality* is solved by writing the quadratic expression in factored form and then solving each of the resulting two cases based on the signs of the factors.

Problem Set 12.9 (Chapter Review)

1–4

Solve by the most convenient method and check by the sum and product of the roots formulas.

1. $x^2 + 2x - 48 = 0$

2. $x^2 - 8x + 11 = 0$

3. $16x^2 - 16x + 1 = 0$

4. $4x^2 + 20x + 41 = 0$

5 and 6

Find the maximum or minimum point of each of the following, sketch the graph, and approximate the x intercepts.

5. $y = 16t^2 - 480t + 3050$

6. $y = -6x^2 + 9x - 3$

7 and 8

Solve and graph the solution on the number line.

7. $5x(5x + 1) < 6$

8. $1 \geq \dfrac{2}{x} + \dfrac{4}{x^2}$

9. Solve: $(r^2 - 3r)^2 - (r^2 - 3r) = 2$.

10. A steel wire 12 ft long is cut into two pieces. One piece is bent into a square and the other into an equilateral triangle.
   (a) Express the sum of the areas of the triangle and the square as a function of x, the part cut off to form the triangle.
   (b) Graph the function determined in part (a).
   (c) Find x so that the sum of the areas is a maximum.
   (d) Find x so that the sum of the areas is a minimum.
   (e) Find x so that the area of the triangle is equal to the area of the square.

11. Find the time of efflux of an SAE 20 oil having a density of 9.18 g/cc if its viscosity as measured on a Saybolt viscosimeter is 250 centipoises.

$$\text{Use } v = d\left(0.0022t - \frac{1.80}{t}\right)$$

   where v = viscosity, poises
   d = density, g/cc
   t = time of efflux, sec

12. After a cubical box is lined with insulating material $\frac{1}{4}$ in. thick, the volume of the box is decreased by 585.125 cu in.
   (a) Find the original dimensions of the box.

(b) What are the allowable thicknesses for the insulating material so that the change in volume for this box is between 480 and 960 cu in.? Approximate the change in volume, $V_2 - V_1$, by

$$V_2 - V_1 = 6ts^2 - 12t^2s$$

where t = thickness of insulating material

s = length of side of interior of box before insulation.

Appendix

TABLE 1
Functions of Numbers

N	N^2	N^3	$\sqrt{N}$	$\sqrt[3]{N}$	$\dfrac{1000}{N}$	N = diameter circum.	area
1/64	0.000 24	0.000 004	0.125 0	0.250 0	64.000 0	0.049 09	0.000 192
1/32	0.000 98	0.000 031	0.176 8	0.315 0	32.000 0	0.098 18	0.000 767
3/64	0.002 20	0.000 103	0.216 5	0.360 6	21.333 3	0.147 26	0.001 726
1/16	0.003 91	0.000 244	0.250 0	0.396 9	16.000 0	0.196 35	0.003 068
5/64	0.006 10	0.000 477	0.279 5	0.427 5	12.800 0	0.245 44	0.004 794
3/32	0.008 79	0.000 824	0.306 2	0.454 3	10.666 7	0.294 52	0.006 903
7/64	0.011 96	0.001 308	0.330 7	0.478 2	9.142 9	0.343 61	0.009 393
1/8	0.015 63	0.001 953	0.353 6	0.500 0	8.000 0	0.392 70	0.012 276
9/64	0.019 78	0.002 782	0.375 0	0.520 0	7.111 1	0.441 79	0.015 535
5/32	0.024 41	0.003 814	0.395 3	0.538 6	6.400 0	0.490 87	0.019 172
11/64	0.029 54	0.005 077	0.414 6	0.556 0	5.818 2	0.539 96	0.023 201
3/16	0.035 16	0.006 592	0.433 0	0.572 4	5.333 3	0.589 05	0.027 615
13/64	0.041 26	0.008 381	0.450 7	0.587 8	4.923 1	0.638 14	0.032 406
7/32	0.047 85	0.010 468	0.467 7	0.602 5	4.571 4	0.687 22	0.037 581
15/64	0.054 93	0.012 875	0.484 1	0.616 6	4.266 7	0.736 31	0.043 142
1/4	0.062 50	0.015 625	0.500 0	0.630 0	4.000 0	0.785 40	0.049 087
17/64	0.070 56	0.018 742	0.515 4	0.642 8	3.764 7	0.834 48	0.055 418
9/32	0.079 10	0.022 247	0.530 3	0.655 2	3.555 6	0.883 57	0.062 125
19/64	0.088 13	0.026 165	0.544 9	0.667 1	3.368 4	0.932 66	0.069 217
5/16	0.097 66	0.030 516	0.559 0	0.678 6	3.200 0	0.981 75	0.076 702
21/64	0.107 67	0.035 326	0.572 8	0.689 7	3.047 6	1.030 8	0.084 56
11/32	0.118 16	0.040 619	0.586 3	0.700 5	2.909 1	1.079 9	0.092 81
23/64	0.129 15	0.046 413	0.599 5	0.711 0	2.782 6	1.129 0	0.101 43
3/8	0.140 63	0.052 734	0.612 4	0.721 1	2.666 7	1.178 1	0.110 45
25/64	0.152 59	0.059 605	0.625 0	0.731 0	2.560 0	1.227 2	0.119 84
13/32	0.165 04	0.067 047	0.637 4	0.740 6	2.461 5	1.276 3	0.129 62
27/64	0.177 98	0.075 079	0.649 5	0.750 0	2.370 4	1.325 4	0.139 79
7/16	0.191 41	0.083 740	0.661 4	0.759 2	2.285 7	1.374 4	0.150 33
29/64	0.205 32	0.093 037	0.673 2	0.768 1	2.206 9	1.423 5	0.161 26
15/32	0.219 73	0.102 997	0.684 7	0.776 8	2.133 3	1.472 6	0.172 57
31/64	0.234 62	0.113 644	0.696 0	0.785 4	2.064 5	1.521 7	0.184 27
1/2	0.250 00	0.125 000	0.707 1	0.793 7	2.000 0	1.570 8	0.196 35
33/64	0.265 87	0.137 089	0.718 1	0.801 9	1.939 4	1.619 9	0.208 81
17/32	0.282 23	0.149 933	0.728 9	0.809 9	1.882 4	1.669 0	0.221 66
35/64	0.299 07	0.163 555	0.739 5	0.817 8	1.828 6	1.718 1	0.234 89
9/16	0.316 41	0.177 979	0.750 0	0.825 5	1.777 8	1.767 1	0.248 50
37/64	0.334 23	0.193 226	0.760 4	0.833 1	1.729 7	1.816 2	0.262 50
19/32	0.352 54	0.209 320	0.770 6	0.840 5	1.684 2	1.865 3	0.276 88
39/64	0.371 34	0.226 284	0.780 6	0.847 8	1.641 0	1.914 4	0.291 65
5/8	0.390 63	0.244 141	0.790 6	0.855 0	1.600 0	1.963 5	0.306 80
41/64	0.410 40	0.262 913	0.800 4	0.862 1	1.561 0	2.012 6	0.322 33
21/32	0.430 66	0.282 621	0.810 1	0.869 0	1.523 8	2.061 7	0.338 24
43/64	0.451 42	0.303 295	0.819 7	0.875 9	1.488 4	2.110 8	0.354 54
11/16	0.472 66	0.324 951	0.829 7	0.882 6	1.454 5	2.159 8	0.371 22
45/64	0.494 38	0.347 614	0.838 5	0.889 2	1.422 2	2.208 9	0.388 29
23/32	0.516 60	0.371 307	0.847 8	0.895 8	1.391 3	2.258 0	0.405 74
47/64	0.539 31	0.396 053	0.857 0	0.902 2	1.361 7	2.307 1	0.423 57
3/4	0.562 50	0.421 875	0.866 0	0.908 6	1.333 3	2.356 2	0.441 79
49/64	0.586 18	0.448 795	0.875 0	0.914 8	1.306 1	2.405 3	0.460 38
25/32	0.610 35	0.476 837	0.883 9	0.921 0	1.280 0	2.454 4	0.479 37
51/64	0.635 01	0.506 023	0.892 7	0.927 1	1.254 9	2.503 5	0.498 74
13/16	0.660 16	0.536 377	0.901 4	0.933 1	1.230 8	2.552 5	0.518 49
53/64	0.685 79	0.567 921	0.910 0	0.939 1	1.207 5	2.601 6	0.538 62
27/32	0.711 91	0.600 677	0.918 6	0.944 9	1.185 2	2.650 7	0.559 14
55/64	0.738 53	0.634 608	0.927 0	0.950 7	1.163 6	2.699 8	0.580 04
7/8	0.765 63	0.669 922	0.935 4	0.956 5	1.142 9	2.748 9	0.601 83
57/64	0.793 21	0.706 455	0.943 7	0.962 1	1.122 8	2.798 0	0.622 99
29/32	0.821 29	0.744 293	0.952 0	0.967 7	1.103 4	2.847 1	0.645 04
59/64	0.849 85	0.783 459	0.960 1	0.973 3	1.084 7	2.896 2	0.667 47
15/16	0.878 91	0.823 975	0.968 3	0.978 7	1.066 7	2.945 2	0.690 29
61/64	0.908 45	0.865 864	0.976 3	0.984 1	1.049 2	2.994 3	0.713 49
31/32	0.938 48	0.909 149	0.984 3	0.989 5	1.032 3	3.043 4	0.737 08
63/64	0.968 99	0.953 854	0.992 2	0.994 8	1.015 9	3.092 5	0.761 04
1 1/8	1.265 6	1.423 8	1.060 6	1.040 0	0.888 89	3.534 3	0.994 00
1 3/8	1.890 6	2.599 6	1.172 6	1.112 0	0.727 27	4.319 7	1.484 9
1 5/8	2.640 6	4.291 0	1.274 8	1.175 7	0.615 38	5.105 1	2.073 9
1 7/8	3.515 6	6.591 8	1.369 3	1.233 1	0.533 33	5.890 5	2.761 2

N	N^2	N^3	$\sqrt{N}$	$\sqrt[3]{N}$	$\dfrac{1000}{N}$	N = diameter	
						circum.	area
2 1/8	4.515 6	9.595 7	1.457 7	1.285 6	0.470 59	6.675 9	3.546 6
2 3/8	5.640 6	13.396 5	1.541 1	1.334 2	0.421 05	7.461 3	4.430 1
2 5/8	6.890 6	18.087 9	1.620 2	1.379 5	0.380 95	8.246 7	5.411 9
2 7/8	8.265 6	23.763 7	1.695 6	1.421 9	0.347 83	9.032 1	6.491 8
3 1/8	9.765 6	30.517 6	1.767 8	1.462 0	0.320 00	9.817 5	7.669 9
3 3/8	11.390 6	38.443 4	1.837 1	1.500 0	0.296 30	10.602 9	8.946 2
3 5/8	13.140 6	47.634 8	1.903 9	1.536 2	0.275 86	11.388 3	10.320 6
3 7/8	15.015 6	58.185 6	1.968 5	1.570 7	0.258 06	12.173 7	11.793 2
1	1	1	1.000 0	1.000 0	1000.000	3.142	0.785 4
2	4	8	1.414 2	1.259 9	500.000	6.283	3.141 6
3	9	27	1.732 1	1.442 2	333.333	9.425	7.068 6
4	16	64	2.000 0	1.587 4	250.000	12.566	12.566 4
5	25	125	2.236 1	1.710 0	200.000	15.708	19.635 0
6	36	216	2.449 5	1.817 1	166.667	18.850	28.274 3
7	49	343	2.645 8	1.912 9	142.857	21.991	38.484 5
8	64	512	2.828 4	2.000 0	125.000	25.133	50.265 5
9	81	729	3.000 0	2.080 1	111.111	28.274	63.617 3
10	100	1000	3.162 3	2.154 4	100.000	31.416	78.539 8
11	121	1331	3.316 6	2.224 0	90.909 1	34.558	95.033 2
12	144	1728	3.464 1	2.289 4	83.333 3	37.699	113.097
13	169	2197	3.605 6	2.351 3	76.923 1	40.841	132.732
14	196	2744	3.741 7	2.410 1	71.428 6	43.982	153.938
15	225	3375	3.873 0	2.466 2	66.666 7	47.124	176.715
16	256	4096	4.000 0	2.519 8	62.500 0	50.265	201.062
17	289	4913	4.123 1	2.571 3	58.823 5	53.407	226.980
18	324	5832	4.242 6	2.620 7	55.555 6	56.549	254.469
19	361	6859	4.358 9	2.668 4	52.631 6	59.690	283.529
20	400	8000	4.472 1	2.714 4	50.000 0	62.832	314.159
21	441	9261	4.582 6	2.758 9	47.619 0	65.973	346.361
22	484	10648	4.690 4	2.802 0	45.454 5	69.115	380.133
23	529	12167	4.795 8	2.843 9	43.478 3	72.257	415.476
24	576	13824	4.899 0	2.884 5	41.666 7	75.398	452.389
25	625	15625	5.000 0	2.924 0	40.000 0	78.540	490.874
26	676	17576	5.099 0	2.962 5	38.461 5	81.681	530.929
27	729	19683	5.196 2	3.000 0	37.037 0	84.823	572.555
28	784	21952	5.291 5	3.036 6	35.714 3	87.965	615.752
29	841	24389	5.385 2	3.072 3	34.482 8	91.106	660.520
30	900	27000	5.477 2	3.107 2	33.333 3	94.248	706.858
31	961	29791	5.567 8	3.141 4	32.258 1	97.389	754.768
32	1024	32768	5.656 9	3.174 8	31.250 0	100.531	804.248
33	1089	35937	5.744 6	3.207 5	30.303 0	103.673	855.299
34	1156	39304	5.831 0	3.239 6	29.411 8	106.814	907.920
35	1225	42875	5.916 1	3.271 1	28.571 4	109.956	962.113
36	1296	46656	6.000 0	3.301 9	27.777 8	113.097	1017.88
37	1369	50653	6.082 8	3.332 2	27.027 0	116.239	1075.21
38	1444	54872	6.164 4	3.362 0	26.315 8	119.381	1134.11
39	1521	59319	6.245 0	3.391 2	25.641 0	122.522	1194.59
40	1600	64000	6.324 6	3.420 0	25.000 0	125.664	1256.64
41	1681	68921	6.403 1	3.448 2	24.390 2	128.81	1320.25
42	1764	74088	6.480 7	3.476 0	23.809 5	131.95	1385.44
43	1849	79507	6.557 4	3.503 4	23.255 8	135.09	1452.20
44	1936	85184	6.633 2	3.530 3	22.727 3	138.23	1520.53
45	2025	91125	6.708 2	3.556 9	22.222 2	141.37	1590.43
46	2116	97336	6.782 3	3.583 0	21.739 1	144.51	1661.90
47	2209	103823	6.855 7	3.608 8	21.276 6	147.65	1734.94
48	2304	110592	6.928 2	3.634 2	20.833 3	150.80	1809.56
49	2401	117649	7.000 0	3.659 3	20.408 2	153.94	1885.74
50	2500	125000	7.071 1	3.684 0	20.000 0	157.08	1963.50
51	2601	132651	7.141 4	3.708 4	19.607 8	160.22	2042.82
52	2704	140608	7.211 1	3.732 5	19.230 8	163.36	2123.72
53	2809	148877	7.280 1	3.756 3	18.867 9	166.50	2206.18
54	2916	157464	7.348 5	3.779 8	18.518 5	169.65	2290.22

N	N^2	N^3	$\sqrt{N}$	$\sqrt[3]{N}$	$\dfrac{1000}{N}$	N = diameter	
						circum.	area
55	**3025**	**166375**	**7.416 2**	**3.803 0**	**18.181 8**	**172.79**	**2375.83**
56	3136	175616	7.483 3	3.825 9	17.857 1	175.93	2463.01
57	3249	185193	7.549 8	3.848 5	17.543 9	179.07	2551.76
58	3364	195112	7.615 8	3.870 9	17.241 4	182.21	2642.08
59	3481	205379	7.681 1	3.893 0	16.949 2	185.35	2733.97
60	**3600**	**216000**	**7.746 0**	**3.914 9**	**16.666 7**	**188.50**	**2827.43**
61	3721	226981	7.810 2	3.936 5	16.393 4	191.64	2922.47
62	3844	238328	7.874 0	3.957 9	16.129 0	194.78	3019.07
63	3969	250047	7.937 3	3.979 1	15.873 0	197.92	3117.25
64	4096	262144	8.000 0	4.000 0	15.625 0	201.06	3216.99
65	**4225**	**274625**	**8.062 3**	**4.020 7**	**15.384 6**	**204.20**	**3318.31**
66	4356	287496	8.124 0	4.041 2	15.151 5	207.35	3421.19
67	4489	300763	8.185 4	4.061 5	14.925 4	210.49	3525.65
68	4624	314432	8.246 2	4.081 7	14.705 9	213.63	3631.68
69	4761	328509	8.306 6	4.101 6	14.492 8	216.77	3739.28
70	**4900**	**343000**	**8.366 6**	**4.121 3**	**14.285 7**	**219.91**	**3848.45**
71	5041	357911	8.426 1	4.140 8	14.084 5	223.05	3959.19
72	5184	373248	8.485 3	4.160 2	13.888 9	226.19	4071.50
73	5329	389017	8.544 0	4.179 3	13.698 6	229.34	4185.39
74	5476	405224	8.602 3	4.198 3	13.513 5	232.48	4300.84
75	**5625**	**421875**	**8.660 3**	**4.217 2**	**13.333 3**	**235.62**	**4417.86**
76	5776	438976	8.717 8	4.235 8	13.157 9	238.76	4536.46
77	5929	456533	8.775 0	4.254 3	12.987 0	241.90	4656.63
78	6084	474552	8.831 8	4.272 7	12.820 5	245.04	4778.36
79	6241	493039	8.888 2	4.290 8	12.658 2	248.19	4901.67
80	**6400**	**512000**	**8.944 3**	**4.308 9**	**12.500 0**	**251.33**	**5026.55**
81	6561	531441	9.000 0	4.326 7	12.345 7	254.47	5153.00
82	6724	551368	9.055 4	4.344 5	12.195 1	257.61	5281.02
83	6889	571787	9.110 4	4.362 1	12.048 2	260.75	5410.61
84	7056	592704	9.165 2	4.379 5	11.904 8	263.89	5541.77
85	**7225**	**614125**	**9.219 5**	**4.396 8**	**11.764 7**	**267.04**	**5674.50**
86	7396	636056	9.273 6	4.414 0	11.627 9	270.18	5808.80
87	7569	658503	9.327 4	4.431 0	11.494 3	273.32	5944.68
88	7744	681472	9.380 8	4.448 0	11.363 6	276.46	6082.12
89	7921	704969	9.434 0	4.464 7	11.236 0	279.60	6221.14
90	**8100**	**729000**	**9.486 8**	**4.481 4**	**11.111 1**	**282.74**	**6361.73**
91	8281	753571	9.539 4	4.497 9	10.989 0	285.88	6503.88
92	8464	778688	9.591 7	4.514 4	10.869 6	289.03	6647.61
93	8649	804357	9.643 7	4.530 7	10.752 7	292.17	6792.91
94	8836	830584	9.695 4	4.546 8	10.638 3	295.31	6939.78
95	**9025**	**857375**	**9.746 8**	**4.562 9**	**10.526 3**	**298.45**	**7088.22**
96	9216	884736	9.798 0	4.578 9	10.416 7	301.59	7238.23
97	9409	912673	9.848 9	4.594 7	10.309 3	304.73	7389.81
98	9604	941192	9.899 5	4.610 4	10.204 1	307.88	7542.96
99	9801	970299	9.949 9	4.626 1	10.101 0	311.02	7697.69
100	**10000**	**1000000**	**10.000 0**	**4.641 6**	**10.000 0**	**314.16**	**7853.98**
101	10201	1030301	10.049 9	4.657 0	9.900 99	317.30	8011.85
102	10404	1061208	10.099 5	4.672 3	9.803 92	320.44	8171.28
103	10609	1092727	10.148 9	4.687 5	9.708 74	323.58	8332.29
104	10816	1124864	10.198 0	4.702 7	9.615 38	326.73	8494.87
105	**11025**	**1157625**	**10.247 0**	**4.717 7**	**9.523 81**	**329.87**	**8659.01**
106	11236	1191016	10.295 6	4.732 6	9.433 96	333.01	8824.73
107	11449	1225043	10.344 1	4.747 5	9.345 79	336.15	8992.02
108	11664	1259712	10.392 3	4.762 2	9.259 26	339.29	9160.88
109	11881	1295029	10.440 3	4.776 9	9.174 31	342.43	9331.32
110	**12100**	**1331000**	**10.488 1**	**4.791 4**	**9.090 91**	**345.58**	**9503.32**
111	12321	1367631	10.535 7	4.805 9	9.009 01	348.72	9676.89
112	12544	1404928	10.583 0	4.820 3	8.928 57	351.86	9852.03
113	12769	1442897	10.630 1	4.834 6	8.849 56	355.00	10028.7
114	12996	1481544	10.677 1	4.848 8	8.771 93	358.14	10207.0
115	**13225**	**1520875**	**10.723 8**	**4.862 9**	**8.695 65**	**361.28**	**10386.9**
116	13456	1560896	10.770 3	4.877 0	8.620 69	364.42	10568.3
117	13689	1601613	10.816 7	4.891 0	8.547 01	367.57	10751.3
118	13924	1643032	10.862 8	4.904 9	8.474 58	370.71	10935.9
119	14161	1685159	10.908 7	4.918 7	8.403 36	373.85	11122.0

Table 1 / Functions of numbers □ **603**

N	N^2	N^3	$\sqrt{N}$	$\sqrt[3]{N}$	$\dfrac{1000}{N}$	circum.	area
						$N =$ diameter	
120	**14400**	**1728000**	**10.954 5**	**4.932 4**	**8.333 33**	**376.99**	**11309.7**
121	14641	1771561	11.000 0	4.946 1	8.264 46	380.13	11499.0
122	14884	1815848	11.045 4	4.959 7	8.196 72	383.27	11689.9
123	15129	1860867	11.090 5	4.973 2	8.130 08	386.42	11882.3
124	15376	1906624	11.135 5	4.986 6	8.064 52	389.56	12076.3
125	**15625**	**1953125**	**11.180 3**	**5.000 0**	**8.000 00**	**392.70**	**12271.8**
126	15876	2000376	11.225 0	5.013 3	7.936 51	395.84	12469.0
127	16129	2048383	11.269 4	5.026 5	7.874 02	398.98	12667.7
128	16384	2097152	11.313 7	5.039 7	7.812 50	402.12	12868.0
129	16641	2146689	11.357 8	5.052 8	7.751 94	405.27	13069.8
130	**16900**	**2197000**	**11.401 8**	**5.065 8**	**7.692 31**	**408.41**	**13273.2**
131	17161	2248091	11.445 5	5.078 8	7.633 59	411.55	13478.2
132	17424	2299968	11.489 1	5.091 6	7.575 76	414.69	13684.8
133	17689	2352637	11.532 6	5.104 5	7.518 80	417.83	13892.9
134	17956	2406104	11.575 8	5.117 2	7.462 69	420.97	14102.6
135	**18225**	**2460375**	**11.619 0**	**5.129 9**	**7.407 41**	**424.12**	**14313.9**
136	18496	2515456	11.661 9	5.142 6	7.352 94	427.26	14526.7
137	18769	2571353	11.704 7	5.155 1	7.299 27	430.40	14741.1
138	19044	2628072	11.747 3	5.167 6	7.246 38	433.54	14957.1
139	19321	2685619	11.789 8	5.180 1	7.194 24	436.68	15174.7
140	**19600**	**2744000**	**11.832 2**	**5.192 5**	**7.142 86**	**439.82**	**15393.8**
141	19881	2803221	11.874 3	5.204 8	7.092 20	442.96	15614.5
142	20164	2863288	11.916 4	5.217 1	7.042 25	446.11	15836.8
143	20449	2924207	11.958 3	5.229 3	6.993 01	449.25	16060.6
144	20736	2985984	12.000 0	5.241 5	6.944 44	452.39	16286.0
145	**21025**	**3048625**	**12.041 6**	**5.253 6**	**6.896 55**	**455.53**	**16513.0**
146	21316	3112136	12.083 0	5.265 6	6.849 32	458.67	16741.5
147	21609	3176523	12.124 4	5.277 6	6.802 72	461.81	16971.7
148	21904	3241792	12.165 5	5.289 6	6.756 76	464.96	17203.4
149	22201	3307949	12.206 6	5.301 5	6.711 41	468.10	17436.6
150	**22500**	**3375000**	**12.247 4**	**5.313 3**	**6.666 67**	**471.24**	**17671.5**
151	22801	3442951	12.288 2	5.325 1	6.622 52	474.38	17907.9
152	23104	3511808	12.328 8	5.336 8	6.578 95	477.52	18145.8
153	23409	3581577	12.369 3	5.348 5	6.535 95	480.66	18385.4
154	23716	3652264	12.409 7	5.360 1	6.493 51	483.81	18626.5
155	**24025**	**3723875**	**12.449 9**	**5.371 7**	**6.451 61**	**486.95**	**18869.2**
156	24336	3796416	12.490 0	5.383 2	6.410 26	490.09	19113.4
157	24649	3869893	12.530 0	5.394 7	6.369 43	493.23	19359.3
158	24964	3944312	12.569 8	5.406 1	6.329 11	496.37	19606.7
159	25281	4019679	12.609 5	5.417 5	6.289 31	499.51	19855.7
160	**25600**	**4096000**	**12.649 1**	**5.428 8**	**6.250 00**	**502.65**	**20106.2**
161	25921	4173281	12.688 6	5.440 1	6.211 18	505.80	20358.3
162	26244	4251528	12.727 9	5.451 4	6.172 84	508.94	20612.0
163	26569	4330747	12.767 1	5.462 6	6.134 97	512.08	20867.2
164	26896	4410944	12.806 2	5.473 7	6.097 56	515.22	21124.1
165	**27225**	**4492125**	**12.845 2**	**5.484 8**	**6.060 61**	**518.36**	**21382.5**
166	27556	4574296	12.884 1	5.495 9	6.024 10	521.50	21642.4
167	27889	4657463	12.922 8	5.506 9	5.988 02	524.65	21904.0
168	28224	4741632	12.961 5	5.517 8	5.952 38	527.79	22167.1
169	28561	4826809	13.000 0	5.528 8	5.917 16	530.93	22431.8
170	**28900**	**4913000**	**13.038 4**	**5.539 7**	**5.882 35**	**534.07**	**22698.0**
171	29241	5000211	13.076 7	5.550 5	5.847 95	537.21	22965.8
172	29584	5088448	13.114 9	5.561 3	5.813 95	540.35	23235.2
173	29929	5177717	13.152 9	5.572 1	5.780 35	543.50	23506.2
174	30276	5268024	13.190 9	5.582 8	5.747 13	546.64	23778.7
175	**30625**	**5359375**	**13.228 8**	**5.593 4**	**5.714 29**	**549.78**	**24052.8**
176	30976	5451776	13.266 5	5.604 1	5.681 82	552.92	24328.5
177	31329	5545233	13.304 1	5.614 7	5.649 72	556.06	24605.7
178	31684	5639752	13.341 7	5.625 2	5.617 98	559.20	24884.6
179	32041	5735339	13.379 1	5.635 7	5.586 59	562.35	25164.9
180	**32400**	**5832000**	**13.416 4**	**5.646 2**	**5.555 56**	**565.49**	**25446.9**
181	32761	5929741	13.453 6	5.656 7	5.524 86	568.63	25730.4
182	33124	6028568	13.490 7	5.667 1	5.494 51	571.77	26015.5
183	33489	6128487	13.527 7	5.677 4	5.464 48	574.91	26302.2
184	33856	6229504	13.564 7	5.687 7	5.434 78	578.05	26590.4

N	N^2	N^3	$\sqrt{N}$	$\sqrt[3]{N}$	$\dfrac{1000}{N}$	N = diameter circum.	area
185	**34225**	**6331625**	**13.601 5**	**5.698 0**	**5.405 41**	**581.19**	**26880.3**
186	34596	6434856	13.638 2	5.708 3	5.376 34	584.34	27171.6
187	34969	6539203	13.674 8	5.718 5	5.347 59	587.48	27464.6
188	35344	6644672	13.711 3	5.728 7	5.319 15	590.62	27759.1
189	35721	6751269	13.747 7	5.738 8	5.291 01	593.76	28055.2
190	**36100**	**6859000**	**13.784 0**	**5.748 9**	**5.263 16**	**596.90**	**28352.9**
191	36481	6967871	13.820 3	5.759 0	5.235 60	600.04	28652.1
192	36864	7077888	13.856 4	5.769 0	5.208 33	603.19	28952.9
193	37249	7189057	13.892 4	5.779 0	5.181 35	606.33	29255.3
194	37636	7301384	13.928 4	5.789 0	5.154 64	609.47	29559.2
195	**38025**	**7414875**	**13.964 2**	**5.798 9**	**5.128 21**	**612.61**	**29864.8**
196	38416	7529536	14.000 0	5.808 8	5.102 04	615.75	30171.9
197	38809	7645373	14.035 7	5.818 6	5.076 14	618.89	30480.5
198	39204	7762392	14.071 2	5.828 5	5.050 51	622.04	30790.7
199	39601	7880599	14.106 7	5.838 3	5.025 13	625.18	31102.6
200	**40000**	**8000000**	**14.142 1**	**5.848 0**	**5.000 00**	**628.32**	**31415.9**
201	40401	8120601	14.177 4	5.857 8	4.975 12	631.46	31730.9
202	40804	8242408	14.212 7	5.867 5	4.950 50	634.60	32047.4
203	41209	8365427	14.247 8	5.877 1	4.926 11	637.74	32365.5
204	41616	8489664	14.282 9	5.886 8	4.901 96	640.88	32685.1
205	**42025**	**8615125**	**14.317 8**	**5.896 4**	**4.878 05**	**644.03**	**33006.4**
206	42436	8741816	14.352 7	5.905 9	4.854 37	647.17	33329.2
207	42849	8869743	14.387 5	5.915 5	4.830 92	650.31	33653.5
208	43264	8998912	14.422 2	5.925 0	4.807 69	653.45	33979.5
209	43681	9129329	14.456 8	5.934 5	4.784 69	656.59	34307.0
210	**44100**	**9261000**	**14.491 4**	**5.943 9**	**4.761 90**	**659.73**	**34636.1**
211	44521	9393931	14.525 8	5.953 3	4.739 34	662.88	34966.7
212	44944	9528128	14.560 2	5.962 7	4.716 98	666.02	35298.9
213	45369	9663597	14.594 5	5.972 1	4.694 84	669.16	35632.7
214	45796	9800344	14.628 7	5.981 4	4.672 90	672.30	35968.1
215	**46225**	**9938375**	**14.662 9**	**5.990 7**	**4.651 16**	**675.44**	**36305.0**
216	46656	10077696	14.696 9	6.000 0	4.629 63	678.58	36643.5
217	47089	10218313	14.730 9	6.009 2	4.608 29	681.73	36983.6
218	47524	10360232	14.764 8	6.018 5	4.587 16	684.87	37325.3
219	47961	10503459	14.798 6	6.027 7	4.566 21	688.01	37668.5
220	**48400**	**10648000**	**14.832 4**	**6.036 8**	**4.545 45**	**691.15**	**38013.3**
221	48841	10793861	14.866 1	6.045 9	4.524 89	694.29	38359.6
222	49284	10941048	14.899 7	6.055 0	4.504 50	697.43	38707.6
223	49729	11089567	14.933 2	6.064 1	4.484 30	700.58	39057.1
224	50176	11239424	14.966 6	6.073 2	4.464 29	703.72	39408.1
225	**50625**	**11390625**	**15.000 0**	**6.082 2**	**4.444 44**	**706.86**	**39760.8**
226	51076	11543176	15.033 3	6.091 2	4.424 78	710.00	40115.0
227	51529	11697083	15.066 5	6.100 2	4.405 29	713.14	40470.8
228	51984	11852352	15.099 7	6.109 1	4.385 96	716.28	40828.1
229	52441	12008989	15.132 7	6.118 0	4.366 81	719.42	41187.1
230	**52900**	**12167000**	**15.165 8**	**6.126 9**	**4.347 83**	**722.57**	**41547.6**
231	53361	12326391	15.198 7	6.135 8	4.329 00	725.71	41909.6
232	53824	12487168	15.231 5	6.144 6	4.310 34	728.85	42273.3
233	54289	12649337	15.264 3	6.153 4	4.291 85	731.99	42638.5
234	54756	12812904	15.297 1	6.162 2	4.273 50	735.13	43005.3
235	**55225**	**12977875**	**15.329 7**	**6.171 0**	**4.255 32**	**738.27**	**43373.6**
236	55696	13144256	15.362 3	6.179 7	4.237 29	741.42	43743.5
237	56169	13312053	15.394 8	6.188 5	4.219 41	744.56	44115.0
238	56644	13481272	15.427 2	6.197 2	4.201 68	747.70	44488.1
239	57121	13651919	15.459 6	6.205 8	4.184 10	750.84	44862.7
240	**57600**	**13824000**	**15.491 9**	**6.214 5**	**4.166 67**	**753.98**	**45238.9**
241	58081	13997521	15.524 2	6.223 1	4.149 38	757.12	45616.7
242	58564	14172488	15.556 3	6.231 7	4.132 23	760.27	45996.1
243	59049	14348907	15.588 5	6.240 3	4.115 23	763.41	46377.0
244	59536	14526784	15.620 5	6.248 8	4.098 36	766.55	46759.5
245	**60025**	**14706125**	**15.652 5**	**6.257 3**	**4.081 63**	**769.69**	**47143.5**
246	60516	14886936	15.684 4	6.265 8	4.065 04	772.83	47529.2
247	61009	15069223	15.716 2	6.274 3	4.048 58	775.97	47916.4
248	61504	15252992	15.748 0	6.282 8	4.032 26	779.12	48305.1
249	62001	15438249	15.779 7	6.291 2	4.016 06	782.26	48695.5

Table 1 / Functions of numbers □ **605**

N	N^2	N^3	$\sqrt{N}$	$\sqrt[3]{N}$	$\dfrac{1000}{N}$	N = diameter circum.	area
250	**62500**	**15625000**	**15.811.4**	**6.299 6**	**4.000 00**	**785.40**	**49087.4**
251	63001	15813251	15.843 0	6.308 0	3.984 06	788.54	49480.9
252	63504	16003008	15.874 5	6.316 4	3.968 25	791.68	49875.9
253	64009	16194277	15.906 0	6.324 7	3.952 57	794.82	50272.6
254	64516	16387064	15.937 4	6.333 0	3.937 01	797.96	50670.7
255	**65025**	**16581375**	**15.968 7**	**6.341 3**	**3.921 57**	**801.11**	**51070.5**
256	65536	16777216	16.000 0	6.349 6	3.906 25	804.25	51471.9
257	66049	16974593	16.031 2	6.357 9	3.891 05	807.39	51874.8
258	66564	17173512	16.062 4	6.366 1	3.875 97	810.53	52279.2
259	67081	17373979	16.093 5	6.374 3	3.861 00	813.67	52685.3
260	**67600**	**17576000**	**16.124 5**	**6.382 5**	**3.846 15**	**816.81**	**53092.9**
261	68121	17779581	16.155 5	6.390 7	3.831 42	819.96	53502.1
262	68644	17984728	16.186 4	6.398 8	3.816 79	823.10	53912.9
263	69169	18191447	16.217 3	6.407 0	3.802 28	826.24	54325.2
264	69696	18399744	16.248 1	6.415 1	3.787 88	829.38	54739.1
265	**70225**	**18609625**	**16.278 8**	**6.423 2**	**3.773 58**	**832.52**	**55154.6**
266	70756	18821096	16.309 5	6.431 2	3.759 40	835.66	55571.6
267	71289	19034163	16.340 1	6.439 3	3.745 32	838.81	55990.2
268	71824	19248832	16.370 7	6.447 3	3.731 34	841.95	56410.4
269	72361	19465109	16.401 2	6.455 3	3.717 47	845.09	56832.2
270	**72900**	**19683000**	**16.431 7**	**6.463 3**	**3.703 70**	**848.23**	**57255.5**
271	73441	19902511	16.462 1	6.471 3	3.690 04	851.37	57680.4
272	73984	20123648	16.492 4	6.479 2	3.676 47	854.51	58106.9
273	74529	20346417	16.522 7	6.487 2	3.663 00	857.65	58534.9
274	75076	20570824	16.552 9	6.495 1	3.649 64	860.80	58964.6
275	**75625**	**20796875**	**16.583 1**	**6.503 0**	**3.636 36**	**863.94**	**59395.7**
276	76176	21024576	16.613 2	6.510 8	3.623 19	867.08	59828.5
277	76729	21253933	16.643 3	6.518 7	3.610 11	870.22	60262.8
278	77284	21484952	16.673 3	6.526 5	3.597 12	873.36	60698.7
279	77841	21717639	16.703 3	6.534 3	3.584 23	876.50	61136.2
280	**78400**	**21952000**	**16.733 2**	**6.542 1**	**3.571 43**	**879.65**	**61575.2**
281	78961	22188041	16.763 1	6.549 9	3.558 72	882.79	62015.8
282	79524	22425768	16.792 9	6.557 7	3.546 10	885.93	62458.0
283	80089	22665187	16.822 6	6.565 4	3.533 57	889.07	62901.8
284	80656	22906304	16.852 3	6.573 1	3.521 13	892.21	63347.1
285	**81225**	**23149125**	**16.881 9**	**6.580 8**	**3.508 77**	**895.35**	**63794.0**
286	81796	23393656	16.911 5	6.588 5	3.496 50	898.50	64242.4
287	82369	23639903	16.941 1	6.596 2	3.484 32	901.64	64692.5
288	82944	23887872	16.970 6	6.603 9	3.472 22	904.78	65144.1
289	83521	24137569	17.000 0	6.611 5	3.460 21	907.92	65597.2
290	**84100**	**24389000**	**17.029 4**	**6.619 1**	**3.448 28**	**911.06**	**66052.0**
291	84681	24642171	17.058 7	6.626 7	3.436 43	914.20	66508.3
292	85264	24897088	17.088 0	6.634 3	3.424 66	917.35	66966.2
293	85849	25153757	17.117 2	6.641 9	3.412 97	920.49	67425.6
294	86436	25412184	17.146 4	6.649 4	3.401 36	923.63	67886.7
295	**87025**	**25672375**	**17.175 6**	**6.656 9**	**3.389 83**	**926.77**	**68349.3**
296	87616	25934336	17.204 7	6.664 4	3.378 38	929.91	68813.4
297	88209	26198073	17.233 7	6.671 9	3.367 00	933.05	69279.2
298	88804	26463592	17.262 7	6.679 4	3.355 70	936.19	69746.5
299	89401	26730899	17.291 6	6.686 9	3.344 48	939.34	70215.4
300	**90000**	**27000000**	**17.320 5**	**6.694 3**	**3.333 33**	**942.48**	**70685.8**
301	90601	27270901	17.349 4	6.701 8	3.322 26	945.62	71157.9
302	91204	27543608	17.378 1	6.709 2	3.311 26	948.76	71631.5
303	91809	27818127	17.406 9	6.716 6	3.300 33	951.90	72106.6
304	92416	28094464	17.435 6	6.724 0	3.289 47	955.04	72583.4
305	**93025**	**28372625**	**17.464 2**	**6.731 3**	**3.278 69**	**958.19**	**73061.7**
306	93636	28652616	17.492 9	6.738 7	3.267 97	961.33	73541.5
307	94249	28934443	17.521 4	6.746 0	3.257 33	964.47	74023.0
308	94864	29218112	17.549 9	6.753 3	3.246 75	967.61	74506.0
309	95481	29503629	17.578 4	6.760 6	3.236 25	970.75	74990.6
310	**96100**	**29791000**	**17.606 8**	**6.767 9**	**3.225 81**	**973.89**	**75476.8**
311	96721	30080231	17.635 2	6.775 2	3.215 43	977.04	75964.5
312	97344	30371328	17.663 5	6.782 4	3.205 13	980.18	76453.8
313	97969	30664297	17.691 8	6.789 7	3.194 89	983.32	76944.7
314	98596	30959144	17.720 0	6.796 9	3.184 71	986.46	77437.1

N	N^2	N^3	$\sqrt{N}$	$\sqrt[3]{N}$	$\dfrac{1000}{N}$	N = diameter circum.	area
315	**99225**	**31255875**	**17.748 2**	**6.804 1**	**3.174 60**	**989.60**	**77931.1**
316	99856	31554496	17.776 4	6.811 3	3.164 56	992.74	78426.7
317	100489	31855013	17.804 5	6.818 5	3.154 57	995.88	78923.9
318	101124	32157432	17.832 6	6.825 6	3.144 65	999.03	79422.6
319	101761	32461759	17.860 6	6.832 8	3.134 80	1002.2	79922.9
320	**102400**	**32768000**	**17.888 5**	**6.839 9**	**3.125 00**	**1005.3**	**80424.8**
321	103041	33076161	17.916 5	6.847 0	3.115 26	1008.5	80928.2
322	103684	33386248	17.944 4	6.854 1	3.105 59	1011.6	81433.2
323	104329	33698267	17.972 2	6.861 2	3.095 98	1014.7	81939.8
324	104976	34012224	18.000 0	6.868 3	3.086 42	1017.9	82448.0
325	**105625**	**34328125**	**18.027 8**	**6.875 3**	**3.076 92**	**1021.0**	**82957.7**
326	106276	34645976	18.055 5	6.882 4	3.067 49	1024.2	83469.0
327	106929	34965783	18.083 1	6.889 4	3.058 10	1027.3	83981.8
328	107584	35287552	18.110 8	6.896 4	3.048 78	1030.4	84496.3
329	108241	35611289	18.138 4	6.903 4	3.039 51	1033.6	85012.3
330	**108900**	**35937000**	**18.165 9**	**6.910 4**	**3.030 30**	**1036.7**	**85529.9**
331	109561	36264691	18.193 4	6.917 4	3.021 15	1039.9	86049.0
332	110224	36594368	18.220 9	6.924 4	3.012 05	1043.0	86569.7
333	110889	36926037	18.248 3	6.931 3	3.003 00	1046.2	87092.0
334	111556	37259704	18.275 7	6.938 2	2.994 01	1049.3	87615.9
335	**112225**	**37595375**	**18.303 0**	**6.945 1**	**2.985 07**	**1052.4**	**88141.3**
336	112896	37933056	18.330 3	6.952 1	2.976 19	1055.6	88668.3
337	113569	38272753	18.357 6	6.958 9	2.967 36	1058.7	89196.9
338	114244	38614472	18.384 8	6.965 8	2.958 58	1061.9	89727.0
339	114921	38958219	18.412 0	6.972 7	2.949 85	1065.0	90258.7
340	**115600**	**39304000**	**18.439 1**	**6.979 5**	**2.941 18**	**1068.1**	**90792.0**
341	116281	39651821	18.466 2	6.986 4	2.932 55	1071.3	91326.9
342	116964	40001688	18.493 2	6.993 2	2.923 98	1074.4	91863.3
343	117649	40353607	18.520 3	7.000 0	2.915 45	1077.6	92401.3
344	118336	40707584	18.547 2	7.006 8	2.906 98	1080.7	92940.9
345	**119025**	**41063625**	**18.574 2**	**7.013 6**	**2 898 55**	**1083.8**	**93482.0**
346	119716	41421736	18.601 1	7.020 3	2.890 17	1087.0	94024.7
347	120409	41781923	18.627 9	7.027 1	2.881 84	1090.1	94569.0
348	121104	42144192	18.654 8	7.033 8	2.873 56	1093.3	95114.9
349	121801	42508549	18.681 5	7.040 6	2.865 33	1096.4	95662.3
350	**122500**	**42875000**	**18.708 3**	**7.047 3**	**2.857 14**	**1099.6**	**96211.3**
351	123201	43243551	18.735 0	7.054 0	2.849 00	1102.7	96761.8
352	123904	43614208	18.761 7	7.060 7	2.840 91	1105.8	97314.0
353	124609	43986977	18.788 3	7.067 4	2.832 86	1109.0	97867.7
354	125316	44361864	18.814 9	7.074 0	2.824 86	1112.1	98423.0
355	**126025**	**44738875**	**18.841 4**	**7.080 7**	**2.816 90**	**1115.3**	**98979.8**
356	126736	45118016	18.868 0	7.087 3	2.808 99	1118.4	99538.2
357	127449	45499293	18.894 4	7.094 0	2.801 12	1121.5	100098
358	128164	45882712	18.920 9	7.100 6	2.793 30	1124.7	100660
359	128881	46268279	18.947 3	7.107 2	2.785 52	1127.8	101223
360	**129600**	**46656000**	**18.973 7**	**7.113 8**	**2.777 78**	**1131.0**	**101788**
361	130321	47045881	19.000 0	7.120 4	2.770 08	1134.1	102354
362	131044	47437928	19.026 3	7.126 9	2.762 43	1137.3	102922
363	131769	47832147	19.052 6	7.133 5	2.754 82	1140.4	103491
364	132496	48228544	19.078 8	7.140 0	2.747 25	1143.5	104062
365	**133225**	**48627125**	**19.105 0**	**7.146 6**	**2.739 73**	**1146.7**	**104635**
366	133956	49027896	19.131 1	7.153 1	2.732 24	1149.8	105209
367	134689	49430863	19.157 2	7.159 6	2.724 80	1153.0	105785
368	135424	49836032	19.183 3	7.166 1	2.717 39	1156.1	106362
369	136161	50243409	19.209 4	7.172 6	2.710 03	1159.2	106941
370	**136900**	**50653000**	**19.235 4**	**7.179 1**	**2.702 70**	**1162.4**	**107521**
371	137641	51064811	19.261 4	7.185 5	2.695 42	1165.5	108103
372	138384	51478848	19.287 3	7.192 0	2.688 17	1168.7	108687
373	139129	51895117	19.313 2	7.198 4	2.680 97	1171.8	109272
374	139876	52313624	19.339 1	7.204 8	2.673 80	1175.0	109858
375	**140625**	**52734375**	**19.364 9**	**7.211 2**	**2.666 67**	**1178.1**	**110447**
376	141376	53157376	19.390 7	7.217 7	2.659 57	1181.2	111036
377	142129	53582633	19.416 5	7.224 0	2.652 52	1184.4	111628
378	142884	54010152	19.442 2	7.230 4	2.645 50	1187.5	112221
379	143641	54439939	19.467 9	7.236 8	2.638 52	1190.7	112815

Table 1 / Functions of numbers   □   **607**

N	N^2	N^3	$\sqrt{N}$	$\sqrt[3]{N}$	$\dfrac{1000}{N}$	N = diameter circum.	area
380	**144400**	**54872000**	**19.493 6**	**7.243 2**	**2.631 58**	**1193.8**	**113411**
381	145161	55306341	19.519 2	7.249 5	2.624 67	1196.9	114009
382	145924	55742968	19.544 8	7.255 8	2.617 80	1200.1	114608
383	146689	56181887	19.570 4	7.262 2	2.610 97	1203.2	115209
384	147456	56623104	19.595 9	7.268 5	2.604 17	1206.4	115812
385	**148225**	**57066625**	**19.621 4**	**7.274 8**	**2.597 40**	**1209.5**	**116416**
386	148996	57512456	19.646 9	7.281 1	2.590 67	1212.7	117021
387	149769	57960603	19.672 3	7.287 4	2.583 98	1215.8	117628
388	150544	58411072	19.697 7	7.293 6	2.577 32	1218.9	118237
389	151321	58863869	19.723 1	7.299 9	2.570 69	1222.1	118847
390	**152100**	**59319000**	**19.748 4**	**7.306 1**	**2.564 10**	**1225.2**	**119459**
391	152881	59776471	19.773 7	7.312 4	2.557 54	1228.4	120072
392	153664	60236288	19.799 0	7.318 6	2.551 02	1231.5	120687
393	154449	60698457	19.824 2	7.324 8	2.544 53	1234.6	121304
394	155236	61162984	19.849 4	7.331 0	2.538 07	1237.8	121922
395	**156025**	**61629875**	**19.874 6**	**7.337 2**	**2.531 65**	**1240.9**	**122542**
396	156816	62099136	19.899 7	7.343 4	2.525 25	1244.1	123163
397	157609	62570773	19.924 9	7.349 6	2.518 89	1247.2	123786
398	158404	63044792	19.949 9	7.355 8	2.512 56	1250.4	124410
399	159201	63521199	19.975 0	7.361 9	2.506 27	1253.5	125036
400	**160000**	**64000000**	**20.000 0**	**7.368 1**	**2.500 00**	**1256.6**	**125664**
401	160801	64481201	20.025 0	7.374 2	2.493 77	1259.8	126293
402	161604	64964808	20.049 9	7.380 3	2.487 56	1262.9	126923
403	162409	65450827	20.074 9	7.386 4	2.481 39	1266.1	127556
404	163216	65939264	20.099 8	7.392 5	2.475 25	1269.2	128190
405	**164025**	**66430125**	**20.124 6**	**7.398 6**	**2.469 14**	**1272.3**	**128825**
406	164836	66923416	20.149 4	7.404 7	2.463 05	1275.5	129462
407	165649	67419143	20.174 2	7.410 8	2.457 00	1278.6	130100
408	166464	67917312	20.199 0	7.416 9	2.450 98	1281.8	130741
409	167281	68417929	20.223 7	7.422 9	2.444 99	1284.9	131382
410	**168100**	**68921000**	**20.248 5**	**7.429 0**	**2.439 02**	**1288.1**	**132025**
411	168921	69426531	20.273 1	7.435 0	2.433 09	1291.2	132670
412	169744	69934528	20.297 8	7.441 0	2.427 18	1294.3	133317
413	170569	70444997	20.322 4	7.447 0	2.421 31	1297.5	133965
414	171396	70957944	20.347 0	7.453 0	2.415 46	1300.6	134614
415	**172225**	**71473375**	**20.371 5**	**7.459 0**	**2.409 64**	**1303.8**	**135265**
416	173056	71991296	20.396 1	7.465 0	2.403 85	1306.9	135918
417	173889	72511713	20.420 6	7.471 0	2.398 08	1310.0	136572
418	174724	73034632	20.445 0	7.477 0	2.392 34	1313.2	137228
419	175561	73560059	20.469 5	7.482 9	2.386 63	1316.3	137885
420	**176400**	**74088000**	**20.493 9**	**7.488 9**	**2.380 95**	**1319.5**	**138544**
421	177241	74618461	20.518 3	7.494 8	2.375 30	1322.6	139205
422	178084	75151448	20.542 6	7.500 7	2.369 67	1325.8	139867
423	178929	75686967	20.567 0	7.506 7	2.364 07	1328.9	140531
424	179776	76225024	20.591 3	7.512 6	2.358 49	1332.0	141196
425	**180625**	**76765625**	**20.615 5**	**7.518 5**	**2.352 94**	**1335.2**	**141863**
426	181476	77308776	20.639 8	7.524 4	2.347 42	1338.3	142531
427	182329	77854483	20.664 0	7.530 2	2.341 92	1341.5	143201
428	183184	78402752	20.688 2	7.536 1	2.336 45	1344.6	143872
429	184041	78953589	20.712 3	7.542 0	2.331 00	1347.7	144545
430	**184900**	**79507000**	**20.736 4**	**7.547 8**	**2.325 58**	**1350.9**	**145220**
431	185761	80062991	20.760 5	7.553 7	2.320 19	1354.0	145896
432	186624	80621568	20.784 6	7.559 5	2.314 81	1357.2	146574
433	187489	81182737	20.808 7	7.565 4	2.309 47	1360.3	147254
434	188356	81746504	20.832 7	7.571 2	2.304 15	1363.5	147934
435	**189225**	**82312875**	**20.856 7**	**7.577 0**	**2.298 85**	**1366.6**	**148617**
436	190096	82881856	20.880 6	7.582 8	2.293 58	1369.7	149301
437	190969	83453453	20.904 5	7.588 6	2.288 33	1372.9	149987
438	191844	84027672	20.928 4	7.594 4	2.283 11	1376.0	150674
439	192721	84604519	20.952 3	7.600 1	2.277 90	1379.2	151363
440	**193600**	**85184000**	**20.976 2**	**7.605 9**	**2.272 73**	**1382.3**	**152053**
441	194481	85766121	21.000 0	7.611 7	2.267 57	1385.4	152745
442	195364	86350888	21.023 8	7.617 4	2.262 44	1388.6	153439
443	196249	86938307	21.047 6	7.623 2	2.257 34	1391.7	154134
444	197136	87528384	21.071 3	7.628 9	2.252 25	1394.9	154830

N	N^2	N^3	$\sqrt{N}$	$\sqrt[3]{N}$	$\dfrac{1000}{N}$	N = diameter circum.	area
445	198025	88121125	21.095 0	7.634 6	2.247 19	1398.0	155528
446	198916	88716536	21.118 7	7.640 3	2.242 15	1401.2	156228
447	199809	89314623	21.142 4	7.646 0	2.237 14	1404.3	156930
448	200704	89915392	21.166 0	7.651 7	2.232 14	1407.4	157633
449	201601	90518849	21.189 6	7.657 4	2.227 17	1410.6	158337
450	202500	91125000	21.213 2	7.663 1	2.222 22	1413.7	159043
451	203401	91733851	21.236 8	7.668 8	2.217 29	1416.9	159751
452	204304	92345408	21.260 3	7.674 4	2.212 39	1420.0	160460
453	205209	92959677	21.283 8	7.680 1	2.207 51	1423.1	161171
454	206116	93576664	21.307 3	7.685 7	2.202 64	1426.3	161883
455	207025	94196375	21.330 7	7.691 4	2.197 80	1429.4	162597
456	207936	94818816	21.354 2	7.697 0	2.192 98	1432.6	163313
457	208849	95443993	21.377 6	7.702 6	2.188 18	1435.7	164030
458	209764	96071912	21.400 9	7.708 2	2.183 41	1438.8	164748
459	210681	96702579	21.424 3	7.713 8	2.178 65	1442.0	165468
460	211600	97336000	21.447 6	7.719 4	2.173 91	1445.1	166190
461	212521	97972181	21.470 9	7.725 0	2.169 20	1448.3	166914
462	213444	98611128	21.494 2	7.730 6	2.164 50	1451.4	167639
463	214369	99252847	21.517 4	7.736 2	2.159 83	1454.6	168365
464	215296	99897344	21.540 7	7.741 8	2.155 17	1457.7	169093
465	216225	100544625	21.563 9	7.747 3	2.150 54	1460.8	169823
466	217156	101194696	21.587 0	7.752 9	2.145 92	1464.0	170554
467	218089	101847563	21.610 2	7.758 4	2.141 33	1467.1	171287
468	219024	102503232	21.633 3	7.763 9	2.136 75	1470.3	172021
469	219961	103161709	21.656 4	7.769 5	2.132 20	1473.4	172757
470	220900	103823000	21.679 5	7.775 0	2.127 66	1476.5	173494
471	221841	104487111	21.702 5	7.780 5	2.123 14	1479.7	174234
472	222784	105154048	21.725 6	7.786 0	2.118 64	1482.8	174974
473	223729	105823817	21.748 6	7.791 5	2.114 16	1486.0	175716
474	224676	106496424	21.771 5	7.797 0	2.109 70	1489.1	176460
475	225625	107171875	21.794 5	7.802 5	2.105 26	1492.3	177205
476	226576	107850176	21.817 4	7.807 9	2.100 84	1495.4	177952
477	227529	108531333	21.840 3	7.813 4	2.096 44	1498.5	178701
478	228484	109215352	21.863 2	7.818 8	2.092 05	1501.7	179451
479	229441	109902239	21.886 1	7.824 3	2.087 68	1504.8	180203
480	230400	110592000	21.908 9	7.829 7	2.083 33	1508.0	180956
481	231361	111284641	21.931 7	7.835 2	2.079 00	1511.1	181711
482	232324	111980168	21.954 5	7.840 6	2.074 69	1514.2	182467
483	233289	112678587	21.977 3	7.846 0	2.070 39	1517.4	183225
484	234256	113379904	22.000 0	7.851 4	2.066 12	1520.5	183984
485	235225	114084125	22.022 7	7.856 8	2.061 86	1523.7	184745
486	236196	114791256	22.045 4	7.862 2	2.057 61	1526.8	185508
487	237169	115501303	22.068 1	7.867 6	2.053 39	1530.0	186272
488	238144	116214272	22.090 7	7.873 0	2.049 18	1533.1	187038
489	239121	116930169	22.113 3	7.878 4	2.044 99	1536.2	187805
490	240100	117649000	22.135 9	7.883 7	2.040 82	1539.4	188574
491	241081	118370701	22.158 5	7.889 1	2.036 66	1542.5	189345
492	242064	119095488	22.181 1	7.894 4	2.032 52	1545.7	190117
493	243049	119823157	22.203 6	7.899 8	2.028 40	1548.8	190890
494	244036	120553784	22.226 1	7.905 1	2.024 29	1551.9	191665
495	245025	121287375	22.248 6	7.910 5	2.020 20	1555.1	192442
496	246016	122023936	22.271 1	7.915 8	2.016 13	1558.2	193221
497	247009	122763473	22.293 5	7.921 1	2.012 07	1561.4	194000
498	248004	123505992	22.315 9	7.926 4	2.008 03	1564.5	194782
499	249001	124251499	22.338 3	7.931 7	2.004 01	1567.7	195565
500	250000	125000000	22.360 7	7.937 0	2.000 00	1570.8	196350
501	251001	125751501	22.383 0	7.942 3	1.996 01	1573.9	197136
502	252004	126506008	22.405 4	7.947 6	1.992 03	1577.1	197923
503	253009	127263527	22.427 7	7.952 8	1.988 07	1580.2	198713
504	254016	128024064	22.449 9	7.958 1	1.984 13	1583.4	199504
505	255025	128787625	22.472 2	7.963 4	1.980 20	1586.5	200296
506	256036	129554216	22.494 4	7.968 6	1.976 28	1589.6	201090
507	257049	130323843	22.516 7	7.973 9	1.972 39	1592.8	201886
508	258064	131096512	22.538 9	7.979 1	1.968 50	1595.9	202683
509	259081	131872229	22.561 0	7.984 3	1.964 64	1599.1	203482

Table 1 / Functions of numbers □ 609

N	N^2	N^3	$\sqrt{N}$	$\sqrt[3]{N}$	$\dfrac{1000}{N}$	N = diameter circum.	area
510	260100	132651000	22.583 2	7.989 6	1.960 78	1602.2	204282
511	261121	133432831	22.605 3	7.994 8	1.956 95	1605.4	205084
512	262144	134217728	22.627 4	8.000 0	1.953 12	1608.5	205887
513	263169	135005697	22.649 5	8.005 2	1.949 32	1611.6	206692
514	264196	135796744	22.671 6	8.010 4	1.945 53	1614.8	207499
515	265225	136590875	22.693 6	8.015 6	1.941 75	1617.9	208307
516	266256	137388096	22.715 6	8.020 8	1.937 98	1621.1	209117
517	267289	138188413	22.737 6	8.026 0	1.934 24	1624.2	209928
518	268324	138991832	22.759 6	8.031 1	1.930 50	1627.3	210741
519	269361	139798359	22.781 6	8.036 3	1.926 78	1630.5	211556
520	270400	140608000	22.803 5	8.041 5	1.923 08	1633.6	212372
521	271441	141420761	22.825 4	8.046 6	1.919 39	1636.8	213189
522	272484	142236648	22.847 3	8.051 7	1.915 71	1639.9	214008
523	273529	143055667	22.869 2	8.056 9	1.912 05	1643.1	214829
524	274576	143877824	22.891 0	8.062 0	1.908 40	1646.2	215651
525	275625	144703125	22.912 9	8.067 1	1.904 76	1649.3	216475
526	276676	145531576	22.934 7	8.072 3	1.901 14	1652.5	217301
527	277729	146363183	22.956 5	8.077 4	1.897 53	1655.6	218128
528	278784	147197952	22.978 3	8.082 5	1.893 94	1658.8	218956
529	279841	148035889	23.000 0	8.087 6	1.890 36	1661.9	219787
530	280900	148877000	23.021 7	8.092 7	1.886 79	1665.0	220618
531	281961	149721291	23.043 4	8.097 8	1.883 24	1668.2	221452
532	283024	150568768	23.065 1	8.102 8	1.879 70	1671.3	222287
533	284089	151419437	23.086 8	8.107 9	1.876 17	1674.5	223123
534	285156	152273304	23.108 4	8.113 0	1.872 66	1677.6	223961
535	286225	153130375	23.130 1	8.118 0	1.869 16	1680.8	224801
536	287296	153990656	23.151 7	8.123 1	1.865 67	1683.9	225642
537	288369	154854153	23.173 3	8.128 1	1.862 20	1687.0	226484
538	289444	155720872	23.194 8	8.133 2	1.858 74	1690.2	227329
539	290521	156590819	23.216 4	8.138 2	1.855 29	1693.3	228175
540	291600	157464000	23.237 9	8.143 3	1.851 85	1696.5	229022
541	292681	158340421	23.259 4	8.148 3	1.848 43	1699.6	229871
542	293764	159220088	23.280 9	8.153 3	1.845 02	1702.7	230722
543	294849	160103007	23.302 4	8.158 3	1.841 62	1705.9	231574
544	295936	160989184	23.323 8	8.163 3	1.838 24	1709.0	232428
545	297025	161878625	23.345 2	8.168 3	1.834 86	1712.2	233283
546	298116	162771336	23.366 6	8.173 3	1.831 50	1715.3	234140
547	299209	163667323	23.388 0	8.178 3	1.828 15	1718.5	234998
548	300304	164566592	23.409 4	8.183 3	1.824 82	1721.6	235858
549	301401	165469149	23.430 7	8.188 2	1.821 49	1724.7	236720
550	302500	166375000	23.452 1	8.193 2	1.818 18	1727.9	237583
551	303601	167284151	23.473 4	8.198 2	1.814 88	1731.0	238448
552	304704	168196608	23.494 7	8.203 1	1.811 59	1734.2	239314
553	305809	169112377	23.516 0	8.208 1	1.808 32	1737.3	240182
554	306916	170031464	23.537 2	8.213 0	1.805 05	1740.4	241051
555	308025	170953875	23.558 4	8.218 0	1.801 80	1743.6	241922
556	309136	171879616	23.579 7	8.222 9	1.798 56	1746.7	242795
557	310249	172808693	23.600 8	8.227 8	1.795 33	1749.9	243669
558	311364	173741112	23.622 0	8.232 7	1.792 11	1753.0	244545
559	312481	174676879	23.643 2	8.237 7	1.788 91	1756.2	245422
560	313600	175616000	23.664 3	8.242 6	1.785 71	1759.3	246301
561	314721	176558481	23.685 4	8.247 5	1.782 53	1762.4	247181
562	315844	177504328	23.706 5	8.252 4	1.779 36	1765.6	248063
563	316969	178453547	23.727 6	8.257 3	1.776 20	1768.7	248947
564	318096	179406144	23.748 7	8.262 1	1.773 05	1771.9	249832
565	319225	180362125	23.769 7	8.267 0	1.769 91	1775.0	250719
566	320356	181321496	23.790 8	8.271 9	1.766 78	1778.1	251607
567	321489	182284263	23.811 8	8.276 8	1.763 67	1781.3	252497
568	322624	183250432	23.832 8	8.281 6	1.760 56	1784.4	253388
569	323761	184220009	23.853 7	8.286 5	1.757 47	1787.6	254281
570	324900	185193000	23.874 7	8.291 3	1.754 39	1790.7	255176
571	326041	186169411	23.895 6	8.296 2	1.751 31	1793.8	256072
572	327184	187149248	23.916 5	8.301 0	1.748 25	1797.0	256970
573	328329	188132517	23.937 4	8.305 9	1.745 20	1800.1	257869
574	329476	189119224	23.958 3	8.310 7	1.742 16	1803.3	258770

N	N^2	N^3	$\sqrt{N}$	$\sqrt[3]{N}$	$\dfrac{1000}{N}$	N = diameter	
						circum.	area
575	**330625**	**190109375**	**23.979 2**	**8.315 5**	**1.739 13**	**1806.4**	**259672**
576	331776	191102976	24.000 0	8.320 3	1.736 11	1809.6	260576
577	332929	192100033	24.020 8	8.325 1	1.733 10	1812.7	261482
578	334084	193100552	24.041 6	8.330 0	1.730 10	1815.8	262389
579	335241	194104539	24.062 4	8.334 8	1.727 12	1819.0	263298
580	**336400**	**195112000**	**24.083 2**	**8.339 6**	**1.724 14**	**1822.1**	**264208**
581	337561	196122941	24.103 9	8.344 3	1.721 17	1825.3	265120
582	338724	197137368	24.124 7	8.349 1	1.718 21	1828.4	266033
583	339889	198155287	24.145 4	8.353 9	1.715 27	1831.6	266948
584	341056	199176704	24.166 1	8.358 7	1.712 33	1834.7	267865
585	**342225**	**200201625**	**24.186 8**	**8.363 4**	**1.709 40**	**1837.8**	**268783**
586	343396	201230056	24.207 4	8.368 2	1.706 48	1841.0	269703
587	344569	202262003	24.228 1	8.373 0	1.703 58	1844.1	270624
588	345744	203297472	24.248 7	8.377 7	1.700 68	1847.3	271547
589	346921	204336469	24.269 3	8.382 5	1.697 79	1850.4	272471
590	**348100**	**205379000**	**24.289 9**	**8.387 2**	**1.694 92**	**1853.5**	**273397**
591	349281	206425071	24.310 5	8.391 9	1.692 05	1856.7	274325
592	350464	207474688	24.331 1	8.396 7	1.689 19	1859.8	275254
593	351649	208527857	24.351 6	8.401 4	1.686 34	1863.0	276184
594	352836	209584584	24.372 1	8.406 1	1.683 50	1866.1	277117
595	**354025**	**210644875**	**24.392 6**	**8.410 8**	**1.680 67**	**1860.2**	**278051**
596	355216	211708736	24.413 1	8.415 5	1.677 85	1872.4	278986
597	356409	212776173	24.433 6	8.420 2	1.675 04	1875.5	279923
598	357604	213847192	24.454 0	8.424 9	1.672 24	1878.7	280862
599	358801	214921799	24.474 5	8.429 6	1.669 45	1881.8	281802
600	**360000**	**216000000**	**24.494 9**	**8.434 3**	**1.666 67**	**1885.0**	**282743**
601	361201	217081801	24.515 3	8.439 0	1.663 89	1888.1	283687
602	362404	218167208	24.535 7	8.443 7	1.661 13	1891.2	284631
603	363609	219256227	24.556 1	8.448 4	1.658 37	1894.4	285578
604	364816	220348864	24.576 4	8.453 0	1.655 63	1897.5	286526
605	**366025**	**221445125**	**24.596 7**	**8.457 7**	**1.652 89**	**1900.7**	**287475**
606	367236	222545016	24.617 1	8.462 3	1.650 17	1903.8	288426
607	368449	223648543	24.637 4	8.467 0	1.647 45	1906.9	289379
608	369664	224755712	24.657 7	8.471 6	1.644 74	1910.1	290333
609	370881	225866529	24.677 9	8.476 3	1.642 04	1913.2	291289
610	**372100**	**226981000**	**24.698 2**	**8.480 9**	**1.639 34**	**1916.4**	**292247**
611	373321	228099131	24.718 4	8.485 6	1.636 66	1919.5	293206
612	374544	229220928	24.738 6	8.490 2	1.633 99	1922.7	294166
613	375769	230346397	24.758 8	8.494 8	1.631 32	1925.8	295128
614	376996	231475544	24.779 0	8.499 4	1.628 66	1928.9	296092
615	**378225**	**232608375**	**24.799 2**	**8.504 0**	**1.626 02**	**1932.1**	**297057**
616	379456	233744896	24.819 3	8.508 6	1.623 38	1935.2	298024
617	380689	234885113	24.839 5	8.513 2	1.620 75	1938.4	298992
618	381924	236029032	24.859 6	8.517 8	1.618 12	1941.5	299962
619	383161	237176659	24.879 7	8.522 4	1.615 51	1944.6	300934
620	**384400**	**238328000**	**24.899 8**	**8.527 0**	**1.612 90**	**1947.8**	**301907**
621	385641	239483061	24.919 9	8.531 6	1.610 31	1950.9	302882
622	386884	240641848	24.939 9	8.536 2	1.607 72	1954.1	303858
623	388129	241804367	24.960 0	8.540 8	1.605 14	1957.2	304836
624	389376	242970624	24.980 0	8.545 3	1.602 56	1960.4	305815
625	**390625**	**244140625**	**25.000 0**	**8.549 9**	**1.600 00**	**1963.5**	**306796**
626	391876	245314376	25.020 0	8.554 4	1.597 44	1966.6	307779
627	393129	246491883	25.040 0	8.559 0	1.594 90	1969.8	308763
628	394384	247673152	25.059 9	8.563 5	1.592 36	1972.9	309748
629	395641	248858189	25.079 9	8.568 1	1.589 83	1976.1	310736
630	**396900**	**250047000**	**25.099 8**	**8.572 6**	**1.587 30**	**1979 2**	**311725**
631	398161	251239591	25.119 7	8.577 2	1.584 79	1982.3	312715
632	399424	252435968	25.139 6	8.581 7	1.582 28	1985.5	313707
633	400689	253636137	25.159 5	8.586 2	1.579 78	1988.6	314700
634	401956	254840104	25.179 4	8.590 7	1.577 29	1991.8	315696
635	**403225**	**256047875**	**25.199 2**	**8.595 2**	**1.574 80**	**1994.9**	**316692**
636	404496	257259456	25.219 0	8.599 7	1.572 33	1998.1	317690
637	405769	258474853	25.238 9	8.604 3	1.569 86	2001.2	318690
638	407044	259694072	25.258 7	8.608 8	1.567 40	2004.3	319692
639	408321	260917119	25.278 4	8.613 2	1.564 95	2007.5	320695

Table 1 / Functions of numbers   □   **611**

N	N^2	N^3	$\sqrt{N}$	$\sqrt[3]{N}$	$\dfrac{1000}{N}$	N = diameter circum.	area
640	**409600**	**262144000**	**25.298 2**	**8.617 7**	**1.562 50**	**2010.6**	**321699**
641	410881	263374721	25.318 0	8.622 2	1.560 06	2013.8	322705
642	412164	264609288	25.337 7	8.626 7	1.557 63	2016.9	323713
643	413449	265847707	25.357 4	8.631 2	1.555 21	2020.0	324722
644	414736	267089984	25.377 2	8.635 7	1.552 80	2023.2	325733
645	**416025**	**268336125**	**25.396 9**	**8.640 1**	**1.550 39**	**2026.3**	**326745**
646	417316	269586136	25.416 5	8.644 6	1.547 99	2029.5	327759
647	418609	270840023	25.436 2	8.649 0	1.545 60	2032.6	328775
648	419904	272097792	25.455 8	8.653 5	1.543 21	2035.8	329792
649	421201	273359449	25.475 5	8.657 9	1.540 83	2038.9	330810
650	**422500**	**274625000**	**25.495 1**	**8.662 4**	**1.538 46**	**2042.0**	**331831**
651	423801	275894451	25.514 7	8.666 8	1.536 10	2045.2	332853
652	425104	277167808	25.534 3	8.671 3	1.533 74	2048.3	333876
653	426409	278445077	25.553 9	8.675 7	1.531 39	2051.5	334901
654	427716	279726264	25.573 4	8.680 1	1.529 05	2054.6	335927
655	**429025**	**281011375**	**25.593 0**	**8.684 5**	**1.526 72**	**2057.7**	**336955**
656	430336	282300416	25.612 5	8.689 0	1.524 39	2060.9	337985
657	431649	283593393	25.632 0	8.693 4	1.522 07	2064.0	339016
658	432964	284890312	25.651 5	8.697 8	1.519 76	2067.2	340049
659	434281	286191179	25.671 0	8.702 2	1.517 45	2070.3	341084
660	**435600**	**287496000**	**25.690 5**	**8.706 6**	**1.515 15**	**2073.5**	**342119**
661	436921	288804781	25.709 9	8.711 0	1.512 86	2076.6	343157
662	438244	290117528	25.729 4	8.715 4	1.510 57	2079.7	344196
663	439569	291434247	25.748 8	8.719 8	1.508 30	2082.9	345237
664	440896	292754944	25.768 2	8.724 1	1.506 02	2086.0	346279
665	**442225**	**294079625**	**25.787 6**	**8.728 5**	**1.503 76**	**2089.2**	**347323**
666	443556	295408296	25.807 0	8.732 9	1.501 50	2092.3	348368
667	444889	296740963	25.826 3	8.737 3	1.499 25	2095.4	349415
668	446224	298077632	25.845 7	8.741 6	1.497 01	2098.6	350464
669	447561	299418309	25.865 0	8.746 0	1.494 77	2101.7	351514
670	**448900**	**300763000**	**25.884 4**	**8.750 3**	**1.492 54**	**2104.9**	**352565**
671	450241	302111711	25.903 7	8.754 7	1.490 31	2108.0	353618
672	451584	303464448	25.923 0	8.759 0	1.488 10	2111.2	354673
673	452929	304821217	25.942 2	8.763 4	1.485 88	2114.3	355730
674	454276	306182024	25.961 5	8.767 7	1.483 68	2117.4	356788
675	**455625**	**307546875**	**25.980 8**	**8.772 1**	**1.481 48**	**2120.6**	**357847**
676	456976	308915776	26.000 0	8.776 4	1.479 29	2123.7	358908
677	458329	310288733	26.019 2	8.780 7	1.477 10	2126.9	359971
678	459684	311665752	26.038 4	8.785 0	1.474 93	2130.0	361035
679	461041	313046839	26.057 6	8.789 3	1.472 75	2133.1	362101
680	**462400**	**314432000**	**26.076 8**	**8.793 7**	**1.470 59**	**2136.3**	**363168**
681	463761	315821241	26.096 0	8.798 0	1.468 43	2139.4	364237
682	465124	317214568	26.115 1	8.802 3	1.466 28	2142.6	365308
683	466489	318611987	26.134 2	8.806 6	1.464 13	2145.7	366380
684	467856	320013504	26.153 4	8.810 9	1.461 99	2148.8	367453
685	**469225**	**321419125**	**26.172 5**	**8.815 2**	**1.459 85**	**2152.0**	**368528**
686	470596	322828856	26.191 6	8.819 4	1.457 73	2155.1	369605
687	471969	324242703	26.210 7	8.823 7	1.455 60	2158.3	370684
688	473344	325660672	26.229 8	8.828 0	1.453 49	2161.4	371764
689	474721	327082769	26.248 8	8.832 3	1.451 38	2164.6	372845
690	**476100**	**328509000**	**26.267 9**	**8.836 6**	**1.449 28**	**2167.7**	**373928**
691	477481	329939371	26.286 9	8.840 8	1.447 18	2170.8	375013
692	478864	331373888	26.305 9	8.845 1	1.445 09	2174.0	376099
693	480249	332812557	26.324 9	8.849 3	1.443 00	2177.1	377187
694	481636	334255384	26.343 9	8.853 6	1.440 92	2180.3	378276
695	**483025**	**335702375**	**26.362 9**	**8.857 8**	**1.438 85**	**2183.4**	**379367**
696	484416	337153536	26.381 8	8.862 1	1.436 78	2186.5	380459
697	485809	338608873	26.400 8	8.866 3	1.434 72	2189.7	381553
698	487204	340068392	26.419 7	8.870 6	1.432 66	2192.8	382649
699	488601	341532099	26.438 6	8.874 8	1.430 62	2196.0	383746
700	**490000**	**343000000**	**26.457 5**	**8.879 0**	**1.428 57**	**2199.1**	**384845**
701	491401	344472101	26.476 4	8.883 3	1.426 53	2202.3	385945
702	492804	345948408	26.495 3	8.887 5	1.424 50	2205.4	387047
703	494209	347428927	26.514 1	8.891 7	1.422 48	2208.5	388151
704	495616	348913664	26.533 0	8.895 9	1.420 45	2211.7	389256

N	N^2	N^3	$\sqrt{N}$	$\sqrt[3]{N}$	$\dfrac{1000}{N}$	N = diameter circum.	area
705	497025	350402625	26.551 8	8.900 1	1.418 44	2214.8	390363
706	498436	351895816	26.570 7	8.904 3	1.416 43	2218.0	391471
707	499849	353393243	26.589 5	8.908 5	1.414 43	2221.1	392580
708	501264	354894912	26.608 3	8.912 7	1.412 43	2224.2	393692
709	502681	356400829	26.627 1	8.916 9	1.410 44	2227.4	394805
710	504100	357911000	26.645 8	8.921 1	1.408 45	2230.5	395919
711	505521	359425431	26.664 6	8.925 3	1.406 47	2233.7	397035
712	506944	360944128	26.683 3	8.929 5	1.404 49	2236.8	398153
713	508369	362467097	26.702 1	8.933 7	1.402 52	2240.0	399272
714	509796	363994344	26.720 8	8.937 8	1.400 56	2243.1	400393
715	511225	365525875	26.739 5	8.942 0	1.398 60	2246.2	401515
716	512656	367061696	26.758 2	8.946 2	1.396 65	2249.4	402639
717	514089	368601813	26.776 9	8.950 3	1.394 70	2252.5	403765
718	515524	370146232	26.795 5	8.954 5	1.392 76	2255.7	404892
719	516961	371694959	26.814 2	8.958 7	1.390 82	2258.8	406020
720	518400	373248000	26.832 8	8.962 8	1.388 89	2261.9	407150
721	519841	374805361	26.851 4	8.967 0	1.386 96	2265.1	408282
722	521284	376367048	26.870 1	8.971 1	1.385 04	2268.2	409415
723	522729	377933067	26.888 7	8.975 2	1.383 13	2271.4	410550
724	524176	379503424	26.907 2	8.979 4	1.381 22	2274.5	411687
725	525625	381078125	26.925 8	8.983 5	1.379 31	2277.7	412825
726	527076	382657176	26.944 4	8.987 6	1.377 41	2280.8	413965
727	528529	384240583	26.962 9	8.991 8	1.375 52	2283.9	415106
728	529984	385828352	26.981 5	8.995 9	1.373 63	2287.1	416248
729	531441	387420489	27.000 0	9.000 0	1.371 74	2290.2	417393
730	532900	389017000	27.018 5	9.004 1	1.369 86	2293.4	418539
731	534361	390617891	27.037 0	9.008 2	1.367 99	2296.5	419686
732	535824	392223168	27.055 5	9.012 3	1.366 12	2299.6	420835
733	537289	393832837	27.074 0	9.016 4	1.364 26	2302.8	421986
734	538756	395446904	27.092 4	9.020 5	1.362 40	2305.9	423138
735	540225	397065375	27.110 9	9.024 6	1.360 54	2309.1	424293
736	541696	398688256	27.129 3	9.028 7	1.358 70	2312.2	425447
737	543169	400315553	27.147 7	9.032 8	1.356 85	2315.4	426604
738	544644	401947272	27.166 2	9.036 9	1.355 01	2318.5	427762
739	546121	403583419	27.184 6	9.041 0	1.353 18	2321.6	428922
740	547600	405224000	27.202 9	9.045 0	1.351 35	2324.8	430084
741	549081	406869021	27.221 3	9.049 1	1.349 53	2327.9	431247
742	550564	408518488	27.239 7	9.053 2	1.347 71	2331.1	432412
743	552049	410172407	27.258 0	9.057 2	1.345 90	2334.2	433578
744	553536	411830784	27.276 4	9.061 3	1.344 09	2337.3	434746
745	555025	413493625	27.294 7	9.065 4	1.342 28	2340.5	435916
746	556516	415160936	27.313 0	9.069 4	1.340 48	2343.6	437087
747	558009	416832723	27.331 3	9.073 5	1.338 69	2346.8	438259
748	559504	418508992	27.349 6	9.077 5	1.336 90	2349.9	439433
749	561001	420189749	27.367 9	9.081 6	1.335 11	2353.1	440609
750	562500	421875000	27.386 1	9.085 6	1.333 33	2356.2	441786
751	564001	423564751	27.404 4	9.089 6	1.331 56	2359.3	442965
752	565504	425259008	27.422 6	9.093 7	1.329 79	2362.5	444146
753	567009	426957777	27.440 8	9.097 7	1.328 02	2365.6	445328
754	568516	428661064	27.459 1	9.101 7	1.326 26	2368.8	446511
755	570025	430368875	27.477 3	9.105 7	1.324 50	2371.9	447697
756	571536	432081216	27.495 5	9.109 8	1.322 75	2375.0	448883
757	573049	433798093	27.513 6	9.113 8	1.321 00	2378.2	450072
758	574564	435519512	27.531 8	9.117 8	1.319 26	2381.3	451262
759	576081	437245479	27.550 0	9.121 8	1.317 52	2384.5	452453
760	577600	438976000	27.568 1	9.125 8	1.315 79	2387.6	453646
761	579121	440711081	27.586 2	9.129 8	1.314 06	2390.8	454841
762	580644	442450728	27.604 3	9.133 8	1.312 34	2393.9	456037
763	582169	444194947	27.622 5	9.137 8	1.310 62	2397.0	457234
764	583696	445943744	27.640 5	9.141 8	1.308 90	2400.2	458434
765	585225	447697125	27.658 6	9.145 8	1.307 19	2403.3	459635
766	586756	449455096	27.676 7	9.149 8	1.305 48	2406.5	460837
767	588289	451217663	27.694 8	9.153 7	1.303 78	2409.6	462041
768	589824	452984832	27.712 8	9.157 7	1.302 08	2412.7	463247
769	591361	454756609	27.730 8	9.161 7	1.300 39	2415.9	464454

Table 1 / Functions of numbers   □   **613**

N	N^2	N^3	$\sqrt{N}$	$\sqrt[3]{N}$	$\dfrac{1000}{N}$	$N =$ diameter	
						circum.	area
770	592900	456533000	27.748 9	9.165 7	1.298 70	2419.0	465663
771	594441	458314011	27.766 9	9.169 6	1.297 02	2422.2	466873
772	595984	460099648	27.784 9	9.173 6	1.295 34	2425.3	468085
773	597529	461889917	27.802 9	9.177 5	1.293 66	2428.5	469298
774	599076	463684824	27.820 9	9.181 5	1.291 99	2431.6	470513
775	600625	465484375	27.838 8	9.185 5	1.290 32	2434.7	471730
776	602176	467288576	27.856 8	9.189 4	1.288 66	2437.9	472948
777	603729	469097433	27.874 7	9.193 3	1.287 00	2441.9	474168
778	605284	470910952	27.892 7	9.197 3	1.285 35	2444.2	475389
779	606841	472729139	27.910 6	9.201 2	1.283 70	2447.3	476612
780	608400	474552000	27.928 5	9.205 2	1.282 05	2450.5	477836
781	609961	476379541	27.946 4	9.209 1	1.280 41	2453.6	479062
782	611524	478211768	27.964 3	9.213 0	1.278 77	2456.7	480290
783	613089	480048687	27.982 1	9.217 0	1.277 14	2459.9	481519
784	614656	481890304	28.000 0	9.220 9	1.275 51	2463.0	482750
785	616225	483736625	28.017 9	9.224 8	1.273 89	2466.2	483982
786	617796	485587656	28.035 7	9.228 7	1.272 26	2469.2	485216
787	619369	487443403	28.053 5	0.232 6	1.270 65	2472.4	486451
788	620944	489303872	28.071 3	9.236 5	1.269 04	2475.6	487688
789	622521	491169069	28.089 1	9.240 4	1.267 43	2478.7	488927
790	624100	493039000	28.106 9	9.244 3	1.265 82	2481.9	490167
791	625681	494913671	28.124 7	9.248 2	1.264 22	2485.0	491409
792	627264	496793088	28.142 5	9.242 1	1.262 63	2488.1	492652
793	628849	498677257	28.160 3	9.256 0	1.261 03	2491.3	493897
794	630436	500566184	28.178 0	9.259 9	1.259 45	2494.4	495143
795	632025	502459875	28.195 7	9.263 8	1.257 86	2497.6	496391
796	633616	504358336	28.213 5	9.267 7	1.256 28	2500.7	497641
797	635209	506261573	28.231 2	9.271 6	1.254 71	2503.8	498892
798	636804	508169592	28.248 9	9.275 4	1.253 13	2507.0	500145
799	638401	510082399	28.266 6	9.279 3	1.251 56	2510.1	501399
800	640000	512000000	28.284 3	9.283 2	1.250 00	2513.3	502655
801	641601	513922401	28.301 9	9.287 0	1.248 44	2516.4	503912
802	643204	515849608	28.319 6	9.290 9	1.246 88	2519.6	505171
803	644809	517781627	28.337 3	9.294 8	1.245 33	2522.7	506432
804	646416	519718464	28.354 9	9.298 6	1.243 78	2525.8	507694
805	648025	521660125	28.372 5	9.302 5	1.242 24	2529.0	508958
806	649636	523606616	28.390 1	9.306 3	1.240 69	2532.1	510223
807	651249	525557943	28.407 7	9.310 2	1.239 16	2535.3	511490
808	652864	527514112	28.425 3	9.314 0	1.237 62	2538.4	512758
809	654481	529475129	28.442 9	9.317 9	1.236 09	2541.5	514028
810	656100	531441000	28.460 5	9.321 7	1.234 57	2544.7	515300
811	657721	533411731	28.478 1	9.325 5	1.233 05	2547.8	516573
812	659344	535387328	28.495 6	9.329 4	1.231 53	2551.0	517848
813	660969	537367797	28.513 2	9.333 2	1.230 01	2554.1	519124
814	662596	539353144	28.530 7	9.337 0	1.228 50	2557.3	520402
815	664225	541343375	28.548 2	9.340 8	1.226 99	2560.4	521681
816	665856	543338496	28.565 7	9.344 7	1.225 49	2563.5	522962
817	667489	545338513	28.583 2	9.348 5	1.223 99	2566.7	524245
818	669124	547343432	28.600 7	9.352 3	1.222 49	2569.8	525529
819	670761	549353259	28.618 2	9.356 1	1.221 00	2573.0	526814
820	672400	551368000	28.635 6	9.359 9	1.219 51	2576.1	528102
821	674041	553387661	28.653 1	9.363 7	1.218 03	2579.2	529391
822	675684	555412248	28.670 5	9.367 5	1.216 55	2582.4	530681
823	677329	557441767	28.688 0	9.371 3	1.215 07	2585.5	531973
824	678976	559476224	28.705 4	9.375 1	1.213 59	2588.7	533267
825	680625	561515625	28.722 8	9.378 9	1.212 12	2591.8	534562
826	682276	563559976	28.740 2	9.382 7	1.210 65	2595.0	535858
827	683929	565609283	28.757 6	9.386 5	1.209 19	2598.1	537157
828	685584	567663552	28.775 0	9.390 2	1.207 73	2601.2	538456
829	687241	569722789	28.792 4	9.394 0	1.206 27	2604.4	539758
830	688900	571787000	28.809 7	9.397 8	1.204 82	2607.5	541061
831	690561	573856191	28.827 1	9.401 6	1.203 37	2610.7	542365
832	692224	575930368	28.844 4	9.405 3	1.201 92	2613.8	543671
833	693889	578009537	28.861 7	9.409 1	1.200 48	2616.9	544979
834	695556	580093704	28.879 1	9.412 9	1.199 04	2620.1	546288

N	N^2	N^3	$\sqrt{N}$	$\sqrt[3]{N}$	$\dfrac{1000}{N}$	N = diameter	
						circum.	area
835	**697225**	**582182875**	**28.896 4**	**9.416 6**	**1.197 60**	**2623.2**	**547599**
836	698896	584277056	28.913 7	9.420 4	1.196 17	2626.4	548912
837	700569	586376253	28.931 0	9.424 1	1.194 74	2629.5	550226
838	702244	588480472	28.948 2	9.427 9	1.193 32	2632.7	551541
839	703921	590589719	28.965 5	9.431 6	1.191 90	2635.8	552858
840	**705600**	**592704000**	**28.982 8**	**9.435 4**	**1.190 48**	**2638.9**	**554177**
841	707281	594823321	29.000 0	9.439 1	1.189 06	2642.1	555497
842	708964	596947688	29.017 2	9.442 9	1.187 65	2645.2	556819
843	710649	599077107	29.034 5	9.446 6	1.186 24	2648.4	558142
844	712336	601211584	29.051 7	9.450 3	1.184 83	2651.5	559467
845	**714025**	**603351125**	**29.068 9**	**9.454 1**	**1.183 43**	**2654.6**	**560794**
846	715716	605495736	29.086 1	9.457 8	1.182 03	2657.8	562122
847	717409	607645423	29.103 3	9.461 5	1.180 64	2660.9	563452
848	719104	609800192	29.120 4	9.462 2	1.179 25	2664.1	564783
849	720801	611960049	29.137 6	9.469 0	1.177 86	2667.2	566116
850	**722500**	**614125000**	**29.154 8**	**9.472 7**	**1.176 47**	**2670.4**	**567450**
851	724201	616295051	29.171 9	9.476 4	1.175 09	2673.5	568786
852	725904	618470208	29.189 0	9.480 1	1.173 71	2676.6	570124
853	727609	620650477	29.206 2	9.483 8	1.172 33	2679.8	571463
854	729316	622835864	29.223 3	9.487 5	1.170 96	2682.9	572803
855	**731025**	**625026375**	**29.240 4**	**9.491 2**	**1.169 59**	**2686.1**	**574146**
856	732736	627222016	29.257 5	9.494 9	1.168 22	2689.2	575490
857	734449	629422793	29.274 6	9.498 6	1.166 86	2692.3	576835
858	736164	631628712	29.291 6	9.502 3	1.165 50	2695.5	578182
859	737881	633839779	29.308 7	9.506 0	1.164 14	2698.6	579530
860	**739600**	**636056000**	**29.325 8**	**9.509 7**	**1.162 79**	**2701.8**	**580880**
861	741321	638277381	29.342 8	9.513 4	1.161 44	2704.9	582232
862	743044	640503928	29.359 8	9.517 1	1.160 09	2708.1	583585
863	744769	642735647	29.376 9	9.520 7	1.158 75	2711.2	584940
864	746496	644972544	29.393 9	9.524 4	1.157 41	2714.3	586297
865	**748225**	**647214625**	**29.410 9**	**9.528 1**	**1.156 07**	**2717.5**	**587655**
866	749956	649461896	29.427 9	9.531 7	1.154 73	2720.6	589014
867	751689	651714363	29.444 9	9.535 4	1.153 40	2723.8	590375
868	753424	653972032	29.461 8	9.539 1	1.152 07	2726.9	591738
869	755161	656234909	29.478 8	9.542 7	1.150 75	2730.0	593102
870	**756900**	**658503000**	**29.495 8**	**9.546 4**	**1.149 43**	**2733.2**	**594468**
871	758641	660776311	29.512 7	9.550 1	1.148 11	2736.3	595835
872	760384	663054848	29.529 6	9.553 7	1.146 79	2739.5	597204
873	762129	665338617	29.546 6	9.557 4	1.145 48	2742.6	598575
874	763876	667627624	29.563 5	9.561 0	1.144 16	2745.8	599947
875	**765625**	**669921875**	**29.580 4**	**9.564 7**	**1.142 86**	**2748.9**	**601320**
876	767376	672221376	29.597 3	9.568 3	1.141 55	2752.0	602696
877	769129	674526133	29.614 2	9.571 9	1.140 25	2755.2	604073
878	770884	676836152	29.631 1	9.575 6	1.138 95	2758.3	605451
879	772641	679151439	29.647 9	9.579 2	1.137 66	2761.5	606831
880	**774400**	**681472000**	**29.664 8**	**9.582 8**	**1.136 36**	**2764.6**	**608112**
881	776161	683797841	29.681 6	9.586 5	1.135 07	2767.7	609595
882	777924	686128968	29.698 5	9.590 1	1.133 79	2770.9	610980
883	779689	688465387	29.715 3	9.593 7	1.132 50	2774.0	612366
884	781456	690807104	29.732 1	9.597 3	1.131 22	2777.2	613754
885	**783225**	**693154125**	**29.748 9**	**9.601 0**	**1.129 94**	**2780.3**	**615143**
886	784996	695506456	29.765 8	9.604 6	1.128 67	2783.5	616534
887	786769	697864103	29.782 5	9.608 2	1.127 40	2786.6	617927
888	788544	700227072	29.799 3	9.611 8	1.126 13	2789.7	619321
889	790321	702595369	29.816 1	9.615 4	1.124 86	2792.9	620717
890	**792100**	**704969000**	**29.832 9**	**9.619 0**	**1.123 60**	**2796.0**	**622114**
891	793881	707347081	29.849 6	9.622 6	1.122 33	2799.2	623513
892	795664	709732288	29.866 4	9.626 2	1.121 08	2802.3	624913
893	797449	712121957	29.883 1	9.629 8	1.119 82	2805.4	626315
894	799236	714516984	29.899 8	9.633 4	1.118 57	2808.6	627718
895	**801025**	**716917375**	**29.916 6**	**9.637 0**	**1.117 32**	**2811.7**	**629124**
896	802816	719323136	29.933 3	9.640 6	1.116 07	2814.9	630530
897	804609	721734273	29.950 0	9.644 2	1.114 83	2818.0	631938
898	806404	724150792	29.966 6	9.647 7	1.113 59	2821.2	633348
899	808201	726572699	29.983 3	9.651 3	1.112 35	2824.3	634760

Table 1 / Functions of numbers   □   **615**

N	N²	N³	√N	³√N	1000/N	N = diameter circum.	area
900	**810000**	**729000000**	**30.000 0**	**9.654 9**	**1.111 11**	**2827.4**	**636173**
901	811801	731432701	30.016 7	9.658 5	1.109 88	2830.6	637587
902	813604	733870808	30.033 3	9.662 0	1.108 65	2833.7	639003
903	815409	736314327	30.050 0	9.665 6	1.107 42	2836.9	640421
904	817216	738763264	30.066 6	9.669 2	1.106 19	2840.0	641840
905	**819025**	**741217625**	**30.083 2**	**9.672 7**	**1.104 97**	**2843.1**	**643261**
906	820836	743677416	30.099 8	9.676 3	1.103 75	2846.3	644683
907	822649	746142643	30.116 4	9.679 9	1.102 54	2849.4	646107
908	824464	748613312	30.133 0	9.683 4	1.101 32	2852.6	647533
909	826281	751089429	30.149 6	9.687 0	1.100 11	2855.7	648960
910	**828100**	**753571000**	**30.166 2**	**9.690 5**	**1.098 90**	**2858.8**	**650388**
911	829921	756058031	30.182 8	9.694 1	1.097 69	2862.0	651818
912	831744	758550528	30.199 3	9.697 6	1.096 49	2865.1	653250
913	833569	761048497	30.215 9	9.701 2	1.095 29	2868.3	654684
914	835396	763551944	30.232 4	9.704 7	1.094 09	2871.4	656118
915	**837225**	**766060875**	**30.294 0**	**9.708 2**	**1.092 90**	**2874.6**	**657555**
916	839056	768575296	30.265 5	9.711 8	1.091 70	2877.7	658993
917	840889	771095213	30.282 0	9.715 3	1.090 51	2880.8	660433
918	842724	773620632	30.298 5	9.718 8	1.089 32	2884.0	661874
919	844561	776151559	30.315 0	9.722 4	1.088 14	2887.1	663317
920	**846400**	**778688000**	**30.331 5**	**9.725 9**	**1.086 96**	**2890.3**	**664761**
921	848241	781229961	30.348 0	9.729 4	1.085 78	2893.4	666207
922	850084	783777448	30.364 5	9.732 9	1.084 60	2896.5	667654
923	851929	786330467	30.380 9	9.736 4	1.083 42	2899.7	669103
924	853776	788889024	30.397 4	9.740 0	1.082 25	2902.8	670554
925	**855625**	**791453125**	**30.413 8**	**9.743 5**	**1.081 08**	**2906.0**	**672006**
926	857476	794022776	30.430 2	9.747 0	1.079 91	2909.1	673460
927	859329	796597983	30.446 7	9.750 5	1.078 75	2912.3	674915
928	861184	799178752	30.463 1	9.754 0	1.077 59	2915.4	676372
929	863041	801765089	30.479 5	9.757 5	1.076 43	2918.5	677831
930	**864900**	**804357000**	**30.495 9**	**9.761 0**	**1.075 27**	**2921.7**	**679291**
931	866761	806954491	30.512 3	9.764 5	1.074 11	2924.8	680752
932	868624	809557568	30.528 7	9.768 0	1.072 96	2928.0	682216
933	870489	812166237	30.545 0	9.771 5	1.071 81	2931.1	683680
934	872356	814780504	30.561 4	9.775 0	1.070 66	2934.2	685147
935	**874225**	**817400375**	**30.577 8**	**9.778 5**	**1.069 52**	**2937.4**	**686615**
936	876096	820025856	30.594 1	9.781 9	1.068 38	2940.5	688084
937	877969	822656953	30.610 5	9.785 4	1.067 24	2943.7	689555
938	879844	825293672	30.626 8	9.788 9	1.066 10	2946.8	691028
939	881721	827936019	30.643 1	9.792 4	1.064 96	2950.0	692502
940	**883600**	**830584000**	**30.659 4**	**9.795 9**	**1.063 83**	**2953.1**	**693978**
941	885481	833237621	30.675 7	9.799 3	1.062 70	2956.2	695455
942	887364	835896888	30.692 0	9.802 8	1.061 57	2959.4	696934
943	889249	838561807	30.708 3	9.806 3	1.060 45	2962.5	698415
944	891136	841232384	30.724 6	9.809 7	1.059 32	2965.7	699897
945	**893025**	**843908625**	**30.740 9**	**9.813 2**	**1.058 20**	**2968.8**	**701380**
946	894916	846590536	30.757 1	9.816 7	1.057 08	2971.9	702865
947	896809	849278123	30.773 4	9.820 1	1.055 97	2975.1	704352
948	898704	851971392	30.789 6	9.823 6	1.054 85	2978.2	705840
949	900601	854670349	30.805 8	9.827 0	1.053 74	2981.4	707330
950	**902500**	**857375000**	**30.822 1**	**9.803 5**	**1.052 63**	**2984.5**	**708822**
951	904401	860085351	30.838 3	9.833 9	1.051 52	2987.7	710315
952	906304	862801408	30.854 5	9.837 4	1.050 42	2990.8	711809
953	908209	865523177	30.870 7	9.840 8	1.049 32	2993.9	713306
954	910116	868250664	30.886 9	9.844 3	1.048 22	2997.1	714803
955	**912025**	**870983875**	**30.903 1**	**9.847 7**	**1.047 12**	**3000.2**	**716303**
956	913936	873722816	30.919 2	9.851 1	1.046 03	3003.4	717804
957	915849	876467493	30.935 4	9.854 6	1.044 93	3006.5	719306
958	917764	879217912	30.951 6	9.858 0	1.043 84	3009.6	720810
959	919681	881974079	30.967 7	9.861 4	1.042 75	3012.8	722316
960	**921600**	**884736000**	**30.983 9**	**9.864 8**	**1.041 67**	**3015.9**	**723823**
961	923521	887503681	31.000 0	9.868 3	1.040 58	3019.1	725332
962	925444	890277128	31.016 1	9.871 7	1.039 50	3022.2	726842
963	927369	893056347	31.032 2	9.875 1	1.038 42	3025.4	728354
964	929296	895841344	31.048 3	9.878 5	1.037 34	3028.5	729867

N	N²	N³	$\sqrt{N}$	$\sqrt[3]{N}$	$\dfrac{1000}{N}$	$N = $ diameter	
						circum.	area
965	**931225**	**898632125**	**31.064 4**	**9.881 9**	**1.036 27**	**3031.6**	**731382**
966	933156	901428696	31.080 5	9.885 4	1.035 20	3034.8	732899
967	935089	904231063	31.096 6	9.888 8	1.034 13	3037.9	734417
968	937024	907039232	31.112 7	9.892 2	1.033 06	3041.1	735937
969	938961	909853209	31.128 8	9.895 6	1.031 99	3044.2	737458
970	**940900**	**912673000**	**31.144 8**	**9.899 0**	**1.030 93**	**3047.3**	**738981**
971	942841	915498611	31.160 9	9.902 4	1.029 87	3050.5	740506
972	944784	918330048	31.176 9	9.905 8	1.028 81	3053.6	742032
973	946729	921167317	31.192 9	9.909 2	1.027 75	3056.8	743559
974	948676	924010424	31.209 0	9.912 6	1.026 69	3059.9	745088
975	**950625**	**926859375**	**31.225 0**	**9.916 0**	**1.025 64**	**3063.1**	**746619**
976	952576	929714176	31.241 0	9.919 4	1.024 59	3066.2	748151
977	954529	932574833	31.257 0	9.922 7	1.023 54	3069.3	749685
978	956484	935441352	31.273 0	9.926 1	1.022 49	3072.5	751221
979	958441	938313739	31.289 0	9.929 5	1.021 45	3075.6	752758
980	**960400**	**941192000**	**31.305 0**	**9.932 9**	**1.020 41**	**3078.8**	**754296**
981	962361	944076141	31.320 9	9.936 3	1.019 37	3081.9	755837
982	964324	946966168	31.336 9	9.939 6	1.018 33	3085.0	757378
983	966289	949862087	31.352 8	9.943 0	1.017 29	3088.2	758922
984	968256	952763904	31.368 8	9.946 4	1.016 26	3091.3	760466
985	**970225**	**955671625**	**31.384 7**	**9.949 7**	**1.015 23**	**3094.5**	**762013**
986	972196	958585256	31.400 6	9.953 1	1.014 20	3097.6	763561
987	974169	961504803	31.416 6	9.956 5	1.013 17	3100.8	765111
988	976144	964430272	31.432 5	9.959 8	1.012 15	3103.9	766662
989	978121	967361669	31.448 4	9.963 2	1.011 12	3107.0	768214
990	**980100**	**970299000**	**31.464 3**	**9.966 6**	**1.010 10**	**3110.2**	**769769**
991	982081	973242271	31.480 2	9.969 9	1.009 08	3113.3	771325
992	984064	976191488	31.496 0	9.973 3	1.008 06	3116.5	772882
993	986049	979146657	31.511 9	9.976 6	1.007 05	3119.6	774441
994	988036	982107784	31.527 8	9.980 0	1.006 04	3122.7	776002
995	**990025**	**985074875**	**31.543 6**	**9.983 3**	**1.005 03**	**3125.9**	**777564**
996	992016	988047936	31.559 5	9.986 6	1.004 02	2129.0	779128
997	994009	991026973	31.575 3	9.990 0	1.003 01	3132.2	780693
998	996004	994011992	31.591 1	9.993 3	1.002 00	3135.3	782260
999	998001	997002999	31.607 0	9.996 7	1.001 00	3138.5	783828

Table 1 / *Functions of numbers* □ 617

TABLE 2
Angular Conversion

Table 2A
Minutes and seconds to decimals of degree (decitrig)

′	°	″	°	″	°
0	**0.000 00**	0	**0.000 00**	0.1	**0.000 03**
1	0.016 67	1	0.000 28	0.2	0.000 06
2	0.033 33	2	0.000 55	0.3	0.000 08
3	0.050 00	3	0.000 83	0.4	0.000 11
4	0.066 67	4	0.001 11	0.5	0.000 14
5	**0.083 33**	5	**0.001 39**	0.6	**0.000 17**
6	0.100 00	6	0.001 67	0.7	0.000 19
7	0.116 67	7	0.001 94	0.8	0.000 22
8	0.133 33	8	0.002 22	0.9	0.000 25
9	0.150 00	9	0.002 50	1.0	0.000 28
10	**0.166 67**	10	**0.002 78**		
11	0.183 33	11	0.003 06		
12	0.200 00	12	0.003 33		
13	0.216 67	13	0.003 61		
14	0.233 33	14	0.003 89		
15	**0.250 00**	15	**0.004 17**		
16	0.266 67	16	0.004 44		
17	0.283 33	17	0.004 72		
18	0.300 00	18	0.005 00		
19	0.316 67	19	0.005 28		
20	**0.333 33**	20	**0.005 56**		
21	0.350 00	21	0.005 83		
22	0.366 67	22	0.006 11		
23	0.383 33	23	0.006 39		
24	0.400 00	24	0.006 67		
25	**0.416 67**	25	**0.006 94**		
26	0.433 33	26	0.007 22		
27	0.450 00	27	0.007 50		
28	0.466 67	28	0.007 78		
29	0.483 33	29	0.008 06		
30	**0.500 00**	30	**0.008 33**		
31	0.516 67	31	0.008 61		
32	0.533 33	32	0.008 89		
33	0.550 00	33	0.009 17		
34	0.566 67	34	0.009 44		
35	**0.583 33**	35	**0.009 72**		
36	0.600 00	36	0.010 00		
37	0.616 67	37	0.010 28		
38	0.633 33	38	0.010 56		
39	0.650 00	39	0.010 83		
40	**0.666 67**	40	**0.011 11**		
41	0.683 33	41	0.011 39		
42	0.700 00	42	0.011 67		
43	0.716 67	43	0.011 94		
44	0.733 33	44	0.012 22		
45	**0.750 00**	45	**0.012 50**		
46	0.766 67	46	0.012 78		
47	0.783 33	47	0.013 06		
48	0.800 00	48	0.013 33		
49	0.816 67	49	0.013 61		
50	**0.833 33**	50	**0.013 89**		
51	0.850 00	51	0.014 17		
52	0.866 67	52	0.014 44		
53	0.883 33	53	0.014 72		
54	0.900 00	54	0.015 00		
55	**0.916 67**	55	**0.015 28**		
56	0.933 33	56	0.015 56		
57	0.950 00	57	0.015 83		
58	0.966 67	58	0.016 11		
59	0.983 33	59	0.016 39		
60	**1.000 00**	60	**0.016 67**		

Table 2B
Decimals of degree (decitrig) to minutes and seconds

°	′	″	°	′	″	°	″
0.00	0	00	0.50	30	00	0.000	0.0
0.01	0	36	0.51	30	36	0.001	3.6
0.02	1	12	0.52	31	12	0.002	7.2
0.03	1	48	0.53	31	48	0.003	10.8
0.04	2	24	0.54	32	24	0.004	14.4
0.05	3	00	0.55	33	00	0.005	18.0
0.06	3	36	0.56	33	36	0.006	21.6
0.07	4	12	0.57	34	12	0.007	25.2
0.08	4	48	0.58	34	48	0.008	28.8
0.09	5	24	0.59	35	24	0.009	32.4
0.10	6	00	0.60	36	00	0.010	36.0
0.11	6	36	0.61	36	36		
0.12	7	12	0.62	37	12		
0.13	7	48	0.63	37	48		
0.14	8	24	0.64	38	24		
0.15	9	00	0.55	39	00		
0.16	9	36	0.66	39	36	0.0001	0.4
0.17	10	12	0.67	40	12	0.0002	0.7
0.18	10	48	0.68	40	48	0.0003	1.1
0.19	11	24	0.69	41	24	0.0004	1.4
0.20	12	00	0.70	42	00	0.0005	1.8
0.21	12	36	0.71	42	36	0.0006	2.2
0.22	13	12	0.72	43	12	0.0007	2.5
0.23	13	48	0.73	43	48	0.0008	2.9
0.24	14	24	0.74	44	24	0.0009	3.2
0.25	15	00	0.75	45	00	0.0010	3.6
0.26	15	36	0.76	45	36		
0.27	16	12	0.77	46	12		
0.28	16	48	0.78	46	48		
0.29	17	24	0.79	47	24		
0.30	18	00	0.80	48	00		
0.31	18	36	0.81	48	36		
0.32	19	12	0.82	49	12		
0.33	19	48	0.83	49	48		
0.34	20	24	0.84	50	24		
0.35	21	00	0.85	51	00		
0.36	21	36	0.86	51	36		
0.37	22	12	0.87	52	12		
0.38	22	48	0.88	52	48		
0.39	23	24	0.89	53	24		
0.40	24	00	0.90	54	00		
0.41	24	36	0.91	54	36		
0.42	25	12	0.92	55	12		
0.43	25	48	0.93	55	48		
0.44	26	24	0.94	56	24		
0.45	27	00	0.95	57	00		
0.46	27	36	0.96	57	36		
0.47	28	12	0.97	58	12		
0.48	28	48	0.98	58	48		
0.49	29	24	0.99	59	24		
0.50	30	00	1.00	60	00		

Table 2 / Angular conversion □ 619

Table 2C

Radians to degrees, minutes, and seconds

Rad	°	′	″	Rad	°	′	″	Rad	°	′	″
1	57	17	44.8	0.1	5	43	46.5	0.01	0	34	22.6
2	114	35	29.6	0.2	11	27	33.0	0.02	1	8	45.3
3	171	53	14.4	0.3	17	11	19.4	0.03	1	43	7.9
4	229	10	59.2	0.4	22	55	5.9	0.04	2	17	30.6
5	286	28	44.0	0.5	28	38	52.4	0.05	2	51	53.2
6	343	46	28.8	0.6	34	22	38.9	0.06	3	26	15.9
7	401	4	13.6	0.7	40	6	25.4	0.07	4	0	38.5
8	458	21	58.4	0.8	45	50	11.8	0.08	4	35	1.2
9	515	39	43.3	0.9	51	33	58.3	0.09	5	9	23.8

Rad	°	′	″	Rad	°	′	″
0.001	0	3	26.3	0.000 1	0	0	20.6
0.002	0	6	52.5	0.000 2	0	0	41.3
0.003	0	10	18.8	0.000 3	0	1	1.9
0.004	0	13	45.1	0.000 4	0	1	22.5
0.005	0	17	11.3	0.000 5	0	1	43.1
0.006	0	20	37.6	0.000 6	0	2	3.8
0.007	0	24	3.9	3.000 7	0	2	24.4
0.008	0	27	30.1	0.000 8	0	2	45.0
0.009	0	30	56.4	0.000 9	0	3	5.6

Table 2D

Radians to degrees and decimals (decitrig)

Rad	°	Rad	°	Rad	°	Rad	°
1	57.295 8	0.1	5.729 6	0.01	0.573 0	0.001	0.057 3
2	114.591 6	0.2	11.459 2	0.02	1.145 9	0.002	0.114 6
3	171.887 3	0.3	17.188 7	0.03	1.718 9	0.003	0.171 9
4	229.183 1	0.4	22.918 3	0.04	2.291 8	0.004	0.229 2
5	286.478 9	0.5	28.647 9	0.05	2.864 8	0.005	0.286 5
6	343.774 7	0.6	34.377 5	0.06	3.437 7	0.006	0.343 8
7	401.070 5	0.7	40.107 0	0.07	4.010 7	0.007	0.401 1
8	458.366 2	0.8	45.836 6	0.08	4.583 7	0.008	0.458 4
9	515.662 0	0.9	51.566 2	0.09	5.156 6	0.009	0.515 7
10	572.957 8	1.0	57.295 8	0.10	5.729 6	0.010	0.573 0

Table 2E

Degrees, minutes, and seconds to radians*

Degrees		Degrees		Degrees		Minutes		Seconds	
°		°		°		′		″	
0	0.000 000 0	60	1.047 197 6	120	2.094 395 1	0	0.000 000 0	0	0.000 000 0
1	0.017 453 3	61	1.064 650 8	121	2.111 848 4	1	0.000 290 9	1	0.000 004 8
2	0.034 906 6	62	1.082 104 1	122	2.129 301 7	2	0.000 581 8	2	0.000 009 7
3	0.052 359 9	63	1.099 557 4	123	2.146 755 0	3	0.000 872 7	3	0.000 014 5
4	0.069 813 2	64	1.117 010 7	124	2.164 208 3	4	0.001 163 6	4	0.000 019 4
5	0.087 266 5	65	1.134 464 0	125	2.181 661 6	5	0.001 454 4	5	0.000 024 2
6	0.104 719 8	66	1.151 917 3	126	2.199 114 9	6	0.001 745 3	6	0.000 029 1
7	0.122 173 0	67	1.169 370 6	127	2.216 568 2	7	0.002 036 2	7	0.000 033 9
8	0.139 626 3	68	1.186 823 9	128	2.234 021 4	8	0.002 327 1	8	0.000 038 8
9	0.157 079 6	69	1.204 277 2	129	2.251 474 7	9	0.002 618 0	9	0.000 043 6
10	0.174 532 9	70	1.221 730 5	130	2.268 928 0	10	0.002 908 9	10	0.000 048 5
11	0.191 986 2	71	1.239 183 8	131	2.286 381 3	11	0.003 199 8	11	0.000 053 3
12	0.209 439 5	72	1.256 637 1	132	2.303 834 6	12	0.003 490 7	12	0.000 058 2
13	0.226 892 8	73	1.274 090 4	133	2.321 287 9	13	0.003 781 5	13	0.000 063 0
14	0.244 346 1	74	1.291 543 6	134	2.338 741 2	14	0.004 072 4	14	0.000 067 9
15	0.261 799 4	75	1.308 996 9	135	2.356 194 5	15	0.004 363 3	15	0.000 072 7
16	0.279 252 7	76	1.326 450 2	136	2.373 647 8	16	0.004 654 2	16	0.000 077 6
17	0.296 706 0	77	1.343 903 5	137	2.391 101 1	17	0.004 945 1	17	0.000 082 4
18	0.314 159 3	78	1.361 356 8	138	2.408 554 4	18	0.005 236 0	18	0.000 087 3
19	0.331 612 6	79	1.378 810 1	139	2.426 007 7	19	0.005 526 9	19	0.000 092 1
20	0.349 065 9	80	1.396 263 4	140	2.443 461 0	20	0.005 817 8	20	0.000 097 0
21	0.366 519 1	81	1.413 716 7	141	2.460 914 2	21	0.006 108 7	21	0.000 101 8
22	0.383 972 4	82	1.431 170 0	142	2.478 367 5	22	0.006 399 5	22	0.000 106 7
23	0.401 425 7	83	1.448 623 3	143	2.495 820 8	23	0.006 690 4	23	0.000 111 5
24	0.418 879 0	84	1.466 076 6	144	2.513 274 1	24	0.006 981 3	24	0.000 116 4
25	0.436 332 3	85	1.483 529 9	145	2.530 727 4	25	0.007 272 2	25	0.000 121 2
26	0.453 785 6	86	1.500 983 2	146	2.548 180 7	26	0.007 563 1	26	0.000 126 1
27	0.471 238 9	87	1.518 436 4	147	2.565 634 0	27	0.007 854 0	27	0.000 130 9
28	0.488 692 2	88	1.535 889 7	148	2.583 087 3	28	0.008 144 9	28	0.000 135 7
29	0.506 145 5	89	1.553 343 0	149	2.600 540 6	29	0.008 435 8	29	0.000 140 6
30	0.523 598 8	90	1.570 796 3	150	2.617 993 9	30	0.008 726 6	30	0.000 145 4
31	0.541 052 1	91	1.588 249 6	151	2.635 447 2	31	0.009 017 5	31	0.000 150 3
32	0.558 505 4	92	1.605 702 9	152	2.652 900 5	32	0.009 308 4	32	0.000 155 1
33	0.575 958 7	93	1.623 156 2	153	2.670 353 8	33	0.009 599 3	33	0.000 160 0
34	0.593 411 9	94	1.640 609 5	154	2.687 807 0	34	0.009 890 2	34	0.000 164 8
35	0.610 865 2	95	1.658 062 8	155	2.705 260 3	35	0.010 181 1	35	0.000 169 7
36	0.628 318 5	96	1.675 516 1	156	2.722 713 6	36	0.010 472 0	36	0.000 174 5
37	0.645 771 8	97	1.692 969 4	157	2.740 166 9	37	0.010 762 9	37	0.000 179 4
38	0.663 225 1	98	1.710 422 7	158	2.757 620 2	38	0.011 053 8	38	0.000 184 2
39	0.680 678 4	99	1.727 876 0	159	2.775 073 5	39	0.011 344 6	39	0.000 189 1
40	0.698 131 7	100	1.745 329 3	160	2.792 526 8	40	0.011 635 5	40	0.000 193 9
41	0.715 585 0	101	1.762 782 5	161	2.809 980 1	41	0.011 926 4	41	0.000 198 8
42	0.733 038 3	102	1.780 235 8	162	2.827 433 4	42	0.012 217 3	42	0.000 203 6
43	0.750 491 6	103	1.797 689 1	163	2.844 886 7	43	0.012 508 2	43	0.000 208 5
44	0.767 944 9	104	1.815 142 4	164	2.862 340 0	44	0.012 799 1	44	0.000 213 3
45	0.785 398 2	105	1.832 595 7	165	2.879 793 3	45	0.013 090 0	45	0.000 218 2
46	0.802 851 5	106	1.850 049 0	166	2.897 246 6	46	0.013 380 9	46	0.000 223 0
47	0.820 304 7	107	1.867 502 3	167	2.914 699 9	47	0.013 671 7	47	0.000 227 9
48	0.837 758 0	108	1.884 955 6	168	2.932 153 1	48	0.013 962 6	48	0.000 232 7
49	0.855 211 3	109	1.902 408 0	169	2.949 606 4	49	0.014 253 5	49	0.000 237 6
50	0.872 664 6	110	1.919 862 2	170	2.967 059 7	50	0.014 544 4	50	0.000 242 4
51	0.890 117 9	111	1.937 315 5	171	2.984 513 0	51	0.014 835 3	51	0.000 247 3
52	0.907 571 2	112	1.954 768 8	172	3.001 966 3	52	0.015 126 2	52	0.000 252 1
53	0.925 024 5	113	1.972 222 1	173	3.019 419 6	53	0.015 417 1	53	0.000 257 0
54	0.942 477 8	114	1.989 675 3	174	3.036 872 9	54	0.015 708 0	54	0.000 261 8
55	0.959 931 1	115	2.007 128 6	175	3.054 326 2	55	0.015 998 9	55	0.000 266 6
56	0.977 384 4	116	2.024 581 9	176	3.071 779 5	56	0.016 289 7	56	0.000 271 5
57	0.994 837 7	117	2.042 035 2	177	3.089 232 8	57	0.016 580 6	57	0.000 276 3
58	1.012 291 0	118	2.059 488 5	178	3.106 686 1	58	0.016 871 5	58	0.000 281 2
59	1.029 744 3	119	2.076 941 8	179	3.124 139 4	59	0.017 162 4	59	0.000 286 0
60	1.047 197 6	120	2.094 395 1	180	3.141 592 7	60	0.017 453 3	60	0.000 290 9

* From H. B. Dwight, *Tables of Integrals.* New York: The Macmillan Company, 4th ed., 1961, p. 266.

Table 2 / Angular conversion   □   621

Table 2F

Degrees and decimals (decitrig) to radians

°	Rad	°	Rad	°	Rad
100	1.745 329	10	0.174 533	1	0.017 453
200	3.490 659	20	0.349 066	2	0.034 907
300	5.235 988	30	0.523 599	3	0.052 360
400	6.981 317	40	0.698 132	4	0.069 813
500	8.726 646	50	0.872 665	5	0.087 266
600	10.471 976	60	1.047 198	6	0.104 720
700	12.217 305	70	1.221 730	7	0.122 173
800	13.962 634	80	1.396 263	8	0.139 626
900	15.707 963	90	1.570 796	9	0.157 080

°	Rad	°	Rad	°	Rad
0.1	0.001 745	0.01	0.000 175	0.001	0.000 017
0.2	0.003 491	0.02	0.000 349	0.002	0.000 035
0.3	0.005 236	0.03	0.000 524	0.003	0.000 052
0.4	0.006 981	0.04	0.000 698	0.004	0.000 070
0.5	0.008 727	0.05	0.000 873	0.005	0.000 087
0.6	0.010 472	0.06	0.001 047	0.006	0.000 105
0.7	0.012 217	0.07	0.001 222	0.007	0.000 122
0.8	0.013 963	0.08	0.001 396	0.008	0.000 140
0.9	0.015 708	0.09	0.001 571	0.009	0.000 157

TABLE 3
Five-Place Natural Trigonometric Functions;
Angles in Degrees, Minutes, and Seconds

0° (180°)   (359°) **179°**

′	Sin	Tan	Cot	Cos	Sec	Csc	′
0	**0.000 00**	**0.000 00**	—	**1.000 0**	**1.000 0**	—	60
1	0.000 29	0.000 29	3437.7	1.000 0	1.000 0	3437.7	59
2	0.000 58	0.000 58	1718.9	1.000 0	1.000 0	1718.9	58
3	0.000 87	0.000 87	1145.9	1.000 0	1.000 0	1145.9	57
4	0.001 16	0.001 16	859.44	1.000 0	1.000 0	859.44	56
5	**0.001 45**	**0.001 45**	**687.55**	**1.000 0**	**1.000 0**	**687.55**	55
6	0.001 75	0.001 75	572.96	1.000 0	1.000 0	572.96	54
7	0.002 04	0.002 04	491.11	1.000 0	1.000 0	491.11	53
8	0.002 33	0.002 33	429.72	1.000 0	1.000 0	429.72	52
9	0.002 62	0.002 62	381.97	1.000 0	1.000 0	381.97	51
10	**0.002 91**	**0.002 91**	**343.77**	**1.000 0**	**1.000 0**	**343.78**	50
11	0.003 20	0.003 20	312.52	0.999 99	1.000 0	312.52	49
12	0.003 49	0.003 49	286.48	0.999 99	1.000 0	286.48	48
13	0.003 78	0.003 78	264.44	0.999 99	1.000 0	264.44	47
14	0.004 07	0.004 07	245.55	0.999 99	1.000 0	245.55	46
15	**0.004 36**	**0.004 36**	**229.18**	**0.999 99**	**1.000 0**	**229.18**	45
16	0.004 65	0.004 65	214.86	0.999 99	1.000 0	214.86	44
17	0.004 95	0.004 95	202.22	0.999 99	1.000 0	202.22	43
18	0.005 24	0.005 24	190.98	0.999 99	1.000 0	190.99	42
19	0.005 53	0.005 53	180.93	0.999 99	1.000 0	180.93	41
20	**0.005 82**	**0.005 82**	**171.89**	**0.999 98**	**1.000 0**	**171.89**	40
21	0.006 11	0.006 11	163.70	0.999 98	1.000 0	163.70	39
22	0.006 40	0.006 40	156.26	0.999 98	1.000 0	156.26	38
23	0.006 69	0.006 69	149.47	0.999 98	1.000 0	149.47	37
24	0.006 98	0.006 98	143.24	0.999 98	1.000 0	143.24	36
25	**0.007 27**	**0.007 27**	**137.51**	**0.999 97**	**1.000 0**	**137.51**	35
26	0.007 56	0.007 56	132.22	0.999 97	1.000 0	132.22	34
27	0.007 85	0.007 85	127.32	0.999 97	1.000 0	127.33	33
28	0.008 14	0.008 15	122.77	0.999 97	1.000 0	122.78	32
29	0.008 44	0.008 44	118.54	0.999 96	1.000 0	118.54	31
30	**0.008 73**	**0.008 73**	**114.59**	**0.999 96**	**1.000 0**	**114.59**	30
31	0.009 02	0.009 02	110.89	0.999 96	1.000 0	110.90	29
32	0.009 31	0.009 31	107.43	0.999 96	1.000 0	107.43	28
33	0.009 60	0.009 60	104.17	0.999 95	1.000 0	104.18	27
34	0.009 89	0.009 89	101.11	0.999 95	1.000 0	101.11	26
35	**0.010 18**	**0.010 18**	**98.218**	**0.999 95**	**1.000 1**	**98.223**	25
36	0.010 47	0.010 47	95.489	0.999 95	1.000 1	95.495	24
37	0.010 76	0.010 76	92.908	0.999 94	1.000 1	92.914	23
38	0.011 05	0.011 05	90.463	0.999 94	1.000 1	90.469	22
39	0.011 35	0.011 34	88.144	0.999 94	1.000 1	88.149	21
40	**0.011 64**	**0.011 64**	**85.940**	**0.999 93**	**1.000 1**	**85.946**	20
41	0.011 93	0.011 93	83.844	0.999 93	1.000 1	83.849	19
42	0.012 22	0.012 22	81.847	0.999 93	1.000 1	81.853	18
43	0.012 51	0.012 51	79.943	0.999 92	1.000 1	79.950	17
44	0.012 80	0.012 80	78.126	0.999 92	1.000 1	78.133	16
45	**0.013 09**	**0.013 09**	**76.390**	**0.999 91**	**1.000 1**	**76.397**	15
46	0.013 38	0.013 38	74.729	0.999 91	1.000 1	74.736	14
47	0.013 67	0.013 67	73.139	0.999 91	1.000 1	73.146	13
48	0.013 96	0.013 96	71.615	0.999 90	1.000 1	71.622	12
49	0.014 25	0.014 25	70.153	0.999 90	1.000 1	70.160	11
50	**0.014 54**	**0.014 55**	**68.750**	**0.999 89**	**1.000 1**	**68.757**	10
51	0.014 83	0.014 84	67.402	0.999 89	1.000 1	67.409	9
52	0.015 13	0.015 13	66.105	0.999 89	1.000 1	66.113	8
53	0.015 42	0.015 42	64.858	0.999 88	1.000 1	64.866	7
54	0.015 71	0.015 71	63.657	0.999 88	1.000 1	63.665	6
55	**0.016 00**	**0.016 00**	**62.499**	**0.999 87**	**1.000 1**	**62.507**	5
56	0.016 29	0.016 29	61.383	0.999 87	1.000 1	61.391	4
57	0.016 58	0.016 58	60.306	0.999 86	1.000 1	60.314	3
58	0.016 87	0.016 87	59.266	0.999 86	1.000 1	59.274	2
59	0.017 16	0.017 16	58.261	0.999 85	1.000 1	58.270	1
60	**0.017 45**	**0.017 46**	**57.290**	**0.999 85**	**1.000 2**	**57.299**	0
′	Cos	Cot	Tan	Sin	Csc	Sec	′

90° (270°)   (269°) **89°**

623

′	Sin	Tan	Cot	Cos	Sec	Csc	′
0	0.017 45	0.017 46	57.290	0.999 85	1.000 2	57.299	60
1	0.017 74	0.017 75	56.351	0.999 84	1.000 2	56.359	59
2	0.018 03	0.018 04	55.442	0.999 84	1.000 2	55.451	58
3	0.018 32	0.018 33	54.561	0.999 83	1.000 2	54.570	57
4	0.018 62	0.018 62	53.709	0.999 83	1.000 2	53.718	56
5	0.018 91	0.018 91	52.882	0.999 82	1.000 2	52.892	55
6	0.019 20	0.019 20	52.081	0.999 82	1.000 2	52.090	54
7	0.019 49	0.019 49	51.303	0.999 81	1.000 2	51.313	53
8	0.019 78	0.019 78	50.549	0.999 80	1.000 2	50.558	52
9	0.020 07	0.020 07	49.816	0.999 80	1.000 2	49.826	51
10	0.020 36	0.020 36	49.104	0.999 79	1.000 2	49.114	50
11	0.020 65	0.020 66	48.412	0.999 79	1.000 2	48.422	49
12	0.020 94	0.020 95	47.740	0.999 78	1.000 2	47.750	48
13	0.021 23	0.021 24	47.085	0.999 77	1.000 2	47.096	47
14	0.021 52	0.021 53	46.449	0.999 77	1.000 2	46.460	46
15	0.021 81	0.021 82	45.829	0.999 76	1.000 2	45.840	45
16	0.022 11	0.022 11	45.226	0.999 76	1.000 2	45.237	44
17	0.022 40	0.022 40	44.639	0.999 75	1.000 3	44.650	43
18	0.022 69	0.022 69	44.066	0.999 74	1.000 3	44.077	42
19	0.022 98	0.022 98	43.508	0.999 74	1.000 3	43.520	41
20	0.023 27	0.023 28	42.964	0.999 73	1.000 3	42.976	40
21	0.023 56	0.023 57	42.433	0.999 72	1.000 3	42.445	39
22	0.023 85	0.023 86	41.916	0.999 72	1.000 3	41.928	38
23	0.024 14	0.024 15	41.411	0.999 71	1.000 3	41.423	37
24	0.024 43	0.024 44	40.917	0.999 70	1.000 3	40.930	36
25	0.024 72	0.024 73	40.436	0.999 69	1.000 3	40.448	35
26	0.025 01	0.025 02	39.965	0.999 69	1.000 3	39.978	34
27	0.025 30	0.025 31	39.506	0.999 68	1.000 3	39.519	33
28	0.025 60	0.025 60	39.057	0.999 67	1.000 3	39.070	32
29	0.025 89	0.025 89	38.618	0.999 66	1.000 3	38.631	31
30	0.026 18	0.026 19	38.188	0.999 66	1.000 3	38.202	30
31	0.026 47	0.026 48	37.769	0.999 65	1.000 4	37.782	29
32	0.026 76	0.026 77	37.358	0.999 64	1.000 4	37.371	28
33	0.027 05	0.027 06	36.956	0.999 63	1.000 4	36.970	27
34	0.027 34	0.027 35	36.563	0.999 63	1.000 4	36.576	26
35	0.027 63	0.027 64	36.178	0.999 62	1.000 4	36.191	25
36	0.027 92	0.027 93	35.801	0.999 61	1.000 4	35.815	24
37	0.028 21	0.028 22	35.431	0.999 60	1.000 4	35.445	23
38	0.028 50	0.028 51	35.070	0.999 59	1.000 4	35.084	22
39	0.028 79	0.028 81	34.715	0.999 59	1.000 4	34.730	21
40	0.029 08	0.029 10	34.368	0.999 58	1.000 4	34.382	20
41	0.029 38	0.029 39	34.027	0.999 57	1.000 4	34.042	19
42	0.029 67	0.029 68	33.694	0.999 56	1.000 4	33.708	18
43	0.029 96	0.029 97	33.366	0.999 55	1.000 4	33.381	17
44	0.030 25	0.030 26	33.045	0.999 54	1.000 5	33.060	16
45	0.030 54	0.030 55	32.730	0.999 53	1.000 5	32.746	15
46	0.030 83	0.030 84	32.421	0.999 52	1.000 5	32.437	14
47	0.031 12	0.031 14	32.118	0.999 52	1.000 5	32.134	13
48	0.031 41	0.031 43	31.821	0.999 51	1.000 5	31.836	12
49	0.031 70	0.031 72	31.528	0.999 50	1.000 5	31.544	11
50	0.031 99	0.032 01	31.242	0.999 49	1.000 5	31.258	10
51	0.032 28	0.032 30	30.960	0.999 48	1.000 5	30.976	9
52	0.032 57	0.032 59	30.683	0.999 47	1.000 5	30.700	8
53	0.032 86	0.032 88	30.412	0.999 46	1.000 5	30.428	7
54	0.033 16	0.033 17	30.145	0.999 45	1.000 6	30.161	6
55	0.033 45	0.033 46	29.882	0.999 44	1.000 6	29.899	5
56	0.033 74	0.033 76	29.624	0.999 43	1.000 6	29.641	4
57	0.034 03	0.034 05	29.371	0.999 42	1.000 6	29.388	3
58	0.034 32	0.034 34	29.122	0.999 41	1.000 6	29.139	2
59	0.034 61	0.034 63	28.877	0.999 40	1.000 6	28.894	1
60	0.034 90	0.034 92	28.636	0.999 39	1.000 6	28.654	0
′	Cos	Cot	Tan	Sin	Csc	Sec	′

′	Sin	Tan	Cot	Cos	Sec	Csc	
0	0.034 90	0.034 92	28.636	0.999 39	1.000 6	28.654	60
1	0.035 19	0.035 21	28.399	0.999 38	1.000 6	28.417	59
2	0.035 48	0.035 50	28.166	0.999 37	1.000 6	28.184	58
3	0.035 77	0.035 79	27.937	0.999 36	1.000 6	27.955	57
4	0.036 06	0.036 09	27.712	0.999 35	1.000 7	27.730	56
5	0.036 35	0.036 38	27.490	0.999 34	1.000 7	27.508	55
6	0.036 64	0.036 67	27.271	0.999 33	1.000 7	27.290	54
7	0.036 93	0.036 96	27.057	0.999 32	1.000 7	27.075	53
8	0.037 23	0.037 25	26.845	0.999 31	1.000 7	26.864	52
9	0.037 52	0.037 54	26.637	0.999 30	1.000 7	26.655	51
10	0.037 81	0.037 83	26.432	0.999 29	1.000 7	26.451	50
11	0.038 10	0.038 12	26.230	0.999 27	1.000 7	26.249	49
12	0.038 39	0.038 42	26.031	0.999 26	1.000 7	26.050	48
13	0.038 68	0.038 71	25.835	0.999 25	1.000 7	25.854	47
14	0.038 97	0.039 00	25.642	0.999 24	1.000 8	25.661	46
15	0.039 26	0.039 29	25.452	0.999 23	1.000 8	25.471	45
16	0.039 55	0.039 58	25.264	0.999 22	1.000 8	25.284	44
17	0.039 84	0.039 87	25.080	0.999 21	1.000 8	25.100	43
18	0.040 13	0.040 16	24.898	0.999 19	1.000 8	24.918	42
19	0.040 42	0.040 46	24.719	0.999 18	1.000 8	24.739	41
20	0.040 71	0.040 75	24.542	0.999 17	1.000 8	24.562	40
21	0.041 00	0.041 04	24.368	0.999 16	1.000 8	24.388	39
22	0.041 29	0.041 33	24.196	0.999 15	1.000 9	24.216	38
23	0.041 59	0.041 62	24.026	0.999 13	1.000 9	24.047	37
24	0.041 88	0.041 91	23.859	0.999 12	1.000 9	23.880	36
25	0.042 17	0.042 20	23.695	0.999 11	1.000 9	23.716	35
26	0.042 46	0.042 50	23.532	0.999 10	1.000 9	23.553	34
27	0.042 75	0.042 79	23.372	0.999 09	1.000 9	23.393	33
28	0.043 04	0.043 08	23.214	0.999 07	1.000 9	23.235	32
29	0.043 33	0.043 37	23.058	0.999 06	1.000 9	23.079	31
30	0.043 62	0.043 66	22.904	0.999 05	1.001 0	22.926	30
31	0.043 91	0.043 95	22.752	0.999 04	1.001 0	22.774	29
32	0.044 20	0.044 24	22.602	0.999 02	1.001 0	22.624	28
33	0.044 49	0.044 54	22.454	0.999 01	1.001 0	22.476	27
34	0.044 78	0.044 83	22.308	0.999 00	1.001 0	22.330	26
35	0.045 07	0.045 12	22.164	0.998 98	1.001 0	22.187	25
36	0.045 36	0.045 41	22.022	0.998 97	1.001 0	22.044	24
37	0.045 65	0.045 70	21.881	0.998 96	1.001 0	21.904	23
38	0.045 94	0.045 99	21.743	0.998 94	1.001 1	21.766	22
39	0.046 23	0.046 28	21.606	0.998 93	1.001 1	21.629	21
40	0.046 53	0.046 58	21.470	0.998 92	1.001 1	21.494	20
41	0.046 82	0.046 87	21.337	0.998 90	1.001 1	21.360	19
42	0.047 11	0.047 16	21.205	0.998 89	1.001 1	21.229	18
43	0.047 40	0.047 45	21.075	0.998 88	1.001 1	21.098	17
44	0.047 69	0.047 74	20.946	0.998 86	1.001 1	20.970	16
45	0.047 98	0.048 03	20.819	0.998 85	1.001 2	20.843	15
46	0.048 27	0.048 33	20.693	0.998 83	1.001 2	20.717	14
47	0.048 56	0.048 62	20.569	0.998 82	1.001 2	20.593	13
48	0.048 85	0.048 91	20.446	0.998 81	1.001 2	20.471	12
49	0.049 14	0.049 20	20.325	0.998 79	1.001 2	20.350	11
50	0.049 43	0.049 49	20.206	0.998 78	1.001 2	20.230	10
51	0.049 72	0.049 78	20.087	0.998 76	1.001 2	20.112	9
52	0.050 01	0.050 07	19.970	0.998 75	1.001 3	19.995	8
53	0.050 30	0.050 37	19.855	0.998 73	1.001 3	19.880	7
54	0.050 59	0.050 66	19.740	0.998 72	1.001 3	19.766	6
55	0.050 88	0.050 95	19.627	0.998 70	1.001 3	19.653	5
56	0.051 17	0.051 24	19.516	0.998 69	1.001 3	19.541	4
57	0.051 46	0.051 53	19.405	0.998 67	1.001 3	19.431	3
58	0.051 75	0.051 82	19.296	0.998 66	1.001 3	19.322	2
59	0.052 05	0.052 12	19.188	0.998 64	1.001 4	19.214	1
60	0.052 34	0.052 41	19.081	0.998 63	1.001 4	19.107	0
′	Cos	Cot	Tan	Sin	Csc	Sec	′

Table 3 / Five-place natural trigonometric functions □ 625

′	Sin	Tan	Cot	Cos	Sec	Csc	′
0	**0.052 34**	**0.052 41**	**19.081**	**0.998 63**	**1.0014**	19.107	**60**
1	0.052 63	0.052 70	18.976	0.998 61	1.0014	19.002	59
2	0.052 92	0.052 99	18.871	0.998 60	1.0014	18.898	58
3	0.053 21	0.053 28	18.768	0.998 58	1.0014	18.794	57
4	0.053 50	0.053 57	18.666	0.998 57	1.0014	18.692	56
5	**0.053 79**	**0.053 87**	**18.564**	**0.998 55**	**1.0014**	**18.591**	**55**
6	0.054 08	0.054 16	18.464	0.998 54	1.0015	18.492	54
7	0.054 37	0.054 45	18.366	0.998 52	1.0015	18.393	53
8	0.054 66	0.054 74	18.268	0.998 51	1.0015	18.295	52
9	0.054 95	0.055 03	18.171	0.998 49	1.0015	18.198	51
10	**0.055 24**	**0.055 33**	**18.075**	**0.998 47**	**1.0015**	**18.103**	**50**
11	0.055 53	0.055 62	17.980	0.998 46	1.0015	18.008	49
12	0.055 82	0.055 91	17.886	0.998 44	1.0016	17.914	48
13	0.056 11	0.056 20	17.793	0.998 42	1.0016	17.822	47
14	0.056 40	0.056 49	17.702	0.998 41	1.0016	17.730	46
15	**0.056 69**	**0.056 78**	**17.611**	**0.998 39**	**1.0016**	**17.639**	**45**
16	0.056 98	0.057 08	17.521	0.998 38	1.0016	17.549	44
17	0.057 27	0.057 37	17.431	0.998 36	1.0016	17.460	43
18	0.057 56	0.057 66	17.343	0.998 34	1.0017	17.372	42
19	0.057 85	0.057 95	17.256	0.998 33	1.0017	17.285	41
20	**0.058 14**	**0.058 24**	**17.169**	**0.998 31**	**1.0017**	**17.198**	**40**
21	0.058 44	0.058 54	17.084	0.998 29	1.0017	17.113	39
22	0.058 73	0.058 83	16.999	0.998 27	1.0017	17.028	38
23	0.059 02	0.059 12	16.915	0.998 26	1.0017	16.945	37
24	0.059 31	0.059 41	16.832	0.998 24	1.0018	16.862	36
25	**0.059 60**	**0.059 70**	**16.750**	**0.998 22**	**1.0018**	**16.779**	**35**
26	0.059 89	0.059 99	16.668	0.998 21	1.0018	16.698	34
27	0.060 18	0.060 29	16.587	0.998 19	1.0018	16.618	33
28	0.060 47	0.060 58	16.507	0.998 17	1.0018	16.538	32
29	0.060 76	0.060 87	16.428	0.998 15	1.0019	16.459	31
30	**0.061 05**	**0.061 16**	**16.350**	**0.998 13**	**1.0019**	**16.380**	**30**
31	0.061 34	0.061 45	16.272	0.998 12	1.0019	16.303	29
32	0.061 63	0.061 75	16.195	0.998 10	1.0019	16.226	28
33	0.061 92	0.062 04	16.119	0.998 08	1.0019	16.150	27
34	0.062 21	0.062 33	16.043	0.998 06	1.0019	16.075	26
35	**0.062 50**	**0.062 62**	**15.969**	**0.998 04**	**1.0020**	**16.000**	**25**
36	0.062 79	0.062 91	15.895	0.998 03	1.0020	15.926	24
37	0.063 08	0.063 21	15.821	0.998 01	1.0020	15.853	23
38	0.063 37	0.063 50	15.748	0.997 99	1.0020	15.780	22
39	0.063 66	0.063 79	15.676	0.997 97	1.0020	15.708	21
40	**0.063 95**	**0.064 08**	**15.605**	**0.997 95**	**1.0021**	**15.637**	**20**
41	0.064 24	0.064 38	15.534	0.997 93	1.0021	15.566	19
42	0.064 53	0.064 67	15.464	0.997 92	1.0021	15.496	18
43	0.064 82	0.064 96	15.394	0.997 90	1.0021	15.427	17
44	0.065 11	0.065 25	15.325	0.997 88	1.0021	15.358	16
45	**0.065 40**	**0.065 54**	**15.257**	**0.997 86**	**1.0021**	**15.290**	**15**
46	0.065 69	0.065 84	15.189	0.997 84	1.0022	15.222	14
47	0.065 98	0.066 13	15.122	0.997 82	1.0022	15.155	13
48	0.066 27	0.066 42	15.056	0.997 80	1.0022	15.089	12
49	0.066 56	0.066 71	14.990	0.997 78	1.0022	15.023	11
50	**0.066 85**	**0.067 00**	**14.924**	**0.997 76**	**1.0022**	**14.958**	**10**
51	0.067 14	0.067 30	14.860	0.997 74	1.0023	14.893	9
52	0.067 43	0.067 59	14.795	0.997 72	1.0023	14.829	8
53	0.067 73	0.067 88	14.732	0.997 70	1.0023	14.766	7
54	0.068 02	0.068 17	14.669	0.997 68	1.0023	14.703	6
55	**0.068 31**	**0.068 47**	**14.606**	**0.997 66**	**1.0023**	**14.640**	**5**
56	0.068 60	0.068 76	14.544	0.997 64	1.0024	14.578	4
57	0.068 89	0.069 05	14.482	0.997 62	1.0024	14.517	3
58	0.069 18	0.069 34	14.421	0.997 60	1.0024	14.456	2
59	0.069 47	0.069 63	14.361	0.997 58	1.0024	14.395	1
60	**0.069 76**	**0.069 93**	**14.301**	**0.997 56**	**1.0024**	**14.336**	**0**
′	Cos	Cot	Tan	Sin	Csc	Sec	

′	Sin	Tan	Cot	Cos	Sec	Csc	′
0	**0.069 76**	**0.069 93**	**14.301**	**0.997 56**	**1.002 4**	**14.336**	60
1	0.070 05	0.070 22	14.241	0.997 54	1.002 5	14.276	59
2	0.070 34	0.070 51	14.182	0.997 52	1.002 5	14.217	58
3	0.070 63	0.070 80	14.124	0.997 50	1.002 5	14.159	57
4	0.070 92	0.071 10	14.065	0.997 48	1.002 5	14.101	56
5	**0.071 21**	**0.071 39**	**14.008**	**0.997 46**	**1.002 5**	**14.044**	55
6	0.071 50	0.071 68	13.951	0.997 44	1.002 6	13.987	54
7	0.071 79	0.071 97	13.894	0.997 42	1.002 6	13.930	53
8	0.072 08	0.072 27	13.838	0.997 40	1.002 6	13.874	52
9	0.072 37	0.072 56	13.782	0.997 38	1.002 6	13.818	51
10	**0.072 66**	**0.072 85**	**13.727**	**0.997 36**	**1.002 7**	**13.763**	50
11	0.072 95	0.073 14	13.672	0.997 34	1.002 7	13.708	49
12	0.073 24	0.073 44	13.617	0.997 31	1.002 7	13.654	48
13	0.073 53	0.073 73	13.563	0.997 29	1.002 7	13.600	47
14	0.073 82	0.074 02	13.510	0.997 27	1.002 7	13.547	46
15	**0.074 11**	**0.074 31**	**13.457**	**0.997 25**	**1.002 8**	**13.494**	45
16	0.074 40	0.074 61	13.404	0.997 23	1.002 8	13.441	44
17	0.074 69	0.074 90	13.352	0.997 21	1.002 8	13.389	43
18	0.074 98	0.075 19	13.300	0.997 19	1.002 8	13.337	42
19	0.075 27	0.075 48	13.248	0.997 16	1.002 8	13.286	41
20	**0.075 56**	**0.075 78**	**13.197**	**0.997 14**	**1.002 9**	**13.235**	40
21	0.075 85	0.076 07	13.146	0.997 12	1.002 9	13.184	39
22	0.076 14	0.076 36	13.096	0.997 10	1.002 9	13.134	38
23	0.076 43	0.076 65	13.046	0.997 08	1.002 9	13.084	37
24	0.076 72	0.076 95	12.996	0.997 05	1.003 0	13.035	36
25	**0.077 01**	**0.077 24**	**12.947**	**0.997 03**	**1.003 0**	**12.985**	35
26	0.077 30	0.077 53	12.898	0.997 01	1.003 0	12.937	34
27	0.077 59	0.077 82	12.850	0.996 99	1.003 0	12.888	33
28	0.077 88	0.078 12	12.801	0.996 96	1.003 0	12.840	32
29	0.078 17	0.078 41	12.754	0.996 94	1.003 1	12.793	31
30	**0.078 46**	**0.078 70**	**12.706**	**0.996 92**	**1.003 1**	**12.745**	30
31	0.078 75	0.078 99	12.659	0.996 89	1.003 1	12.699	29
32	0.079 04	0.079 29	12.612	0.996 87	1.003 1	12.652	28
33	0.079 33	0.079 58	12.566	0.996 85	1.003 2	12.606	27
34	0.079 62	0.079 87	12.520	0.996 83	1.003 2	12.560	26
35	**0.079 91**	**0.080 17**	**12.474**	**0.996 80**	**1.003 2**	**12.514**	25
36	0.080 20	0.080 46	12.429	0.996 78	1.003 2	12.469	24
37	0.080 49	0.080 75	12.384	0.996 76	1.003 3	12.424	23
38	0.080 78	0.081 04	12.339	0.996 73	1.003 3	12.379	22
39	0.081 07	0.081 34	12.295	0.996 71	1.003 3	12.335	21
40	**0.081 36**	**0.081 63**	**12.251**	**0.996 68**	**1.003 3**	**12.291**	20
41	0.081 65	0.081 92	12.207	0.996 66	1.003 4	12.248	19
42	0.081 94	0.082 21	12.163	0.996 64	1.003 4	12.204	18
43	0.082 23	0.082 51	12.120	0.996 61	1.003 4	12.161	17
44	0.082 52	0.082 80	12.077	0.996 59	1.003 4	12.119	16
45	**0.082 81**	**0.083 09**	**12.035**	**0.996 57**	**1.003 4**	**12.076**	15
46	0.083 10	0.083 39	11.992	0.996 54	1.003 5	12.034	14
47	0.083 39	0.083 68	11.950	0.996 52	1.003 5	11.992	13
48	0.083 68	0.083 97	11.909	0.996 49	1.003 5	11.951	12
49	0.083 97	0.084 27	11.867	0.996 47	1.003 5	11.909	11
50	**0.084 26**	**0.084 56**	**11.826**	**0.996 44**	**1.003 6**	**11.868**	10
51	0.084 55	0.084 85	11.785	0.996 42	1.003 6	11.828	9
52	0.084 84	0.085 14	11.745	0.996 39	1.003 6	11.787	8
53	0.085 13	0.085 44	11.705	0.996 37	1.003 6	11.747	7
54	0.085 42	0.085 73	11.664	0.996 35	1.003 7	11.707	6
55	**0.085 71**	**0.086 02**	**11.625**	**0.996 32**	**1.003 7**	**11.668**	5
56	0.086 00	0.086 32	11.585	0.996 30	1.003 7	11.628	4
57	0.086 29	0.086 61	11.546	0.996 27	1.003 7	11.589	3
58	0.086 58	0.086 90	11.507	0.996 25	1.003 8	11.551	2
59	0.086 87	0.087 20	11.468	0.996 22	1.003 8	11.512	1
60	**0.087 16**	**0.087 49**	**11.430**	**0.996 19**	**1.003 8**	**11.474**	0
′	Cos	Cot	Tan	Sin	Csc	Sec	′

Table 3 / Five-place natural trigonometric functions □ **627**

′	Sin	Tan	Cot	Cos	Sec	Csc	′
0	**0.087 16**	**0.087 49**	**11.430**	**0.996 19**	**1.003 8**	**11.474**	60
1	0.087 45	0.087 78	11.392	0.996 17	1.003 8	11.436	59
2	0.087 74	0.088 07	11.354	0.996 14	1.003 9	11.398	58
3	0.088 03	0.088 37	11.316	0.996 12	1.003 9	11.360	57
4	0.088 31	0.088 66	11.279	0.996 09	1.003 9	11.323	56
5	**0.088 60**	**0.088 95**	**11.242**	**0.996 07**	**1.003 9**	**11.286**	55
6	0.088 89	0.089 25	11.205	0.996 04	1.004 0	11.249	54
7	0.089 18	0.089 54	11.168	0.996 02	1.004 0	11.213	53
8	0.089 47	0.089 83	11.132	0.995 99	1.004 0	11.176	52
9	0.089 76	0.090 13	11.095	0.995 96	1.004 1	11.140	51
10	**0.090 05**	**0.090 42**	**11.059**	**0.995 94**	**1.004 1**	**11.105**	50
11	0.090 34	0.090 71	11.024	0.995 91	1.004 1	11.069	49
12	0.090 63	0.091 01	10.988	0.995 88	1.004 1	11.034	48
13	0.090 92	0.091 30	10.953	0.995 86	1.004 2	10.998	47
14	0.091 21	0.091 59	10.918	0.995 83	1.004 2	10.963	46
15	**0.091 50**	**0.091 89**	**10.883**	**0.995 80**	**1.004 2**	**10.929**	45
16	0.091 79	0.092 18	10.848	0.995 78	1.004 2	10.894	44
17	0.092 08	0.092 47	10.814	0.995 75	1.004 3	10.860	43
18	0.092 37	0.092 77	10.780	0.995 72	1.004 3	10.826	42
19	0.092 66	0.093 06	10.746	0.995 70	1.004 3	10.792	41
20	**0.092 95**	**0.093 35**	**10.712**	**0.995 67**	**1.004 3**	**10.758**	40
21	0.093 24	0.093 65	10.678	0.995 64	1.004 4	10.725	39
22	0.093 53	0.093 94	10.645	0.995 62	1.004 4	10.692	38
23	0.093 82	0.094 23	10.612	0.995 59	1.004.4	10.659	37
24	0.094 11	0.094 53	10.579	0.995 56	1.004 5	10.626	36
25	**0.094 40**	**0.094 82**	**10.546**	**0.995 53**	**1.004 5**	**10.593**	35
26	0.094 69	0.095 11	10.514	0.995 51	1.004 5	10.561	34
27	0.094 98	0.095 41	10.481	0.995 48	1.004 5	10.529	33
28	0.095 27	0.095 70	10.449	0.995 45	1.004 6	10.497	32
29	0.095 56	0.096 00	10.417	0.995 42	1.004 6	10.465	31
30	**0.095 85**	**0.096 29**	**10.385**	**0.995 40**	**1.004 6**	**10.433**	30
31	0.096 14	0.096 58	10.354	0.995 37	1.004 7	10.402	29
32	0.096 42	0.096 88	10.322	0.995 34	1.004 7	10.371	28
33	0.096 71	0.097 17	10.291	0.995 31	1.004 7	10.340	27
34	0.097 00	0.097 46	10.260	0.995 28	1.004 7	10.309	26
35	**0.097 29**	**0.097 76**	**10.229**	**0.995 26**	**1.004 8**	**10.278**	25
36	0.097 58	0.098 05	10.199	0.995 23	1.004 8	10.248	24
37	0.097 87	0.098 34	10.168	0.995 20	1.004 8	10.217	23
38	0.098 16	0.098 64	10.138	0.995 17	1.004 9	10.187	22
39	0.098 45	0.098 93	10.108	0.995 14	1.004 9	10.157	21
40	**0.098 74**	**0.099 23**	**10.078**	**0.995 11**	**1.004 9**	**10.128**	20
41	0.099 03	0.099 52	10.048	0.995 08	1.004 9	10.098	19
42	0.099 32	0.099 81	10.019	0.995 06	1.005 0	10.068	18
43	0.099 61	0.100 11	9.989 3	0.995 03	1.005 0	10.039	17
44	0.099 90	0.100 40	9.960 1	0.995 00	1.005 0	10.010	16
45	**0.100 19**	**0.100 69**	**9.931 0**	**0.994 97**	**1.005 1**	**9.981 2**	15
46	0.100 48	0.100 99	9.902 1	0.994 94	1.005 1	9.952 5	14
47	0.100 77	0.101 28	9.873 4	0.994 91	1.005 1	9.923 9	13
48	0.101 06	0.101 58	9.844 8	0.994 88	1.005 1	9.895 5	12
49	0.101 35	0.101 87	9.816 4	0.994 85	1.005 2	9.867 2	11
50	**0.101 64**	**0.102 16**	**9.788 2**	**0.994 82**	**1.005 2**	**9.839 1**	10
51	0.101 92	0.102 46	9.760 1	0.994 79	1.005 2	9.811 2	9
52	0.102 21	0.102 75	9.732 2	0.994 76	1.005 3	9.783 4	8
53	0.102 50	0.103 05	9.704 4	0.994 73	1.005 3	9.755 8	7
54	0.102 79	0.103 34	9.676 8	0.994 70	1.005 3	9.728 3	6
55	**0.103 08**	**0.103 63**	**9.649 3**	**0.994 67**	**1.005 4**	**9.701 0**	5
56	0.103 37	0.103 93	9.622 0	0.994 64	1.005 4	9.673 9	4
57	0.103 66	0.104 22	9.594 9	0.994 61	1.005 4	9.646 9	3
58	0.103 95	0.104 52	9.567 9	0.994 58	1.005 4	9.620 0	2
59	0.104 24	0.104 81	9.541 1	0.994 55	1.005 5	9.593 3	1
60	**0.104 53**	**0.105 10**	**9.514 4**	**0.994 52**	**1.005 5**	**9.566 8**	0
′	Cos	Cot	Tan	Sin	Csc	Sec	′

′	Sin	Tan	Cot	Cos	Sec	Csc	′
0	**0.104 53**	**0.105 10**	**9.514 4**	**0.994 52**	**1.005 5**	**9.566 8**	60
1	0.104 82	0.105 40	9.487 8	0.994 49	1.005 5	9.540 4	59
2	0.105 11	0.105 69	9.461 4	0.994 46	1.005 6	9.514 1	58
3	0.105 40	0.105 99	9.435 2	0.994 43	1.005 6	9.488 0	57
4	0.105 69	0.106 28	9.409 0	0.994 40	1.005 6	9.462 0	56
5	**0.105 97**	**0.106 57**	**9.383 1**	**0.994 37**	**1.005 7**	**9.436 2**	55
6	0.106 26	0.106 87	9.357 2	0.994 34	1.005 7	9.410 5	54
7	0.106 55	0.107 16	9.331 5	0.994 31	1.005 7	9.385 0	53
8	0.106 84	0.107 46	9.306 0	0.994 28	1.005 8	9.359 6	52
9	0.107 13	0.107 75	9.280 6	0.994 24	1.005 8	9.334 3	51
10	**0.107 42**	**0.108 05**	**9.255 3**	**0.994 21**	**1.005 8**	**9.309 2**	50
11	0.107 71	0.108 34	9.230 2	0.994 18	1.005 9	9.284 2	49
12	0.108 00	0.108 63	9.205 2	0.994 15	1.005 9	9.259 3	48
13	0.108 29	0.108 93	9.180 3	0.994 12	1.005 9	9.234 6	47
14	0.108 58	0.109 22	9.155 5	0.994 09	1.005 9	9.210 0	46
15	**0.108 87**	**0.109 52**	**9.130 9**	**0.994 06**	**1.006 0**	**9.185 5**	45
16	0.109 16	0.109 81	9.106 5	0.994 02	1.006 0	9.161 2	44
17	0.109 45	0.110 11	9.082 1	0.993 99	1.006 0	9.137 0	43
18	0.109 73	0.110 40	9.057 9	0.993 96	1.006 1	9.112 9	42
19	0.110 02	0.110 70	9.033 8	0.993 93	1.006 1	9.089 0	41
20	**0.110 31**	**0.110 99**	**9.009 8**	**0.993 90**	**1.006 1**	**9.065 2**	40
21	0.110 60	0.111 28	8.986 0	0.993 86	1.006 2	9.041 5	39
22	0.110 89	0.111 58	8.962 3	0.993 83	1.006 2	9.017 9	38
23	0.111 18	0.111 87	8.938 7	0.993 80	1.006 2	8.994 4	37
24	0.111 47	0.112 17	8.915 2	0.993 77	1.006 3	8.971 1	36
25	**0.111 76**	**0.112 46**	**8.891 9**	**0.993 74**	**1.006 3**	**8.947 9**	35
26	0.112 05	0.112 76	8.868 6	0.993 70	1.006 3	8.924 8	34
27	0.112 34	0.113 05	8.845 5	0.993 67	1.006 4	8.901 9	33
28	0.112 63	0.113 35	8.822 5	0.993 64	1.006 4	8.879 0	32
29	0.112 91	0.113 64	8.799 6	0.993 60	1.006 4	8.856 3	31
30	**0.113 20**	**0.113 94**	**8.776 9**	**0.993 57**	**1.006 5**	**8.833 7**	30
31	0.113 49	0.114 23	8.754 2	0.993 54	1.006 5	8.811 2	29
32	0.113 78	0.114 52	8.731 7	0.993 51	1.006 5	8.788 8	28
33	0.114 07	0.114 82	8.709 3	0.993 47	1.006 6	8.766 5	27
34	0.114 36	0.115 11	8.687 0	0.993 44	1.006 6	8.744 4	26
35	**0.114 65**	**0.115 41**	**8.664 8**	**0.993 41**	**1.006 6**	**8.722 3**	25
36	0.114 94	0.115 70	8.642 7	0.993 37	1.006 7	8.700 4	24
37	0.115 23	0.116 00	8.620 8	0.993 34	1.006 7	8.678 6	23
38	0.115 52	0.116 29	8.598 9	0.993 31	1.006 7	8.656 9	22
39	0.115 80	0.116 59	8.577 2	0.993 27	1.006 8	8.635 3	21
40	**0.116 09**	**0.116 88**	**8.555 5**	**0.993 24**	**1.006 8**	**8.613 8**	20
41	0.116 38	0.117 18	8.534 0	0.993 20	1.006 8	8.592 4	19
42	0.116 67	0.117 47	8.512 6	0.993 17	1.006 9	8.571 1	18
43	0.116 96	0.117 77	8.491 3	0.993 14	1.006 9	8.550 0	17
44	0.117 25	0.118 06	8.470 1	0.993 10	1.006 9	8.528 9	16
45	**0.117 54**	**0.118 36**	**8.449 0**	**0.993 07**	**1.007 0**	**8.507 9**	15
46	0.117 83	0.118 65	8.428 0	0.993 03	1.007 0	8.487 1	14
47	0.118 12	0.118 95	8.407 1	0.993 00	1.007 0	8.466 3	13
48	0.118 40	0.119 24	8.386 3	0.992 97	1.007 1	8.445 7	12
49	0.118 69	0.119 54	8.365 6	0.992 93	1.007 1	8.425 1	11
50	**0.118 98**	**0.119 83**	**8.345 0**	**0.992 90**	**1.007 2**	**8.404 7**	10
51	0.119 27	0.120 13	8.324 5	0.992 86	1.007 2	8.384 3	9
52	0.119 56	0.120 42	8.304 1	0.992 83	1.007 2	8.364 1	8
53	0.119 85	0.120 72	8.283 8	0.992 79	1.007 3	8.343 9	7
54	0.120 14	0.121 01	8.263 6	0.992 76	1.007 3	8.323 8	6
55	**0.120 43**	**0.121 31**	**8.243 4**	**0.992 72**	**1.007 3**	**8.303 9**	5
56	0.120 71	0.121 60	8.223 4	0.992 69	1.007 4	8.284 0	4
57	0.121 00	0.121 90	8.203 5	0.992 65	1.007 4	8.264 2	3
58	0.121 29	0.122 19	8.183 7	0.992 62	1.007 4	8.244 6	2
59	0.121 58	0.122 49	8.164 0	0.992 58	1.007 5	8.225 0	1
60	**0.121 87**	**0.122 78**	**8.144 3**	**0.992 55**	**1.007 5**	**8.205 5**	0
′	Cos	Cot	Tan	Sin	Csc	Sec	′

Table 3 / Five-place natural trigonometric functions   □   **629**

′	Sin	Tan	Cot	Cos	Sec	Csc	
0	**0.121 87**	**0.122 78**	**8.144 3**	**0.992 55**	**1.007 5**	**8.205 5**	60
1	0.122 16	0.123 08	8.124 8	0.992 51	1.007 5	8.186 1	59
2	0.122 45	0.123 38	8.105 4	0.992 48	1.007 6	8.166 8	58
3	0.122 74	0.123 67	8.086 0	0.992 44	1.007 6	8.147 6	57
4	0.123 02	0.123 97	8.066 7	0.992 40	1.007 7	8.128 5	56
5	**0.123 31**	**0.124 26**	**8.047 6**	**0.992 37**	**1.007 7**	**8.109 5**	55
6	0.123 60	0.124 56	8.028 5	0.992 33	1.007 7	8.090 5	54
7	0.123 89	0.124 85	8.009 5	0.992 30	1.007 8	8.071 7	53
8	0.124 18	0.125 15	7.990 6	0.992 26	1.007 8	8.052 9	52
9	0.124 47	0.125 44	7.971 8	0.992 22	1.007 8	8.034 2	51
10	**0.124 76**	**0.125 74**	**7.953 0**	**0.992 19**	**1.007 9**	**8.015 6**	50
11	0.125 04	0.126 03	7.934 4	0.992 15	1.007 9	7.997 1	49
12	0.125 33	0.126 33	7.915 8	0.992 11	1.007 9	7.978 7	48
13	0.125 62	0.126 62	7.897 3	0.992 08	1.008 0	7.960 4	47
14	0.125 91	0.126 92	7.878 9	0.992 04	1.008 0	7.942 2	46
15	**0.126 20**	**0.127 22**	**7.860 6**	**0.992 00**	**1.008 1**	**7.924 0**	45
16	0.126 49	0.127 51	7.842 4	0.991 97	1.008 1	7.905 9	44
17	0.126 78	0.127 81	7.824 3	0.991 93	1.008 1	7.887 9	43
18	0.127 06	0.128 10	7.806 2	0.991 89	1.008 2	7.870 0	42
19	0.127 35	0.128 40	7.788 2	0.991 86	1.008 2	7.852 2	41
20	**0.127 64**	**0.128 69**	**7.770 4**	**0.991 82**	**1.008 2**	**7.834 4**	40
21	0.127 93	0.128 99	7.752 5	0.991 78	1.008 3	7.816 8	39
22	0.128 22	0.129 29	7.734 8	0.991 75	1.008 3	7.799 2	38
23	0.128 51	0.129 58	7.717 1	0.991 71	1.008 4	7.781 7	37
24	0.128 80	0.129 88	7.699 6	0.991 67	1.008 4	7.764 2	36
25	**0.129 08**	**0.130 17**	**7.682 1**	**0.991 63**	**1.008 4**	**7.746 9**	35
26	0.129 37	0.130 47	7.664 7	0.991 60	1.008 5	7.729 6	34
27	0.129 66	0.130 76	7.647 3	0.991 56	1.008 5	7.712 4	33
28	0.129 95	0.131 06	7.630 1	0.991 52	1.008 6	7.695 3	32
29	0.130 24	0.131 36	7.612 9	0.991 48	1.008 6	7.678 3	31
30	**0.130 53**	**0.131 65**	**7.595 8**	**0.991 44**	**1.008 6**	**7.661 3**	30
31	0.130 81	0.131 95	7.578 7	0.991 41	1.008 7	7.644 4	29
32	0.131 10	0.132 24	7.561 8	0.991 37	1.008 7	7.627 6	28
33	0.131 39	0.132 54	7.544 9	0.991 33	1.008 7	7.610 9	27
34	0.131 68	0.132 84	7.528 1	0.991 29	1.008 8	7.594 2	26
35	**0.131 97**	**0.133 13**	**7.511 3**	**0.991 25**	**1.008 8**	**7.577 6**	25
36	0.132 26	0.133 43	7.494 7	0.991 22	1.008 8	7.561 1	24
37	0.132 54	0.133 72	7.478 1	0.991 18	1.008 9	7.544 6	23
38	0.132 83	0.134 02	7.461 5	0.991 14	1.008 9	7.528 2	22
39	0.133 12	0.134 32	7.445 1	0.991 10	1.009 0	7.511 9	21
40	**0.133 41**	**0.134 61**	**7.428 7**	**0.991 06**	**1.009 0**	**7.495 7**	20
41	0.133 70	0.134 91	7.412 4	0.991 02	1.009 1	7.479 5	19
42	0.133 99	0.135 21	7.396 2	0.990 98	1.009 1	7.463 5	18
43	0.134 27	0.135 50	7.380 0	0.990 94	1.009 1	7.447 4	17
44	0.134 56	0.135 80	7 363 9	0.990 91	1.009 2	7.431 5	16
45	**0.134 85**	**0.136 09**	**7.347 9**	**0.990 87**	**1.009 2**	**7.415 6**	15
46	0.135 14	0.136 39	7.331 9	0.990 83	1.009 3	7.399 8	14
47	0.135 43	0.136 69	7.316 0	0.990 79	1.009 3	7.384 0	13
48	0.135 72	0.136 98	7.300 2	0.990 75	1.009 3	7.368 4	12
49	0.136 00	0.137 28	7.284 4	0.990 71	1.009 4	7.352 7	11
50	**0.136 29**	**0.137 58**	**7.268 7**	**0.990 67**	**1.009 4**	**7.337 2**	10
51	0.136 58	0.137 87	7.253 1	0.990 63	1.009 5	7.321 7	9
52	0.136 87	0.138 17	7.237 5	0.990 59	1.009 5	7.306 3	8
53	0.137 16	0.138 46	7.222 0	0.990 55	1.009 5	7.290 5	7
54	0.137 44	0.138 76	7.206 6	0.990 51	1.009 6	7.275 7	6
55	**0.137 73**	**0.139 06**	**7.191 2**	**0.990 47**	**1.009 6**	**7.260 4**	5
56	0.138 02	0.139 35	7.175 9	0.990 43	1.009 7	7.245 3	4
57	0.138 31	0.139 65	7.160 7	0.990 39	1.009 7	7.230 2	3
58	0.138 60	0.139 95	7.145 5	0.990 35	1.009 7	7.215 2	2
59	0.138 89	0.140 24	7.130 4	0.990 31	1.009 8	7.200 2	1
60	**0.139 17**	**0.140 54**	**7.115 4**	**0.990 27**	**1.009 8**	**7.185 3**	0
′	Cos	Cot	Tan	Sin	Csc	Sec	′

′	Sin	Tan	Cot	Cos	Sec	Csc	′
0	**0.139 17**	**0.140 54**	**7.115 4**	**0.990 27**	**1.009 8**	**7.185 3**	60
1	0.139 46	0.140 84	7.100 4	0.990 23	1.009 9	7.170 5	59
2	0.139 75	0.141 13	7.085 5	0.990 19	1.009 9	7.155 7	58
3	0.140 04	0.141 43	7.070 6	0.990 15	1.010 0	7.141 0	57
4	0.140 33	0.141 73	7.055 8	0.990 11	1.010 0	7.126 3	56
5	**0.140 61**	**0.142 02**	**7.041 0**	**0.990 06**	**1.010 0**	**7.111 7**	55
6	0.140 90	0.142 32	7.026 4	0.990 02	1.010 1	7.097 2	54
7	0.141 19	0.142 62	7.011 7	0.989 98	1.010 1	7.082 7	53
8	0.141 48	0.142 91	6.997 2	0.989 94	1.010 2	7.068 3	52
9	0.141 77	0.143 21	6.982 7	0.989 90	1.010 2	7.053 9	51
10	**0.142 05**	**0.143 51**	**6.968 2**	**0.989 86**	**1.010 2**	**7.039 6**	50
11	0.142 34	0.143 81	6.953 8	0.989 82	1.010 3	7.025 4	49
12	0.142 63	0.144 10	6.939 5	0.989 78	1.010 3	7.011 2	48
13	0.142 92	0.144 40	6.925 2	0.989 73	1.010 4	6.997 1	47
14	0.143 20	0.144 70	6.911 0	0.989 69	1.010 4	6.983 0	46
15	**0.143 49**	**0.144 99**	**6.896 9**	**0.989 65**	**1.010 5**	**6.969 0**	45
16	0.143 78	0.145 29	6.882 8	0.989 61	1.010 5	6.955 0	44
17	0.144 07	0.145 59	6.868 7	0.989 57	1.010 5	6.941 1	43
18	0.144 36	0.145 88	6.854 8	0.989 53	1.010 6	6.927 3	42
19	0.144 64	0.146 18	6.840 8	0.989 48	1.010 6	6.913 5	41
20	**0.144 93**	**0.146 48**	**6.826 9**	**0.989 44**	**1.010 7**	**6.899 8**	40
21	0.145 22	0.146 78	6.813 1	0.989 40	1.010 7	6.886 1	39
22	0.145 51	0.147 07	6.799 4	0.989 36	1.010 8	6.872 5	38
23	0.145 80	0.147 37	6.785 6	0.989 31	1.010 8	6.858 9	37
24	0.146 08	0.147 67	6.772 0	0.989 27	1.010 8	6.845 4	36
25	**0.146 37**	**0.147 96**	**6.758 4**	**0.989 23**	**1.010 9**	**6.832 0**	35
26	0.146 66	0.148 26	6.744 8	0.989 19	1.010 9	6.818 6	34
27	0.146 95	0.148 56	6.731 3	0.989 14	1.011 0	6.805 2	33
28	0.147 23	0.148 86	6.717 9	0.989 10	1.011 0	6.791 9	32
29	0.147 52	0.149 15	6.704 5	0.989 06	1.011 1	6.778 9	31
30	**0.147 81**	**0.149 45**	**6.691 2**	**0.989 02**	**1.011 1**	**6.765 5**	30
31	0.148 10	0.149 75	6.677 9	0.988 97	1.011 1	6.752 3	29
32	0.148 38	0.150 05	6.664 6	0.988 93	1.011 2	6.739 2	28
33	0.148 67	0.150 34	6.651 4	0.988 89	1.011 2	6.726 2	27
34	0.148 96	0.150 64	6.638 3	0.988 84	1.011 3	6.713 2	26
35	**0.149 25**	**0.150 94**	**6.625 2**	**0.988 80**	**1.011 3**	**6.700 3**	25
36	0.149 54	0.151 24	6.612 2	0.988 76	1.011 4	6.687 4	24
37	0.149 82	0.151 53	6.599 2	0.988 71	1.011 4	6.674 5	23
38	0.150 11	0.151 83	6.586 3	0.988 67	1.011 5	6.661 8	22
39	0.150 40	0.152 13	6.573 4	0.988 63	1.011 5	6.649 0	21
40	**0.150 69**	**0.152 43**	**6.560 6**	**0.988 58**	**1.011 6**	**6.636 3**	20
41	0.150 97	0.152 72	6.547 8	0.988 54	1.011 6	6.623 7	19
42	0.151 26	0.153 02	6.535 0	0.988 49	1.011 6	6.611 1	18
43	0.151 55	0.153 32	6.522 3	0.988 45	1.011 7	6.598 6	17
44	0.151 84	0.153 62	6.509 7	0.988 41	1.011 7	6.586 1	16
45	**0.152 12**	**0.153 91**	**6.497 1**	**0.988 36**	**1.011 8**	**6.573 6**	15
46	0.152 41	0.154 21	6.484 6	0.988 32	1.011 8	6.561 2	14
47	0.152 70	0.154 51	6.472 1	0.988 27	1.011 9	6.548 9	13
48	0.152 99	0.154 81	6.459 6	0.988 23	1.011 9	6.536 6	12
49	0.153 27	0.155 11	6.447 2	0.988 18	1.012 0	6.524 3	11
50	**0.153 56**	**0.155 40**	**6.434 8**	**0.988 14**	**1.012 0**	**6.511 1**	10
51	0.153 85	0.155 70	6.422 5	0.988 09	1.012 0	6.499 9	9
52	0.154 14	0.156 00	6.410 3	0.988 05	1.012 1	6.487 8	8
53	0.154 42	0.156 30	6.398 0	0.988 00	1.012 1	6.475 7	7
54	0.154 71	0.156 60	6.385 9	0.987 96	1.012 2	6.463 7	6
55	**0.155 00**	**0.156 89**	**6.373 7**	**0.987 91**	**1.012 2**	**6.451 7**	5
56	0.155 29	0.157 19	6.361 7	0.987 87	1.012 3	6.439 8	4
57	0.155 57	0.157 49	6.349 6	0.987 82	1.012 3	6.427 9	3
58	0.155 86	0.157 79	6.337 6	0.987 78	1.012 4	6.416 0	2
59	0.156 15	0.158 09	6.325 7	0.987 73	1.012 4	6.404 2	1
60	**0.156 43**	**0.158 38**	**6.313 8**	**0.987 69**	**1.012 5**	**6.392 5**	0
′	Cos	Cot	Tan	Sin	Csc	Sec	′

Table 3 / Five-place natural trigonometric functions □ 631

′	Sin	Tan	Cot	Cos	Sec	Csc	′
0	**0.156 43**	**0.158 38**	**6.313 8**	**0.987 69**	**1.012 5**	**6.392 5**	**60**
1	0.156 72	0.158 68	6.301 9	0.987 64	1.012 5	6.380 7	59
2	0.157 01	0.158 98	6.290 1	0.987 60	1.012 6	6.369 1	58
3	0.157 30	0.159 28	6.278 3	0.987 55	1.012 6	6.357 4	57
4	0.157 58	0.159 58	6.266 6	0.987 51	1.012 7	6.345 8	56
5	**0.157 87**	**0.159 88**	**6.254 9**	**0.987 46**	**1.012 7**	**6.334 4**	**55**
6	0.158 16	0.160 17	6.243 2	0.987 41	1.012 7	6.322 8	54
7	0.158 45	0.160 47	6.231 6	0.987 37	1.012 8	6.311 3	53
8	0.158 73	0.160 77	6.220 0	0.987 32	1.012 8	6.299 9	52
9	0.159 02	0.161 07	6.208 5	0.987 28	1.012 9	6.288 5	51
10	**0.159 31**	**0.161 37**	**6.197 0**	**0.987 23**	**1.012 9**	**6.277 2**	**50**
11	0.159 59	0.161 67	6.185 6	0.987 18	1.013 0	6.265 9	49
12	0.159 88	0.161 96	6.174 2	0.987 14	1.013 0	6.254 6	48
13	0.160 17	0.162 26	6.162 8	0.987 09	1.013 1	6.243 4	47
14	0.160 46	0.162 56	6.151 5	0.987 04	1.013 1	6.232 3	46
15	**0.160 74**	**0.162 86**	**6.140 2**	**0.987 00**	**1.013 2**	**6.221 1**	**45**
16	0.161 03	0.163 16	6.129 0	0.986 95	1.013 2	6.210 0	44
17	0.161 32	0.163 46	6.117 8	0.986 90	1.013 3	6.199 0	43
18	0.161 60	0.163 76	6.106 6	0.986 86	1.013 3	6.188 0	42
19	0.161 89	0.164 05	6.095 5	0.986 81	1.013 4	6.177 0	41
20	**0.162 18**	**0.164 35**	**6.084 4**	**0.986 76**	**1.013 4**	**6.166 1**	**40**
21	0.162 46	0.164 65	6.073 4	0.986 71	1.013 5	6.155 2	39
22	0.162 75	0.164 95	6.062 4	0.986 67	1.013 5	6.144 3	38
23	0.163 04	0.165 25	6.051 4	0.986 62	1.013 6	6.133 5	37
24	0.163 33	0.165 55	6.040 5	0.986 57	1.013 6	6.122 7	36
25	**0.163 61**	**0.165 85**	**6.029 6**	**0.986 52**	**1.013 7**	**6.112 0**	**35**
26	0.163 90	0.166 15	6.018 8	0.986 48	1.013 7	6.101 3	34
27	0.164 19	0.166 45	6.008 0	0.986 43	1.013 8	6.090 6	33
28	0.164 47	0.166 74	5.997 2	0.986 38	1.013 8	6.080 0	32
29	0.164 76	0.167 04	5.986 5	0.986 33	1.013 9	6.069 4	31
30	**0.165 05**	**0.167 34**	**5.975 8**	**0.986 29**	**1.013 9**	**6.058 9**	**30**
31	0.165 33	0.167 64	5.965 1	0.986 24	1.014 0	6.048 3	29
32	0.165 62	0.167 94	5.954 5	0.986 19	1.014 0	6.037 9	28
33	0.165 91	0.168 24	5.943 9	0.986 14	1.014 1	6.027 4	27
34	0.166 20	0.168 54	5.933 3	0.986 09	1.014 1	6.017 0	26
35	**0.166 48**	**0.168 84**	**5.922 8**	**0.986 04**	**1.014 2**	**6.006 7**	**25**
36	0.166 77	0.169 14	5.912 4	0.986 00	1.014 2	5.996 3	24
37	0.167 06	0.169 44	5.901 9	0.985 95	1.014 3	5.986 0	23
38	0.167 34	0.169 74	5.891 5	0.985 90	1.014 3	5.975 8	22
39	0.167 63	0.170 04	5.881 1	0.985 85	1.014 4	5.965 6	21
40	**0.167 92**	**0.170 33**	**5.870 8**	**0.985 80**	**1.014 4**	**5.955 4**	**20**
41	0.168 20	0.170 63	5.860 5	0.985 75	1.014 5	5.945 2	19
42	0.168 49	0.170 93	5.850 2	0.985 70	1.014 5	5.935 1	18
43	0.168 78	0.171 23	5.840 0	0.985 65	1.014 6	5.925 0	17
44	0.169 06	0.171 53	5.829 8	0.985 61	1.014 6	5.915 0	16
45	**0.169 35**	**0.171 83**	**5.819 7**	**0.985 56**	**1.014 7**	**5.904 9**	**15**
46	0.169 64	0.172 13	5.809 5	0.985 51	1.014 7	5.895 0	14
47	0.169 92	0.172 43	5.799 4	0.985 46	1.014 8	5.885 0	13
48	0.170 21	0.172 73	5.789 4	0.985 41	1.014 8	5.875 1	12
49	0.170 50	0.173 03	5.779 4	0.985 36	1.014 9	5.865 2	11
50	**0.170 78**	**0.173 33**	**5.769 4**	**0.985 31**	**1.014 9**	**5.855 4**	**10**
51	0.171 07	0.173 63	5.759 4	0.985 26	1.015 0	5.845 6	9
52	0.171 36	0.173 93	5.749 5	0.985 21	1.015 0	5.835 8	8
53	0.171 64	0.174 23	5.739 6	0.985 16	1.015 1	5.826 1	7
54	0.171 93	0.174 53	5.729 7	0.985 11	1.015 1	5.816 4	6
55	**0.172 22**	**0.174 83**	**5.719 9**	**0.985 06**	**1.015 2**	**5.806 7**	**5**
56	0.172 50	0.175 13	5.710 1	0.985 01	1.015 2	5.797 0	4
57	0.172 79	0.175 43	5.700 4	0.984 96	1.015 3	5.787 4	3
58	0.173 08	0.175 73	5.690 6	0.984 91	1.015 3	5.777 8	2
59	0.173 36	0.176 03	5.680 9	0.984 86	1.015 4	5.768 3	1
60	**0.173 65**	**0.176 33**	**5.671 3**	**0.984 81**	**1.015 4**	**5.758 8**	**0**
′	Cos	Cot	Tan	Sin	Csc	Sec	′

′	Sin	Tan	Cot	Cos	Sec	Csc	′
0	**0.173 65**	**0.176 33**	**5.671 3**	**0.984 81**	**1.015 4**	**5.758 8**	60
1	0.173 93	0.176 63	5.661 7	0.984 76	1.015 5	5.749 3	59
2	0.174 22	0.176 93	5.652 1	0.984 71	1.015 5	5.739 8	58
3	0.174 51	0.177 23	5.642 5	0.984 66	1.015 6	5.730 4	57
4	0.174 79	0.177 53	5.632 9	0.984 61	1.015 6	5.721 0	56
5	**0.175 08**	**0.177 83**	**5 623 4**	**0.984 55**	**1.015 7**	**5.711 7**	**55**
6	0.175 37	0.178 13	5.614 0	0.984 50	1.015 7	5.702 3	54
7	0.175 65	0.178 43	5.604 5	0.984 45	1.015 8	5.693 0	53
8	0.175 94	0.178 73	5.595 1	0.984 40	1.015 8	5.683 8	52
9	0.176 23	0.179 03	5.585 7	0.984 35	1.015 9	5.674 5	51
10	**0.176 51**	**0.179 33**	**5.576 4**	**0.984 30**	**1.016 0**	**5.665 3**	**50**
11	0.176 80	0.179 63	5.567 1	0.984 25	1.016 0	5.656 2	49
12	0.177 08	0.179 93	5.557 8	0.984 20	1.016 1	5.647 0	48
13	0.177 37	0.180 23	5.548 5	0.984 14	1.016 1	5.637 9	47
14	0.177 66	0.180 53	5.539 3	0.984 09	1.016 2	5.628 8	46
15	**0.177 94**	**0.180 83**	**5.530 1**	**0.984 04**	**1.016 2**	**5.619 8**	**45**
16	0.178 23	0.181 13	5.520 9	0.983 99	1.016 3	5.610 7	44
17	0.178 52	0.181 43	5.511 8	0.983 94	1.016 3	5.601 7	43
18	0.178 80	0.181 73	5.502 6	0.983 89	1.016 4	5.592 8	42
19	0.179 09	0.182 03	5.493 6	0.983 83	1.016 4	5.583 8	41
20	**0.179 37**	**0.182 33**	**5.484 5**	**0.983 78**	**1.016 5**	**5.574 9**	**40**
21	0.179 66	0.182 63	5.475 5	0.983 73	1.016 5	5.566 0	39
22	0.179 95	0.182 93	5.466 5	0.983 68	1.016 6	5.557 2	38
23	0.180 23	0.183 23	5.457 5	0.983 62	1.016 6	5.548 4	37
24	0.180 52	0.183 53	5.448 6	0.983 57	1.016 7	5.539 6	36
25	**0.180 81**	**0.183 84**	**5.439 7**	**0.983 52**	**1.016 8**	**5.530 8**	**35**
26	0.181 09	0.184 14	5.430 8	0.983 47	1.016 8	5.522 1	34
27	0.181 38	0.184 44	5.421 9	0.983 41	1.016 9	5.513 4	33
28	0.181 66	0.184 74	5.413 1	0.983 36	1.016 9	5.504 7	32
29	0.181 95	0.185 04	5.404 3	0.983 31	1.017 0	5.496 0	31
30	**0.182 24**	**0.185 34**	**5.395 5**	**0.983 25**	**1.017 0**	**5.487 4**	**30**
31	0.182 52	0.185 64	5.386 8	0.983 20	1.017 1	5.478 8	29
32	0.182 81	0.185 94	5.378 1	0.983 15	1.017 1	5.470 2	28
33	0.183 09	0.186 24	5.369 4	0.983 10	1.017 2	5.461 7	27
34	0.183 38	0.186 54	5.360 7	0.983 04	1.017 3	5.453 2	26
35	**0.183 67**	**0.186 84**	**5.352 1**	**0.982 99**	**1.017 3**	**5.444 7**	**25**
36	0.183 95	0.187 14	5.343 5	0.982 94	1.017 4	5.436 2	24
37	0.184 24	0.187 45	5.334 9	0.982 88	1.017 4	5.427 8	23
38	0.184 52	0.187 75	5.326 3	0.982 83	1.017 5	5.419 4	22
39	0.184 81	0.188 05	5.317 8	0.982 77	1.017 5	5.411 0	21
40	**0.185 09**	**0.188 35**	**5.309 3**	**0.982 72**	**1.017 6**	**5.402 6**	**20**
41	0.185 38	0.188 65	5.300 8	0.982 67	1.017 6	5.394 3	19
42	0.185 67	0.188 95	5.292 4	0.982 61	1.017 7	5.386 0	18
43	0.185 95	0.189 25	5.283 9	0.982 56	1.017 8	5.377 7	17
44	0.186 24	0.189 55	5.275 5	0.982 50	1.017 8	5.369 5	16
45	**0.186 52**	**0.189 86**	**5.267 2**	**0.982 45**	**1.017 9**	**5.361 2**	**15**
46	0.186 81	0.190 16	5.258 8	0.982 40	1.017 9	5.353 0	14
47	0.187 10	0.190 46	5.250 5	0.982 34	1.018 0	5.344 9	13
48	0.187 38	0.190 76	5.242 2	0.982 29	1.018 0	5.336 7	12
49	0.187 67	0.191 06	5.233 9	0.982 23	1.018 1	5.328 6	11
50	**0.187 95**	**0.191 36**	**5.225 7**	**0.982 18**	**1.018 1**	**5.320 5**	**10**
51	0.188 24	0.191 66	5.217 4	0.982 12	1.018 2	5.312 4	9
52	0.188 52	0.191 97	5.209 2	0.982 07	1.018 3	5.304 4	8
53	0.188 81	0.192 27	5.201 1	0.982 01	1.018 3	5.296 3	7
54	0.189 10	0.192 57	5.192 9	0.981 96	1.018 4	5.288 3	6
55	**0.189 38**	**0.192 87**	**5.184 8**	**0.981 90**	**1.018 4**	**5.280 4**	**5**
56	0.189 67	0.193 17	5.176 7	0.981 85	1.018 5	5.272 4	4
57	0.189 95	0.193 47	5.168 6	0.981 79	1.018 5	5.264 5	3
58	0.190 24	0.193 78	5.160 6	0.981 74	1.018 6	5.256 6	2
59	0.190 52	0.194 08	5.152 6	0.981 68	1.018 7	5.248 7	1
60	**0.190 81**	**0.194 38**	**5.144 6**	**0.981 63**	**1.018 7**	**5.240 8**	0
′	Cos	Cot	Tan	Sin	Csc	Sec	′

Table 3 / Five-place natural trigonometric functions □ 633

′	Sin	Tan	Cot	Cos	Sec	Csc	′
0	0.190 81	0.194 38	5.144 6	0.981 63	1.018 7	5.240 8	60
1	0.191 09	0.194 68	5.136 6	0.981 57	1.018 8	5.233 0	59
2	0.191 38	0.194 98	5.128 6	0.981 52	1.018 8	5.225 2	58
3	0.191 67	0.195 29	5.120 7	0.981 46	1.018 9	5.217 4	57
4	0.191 95	0.195 59	5.112 8	0.981 40	1.018 9	5.209 7	56
5	0.192 24	0.195 89	5.104 9	0.981 35	1.019 0	5.201 9	55
6	0.192 52	0.196 19	5.097 0	0.981 29	1.019 1	5.194 2	54
7	0.192 81	0.196 49	5.089 2	0.981 24	1.019 1	5.186 5	53
8	0.193 09	0.196 80	5.081 4	0.981 18	1.019 2	5.178 9	52
9	0.193 38	0.197 10	5.073 6	0.981 12	1.019 2	5.171 2	51
10	0.193 66	0.197 40	5.065 8	0.981 07	1.019 3	5.163 6	50
11	0.193 95	0.197 70	5.058 1	0.981 01	1.019 4	5.156 0	49
12	0.194 23	0.198 01	5.050 4	0.980 96	1.019 4	5.148 4	48
13	0.194 52	0.198 31	5.042 7	0.980 90	1.019 5	5.140 9	47
14	0.194 81	0.198 61	5.035 0	0.980 84	1.019 5	5.133 3	46
15	0.195 09	0.198 91	5.027 3	0.980 79	1.019 6	5.125 8	45
16	0.195 38	0.199 21	5.019 7	0.980 73	1.019 7	5.118 3	44
17	0.195 66	0.199 52	5.012 1	0.980 67	1.019 7	5.110 9	43
18	0.195 95	0.199 82	5.004 5	0.980 61	1.019 8	5.103 4	42
19	0.196 23	0.200 12	4.996 9	0.980 56	1.019 8	5.096 0	41
20	0.196 52	0.200 42	4.989 4	0.980 50	1.019 9	5.088 6	40
21	0.196 80	0.200 73	4.981 9	0.980 44	1.019 9	5.081 3	39
22	0.197 09	0.201 03	4.974 4	0.980 39	1.020 0	5.073 9	38
23	0.197 37	0.201 33	4.966 9	0.980 33	1.020 1	5.066 6	37
24	0.197 66	0.201 64	4.959 4	0.980 27	1.020 1	5.059 3	36
25	0.197 94	0.201 94	4.952 0	0.980 21	1.020 2	5.052 0	35
26	0.198 23	0.202 24	4.944 6	0.980 16	1.020 2	5.044 7	34
27	0.198 51	0.202 54	4.937 2	0.980 10	1.020 3	5.037 5	33
28	0.198 80	0.202 85	4.929 8	0.980 04	1.020 4	5.030 2	32
29	0.199 08	0.203 15	4.922 5	0.979 98	1.020 4	5.023 0	31
30	0.199 37	0.203 45	4.915 2	0.979 92	1.020 5	5.015 9	30
31	0.199 65	0.203 76	4.907 8	0.979 87	1.020 5	5.008 7	29
32	0.199 94	0.204 06	4.900 6	0.979 81	1.020 6	5.001 6	28
33	0.200 22	0.204 36	4.893 3	0.979 75	1.020 7	4.994 4	27
34	0.200 51	0.204 66	4.886 0	0.979 69	1.020 7	4.987 3	26
35	0.200 79	0.204 97	4.878 8	0.979 63	1.020 8	4.980 3	25
36	0.201 08	0.205 27	4.871 6	0.979 58	1.020 9	4.973 2	24
37	0.201 36	0.205 57	4.864 4	0.979 52	1.020 9	4.966 2	23
38	0.201 65	0.205 88	4.857 3	0.979 46	1.021 0	4.959 1	22
39	0.201 93	0.206 18	4.850 1	0.979 40	1.021 0	4.952 1	21
40	0.202 22	0.206 48	4.843 0	0.979 34	1.021 1	4.945 2	20
41	0.202 50	0.206 79	4.835 9	0.979 28	1.021 2	4.938 2	19
42	0.202 79	0.207 09	4.828 8	0.979 22	1.021 2	4.931 3	18
43	0.203 07	0.207 39	4.821 8	0.979 16	1.021 3	4.924 4	17
44	0.203 36	0.207 70	4.814 7	0.979 10	1.021 3	4.917 5	16
45	0.203 64	0.208 00	4.807 7	0.979 05	1.021 4	4.910 6	15
46	0.203 93	0.208 30	4.800 7	0.978 99	1.021 5	4.903 7	14
47	0.204 21	0.208 61	4.793 7	0.978 93	1.021 5	4.896 9	13
48	0.204 50	0.208 91	4.786 7	0.978 87	1.021 6	4.890 1	12
49	0.204 78	0.209 21	4.779 8	0.978 81	1.021 7	4.883 3	11
50	0.205 07	0.209 52	4.772 9	0.978 75	1.021 7	4.876 5	10
51	0.205 35	0.209 82	4.765 9	0.978 69	1.021 8	4.869 7	9
52	0.205 63	0.210 13	4.759 1	0.978 63	1.021 8	4.863 0	8
53	0.205 92	0.210 43	4.752 2	0.978 57	1.021 9	4.856 3	7
54	0.206 20	0.210 73	4.745 3	0.978 51	1.022 0	4.849 6	6
55	0.206 49	0.211 04	4.738 5	0.978 45	1.022 0	4.842 9	5
56	0.206 77	0.211 34	4.731 7	0.978 39	1.022 1	4.836 2	4
57	0.207 06	0.211 64	4.724 9	0.978 33	1.022 2	4.829 6	3
58	0.207 34	0.211 95	4.718 1	0.978 27	1.022 2	4.822 9	2
59	0.207 63	0.212 25	4.711 4	0.978 21	1.022 3	4.816 3	1
60	0.207 91	0.212 56	4.704 6	0.978 15	1.022 3	4.809 7	0
′	Cos	Cot	Tan	Sin	Csc	Sec	′

′	Sin	Tan	Cot	Cos	Sec	Csc	′
0	**0.207 91**	**0.212 56**	**4.704 6**	**0.978 15**	**1.022 3**	**4.809 7**	**60**
1	0.208 20	0.212 86	4.697 9	0.978 09	1.022 4	4.803 2	59
2	0.208 48	0.213 16	4.691 2	0.978 03	1.022 5	4.796 6	58
3	0.208 77	0.213 47	4.684 5	0.977 97	1.022 5	4.790 1	57
4	0.209 05	0.213 77	4.677 9	0.977 91	1.022 6	4.783 6	56
5	**0.209 33**	**0.214 08**	**4.671 2**	**0.977 84**	**1.022 7**	**4.777 1**	**55**
6	0.209 62	0.214 38	4.664 6	0.977 78	1.022 7	4.770 6	54
7	0.209 90	0.214 69	4.658 0	0.977 72	1.022 8	4.764 1	53
8	0.210 19	0.214 99	4.651 4	0.977 66	1.022 8	4.757 7	52
9	0.210 47	0.215 29	4.644 8	0.977 60	1.022 9	4.751 2	51
10	**0.210 76**	**0.215 60**	**4.638 2**	**0.977 54**	**1.023 0**	**4.774 8**	**50**
11	0.211 04	0.215 90	4.631 7	0.977 48	1.023 0	4.738 4	49
12	0.211 32	0.216 21	4.625 2	0.977 42	1.023 1	4.732 1	48
13	0.211 61	0.216 51	4.618 7	0.977 35	1.023 2	4.725 7	47
14	0.211 89	0.216 82	4.612 2	0.977 29	1.023 2	4.719 4	46
15	**0.212 18**	**0.217 12**	**4.605 7**	**0.977 23**	**1.023 3**	**4.713 0**	**45**
16	0.212 46	0.217 43	4.599 3	0.977 17	1.023 4	4.706 7	44
17	0.212 75	0.217 73	4.592 8	0.977 11	1.023 4	4.700 4	43
18	0.213 03	0.218 04	4.586 4	0.977 05	1.023 5	4.694 2	42
19	0.213 31	0.218 34	4.580 0	0.976 98	1.023 6	4.687 9	41
20	**0.213 60**	**0.218 64**	**4.573 6**	**0.976 92**	**1.023 6**	**4.681 7**	**40**
21	0.213 88	0.218 95	4.567 3	0.976 86	1.023 7	4.675 5	39
22	0.214 17	0.219 25	4.560 9	0.976 80	1.023 8	4.669 3	38
23	0.214 45	0.219 56	4.554 6	0.976 73	1.023 8	4.663 1	37
24	0.214 74	0.219 86	4.548 3	0.976 67	1.023 9	4.656 9	36
25	**0.215 02**	**0.220 17**	**4.542 0**	**0.976 61**	**1.024 0**	**4.650 7**	**35**
26	0.215 30	0.220 47	4.535 7	0.976 55	1.024 0	4.644 6	34
27	0.215 59	0.220 78	4.529 4	0.976 48	1.024 1	4.638 5	33
28	0.215 87	0.221 08	4.523 2	0.976 42	1.024 1	4.632 4	32
29	0.216 16	0.221 39	4.516 9	0.976 36	1.024 2	4.626 3	31
30	**0.216 44**	**0.221 69**	**4.510 7**	**0.976 30**	**1.024 3**	**4.620 2**	**30**
31	0.216 72	0.222 00	4.504 5	0.976 23	1.024 3	4.614 2	29
32	0.217 01	0.222 31	4.498 3	0.976 17	1.024 4	4.608 1	28
33	0.217 29	0.222 61	4.492 2	0.976 11	1.024 5	4.602 1	27
34	0.217 58	0.222 92	4.486 0	0.976 04	1.024 5	4.596 1	26
35	**0.217 86**	**0.223 22**	**4.479 9**	**0.975 98**	**1.024 6**	**4.590 1**	**25**
36	0.218 14	0.223 53	4.473 7	0.975 92	1.024 7	4.584 1	24
37	0.218 43	0.223 83	4.467 6	0.975 85	1.024 7	4.578 2	23
38	0.218 71	0.224 14	4.461 5	0.975 79	1.024 8	4.572 2	22
39	0.218 99	0.224 44	4.455 5	0.975 73	1.024 9	4.566 3	21
40	**0.219 28**	**0.224 75**	**4.449 4**	**0.975 66**	**1.024 9**	**4.560 4**	**20**
41	0.219 56	0.225 05	4.443 4	0.975 60	1.025 0	4.554 5	19
42	0.219 85	0.225 36	4.437 3	0.975 53	1.025 1	4.548 6	18
43	0.220 13	0.225 67	4.431 3	0.975 47	1.025 1	4.542 8	17
44	0.220 41	0.225 97	4.425 3	0.975 41	1.025 2	4.536 9	16
45	**0.220 70**	**0.226 28**	**4.419 4**	**0.975 34**	**1.025 3**	**4.531 1**	**15**
46	0.220 98	0.226 58	4.413 4	0.975 28	1.025 3	4.525 3	14
47	0.221 26	0.226 89	4.407 5	0.975 21	1.025 4	4.519 5	13
48	0.221 55	0.227 19	4.401 5	0.975 15	1.025 5	4.513 7	12
49	0.221 83	0.227 50	4.395 6	0.975 08	1.025 6	4.507 9	11
50	**0.222 12**	**0.227 81**	**4.389 7**	**0.975 02**	**1.025 6**	**4.502 2**	**10**
51	0.222 40	0.228 11	4.383 8	0.974 96	1.025 7	4.496 4	9
52	0.222 68	0.228 42	4.377 9	0.974 89	1.025 8	4.490 7	8
53	0.222 97	0.228 72	4.372 1	0.974 83	1.025 8	4.485 0	7
54	0.223 25	0.229 03	4.366 2	0.974 76	1.025 9	4.479 3	6
55	**0.223 53**	**0.229 34**	**4.360 4**	**0.974 70**	**1.026 0**	**4.473 6**	**5**
56	0.223 82	0.229 64	4.354 6	0.974 63	1.026 0	4.467 9	4
57	0.224 10	0.229 95	4.348 8	0.974 57	1.026 1	4.462 3	3
58	0.224 38	0.230 26	4.343 0	0.974 50	1.026 2	4.456 6	2
59	0.224 67	0.230 56	4.337 2	0.974 44	1.026 2	4.451 0	1
60	**0.224 95**	**0.230 87**	**4.331 5**	**0.974 37**	**1.026 3**	**4.445 4**	**0**
′	Cos	Cot	Tan	Sin	Csc	Sec	′

Table 3 / Five-place natural trigonometric functions   □   **635**

′	Sin	Tan	Cot	Cos	Sec	Csc	′
0	**0.224 95**	**0.230 87**	**4.331 5**	**0.974 37**	**1.026 3**	**4.445 4**	60
1	0.225 23	0.231 17	4.325 7	0.974 30	1.026 4	4.439 8	59
2	0.225 52	0.231 48	4.320 0	0.974 24	1.026 4	4.434 2	58
3	0.225 80	0.231 79	4.314 3	0.974 17	1.026 5	4.428 7	57
4	0.226 08	0.232 09	4.308 6	0.974 11	1.026 6	4.423 1	56
5	**0.226 37**	**0.232 40**	**4.302 9**	**0.974 04**	**1.026 6**	**4.417 6**	55
6	0.226 65	0.232 71	4.297 2	0.973 98	1.026 7	4.412 1	54
7	0.226 93	0.233 01	4.291 6	0.973 91	1.026 8	4.406 6	53
8	0.227 22	0.233 32	4.285 9	0.973 84	1.026 9	4.401 1	52
9	0.227 50	0.233 63	4.280 3	0.973 78	1.026 9	4.395 6	51
10	**0.227 78**	**0.233 93**	**4.274 7**	**0.973 71**	**1.027 0**	**4.390 1**	50
11	0.228 07	0.234 24	4.269 1	0.973 65	1.027 1	4.384 7	49
12	0.228 35	0.234 55	4.263 5	0.973 58	1.027 1	4.379 2	48
13	0.228 63	0.234 85	4.258 0	0.973 51	1.027 2	4.373 8	47
14	0.228 92	0.235 16	4.252 4	0.973 45	1.027 3	4.368 4	46
15	**0.229 20**	**0.235 47**	**4.246 8**	**0.973 38**	**1.027 3**	**4.363 0**	45
16	0.229 48	0.235 78	4.241 3	0.973 31	1.027 4	4.357 6	44
17	0.229 77	0.236 08	4.235 8	0.973 25	1.027 5	4.352 2	43
18	0.230 05	0.236 39	4.230 3	0.973 18	1.027 6	4.346 9	42
19	0.230 33	0.236 70	4.224 8	0.973 11	1.027 6	4.341 5	41
20	**0.230 62**	**0.237 00**	**4.219 3**	**0.973 04**	**1.027 7**	**4.336 2**	40
21	0.230 90	0.237 31	4.213 9	0.972 98	1.027 8	4.330 9	39
22	0.231 18	0.237 62	4.208 4	0.972 91	1.027 8	4.325 6	38
23	0.231 46	0.237 93	4.203 0	0.972 84	1.027 9	4.320 3	37
24	0.231 75	0.238 23	4.197 6	0.972 78	1.028 0	4.315 0	36
25	**0.232 03**	**0.238 54**	**4.192 2**	**0.972 71**	**1.028 1**	**4.309 8**	35
26	0.232 31	0.238 85	4.186 8	0.972 64	1.028 1	4.304 5	34
27	0.232 60	0.239 16	4.181 4	0.972 57	1.028 2	4.299 3	33
28	0.232 88	0.239 46	4.176 0	0.972 51	1.028 3	4.294 1	32
29	0.233 16	0.239 77	4.170 6	0.972 44	1.028 3	4.288 9	31
30	**0.233 45**	**0.240 08**	**4.165 3**	**0.972 37**	**1.028 4**	**4.283 7**	30
31	0.233 73	0.240 39	4.160 0	0.972 30	1.028 5	4.278 5	29
32	0.234 01	0.240 69	4.154 7	0.972 23	1.028 6	4.273 3	28
33	0.234 29	0.241 00	4.149 3	0.972 17	1.028 6	4.268 1	27
34	0.234 58	0.241 31	4.144 1	0.972 10	1.028 7	4.263 0	26
35	**0.234 86**	**0.241 62**	**4.138 8**	**0.972 03**	**1.028 8**	**4.257 9**	25
36	0.235 14	0.241 93	4.133 5	0.971 96	1.028 8	4.252 7	24
37	0.235 42	0.242 23	4.128 2	0.971 89	1.028 9	4.247 6	23
38	0.235 71	0.242 54	4.123 0	0.971 82	1.029 0	4.242 5	22
39	0.235 99	0.242 85	4.117 8	0.971 76	1.029 1	4.237 5	21
40	**0.236 27**	**0.243 16**	**4.112 6**	**0.971 69**	**1.029 1**	**4.232 4**	20
41	0.236 56	0.243 47	4.107 4	0.971 62	1.029 2	4.227 3	19
42	0.236 84	0.243 77	4.102 2	0.971 55	1.029 3	4.222 3	18
43	0.237 12	0.244 08	4.097 0	0.971 48	1.029 4	4.217 3	17
44	0.237 40	0.244 39	4.091 8	0.971 41	1.029 4	4.212 2	16
45	**0.237 69**	**0.244 70**	**4.086 7**	**0.971 34**	**1.029 5**	**4.207 2**	15
46	0.237 97	0.245 01	4.081 5	0.971 27	1.029 6	4.202 2	14
47	0.238 25	0.245 32	4.076 4	0.971 20	1.029 7	4.197 3	13
48	0.238 53	0.245 62	4.071 3	0.971 13	1.029 7	4.192 3	12
49	0.238 82	0.245 93	4.066 2	0.971 06	1.029 8	4.187 3	11
50	**0.239 10**	**0.246 24**	**4.061 1**	**0.971 00**	**1.029 9**	**4.182 4**	10
51	0.239 38	0.246 55	4.056 0	0.970 93	1.029 9	4.177 4	9
52	0.239 66	0.246 86	4.050 9	0.970 86	1.030 0	4.172 5	8
53	0.239 95	0.247 17	4.045 9	0.970 79	1.030 1	4.167 6	7
54	0.240 23	0.247 47	4.040 8	0.970 72	1.030 2	4.162 7	6
55	**0.240 51**	**0.247 78**	**4.035 8**	**0.970 65**	**1.030 2**	**4.157 8**	5
56	0.240 79	0.248 09	4.030 8	0.970 58	1.030 3	4.152 9	4
57	0.241 08	0.248 40	4.025 7	0.970 51	1.030 4	4.148 1	3
58	0.241 36	0.248 71	4.020 7	0.970 44	1.030 5	4.143 2	2
59	0.241 64	0.249 02	4.015 8	0.970 37	1.030 5	4.138 4	1
60	**0.241 92**	**0.249 33**	**4.010 8**	**0.970 30**	**1.030 6**	**4.133 6**	0
′	Cos	Cot	Tan	Sin	Csc	Sec	′

′	Sin	Tan	Cot	Cos	Sec	Csc	′
0	**0.241 92**	**0.249 33**	**4.010 8**	**0.970 30**	**1.030 6**	**4.133 6**	**60**
1	0.242 20	0.249 64	4.005 8	0.970 23	1.030 7	4.128 7	59
2	0.242 49	0.249 95	4.000 9	0.970 15	1.030 8	4.123 9	58
3	0.242 77	0.250 26	3.995 9	0.970 08	1.030 8	4.119 1	57
4	0.243 05	0.250 56	3.991 0	0.970 01	1.030 9	4.114 4	56
5	**0.243 33**	**0.250 87**	**3.986 1**	**0.969 94**	**1.031 0**	**4.109 6**	**55**
6	0.243 62	0.251 18	3.981 2	0.969 87	1.031 1	4.104 8	54
7	0.243 90	0.251 49	3.976 3	0.969 80	1.031 1	4.100 1	53
8	0.244 18	0.251 80	3.971 4	0.969 73	1.031 2	4.095 4	52
9	0.244 46	0.252 11	3.966 5	0.969 66	1.031 3	4.090 6	51
10	**0.244 74**	**0.252 42**	**3.961 7**	**0.969 59**	**1.031 4**	**4.085 9**	**50**
11	0.245 03	0.252 73	3.956 8	0.969 52	1.031 4	4.081 2	49
12	0.245 31	0.253 04	3.952 0	0.969 45	1.031 5	4.076 5	48
13	0.245 59	0.253 35	3.947 1	0.969 37	1.031 6	4.071 8	47
14	0.245 87	0.253 66	3.942 3	0.969 30	1.031 7	4.067 2	46
15	**0.246 15**	**0.253 97**	**3.937 5**	**0.969 23**	**1.031 7**	**4.062 5**	**45**
16	0.246 44	0.254 28	3.932 7	0.969 16	1.031 8	4.057 9	44
17	0.246 72	0.254 59	3.927 9	0.969 09	1.031 9	4.053 2	43
18	0.247 00	0.254 90	3.923 2	0.969 02	1.032 0	4.048 6	42
19	0.247 28	0.255 21	3.918 4	0.968 94	1.032 1	4.044 0	41
20	**0.247 56**	**0.255 52**	**3.913 6**	**0.968 87**	**1.032 1**	**4.039 4**	**40**
21	0.247 84	0.255 83	3.908 9	0.968 80	1.032 2	4.034 8	39
22	0.248 13	0.256 14	3.904 2	0.968 73	1.032 3	4.030 2	38
23	0.248 41	0.256 45	3.899 5	0.968 66	1.032 4	4.025 6	37
24	0.248 69	0.256 76	3.894 7	0.968 58	1.032 4	4.021 1	36
25	**0.248 97**	**0.257 07**	**3.890 0**	**0.968 51**	**1.032 5**	**4.016 5**	**35**
26	0.249 25	0.257 38	3.885 4	0.968 44	1.032 6	4.012 0	34
27	0.249 54	0.257 69	3.880 7	0.968 37	1.032 7	4.007 5	33
28	0.249 82	0.258 00	3.876 0	0.968 29	1.032 7	4.002 9	32
29	0.250 10	0.258 31	3.871 4	0.968 22	1.032 8	3.998 4	31
30	**0.250 38**	**0.258 62**	**3.866 7**	**0.968 15**	**1.032 9**	**3.993 9**	**30**
31	0.250 66	0.258 93	3.862 1	0.968 07	1.033 0	3.989 4	29
32	0.250 94	0.259 24	3.857 5	0.968 00	1.033 1	3.985 0	28
33	0.251 22	0.259 55	3.852 8	0.967 93	1.033 1	3.980 5	27
34	0.251 51	0.259 86	3.848 2	0.967 86	1.033 2	3.976 0	26
35	**0.251 79**	**0.260 17**	**3.843 6**	**0.967 78**	**1.033 3**	**3.971 6**	**25**
36	0.252 07	0.260 48	3.839 1	0.967 71	1.033 4	3.967 2	24
37	0.252 35	0.260 79	3.834 5	0.967 64	1.033 4	3.962 7	23
38	0.252 63	0.261 10	3.829 9	0.967 56	1.033 5	3.958 3	22
39	0.252 91	0.261 41	3.825 4	0.967 49	1.033 6	3.953 9	21
40	**0.253 20**	**0.261 72**	**3.820 8**	**0.967 42**	**1.033 7**	**3.949 5**	**20**
41	0.253 48	0.262 03	3.816 3	0.967 34	1.033 8	3.945 1	19
42	0.253 76	0.262 35	3.811 8	0.967 27	1.033 8	3.940 8	18
43	0.254 04	0.262 66	3.807 3	0.967 19	1.033 9	3.936 4	17
44	0.254 32	0.262 97	3.802 8	0.967 12	1.034 0	3.932 0	16
45	**0.254 60**	**0.263 28**	**3.798 3**	**0.967 05**	**1.034 1**	**3.927 7**	**15**
46	0.254 88	0.263 59	3.793 8	0.966 97	1.034 2	3.923 4	14
47	0.255 16	0.263 90	3.789 3	0.966 90	1.034 2	3.919 0	13
48	0.255 45	0.264 21	3.784 8	0.966 82	1.034 3	3.914 7	12
49	0.255 73	0.264 52	3.780 4	0.966 75	1.034 4	3.910 4	11
50	**0.256 01**	**0.264 83**	**3.776 0**	**0.966 67**	**1.034 5**	**3.906 1**	**10**
51	0.256 29	0.265 15	3.771 5	0.966 60	1.034 6	3.901 8	9
52	0.256 57	0.265 46	3.767 1	0.966 53	1.034 6	3.897 6	8
53	0.256 85	0.265 77	3.762 7	0.966 45	1.034 7	3.893 3	7
54	0.257 13	0.266 08	3.758 3	0.966 38	1.034 8	3.889 0	6
55	**0.257 41**	**0.266 39**	**3.753 9**	**0.966 30**	**1.034 9**	**3.884 8**	**5**
56	0.257 69	0.266 70	3.749 5	0.966 23	1.035 0	3.880 6	4
57	0.257 98	0.267 01	3.745 1	0.966 15	1.035 0	3.876 3	3
58	0.258 26	0.267 33	3.740 8	0.966 08	1.035 1	3.872 1	2
59	0.258 54	0.267 64	3.736 4	0.966 00	1.035 2	3.867 9	1
60	**0.258 82**	**0.267 95**	**3.732 1**	**0.965 93**	**1.035 3**	**3.863 7**	**0**
′	Cos	Cot	Tan	Sin	Csc	Sec	′

Table 3 / *Five-place natural trigonometric functions* ☐ 637

′	Sin	Tan	Cot	Cos	Sec	Csc	′
0	**0.258 82**	**0.267 95**	**3.732 1**	**0.965 93**	**1.035 3**	**3.863 7**	60
1	0.259 10	0.268 26	3.727 7	0.965 85	1.035 4	3.859 5	59
2	0.259 38	0.268 57	3.723 4	0.965 78	1.035 4	3.855 3	58
3	0.259 66	0.268 88	3.719 1	0.965 70	1.035 5	3.851 2	57
4	0.259 94	0.269 20	3.714 8	0.965 62	1.035 6	3.847 0	56
5	**0.260 22**	**0.269 51**	**3.710 5**	**0.965 55**	**1.035 7**	**3.842 8**	55
6	0.260 50	0.269 82	3.706 2	0.965 47	1.035 8	3.838 7	54
7	0.260 79	0.270 13	3.701 9	0.965 40	1.035 8	3.834 6	53
8	0.261 07	0.270 44	3.697 6	0.965 32	1.035 9	3.830 4	52
9	0.261 35	0.270 76	3.693 3	0.965 24	1.036 0	3.826 3	51
10	**0.261 63**	**0.271 07**	**3.689 1**	**0.965 17**	**1.036 1**	**3.822 2**	50
11	0.261 91	0.271 38	3.684 8	0.965 09	1.036 2	3.818 1	49
12	0.262 19	0.271 69	3.680 6	0.965 02	1.036 3	3.814 0	48
13	0.262 47	0.272 01	3.676 4	0.964 94	1.036 3	3.810 0	47
14	0.262 75	0.272 32	3.672 2	0.964 86	1.036 4	3.805 9	46
15	**0.263 03**	**0.272 63**	**3.668 0**	**0.964 79**	**1.036 5**	**3.801 8**	45
16	0.263 31	0.272 94	3.663 8	0.964 71	1.036 6	3.797 8	44
17	0.263 59	0.273 26	3.659 6	0.964 63	1.036 7	3.793 7	43
18	0.263 87	0.273 57	3.655 4	0.964 56	1.036 7	3.789 7	42
19	0.264 15	0.273 88	3.651 2	0.964 48	1.036 8	3.785 7	41
20	**0.264 43**	**0.274 19**	**3.647 0**	**0.964 40**	**1.036 9**	**3.781 7**	40
21	0.264 71	0.274 51	3.642 9	0.964 33	1.037 0	3.777 7	39
22	0.265 00	0.274 82	3.638 7	0.964 25	1.037 1	3.773 7	38
23	0.265 28	0.275 13	3.634 6	0.964 17	1.037 2	3.769 7	37
24	0.265 56	0.275 45	3.630 5	0.964 10	1.037 2	3.765 7	36
25	**0.265 84**	**0.275 76**	**3.626 4**	**0.964 02**	**1.037 3**	**3.761 7**	35
26	0.266 12	0.276 07	3.622 2	0.963 94	1.037 4	3.757 7	34
27	0.266 40	0.276 38	3.618 1	0.963 86	1.037 5	3.753 8	33
28	0.266 68	0.276 70	3.614 0	0.963 79	1.037 6	3.749 8	32
29	0.266 96	0.277 01	3.610 0	0.963 71	1.037 7	3.745 9	31
30	**0.267 24**	**0.277 32**	**3.605 9**	**0.963 63**	**1.037 7**	**3.742 0**	30
31	0.267 52	0.277 64	3.601 8	0.963 55	1.037 8	3.738 1	29
32	0.267 80	0.277 95	3.597 8	0.963 47	1.037 9	3.734 1	28
33	0.268 08	0.278 26	3.593 7	0.963 40	1.038 0	3.730 2	27
34	0.268 36	0.278 58	3.589 7	0.963 32	1.038 1	3.726 3	26
35	**0.268 64**	**0.278 89**	**3.585 6**	**0.963 24**	**1.038 2**	**3.722 5**	25
36	0.268 92	0.279 21	3.581 6	0.963 16	1.038 2	3.718 6	24
37	0.269 20	0.279 52	3.577 6	0.963 08	1.038 3	3.714 7	23
38	0.269 48	0.279 83	3.573 6	0.963 01	1.038 4	3.710 8	22
39	0.269 76	0.280 15	3.569 6	0.962 93	1.038 5	3.707 0	21
40	**0.270 04**	**0.280 46**	**3.565 6**	**0.962 85**	**1.038 6**	**3.703 2**	20
41	0.270 32	0.280 77	3.561 6	0.962 77	1.038 7	3.699 3	19
42	0.270 60	0.281 09	3.557 6	0.962 69	1.038 8	3.695 5	18
43	0.270 88	0.281 40	3.553 6	0.962 61	1.038 8	3.691 7	17
44	0.271 16	0.281 72	3.549 7	0.962 53	1.038 9	3.687 9	16
45	**0.271 44**	**0.282 03**	**3.545 7**	**0.962 46**	**1.039 0**	**3.684 0**	15
46	0.271 72	0.282 34	3.541 8	0.962 38	1.039 1	3.680 3	14
47	0.272 00	0.282 66	3.537 9	0.962 30	1.039 2	3.676 5	13
48	0.272 28	0.282 97	3.533 9	0.962 22	1.039 3	3.672 7	12
49	0.272 56	0.283 29	3.530 0	0.962 14	1.039 4	3.668 9	11
50	**0.272 84**	**0.283 60**	**3.526 1**	**0.962 06**	**1.039 4**	**3.665 2**	10
51	0.273 12	0.283 91	3.522 2	0.961 98	1.039 5	3.661 4	9
52	0.273 40	0.284 23	3.518 3	0.961 90	1.039 6	3.657 6	8
53	0.273 68	0.284 54	3.514 4	0.961 82	1.039 7	3.653 9	7
54	0.273 96	0.284 86	3.510 5	0.961 74	1.039 8	3.650 2	6
55	**0.274 24**	**0.285 17**	**3.506 7**	**0.961 66**	**1.039 9**	**3.646 5**	5
56	0.274 52	0.285 49	3.502 8	0.961 58	1.040 0	3.642 7	4
57	0.274 80	0.285 80	3.498 9	0.961 50	1.040 0	3.639 0	3
58	0.275 08	0.286 12	3.495 1	0.961 42	1.040 1	3.635 3	2
59	0.275 36	0.286 43	3.491 2	0.961 34	1.040 2	3.631 6	1
60	**0.275 64**	**0.286 75**	**3.487 4**	**0.961 26**	**1.040 3**	**3.628 0**	0
′	Cos	Cot	Tan	Sin	Csc	Sec	′

′	Sin	Tan	Cot	Cos	Sec	Csc	′
0	**0.275 64**	**0.286 75**	**3.487 4**	**0.961 26**	**1.040 3**	**3.628 0**	60
1	0.275 92	0.287 06	3.483 6	0.961 18	1.040 4	3.624 3	59
2	0.276 20	0.287 38	3.479 8	0.961 10	1.040 5	3.620 6	58
3	0.276 48	0.287 69	3.476 0	0.961 02	1.040 6	3.616 9	57
4	0.276 76	0.288 01	3.472 2	0.960 94	1.040 6	3.613 3	56
5	**0.277 04**	**0.288 32**	**3.468 4**	**0.960 86**	**1.040 7**	**3.609 7**	55
6	0.277 31	0.288 64	3.464 6	0.960 78	1.040 8	3.606 0	54
7	0.277 59	0.288 95	3.460 8	0.960 70	1.040 9	3.602 4	53
8	0.277 87	0.289 27	3.457 0	0.960 62	1.041 0	3.598 8	52
9	0.278 15	0.289 58	3.453 3	0.960 54	1.041 1	3.595 1	51
10	**0.278 43**	**0.289 90**	**3.449 5**	**0.960 46**	**1.041 2**	**3.591 5**	50
11	0.278 71	0.290 21	3.445 8	0.960 37	1.041 3	3.587 9	49
12	0.278 99	0.290 53	3.442 0	0.960 29	1.041 3	3.584 3	48
13	0.279 27	0.290 84	3.438 3	0.960 21	1.041 4	3.580 8	47
14	0.279 55	0.291 16	3.434 6	0.960 13	1.041 5	3.577 2	46
15	**0.279 83**	**0.291 47**	**3.430 8**	**0.960 05**	**1.041 6**	**3.573 6**	45
16	0.280 11	0.291 79	3.427 1	0.959 97	1.041 7	3.570 0	44
17	0.280 39	0.292 10	3.423 4	0.959 89	1.041 8	3.566 5	43
18	0.280 67	0.292 42	3.419 7	0.959 81	1.041 9	3.562 9	42
19	0.280 95	0.292 74	3.416 0	0.959 72	1.042 0	3.559 4	41
20	**0.281 23**	**0.293 05**	**3.412 4**	**0.959 64**	**1.042 1**	**3.555 9**	40
21	0.281 50	0.293 37	3.408 7	0.959 56	1.042 1	3.552 3	39
22	0.281 78	0.293 68	3.405 0	0.959 48	1.042 2	3.548 8	38
23	0.282 06	0.294 00	3.401 4	0.959 40	1.042 3	3.545 3	37
24	0.282 34	0.294 32	3.397 7	0.959 31	1.042 4	3.541 8	36
25	**0.282 62**	**0.294 63**	**3.394 1**	**0.959 23**	**1.042 5**	**3.538 3**	35
26	0.282 90	0.294 95	3.390 4	0.959 15	1.042 6	3.534 8	34
27	0.283 18	0.295 26	3.386 8	0.959 07	1.042 7	3.531 3	33
28	0.283 46	0.295 58	3.383 2	0.958 98	1.042 8	3.527 9	32
29	0.283 74	0.295 90	3.379 6	0.958 90	1.042 9	3.524 4	31
30	**0.284 02**	**0.296 21**	**3.375 9**	**0.958 82**	**1.042 9**	**3.520 9**	30
31	0.284 29	0.296 53	3.372 3	0.958 74	1.043 0	3.517 5	29
32	0.284 57	0.296 85	3.368 7	0.958 65	1.043 1	3.514 0	28
33	0.284 85	0.297 16	3.365 2	0.958 57	1.043 2	3.510 6	27
34	0.285 13	0.297 48	3.361 6	0.958 49	1.043 3	3.507 2	26
35	**0.285 41**	**0.297 80**	**3.358 0**	**0.958 41**	**1.043 4**	**3.503 7**	25
36	0.285 69	0.298 11	3.354 4	0.958 32	1.043 5	3.500 3	24
37	0.285 97	0.298 43	3.350 9	0.958 24	1.043 6	3.496 9	23
38	0.286 25	0.298 75	3.347 3	0.958 16	1.043 7	3.493 5	22
39	0.286 52	0.299 06	3.343 8	0.958 07	1.043 8	3.490 1	21
40	**0.286 80**	**0.299 38**	**3.340 2**	**0.957 99**	**1.043 9**	**3.486 7**	20
41	0.287 08	0.299 70	3.336 7	0.957 91	1.043 9	3.483 9	19
42	0.287 36	0.300 01	3.333 2	0.957 82	1.044 0	3.479 9	18
43	0.287 64	0.300 33	3.329 7	0.957 74	1.044 1	3.476 6	17
44	0.287 92	0.300 65	3.326 1	0.957 66	1.044 2	3.473 2	16
45	**0.288 20**	**0.300 97**	**3.322 6**	**0.957 57**	**1.044 3**	**3.469 9**	15
46	0.288 47	0.301 28	3.319 1	0.957 49	1.044 4	3.466 5	14
47	0.288 75	0.301 60	3.315 6	0.957 40	1.044 5	3.463 2	13
48	0.289 03	0.301 92	3.312 2	0.957 32	1.044 6	3.459 8	12
49	0.289 31	0.302 24	3.308 7	0.957 24	1.044 7	3.456 5	11
50	**0.289 59**	**0.302 55**	**3.305 2**	**0.957 15**	**1.044 8**	**3.453 2**	10
51	0.289 87	0.302 87	3.301 7	0.957 07	1.044 9	3.449 9	9
52	0.290 15	0.303 19	3.298 3	0.956 98	1.045 0	3.446 5	8
53	0.290 42	0.303 51	3.294 8	0.956 90	1.045 0	3.443 2	7
54	0.290 70	0.303 82	3.291 4	0.956 81	1.045 1	3.439 9	6
55	**0.290 98**	**0.304 14**	**3.287 9**	**0.956 73**	**1.045 2**	**3.436 7**	5
56	0.291 26	0.304 46	3.284 5	0.956 64	1.045 3	3.433 4	4
57	0.291 54	0.304 78	3.281 1	0.956 56	1.045 4	3.430 1	3
58	0.291 82	0.305 09	3.277 7	0.956 47	1.045 5	3.426 8	2
59	0.292 09	0.305 41	3.274 3	0.956 39	1.045 6	3.423 6	1
60	**0.292 37**	**0.305 73**	**3.270 9**	**0.956 30**	**1.045 7**	**3.420 3**	0
′	Cos	Cot	Tan	Sin	Csc	Sec	′

′	Sin	Tan	Cot	Cos	Sec	Csc	′
0	0.292 37	0.305 73	3.270 9	0.956 30	1.045 7	3.420 3	60
1	0.292 65	0.306 05	3.267 5	0.956 22	1.045 8	3.417 1	59
2	0.292 93	0.306 37	3.264 1	0.956 13	1.045 9	3.413 8	58
3	0.293 21	0.306 69	3.260 7	0.956 05	1.046 0	3.410 6	57
4	0.293 48	0.307 00	3.257 3	0.955 96	1.046 1	3.407 3	56
5	0.293 76	0.307 32	3.253 9	0.955 88	1.046 2	3.404 1	55
6	0.294 04	0.307 64	3.250 6	0.955 79	1.046 3	3.400 9	54
7	0.294 32	0.307 96	3.247 2	0.955 71	1.046 3	3.397 7	53
8	0.294 60	0.308 28	3.243 8	0.955 62	1.046 4	3.394 5	52
9	0.294 87	0.308 60	3.240 5	0.955 54	1.046 5	3.391 3	51
10	0.295 15	0.308 91	3.237 1	0.955 45	1.046 6	3.388 1	50
11	0.295 43	0.309 23	3.233 8	0.955 36	1.046 7	3.384 9	49
12	0.295 71	0.309 55	3.230 5	0.955 28	1.046 8	3.381 7	48
13	0.295 99	0.309 87	3.227 2	0.955 19	1.046 9	3.378 5	47
14	0.296 26	0.310 19	3.223 8	0.955 11	1.047 0	3.375 4	46
15	0.296 54	0.310 51	3.220 5	0.955 02	1.047 1	3.372 2	45
16	0.296 82	0.310 83	3.217 2	0.954 93	1.047 2	3.369 1	44
17	0.297 10	0.311 15	3.213 9	0.954 85	1.047 3	3.365 9	43
18	0.297 37	0.311 47	3.210 6	0.954 76	1.047 4	3.362 8	42
19	0.297 65	0.311 78	3.207 3	0.954 67	1.047 5	3.359 6	41
20	0.297 93	0.312 10	3.204 1	0.954 59	1.047 6	3.356 5	40
21	0.298 21	0.312 42	3.200 8	0.954 50	1.047 7	3.353 4	39
22	0.298 49	0.312 74	3.197 5	0.954 41	1.047 8	3.350 2	38
23	0.298 76	0.313 06	3.194 3	0.954 33	1.047 9	3.347 1	37
24	0.299 04	0.313 38	3.191 0	0.954 24	1.048 0	3.344 0	36
25	0.299 32	0.313 70	3.187 8	0.954 15	1.048 0	3.340 9	35
26	0.299 60	0.314 02	3.184 5	0.954 07	1.048 1	3.337 8	34
27	0.299 87	0.314 34	3.181 3	0.953 98	1.048 2	3.334 7	33
28	0.300 15	0.314 66	3.178 0	0.953 89	1.048 3	3.331 7	32
29	0.300 43	0.314 98	3.174 8	0.953 80	1.048 4	3.328 6	31
30	0.300 71	0.315 30	3.171 6	0.953 72	1.048 5	3.325 5	30
31	0.300 98	0.315 62	3.168 4	0.953 63	1.048 6	3.322 4	29
32	0.301 26	0.315 94	3.165 2	0.953 54	1.048 7	3.319 4	28
33	0.301 54	0.316 26	3.162 0	0.953 45	1.048 8	3.316 3	27
34	0.301 82	0.316 58	3.158 8	0.953 37	1.048 9	3.313 3	26
35	0.302 09	0.316 90	3.155 6	0.953 28	1.049 0	3.310 2	25
36	0.302 37	0.317 22	3.152 4	0.953 19	1.049 1	3.307 2	24
37	0.302 65	0.317 54	3.149 2	0.953 10	1.049 2	3.304 2	23
38	0.302 92	0.317 86	3.146 0	0.953 01	1.049 3	3.301 2	22
39	0.303 20	0.318 18	3.142 9	0.952 93	1.049 4	3.298 1	21
40	0.303 48	0.318 50	3.139 7	0.952 84	1.049 5	3.295 1	20
41	0.303 76	0.318 82	3.136 6	0.952 75	1.049 6	3.292 1	19
42	0.304 03	0.319 14	3.133 4	0.952 66	1.049 7	3.289 1	18
43	0.304 31	0.319 46	3.130 3	0.952 57	1.049 8	3.286 1	17
44	0.304 59	0.319 78	3.127 1	0.952 48	1.049 9	3.283 1	16
45	0.304 86	0.320 10	3.124 0	0.952 40	1.050 0	3.280 1	15
46	0.305 14	0.320 42	3.120 9	0.952 31	1.050 1	3.277 2	14
47	0.305 42	0.320 74	3.117 8	0.952 22	1.050 2	3.274 2	13
48	0.305 70	0.321 06	3.114 6	0.952 13	1.050 3	3.271 2	12
49	0.305 97	0.321 39	3.111 5	0.952 04	1.050 4	3.268 3	11
50	0.306 25	0.321 71	3.108 4	0.951 95	1.050 5	3.265 3	10
51	0.306 53	0.322 03	3.105 3	0.951 86	1.050 6	3.262 4	9
52	0.306 80	0.322 35	3.102 2	0.951 77	1.050 7	3.259 4	8
53	0.307 08	0.322 67	3.099 1	0.951 68	1.050 8	3.256 5	7
54	0.307 36	0.322 99	3.096 1	0.951 59	1.050 9	3.253 5	6
55	0.307 63	0.323 31	3.093 0	0.951 50	1.051 0	3.250 6	5
56	0.307 91	0.323 63	3.089 9	0.951 42	1.051 1	3.247 7	4
57	0.308 19	0.323 96	3.086 8	0.951 33	1.051 2	3.244 8	3
58	0.308 46	0.324 28	3.083 8	0.951 24	1.051 3	3.241 9	2
59	0.308 74	0.324 60	3.080 7	0.951 15	1.051 4	3.239 0	1
60	0.309 02	0.324 92	3.077 7	0.951 06	1.051 5	3.236 1	0
′	Cos	Cot	Tan	Sin	Csc	Sec	′

′	Sin	Tan	Cot	Cos	Sec	Csc	′
0	**0.309 02**	**0.324 92**	**3.077 7**	**0.951 06**	**1.051 5**	**3.236 1**	60
1	0.309 29	0.325 24	3.074 6	0.950 97	1.051 6	3.233 2	59
2	0.309 57	0.325 56	3.071 6	0.950 88	1.051 7	3.230 3	58
3	0.309 85	0.325 88	3.068 6	0.950 79	1.051 8	3.227 4	57
4	0.310 12	0.326 21	3.065 5	0.950 70	1.051 9	3.224 5	56
5	**0.310 40**	**0.326 53**	**3.062 5**	**0.950 61**	**1.052 0**	**3.221 7**	55
6	0.310 68	0.326 85	3.059 5	0.950 52	1.052 1	3.218 8	54
7	0.310 95	0.327 17	3.056 5	0.950 43	1.052 2	3.215 9	53
8	0.311 23	0.327 49	3.053 5	0.950 33	1.052 3	3.213 1	52
9	0.311 51	0.327 82	3.050 5	0.950 24	1.052 4	3.210 2	51
10	**0.311 78**	**0.328 14**	**3.047 5**	**0.950 15**	**1.052 5**	**3.207 4**	50
11	0.312 06	0.328 46	3.044 5	0.950 06	1.052 6	3.204 5	49
12	0.312 33	0.328 78	3.041 5	0.949 97	1.052 7	3.201 7	48
13	0.312 61	0.329 11	3.038 5	0.949 88	1.052 8	3.198 9	47
14	0.312 89	0.329 43	3.035 6	0.949 79	1.052 9	3.196 0	46
15	**0.313 16**	**0.329 75**	**3.032 6**	**0.949 70**	**1.053 0**	**3.193 2**	45
16	0.313 44	0.330 07	3.029 6	0.949 61	1.053 1	3.190 4	44
17	0.313 72	0.330 40	3.026 7	0.949 52	1.053 2	3.187 6	43
18	0.313 99	0.330 72	3.023 7	0.949 43	1.053 3	3.184 8	42
19	0.314 27	0.331 04	3.020 8	0.949 33	1.053 4	3.182 0	41
20	**0.314 54**	**0.331 36**	**3.017 8**	**0.949 24**	**1.053 5**	**3.179 2**	40
21	0.314 82	0.331 69	3.014 9	0.949 15	1.053 6	3.176 4	39
22	0.315 10	0.332 01	3.012 0	0.949 06	1.053 7	3.173 6	38
23	0.315 37	0.332 33	3.009 0	0.948 97	1.053 8	3.170 8	37
24	0.315 65	0.332 66	3.006 1	0.948 88	1.053 9	3.168 1	36
25	**0.315 93**	**0.332 98**	**3.003 2**	**0.948 58**	**1.054 0**	**3.165 3**	35
26	0.316 20	0.333 30	3.000 3	0.948 69	1.054 1	3.162 5	34
27	0.316 48	0.333 63	2.997 4	0.948 60	1.054 2	3.159 8	33
28	0.316 75	0.333 95	2.994 5	0.948 51	1.054 3	3.157 0	32
29	0.317 03	0.334 27	2.991 6	0.948 42	1.054 4	3.154 3	31
30	**0.317 30**	**0.334 60**	**2.988 7**	**0.948 32**	**1.054 5**	**3.151 5**	30
31	0.317 58	0.334 92	2.985 8	0.948 23	1.054 6	3.148 8	29
32	0.317 86	0.335 24	2.982 9	0.948 14	1.054 7	3.146 1	28
33	0.318 13	0.335 57	2.980 0	0.948 05	1.054 8	3.143 3	27
34	0.318 41	0.335 89	2.977 2	0.947 95	1.054 9	3.140 6	26
35	**0.318 68**	**0.336 21**	**2.974 3**	**0.947 86**	**1.055 0**	**3.137 9**	25
36	0.318 96	0.336 54	2.971 4	0.947 77	1.055 1	3.135 2	24
37	0.319 23	0.336 86	2.968 6	0.947 68	1.055 2	3.132 5	23
38	0.319 51	0.337 18	2.965 7	0.947 58	1.055 3	3.129 8	22
39	0.319 79	0.337 51	2.962 9	0.947 49	1.055 4	3.127 1	21
40	**0.320 06**	**0.337 83**	**2.960 0**	**0.947 40**	**1.055 5**	**3.124 4**	20
41	0.320 34	0.338 16	2.957 2	0.947 30	1.055 6	3.121 7	19
42	0.320 61	0.338 48	2.954 4	0.947 21	1.055 7	3.119 0	18
43	0.320 89	0.338 81	2.951 5	0.947 12	1.055 8	3.116 3	17
44	0.321 16	0.339 13	2.948 7	0.947 02	1.055 9	3.113 7	16
45	**0.321 44**	**0.339 45**	**2.945 9**	**0.946 93**	**1.056 0**	**3.111 0**	15
46	0.321 71	0.339 78	2.943 1	0.946 84	1.056 1	3.108 3	14
47	0.321 99	0.340 10	2.940 3	0.946 74	1.056 3	3.105 7	13
48	0.322 27	0.340 43	2.937 5	0.946 65	1.056 4	3.103 0	12
49	0.322 54	0.340 75	2.934 7	0.946 56	1.056 5	3.100 4	11
50	**0.322 82**	**0.341 08**	**2.931 9**	**0.946 46**	**1.056 6**	**3.097 7**	10
51	0.323 09	0.341 40	2.929 1	0.946 37	1.056 7	3.095 1	9
52	0.323 37	0.341 73	2.926 3	0.946 27	1.056 8	3.092 5	8
53	0.323 64	0.342 05	2.923 5	0.946 18	1.056 9	3.089 8	7
54	0.323 92	0.342 38	2.920 8	0.946 09	1.057 0	3.087 2	6
55	**0.324 19**	**0.342 70**	**2.918 0**	**0.945 99**	**1.057 1**	**3.084 6**	5
56	0.324 47	0.343 03	2.915 2	0.945 90	1.057 2	3.082 0	4
57	0.324 74	0.343 35	2.912 5	0.945 80	1.057 3	3.079 4	3
58	0.325 02	0.343 68	2.909 7	0.945 71	1.057 4	3.076 8	2
59	0.325 29	0.344 00	2.907 0	0.945 61	1.057 5	3.074 2	1
60	**0.325 57**	**0.344 33**	**2.904 2**	**0.945 52**	**1.057 6**	**3.071 6**	0
′	Cos	Cot	Tan	Sin	Csc	Sec	′

Table 3 / Five-place natural trigonometric functions   □   **641**

′	Sin	Tan	Cot	Cos	Sec	Csc	′
0	**0.325 57**	**0.344 33**	**2.904 2**	**0.945 52**	**1.057 6**	**3.071 6**	60
1	0.325 84	0.344 65	2.901 5	0.945 42	1.057 7	3.069 0	59
2	0.326 12	0.344 98	2.898 7	0.945 33	1.057 8	3.066 4	58
3	0.326 39	0.345 30	2.896 0	0.945 23	1.057 9	3.063 8	57
4	0.326 67	0.345 63	2.893 3	0.945 14	1.058 0	3.061 2	56
5	**0.326 94**	**0.345 96**	**2.890 5**	**0.945 05**	**1.058 2**	**3.058 6**	55
6	0.327 22	0.346 28	2.887 8	0.944 95	1.058 3	3.056 1	54
7	0.327 49	0.346 61	2.885 1	0.944 85	1.058 4	3.053 5	53
8	0.327 77	0.346 93	2.882 4	0.944 76	1.058 5	3.050 9	52
9	0.328 04	0.347 26	2.879 7	0.944 66	1.058 6	3.048 4	51
10	**0.328 32**	**0.347 58**	**2.877 0**	**0.944 57**	**1.058 7**	**3.045 8**	50
11	0.328 59	0.347 91	2.874 3	0.944 47	1.058 8	3.043 3	49
12	0.328 87	0.348 24	2.871 6	0.944 38	1.058 9	3.040 7	48
13	0.329 14	0.348 56	2.868 9	0.944 28	1.059 0	3,038 2	47
14	0.329 42	0.348 89	2.866 2	0.944 18	1.059 1	3.035 7	46
15	**0.329 69**	**0.349 22**	**2.863 6**	**0.944 09**	**1.059 2**	**3.033 1**	45
16	0.329 97	0.349 54	2.860 9	0.943 99	1.059 3	3.030 6	44
17	0.330 24	0.349 87	2.858 2	0.943 90	1.059 4	3.028 1	43
18	0.330 51	0.350 20	2.855 6	0.943 80	1.059 5	3.025 6	42
19	0.330 79	0.350 52	2.852 9	0.943 70	1.059 7	3.023 1	41
20	**0.331 06**	**0.350 85**	**2.850 2**	**0.943 61**	**1.059 8**	**3.020 6**	40
21	0.331 34	0.351 18	2.847 6	0.943 51	1.059 9	3.018 1	39
22	0.331 61	0.351 50	2.844 9	0.943 42	1.060 0	3.015 6	38
23	0.331 89	0.351 83	2.842 3	0.943 32	1.060 1	3.013 1	37
24	0.332 16	0.352 16	2.839 7	0.943 22	1.060 2	3.010 6	36
25	**0.332 44**	**0.352 48**	**2.837 0**	**0.943 13**	**1.060 3**	**3.008 1**	35
26	0.332 71	0.352 81	2.834 4	0.943 03	1.060 4	3.005 6	34
27	0.332 98	0.353 14	2.831 8	0.942 93	1.060 5	3.003 1	33
28	0.333 26	0.353 46	2.829 1	0.942 84	1.060 6	3.000 7	32
29	0.333 53	0.353 79	2.826 5	0.942 74	1.060 7	2.998 2	31
30	**0.333 81**	**0.354 12**	**2.823 9**	**0.942 64**	**1.060 8**	**2.995 7**	30
31	0.334 08	0.354 45	2.821 3	0.942 54	1.061 0	2.993 3	29
32	0.334 36	0.354 77	2.818 7	0.942 45	1.061 1	2.990 8	28
33	0.334 63	0.355 10	2.816 1	0.942 35	1.061 2	2.988 4	27
34	0.334 90	0.355 43	2.813 5	0.942 25	1.061 3	2.985 9	26
35	**0.335 18**	**0.355 76**	**2.810 9**	**0.942 15**	**1.061 4**	**2.983 5**	25
36	0.335 45	0.356 08	2.808 3	0.942 06	1.061 5	2.981 1	24
37	0.335 73	0.356 41	2.805 7	0.941 96	1.061 6	2.978 6	23
38	0.336 00	0.356 74	2.803 2	0.941 86	1.061 7	2.976 2	22
39	0.336 27	0.357 07	2.800 6	0.941 76	1.061 8	2.973 8	21
40	**0.336 55**	**0.357 40**	**2.798 0**	**0.941 67**	**1.061 9**	**2.971 3**	20
41	0.336 82	0.357 72	2.795 5	0.941 57	1.062 1	2.968 9	19
42	0.337 10	0.358 05	2.792 9	0.941 47	1.062 2	2.966 5	18
43	0.337 37	0.358 38	2.790 3	0.941 37	1.062 3	2.964 1	17
44	0.337 64	0.358 71	2.787 8	0.941 27	1.062 4	2.961 7	16
45	**0.337 92**	**0.359 04**	**2.785 2**	**0.941 18**	**1.062 5**	**2.959 3**	15
46	0.338 19	0.359 37	2.782 7	0.941 08	1.062 6	2.956 9	14
47	0.338 46	0.359 69	2.780 1	0.940 98	1.062 7	2.954 5	13
48	0.338 74	0.360 02	2.777 6	0.940 88	1.062 8	2.952 1	12
49	0.339 01	0.360 35	2.775 1	0.940 78	1.062 9	2.949 8	11
50	**0.339 29**	**0.360 68**	**2.772 5**	**0.940 68**	**1.063 1**	**2.947 4**	10
51	0.339 56	0.361 01	2.770 0	0.940 58	1.063 2	2.945 0	9
52	0.339 83	0.361 34	2.767 5	0.940 49	1.063 3	2.942 6	8
53	0.340 11	0.361 67	2.765 0	0.940 39	1.063 4	2.940 3	7
54	0.340 38	0.361 99	2.762 5	0.940 29	1.063 5	2.937 9	6
55	**0.340 65**	**0.362 32**	**2.760 0**	**0.940 19**	**1.063 6**	**2.935 5**	5
56	0.340 93	0.362 65	2.757 5	0.940 09	1.063 7	2.933 2	4
57	0.341 20	0.362 98	2.755 0	0.939 99	1.063 8	2.930 8	3
58	0.341 47	0.363 31	2.752 5	0.939 89	1.064 0	2.928 5	2
59	0.341 75	0.363 64	2.750 0	0.939 79	1.064 1	2.926 1	1
60	**0.342 02**	**0.363 97**	**2.747 5**	**0.939 69**	**1.064 2**	**2.923 8**	0
′	Cos	Cot	Tan	Sin	Csc	Sec	′

'	Sin	Tan	Cot	Cos	Sec	Csc	'
0	**0.342 02**	**0.363 97**	**2.747 5**	**0.939 60**	1.064 2	**2.923 8**	60
1	0.342 29	0.364 30	2.745 0	0.939 59	1.064 3	2.921 5	59
2	0.342 57	0.364 63	2.742 5	0.939 49	1.064 4	2.919 1	58
3	0.342 84	0.364 96	2.740 0	0.939 39	1.064 5	2.916 8	57
4	0.343 11	0.365 29	2.737 6	0.939 29	1.064 6	2.914 5	56
5	**0.343 39**	**0.365 62**	**2.735 1**	**0.939 19**	1.064 7	**2.912 2**	55
6	0.343 66	0.365 95	2.732 6	0.939 09	1.064 9	2.909 9	54
7	0.343 93	0.366 28	2.730 2	0.938 99	1.065 0	2.907 5	53
8	0.344 21	0.366 61	2.727 7	0.938 89	1.065 1	2.905 2	52
9	0.344 48	0.366 94	2.725 3	0.938 79	1.065 2	2.902 9	51
10	**0.344 75**	**0.367 27**	**2.722 8**	**0.938 69**	1.065 3	**2.900 3**	50
11	0.345 03	0.367 60	2.720 4	0.938 59	1.065 4	2.898 3	49
12	0.345 30	0.367 93	2.717 9	0.938 49	1.065 5	2.896 0	48
13	0.345 57	0.368 26	2.715 5	0.938 39	1.065 7	2.893 8	47
14	0.345 84	0.368 59	2.713 0	0.938 29	1.065 8	2.891 5	46
15	**0.346 12**	**0.368 92**	**2.710 6**	**0.938 19**	1.065 9	**2.889 2**	45
16	0.346 39	0.369 25	2.708 2	0.938 09	1.066 0	2.886 9	44
17	0.346 66	0.369 58	2.705 8	0.937 99	1.066 1	2.884 6	43
18	0.346 94	0.369 91	2.703 4	0.937 89	1.066 2	2.882 4	42
19	0.347 21	0.370 24	2.700 9	0.937 79	1.066 3	2.880 1	41
20	**0.347 48**	**0.370 57**	**2.698 5**	**0.937 69**	1.066 5	**2.877 9**	40
21	0.347 75	0.370 90	2.696 1	0.937 59	1.066 6	2.875 6	39
22	0.348 03	0.371 23	2.693 7	0.937 48	1.066 7	2.873 3	38
23	0.348 30	0.371 57	2.691 3	0.937 38	1.066 8	2.871 1	37
24	0.348 57	0.371 90	2.688 9	0.937 28	1.066 9	2.868 8	36
25	**0.348 84**	**0.372 23**	**2.686 5**	**0.937 18**	1.067 0	**2.866 6**	35
26	0.349 12	0.372 56	2.684 1	0.937 08	1.067 1	2.864 4	34
27	0.349 39	0.372 89	2.681 8	0.936 98	1.067 3	2.862 1	33
28	0.349 66	0.373 22	2.679 4	0.936 88	1.067 4	2.859 9	32
29	0.349 93	0.373 55	2.677 0	0.936 77	1.067 5	2.857 7	31
30	**0.350 21**	**0.373 88**	**2.674 6**	**0.936 67**	1.067 6	**2.855 5**	30
31	0.350 48	0.374 22	2.672 3	0.936 57	1.067 7	2.853 2	29
32	0.350 75	0.374 55	2.669 9	0.936 47	1.067 8	2.851 0	28
33	0.351 02	0.374 88	2.667 5	0.936 37	1.068 0	2.848 8	27
34	0.351 30	0.375 21	2.665 2	0.936 26	1.068 1	2.846 6	26
35	**0.351 57**	**0.375 54**	**2.662 8**	**0.936 16**	1.068 2	**2.844 4**	25
36	0.351 84	0.375 88	2.660 5	0.936 06	1.068 3	2.842 2	24
37	0.352 11	0.376 21	2.658 1	0.935 96	1.068 4	2.840 0	23
38	0.352 39	0.376 54	2.655 8	0.935 85	1.068 5	2.837 8	22
39	0.352 66	0.376 87	2.653 4	0.935 75	1.068 7	2.835 6	21
40	**0 352 93**	**0.377 20**	**2.651 1**	**0.935 65**	1.068 8	**2.833 4**	20
41	0.353 20	0.377 54	2.648 8	0.935 55	1.068 9	2.831 2	19
42	0.353 47	0.377 87	2.646 4	0.935 44	1.069 0	2.829 1	18
43	0.353 75	0.378 20	2.644 1	0.935 34	1.069 1	2.826 9	17
44	0.354 02	0.378 53	2.641 8	0.935 24	1.069 2	2.824 7	16
45	**0.354 29**	**0.378 87**	**2.639 5**	**0.935 14**	1.069 4	**2.822 5**	15
46	0.354 56	0.379 20	2.637 1	0.935 03	1.069 5	2.820 4	14
47	0.354 84	0.379 53	2.634 8	0.934 93	1.069 6	2.818 2	13
48	0.355 11	0.379 86	2.632 5	0.934 83	1.069 7	2.816 1	12
49	0.355 38	0.380 20	2.630 2	0.934 72	1.069 8	2.813 9	11
50	**0.355 65**	**0.380 53**	**2.627 9**	**0.934 62**	1.070 0	**2.811 7**	10
51	0.355 92	0.380 86	2.625 6	0.934 52	1.070 1	2.809 6	9
52	0.356 19	0.381 20	2.623 3	0.934 41	1.070 2	2.807 5	8
53	0.356 47	0.381 53	2.621 0	0.934 31	1.070 3	2.805 3	7
54	0.356 74	0.381 86	2.618 7	0.934 20	1.070 4	2.803 2	6
55	**0.357 01**	**0.382 20**	**2.616 5**	**0.934 10**	1.070 5	**2.801 0**	5
56	0.357 28	0.382 53	2.614 2	0.934 00	1.070 7	2.798 9	4
57	0.357 55	0.382 86	2.611 9	0.933 89	1.070 8	2.796 8	3
58	0.357 82	0.383 20	2.609 6	0.933 79	1.070 9	2.794 7	2
59	0.358 10	0.383 53	2.607 4	0.933 68	1.071 0	2.792 5	1
60	**0.358 37**	**0.383 86**	**2.605 1**	**0.933 58**	1.071 1	**2.790 4**	0
'	Cos	Cot	Tan	Sin	Csc	Sec	'

Table 3 / Five-place natural trigonometric functions □ **643**

′	Sin	Tan	Cot	Cos	Sec	Csc	′
0	0.358 37	0.383 86	2.605 1	0.933 58	1.071 1	2.790 4	60
1	0.358 64	0.384 20	2.602 8	0.933 48	1.071 3	2.788 3	59
2	0.358 91	0.384 53	2.600 6	0.933 37	1.071 4	2.786 2	58
3	0.359 18	0.384 87	2.598 3	0.933 27	1.071 5	2.784 1	57
4	0.359 45	0.385 20	2.596 1	0.933 16	1.071 6	2.782 0	56
5	0.359 73	0.385 53	2.593 8	0.933 06	1.071 7	2.779 9	55
6	0.360 00	0.385 87	2.591 6	0.932 95	1.071 9	2.777 8	54
7	0.360 27	0.386 20	2.589 3	0.932 85	1.072 0	2.775 7	53
8	0.360 54	0.386 54	2.587 1	0.932 74	1.072 1	2.773 6	52
9	0.360 81	0.386 87	2.584 8	0.932 64	1.072 2	2.771 5	51
10	0.361 08	0.387 21	2.582 6	0.932 53	1.072 3	2.769 5	50
11	0.361 35	0.387 54	2.580 4	0.932 43	1.072 5	2.767 4	49
12	0.361 62	0.387 87	2.578 2	0.932 32	1.072 6	2.765 3	48
13	0.361 90	0.388 21	2.575 9	0.932 22	1.072 7	2.763 2	47
14	0.362 17	0.388 54	2.573 7	0.932 11	1.072 8	2.761 2	46
15	0.362 44	0.388 88	2.571 5	0.932 01	1.073 0	2.759 1	45
16	0.362 71	0.389 21	2.569 3	0.931 90	1.073 1	2.757 0	44
17	0.362 98	0.389 55	2.567 1	0.931 80	1.073 2	2.755 0	43
18	0.363 25	0.389 88	2.564 9	0.931 69	1.073 3	2.752 9	42
19	0.363 52	0.390 22	2.562 7	0.931 59	1.073 4	2.750 9	41
20	0.363 79	0.390 55	2.560 5	0.931 48	1.073 6	2.748 8	40
21	0.364 06	0.390 89	2.558 3	0.931 37	1.073 7	2.746 8	39
22	0.364 34	0.391 22	2.556 1	0.931 27	1.073 8	2.744 7	38
23	0.364 61	0.391 56	2.553 9	0.931 16	1.073 9	2.742 7	37
24	0.364 88	0.391 90	2.551 7	0.931 06	1.074 0	2.740 7	36
25	0.365 15	0.392 23	2.549 5	0.930 95	1.074 2	2.738 6	35
26	0.365 42	0.392 57	2.547 3	0.930 84	1.074 3	2.736 6	34
27	0.365 69	0.392 90	2.545 2	0.930 74	1.074 4	2.734 6	33
28	0.365 96	0.393 24	2.543 0	0.930 63	1.074 5	2.732 5	32
29	0.366 23	0.393 57	2.540 8	0.930 52	1.074 7	2.730 5	31
30	0.366 50	0.393 91	2.538 6	0.930 42	1.074 8	2.728 5	30
31	0.366 77	0.394 25	2.536 5	0.930 31	1.074 9	2.726 5	29
32	0.367 04	0.394 58	2.534 3	0.930 20	1.075 0	2.724 5	28
33	0.367 31	0.394 92	2.532 2	0.930 10	1.075 2	2.722 5	27
34	0.367 58	0.395 26	2.530 0	0.929 99	1.075 3	2.720 5	26
35	0.367 85	0.395 59	2.527 9	0.929 88	1.075 4	2.718 5	25
36	0.368 12	0.395 93	2.525 7	0.929 78	1.075 5	2.716 5	24
37	0.368 39	0.396 26	2.523 6	0.929 67	1.075 7	2.714 5	23
38	0.368 67	0.396 60	2.521 4	0.929 56	1.075 8	2.712 5	22
39	0.368 94	0.396 94	2.519 3	0.929 45	1.075 9	2.710 5	21
40	0.369 21	0.397 27	2.517 2	0.929 35	1.076 0	2.708 5	20
41	0.369 48	0.397 61	2.515 0	0.929 24	1.076 1	2.706 5	19
42	0.369 75	0.397 95	2.512 9	0.929 13	1.076 3	2.704 6	18
43	0.370 02	0.398 29	2.510 8	0.929 02	1.076 4	2.702 6	17
44	0.370 29	0.398 62	2.508 6	0.928 92	1.076 5	2.700 6	16
45	0.370 56	0.398 96	2.506 5	0.928 81	1.076 6	2.698 6	15
46	0.370 83	0.399 30	2.504 4	0.928 70	1.076 8	2.696 7	14
47	0.371 10	0.399 63	2.502 3	0.928 59	1.076 9	2.694 7	13
48	0.371 37	0.399 97	2.500 2	0.928 49	1.077 0	2.692 7	12
49	0.371 64	0.400 31	2.498 1	0.928 38	1.077 1	2.690 8	11
50	0.371 91	0.400 65	2.496 0	0.928 27	1.077 3	2.688 8	10
51	0.372 18	0.400 98	2.493 9	0.928 16	1.077 4	2.686 9	9
52	0.372 45	0.401 32	2.491 8	0.928 05	1.077 5	2.684 9	8
53	0.372 72	0.401 66	2.489 7	0.927 94	1.077 7	2.683 0	7
54	0.372 99	0.402 00	2.487 6	0.927 84	1.077 8	2.681 1	6
55	0.373 26	0.402 34	2.485 5	0.927 73	1.077 9	2.679 1	5
56	0.373 53	0.402 67	2.483 4	0.927 62	1.078 0	2.677 2	4
57	0.373 80	0.403 01	2.481 3	0.927 51	1.078 2	2.675 2	3
58	0.374 07	0.403 35	2.479 2	0.927 40	1.078 3	2.673 3	2
59	0.374 34	0.403 69	2.477 2	0.927 29	1.078 4	2.671 4	1
60	0.374 61	0.404 03	2.475 1	0.927 18	1.078 5	2.669 5	0
′	Cos	Cot	Tan	Sin	Csc	Sec	′

′	Sin	Tan	Cot	Cos	Sec	Csc	
0	**0.374 61**	**0.404 03**	**2.465 1**	**0.927 18**	**1.078 5**	**2.669 5**	**60**
1	0.374 88	0.404 36	2.473 0	0.927 07	1.078 7	2.667 5	59
2	0.375 15	0.404 70	2.470 9	0.926 97	1.078 8	2.665 6	58
3	0.375 42	0.405 04	2.468 9	0.926 82	1.078 9	2.663 7	57
4	0.375 69	0.405 38	2.466 8	0.926 75	1.079 0	2.661 8	56
5	**0.375 95**	**0.405 72**	**2.464 8**	**0.926 64**	**1.079 2**	**2.659 9**	**55**
6	0.376 22	0.406 06	2.462 7	0.926 53	1.079 3	2.658 0	54
7	0.376 49	0.406 40	2.460 6	0.926 42	1.079 4	2.656 1	53
8	0.376 76	0.406 74	2.458 6	0.926 31	1.079 6	2.654 2	52
9	0.377 03	0.407 07	2.456 6	0.926 20	1.079 7	2.652 3	51
10	**0.377 30**	**0.407 41**	**2.454 5**	**0.926 09**	**1.079 8**	**2.650 4**	**50**
11	0.377 57	0.407 75	2.452 5	0.925 98	1.079 9	2.648 5	49
12	0.377 84	0.408 09	2.450 4	0.925 87	1.080 1	2.646 6	48
13	0.378 11	0.408 43	2.448 4	0.925 76	1.080 2	2.644 7	47
14	0.378 38	0.408 77	2.446 4	0.925 65	1.080 3	2.642 9	46
15	**0.378 65**	**0.409 11**	**2.444 3**	**0.925 54**	**1.080 4**	**2.641 0**	**45**
16	0.378 92	0.409 45	2.442 3	0.925 43	1.080 6	2.639 1	44
17	0.379 19	0.409 79	2.440 3	0.925 32	1.080 7	2.637 2	43
18	0.379 46	0.410 13	2.438 3	0.925 21	1.080 8	2.635 4	42
19	0.379 73	0.410 47	2.436 2	0.925 10	1.081 0	2.633 5	41
20	**0.379 99**	**0.410 81**	**2.434 2**	**0.924 99**	**1.081 1**	**2.631 6**	**40**
21	0.380 26	0.411 15	2.432 2	0.924 88	1.081 2	2.629 8	39
22	0.380 53	0.411 49	2.430 2	0.924 77	1.081 4	2.627 9	38
23	0.380 80	0.411 83	2.428 2	0.924 66	1.081 5	2.626 0	37
24	0.381 07	0.412 17	2.426 2	0.924 55	1.081 6	2.624 2	36
25	**0.381 34**	**0.412 51**	**2.424 2**	**0.924 44**	**1.081 7**	**2.622 3**	**35**
26	0.381 61	0.412 85	2.422 2	0.924 32	1.081 9	2.620 5	34
27	0.381 88	0.413 19	2.420 2	0.924 21	1.082 0	2.618 6	33
28	0.382 15	0.413 53	2.418 2	0.924 10	1.082 1	2.616 8	32
29	0.382 41	0.413 87	2.416 2	0.923 99	1.082 3	2.615 0	31
30	**0.382 68**	**0.414 21**	**2.414 2**	**0.923 88**	**1.082 4**	**2.613 1**	**30**
31	0.382 95	0.414 55	2.412 2	0.923 77	1.082 5	2.611 3	29
32	0.383 22	0.414 90	2.410 2	0.923 66	1.082 7	2.609 5	28
33	0.383 49	0.415 24	2.408 3	0.923 55	1.082 8	2.607 6	27
34	0.383 76	0.415 58	2.406 3	0.923 43	1.082 9	2.605 8	26
35	**0.384 03**	**0.415 92**	**2.404 3**	**0.923 32**	**1.083 0**	**2.604 0**	**25**
36	0.384 30	0.416 26	2.402 3	0.923 21	1.083 2	2.602 2	24
37	0.384 56	0.416 60	2.400 4	0.923 10	1.083 3	2.600 3	23
38	0.384 83	0.416 94	2.398 4	0.922 99	1.083 4	2.598 5	22
39	0.385 10	0.417 28	2.396 4	0.922 87	1.083 6	2.596 7	21
40	**0.385 37**	**0.417 63**	**2.394 5**	**0.922 76**	**1.083 7**	**2.594 9**	**20**
41	0.385 64	0.417 97	2.392 5	0.922 65	1.083 8	2.593 1	19
42	0.385 91	0.418 31	2.390 6	0.922 54	1.084 0	2.591 3	18
43	0.386 17	0.418 65	2.388 6	0.922 43	1.084 1	2.589 5	17
44	0.386 44	0.418 99	2.386 7	0.922 31	1.084 2	2.587 7	16
45	**0.386 71**	**0.419 33**	**2.384 7**	**0.922 20**	**1.084 4**	**2.585 9**	**15**
46	0.386 98	0.419 68	2.382 8	0.922 09	1.084 5	2.584 1	14
47	0.387 25	0.420 02	2.380 8	0.921 98	1.084 6	2.582 3	13
48	0.387 52	0.420 36	2.378 9	0.921 86	1.084 8	2.580 5	12
49	0.387 78	0.420 70	2.377 0	0.921 75	1.084 9	2.578 8	11
50	**0.388 05**	**0.421 05**	**2.375 0**	**0.921 64**	**1.085 0**	**2.577 0**	**10**
51	0.388 32	0.421 39	2.373 1	0.921 52	1.085 2	2.575 2	9
52	0.388 59	0.421 73	2.371 2	0.921 41	1.085 3	2.573 4	8
53	0.388 86	0.422 07	2.369 3	0.921 30	1.085 4	2.571 6	7
54	0.389 12	0.422 42	2.367 3	0.921 19	1.085 6	2.569 9	6
55	**0.389 39**	**0.422 76**	**2.365 4**	**0.921 07**	**1.085 7**	**2.568 1**	**5**
56	0.389 66	0.423 10	2.363 5	0.920 96	1.085 8	2.566 3	4
57	0.389 93	0.423 45	2.361 6	0.920 85	1.086 0	2.564 6	3
58	0.390 20	0.423 79	2.359 7	0.920 73	1.086 1	2.562 8	2
59	0.390 46	0.424 13	2.357 8	0.920 62	1.086 2	2.561 1	1
60	**0.390 73**	**0.424 47**	**2.355 9**	**0.920 50**	**1.086 4**	**2.559 3**	**0**
′	Cos	Cot	Tan	Sin	Csc	Sec	′

Table 3 / Five-place natural trigonometric functions □ **645**

′	Sin	Tan	Cot	Cos	Sec	Csc	′
0	**0.390 73**	**0.424 47**	**2.355 9**	**0.920 50**	**1.086 4**	**2.559 3**	60
1	0.391 00	0.424 82	2.353 9	0.920 39	1.086 5	2.557 6	59
2	0.391 27	0.425 16	2.352 0	0.920 28	1.086 6	2.555 8	58
3	0.391 53	0.425 51	2.350 1	0.920 16	1.086 8	2.554 1	57
4	0.391 80	0.425 85	2.348 3	0.920 05	1.086 9	2.552 3	56
5	**0.392 07**	**0.426 19**	**2.346 4**	**0.919 94**	**1.087 0**	**2.550 6**	55
6	0.392 34	0.426 54	2.344 5	0.919 82	1.087 2	2.548 8	54
7	0.392 60	0.426 88	2.342 6	0.919 71	1.087 3	2.547 1	53
8	0.392 87	0.427 22	2.340 7	0.919 59	1.087 4	2.545 4	52
9	0.393 14	0.427 57	2.338 8	0.919 48	1.087 6	2.543 6	51
10	**0.393 41**	**0.427 91**	**2.336 9**	**0.919 36**	**1.087 7**	**2.541 9**	50
11	0.393 67	0.428 26	2.335 1	0.919 25	1.087 8	2.540 2	49
12	0.393 94	0.428 60	2.333 2	0.919 14	1.088 0	2.538 4	48
13	0.394 21	0.428 94	2.331 3	0.919 02	1.088 1	2.536 7	47
14	0.394 48	0.429 29	2.329 4	0.918 91	1.088 3	2.535 0	46
15	**0.394 74**	**0.429 63**	**2.327 6**	**0.918 79**	**1.088 4**	**2.533 3**	45
16	0.395 01	0.429 98	2.325 7	0.918 68	1.088 5	2.531 6	44
17	0.395 28	0.430 32	2.323 8	0.918 56	1.088 7	2.529 9	43
18	0.395 55	0.430 67	2.322 0	0.918 45	1.088 8	2.528 2	42
19	0.395 81	0.431 01	2.320 1	0.918 33	1.088 9	2.526 4	41
20	**0.396 08**	**0.431 36**	**2.318 3**	**0.918 22**	**1.089 1**	**2.524 7**	40
21	0.396 35	0.431 70	2.316 4	0.918 10	1.089 2	2.523 0	39
22	0.396 61	0.432 05	2.314 6	0.917 99	1.089 3	2.521 3	38
23	0.396 88	0.432 39	2.312 7	0.917 87	1.089 5	2.519 6	37
24	0.397 15	0.432 74	2.310 9	0.917 75	1.089 6	2.518 0	36
25	**0.397 41**	**0.433 08**	**2.309 0**	**0.917 64**	**1.089 8**	**2.516 3**	35
26	0.397 68	0.433 43	2.307 2	0.917 52	1.089 9	2.514 6	34
27	0.397 95	0.433 78	2.305 3	0.917 41	1.090 0	2.512 9	33
28	0.398 22	0.434 12	2.303 5	0.917 29	1.090 2	2.511 2	32
29	0.398 48	0.434 47	2.301 7	0.917 18	1.090 3	2.509 5	31
30	**0.398 75**	**0.434 81**	**2.299 8**	**0.917 06**	**1.090 4**	**2.507 8**	30
31	0.399 02	0.435 16	2.298 0	0.916 94	1.090 6	2.506 2	29
32	0.399 28	0.435 50	2.296 2	0.916 83	1.090 7	2.504 5	28
33	0.399 55	0.435 85	2.294 4	0.916 71	1.090 9	2.502 8	27
34	0.399 82	0.436 20	2.292 5	0.916 60	1.091 0	2.501 2	26
35	**0.400 08**	**0.436 54**	**2.290 7**	**0.916 48**	**1.091 1**	**2.499 5**	25
36	0.400 35	0.436 89	2.288 9	0.916 36	1.091 3	2.497 8	24
37	0.400 62	0.437 24	2.287 1	0.916 25	1.091 4	2.496 2	23
38	0.400 88	0.437 58	2.285 3	0.916 13	1.091 5	2.494 5	22
39	0.401 15	0.437 93	2.283 5	0.916 01	1.091 7	2.492 8	21
40	**0.401 41**	**0.438 28**	**2.281 7**	**0.915 90**	**1.091 8**	**2.491 2**	20
41	0.401 68	0.438 62	2.279 9	0.915 78	1.092 0	2.489 5	19
42	0.401 95	0.438 97	2.278 1	0.915 66	1.092 1	2.487 9	18
43	0.402 21	0.439 32	2.276 3	0.915 55	1.092 2	2.486 2	17
44	0.402 48	0.439 66	2.274 5	0.915 43	1.092 4	2.484 6	16
45	**0.402 75**	**0.440 01**	**2.272 7**	**0.915 31**	**1.092 5**	**2.483 0**	15
46	0.403 01	0.440 36	2.270 9	0.915 19	1.092 7	2.481 3	14
47	0.403 28	0.440 71	2.269 1	0.915 08	1.092 8	2.479 7	13
48	0.403 55	0.441 05	2.267 3	0.914 96	1.092 9	2.478 0	12
49	0.403 81	0.441 40	2.265 5	0.914 84	1.093 1	2.476 4	11
50	**0.404 08**	**0.441 75**	**2.263 7**	**0.914 72**	**1.093 2**	**2.474 8**	10
51	0.404 34	0.442 10	2.262 0	0.914 61	1.093 4	2.473 1	9
52	0.404 61	0.442 44	2.260 2	0.914 49	1.093 5	2.471 5	8
53	0.404 88	0.442 79	2.258 4	0.914 37	1.093 6	2.469 9	7
54	0.405 14	0.443 14	2.256 6	0.914 25	1.093 8	2.468 3	6
55	**0.405 41**	**0.443 49**	**2.254 9**	**0.914 14**	**1.093 9**	**2.466 7**	5
56	0.405 67	0.443 84	2.253 1	0.914 02	1.094 1	2.465 0	4
57	0.405 94	0.444 18	2.251 3	0.913 90	1.094 2	2.463 4	3
58	0.406 21	0.444 53	2.249 6	0.913 78	1.094 4	2.461 8	2
59	0.406 47	0.444 88	2.247 8	0.913 66	1.094 5	2.460 2	1
60	**0.406 74**	**0.445 23**	**2.246 0**	**0.913 55**	**1.094 6**	**2.458 6**	0
′	Cos	Cot	Tan	Sin	Csc	Sec	′

′	Sin	Tan	Cot	Cos	Sec	Csc	′
0	0.406 74	0.445 23	2.246 0	0.913 55	1.094 6	2.458 6	60
1	0.407 00	0.445 58	2.244 3	0.913 43	1.094 8	2.457 0	59
2	0.407 27	0.445 93	2.242 5	0.913 31	1.094 9	2.455 4	58
3	0.407 53	0.446 27	2.240 8	0.913 19	1.095 1	2.453 8	57
4	0.407 80	0.446 62	2.239 0	0.913 07	1.095 2	2.452 2	56
5	0.408 06	0.446 97	2.237 3	0.912 95	1.095 3	2.450 6	55
6	0.408 33	0.447 32	2.235 5	0.912 83	1.095 5	2.449 0	54
7	0.408 60	0.447 67	2.233 8	0.912 72	1.095 6	2.447 4	53
8	0.408 86	0.448 02	2.232 0	0.912 60	1.095 8	2.445 8	52
9	0.409 13	0.448 37	2.230 3	0.912 48	1.095 9	2.444 2	51
10	0.409 39	0.448 72	2.228 6	0.912 36	1.096 1	2.442 6	50
11	0.409 66	0.449 07	2.226 8	0.912 24	1.096 2	2.441 1	49
12	0.409 92	0.449 42	2.225 1	0.912 12	1.096 3	2.439 5	48
13	0.410 19	0.449 77	2.223 4	0.912 00	1.096 5	2.437 9	47
14	0.410 45	0.450 12	2.221 6	0.911 88	1.096 6	2.436 3	46
15	0.410 72	0.450 47	2.219 9	0.911 76	1.096 8	2.434 8	45
16	0.410 98	0.450 82	2.218 2	0.911 64	1.096 9	2.433 2	44
17	0.411 25	0.451 17	2.216 5	0.911 52	1.097 1	2.431 6	43
18	0.411 51	0.451 52	2.214 8	0.911 40	1.097 2	2.430 0	42
19	0.411 78	0.451 87	2.213 0	0.911 28	1.097 4	2.428 5	41
20	0.412 04	0.452 22	2.211 3	0.911 16	1.097 5	2.426 9	40
21	0.412 31	0.452 57	2.209 6	0.911 04	1.097 6	2.425 4	39
22	0.412 57	0.452 92	2.207 9	0.910 92	1.097 8	2.423 8	38
23	0.412 84	0.453 27	2.206 2	0.910 80	1.097 9	2.422 2	37
24	0.413 10	0.453 62	2.204 5	0.910 68	1.098 1	2.420 7	36
25	0.413 37	0.453 97	2.202 8	0.910 56	1.098 2	2.419 1	35
26	0.413 63	0.454 32	2.201 1	0.910 44	1.098 4	2.417 6	34
27	0.413 90	0.454 67	2.199 4	0.910 32	1.098 5	2.416 0	33
28	0.414 16	0.455 02	2.197 7	0.910 20	1.098 7	2.414 5	32
29	0.414 43	0.455 38	2.196 0	0.910 08	1.098 8	2.413 0	31
30	0.414 69	0.455 73	2.194 3	0.909 96	1.098 9	2.411 4	30
31	0.414 96	0.456 08	2.192 6	0.909 84	1.099 1	2.409 9	29
32	0.415 22	0.456 43	2.190 9	0.909 72	1.099 2	2.408 3	28
33	0.415 49	0.456 78	2.189 2	0.909 60	1.099 4	2.406 8	27
34	0.415 75	0.457 13	2.187 6	0.909 48	1.099 5	2.405 3	26
35	0.416 02	0.457 48	2.185 9	0.909 36	1.099 7	2.403 8	25
36	0.416 28	0.457 84	2.184 2	0.909 24	1.099 8	2.402 2	24
37	0.416 55	0.458 19	2.182 5	0.909 11	1.100 0	2.400 7	23
38	0.416 81	0.458 54	2.180 8	0.908 99	1.100 1	2.399 2	22
39	0.417 07	0.458 89	2.179 2	0.908 87	1.100 3	2.397 7	21
40	0.417 34	0.459 24	2.177 5	0.908 75	1.100 4	2.396 1	20
41	0.417 60	0.459 60	2.175 8	0.908 63	1.100 6	2.394 6	19
42	0.417 87	0.459 95	2.174 2	0.908 51	1.100 7	2.393 1	18
43	0.418 13	0.460 30	2.172 5	0.908 39	1.100 9	2.391 6	17
44	0.418 40	0.460 65	2.170 8	0.908 26	1.101 0	2.390 1	16
45	0.418 66	0.461 01	2.169 2	0.908 14	1.101 1	2.388 6	15
46	0.418 92	0.461 36	2.167 5	0.908 02	1.101 3	2.387 1	14
47	0.419 19	0.461 71	2.165 9	0.907 90	1.101 4	2.385 6	13
48	0.419 45	0.462 06	2.164 2	0.907 78	1.101 6	2.384 1	12
49	0.419 72	0.462 42	2.162 5	0.907 66	1.101 7	2.382 6	11
50	0.419 98	0.462 77	2.160 9	0.907 53	1.101 9	2.381 1	10
51	0.420 24	0.463 12	2.159 2	0.907 41	1.102 0	2.379 6	9
52	0.420 51	0.463 48	2.157 6	0.907 29	1.102 2	2.378 1	8
53	0.420 77	0.463 83	2.156 0	0.907 17	1.102 3	2.376 6	7
54	0.421 04	0.464 18	2.154 3	0.907 04	1.102 5	2.375 1	6
55	0.421 30	0.464 54	2.152 7	0.906 92	1.102 6	2.373 6	5
56	0.421 56	0.464 89	2.151 0	0.906 80	1.102 8	2.372 1	4
57	0.421 83	0.465 25	2.149 4	0.906 68	1.102 9	2.370 6	3
58	0.422 09	0.465 60	2.147 8	0.906 55	1.103 1	2.369 2	2
59	0.422 35	0.465 95	2.146 1	0.906 43	1.103 2	2.367 7	1
60	0.422 62	0.466 31	2.144 5	0.906 31	1.103 4	2.366 2	0
′	Cos	Cot	Tan	Sin	Csc	Sec	′

Table 3 / *Five-place natural trigonometric functions* □ 647

′	Sin	Tan	Cot	Cos	Sec	Csc	
0	**0.422 62**	**0.466 31**	**2.144 5**	**0.906 31**	**1.103 4**	**2.366 2**	60
1	0.422 88	0.466 66	2.142 9	0.906 18	1.103 5	2.364 7	59
2	0.423 15	0.467 02	2.141 3	0.906 06	1.103 7	2.363 3	58
3	0.423 41	0.467 37	2.139 6	0.905 94	1.103 8	2.361 8	57
4	0.423 67	0.467 72	2.138 0	0.905 82	1.104 0	2.360 3	56
5	**0.423 94**	**0.468 08**	**2.136 4**	**0.905 69**	**1.104 1**	**2.358 8**	55
6	0.424 20	0.468 43	2.134 8	0.905 57	1.104 3	2.357 4	54
7	0.424 46	0.468 79	2.133 2	0.905 45	1.104 4	2.355 9	53
8	0.424 73	0.469 14	2.131 5	0.905 32	1.104 6	2.354 5	52
9	0.424 99	0.469 50	2.129 9	0.905 20	1.104 7	2.353 0	51
10	**0.425 25**	**0.469 85**	**2.128 3**	**0.905 07**	**1.104 9**	**2.351 5**	50
11	0.425 52	0.470 21	2.126 7	0.904 95	1.105 0	2.350 1	49
12	0.425 78	0.470 56	2.125 1	0.904 83	1.105 2	2.348 6	48
13	0.426 04	0.470 92	2.123 5	0.904 70	1.105 3	2.347 2	47
14	0.426 31	0.471 28	2.121 9	0.904 58	1.105 5	2.345 7	46
15	**0.426 57**	**0.471 63**	**2.120 3**	**0.904 46**	**1.105 6**	**2.344 3**	45
16	0.426 83	0.471 99	2.118 7	0.904 33	1.105 8	2.342 8	44
17	0.427 09	0.472 34	2.117 1	0.904 21	1.105 9	2.341 4	43
18	0.427 36	0.472 70	2.115 5	0.904 08	1.106 1	2.340 0	42
19	0.427 62	0.473 05	2.113 9	0.903 96	1.106 2	2.338 5	41
20	**0.427 88**	**0.473 41**	**2.112 3**	**0.903 83**	**1.106 4**	**2.337 1**	40
21	0.428 15	0.473 77	2.110 7	0.903 71	1.106 6	2.335 6	39
22	0.428 41	0.474 12	2.109 2	0.903 58	1.106 7	2.334 2	38
23	0.428 67	0.474 48	2.107 6	0.903 46	1.106 9	2.332 8	37
24	0.428 94	0.474 83	2.106 0	0.903 34	1.107 0	2.331 4	36
25	**0.429 20**	**0.475 19**	**2.104 4**	**0.903 21**	**1.107 2**	**2.329 9**	35
26	0.429 46	0.475 55	2.102 8	0.903 09	1.107 3	2.328 5	34
27	0.429 72	0.475 90	2.101 3	0.902 96	1.107 5	2.327 1	33
28	0.429 99	0.476 26	2.099 7	0.902 84	1.107 6	2.325 7	32
29	0.430 25	0.476 62	2.098 1	0.902 71	1.107 8	2.324 2	31
30	**0.430 51**	**0.476 98**	**2.096 5**	**0.902 59**	**1.107 9**	**2.322 8**	30
31	0.430 77	0.477 33	2.095 0	0.902 46	1.108 1	2.321 4	29
32	0.431 04	0.477 69	2.093 4	0.902 33	1.108 2	2.320 0	28
33	0.431 30	0.478 05	2.091 8	0.902 21	1.108 4	2.318 6	27
34	0.431 56	0.478 40	2.090 3	0.902 08	1.108 5	2.317 2	26
35	**0.431 82**	**0.478 76**	**2.088 7**	**0.901 96**	**1.108 7**	**2.315 8**	25
36	0.432 09	0.479 12	2.087 2	0.901 83	1.108 9	2.314 4	24
37	0.432 35	0.479 48	2.085 6	0.901 71	1.109 0	2.313 0	23
38	0.432 61	0.479 84	2.084 0	0.901 58	1.109 2	2.311 5	22
39	0.432 87	0.480 19	2.082 5	0.901 46	1.109 3	2.310 1	21
40	**0.433 13**	**0.480 55**	**2.080 9**	**0.901 33**	**1.109 5**	**2.308 8**	20
41	0.433 40	0.480 91	2.079 4	0.901 20	1.109 6	2.307 4	19
42	0.433 66	0.481 27	2.077 8	0.901 08	1.109 8	2.306 0	18
43	0.433 92	0.481 63	2.076 3	0.900 95	1.109 9	2.304 6	17
44	0.434 18	0.481 98	2.074 8	0.900 82	1.110 1	2.303 2	16
45	**0.434 45**	**0.482 34**	**2.073 2**	**0.900 70**	**1.110 2**	**2.301 8**	15
46	0.434 71	0.482 70	2.071 7	0.900 57	1.110 4	2.300 4	14
47	0.434 97	0.483 06	2.070 1	0.900 45	1.110 6	2.299 0	13
48	0.435 23	0.483 42	2.068 6	0.900 32	1.110 7	2.297 6	12
49	0.435 49	0.483 78	2.067 1	0.900 19	1.110 9	2.296 2	11
50	**0.435 75**	**0.484 14**	**2.065 5**	**0.900 07**	**1.111 0**	**2.294 9**	10
51	0.436 02	0.484 50	2.064 0	0.899 94	1.111 2	2.293 5	9
52	0.436 28	0.484 86	2.062 5	0.899 81	1.111 3	2.292 1	8
53	0.436 54	0.485 21	2.060 9	0.899 68	1.111 5	2.290 7	7
54	0.436 80	0.485 57	2.059 4	0.899 56	1.111 7	2.289 4	6
55	**0.437 06**	**0.485 93**	**2.057 9**	**0.899 43**	**1.111 8**	**2.288 0**	5
56	0.437 33	0.486 29	2.056 4	0.899 30	1.112 0	2.286 6	4
57	0.437 59	0.486 65	2.054 9	0.899 18	1.112 1	2.285 3	3
58	0.437 85	0.487 01	2.053 3	0.899 05	1.112 3	2.283 9	2
59	0.438 11	0.487 37	2.051 8	0.898 92	1.112 4	2.282 5	1
60	**0.438 37**	**0.487 73**	**2.050 3**	**0.898 79**	**1.112 6**	**2.281 2**	0
′	Cos	Cot	Tan	Sin	Csc	Sec	′

′	Sin	Tan	Cot	Cos	Sec	Csc	′
0	**0.438 37**	**0.487 73**	**2.050 3**	**0.898 79**	**1.112 6**	**2.281 2**	60
1	0.438 63	0.488 09	2.048 8	0.898 67	1.112 8	2.279 8	59
2	0.438 89	0.488 45	2.047 3	0.898 54	1.112 9	2.278 5	58
3	0.439 16	0.488 81	2.045 8	0.898 41	1.113 1	2.277 1	57
4	0.439 42	0.489 17	2.044 3	0.898 28	1.113 2	2.275 7	56
5	**0.439 68**	**0.489 53**	**2.042 8**	**0.898 16**	**1.113 4**	**2.274 4**	55
6	0.439 94	0.489 89	2.041 3	0.898 03	1.113 6	2.273 0	54
7	0.440 20	0.490 26	2.039 8	0.897 90	1.113 7	2.271 7	53
8	0.440 46	0.490 62	2.038 3	0.897 77	1.113 9	2.270 3	52
9	0.440 72	0.490 98	2.036 8	0.897 64	1.114 0	2.269 0	51
10	**0.440 98**	**0.491 34**	**2.035 3**	**0.897 52**	**1.114 2**	**2.267 7**	50
11	0.441 24	0.491 70	2.033 8	0.897 39	1.114 3	2.266 3	49
12	0.441 51	0.492 06	2.032 3	0.897 26	1.114 5	2.265 0	48
13	0.441 77	0.492 42	2.030 8	0.897 13	1.114 7	2.263 6	47
14	0.442 03	0.492 78	2.029 3	0.897 00	1.114 8	2.262 3	46
15	**0.442 29**	**0.493 15**	**2.027 8**	**0.896 87**	**1.115 0**	**2.261 0**	45
16	0.442 55	0.493 51	2.026 3	0.896 74	1.115 1	2.259 6	44
17	0.442 81	0.493 87	2.024 8	0.896 62	1.115 3	2.258 3	43
18	0.443 07	0.494 23	2.023 3	0.896 49	1.115 5	2.257 0	42
19	0.443 33	0.494 59	2.021 9	0.896 36	1.115 6	2.255 6	41
20	**0.443 59**	**0.494 95**	**2.020 4**	**0.896 23**	**1.115 8**	**2.254 3**	40
21	0.443 85	0.495 32	2.018 9	0.896 10	1.115 9	2.253 0	39
22	0.444 11	0.495 68	2.017 4	0.895 97	1.116 1	2.251 7	38
23	0.444 37	0.496 04	2.016 0	0.895 84	1.116 3	2.250 4	37
24	0.444 64	0.496 40	2.014 5	0.895 71	1.116 4	2.249 0	36
25	**0.444 90**	**0.496 77**	**2.013 0**	**0.895 58**	**1.116 6**	**2.247 7**	35
26	0.445 16	0.497 13	2.011 5	0.895 45	1.116 8	2.246 4	34
27	0.445 42	0.497 49	2.010 1	0.895 32	1.116 9	2.245 1	33
28	0.445 68	0.497 86	2.008 6	0.895 19	1.117 1	2.243 8	32
29	0.445 94	0.498 22	2.007 2	0.895 06	1.117 2	2.242 5	31
30	**0.446 20**	**0.498 58**	**2.005 7**	**0.894 93**	**1.117 4**	**2.241 2**	30
31	0.446 46	0.498 94	2.004 2	0.894 80	1.117 6	2.239 9	29
32	0.446 72	0.499 31	2.002 8	0.894 67	1.117 7	2.238 5	28
33	0.446 98	0.499 67	2.001 3	0.894 54	1.117 9	2.237 2	27
34	0.447 24	0.500 04	1.999 9	0.894 41	1.118 0	2.235 9	26
35	**0.447 50**	**0.500 40**	**1.998 4**	**0.894 28**	**1.118 2**	**2.234 6**	25
36	0.447 76	0.500 76	1.997 0	0.894 15	1.118 4	2.233 3	24
37	0.448 02	0.501 13	1.995 5	0.894 02	1.118 5	2.232 0	23
38	0.448 28	0.501 49	1.994 1	0.893 89	1.118 7	2.230 8	22
39	0.448 54	0.501 85	1.992 6	0.893 76	1.118 9	2.229 5	21
40	**0.448 80**	**0.502 22**	**1.991 2**	**0.893 63**	**1.119 0**	**2.228 2**	20
41	0.449 06	0.502 58	1.989 7	0.893 50	1.119 2	2.226 9	19
42	0.449 32	0.502 95	1.988 3	0.893 37	1.119 4	2.225 6	18
43	0.449 58	0.503 31	1.986 8	0.893 24	1.119 5	2.224 3	17
44	0.449 84	0.503 68	1.985 4	0.893 11	1.119 7	2.223 0	16
45	**0.450 10**	**0.504 04**	**1.984 0**	**0.892 98**	**1.119 8**	**2.221 7**	15
46	0.450 36	0.504 41	1.982 5	0.892 85	1.120 0	2.220 5	14
47	0.450 62	0.504 77	1.981 1	0.892 72	1.120 2	2.219 2	13
48	0.450 88	0.505 14	1.979 7	0.892 59	1.120 3	2.217 9	12
49	0.451 14	0.505 50	1.978 2	0.892 45	1.120 5	2.216 6	11
50	**0.451 40**	**0.505 87**	**1.976 8**	**0.892 32**	**1.120 7**	**2.215 3**	10
51	0.451 66	0.506 23	1.975 4	0.892 19	1.120 8	2.214 1	9
52	0.451 92	0.506 60	1.974 0	0.892 06	1.121 0	2.212 8	8
53	0.452 18	0.506 96	1.972 5	0.891 93	1.121 2	2.211 5	7
54	0.452 43	0.507 33	1.971 1	0.891 80	1.121 3	2.210 3	6
55	**0.452 69**	**0.507 69**	**1.969 7**	**0.891 67**	**1.121 5**	**2.209 0**	5
56	0.452 95	0.508 06	1.968 3	0.891 53	1.121 7	2.207 7	4
57	0.453 21	0.508 43	1.966 9	0.891 40	1.121 8	2.206 5	3
58	0.453 47	0.508 79	1.965 4	0.891 27	1.122 0	2.205 2	2
59	0.453 73	0.509 16	1.964 0	0.891 14	1.122 2	2.203 9	1
60	**0.453 99**	**0.509 53**	**1.962 6**	**0.891 01**	**1.122 3**	**2.202 7**	0
′	Cos	Cot	Tan	Sin	Csc	Sec	′

Table 3 / Five-place natural trigonometric functions □ 649

′	Sin	Tan	Cot	Cos	Sec	Csc	′
0	**0.453 99**	**0.509 53**	**1.962 6**	**0.891 01**	**1.122 3**	**2.202 7**	60
1	0.454 25	0.509 89	1.961 2	0.890 87	1.122 5	2.201 4	59
2	0.454 51	0.510 26	1.959 8	0.890 74	1.122 7	2.200 2	58
3	0.454 77	0.510 63	1.958 4	0.890 61	1.122 8	2.198 9	57
4	0.455 03	0.510 99	1.957 0	0.890 48	1.123 0	2.197 7	56
5	**0.455 29**	**0.511 36**	**1.955 6**	**0.890 35**	**1.123 2**	**2.196 4**	55
6	0.455 54	0.511 73	1.954 2	0.890 21	1.123 3	2.195 2	54
7	0.455 80	0.512 09	1.952 8	0.890 08	1.123 5	2.193 9	53
8	0.456 06	0.512 46	1.951 4	0.889 95	1.123 7	2.192 7	52
9	0.456 32	0.512 83	1.950 0	0.889 81	1.123 8	2.191 4	51
10	**0.456 58**	**0.513 19**	**1.948 6**	**0.889 68**	**1.124 0**	**2.190 2**	50
11	0.456 84	0.513 56	1.947 2	0.889 55	1.124 2	2.189 0	49
12	0.457 10	0.513 93	1.945 8	0.889 42	1.124 3	2.187 7	48
13	0.457 36	0.514 30	1.944 4	0.889 28	1.124 5	2.186 5	47
14	0.457 62	0.514 67	1.943 0	0.889 15	1.124 7	2.185 2	46
15	**0.457 87**	**0.515 03**	**1.941 6**	**0.889 02**	**1.124 8**	**2.184 0**	45
16	0.458 13	0.515 40	1.940 2	0.888 88	1.125 0	2.182 8	44
17	0.458 39	0.515 77	1.938 8	0.888 75	1.125 2	2.181 5	43
18	0.458 65	0.516 14	1.937 5	0.888 62	1.125 3	2.180 3	42
19	0.458 91	0.516 51	1.936 1	0.888 48	1.125 5	2.179 1	41
20	**0.459 17**	**0.516 88**	**1.934 7**	**0.888 35**	**1.125 7**	**2.177 9**	40
21	0.459 42	0.517 24	1.933 3	0.888 22	1.125 9	2.176 6	39
22	0.459 68	0.517 61	1.931 9	0.888 08	1.126 0	2.175 4	38
23	0.459 94	0.517 98	1.930 6	0.887 95	1.126 2	2.174 2	37
24	0.460 20	0.518 35	1.929 2	0.887 82	1.126 4	2.173 0	36
25	**0.460 46**	**0.518 72**	**1.927 8**	**0.887 68**	**1.126 5**	**2.171 8**	35
26	0.460 72	0.519 09	1.926 5	0.887 55	1.126 7	2.170 5	34
27	0.460 97	0.519 46	1.925 1	0.887 41	1.126 9	2.169 3	33
28	0.461 23	0.519 83	1.923 7	0.887 28	1.127 0	2.168 1	32
29	0.461 49	0.520 20	1.922 3	0.887 15	1.127 2	2.166 9	31
30	**0.461 75**	**0.520 57**	**1.921 0**	**0.887 01**	**1.127 4**	**2.165 7**	30
31	0.462 01	0.520 94	1.919 6	0.886 88	1.127 6	2.164 5	29
32	0.462 26	0.521 31	1.918 3	0.886 74	1.127 7	2.163 3	28
33	0.462 52	0.521 68	1.916 9	0.886 61	1.127 9	2.162 1	27
34	0.462 78	0.522 05	1.915 5	0.886 47	1.128 1	2.160 9	26
35	**0.463 04**	**0.522 42**	**1.914 2**	**0.886 34**	**1.128 2**	**2.159 6**	25
36	0.463 30	0.522 79	1.912 8	0.886 20	1.128 4	2.158 4	24
37	0.463 55	0.523 16	1.911 5	0.886 07	1.128 6	2.157 2	23
38	0.463 81	0.523 53	1.910 1	0.885 93	1.128 8	2.156 0	22
39	0.464 07	0.523 90	1.908 8	0.885 80	1.128 9	2.154 9	21
40	**0.464 33**	**0.524 27**	**1.907 4**	**0.885 66**	**1.129 1**	**2.153 7**	20
41	0.464 58	0.524 64	1.906 1	0.885 53	1.129 3	2.152 5	19
42	0.464 84	0.525 01	1.904 7	0.885 39	1.129 4	2.151 3	18
43	0.465 10	0.525 38	1.903 4	0.885 26	1.129 6	2.150 1	17
44	0.465 36	0.525 75	1.902 0	0.885 12	1.129 8	2.148 9	16
45	**0.465 61**	**0.526 13**	**1.900 7**	**0.884 99**	**1.130 0**	**2.147 7**	15
46	0.465 87	0.526 50	1.899 3	0.884 85	1.130 1	2.146 5	14
47	0.466 13	0.526 87	1.898 0	0.884 72	1.130 3	2.145 3	13
48	0.466 39	0.527 24	1.896 7	0.884 58	1.130 5	2.144 1	12
49	0.466 64	0.527 61	1.895 3	0.884 45	1.130 7	2.143 0	11
50	**0.466 90**	**0.527 98**	**1.894 0**	**0.884 31**	**1.130 8**	**2.141 8**	10
51	0.467 16	0.528 36	1.892 7	0.884 17	1.131 0	2.140 6	9
52	0.467 42	0.528 73	1.891 3	0.884 04	1.131 2	2.139 4	8
53	0.467 67	0.529 10	1.890 0	0.883 90	1.131 3	2.138 2	7
54	0.467 93	0.529 47	1.888 7	0.883 77	1.131 5	2.137 1	6
55	**0.468 19**	**0.529 85**	**1.887 3**	**0.883 63**	**1.131 7**	**2.135 9**	5
56	0.468 44	0.530 22	1.886 0	0.883 49	1.131 9	2.134 7	4
57	0.468 70	0.530 59	1.884 7	0.883 36	1.132 0	2.133 6	3
58	0.468 96	0.530 96	1.883 4	0.883 22	1.132 2	2.132 4	2
59	0.469 21	0.531 34	1.882 0	0.883 08	1.132 4	2.131 2	1
60	**0.469 47**	**0.531 71**	**1.880 7**	**0.882 95**	**1.132 6**	**2.130 1**	0
′	Cos	Cot	Tan	Sin	Csc	Sec	′

′	Sin	Tan	Cot	Cos	Sec	Csc	′
0	0.469 47	0.531 71	1.880 7	0.882 95	1.132 6	2.130 1	60
1	0.469 73	0.532 08	1.879 4	0.882 81	1.132 7	2.128 9	59
2	0.469 99	0.532 46	1.878 1	0.882 67	1.132 9	2.127 7	58
3	0.470 24	0.532 83	1.876 8	0.882 54	1.133 1	2.126 6	57
4	0.470 50	0.533 20	1.875 5	0.882 40	1.133 3	2.125 4	56
5	0.470 76	0.533 58	1.874 1	0.882 26	1.133 4	2.124 2	55
6	0.471 01	0.533 95	1.872 8	0.882 13	1.133 6	2.123 1	54
7	0.471 27	0.534 32	1.871 5	0.881 99	1.133 8	2.121 9	53
8	0.471 53	0.534 70	1.870 2	0.881 85	1.134 0	2.120 8	52
9	0.471 78	0.535 07	1.868 9	0.881 72	1.134 2	2.119 6	51
10	0.472 04	0.535 45	1.867 6	0.881 58	1.134 3	2.118 5	50
11	0.472 29	0.535 82	1.866 3	0.881 44	1.134 5	2.117 3	49
12	0.472 55	0.536 20	1.865 0	0.881 30	1.134 7	2.116 2	48
13	0.472 81	0.536 57	1.863 7	0.881 17	1.134 9	2.115 0	47
14	0.473 06	0.536 94	1.862 4	0.881 03	1.135 0	2.113 9	46
15	0.473 32	0.537 32	1.861 1	0.880 89	1.135 2	2.112 7	45
16	0.473 58	0.537 69	1.859 8	0.880 75	1.135 4	2.111 6	44
17	0.473 83	0.538 07	1.858 5	0.880 62	1.135 6	2.110 5	43
18	0.474 09	0.538 44	1.857 2	0.880 48	1.135 7	2.109 3	42
19	0.474 34	0.538 82	1.855 9	0.880 34	1.135 9	2.108 2	41
20	0.474 60	0.539 20	1.854 6	0.880 20	1.136 1	2.107 0	40
21	0.474 86	0.539 57	1.853 3	0.880 06	1.136 3	2.105 9	39
22	0.475 11	0.539 95	1.852 0	0.879 93	1.136 5	2.104 8	38
23	0.475 37	0.540 32	1.850 7	0.879 79	1.136 6	2.103 6	37
24	0.475 62	0.540 70	1.849 5	0.879 65	1.136 8	2.102 5	36
25	0.475 88	0.541 07	1.848 2	0.879 51	1.137 0	2.101 4	35
26	0.476 14	0.541 45	1.846 9	0.879 37	1.137 2	2.100 2	34
27	0.476 39	0.541 83	1.845 6	0.879 23	1.137 4	2.099 1	33
28	0.476 65	0.542 20	1.844 3	0.879 09	1.137 5	2.098 0	32
29	0.476 90	0.542 58	1.843 0	0.878 96	1.137 7	2.096 9	31
30	0.477 16	0.542 96	1.841 8	0.878 82	1.137 9	2.095 7	30
31	0.477 41	0.543 33	1.840 5	0.878 68	1.138 1	2.094 6	29
32	0.477 67	0.543 71	1.839 2	0.878 54	1.138 3	2.093 5	28
33	0.477 93	0.544 09	1.837 9	0.878 40	1.138 4	2.092 4	27
34	0.478 18	0.544 46	1.836 7	0.878 26	1.138 6	2.091 3	26
35	0.478 44	0.544 84	1.835 4	0.878 12	1.138 8	2.090 1	25
36	0.478 69	0.545 22	1.834 1	0.877 98	1.139 0	2.089 0	24
37	0.478 95	0.545 60	1.832 9	0.877 84	1.139 2	2.087 9	23
38	0.479 20	0.545 97	1.831 6	0.877 70	1.139 3	2.086 8	22
39	0.479 46	0.546 35	1.830 3	0.877 56	1.139 5	2.085 7	21
40	0.479 71	0.546 73	1.829 1	0.877 43	1.139 7	2.084 6	20
41	0.479 97	0.547 11	1.827 8	0.877 29	1.139 9	2.083 5	19
42	0.480 22	0.547 48	1.826 5	0.877 15	1.140 1	2.082 4	18
43	0.480 48	0.547 86	1.825 3	0.877 01	1.140 2	2.081 3	17
44	0.480 73	0.548 24	1.824 0	0.876 87	1.140 4	2.080 2	16
45	0.480 99	0.548 62	1.822 8	0.876 73	1.140 6	2.079 1	15
46	0.481 24	0.549 00	1.821 5	0.876 59	1.140 8	2.077 9	14
47	0.481 50	0.549 38	1.820 2	0.876 45	1.141 0	2.076 8	13
48	0.481 75	0.549 75	1.819 0	0.876 31	1.141 2	2.075 7	12
49	0.482 01	0.550 13	1.817 7	0.876 17	1.141 3	2.074 7	11
50	0.482 26	0.550 51	1.816 5	0.876 03	1.141 5	2.073 6	10
51	0.482 52	0.550 89	1.815 2	0.875 89	1.141 7	2.072 5	9
52	0.482 77	0.551 27	1.814 0	0.875 75	1.141 9	2.071 4	8
53	0.483 03	0.551 65	1.812 7	0.875 61	1.142 1	2.070 3	7
54	0.483 28	0.552 03	1.811 5	0.875 46	1.142 3	2.069 2	6
55	0.483 54	0.552 41	1.810 3	0.875 32	1.142 4	2.068 1	5
56	0.483 79	0.552 79	1.809 0	0.875 18	1.142 6	2.067 0	4
57	0.484 05	0.553 17	1.807 8	0.875 04	1.142 8	2.065 9	3
58	0.484 30	0.553 55	1.806 5	0.874 90	1.143 0	2.064 8	2
59	0.484 56	0.553 93	1.805 3	0.874 76	1.143 2	2.063 7	1
60	0.484 81	0.554 31	1.804 0	0.874 62	1.143 4	2.062 7	0
′	Cos	Cot	Tan	Sin	Csc	Sec	′

Table 3 / *Five-place natural trigonometric functions*   □   651

′	Sin	Tan	Cot	Cos	Sec	Csc	
0	**0.484 81**	**0.554 31**	**1.804 0**	**0.874 62**	**1.143 4**	**2.062 7**	**60**
1	0.485 06	0.554 69	1.802 8	0.874 48	1.143 5	2.061 6	59
2	0.485 32	0.555 07	1.801 6	0.874 34	1.143 7	2.060 5	58
3	0.485 57	0.555 45	1.800 3	0.874 20	1.143 9	2.059 4	57
4	0.485 83	0.555 83	1.799 1	0.874 06	1.144 1	2.058 3	56
5	**0.486 08**	**0.556 21**	**1.797 9**	**0.873 91**	**1.144 3**	**2.057 3**	**55**
6	0.486 34	0.556 59	1.796 6	0.873 77	1.144 5	2.056 2	54
7	0.486 59	0.556 97	1.795 4	0.873 63	1.144 6	2.055 1	53
8	0.486 84	0.557 36	1.794 2	0.873 49	1.144 8	2.054 0	52
9	0.487 10	0.557 74	1.793 0	0.873 35	1.145 0	2.053 0	51
10	**0.487 35**	**0.558 12**	**1.791 7**	**0.873 21**	**1.145 2**	**2.051 9**	**50**
11	0.487 61	0.558 50	1.790 5	0.873 06	1.145 4	2.050 8	49
12	0.487 86	0.558 88	1.789 3	0.872 92	1.145 6	2.049 8	48
13	0.488 11	0.559 26	1.788 1	0.872 78	1.145 8	2.048 7	47
14	0.488 37	0.559 64	1.786 8	0.872 64	1.146 0	2.047 6	46
15	**0.488 62**	**0.560 03**	**1.785 6**	**0.872 50**	**1.146 1**	**2.046 6**	**45**
16	0.488 88	0.560 41	1.784 4	0.872 35	1.146 3	2.045 5	44
17	0.489 13	0.560 79	1.783 2	0.872 21	1.146 5	2.044 5	43
18	0.489 38	0.561 17	1.782 0	0.872 07	1.146 7	2.043 4	42
19	0.489 64	0.561 56	1.780 8	0.871 93	1.146 9	2.042 3	41
20	**0.489 89**	**0.561 94**	**1.779 6**	**0.871 78**	**1.147 1**	**2.041 3**	**40**
21	0.490 14	0.562 32	1.778 3	0.871 64	1.147 3	2.040 2	39
22	0.490 40	0.562 70	1.777 1	0.871 50	1.147 4	2.039 2	38
23	0.490 65	0.563 09	1.775 9	0.871 36	1.147 6	2.038 1	37
24	0.490 90	0.563 47	1.774 7	0.871 21	1.147 8	2.037 1	36
25	**0.491 16**	**0.563 85**	**1.773 5**	**0.871 07**	**1.148 0**	**2.036 0**	**35**
26	0.491 41	0.564 24	1.772 3	0.870 93	1.148 4	2.035 0	34
27	0.491 66	0.564 62	1.771 1	0.870 79	1.148 4	2.033 9	33
28	0.491 92	0.565 01	1.769 9	0.870 64	1.148 6	2.032 9	32
29	0.492 17	0.565 39	1.768 7	0.870 50	1.148 8	2.031 8	31
30	**0.492 42**	**0.565 77**	**1.767 5**	**0.870 36**	**1.149 0**	**2.030 8**	**30**
31	0.492 68	0.566 16	1.766 3	0.870 21	1.149 1	2.029 7	29
32	0.492 93	0.566 54	1.765 1	0.870 07	1.149 3	2.022 7	28
33	0.493 18	0.566 93	1.763 9	0.869 93	1.149 5	2.027 6	27
34	0.493 44	0.567 31	1.762 7	0.869 78	1.149 7	2.026 6	26
35	**0.493 69**	**0.567 69**	**1.761 5**	**0.869 64**	**1.149 9**	**2.025 6**	**25**
36	0.493 94	0.568 08	1.760 3	0.869 49	1.150 1	2.024 5	24
37	0.494 19	0.568 46	1.759 1	0.869 35	1.150 3	2.023 5	23
38	0.494 45	0.568 85	1.757 9	0.869 21	1.150 5	2.022 5	22
39	0.494 70	0.569 23	1.756 7	0.869 06	1.150 7	2.021 4	21
40	**0.494 95**	**0.569 62**	**1.755 6**	**0.868 92**	**1.150 9**	**2.020 4**	**20**
41	0.495 21	0.570 00	1.754 4	0.868 78	1.151 0	2.019 4	19
42	0.495 46	0.570 39	1.753 2	0.868 63	1.151 2	2.018 3	18
43	0.495 71	0.570 78	1.752 0	0.868 49	1.151 4	2.017 3	17
44	0.495 96	0.571 16	1.750 8	0.868 34	1.151 6	2.016 3	16
45	**0.496 22**	**0.571 55**	**1.749 6**	**0.868 20**	**1.151 8**	**2.015 2**	**15**
46	0.496 47	0.571 93	1.748 5	0.868 05	1.152 0	2.014 2	14
47	0.496 72	0.572 32	1.747 3	0.867 91	1.152 2	2.013 2	13
48	0.496 97	0.572 71	1.746 1	0.867 77	1.152 4	2.012 2	12
49	0.497 23	0.573 09	1.744 9	0.867 62	1.152 6	2.011 2	11
50	**0.497 48**	**0.573 48**	**1.743 7**	**0.867 48**	**1.152 8**	**2.010 1**	**10**
51	0.497 73	0.573 86	1.742 6	0.867 33	1.153 0	2.009 1	9
52	0.497 98	0.574 25	1.741 4	0.867 19	1.153 2	2.008 1	8
53	0.498 24	0.574 64	1.740 2	0.867 04	1.153 3	2.007 1	7
54	0.498 49	0.575 03	1.739 1	0.866 90	1.153 5	2.006 1	6
55	**0.498 74**	**0.575 41**	**1.737 9**	**0.866 75**	**1.153 7**	**2.005 1**	**5**
56	0.498 99	0.575 80	1.736 7	0.866 61	1.153 9	2.004 0	4
57	0.499 24	0.576 19	1.735 5	0.866 46	1.154 1	2.003 0	3
58	0.499 50	0.576 57	1.734 4	0.866 32	1.154 3	2.002 0	2
59	0.499 75	0.576 96	1.733 2	0.866 17	1.154 5	2.001 0	1
60	**0.500 00**	**0.577 35**	**1.732 1**	**0.866 03**	**1.154 7**	**2.000 0**	**0**
′	Cos	Cot	Tan	Sin	Csc	Sec	′

′	Sin	Tan	Cot	Cos	Sec	Csc	
0	**0.500 00**	**0.577 35**	**1.732 1**	**0.866 03**	**1.154 7**	**2.000 0**	60
1	0.500 25	0.577 74	1.730 9	0.865 88	1.154 9	1.999 0	59
2	0.500 50	0.578 13	1.729 7	0.865 73	1.155 1	1.998 0	58
3	0.500 76	0.578 51	1.728 6	0.865 59	1.155 3	1.997 0	57
4	0.501 01	0.578 90	1.727 4	0.865 44	1.155 5	1.996 0	56
5	**0.501 26**	**0.579 29**	**1.726 2**	**0.865 30**	**1.155 7**	**1.995 0**	55
6	0.501 51	0.579 68	1.725 1	0.865 15	1.155 9	1.994 0	54
7	0.501 76	0.580 07	1.723 9	0.865 01	1.156 1	1.993 0	53
8	0.502 01	0.580 46	1.722 8	0.864 86	1.156 3	1.992 0	52
9	0.502 27	0.580 85	1.721 6	0.864 71	1.156 5	1.991 0	51
10	**0.502 52**	**0.581 24**	**1.720 5**	**0.864 57**	**1.156 6**	**1.990 0**	50
11	0.502 77	0.581 62	1.719 3	0.864 42	1.156 8	1.989 0	49
12	0.503 02	0.582 01	1.718 2	0.864 27	1.157 0	1.988 0	48
13	0.503 27	0.582 40	1.717 0	0.864 13	1.157 2	1.987 0	47
14	0.503 52	0.582 79	1.715 9	0.863 98	1.157 4	1.986 0	46
15	**0.503 77**	**0.583 18**	**1.714 7**	**0.863 84**	**1.157 6**	**1.985 0**	45
16	0.504 03	0.583 57	1.713 6	0.863 69	1.157 8	1.984 0	44
17	0.504 28	0.583 96	1.712 4	0.863 54	1.158 0	1.983 0	43
18	0.504 53	0.584 35	1.711 3	0.863 40	1.158 2	1.982 1	42
19	0.504 78	0.584 74	1.710 2	0.863 25	1.158 4	1.981 1	41
20	**0.505 03**	**0.585 13**	**1.709 0**	**0.863 10**	**1.158 6**	**1.980 1**	40
21	0.505 28	0.585 52	1.707 9	0.862 95	1.158 8	1.979 1	39
22	0.505 53	0.585 91	1.706 7	0.862 81	1.159 0	1.978 1	38
23	0.505 78	0.586 31	1.705 6	0.862 66	1.159 2	1.977 1	37
24	0.506 03	0.586 70	1.704 5	0.862 51	1.159 4	1.976 2	36
25	**0.506 28**	**0.587 09**	**1.703 3**	**0.862 37**	**1.159 6**	**1.975 2**	35
26	0.506 54	0.587 48	1.702 2	0.862 22	1.159 8	1.974 2	34
27	0.506 79	0.587 87	1.701 1	0.862 07	1.160 0	1.973 2	33
28	0.507 04	0.588 26	1.699 9	0.861 92	1.160 2	1.972 2	32
29	0.507 29	0.588 65	1.698 8	0.861 78	1.160 4	1.971 3	31
30	**0.507 54**	**0.589 05**	**1.697 7**	**0.861 63**	**1.160 6**	**1.970 3**	30
31	0.507 79	0.589 44	1.696 5	0.861 48	1.160 8	1.969 3	29
32	0.508 04	0.589 83	1.695 4	0.861 33	1.161 0	1.968 4	28
33	0.508 29	0.590 22	1.694 3	0.861 19	1.161 2	1.967 4	27
34	0.508 54	0.590 61	1.693 2	0.861 04	1.161 4	1.966 4	26
35	**0.508 79**	**0.591 01**	**1.692 0**	**0.860 89**	**1.161 6**	**1.965 4**	25
36	0.509 04	0.591 40	1.690 9	0.860 74	1.161 8	1.964 5	24
37	0.509 29	0.591 79	1.689 8	0.860 59	1.162 0	1.963 5	23
38	0.509 54	0.592 18	1.688 7	0.860 45	1.162 2	1.962 5	22
39	0.509 79	0.592 58	1.687 5	0.860 30	1.162 4	1.961 6	21
40	**0.510 04**	**0.592 97**	**1.686 4**	**0.860 15**	**1.162 6**	**1.960 6**	20
41	0.510 29	0.593 36	1.685 3	0.860 00	1.162 8	1.959 7	19
42	0.510 54	0.593 76	1.684 2	0.859 85	1.163 0	1.958 7	18
43	0.510 79	0.594 15	1.683 1	0.859 70	1.163 2	1.957 7	17
44	0.511 04	0.594 54	1.682 0	0.859 56	1.163 4	1.956 8	16
45	**0.511 29**	**0.594 94**	**1.680 8**	**0.859 41**	**1.163 6**	**1.955 8**	15
46	0.511 54	0.595 33	1.679 7	0.859 26	1.163 8	1.954 9	14
47	0.511 79	0.595 73	1.678 6	0.859 11	1.164 0	1.953 9	13
48	0.512 04	0.596 12	1.677 5	0.858 96	1.164 2	1.953 0	12
49	0.512 29	0.596 51	1.676 4	0.858 81	1.164 4	1.952 0	11
50	**0.512 54**	**0.596 91**	**1.675 3**	**0.858 66**	**1.164 6**	**1.951 1**	10
51	0.512 79	0.597 30	1.674 2	0.858 51	1.164 8	1.950 1	9
52	0.513 04	0.597 70	1.673 1	0.858 36	1.165 0	1.949 2	8
53	0.513 29	0.598 09	1.672 0	0.858 21	1.165 2	1.948 2	7
54	0.513 54	0.598 49	1.670 9	0.858 06	1.165 4	1.947 3	6
55	**0.513 79**	**0.598 88**	**1.669 8**	**0.857 92**	**1.165 6**	**1.946 3**	5
56	0.514 04	0.599 28	1.668 7	0.857 77	1.165 8	1.945 4	4
57	0.514 29	0.599 67	1.667 6	0.857 62	1.166 0	1.944 4	3
58	0.514 54	0.600 07	1.666 5	0.857 47	1.166 2	1.943 5	2
59	0.514 79	0.600 46	1.665 4	0.857 32	1.166 4	1.942 5	1
60	**0.515 04**	**0.600 86**	**1.664 3**	**0.857 17**	**1.166 6**	**1.941 6**	0
′	Cos	Cot	Tan	Sin	Csc	Sec	′

Table 3 / Five-place natural trigonometric functions   □   **653**

′	Sin	Tan	Cot	Cos	Sec	Csc	′
0	0.515 04	0.600 86	1.664 3	0.857 17	1.166 6	1.941 6	60
1	0.515 29	0.601 26	1.663 2	0.857 02	1.166 8	1.940 7	59
2	0.515 54	0.601 65	1.662 1	0.856 87	1.167 0	1.939 7	58
3	0.515 79	0.602 05	1.661 0	0.856 72	1.167 2	1.938 8	57
4	0.516 04	0.602 45	1.659 9	0.856 57	1.167 5	1.937 9	56
5	0.516 28	0.602 84	1.658 8	0.856 42	1.167 7	1.936 9	55
6	0.516 53	0.603 24	1.657 7	0.856 27	1.167 9	1.936 0	54
7	0.516 78	0.603 64	1.656 6	0.856 12	1.168 1	1.935 1	53
8	0.517 03	0.604 03	1.655 5	0.855 97	1.168 3	1.934 1	52
9	0.517 28	0.604 43	1.654 5	0.855 82	1.168 5	1.933 2	51
10	0.517 53	0.604 83	1.653 4	0.855 67	1.168 7	1.932 3	50
11	0.517 78	0.605 22	1.652 3	0.855 51	1.168 9	1.931 3	49
12	0.518 03	0.605 62	1.651 2	0.855 36	1.169 1	1.930 4	48
13	0.518 38	0.606 02	1.650 1	0.855 21	1.169 3	1.929 5	47
14	0.518 52	0.606 42	1.649 0	0.855 06	1.169 5	1.928 5	46
15	0.518 77	0.606 81	1.647 9	0.854 91	1.169 7	1.927 6	45
16	0.519 02	0.607 21	1.646 9	0.854 76	1.169 9	1.926 7	44
17	0.519 27	0.607 61	1.645 8	0.854 61	1.170 1	1.925 8	43
18	0.519 52	0.608 01	1.644 7	0.854 46	1.170 3	1.924 9	42
19	0.519 77	0.608 41	1.643 6	0.854 31	1.170 5	1.923 9	41
20	0.520 02	0.608 81	1.642 6	0.854 16	1.170 7	1.923 0	40
21	0.520 26	0.609 21	1.641 5	0.854 01	1.170 0	1.922 1	39
22	0.520 51	0.609 60	1.640 4	0.853 85	1.171 2	1.921 2	38
23	0.520 76	0.610 00	1.639 3	0.853 70	1.171 4	1.920 3	37
24	0.521 01	0.610 40	1.638 3	0.853 55	1.171 6	1.919 4	36
25	0.521 26	0.610 80	1.637 2	0.853 40	1.171 8	1.918 4	35
26	0.521 51	0.611 20	1.636 1	0.853 25	1.172 0	1.917 5	34
27	0.521 75	0.611 60	1.635 1	0.853 10	1.172 2	1.916 6	33
28	0.522 00	0.612 00	1.634 0	0.852 94	1.172 4	1.915 7	32
29	0.522 25	0.612 40	1.632 9	0.852 79	1.172 6	1.914 8	31
30	0.522 50	0.612 80	1.631 9	0.852 64	1.172 8	1.913 9	30
31	0.522 75	0.613 20	1.630 8	0.852 49	1.173 0	1.913 0	29
32	0.522 99	0.613 60	1.629 7	0.852 34	1.173 2	1.912 1	28
33	0.523 24	0.614 00	1.628 7	0.852 18	1.173 5	1.911 2	27
34	0.523 49	0.614 40	1.627 6	0.852 03	1.173 7	1.910 3	26
35	0.523 74	0.614 80	1.626 5	0.851 88	1.173 9	1.909 4	25
36	0.523 99	0.615 20	1.625 5	0.851 73	1.174 1	1.908 4	24
37	0.524 23	0.615 61	1.624 4	0.851 57	1.174 3	1.907 5	23
38	0.524 48	0.616 01	1.623 4	0.851 42	1.174 5	1.906 6	22
39	0.524 73	0.616 41	1.622 3	0.851 27	1.174 7	1.905 7	21
40	0.524 98	0.616 81	1.621 2	0.851 12	1.174 9	1.904 8	20
41	0.525 22	0.617 21	1.620 2	0.850 96	1.175 1	1.903 9	19
42	0.525 47	0.617 61	1.619 1	0.850 81	1.175 3	1.903 1	18
43	0.525 72	0.618 01	1.618 1	0.850 66	1.175 6	1.902 2	17
44	0.525 97	0.618 42	1.617 0	0.850 51	1.175 8	1.901 3	16
45	0.526 21	0.618 82	1.616 0	0.850 35	1.176 0	1.900 4	15
46	0.526 46	0.619 22	1.614 9	0.850 20	1.176 2	1.899 5	14
47	0.526 71	0.619 62	1.613 9	0.850 05	1.176 4	1.898 6	13
48	0.526 96	0.620 03	1.612 8	0.849 89	1.176 6	1.897 7	12
49	0.527 20	0.620 43	1.611 8	0.849 74	1.176 8	1.896 8	11
50	0.527 45	0.620 83	1.610 7	0.849 59	1.177 0	1.895 9	10
51	0.527 70	0.621 24	1.609 7	0.849 43	1.177 3	1.895 0	9
52	0.527 94	0.621 64	1.608 7	0.849 28	1.177 5	1.894 1	8
53	0.528 19	0.622 04	1.607 6	0.849 13	1.177 7	1.893 3	7
54	0.528 44	0.622 45	1.606 6	0.848 97	1.177 9	1.892 4	6
55	0.528 69	0.622 85	1.605 5	0.848 82	1.178 1	1.891 5	5
56	0.528 93	0.623 25	1.604 5	0.848 66	1.178 3	1.890 6	4
57	0.529 18	0.623 66	1.603 4	0.848 51	1.178 5	1.889 7	3
58	0.529 43	0.624 06	1.602 4	0.848 36	1.178 8	1.888 8	2
59	0.529 67	0.624 46	1.601 4	0.848 20	1.179 0	1.888 0	1
60	0.529 92	0.624 87	1.600 3	0.848 05	1.179 2	1.887 1	0
′	Cos	Cot	Tan	Sin	Csc	Sec	′

′	Sin	Tan	Cot	Cos	Sec	Csc	′
0	**0.529 92**	**0.624 87**	**1.600 3**	**0.848 05**	**1.179 2**	**1.887 1**	60
1	0.530 17	0.625 27	1.599 3	0.847 89	1.179 4	1.886 2	59
2	0.530 41	0.625 68	1.598 3	0.847 74	1.179 6	1.885 3	58
3	0.530 66	0.626 08	1.597 2	0.847 59	1.179 8	1.884 4	57
4	0.530 91	0.626 49	1.596 2	0.847 43	1.180 0	1.883 6	56
5	**0.531 15**	**0.626 89**	**1.595 2**	**0.847 28**	**1.180 3**	**1.882 7**	55
6	0.531 40	0.627 30	1.594 1	0.847 12	1.180 5	1.881 8	54
7	0.531 64	0.627 70	1.593 1	0.846 97	1.180 7	1.881 0	53
8	0.531 89	0.628 11	1.592 1	0.846 81	1.180 9	1.880 1	52
9	0.532 14	0.628 52	1.591 1	0.846 66	1.181 1	1.879 2	51
10	**0.532 38**	**0.628 92**	**1.590 0**	**0.846 50**	**1.181 3**	**1.878 3**	50
11	0.532 63	0.629 33	1.589 0	0.846 35	1.181 5	1.877 5	49
12	0.532 88	0.629 73	1.588 0	0.846 19	1.181 8	1.876 6	48
13	0.533 12	0.630 14	1.586 9	0.846 04	1.182 0	1.875 7	47
14	0.533 37	0.630 55	1.585 9	0.845 88	1.182 2	1.874 9	46
15	**0.533 61**	**0.630 95**	**1.584 9**	**0.845 73**	**1.182 4**	**1.874 0**	45
16	0.533 86	0.631 36	1.583 9	0.845 57	1.182 6	1.873 1	44
17	0.534 11	0.631 77	1.582 9	0.845 42	1.182 8	1.872 3	43
18	0.534 35	0.632 17	1.581 8	0.845 26	1.183 1	1.871 4	42
19	0.534 60	0.632 58	1.580 8	0.845 11	1.183 3	1.870 6	41
20	**0.534 84**	**0.632 99**	**1.579 8**	**0.844 95**	**1.183 5**	**1.869 7**	40
21	0.535 09	0.633 40	1.578 8	0.844 80	1.183 7	1.868 8	39
22	0.535 34	0.633 80	1.577 8	0.844 64	1.183 9	1.868 0	38
23	0.535 58	0.634 21	1.576 8	0.844 48	1.184 2	1.867 1	37
24	0.535 83	0.634 62	1.575 7	0.844 33	1.184 4	1.866 3	36
25	**0.536 07**	**0.635 03**	**1.574 7**	**0.844 17**	**1.184 6**	**1.865 4**	35
26	0.536 32	0.635 44	1.573 7	0.844 02	1.184 8	1.864 6	34
27	0.536 56	0.635 84	1.572 7	0.843 86	1.185 0	1.863 7	33
28	0.536 81	0.636 25	1.571 7	0.843 70	1.185 2	1.862 9	32
29	0.537 05	0.636 66	1.570 7	0.843 55	1.185 5	1.862 0	31
30	**0.537 30**	**0.637 07**	**1.569 7**	**0.843 39**	**1.185 7**	**1.861 2**	30
31	0.537 54	0.637 48	1.568 7	0.843 24	1.185 9	1.860 3	29
32	0.537 79	0.637 89	1.567 7	0.843 08	1.186 1	1.859 5	28
33	0.538 04	0.638 30	1.566 7	0.842 92	1.186 3	1.858 6	27
34	0.538 28	0.638 71	1.565 7	0.842 77	1.186 6	1.857 8	26
35	**0.538 53**	**0.639 12**	**1.564 7**	**0.842 61**	**1.186 8**	**1.856 9**	25
36	0.538 77	0.639 53	1.563 7	0.842 45	1.187 0	1.856 1	24
37	0.539 02	0.639 94	1.562 7	0.842 30	1.187 2	1.855 2	23
38	0.539 26	0.640 36	1.561 7	0.842 14	1.187 5	1.854 4	22
39	0.539 51	0.640 76	1.560 7	0.841 98	1.187 7	1.853 3	21
40	**0.539 75**	**0.641 17**	**1.559 7**	**0.841 82**	**1.187 9**	**1.852 7**	20
41	0.540 00	0.641 58	1.558 7	0.841 67	1.188 1	1.851 9	19
42	0.540 24	0.641 99	1.557 7	0.841 51	1.188 3	1.851 0	18
43	0.540 49	0.642 40	1.556 7	0.841 35	1.188 6	1.850 2	17
44	0.540 73	0.642 81	1.555 7	0.841 20	1.188 8	1.849 4	16
45	**0.540 97**	**0.643 22**	**1.554 7**	**0.841 04**	**1.189 0**	**1.848 5**	15
46	0.541 22	0.643 63	1.553 7	0.840 88	1.189 2	1.847 7	14
47	0.541 46	0.644 04	1.552 7	0.840 72	1.189 5	1.846 8	13
48	0.541 71	0.644 46	1.551 7	0.840 57	1.189 7	1.846 0	12
49	0.541 95	0.644 87	1.550 7	0.840 41	1.189 9	1.845 2	11
50	**0.542 20**	**0.645 28**	**1.549 7**	**0.840 25**	**1.190 1**	**1.844 3**	10
51	0.542 44	0.645 69	1.548 7	0.840 09	1.190 3	1.843 5	9
52	0.542 69	0.646 10	1.547 7	0.839 94	1.190 6	1.842 7	8
53	0.542 93	0.646 52	1.546 8	0.839 78	1.190 8	1.841 9	7
54	0.543 17	0.646 93	1.545 8	0.839 62	1.191 0	1.841 0	6
55	**0.543 42**	**0.647 34**	**1.544 8**	**0.839 46**	**1.191 2**	**1.840 2**	5
56	0.543 66	0.647 75	1.543 8	0.839 30	1.191 5	1.839 4	4
57	0.543 91	0.648 17	1.542 8	0.839 15	1.191 7	1.838 5	3
58	0.544 15	0.648 58	1.541 8	0.838 99	1.191 9	1.837 7	2
59	0.544 40	0.648 99	1.540 8	0.838 83	1.192 1	1.836 9	1
60	**0.544 64**	**0.649 41**	**1.539 9**	**0.838 67**	**1.192 4**	**1.836 1**	0
′	Cos	Cot	Tan	Sin	Csc	Sec	′

Table 3 / *Five-place natural trigonometric functions*   □   **655**

′	Sin	Tan	Cot	Cos	Sec	Csc	′
0	**0.544 64**	**0.649 41**	**1.539 9**	**0.838 67**	**1.192 4**	**1.836 1**	60
1	0.544 88	0.649 62	1.538 9	0.838 51	1.192 6	1.835 3	59
2	0.545 13	0.650 24	1.537 9	0.838 35	1.192 8	1.834 4	58
3	0.545 37	0.650 65	1.536 9	0.838 19	1.193 0	1.833 6	57
4	0.545 61	0.651 06	1.535 9	0.838 04	1.193 3	1.832 8	56
5	**0.545 86**	**0.651 48**	**1.535 0**	**0.837 88**	**1.193 5**	**1.832 0**	55
6	0.546 10	0.651 89	1.534 0	0.837 72	1.193 7	1.831 2	54
7	0.546 35	0.652 31	1.533 0	0.837 56	1.193 9	1.830 3	53
8	0.546 59	0.652 72	1.532 0	0.837 40	1.194 2	1.829 5	52
9	0.546 83	0.653 14	1.531 1	0.837 24	1.194 4	1.828 7	51
10	**0.547 08**	**0.653 55**	**1.530 1**	**0.837 08**	**1.194 6**	**1.827 9**	50
11	0.547 32	0.653 97	1.529 1	0.836 92	1.194 9	1.827 1	49
12	0.547 56	0.654 38	1.528 2	0.836 76	1.195 1	1.826 3	48
13	0.547 81	0.654 80	1.527 2	0.836 60	1.195 3	1.825 5	47
14	0.548 05	0.655 21	1.526 2	0.836 45	1.195 5	1.824 7	46
15	**0.548 29**	**0.655 63**	**1.525 3**	**0.836 29**	**1.195 8**	**1.823 8**	45
16	0.548 54	0.656 04	1.524 3	0.836 13	1.196 0	1.823 0	44
17	0.548 78	0.656 46	1.523 3	0.835 97	1.196 2	1.822 2	43
18	0.549 02	0.656 88	1.522 4	0.835 81	1.196 4	1.821 4	42
19	0.549 27	0.657 29	1.521 4	0.835 65	1.196 7	1.820 6	41
20	**0.549 51**	**0.657 71**	**1.520 4**	**0.835 49**	**1.196 9**	**1.819 8**	40
21	0.549 75	0.658 13	1.519 5	0.835 33	1.197 1	1.819 0	39
22	0.549 99	0.658 54	1.518 5	0.835 17	1.197 4	1.818 2	38
23	0.550 24	0.658 96	1.517 5	0.835 01	1.197 6	1.817 4	37
24	0.550 48	0.659 38	1.516 6	0.834 85	1.197 8	1.816 6	36
25	**0.550 72**	**0.659 80**	**1.515 6**	**0.834 69**	**1.198 1**	**1.815 8**	35
26	0.550 97	0.660 21	1.514 7	0.834 53	1.198 3	1.815 0	34
27	0.551 21	0.660 63	1.513 7	0.834 37	1.198 5	1.814 2	33
28	0.551 45	0.661 05	1.512 7	0.834 21	1.198 7	1.813 4	32
29	0.551 69	0.661 47	1.511 8	0.834 05	1.199 0	1.812 6	31
30	**0.551 94**	**0.661 89**	**1.510 8**	**0.833 89**	**1.199 2**	**1.811 8**	30
31	0.552 18	0.662 30	1.509 9	0.833 73	1.199 4	1.811 0	29
32	0.552 42	0.662 72	1.508 9	0.833 56	1.199 7	1.810 2	28
33	0.552 66	0.663 14	1.508 0	0.833 40	1.199 9	1.809 4	27
34	0.552 91	0.663 56	1.507 0	0.833 24	1.200 1	1.808 6	26
35	**0.553 15**	**0.663 98**	**1.506 1**	**0.833 08**	**1.200 4**	**1.807 8**	25
36	0.553 39	0.664 40	1.505 1	0.832 92	1.200 6	1.807 0	24
37	0.553 63	0.664 82	1.504 2	0.832 76	1.200 8	1.806 2	23
38	0.553 88	0.665 24	1.503 2	0.832 60	1.201 1	1.805 5	22
39	0.554 12	0.665 66	1.502 3	0.832 44	1.201 3	1.804 7	21
40	**0.554 36**	**0.666 08**	**1.501 3**	**0.832 28**	**1.201 5**	**1.803 9**	20
41	0.554 60	0.666 50	1.500 4	0.832 12	1.201 8	1.803 1	19
42	0.554 84	0.666 92	1.499 4	0.831 95	1.202 0	1.802 3	18
43	0.555 09	0.667 34	1.498 5	0.831 79	1.202 2	1.801 5	17
44	0.555 33	0.667 76	1.497 5	0.831 63	1.202 5	1.800 7	16
45	**0.555 57**	**0.668 18**	**1.496 6**	**0.831 47**	**1.202 7**	**1.800 0**	15
46	0.555 81	0.668 60	1.495 7	0.831 31	1.202 9	1.799 2	14
47	0.556 05	0.669 02	1.494 7	0.831 15	1.203 2	1.798 4	13
48	0.556 30	0.669 44	1.493 8	0.830 98	1.203 4	1.797 6	12
49	0.556 54	0.669 86	1.492 8	0.830 82	1.203 6	1.796 8	11
50	**0.556 78**	**0.670 28**	**1.491 9**	**0.830 66**	**1.203 9**	**1.796 0**	10
51	0.557 02	0.670 71	1.491 0	0.830 50	1.204 1	1.795 3	9
52	0.557 26	0.671 13	1.490 0	0.830 34	1.204 3	1.794 5	8
53	0.557 50	0.671 55	1.489 1	0.830 17	1.204 6	1.793 7	7
54	0.557 75	0.671 97	1.488 2	0.830 01	1.204 8	1.792 9	6
55	**0.557 99**	**0.672 39**	**1.487 2**	**0.829 85**	**1.205 0**	**1.792 2**	5
56	0.558 23	0.672 82	1.486 3	0.829 69	1.205 3	1.791 4	4
57	0.558 47	0.673 24	1.485 4	0.829 53	1.205 5	1.790 6	3
58	0.558 71	0.673 66	1.484 4	0.829 36	1.205 7	1.789 8	2
59	0.558 95	0.674 09	1.483 5	0.829 20	1.206 0	1.789 1	1
60	**0.559 19**	**0.674 51**	**1.482 6**	**0.829 04**	**1.206 2**	**1.788 3**	0
′	Cos	Cot	Tan	Sin	Csc	Sec	′

′	Sin	Tan	Cot	Cos	Sec	Csc	′
0	**0.559 19**	**0.674 51**	**1.482 6**	**0.829 04**	**1.206 2**	**1.788 3**	60
1	0.559 43	0.674 93	1.481 6	0.828 87	1.206 5	1.787 5	59
2	0.559 68	0.675 36	1.480 7	0.828 71	1.206 7	1.786 8	58
3	0.559 92	0.675 78	1.479 8	0.828 55	1.206 9	1.786 0	57
4	0.560 16	0.676 20	1.478 8	0.828 39	1.207 2	1.785 2	56
5	**0.560 40**	**0.676 63**	**1.477 9**	**0.828 22**	**1.207 4**	**1.784 4**	55
6	0.560 64	0.677 05	1.477 0	0.828 06	1.207 6	1.783 7	54
7	0.560 88	0.677 48	1.476 1	0.827 90	1.207 9	1.782 9	53
8	0.561 12	0.677 90	1.475 1	0.827 73	1.208 1	1.782 1	52
9	0.561 36	0.678 32	1.474 2	0.827 57	1.208 4	1.781 4	51
10	**0.561 60**	**0.678 75**	**1.473 3**	**0.827 41**	**1.208 6**	**1.780 6**	50
11	0.561 84	0.679 17	1.472 4	0.827 24	1.208 8	1.779 9	49
12	0.562 08	0.679 60	1.471 5	0.827 08	1.209 1	1.779 1	48
13	0.562 32	0.680 02	1.470 5	0.826 92	1.209 3	1.778 3	47
14	0.562 56	0.680 45	1.469 6	0.826 75	1.209 6	1.777 6	46
15	**0.562 80**	**0.680 88**	**1.468 7**	**0.826 59**	**1.209 8**	**1.776 8**	45
16	0.563 05	0.681 30	1.467 8	0.826 43	1.210 0	1.776 1	44
17	0.563 29	0.681 73	1.466 9	0.826 26	1.210 3	1.775 3	43
18	0.563 53	0.682 15	1.465 9	0.826 10	1.210 5	1.774 5	42
19	0.563 77	0.682 58	1.465 0	0.825 93	1.210 8	1.773 8	41
20	**0.564 01**	**0.683 01**	**1.464 1**	**0.825 77**	**1.211 0**	**1.773 0**	40
21	0.564 25	0.683 43	1.463 2	0.825 61	1.211 2	1.772 3	39
22	0.564 49	0.683 86	1.462 3	0.825 44	1.211 5	1.771 5	38
23	0.564 73	0.684 29	1.461 4	0.825 28	1.211 7	1.770 8	37
24	0.564 97	0.684 71	1.460 5	0.825 11	1.212 0	1.770 0	36
25	**0.565 21**	**0.685 14**	**1.459 6**	**0.824 95**	**1.212 2**	**1.769 3**	35
26	0.565 45	0.685 57	1.458 6	0.824 78	1.212 4	1.768 5	34
27	0.565 69	0.686 00	1.457 7	0.824 62	1.212 7	1.767 8	33
28	0.565 93	0.686 42	1.456 8	0.824 46	1.212 9	1.767 0	32
29	0.566 17	0.686 85	1.455 9	0.824 29	1.213 2	1.766 3	31
30	**0.566 41**	**0.687 28**	**1.455 0**	**0.824 13**	**1.213 4**	**1.765 5**	30
31	0.566 65	0.687 71	1.454 1	0.823 96	1.213 6	1.764 8	29
32	0.566 89	0.688 14	1.453 2	0.823 80	1.213 9	1.764 0	28
33	0.567 13	0.688 57	1.452 3	0.823 63	1.214 1	1.763 3	27
34	0.567 36	0.689 00	1.451 4	0.823 47	1.214 4	1.762 5	26
35	**0.567 60**	**0.689 42**	**1.450 5**	**0.823 30**	**1.214 6**	**1.761 8**	25
36	0.567 84	0.689 85	1.449 6	0.823 14	1.214 9	1.761 0	24
37	0.568 08	0.690 28	1.448 7	0.822 97	1.215 1	1.760 3	23
38	0.568 32	0.690 71	1.447 8	0.822 81	1.215 4	1.759 6	22
39	0.568 56	0.691 14	1.446 9	0.822 64	1.215 6	1.758 8	21
40	**0.568 80**	**0.691 57**	**1.446 0**	**0.822 48**	**1.215 8**	**1.758 1**	20
41	0.569 04	0.692 00	1.445 1	0.822 31	1.216 1	1.757 3	19
42	0.569 28	0.692 43	1.444 2	0.822 14	1.216 3	1.756 6	18
43	0.569 52	0.692 86	1.443 3	0.821 98	1.216 6	1.755 9	17
44	0.569 76	0.693 29	1.442 4	0.821 81	1.216 8	1.755 1	16
45	**0.570 00**	**0.693 72**	**1.441 5**	**0.821 65**	**1.217 1**	**1.754 4**	15
46	0.570 24	0.694 16	1.440 6	0.821 48	1.217 3	1.753 7	14
47	0.570 47	0.694 59	1.439 7	0.821 32	1.217 6	1.752 9	13
48	0.570 71	0.695 02	1.438 8	0.821 15	1.217 8	1.752 2	12
49	0.570 95	0.695 45	1.437 9	0.820 98	1.218 1	1.751 5	11
50	**0.571 19**	**0.695 88**	**1.437 0**	**0.820 82**	**1.218 3**	**1.750 7**	10
51	0.571 43	0.696 31	1.436 1	0.820 65	1.218 5	1.750 0	9
52	0.571 67	0.696 75	1.435 2	0.820 48	1.218 8	1.749 3	8
53	0.571 91	0.697 18	1.434 4	0.820 32	1.219 0	1.748 5	7
54	0.572 15	0.697 61	1.433 5	0.820 15	1.219 3	1.747 8	6
55	**0.572 38**	**0.698 04**	**1.432 6**	**0.819 99**	**1.219 5**	**1.747 1**	5
56	0.572 62	0.698 47	1.431 7	0.819 82	1.219 8	1.746 3	4
57	0.572 86	0.698 91	1.430 8	0.819 65	1.220 0	1.745 6	3
58	0.573 10	0.699 34	1.429 9	0.819 49	1.220 3	1.744 9	2
59	0.573 34	0.699 77	1.429 0	0.819 32	1.220 5	1.744 2	1
60	**0.573 58**	**0.700 21**	**1.428 1**	**0.819 15**	**1.220 8**	**1.743 4**	0
′	Cos	Cot	Tan	Sin	Csc	Sec	′

′	Sin	Tan	Cot	Cos	Sec	Csc	′
0	**0.573 58**	**0.700 21**	**1.428 1**	**0.819 15**	**1.220 8**	**1.743 4**	60
1	0.573 81	0.700 64	1.427 3	0.818 99	1.221 0	1.742 7	59
2	0.574 05	0.701 07	1.426 4	0.818 82	1.221 3	1.742 0	58
3	0.574 29	0.701 51	1.425 5	0.818 65	1.221 5	1.741 3	57
4	0.574 53	0.701 94	1.424 6	0.818 48	1.221 8	1.740 6	56
5	**0.574 77**	**0.702 38**	**1.423 7**	**0.818 32**	**1.222 0**	**1.739 8**	55
6	0.575 01	0.702 81	1.422 9	0.818 15	1.222 3	1.739 1	54
7	0.575 24	0.703 25	1.422 0	0.817 98	1.222 5	1.738 4	53
8	0.575 48	0.703 68	1.421 1	0.817 82	1.222 8	1.737 7	52
9	0.575 72	0.704 12	1.420 2	0.817 65	1.223 0	1.737 0	51
10	**0.575 96**	**0.704 55**	**1.419 3**	**0.817 48**	**1.223 3**	**1.736 2**	50
11	0.576 19	0.704 99	1.418 5	0.817 31	1.223 5	1.735 5	49
12	0.576 43	0.705 42	1.417 6	0.817 14	1.223 8	1.734 8	48
13	0.576 67	0.705 86	1.416 7	0.816 98	1.224 0	1.734 1	47
14	0.576 91	0.706 29	1.415 8	0.816 81	1.224 3	1.733 4	46
15	**0.577 15**	**0.706 73**	**1.415 0**	**0.816 64**	**1.224 5**	**1.732 7**	45
16	0.577 38	0.707 17	1.414 1	0.816 47	1.224 8	1.732 0	44
17	0.577 62	0.707 60	1.413 2	0.816 31	1.225 0	1.731 2	43
18	0.577 86	0.708 04	1.412 4	0.816 14	1.225 3	1.730 5	42
19	0.578 10	0.708 48	1.411 5	0.815 97	1.225 5	1.729 8	41
20	**0.578 33**	**0.708 91**	**1.410 6**	**0.815 80**	**1.225 8**	**1.729 1**	40
21	0.578 57	0.709 35	1.409 7	0.815 63	1.226 0	1.728 4	39
22	0.578 81	0.709 79	1.408 9	0.815 46	1.226 3	1.727 7	38
23	0.579 04	0.710 23	1.408 0	0.815 30	1.226 5	1.727 0	37
24	0.579 28	0.710 66	1.407 1	0.815 13	1.226 8	1.726 3	36
25	**0.579 52**	**0.711 10**	**1.406 3**	**0.814 96**	**1.227 1**	**1.725 6**	35
26	0.579 76	0.711 54	1.405 4	0.814 79	1.227 3	1.724 9	34
27	0.579 99	0.711 98	1.404 5	0.814 62	1.227 6	1.724 2	33
28	0.580 23	0.712 42	1.403 7	0.814 45	1.227 8	1.723 5	32
29	0.580 47	0.712 85	1.402 8	0.814 28	1.228 1	1.722 8	31
30	**0.580 70**	**0.713 29**	**1.401 9**	**0.814 12**	**1.228 3**	**1.722 1**	30
31	0.580 94	0.713 73	1.401 1	0.813 95	1.228 6	1.721 3	29
32	0.581 18	0.714 17	1.400 2	0.813 78	1.228 8	1.720 6	28
33	0.581 41	0.714 61	1.399 4	0.813 61	1.229 1	1.719 9	27
34	0.581 65	0.715 05	1.398 5	0.813 44	1.229 3	1.719 2	26
35	**0.581 89**	**0.715 49**	**1.397 6**	**0.813 27**	**1.229 6**	**1.718 5**	25
36	0.582 12	0.715 93	1.396 8	0.813 10	1.229 9	1.717 9	24
37	0.582 36	0.716 37	1.395 9	0.812 93	1.230 1	1.717 2	23
38	0.582 60	0.716 81	1.395 1	0.812 76	1.230 4	1.716 5	22
39	0.582 83	0.717 25	1.394 2	0.812 59	1.230 6	1.715 8	21
40	**0.583 07**	**0.717 69**	**1.393 4**	**0.812 42**	**1.230 9**	**1.715 1**	20
41	0.583 30	0.718 13	1.392 5	0.812 25	1.231 1	1.714 4	19
42	0.583 54	0.718 57	1.391 6	0.812 08	1.231 4	1.713 7	18
43	0.583 78	0.719 01	1.390 8	0.811 91	1.231 7	1.713 0	17
44	0.584 01	0.719 46	1.389 9	0.811 74	1.231 9	1.712 3	16
45	**0.584 25**	**0.719 90**	**1.389 1**	**0.811 57**	**1.232 2**	**1.711 6**	15
46	0.584 49	0.720 34	1.388 2	0.811 40	1.232 4	1.710 9	14
47	0.584 72	0.720 78	1.387 4	0.811 23	1.232 7	1.710 2	13
48	0.584 96	0.721 22	1.386 5	0.811 06	1.232 9	1.709 5	12
49	0.585 19	0.721 67	1.385 7	0.810 89	1.233 2	1.708 8	11
50	**0.585 43**	**0.722 11**	**1.384 8**	**0.810 72**	**1.233 5**	**1.708 1**	10
51	0.585 67	0.722 55	1.384 0	0.810 55	1.233 7	1.707 5	9
52	0.585 90	0.722 99	1.383 1	0.810 38	1.234 0	1.706 8	8
53	0.586 14	0.723 44	1.382 3	0.810 21	1.234 2	1.706 1	7
54	0.586 37	0.723 88	1.381 4	0.810 04	1.234 5	1.705 4	6
55	**0.586 61**	**0.724 32**	**1.380 6**	**0.809 87**	**1.234 8**	**1.704 7**	5
56	0.586 84	0.724 77	1.379 8	0.809 70	1.235 0	1.704 0	4
57	0.587 08	0.725 21	1.378 9	0.809 53	1.235 3	1.703 3	3
58	0.587 31	0.725 65	1.378 1	0.809 36	1.235 5	1.702 7	2
59	0.587 55	0.726 10	1.377 2	0.809 19	1.235 8	1.702 0	1
60	**0.587 79**	**0.726 54**	**1.376 4**	**0.809 02**	**1.236 1**	**1.701 3**	0
′	Cos	Cot	Tan	Sin	Csc	Sec	′

′	Sin	Tan	Cot	Cos	Sec	Csc	
0	**0.587 79**	**0.726 54**	**1.376 4**	**0.809 02**	**1.236 1**	**1.701 3**	60
1	0.588 02	0.726 99	1.375 5	0.808 85	1.236 3	1.700 6	59
2	0.588 26	0.727 43	1.374 7	0.808 67	1.236 6	1.699 9	58
3	0.588 49	0.727 88	1.373 9	0.808 50	1.236 9	1.699 3	57
4	0.588 73	0.728 32	1.373 0	0.808 33	1.237 1	1.698 6	56
5	**0.588 96**	**0.728 77**	**1.372 2**	**0.808 16**	**1.237 4**	**1.697 9**	55
6	0.589 20	0.729 21	1.371 3	0.807 99	1.237 6	1.697 2	54
7	0.589 43	0.729 66	1.370 5	0.807 82	1.237 9	1.696 6	53
8	0.589 67	0.730 10	1.369 7	0.807 65	1.238 2	1.695 9	52
9	0.589 90	0.730 55	1.368 8	0.807 48	1.238 4	1.695 2	51
10	**0.590 14**	**0.731 00**	**1.368 0**	**0.807 30**	**1.238 7**	**1.694 5**	50
11	0.590 37	0.731 44	1.367 2	0.807 13	1.239 0	1.693 9	49
12	0.590 61	0.731 89	1.366 3	0.806 96	1.239 2	1.693 2	48
13	0.590 84	0.732 34	1.365 5	0.806 79	1.239 5	1.692 5	47
14	0.591 08	0.732 78	1.364 7	0.806 62	1.239 7	1.691 8	46
15	**0.591 31**	**0.733 23**	**1.363 8**	**0.806 44**	**1.240 0**	**1.691 2**	45
16	0.591 54	0.733 68	1.363 0	0.806 27	1.240 3	1.690 5	44
17	0.591 78	0.734 13	1.362 2	0.806 10	1.240 5	1.689 8	43
18	0.592 01	0.734 57	1.361 3	0.805 93	1.240 8	1.689 2	42
19	0.592 25	0.735 02	1.360 5	0.805 76	1.241 1	1.688 5	41
20	**0.592 48**	**0.735 47**	**1.359 7**	**0.805 58**	**1.241 3**	**1.687 8**	40
21	0.592 72	0.735 92	1.358 8	0.805 41	1.241 6	1.687 1	39
22	0.592 95	0.736 37	1.358 0	0.805 24	1.241 9	1.686 5	38
23	0.593 18	0.736 81	1.357 2	0.805 07	1.242 1	1.685 8	37
24	0.593 42	0.737 26	1.356 4	0.804 89	1.242 4	1.685 2	36
25	**0.593 65**	**0.737 71**	**1.355 5**	**0.804 72**	**1.242 7**	**1.684 5**	35
26	0.593 89	0.738 16	1.354 7	0.804 55	1.242 9	1.683 8	34
27	0.594 12	0.738 61	1.353 9	0.804 38	1.243 2	1.683 2	33
28	0.594 36	0.739 06	1.353 1	0.804 20	1.243 5	1.682 5	32
29	0.594 59	0.739 51	1.352 2	0.804 03	1.243 7	1.681 8	31
30	**0.594 82**	**0.739 96**	**1.351 4**	**0.803 86**	**1.244 0**	**1.681 2**	30
31	0.595 06	0.740 41	1.350 6	0.803 68	1.244 3	1.680 5	29
32	0.595 29	0.740 86	1.349 8	0.803 51	1.244 5	1.679 9	28
33	0.595 52	0.741 31	1.349 0	0.803 34	1.244 8	1.679 2	27
34	0.595 76	0.741 76	1.348 1	0.803 16	1.245 1	1.678 5	26
35	**0.595 99**	**0.742 21**	**1.347 3**	**0.802 99**	**1.245 3**	**1.677 9**	25
36	0.596 22	0.742 67	1.346 5	0.802 82	1.245 6	1.677 2	24
37	0.596 46	0.743 12	1.345 7	0.802 64	1.245 9	1.676 6	23
38	0.596 69	0.743 57	1.344 9	0.802 47	1.246 2	1.675 9	22
39	0.596 93	0.744 02	1.344 0	0.802 30	1.246 4	1.675 3	21
40	**0.597 16**	**0.744 47**	**1.343 2**	**0.802 12**	**1.246 7**	**1.674 6**	20
41	0.597 39	0.744 92	1.342 4	0.801 95	1.247 0	1.673 9	19
42	0.597 63	0.745 38	1.341 6	0.801 78	1.247 2	1.673 3	18
43	0.597 86	0.745 83	1.340 8	0.801 60	1.247 5	1.672 6	17
44	0.598 09	0.746 28	1.340 0	0.801 43	1.247 8	1.672 0	16
45	**0.598 32**	**0.746 74**	**1.339 2**	**0.801 25**	**1.248 0**	**1.671 3**	15
46	0.598 56	0.747 19	1.338 4	0.801 08	1.248 3	1.670 7	14
47	0.598 79	0.747 64	1.337 5	0.800 91	1.248 6	1.670 0	13
48	0.599 02	0.748 10	1.336 7	0.800 73	1.248 9	1.669 4	12
49	0.599 26	0.748 55	1.335 9	0.800 56	1.249 1	1.668 7	11
50	**0.599 49**	**0.749 00**	**1.335 1**	**0.800 38**	**1.249 4**	**1.668 1**	10
51	0.599 72	0.749 46	1.334 3	0.800 21	1.249 7	1.667 4	9
52	0.599 95	0.749 91	1.333 5	0.800 03	1.249 9	1.666 8	8
53	0.600 19	0.750 37	1.332 7	0.799 86	1.250 2	1.666 1	7
54	0.600 42	0.750 82	1.331 9	0.799 68	1.250 5	1.665 5	6
55	**0.600 65**	**0.751 28**	**1.331 1**	**0.799 51**	**1.250 8**	**1.664 9**	5
56	0.600 89	0.751 73	1.330 3	0.799 34	1.251 0	1.664 2	4
57	0.601 12	0.752 19	1.329 5	0.799 16	1.251 3	1.663 6	3
58	0.601 35	0.752 64	1.328 7	0.798 99	1.251 6	1.662 9	2
59	0.601 58	0.753 10	1.327 8	0.798 81	1.251 9	1.662 3	1
60	**0.601 82**	**0.753 55**	**1.327 0**	**0.798 64**	**1.252 1**	**1.661 6**	0
′	Cos	Cot	Tan	Sin	Csc	Sec	′

Table 3 / Five-place natural trigonometric functions □ **659**

′	Sin	Tan	Cot	Cos	Sec	Csc	
0	**0.601 82**	**0.753 55**	**1.327 0**	**0.798 64**	**1.252 1**	**1.661 6**	60
1	0.602 05	0.754 01	1.326 2	0.798 46	1.252 4	1.661 0	59
2	0.602 28	0.754 47	1.325 4	0.798 29	1.252 7	1.660 4	58
3	0.602 51	0.754 92	1.324 6	0.798 11	1.253 0	1.659 7	57
4	0.602 74	0.755 38	1.323 8	0.797 93	1.253 2	1.659 1	56
5	**0.602 98**	**0.755 84**	**1.323 0**	**0.797 76**	**1.253 5**	**1.658 4**	55
6	0.603 21	0.756 29	1.322 2	0.797 58	1.253 8	1.657 8	54
7	0.603 44	0.756 75	1.321 4	0.797 41	1.254 1	1.657 2	53
8	0.603 67	0.757 21	1.320 6	0.797 23	1.254 3	1.656 5	52
9	0.603 90	0.757 67	1.319 8	0.797 06	1.254 6	1.655 9	51
10	**0.604 14**	**0.758 12**	**1.319 0**	**0.796 88**	**1.254 9**	**1.655 3**	50
11	0.604 37	0.758 58	1.318 2	0.796 71	1.255 2	1.654 6	49
12	0.604 60	0.759 04	1.317 5	0.796 53	1.255 4	1.654 0	48
13	0.604 83	0.759 50	1.316 7	0.796 35	1.255 7	1.653 4	47
14	0.605 06	0.759 96	1.315 9	0.796 18	1.256 0	1.652 7	46
15	**0.605 29**	**0.760 42**	**1.315 1**	**0.796 00**	**1.256 3**	**1.652 1**	45
16	0.605 53	0.760 88	1.314 3	0.795 83	1.256 6	1.651 5	44
17	0.605 76	0.761 34	1.313 5	0.795 65	1.256 8	1.650 8	43
18	0.605 99	0.761 80	1.312 7	0.795 47	1.257 1	1.650 2	42
19	0.606 22	0.762 26	1.311 9	0.795 30	1.257 4	1.649 6	41
20	**0.606 45**	**0.762 72**	**1.311 1**	**0.795 12**	**1.257 7**	**1.648 9**	40
21	0.606 68	0.763 18	1.310 3	0.794 94	1.257 9	1.648 3	39
22	0.606 91	0.763 64	1.309 5	0.794 77	1.258 2	1.647 7	38
23	0.607 14	0.764 10	1.308 7	0.794 59	1.258 5	1.647 1	37
24	0.607 38	0.764 56	1.307 9	0.794 41	1.258 8	1.646 4	36
25	**0.607 61**	**0.765 02**	**1.307 2**	**0.794 24**	**1.259 1**	**1.645 8**	35
26	0.607 84	0.765 48	1.306 4	0.794 06	1.259 3	1.645 2	34
27	0.608 07	0.765 94	1.305 6	0.793 88	1.259 6	1.644 6	33
28	0.608 30	0.766 40	1.304 8	0.793 71	1.259 9	1.643 9	32
29	0.608 53	0.766 86	1.304 0	0.793 53	1.260 2	1.643 3	31
30	**0.608 76**	**0.767 33**	**1.303 2**	**0.793 35**	**1.260 5**	**1.642 7**	30
31	0.608 99	0.767 79	1.302 4	0.793 18	1.260 8	1.642 1	29
32	0.609 22	0.768 25	1.301 7	0.793 00	1.261 0	1.641 4	28
33	0.609 45	0.768 71	1.300 9	0.792 82	1.261 3	1.640 8	27
34	0.609 68	0.769 18	1.300 1	0.792 64	1.261 6	1.640 2	26
35	**0.609 91**	**0.769 64**	**1.299 3**	**0.792 47**	**1.261 9**	**1.639 6**	25
36	0.610 15	0.770 10	1.298 5	0.792 29	1.262 2	1.639 0	24
37	0.610 38	0.770 57	1.297 7	0.792 11	1.262 4	1.638 3	23
38	0.610 61	0.771 03	1.297 0	0.791 93	1.262 7	1.637 7	22
39	0.610 84	0.771 49	1.296 2	0.791 76	1.263 0	1.637 1	21
40	**0.611 07**	**0.771 96**	**1.295 4**	**0.791 58**	**1.263 3**	**1.636 5**	20
41	0.611 30	0.772 42	1.294 6	0.791 40	1.263 6	1.635 9	19
42	0.611 53	0.772 89	1.293 8	0.791 22	1.263 9	1.635 3	18
43	0.611 76	0.773 35	1.293 1	0.791 05	1.264 1	1.634 6	17
44	0.611 99	0.773 82	1.292 3	0.790 87	1.264 4	1.634 0	16
45	**0.612 22**	**0.774 28**	**1.291 5**	**0.790 69**	**1.264 7**	**1.633 4**	15
46	0.612 45	0.774 75	1.290 7	0.790 51	1.265 0	1.632 8	14
47	0.612 68	0.775 21	1.290 0	0.790 33	1.265 3	1.632 2	13
48	0.612 91	0.775 68	1.289 2	0.790 16	1.265 6	1.631 6	12
49	0.613 14	0.776 15	1.288 4	0.789 98	1.265 9	1.631 0	11
50	**0.613 37**	**0.776 61**	**1.287 6**	**0.789 80**	**1.266 1**	**1.630 3**	10
51	0.613 60	0.777 08	1.286 9	0.789 62	1.266 4	1.629 7	9
52	0.613 83	0.777 54	1.286 1	0.789 44	1.266 7	1.629 1	8
53	0.614 06	0.778 01	1.285 3	0.789 26	1.267 0	1.628 5	7
54	0.614 29	0.778 48	1.284 6	0.789 08	1.267 3	1.627 9	6
55	**0.614 51**	**0.778 95**	**1.283 8**	**0.788 91**	**1.267 6**	**1.627 3**	5
56	0.614 74	0.779 41	1.283 0	0.788 73	1.267 9	1.626 7	4
57	0.614 97	0.779 88	1.282 2	0.788 55	1.268 2	1.626 1	3
58	0.615 20	0.780 35	1.281 5	0.788 37	1.268 4	1.625 5	2
59	0.615 43	0.780 82	1.280 7	0.788 19	1.268 7	1.624 9	1
60	**0.615 66**	**0.781 29**	**1.279 9**	**0.788 01**	**1.269 0**	**1.624 3**	0
′	Cos	Cot	Tan	Sin	Csc	Sec	′

′	Sin	Tan	Cot	Cos	Sec	Csc	′
0	0.615 66	0.781 29	1.279 9	0.788 01	1.269 0	1.624 3	60
1	0.615 89	0.781 75	1.279 2	0.787 83	1.269 3	1.623 7	59
2	0.616 12	0.782 22	1.278 4	0.787 65	1.269 6	1.623 1	58
3	0.616 35	0.782 69	1.277 6	0.787 47	1.269 9	1.622 5	57
4	0.616 58	0.783 16	1.276 9	0.787 29	1.270 2	1.621 9	56
5	0.616 81	0.783 63	1.276 1	0.787 11	1.270 5	1.621 3	55
6	0.617 04	0.784 10	1.275 3	0.786 94	1.270 8	1.620 7	54
7	0.617 26	0.784 57	1.274 6	0.786 76	1.271 0	1.620 1	53
8	0.617 49	0.785 04	1.273 8	0.786 58	1.271 3	1.619 5	52
9	0.617 72	0.785 51	1.273 1	0.786 40	1.271 6	1.618 9	51
10	0.617 95	0.785 98	1.272 3	0.786 22	1.271 9	1.618 3	50
11	0.618 18	0.786 45	1.271 5	0.786 04	1.272 2	1.617 7	49
12	0.618 41	0.786 92	1.270 8	0.785 86	1.272 5	1.617 1	48
13	0.618 64	0.787 39	1.270 0	0.785 68	1.272 8	1.616 5	47
14	0.618 87	0.787 86	1.269 3	0.785 50	1.273 1	1.615 9	46
15	0.619 09	0.788 34	1.268 5	0.785 32	1.273 4	1.615 3	45
16	0.619 32	0.788 81	1.267 7	0.785 14	1.273 7	1.614 7	44
17	0.619 55	0.789 28	1.267 0	0.784 96	1.274 0	1.614 1	43
18	0.619 78	0.789 75	1.266 2	0.784 78	1.274 2	1.613 5	42
19	0.620 01	0.790 22	1.265 5	0.784 60	1.274 5	1.612 9	41
20	0.620 24	0.790 70	1.264 7	0.784 42	1.274 8	1.612 3	40
21	0.620 46	0.791 17	1.264 0	0.784 24	1.275 1	1.611 7	39
22	0.620 69	0.791 64	1.263 2	0.784 05	1.275 4	1.611 1	38
23	0.620 92	0.792 12	1.262 4	0.783 87	1.275 7	1.610 5	37
24	0.621 15	0.792 59	1.261 7	0.783 69	1.276 0	1.609 9	36
25	0.621 38	0.793 06	1.260 9	0.783 51	1.276 3	1.609 3	35
26	0.621 60	0.793 54	1.260 2	0.783 33	1.276 6	1.608 7	34
27	0.621 83	0.794 01	1.259 4	0.783 15	1.276 9	1.608 2	33
28	0.622 06	0.794 49	1.258 7	0.782 97	1.277 2	1.607 6	32
29	0.622 29	0.794 96	1.257 9	0.782 79	1.277 5	1.607 0	31
30	0.622 51	0.795 44	1.257 2	0.782 61	1.277 8	1.606 4	30
31	0.622 74	0.795 91	1.256 4	0.782 43	1.278 1	1.605 8	29
32	0.622 97	0.796 39	1.255 7	0.782 25	1.278 4	1.605 2	28
33	0.623 20	0.796 86	1.254 9	0.782 06	1.278 7	1.604 6	27
34	0.623 42	0.797 34	1.254 2	0.781 88	1.279 0	1.604 0	26
35	0.623 65	0.797 81	1.253 4	0.781 70	1.279 3	1.603 5	25
36	0.623 88	0.798 29	1.252 7	0.781 52	1.279 6	1.602 9	24
37	0.624 11	0.798 77	1.251 9	0.781 34	1.279 9	1.602 3	23
38	0.624 33	0.799 24	1.251 2	0.781 16	1.280 2	1.601 7	22
39	0.624 56	0.799 72	1.250 4	0.780 98	1.280 4	1.601 1	21
40	0.624 79	0.800 20	1.249 7	0.780 79	1.280 7	1.600 5	20
41	0.625 02	0.800 67	1.248 9	0.780 61	1.281 0	1.600 0	19
42	0.625 24	0.801 15	1.248 2	0.780 43	1.281 3	1.599 4	18
43	0.625 47	0.801 63	1.247 5	0.780 25	1.281 6	1.598 8	17
44	0.625 70	0.802 11	1.246 7	0.780 07	1.281 9	1.598 2	16
45	0.625 92	0.802 58	1.246 0	0.779 88	1.282 2	1.597 6	15
46	0.626 15	0.803 06	1.245 2	0.779 70	1.282 5	1.597 1	14
47	0.626 38	0.803 54	1.244 5	0.779 52	1.282 8	1.596 5	13
48	0.626 60	0.804 02	1.243 7	0.779 34	1.283 1	1.595 9	12
49	0.626 83	0.804 50	1.243 0	0.779 16	1.283 4	1.595 3	11
50	0.627 06	0.804 98	1.242 3	0.778 97	1.283 7	1.594 8	10
51	0.627 28	0.805 46	1.241 5	0.778 79	1.284 0	1.594 2	9
52	0.627 51	0.805 94	1.240 8	0.778 61	1.284 3	1.593 6	8
53	0.627 74	0.806 42	1.240 1	0.778 43	1.284 6	1.593 0	7
54	0.627 96	0.806 90	1.239 3	0.778 24	1.284 9	1.592 5	6
55	0.628 19	0.807 38	1.238 6	0.778 06	1.285 2	1.591 9	5
56	0.628 42	0.807 86	1.237 8	0.777 88	1.285 5	1.591 3	4
57	0.628 64	0.808 34	1.237 1	0.777 69	1.285 9	1.590 7	3
58	0.628 87	0.808 82	1.236 4	0.777 51	1.286 2	1.590 2	2
59	0.629 09	0.809 30	1.235 6	0.777 33	1.286 5	1.589 6	1
60	0.629 32	0.809 78	1.234 9	0.777 15	1.286 8	1.589 0	0
′	Cos	Cot	Tan	Sin	Csc	Sec	′

Table 3 / *Five-place natural trigonometric functions* □ 661

′	Sin	Tan	Cot	Cos	Sec	Csc	′
0	0.629 32	0.809 78	1.234 9	0.777 15	1.286 8	1.589 0	60
1	0.629 55	0.810 27	1.234 2	0.776 96	1.287 1	1.588 4	59
2	0.629 77	0.810 75	1.233 4	0.776 78	1.287 4	1.587 9	58
3	0.630 00	0.811 23	1.232 7	0.776 60	1.287 7	1.587 3	57
4	0.630 22	0.811 71	1.232 0	0.776 41	1.288 0	1.586 7	56
5	0.630 45	0.812 20	1.231 2	0.776 23	1.288 3	1.586 2	55
6	0.630 68	0.812 68	1.230 5	0.776 05	1.288 6	1.585 6	54
7	0.630 90	0.813 16	1.229 8	0.775 86	1.288 9	1.585 0	53
8	0.631 13	0.813 64	1.229 0	0.775 68	1.289 2	1.584 5	52
9	0.631 35	0.814 13	1.228 3	0.775 50	1.289 5	1.583 9	51
10	0.631 58	0.814 61	1.227 6	0.775 31	1.289 8	1.583 3	50
11	0.631 80	0.815 10	1.226 8	0.775 13	1.290 1	1.582 8	49
12	0.632 03	0.815 58	1.226 1	0.774 94	1.290 4	1.582 2	48
13	0.632 25	0.816 06	1.225 4	0.774 76	1.290 7	1.581 6	47
14	0.632 48	0.816 55	1.224 7	0.774 58	1.291 0	1.581 1	46
15	0.632 71	0.817 03	1.223 9	0.774 39	1.291 3	1.580 5	45
16	0.632 93	0.817 52	1.223 2	0.774 21	1.291 6	1.580 0	44
17	0.633 16	0.818 00	1.222 5	0.774 02	1.291 9	1.579 4	43
18	0.633 38	0.818 49	1.221 8	0.773 84	1.292 3	1.578 8	42
19	0.633 61	0.818 98	1.221 0	0.773 66	1.292 6	1.578 3	41
20	0.633 83	0.819 46	1.220 3	0.773 47	1.292 9	1.577 7	40
21	0.634 06	0.819 95	1.219 6	0.773 29	1.293 2	1.577 1	39
22	0.634 28	0.820 44	1.218 9	0.773 10	1.293 5	1.576 6	38
23	0.634 51	0.820 92	1.218 1	0.772 92	1.293 8	1.576 0	37
24	0.634 73	0.821 41	1.217 4	0.772 73	1.294 1	1.575 5	36
25	0.634 96	0.821 90	1.216 7	0.772 55	1.294 4	1.574 9	35
26	0.635 18	0.822 38	1.216 0	0.772 36	1.294 7	1.574 4	34
27	0.635 40	0.822 87	1.215 3	0.772 18	1.295 0	1.573 8	33
28	0.635 63	0.823 36	1.214 5	0.771 99	1.295 3	1.573 2	32
29	0.635 85	0.823 85	1.213 8	0.771 81	1.295 7	1.572 7	31
30	0.636 08	0.824 34	1.213 1	0.771 62	1.296 0	1.572 1	30
31	0.636 30	0.824 83	1.212 4	0.771 44	1.296 3	1.571 6	29
32	0.636 53	0.825 31	1.211 7	0.771 25	1.296 6	1.571 0	28
33	0.636 75	0.825 80	1.210 9	0.771 07	1.296 9	1.570 5	27
34	0.636 98	0.826 29	1.210 2	0.770 88	1.297 2	1.569 9	26
35	0.637 20	0.826 78	1.209 5	0.770 70	1.297 5	1.569 4	25
36	0.637 42	0.827 27	1.208 8	0.770 51	1.297 8	1.568 8	24
37	0.637 65	0.827 76	1.208 1	0.770 33	1.298 1	1.568 3	23
38	0.637 87	0.828 25	1.207 4	0.770 14	1.298 5	1.567 7	22
39	0.638 10	0.828 74	1.206 6	0.769 96	1.298 8	1.567 2	21
40	0.638 32	0.829 23	1.205 9	0.769 77	1.299 1	1.566 6	20
41	0.638 54	0.829 72	1.205 2	0.769 59	1.299 4	1.566 1	19
42	0.638 77	0.830 22	1.204 5	0.769 40	1.299 7	1.565 5	18
43	0.638 99	0.830 71	1.203 8	0.769 21	1.300 0	1.565 0	17
44	0.639 22	0.831 20	1.203 1	0.769 03	1.300 3	1.564 4	16
45	0.639 44	0.831 69	1.202 4	0.768 84	1.300 7	1.563 9	15
46	0.639 66	0.832 18	1.201 7	0.768 66	1.301 0	1.563 3	14
47	0.639 89	0.832 68	1.200 9	0.768 47	1.301 3	1.562 8	13
48	0.640 11	0.833 17	1.200 2	0.768 28	1.301 6	1.562 2	12
49	0.640 33	0.833 66	1.199 5	0.768 10	1.301 9	1.561 7	11
50	0.640 56	0.834 15	1.198 8	0.767 91	1.302 2	1.561 1	10
51	0.640 78	0.834 65	1.198 1	0.767 72	1.302 6	1.560 6	9
52	0.641 00	0.835 14	1.197 4	0.767 54	1.302 9	1.560 1	8
53	0.641 23	0.835 64	1.196 7	0.767 35	1.303 2	1.559 5	7
54	0.641 45	0.836 13	1.196 0	0.767 17	1.303 5	1.559 0	6
55	0.641 67	0.836 62	1.195 3	0.766 98	1.303 8	1.558 4	5
56	0.641 90	0.837 12	1.194 6	0.766 79	1.304 1	1.557 9	4
57	0.642 12	0.837 61	1.193 9	0.766 61	1.304 5	1.557 3	3
58	0.642 34	0.838 11	1.193 2	0.766 42	1.304 8	1.556 8	2
59	0.642 56	0.838 60	1.192 5	0.766 23	1.305 1	1.556 3	1
60	0.642 79	0.839 10	1.191 8	0.766 04	1.305 4	1.555 7	0
′	Cos	Cot	Tan	Sin	Csc	Sec	′

′	Sin	Tan	Cot	Cos	Sec	Csc	′
0	**0.642 79**	**0.839 10**	**1.191 8**	**0.766 04**	**1.305 4**	**1.555 7**	**60**
1	0.643 01	0.839 60	1.191 0	0.765 86	1.305 7	1.555 2	59
2	0.643 23	0.840 09	1.190 3	0.765 67	1.306 0	1.554 6	58
3	0.643 46	0.840 59	1.189 6	0.765 48	1.306 4	1.554 1	57
4	0.643 68	0.841 08	1.188 9	0.765 30	1.306 7	1.553 6	56
5	**0.643 90**	**0.841 58**	**1.188 2**	**0.765 11**	**1.307 0**	**1.553 0**	**55**
6	0.644 12	0.842 08	1.187 5	0.764 92	1.307 3	1.552 5	54
7	0.644 35	0.842 58	1.186 8	0.764 73	1.307 6	1.552 0	53
8	0.644 57	0.843 07	1.186 1	0.764 55	1.308 0	1.551 4	52
9	0.644 79	0.843 57	1.185 4	0.764 36	1.308 3	1.550 9	51
10	**0.645 01**	**0.844 07**	**1.184 7**	**0.764 17**	**1.308 6**	**1.550 4**	**50**
11	0.645 24	0.844 57	1.184 0	0.763 98	1.308 9	1.549 8	49
12	0.645 46	0.845 07	1.183 3	0.763 80	1.309 3	1.549 3	48
13	0.645 68	0.845 56	1.182 6	0.763 61	1.309 6	1.548 8	47
14	0.645 90	0.846 06	1.181 9	0.763 42	1.309 9	1.548 2	46
15	**0.646 12**	**0.846 56**	**1.181 2**	**0.763 23**	**1.310 2**	**1.547 7**	**45**
16	0.646 35	0.847 06	1.180 6	0.763 04	1.310 5	1.547 2	44
17	0.646 57	0.847 56	1.179 9	0.762 86	1.310 9	1.546 6	43
18	0.646 79	0.848 06	1.179 2	0.762 67	1.311 2	1.546 1	42
19	0.647 01	0.848 56	1.178 5	0.762 48	1.311 5	1.545 6	41
20	**0.647 23**	**0.849 06**	**1.177 8**	**0.762 29**	**1.311 8**	**1.545 0**	**40**
21	0.647 46	0.849 56	1.177 1	0.762 10	1.312 2	1.544 5	39
22	0.647 68	0.850 06	1.176 4	0.761 92	1.312 5	1.544 0	38
23	0.647 90	0.850 57	1.175 7	0.761 73	1.312 8	1.543 5	37
24	0.648 12	0.851 07	1.175 0	0.761 54	1.313 1	1.542 9	36
25	**0.648 34**	**0.851 57**	**1.174 3**	**0.761 35**	**1.313 5**	**1.542 4**	**35**
26	0.648 56	0.852 07	1.173 6	0.761 16	1.313 8	1.541 9	34
27	0.648 78	0.852 57	1.172 9	0.760 97	1.314 1	1.541 3	33
28	0.649 01	0.853 08	1.172 2	0.760 78	1.314 4	1.540 8	32
29	0.649 23	0.853 58	1.171 5	0.760 59	1.314 8	1.540 3	31
30	**0.649 45**	**0.854 08**	**1.170 8**	**0.760 41**	**1.315 1**	**1.539 8**	**30**
31	0.649 67	0.854 58	1.170 2	0.760 22	1.315 4	1.539 2	29
32	0.649 89	0.855 09	1.169 5	0.760 03	1.315 7	1.538 7	28
33	0.650 11	0.855 59	1.168 8	0.759 84	1.316 1	1.538 2	27
34	0.650 33	0.856 09	1.168 1	0.759 65	1.316 4	1.537 7	26
35	**0.650 55**	**0.856 60**	**1.167 4**	**0.759 46**	**1.316 7**	**1.537 2**	**25**
36	0.650 77	0.857 10	1.166 7	0.759 27	1.317 1	1.536 6	24
37	0.651 00	0.857 61	1.166 0	0.759 08	1.317 4	1.536 1	23
38	0.651 22	0.858 11	1.165 3	0.758 89	1.317 7	1.535 6	22
39	0.651 44	0.858 62	1.164 7	0.758 70	1.318 0	1.535 1	21
40	**0.651 66**	**0.859 12**	**1.164 0**	**0.758 51**	**1.318 4**	**1.534 5**	**20**
41	0.651 88	0.859 63	1.163 3	0.758 32	1.318 7	1.534 0	19
42	0.652 10	0.860 14	1.162 6	0.758 13	1.319 0	1.533 5	18
43	0.652 32	0.860 64	1.161 9	0.757 94	1.319 4	1.533 0	17
44	0.652 54	0.861 15	1.161 2	0.757 75	1.319 7	1.532 5	16
45	**0.652 76**	**0.861 66**	**1.160 6**	**0.757 56**	**1.320 0**	**1.532 0**	**15**
46	0.652 98	0.862 16	1.159 9	0.757 38	1.320 3	1.531 4	14
47	0.653 20	0.862 67	1.159 2	0.757 19	1.320 7	1.530 9	13
48	0.653 42	0.863 18	1.158 5	0.757 00	1.321 0	1.530 4	12
49	0.653 64	0.863 68	1.157 8	0.756 80	1.321 3	1.529 9	11
50	**0.653 86**	**0.864 19**	**1.157 1**	**0.756 61**	**1.321 7**	**1.529 4**	**10**
51	0.654 08	0.864 70	1.156 5	0.756 42	1.322 0	1.528 9	9
52	0.654 30	0.865 21	1.155 8	0.756 23	1.322 3	1.528 3	8
53	0.654 52	0.865 72	1.155 1	0.756 04	1.322 7	1.527 8	7
54	0.654 74	0.866 23	1.154 4	0.755 85	1.323 0	1.527 3	6
55	**0.654 96**	**0.866 74**	**1.153 8**	**0.755 66**	**1.323 3**	**1.526 8**	**5**
56	0.655 18	0.867 25	1.153 1	0.755 47	1.323 7	1.526 3	4
57	0.655 40	0.867 76	1.152 4	0.755 28	1.324 0	1.525 8	3
58	0.655 62	0.868 27	1.151 7	0.755 09	1.324 3	1.525 3	2
59	0.655 84	0.868 78	1.151 0	0.754 90	1.324 7	1.524 8	1
60	**0.656 06**	**0.869 29**	**1.150 4**	**0.754 71**	**1.325 0**	**1.524 3**	**0**
′	Cos	Cot	Tan	Sin	Csc	Sec	′

Table 3 / *Five-place natural trigonometric functions*   □   663

′	Sin	Tan	Cot	Cos	Sec	Csc	′
0	**0.656 06**	**0.869 29**	1.150 4	**0.754 71**	**1.325 0**	**1.524 3**	60
1	0.656 28	0.869 80	1.149 7	0.754 52	1.325 3	1.523 7	59
2	0.656 50	0.870 31	1.149 0	0.754 33	1.325 7	1.523 2	58
3	0.656 72	0.870 82	1.148 3	0.754 14	1.326 0	1.522 7	57
4	0.656 94	0.871 33	1.147 7	0.753 95	1.326 4	1.522 2	56
5	**0.657 16**	**0.871 84**	1.147 0	**0.753 75**	**1.326 7**	**1.521 7**	55
6	0.657 38	0.872 36	1.146 3	0.753 56	1.327 0	1.521 2	54
7	0.657 59	0.872 87	1.145 6	0.753 37	1.327 4	1.520 7	53
8	0.657 81	0.873 38	1.145 0	0.753 18	1.327 7	1.520 2	52
9	0.658 03	0.873 89	1.144 3	0.752 99	1.328 0	1.519 7	51
10	**0.658 25**	**0.874 41**	1.143 6	**0.752 80**	**1.328 4**	**1.519 2**	50
11	0.658 47	0.874 92	1.143 0	0.752 61	1.328 7	1.518 7	49
12	0.658 69	0.875 43	1.142 3	0.752 41	1.329 1	1.518 2	48
13	0.658 91	0.875 95	1.141 6	0.752 22	1.329 4	1.517 7	47
14	0.659 13	0.876 46	1.141 0	0.752 03	1.329 7	1.517 2	46
15	**0.659 35**	**0.876 98**	1.140 3	**0.751 84**	**1.330 1**	**1.516 7**	45
16	0.659 56	0.877 49	1.139 6	0.751 65	1.330 4	1.516 2	44
17	0.659 78	0.878 01	1.138 9	0.751 46	1.330 7	1.515 6	43
18	0.660 00	0.878 52	1.138 3	0.751 26	1.331 1	1.515 1	42
19	0.660 22	0.879 04	1.137 6	0.751 07	1.331 4	1.514 6	41
20	**0.660 44**	**0.879 55**	1.136 9	**0.750 88**	**1.331 8**	**1.514 1**	40
21	0.660 66	0.880 07	1.136 3	0.750 69	1.332 1	1.513 6	39
22	0.660 88	0.880 59	1.135 6	0.750 50	1.332 5	1.513 1	38
23	0.661 09	0.881 10	1.134 9	0.750 30	1.332 8	1.512 6	37
24	0.661 31	0.881 62	1.134 3	0.750 11	1.333 1	1.512 1	36
25	**0.661 53**	**0.882 14**	1.133 6	**0.749 92**	**1.333 5**	**1.511 6**	35
26	0.661 75	0.882 65	1.132 9	0.749 73	1.333 8	1.511 1	34
27	0.661 97	0.883 17	1.132 3	0.749 53	1.334 2	1.510 7	33
28	0.662 18	0.883 69	1.131 6	0.749 34	1.334 5	1.510 2	32
29	0.662 40	0.884 21	1.131 0	0.749 15	1.334 8	1.509 7	31
30	**0.662 62**	**0.884 73**	1.130 3	**0.748 96**	**1.335 2**	**1.509 2**	30
31	0.662 84	0.885 24	1.129 6	0.748 76	1.335 5	1.508 7	29
32	0.663 06	0.885 76	1.129 0	0.748 57	1.335 9	1.508 2	28
33	0.663 27	0.886 28	1.128 3	0.748 38	1.336 2	1.507 7	27
34	0.663 49	0.886 80	1.127 6	0.748 18	1.336 6	1.507 2	26
35	**0.663 71**	**0.887 32**	1.127 0	**0.747 99**	**1.336 9**	**1.506 7**	25
36	0.663 93	0.887 84	1.126 3	0.747 80	1.337 3	1.506 2	24
37	0.664 14	0.888 36	1.125 7	0.747 60	1.337 6	1.505 7	23
38	0.664 36	0.888 88	1.125 0	0.747 41	1.338 0	1.505 2	22
39	0.664 58	0.889 40	1.124 3	0.747 22	1.338 3	1.504 7	21
40	**0.664 80**	**0.889 92**	1.123 7	**0.747 03**	**1.338 6**	**1.504 2**	20
41	0.665 01	0.890 45	1.123 0	0.746 83	1.339 0	1.503 7	19
42	0.665 23	0.890 97	1.122 4	0.746 64	1.339 3	1.503 2	18
43	0.665 45	0.891 49	1.121 7	0.746 44	1.339 7	1.502 7	17
44	0.665 66	0.892 01	1.121 1	0.746 25	1.340 0	1.502 3	16
45	**0.665 88**	**0.892 53**	1.120 4	**0.746 06**	**1.340 4**	**1.501 8**	15
46	0.666 10	0.893 06	1.119 7	0.745 86	1.340 7	1.501 3	14
47	0.666 32	0.893 58	1.119 1	0.745 67	1.341 1	1.500 8	13
48	0.666 53	0.894 10	1.118 4	0.745 48	1.341 4	1.500 3	12
49	0.666 75	0.894 63	1.117 8	0.745 28	1.341 8	1.499 8	11
50	**0.666 97**	**0.895 15**	1.117 1	**0.745 09**	**1.342 1**	**1.499 3**	10
51	0.667 18	0.895 67	1.116 5	0.744 89	1.342 5	1.498 8	9
52	0.667 40	0.896 20	1.115 8	0.744 70	1.342 8	1.498 4	8
53	0.667 62	0.896 72	1.115 2	0.744 51	1.343 2	1.497 9	7
54	0.667 83	0.897 25	1.114 5	0.744 31	1.343 5	1.497 4	6
55	**0.668 05**	**0.897 77**	1.113 9	**0.744 12**	**1.343 9**	**1.496 9**	5
56	0.668 27	0.898 30	1.113 2	0.743 92	1.344 2	1.496 4	4
57	0.668 48	0.898 83	1.112 6	0.743 73	1.344 6	1.495 9	3
58	0.668 70	0.899 35	1.111 9	0.743 53	1.344 9	1.495 4	2
59	0.668 91	0.899 88	1.111 3	0.743 34	1.345 3	1.495 0	1
60	**0.669 13**	**0.900 40**	1.110 6	**0.743 14**	**1.345 6**	**1.494 5**	0
′	Cos	Cot	Tan	Sin	Csc	Sec	′

′	Sin	Tan	Cot	Cos	Sec	Csc	′
0	0.669 13	0.900 40	1.110 6	0.743 14	1.345 6	1.494 5	60
1	0.669 35	0.900 93	1.110 0	0.742 95	1.346 0	1.494 0	59
2	0.669 56	0.901 46	1.109 3	0.742 76	1.346 3	1.493 5	58
3	0.669 78	0.901 99	1.108 7	0.742 56	1.346 7	1.493 0	57
4	0.669 99	0.902 51	1.108 0	0.742 37	1.347 0	1.492 5	56
5	0.670 21	0.903 04	1.107 4	0.742 17	1.347 4	1.492 1	55
6	0.670 43	0.903 57	1.106 7	0.741 98	1.347 8	1.491 6	54
7	0.670 64	0.904 10	1.106 1	0.741 78	1.348 1	1.491 1	53
8	0.670 86	0.904 63	1.105 4	0.741 59	1.348 5	1.490 6	52
9	0.671 07	0.905 16	1.104 8	0.741 39	1.348 8	1.490 1	51
10	0.671 29	0.905 69	1.104 1	0.741 20	1.349 2	1.489 7	50
11	0.671 51	0.906 21	1.103 5	0.741 00	1.349 5	1.489 2	49
12	0.671 72	0.906 74	1.102 8	0.740 80	1.349 9	1.488 7	48
13	0.671 94	0.907 27	1.102 2	0.740 61	1.350 2	1.488 2	47
14	0.672 15	0.907 81	1.101 6	0.740 41	1.350 6	1.487 8	46
15	0.672 37	0.908 34	1.100 9	0.740 22	1.351 0	1.487 3	45
16	0.672 58	0.908 87	1.100 3	0.740 02	1.351 3	1.486 8	44
17	0.672 80	0.909 40	1.099 6	0.739 83	1.351 7	1.486 3	43
18	0.673 01	0.909 93	1.099 0	0.739 63	1.352 0	1.485 9	42
19	0.673 23	0.910 46	1.098 3	0.739 44	1.352 4	1.485 4	41
20	0.673 44	0.910 99	1.097 7	0.739 24	1.352 7	1.484 9	40
21	0.673 66	0.911 53	1.097 1	0.739 04	1.353 1	1.484 4	39
22	0.673 87	0.912 06	1.096 4	0.738 85	1.353 5	1.484 0	38
23	0.674 09	0.912 59	1.095 8	0.738 65	1.353 8	1.483 5	37
24	0.674 30	0.913 13	1.095 1	0.738 46	1.354 2	1.483 0	36
25	0.674 52	0.913 66	1.094 5	0.738 26	1.354 5	1.482 5	35
26	0.674 73	0.914 19	1.093 9	0.738 06	1.354 9	1.482 1	34
27	0.674 95	0.914 73	1.093 2	0.737 87	1.355 3	1.481 6	33
28	0.675 16	0.915 26	1.092 6	0.737 67	1.355 6	1.481 1	32
29	0.675 38	0.915 80	1.091 9	0.737 47	1.356 0	1.480 7	31
30	0.675 59	0.916 33	1.091 3	0.737 28	1.356 3	1.480 2	30
31	0.675 80	0.916 87	1.090 7	0.737 08	1.356 7	1.479 7	29
32	0.676 02	0.917 40	1.090 0	0.736 88	1.357 1	1.479 2	28
33	0.676 23	0.917 94	1.089 4	0.736 69	1.357 4	1.478 8	27
34	0.676 45	0.918 47	1.088 8	0.736 49	1.357 8	1.478 3	26
35	0.676 66	0.919 01	1.088 1	0.736 29	1.358 2	1.477 8	25
36	0.676 88	0.919 55	1.087 5	0.736 10	1.358 5	1.477 4	24
37	0.677 09	0.920 08	1.086 9	0.735 90	1.358 9	1.476 9	23
38	0.677 30	0.920 62	1.086 2	0.735 70	1.359 2	1.476 4	22
39	0.677 52	0.921 16	1.085 6	0.735 51	1.359 6	1.476 0	21
40	0.677 73	0.921 70	1.085 0	0.735 31	1.360 0	1.475 5	20
41	0.677 95	0.922 24	1.084 3	0.735 11	1.360 3	1.475 0	19
42	0.678 16	0.922 77	1.083 7	0.734 91	1.360 7	1.474 6	18
43	0.678 37	0.923 31	1.083 1	0.734 72	1.361 1	1.474 1	17
44	0.678 59	0.923 85	1.082 4	0.734 52	1.361 4	1.473 7	16
45	0.678 80	0.924 39	1.081 8	0.734 32	1.361 8	1.473 2	15
46	0.679 01	0.924 93	1.081 2	0.734 13	1.362 2	1.472 7	14
47	0.679 23	0.925 47	1.080 5	0.733 93	1.362 5	1.472 3	13
48	0.679 44	0.926 01	1.079 9	0.733 73	1.362 9	1.471 8	12
49	0.679 65	0.926 55	1.079 3	0.733 53	1.363 3	1.471 3	11
50	0.679 87	0.927 09	1.078 6	0.733 33	1.363 6	1.470 9	10
51	0.680 08	0.927 63	1.078 0	0.733 14	1.364 0	1.470 4	9
52	0.680 29	0.928 17	1.077 4	0.732 94	1.364 4	1.470 0	8
53	0.680 51	0.928 72	1.076 8	0.732 74	1.364 7	1.469 5	7
54	0.680 72	0.929 26	1.076 1	0.732 54	1.365 1	1.469 0	6
55	0.680 93	0.929 80	1.075 5	0.732 34	1.365 5	1.468 6	5
56	0.681 15	0.930 34	1.074 9	0.732 15	1.365 8	1.468 1	4
57	0.681 36	0.930 88	1.074 2	0.731 95	1.366 2	1.467 7	3
58	0.681 57	0.931 43	1.073 6	0.731 75	1.366 6	1.467 2	2
59	0.681 79	0.931 97	1.073 0	0.731 55	1.367 0	1.466 7	1
60	0.682 00	0.932 52	1.072 4	0.731 35	1.367 3	1.466 3	0
′	Cos	Cot	Tan	Sin	Csc	Sec	′

Table 3 / Five-place natural trigonometric functions □ **665**

′	Sin	Tan	Cot	Cos	Sec	Csc	′
0	**0.682 00**	**0.932 52**	**1.072 4**	**0.731 35**	**1.367 3**	**1.466 3**	**60**
1	0.682 21	0.933 06	1.071 7	0.731 16	1.367 7	1.465 8	59
2	0.682 42	0.933 60	1.071 1	0.730 96	1.368 1	1.465 4	58
3	0.682 64	0.934 15	1.070 5	0.730 76	1.368 4	1.464 9	57
4	0.682 85	0.934 69	1.069 9	0.730 56	1.368 8	1.464 5	56
5	**0.683 06**	**0.935 24**	**1.069 2**	**0.730 36**	**1.369 2**	**1.464 0**	**55**
6	0.683 27	0.935 78	1.068 6	0.730 16	1.369 6	1.463 5	54
7	0.683 49	0.936 33	1.068 0	0.729 96	1.369 9	1.463 1	53
8	0.683 70	0.936 88	1.067 4	0.729 76	1.370 3	1.462 6	52
9	0.683 91	0.937 42	1.066 8	0.729 57	1.370 7	1.462 2	51
10	**0.684 12**	**0.937 97**	**1.066 1**	**0.729 37**	**1.371 1**	**1.461 7**	**50**
11	0.684 34	0.938 52	1.065 5	0.729 17	1.371 4	1.461 3	49
12	0.684 55	0.939 06	1.064 9	0.728 97	1.371 8	1.460 8	48
13	0.684 76	0.939 61	1.064 3	0.728 77	1.372 2	1.460 4	47
14	0.684 97	0.940 16	1.063 7	0.728 57	1.372 6	1.459 9	46
15	**0.685 18**	**0.940 71**	**1.063 0**	**0.728 37**	**1.372 9**	**1.459 5**	**45**
16	0.685 39	0.941 25	1.062 4	0.728 17	1.373 3	1.459 0	44
17	0.685 61	0.941 80	1.061 8	0.727 97	1.373 7	1.458 6	43
18	0.685 82	0.942 35	1.061 2	0.727 77	1.374 1	1.458 1	42
19	0.686 03	0.942 90	1.060 6	0.727 57	1.374 4	1.457 7	41
20	**0.686 24**	**0.943 45**	**1.059 9**	**0.727 37**	**1.374 8**	**1.457 2**	**40**
21	0.686 45	0.944 00	1.059 3	0.727 17	1.375 2	1.456 8	39
22	0.686 66	0.944 55	1.058 7	0.726 97	1.375 6	1.456 3	38
23	0.686 88	0.945 10	1.058 1	0.726 77	1.375 9	1.455 9	37
24	0.687 09	0.945 65	1.057 5	0.726 57	1.376 3	1.455 4	36
25	**0.687 30**	**0.946 20**	**1.056 9**	**0.726 37**	**1.376 7**	**1.455 0**	**35**
26	0.687 51	0.946 76	1.056 2	0.726 17	1.377 1	1.454 5	34
27	0.687 72	0.947 31	1.055 6	0.725 97	1.377 5	1.454 1	33
28	0.687 93	0.947 86	1.055 0	0.725 77	1.377 8	1.453 6	32
29	0.688 14	0.948 41	1.054 4	0.725 57	1.378 2	1.453 2	31
30	**0.688 35**	**0.948 96**	**1.053 8**	**0.725 37**	**1.378 6**	**1.452 7**	**30**
31	0.688 57	0.949 52	1.053 2	0.725 17	1.379 0	1.452 3	29
32	0.688 78	0.950 07	1.052 6	0.724 97	1.379 4	1.451 8	28
33	0.688 99	0.950 62	1.051 9	0.724 77	1.379 7	1.451 4	27
34	0.689 20	0.951 18	1.051 3	0.724 57	1.380 1	1.451 0	26
35	**0.689 41**	**0.951 73**	**1.050 7**	**0.724 37**	**1.380 5**	**1.450 5**	**25**
36	0.689 62	0.952 29	1.050 1	0.724 17	1.380 9	1.450 1	24
37	0.689 83	0.952 84	1.049 5	0.723 97	1.381 3	1.449 6	23
38	0.690 04	0.953 40	1.048 9	0.723 77	1.381 7	1.449 2	22
39	0.690 25	0.953 95	1.048 3	0.723 57	1.382 0	1.448 7	21
40	**0.690 46**	**0.954 51**	**1.047 7**	**0.723 37**	**1.382 4**	**1.448 3**	**20**
41	0.690 67	0.955 06	1.047 0	0.723 17	1.382 8	1.447 9	19
42	0.690 88	0.955 62	1.046 4	0.722 97	1.383 2	1.447 4	18
43	0.691 09	0.956 18	1.045 8	0.722 77	1.383 6	1.447 0	17
44	0.691 30	0.956 73	1.045 2	0.722 57	1.384 0	1.446 5	16
45	**0.691 51**	**0.957 29**	**1.044 6**	**0.722 36**	**1.384 3**	**1.446 1**	**15**
46	0.691 72	0.957 85	1.044 0	0.722 16	1.384 7	1.445 7	14
47	0.691 93	0.958 41	1.043 4	0.721 96	1.385 1	1.445 2	13
48	0.692 14	0.958 97	1.042 8	0.721 76	1.385 5	1.444 8	12
49	0.692 35	0.959 52	1.042 2	0.721 56	1.385 9	1.444 3	11
50	**0.692 56**	**0.960 08**	**1.041 6**	**0.721 36**	**1.386 3**	**1.443 9**	**10**
51	0.692 77	0.960 64	1.041 0	0.721 16	1.386 7	1.443 5	9
52	0.692 98	0.961 20	1.040 4	0.720 95	1.387 1	1.443 0	8
53	0.693 19	0.961 76	1.039 8	0.720 75	1.387 4	1.442 6	7
54	0.693 40	0.962 32	1.039 2	0.720 55	1.387 8	1.442 2	6
55	**0.693 61**	**0.962 88**	**1.038 5**	**0.720 35**	**1.388 2**	**1.441 7**	**5**
56	0.693 82	0.963 44	1.037 9	0.720 15	1.388 6	1.441 3	4
57	0.694 03	0.964 00	1.037 3	0.719 95	1.389 0	1.440 9	3
58	0.694 24	0.964 57	1.036 7	0.719 74	1.389 4	1.440 4	2
59	0.694 45	0.965 13	1.036 1	0.719 54	1.389 8	1.440 0	1
60	**0.694 66**	**0.965 69**	**1.035 5**	**0.719 34**	**1.390 2**	**1.439 6**	**0**

′	Cos	Cot	Tan	Sin	Csc	Sec	′

′	Sin	Tan	Cot	Cos	Sec	Csc	′
0	**0.694 66**	**0.965 69**	**1.035 5**	**0.719 34**	**1.390 2**	**1.439 6**	60
1	0.694 87	0.966 25	1.034 9	0.719 14	1.390 6	1.439 1	59
2	0.695 08	0.966 81	1.034 3	0.718 94	1.390 9	1.438 7	58
3	0.695 29	0.967 38	1.033 7	0.718 73	1.391 3	1.438 3	57
4	0.695 49	0.967 94	1.033 1	0.718 53	1.391 7	1.437 8	56
5	**0.695 70**	**0.968 50**	**1.032 5**	**0.718 33**	**1.392 1**	**1.437 4**	55
6	0.695 91	0.969 07	1.031 9	0.718 13	1.392 5	1.437 0	54
7	0.696 12	0.969 63	1.031 3	0.717 92	1.392 9	1.436 5	53
8	0.696 33	0.970 20	1.030 7	0.717 72	1.393 3	1.436 1	52
9	0.696 54	0.970 76	1.030 1	0.717 52	1.393 7	1.435 7	51
10	**0.696 75**	**0.971 33**	**1.029 5**	**0.717 32**	**1.394 1**	**1.435 2**	50
11	0.696 96	0.971 89	1.028 9	0.717 11	1.394 5	1.434 8	49
12	0.697 17	0.972 46	1.028 3	0.716 91	1.394 9	1.434 4	48
13	0.697 37	0.973 02	1.027 7	0.716 71	1.395 3	1.434 0	47
14	0.697 58	0.973 59	1.027 1	0.716 50	1.395 7	1.433 5	46
15	**0.697 79**	**0.974 16**	**1.026 5**	**0.716 30**	**1.396 1**	**1.433 1**	45
16	0.698 00	0.974 72	1.025 9	0.716 10	1.396 5	1.432 7	44
17	0.698 21	0.975 29	1.025 3	0.715 90	1.396 9	1.432 2	43
18	0.698 42	0.975 86	1.024 7	0.715 69	1.397 2	1.431 8	42
19	0.698 62	0.976 43	1.024 1	0.715 49	1.397 6	1.431 4	41
20	**0.698 83**	**0.977 00**	**1.023 5**	**0.715 29**	**1.398 0**	**1.431 0**	40
21	0.699 04	0.977 56	1.023 0	0.715 08	1.398 4	1.430 5	39
22	0.699 25	0.978 13	1.022 4	0.714 88	1.398 8	1.430 1	38
23	0.699 46	0.978 70	1.021 8	0.714 68	1.399 2	1.429 7	37
24	0.699 66	0.979 27	1.021 2	0.714 47	1.399 6	1.429 3	36
25	**0.699 87**	**0.979 84**	**1.020 6**	**0.714 27**	**1.400 0**	**1.428 8**	35
26	0.700 08	0.980 41	1.020 0	0.714 07	1.400 4	1.428 4	34
27	0.700 29	0.980 98	1.019 4	0.713 86	1.400 8	1.428 0	33
28	0.700 49	0.981 55	1.018 8	0.713 66	1.401 2	1.427 6	32
29	0.700 70	0.982 13	1.018 2	0.713 45	1.401 6	1.427 1	31
30	**0.700 91**	**0.982 70**	**1.017 6**	**0.713 25**	**1.402 0**	**1.426 7**	30
31	0.701 12	0.983 27	1.017 0	0.713 05	1.402 4	1.426 3	29
32	0.701 32	0.983 84	1.016 4	0.712 84	1.402 8	1.425 9	28
33	0.701 53	0.984 41	1.015 8	0.712 64	1.403 2	1.425 5	27
34	0.701 74	0.984 99	1.015 2	0.712 43	1.403 6	1.425 0	26
35	**0.701 95**	**0.985 56**	**1.014 7**	**0.712 23**	**1.404 0**	**1.424 6**	25
36	0.702 15	0.986 13	1.014 1	0.712 03	1.404 4	1.424 2	24
37	0.702 36	0.986 71	1.013 5	0.711 82	1.404 8	1.423 8	23
38	0.702 57	0.987 28	1.012 9	0.711 62	1.405 2	1.423 4	22
39	0.702 77	0.987 86	1.012 3	0.711 41	1.405 7	1.422 9	21
40	**0.702 98**	**0.988 43**	**1.011 7**	**0.711 21**	**1.406 1**	**1.422 5**	20
41	0.703 19	0.989 01	1.011 1	0.711 00	1.406 5	1.422 1	19
42	0.703 39	0.989 58	1.010 5	0.710 80	1.406 9	1.421 7	18
43	0.703 60	0.990 16	1.009 9	0.710 59	1.407 3	1.421 3	17
44	0.703 81	0.990 73	1.009 4	0.710 39	1.407 7	1.420 8	16
45	**0.704 01**	**0.991 31**	**1.008 8**	**0.710 19**	**1.408 1**	**1.420 4**	15
46	0.704 22	0.991 89	1.008 2	0.709 98	1.408 5	1.420 0	14
47	0.704 43	0.992 47	1.007 6	0.709 78	1.408 9	1.419 6	13
48	0.704 63	0.993 04	1.007 0	0.709 57	1.409 3	1.419 2	12
49	0.704 84	0.993 62	1.006 4	0.709 37	1.409 7	1.418 8	11
50	**0.705 05**	**0.994 20**	**1.005 8**	**0.709 16**	**1.410 1**	**1.418 3**	10
51	0.705 25	0.994 78	1.005 2	0.708 96	1.410 5	1.417 9	9
52	0.705 46	0.995 36	1.004 7	0.708 75	1.410 9	1.417 5	8
53	0.705 67	0.995 94	1.004 1	0.708 55	1.411 3	1.417 1	7
54	0.705 87	0.996 52	1.003 5	0.708 34	1.411 8	1.416 7	6
55	**0.706 08**	**0.997 10**	**1.002 9**	**0.708 13**	**1.412 2**	**1.416 3**	5
56	0.706 28	0.997 68	1.002 3	0.707 93	1.412 6	1.415 9	4
57	0.706 49	0.998 26	1.001 7	0.707 72	1.413 0	1.415 4	3
58	0.706 70	0.998 84	1.001 2	0.707 52	1.413 4	1.415 0	2
59	0.706 90	0.999 42	1.000 6	0.707 31	1.413 8	1.414 6	1
60	**0.707 11**	**1.000 00**	**1.000 0**	**0.707 11**	**1.414 2**	**1.414 2**	0
′	Cos	Cot	Tan	Sin	Csc	Sec	′

Table 3 / *Five-place natural trigonometric functions*   ☐   **667**

TABLE 4

Five-Place Common Logarithms of Natural Trigonometric Functions;
Angles in Degrees, Minutes, and Seconds*

Linear interpolation should *not* be used in that part of the table involving angles between 0° and 3° and the logarithms of sines and tangents and in that part of the table involving angles between 87° and 90° and the logarithms of cosines and cotangents. Instead, use the procedure described below, with Table 4A.

$$\text{For angles } 0° \text{ to } 3°, \log \sin \theta = \log(\theta \text{ in seconds}) + S$$

$$\log \tan \theta = \log(\theta \text{ in seconds}) + T$$

$$\text{For angles } 87° \text{ to } 90°, \log \cos \theta = \log([90° - \theta] \text{ in seconds}) + S$$

$$\log \cot \theta = \log([90° - \theta] \text{ in seconds}) + T$$

Table 4A
Values of S and T

θ (minutes)	S	θ (minutes)	T	θ (minutes)	T
0–40	4.685 57 − 10	0–3	4.685 57 − 10	128–130	4.685 78 − 10
41–57	4.685 56 − 10	4–28	4.685 58 − 10	131–133	4.685 79 − 10
58–70	4.685 55 − 10	29–40	4.685 59 − 10	134–136	4.685 80 − 10
71–81	4.685 54 − 10	41–49	4.685 60 − 10	137–139	4.685 81 − 10
82–90	4.685 53 − 10	50–56	4.685 61 − 10	140–142	4.685 82 − 10
91–99	4.685 52 − 10	57–63	4.685 62 − 10	143–145	4.685 83 − 10
100–107	4.685 51 − 10	64–69	4.685 63 − 10	146–148	4.685 84 − 10
108–114	4.685 50 − 10	70–75	4.685 64 − 10	149–151	4.685 85 − 10
115–121	4.685 49 − 10	76–80	4.685 65 − 10	152–153	4.685 86 − 10
122–128	4.685 48 − 10	81–85	4.685 66 − 10	154–156	4.685 87 − 10
129–134	4.685 47 − 10	86–90	4.685 67 − 10	157–158	4.685 88 − 10
135–140	4.685 46 − 10	91–94	4.685 68 − 10	159–161	4.685 89 − 10
141–145	4.685 45 − 10	95–98	4.685 69 − 10	162–163	4.685 90 − 10
146–151	4.685 44 − 10	99–102	4.685 70 − 10	164–166	4.685 91 − 10
152–156	4.685 43 − 10	103–106	4.685 71 − 10	167–168	4.685 92 − 10
157–161	4.685 42 − 10	107–110	4.685 72 − 10	169–171	4.685 93 − 10
162–166	4.685 41 − 10	111–114	4.685 73 − 10	172–173	4.685 94 − 10
167–171	4.685 40 − 10	115–117	4.685 74 − 10	174–175	4.685 95 − 10
172–176	4.685 39 − 10	118–121	4.685 75 − 10	176–178	4.685 96 − 10
177–180	4.685 38 − 10	122–124	4.685 76 − 10	179–180	4.685 97 − 10
		125–127	4.685 77 − 10		

To Find the Logarithm of the Sine or Tangent of a Small Angle:
(1) Convert the original small angle first into minutes and then into seconds and any decimal parts. The value in minutes is used only for entry into Table 4A, with parts of a minute ignored.
(2) Find the logarithm of the number of seconds in the angle, using Table 7.
(3) Select the correction term from Table 4A for the angle in minutes, using the S column for sines and the T column for tangents. Add the S or T value to the logarithm found in step 2.

* This table is adapted from P. R. Rider, *Plane and Spherical Trigonometry*, New York: The Macmillan Company, 1965.

To Find the Angle from the Logarithm of a Sine or Tangent:

(1) Find the approximate size of the angle in minutes, using the main part of Table 4.

(2) Select the correction term from Table 4A for the angle in minutes, using the S column for sines and the T column for tangents. Subtract this S or T term from the given logarithm.

(3) Find the antilogarithm of the result of step 2. This yields the desired angle in seconds.

For the logarithm of a cosine or cotangent of an angle between 87° and 90°, use the sine or tangent, respectively, of the complementary angle and then follow the above procedure. **10 must be subtracted from each tabular entry.**

Table 4 / Logarithms of trigonometric functions □ **669**

"	'	L Sin	d	L Tan	cd	L Cot	L Cos	'
0	**0**	——		——		——	**10.000 00**	**60**
60	1	6.463 73		6.463 73		13.536 27	10.000 00	59
			30103		30103			
120	2	6.764 76		6.764 76		13.235 24	10.000 00	58
			17609		17609			
180	3	6.940 85		6.940 85		13.059 15	10.000 00	57
			12494		12494			
240	4	7.065 79		7.065 79		12.934 21	10.000 00	56
			9691		9691			
300	**5**	**7.162 70**		**7.162 70**		**12.837 30**	**10.000 00**	**55**
			7918		7918			
360	6	7.241 88		7.241 88		12.758 12	10.000 00	54
			6694		6694			
420	7	7.308 82		7.308 82		12.691 18	10.000 00	53
			5800		5800			
480	8	7.366 82		7.366 82		12.633 18	10.000 00	52
			5115		5115			
540	9	7.417 97		7.417 97		12.582 03	10.000 00	51
			4576		4576			
600	**10**	**7.463 73**		**7.463 73**		**12.536 27**	**10.000 00**	**50**
			4139		4139			
660	11	7.505 12		7.505 12		12.494 88	10.000 00	49
			3779		3779			
720	12	7.542 91		7.542 91		12.457 09	10.000 00	48
			3476		3476			
780	13	7.577 67		7.577 67		12.422 33	10.000 00	47
			3218		3219			
840	14	7.609 85		7.609 86		12.390 14	10.000 00	46
			2997		2996			
900	**15**	**7.639 82**		**7.639 82**		**12.360 18**	**10.000 00**	**45**
			2802		2803			
960	16	7.667 84		7.667 85		12.332 15	10.000 00	44
			2633		2633			
1020	17	7.694 17		7.694 18		12.305 82	9.999 99	43
			2483		2482			
1080	18	7.719 00		7.719 00		12.281 00	9.999 99	42
			2348		2348			
1140	19	7.742 48		7.742 48		12.257 52	9.999 99	41
			2227		2228			
1200	**20**	**7.764 75**		**7.764 76**		**12.235 24**	**9.999 99**	**40**
			2119		2119			
1260	21	7.785 94		7.785 95		12.214 05	9.999 99	39
			2021		2020			
1320	22	7.806 15		7.806 15		12.193 85	9.999 99	38
			1930		1931			
1380	23	7.825 45		7.825 46		12.174 54	9.999 99	37
			1848		1848			
1440	24	7.843 93		7.843 94		12.156 06	9.999 99	36
			1773		1773			
1500	**25**	**7.861 66**		**7.861 67**		**12.138 33**	**9.999 99**	**35**
			1704		1704			
1560	26	7.878 70		7.878 71		12.121 29	9.999 99	34
			1639		1639			
1620	27	7.895 09		7.895 10		12.104 90	9.999 99	33
			1579		1579			
1680	28	7.910 88		7.910 89		12.089 11	9.999 99	32
			1524		1524			
1740	29	7.926 12		7.926 13		12.073 87	9.999 98	31
			1472		1473			
1800	**30**	**7.940 84**		**7.940 86**		**12.059 14**	**9.999 98**	**30**
			1424		1424			
1860	31	7.955 08		7.955 10		12.044 90	9.999 98	29
			1379		1379			
1920	32	7.968 87		7.968 89		12.031 11	9.999 98	28
			1336		1336			
1980	33	7.982 23		7.982 25		12.017 75	9.999 98	27
			1297		1297			
2040	34	7.995 20		7.995 22		12.004 78	9.999 98	26
			1259		1259			
2100	**35**	**8.007 79**		**8.007 81**		**11.992 19**	**9.999 98**	**25**
			1223		1223			
2160	36	8.020 02		8.020 04		11.979 96	9.999 98	24
			1190		1190			
2220	37	8.031 92		8.031 94		11.968 06	9.999 97	23
			1158		1159			
2280	38	8.043 50		8.043 53		11.956 47	9.999 97	22
			1128		1128			
2340	39	8.054 78		8.054 81		11.945 19	9.999 97	21
			1100		1100			
2400	**40**	**8.065 78**		**8.065 81**		**11.934 19**	**9.999 97**	**20**
			1072		1072			
2460	41	8.076 50		8.076 53		11.923 47	9.999 97	19
			1046		1047			
2520	42	8.086 96		8.087 00		11.913 00	9.999 97	18
			1022		1022			
2580	43	8.097 18		8.097 22		11.902 78	9.999 97	17
			999		998			
2640	44	8.107 17		8.107 20		11.892 80	9.999 96	16
			976		976			
2700	**45**	**8.116 93**		**8.116 96**		**11.883 04**	**9.999 96**	**15**
			954		955			
2760	46	8.126 47		8.126 51		11.873 49	9.999 96	14
			934		934			
2820	47	8.135 81		8.135 85		11.864 15	9.999 96	13
			914		915			
2880	48	8.144 95		8.145 00		11.855 00	9.999 96	12
			896		895			
2940	49	8.153 91		8.153 95		11.846 05	9.999 96	11
			877		878			
3000	**50**	**8.162 68**		**8.162 73**		**11.837 27**	**9.999 95**	**10**
			860		860			
3060	51	8.171 28		8.171 33		11.828 67	9.999 95	9
			843		843			
3120	52	8.179 71		8.179 76		11.820 24	9.999 95	8
			827		828			
3180	53	8.187 98		8.188 04		11.811 96	9.999 95	7
			812		812			
3240	54	8.196 10		8.196 16		11.803 84	9.999 95	6
			797		797			
3300	**55**	**8.204 07**		**8.204 13**		**11.795 87**	**9.999 94**	**5**
			782		782			
3360	56	8.211 89		8.211 95		11.788 05	9.999 94	4
			769		769			
3420	57	8.219 58		8.219 64		11.780 36	9.999 94	3
			755		756			
3480	58	8.227 13		8.227 20		11.772 80	9.999 94	2
			743		742			
3540	59	8.234 56		8.234 62		11.765 38	9.999 94	1
			730		730			
3600	**60**	**8.241 86**		**8.241 92**		**11.758 08**	**9.999 93**	**0**
"	'	L Cos	d	L Cot	cd	L Tan	L Sin	'

Note: For logarithms of sines or tangents of angles less than 3° (or logarithms of cosines or cotangents of angles greater than 87°), see Table 4A. When the tabular differences are large, that method is usually better.

″	′	L Sin	d	L Tan	cd	L Cot	L Cos	′
3600	**0**	**8.241 86**		**8.241 92**		**11.758 08**	**9.999 93**	**60**
3660	1	8.249 03	717	8.249 10	718	11.750 90	9.999 93	59
3720	2	8.256 09	706	8.256 16	706	11.743 84	9.999 93	58
3780	3	8.263 04	695	8.263 12	696	11.736 88	9.999 93	57
3840	4	8.269 88	684	8.269 96	684	11.730 04	9.999 92	56
			673		673			
3900	**5**	**8.276 61**		**8.276 69**		**11.723 31**	**9.999 92**	**55**
3960	6	8.283 24	663	8.283 32	663	11.716 68	9.999 92	54
4020	7	8.289 77	653	8.289 86	654	11.710 14	9.999 92	53
4080	8	8.296 21	644	8.296 29	643	11.703 71	9.999 92	52
4140	9	8.302 55	634	8.302 63	634	11.697 37	9.999 91	51
			624		625			
4200	**10**	**8.308 79**		**8.308 88**		**11.691 12**	**9.999 91**	**50**
4260	11	8.314 95	616	8.315 05	617	11.684 95	9.999 91	49
4320	12	8.321 03	608	8.321 12	607	11.678 88	9.999 90	48
4380	13	8.327 02	599	8.327 11	599	11.672 89	9.999 90	47
4440	14	8.332 92	590	8.333 02	591	11.666 98	9.999 90	46
			583		584			
4500	**15**	**8.338 75**		**8.338 86**		**11.661 14**	**9.999 90**	**45**
4560	16	8.344 50	575	8.344 61	575	11.655 39	9.999 89	44
4620	17	8.350 18	568	8.350 29	568	11.649 71	9.999 89	43
4680	18	8.355 78	560	8.355 90	561	11.644 10	9.999 89	42
4740	19	8.361 31	553	8.361 43	553	11.638 57	9.999 89	41
			547		546			
4800	**20**	**8.366 78**		**8.366 89**		**11.633 11**	**9.999 88**	**40**
4860	21	8.372 17	539	8.372 29	540	11.627 71	9.999 88	39
4920	22	8.377 50	533	8.377 62	533	11.622 38	9.999 88	38
4980	23	8.382 76	526	8.382 89	527	11.617 11	9.999 87	37
5040	24	8.387 96	520	8.388 09	520	11.611 91	9.999 87	36
			514		514			
5100	**25**	**8.393 10**		**8.393 23**		**11.606 77**	**9.999 87**	**35**
5160	26	8.398 18	508	8.398 32	509	11.601 68	9.999 86	34
5220	27	8.403 20	502	8.403 34	502	11.596 66	9.999 86	33
5280	28	8.408 16	496	8.408 30	496	11.591 70	9.999 86	32
5340	29	8.413 07	491	8.413 21	491	11.586 79	9.999 85	31
			485		486			
5400	**30**	**8.417 92**		**8.418 07**		**11.581 93**	**9.999 85**	**30**
5460	31	8.422 72	480	8.422 87	480	11.577 13	9.999 85	29
5520	32	8.427 46	474	8.427 62	475	11.572 38	9.999 84	28
5580	33	8.432 16	470	8.432 32	470	11.567 68	9.999 84	27
5640	34	8.436 80	464	8.436 96	464	11.563 04	9.999 84	26
			459		460			
5700	**35**	**8.441 39**		**8.441 56**		**11.558 44**	**9.999 83**	**25**
5760	36	8.445 94	455	8.446 11	455	11.553 89	9.999 83	24
5820	37	8.450 44	450	8.450 61	450	11.549 39	9.999 83	23
5880	38	8.454 89	445	8.455 07	446	11.544 93	9.999 82	22
5940	39	8.459 30	441	8.459 48	441	11.540 52	9.999 82	21
			436		437			
6000	**40**	**8.463 66**		**8.463 85**		**11.536 15**	**9.999 82**	**20**
6060	41	8.467 99	433	4.468 17	432	11.531 83	9.999 81	19
6120	42	8.472 26	427	8.472 45	428	11.527 55	9.999 81	18
6180	43	8.476 50	424	8.476 69	424	11.523 31	9.999 81	17
6240	44	8.480 69	419	8.480 89	420	11.519 11	9.999 80	16
			416		416			
6300	**45**	**8.484 85**		**8.485 05**		**11.514 95**	**9.999 80**	**15**
6360	46	8.488 96	411	8.489 17	412	11.510 83	9.999 79	14
6420	47	8.493 04	408	8.493 25	408	11.506 75	9.999 79	13
6480	48	8.497 08	404	8.497 29	404	11.502 71	9.999 79	12
6540	49	8.501 08	400	8.501 30	401	11.498 70	9.999 78	11
			396		397			
6600	**50**	**8.505 04**		**8.505 27**		**11.494 73**	**9.999 78**	**10**
6660	51	8.508 97	393	8.509 20	393	11.490 80	9.999 77	9
6720	52	8.512 87	390	8.513 10	390	11.486 90	9.999 77	8
6780	53	8.516 73	386	8.516 96	386	11.483 04	9.999 77	7
6840	54	8.520 55	382	8.520 79	383	11.479 21	9.999 76	6
			379		380			
6900	**55**	**8.524 34**		**8.524 59**		**11.475 41**	**9.999 76**	**5**
6960	56	8.528 10	376	8.528 35	376	11.471 65	9.999 76	4
7020	57	8.531 83	373	8.532 08	373	11.467 92	9.999 75	3
7080	58	8.535 52	369	8.535 78	370	11.464 22	9.999 75	2
7140	59	8.539 19	367	8.539 45	367	11.460 55	9.999 74	1
			363		363			
7200	**60**	**8.542 82**		**8.543 08**		**11.456 92**	**9.999 74**	**0**
″	′	L Cos	d	L Cot	cd	L Tan	L Sin	′

Note: For logarithms of sines or tangents of angles less than 3° (or logarithms of cosines or cotangents of angles greater than 87°), see Table 4A. When the tabular differences are large, that method is usually better.

Table 4 / Logarithms of trigonometric functions □ 671

"	'	L Sin	d	L Tan	cd	L Cot	L Cos	'
7200	0	**8.542 82**	360	**8.543 08**	361	**11.456 92**	**9.999 74**	60
7260	1	8.546 42	357	8.546 69	358	11.453 31	9.999 73	59
7320	2	8.549 99	355	8.550 27	355	11.449 73	9.999 73	58
7380	3	8.553 54	351	8.553 82	352	11.446 18	9.999 72	57
7440	4	8.557 05	349	8.557 34	349	11.442 66	9.999 72	56
7500	5	**8.560 54**	346	**8.560 83**	346	**11.439 17**	**9.999 71**	55
7560	6	8.564 00	343	8.564 29	344	11.435 71	9.999 71	54
7620	7	8.567 43	341	8.567 73	341	11.432 27	9.999 70	53
7680	8	8.570 84	337	8.571 14	338	11.428 86	9.999 70	52
7740	9	8.574 21	336	8.574 52	336	11.425 48	9.999 69	51
7800	10	**8.577 57**	332	**8.577 88**	333	**11.422 12**	**9.999 69**	50
7860	11	8.580 89	330	8.581 21	330	11.418 79	9.999 68	49
7920	12	8.584 19	328	8.584 51	328	11.415 49	9.999 68	48
7980	13	8.587 47	325	8.587 79	326	11.412 21	9.999 67	47
8040	14	8.590 72	323	8.591 05	323	11.408 95	9.999 67	46
8100	15	**8.593 95**	320	**8.594 28**	321	**11.405 72**	**9.999 67**	45
8160	16	8.597 15	318	8.597 49	319	11.402 51	9.999 66	44
8220	17	8.600 33	316	8.600 68	316	11.399 32	9.999 66	43
8280	18	8.603 49	313	8.603 84	314	11.396 16	9.999 65	42
8340	19	8.606 62	311	8.606 98	311	11.393 02	9.999 64	41
8400	20	**8.609 73**	309	**8.610 09**	310	**11.389 91**	**9.999 64**	40
8460	21	8.612 82	307	8.613 19	307	11.386 81	9.999 63	39
8520	22	8.615 89	305	8.616 26	305	11.383 74	9.999 63	38
8580	23	8.618 94	302	8.619 31	303	11.380 69	9.999 62	37
8640	24	8.621 96	301	8.622 34	301	11.377 66	9.999 62	36
8700	25	**8.624 97**	298	**8.625 35**	299	**11.374 65**	**9.999 61**	35
8760	26	8.627 95	296	8.628 34	297	11.371 66	9.999 61	34
8820	27	8.630 91	294	8.631 31	295	11.368 69	9.999 60	33
8880	28	8.633 85	293	8.634 26	292	11.365 74	9.999 60	32
8940	29	8.636 78	290	8.637 18	291	11.362 82	9.999 59	31
9000	30	**8.639 68**	288	**8.640 09**	289	**11.359 91**	**9.999 59**	30
9060	31	8.642 56	287	8.642 98	287	11.357 02	9.999 58	29
9120	32	8.645 43	284	8.645 85	285	11.354 15	9.999 58	28
9180	33	8.648 27	283	8.648 70	284	11.351 30	9.999 57	27
9240	34	8.651 10	281	8.651 54	281	11.348 46	9.999 56	26
9300	35	**8.653 91**	279	**8.654 35**	280	**11.345 65**	**9.999 56**	25
9360	36	8.656 70	277	8.657 15	278	11.342 85	9.999 55	24
9420	37	8.659 47	276	8.659 93	276	11.340 07	9.999 55	23
9480	38	8.662 23	274	8.662 69	274	11.337 31	9.999 54	22
9540	39	8.664 97	272	8.665 43	272	11.334 57	9.999 54	21
9600	40	**8.667 69**	270	**8.668 16**	271	**11.331 84**	**9.999 53**	20
9660	41	8.670 39	269	8.670 87	269	11.329 13	9.999 52	19
9720	42	8.673 08	267	8.673 56	268	11.326 44	9.999 52	18
9780	43	8.675 75	266	8.676 24	266	11.323 76	9.999 51	17
9840	44	8.678 41	263	8.678 90	264	11.321 10	9.999 51	16
9900	45	**8.681 04**	263	**8.681 54**	263	**11.318 46**	**9.999 50**	15
9960	46	8.683 67	260	8.684 17	261	11.315 83	9.999 49	14
10020	47	8.686 27	259	8.686 78	260	11.313 22	9.999 49	13
10080	48	8.688 86	258	8.689 38	258	11.310 62	9.999 48	12
10140	49	8.691 44	256	8.691 96	257	11.308 04	9.999 48	11
10200	50	**8.694 00**	254	**8.694 53**	255	**11.305 47**	**9.999 47**	10
10260	51	8.696 54	253	8.697 08	254	11.302 92	9.999 46	9
10320	52	8.699 07	252	8.699 62	252	11.300 38	9.999 46	8
10380	53	8.701 59	250	8.702 14	251	11.297 86	9.999 45	7
10440	54	8.704 09	249	8.704 65	249	11.295 35	9.999 44	6
10500	55	**8.706 58**	247	**8.707 14**	248	**11.292 86**	**9.999 44**	5
10560	56	8.709 05	246	8.709 62	246	11.290 38	9.999 43	4
10620	57	8.711 51	244	8.712 08	245	11.287 92	9.999 42	3
10680	58	8.713 95	243	8.714 53	244	11.285 47	9.999 42	2
10740	59	8.716 38	242	8.716 97	243	11.283 03	9.999 41	1
10800	60	**8.718 80**		**8.719 40**		**11.280 60**	**9.999 40**	0
"	'	L Cos	d	L Cot	cd	L Tan	L Sin	'

Note: For logarithms of sines or tangents of angles less than 3° (or logarithms of cosines or cotangents of angles greater than 87°), see Table 4A. When the tabular differences are large, that method is usually better.

′	L Sin	d	L Tan	cd	L Cot	L Cos	′	″	Prop. Pts.			
0	**8.718 80**	240	**8.719 40**	241	**11.280 60**	**9.999 40**	60	″	**240**	**238**	**236**	**234**
1	8.721 20	239	8.721 81	239	11.278 19	9.999 40	59	6	24.0	23.8	23.6	23.4
2	8.723 59	238	8.724 20	239	11.275 80	9.999 39	58	7	28.0	27.8	27.5	27.3
3	8.725 97	237	8.726 59	237	11.273 41	9.999 38	57	8	32.0	31.7	31.5	31.2
4	8.728 34	235	8.728 96	236	11.271 04	9.999 38	56	9	36.0	35.7	35.4	35.1
5	**8.730 69**	234	**8.731 32**	234	**11.268 68**	**9.999 37**	55	10	40.0	39.7	39.3	39.0
6	8.733 03	232	8.733 66	234	11.266 34	9.999 36	54	20	80.0	79.3	78.7	78.0
7	8.735 35	232	8.736 00	232	11.264 00	9.999 36	53	30	120.0	119.0	118.0	117.0
8	8.737 67	230	8.738 32	232	11.261 68	9.999 35	52	40	160.0	158.7	157.3	156.0
9	8.739 97	229	8.740 63	231	11.259 37	9.999 34	51	50	200.0	198.3	196.7	195.0
10	**8.742 26**	228	**8.742 92**	229	**11.257 08**	**9.999 34**	50	″	**232**	**230**	**228**	**226**
11	8.744 54	226	8.745 21	227	11.254 79	9.999 33	49	6	23.2	23.0	22.8	22.6
12	8.746 80	226	8.747 48	226	11.252 52	9.999 32	48	7	27.1	26.8	26.6	26.4
13	8.749 06	224	8.749 74	226	11.250 26	9.999 32	47	8	30.9	30.7	30.4	30.1
14	8.751 30	223	8.751 99	224	11.248 01	9.999 31	46	9	34.8	34.5	34.2	33.9
15	**8.753 53**	222	**8.754 23**	222	**11.245 77**	**9.999 30**	45	10	38.7	38.3	38.0	37.7
16	8.755 75	220	8.756 45	222	11.243 55	9.999 29	44	20	77.3	76.7	76.0	75.3
17	8.757 95	220	8.758 67	220	11.241 33	9.999 29	43	30	116.0	115.0	114.0	113.0
18	8.760 15	219	8.760 87	219	11.239 13	9.999 28	42	40	154.7	153.3	152.0	150.7
19	8.762 34	217	8.763 06	219	11.236 94	9.999 27	41	50	193.3	191.7	190.0	188.3
20	**8.764 51**	216	**8.765 25**	217	**11.234 75**	**9.999 26**	40	″	**224**	**222**	**220**	**218**
21	8.766 67	216	8.767 42	216	11.232 58	9.999 26	39	6	22.4	22.2	22.0	21.8
22	8.768 83	214	8.769 58	215	11.230 42	9.999 25	38	7	26.1	25.9	25.7	25.4
23	8.770 97	213	8.771 73	214	11.228 27	9.999 24	37	8	29.9	29.6	29.3	29.1
24	8.773 10	212	8.773 87	213	11.226 13	9.999 23	36	9	33.6	33.3	33.0	32.7
25	**8.775 22**	211	**8.776 00**	211	**11.224 00**	**9.999 23**	35	10	37.3	37.0	36.7	36.3
26	8.777 33	210	8.778 11	211	11.221 89	9.999 22	34	20	74.7	74.0	73.3	72.7
27	8.779 43	209	8.780 22	210	11.219 78	9.999 21	33	30	112.0	111.0	110.0	109.0
28	8.781 52	208	8.782 32	209	11.217 68	9.999 20	32	40	149.3	148.0	146.7	145.3
29	8.783 60	208	8.784 41	208	11.215 59	9.999 20	31	50	186.7	185.0	183.3	181.7
30	**8.785 68**	206	**8.786 49**	206	**11.213 51**	**9.999 19**	30	″	**216**	**214**	**212**	**210**
31	8.787 74	205	8.788 55	206	11.211 45	9.999 18	29	6	21.6	21.4	21.2	21.0
32	8.789 79	204	8.790 61	205	11.209 39	9.999 17	28	7	25.2	25.0	24.7	24.5
33	8.791 83	203	8.792 66	204	11.207 34	9.999 17	27	8	28.8	28.5	28.3	28.0
34	8.793 86	202	8.794 70	203	11.205 30	9.999 16	26	9	32.4	32.1	31.8	31.5
35	**8.795 88**	201	**8.796 73**	202	**11.203 27**	**9.999 15**	25	10	36.0	35.7	35.3	35.0
36	8.797 89	201	8.798 75	201	11.201 25	9.999 14	24	20	72.0	71.3	70.7	70.0
37	8.799 90	199	8.800 76	201	11.199 24	9.999 13	23	30	108.0	107.0	106.0	105.0
38	8.801 89	199	8.802 77	199	11.197 23	9.999 13	22	40	144.0	142.7	141.3	140.0
39	8.803 88	197	8.804 76	198	11.195 24	9.999 12	21	50	180.0	178.3	176.7	175.0
40	**8.805 85**	197	**8.806 74**	198	**11.193 26**	**9.999 11**	20	″	**208**	**206**	**204**	**202**
41	8.807 82	196	8.808 72	196	11.191 28	9.999 10	19	6	20.8	20.6	20.4	20.2
42	8.809 78	195	8.810 68	196	11.189 32	9.999 09	18	7	24.3	24.0	23.8	23.6
43	8.811 73	194	8.812 64	195	11.187 36	9.999 09	17	8	27.7	27.5	27.2	26.9
44	8.813 67	193	8.814 59	194	11.185 41	9.999 08	16	9	31.2	30.9	30.6	30.3
45	**8.815 60**	192	**8.816 53**	193	**11.183 47**	**9.999 07**	15	10	34.7	34.3	34.0	33.7
46	8.817 52	192	8.818 46	192	11.181 54	9.999 06	14	20	69.3	68.7	68.0	67.3
47	8.819 44	190	8.820 38	192	11.179 62	9.999 05	13	30	104.0	103.0	102.0	101.0
48	8.821 34	190	8.822 30	190	11.177 70	9.999 04	12	40	138.7	137.3	136.0	134.7
49	8.823 24	189	8.824 20	190	11.175 80	9.999 04	11	50	173.3	171.7	170.0	168.3
50	**8.825 13**	188	**8.826 10**	189	**11.173 90**	**9.999 03**	10	″	**200**	**198**	**196**	**194**
51	8.827 01	187	8.827 99	188	11.172 01	9.999 02	9	6	20.0	19.8	19.6	19.4
52	8.828 88	187	8.829 87	188	11.170 13	9.999 01	8	7	23.3	23.1	22.9	22.6
53	8.830 75	186	8.831 75	186	11.168 25	9.999 00	7	8	26.7	26.4	26.1	25.9
54	8.832 61	185	8.833 61	186	11.166 39	9.998 99	6	9	30.0	29.7	29.4	29.1
55	**8.834 46**	184	**8.835 47**	185	**11.164 53**	**9.998 98**	5	10	33.3	33.0	32.7	32.3
56	8.836 30	183	8.837 32	184	11.162 68	9.998 98	4	20	66.7	66.0	65.3	64.7
57	8.838 13	183	8.839 16	184	11.160 84	9.998 97	3	30	100.0	99.0	98.0	97.0
58	8.839 96	181	8.841 00	182	11.159 00	9.998 96	2	40	133.3	132.0	130.7	129.3
59	8.841 77	181	8.842 82	182	11.157 18	9.998 95	1	50	166.7	165.0	163.3	161.7
60	**8.843 58**		**8.844 64**		**11.155 36**	**9.998 94**	0					
′	L Cos	d	L Cot	cd	L Tan	L Sin	′		Prop. Pts.			

Table 4 / Logarithms of trigonometric functions □ 673

′	L Sin	d	L Tan	cd	L Cot	L Cos	′		Prop. Pts.	
0	8.843 58		8.844 64		11.155 36	9.998 94	60			
1	8.845 39	181	8.846 46	182	11.153 54	9.998 93	59			
2	8.847 18	179	8.848 26	180	11.151 74	9.998 92	58			
3	8.848 97	179	8.850 06	180	11.149 94	9.998 91	57			
4	8.850 75	178	8.851 85	179	11.148 15	9.998 91	56			
		177		178						
5	8.852 52		8.853 63		11.146 37	9.998 90	55	″	182	180	178
6	8.854 29	177	8.855 40	177	11.144 60	9.998 89	54	6	18.2	18.0	17.8
7	8.856 05	177	8.857 17	177	11.142 83	9.998 88	53	7	21.2	21.0	20.8
8	8.857 80	175	8.858 93	176	11.141 07	9.998 87	52	8	24.3	24.0	23.7
9	8.859 55	175	8.860 69	176	11.139 31	9.998 86	51	9	27.3	27.0	26.7
		173		174						
10	8.861 28		8.862 43		11.137 57	9.998 85	50	10	30.3	30.0	29.7
11	8.863 01	173	8.864 17	174	11.135 83	9.998 84	49	20	60.7	60.0	59.3
12	8.864 74	173	8.865 91	174	11.134 09	9.998 83	48	30	91.0	90.0	89.0
13	8.866 45	171	8.867 63	172	11.132 37	9.998 82	47	40	121.3	120.0	118.7
14	8.868 16	171	8.869 35	172	11.130 65	9.998 81	46	50	151.7	150.0	148.3
		171		171						
15	8.869 87		8.871 06		11.128 94	9.998 80	45	″	176	174	172	170
16	8.871 56	169	8.872 77	171	11.127 23	9.998 79	44	6	17.6	17.4	17.2	17.0
17	8.873 25	169	8.874 47	170	11.125 53	9.998 79	43	7	20.5	20.3	20.1	19.8
18	8.874 94	169	8.876 16	169	11.123 84	9.998 78	42	8	23.5	23.2	22.9	22.7
19	8.876 61	167	8.877 85	169	11.122 15	9.998 77	41	9	26.4	26.1	25.8	25.5
		168		168						
20	8.878 29		8.879 53		11.120 47	9.998 76	40	10	29.3	29.0	28.7	28.3
21	8.879 95	166	8.881 20	167	11.118 80	9.998 75	39	20	58.7	58.0	57.3	56.7
22	8.881 61	166	8.882 87	167	11.117 13	9.998 74	38	30	88.0	87.0	86.0	85.0
23	8.883 26	165	8.884 53	166	11.115 47	9.998 73	37	40	117.3	116.0	114.7	113.3
24	8.884 90	164	8.886 18	165	11.113 82	9.998 72	36	50	146.7	145.0	143.3	141.7
		164		165						
25	8.886 54		8.887 83		11.112 17	9.998 71	35	″	168	166	164	162
26	8.888 17	163	8.889 48	165	11.110 52	9.998 70	34	6	16.8	16.6	16.4	16.2
27	8.889 80	163	8.891 11	163	11.108 89	9.998 69	33	7	19.6	19.4	19.1	18.9
28	8.891 42	162	8.892 74	163	11.107 26	9.998 68	32	8	22.4	22.1	21.9	21.6
29	8.893 04	162	8.894 37	163	11.105 63	9.998 67	31	9	25.2	24.9	24.6	24.3
		160		161						
30	8.894 64		8.895 98		11.104 02	9.998 66	30	10	28.0	27.7	27.3	27.0
31	8.896 25	161	8.897 60	162	11.102 40	9.998 65	29	20	56.0	55.3	54.7	54.0
32	8.897 84	159	8.899 20	160	11.100 80	9.998 64	28	30	84.0	83.0	82.0	81.0
33	8.899 43	159	8.900 80	160	11.099 20	9.998 63	27	40	112.0	110.7	109.3	108.0
34	8.901 02	159	8.902 40	160	11.097 60	9.998 62	26	50	140.0	138.3	136.7	135.0
		158		159						
35	8.902 60		8.903 99		11.096 01	9.998 61	25	″	160	158	156	154
36	8.904 17	157	8.905 57	158	11.094 43	9.998 60	24	6	16.0	15.8	15.6	15.4
37	8.905 74	157	8.907 15	158	11.092 85	9.998 59	23	7	18.7	18.4	18.2	18.0
38	8.907 30	156	8.908 72	157	11.091 28	9.998 58	22	8	21.3	21.1	20.8	20.5
39	8.908 85	155	8.910 29	157	11.089 71	9.998 57	21	9	24.0	23.7	23.4	23.1
		155		156						
40	8.910 40		8.911 85		11.088 15	9.998 56	20	10	26.7	26.3	26.0	25.7
41	8.911 95	155	8.913 40	155	11.086 60	9.998 55	19	20	53.3	52.7	52.0	51.3
42	8.913 49	154	8.914 95	155	11.085 05	9.998 54	18	30	80.0	79.0	78.0	77.0
43	8.915 02	153	8.916 50	155	11.083 50	9.998 53	17	40	106.7	105.3	104.0	102.7
44	8.916 55	153	8.918 03	153	11.081 97	9.998 52	16	50	133.3	131.7	130.0	128.3
		152		154						
45	8.918 07		8.919 57		11.080 43	9.998 51	15	″	152	150	148	146
46	8.919 59	152	8.921 10	153	11.078 90	9.998 50	14	6	15.2	15.0	14.8	14.6
47	8.921 10	151	8.922 62	152	11.077 38	9.998 48	13	7	17.7	17.5	17.3	17.0
48	8.922 61	151	8.924 14	152	11.075 86	9.998 47	12	8	20.3	20.0	19.7	19.5
49	8.924 11	150	8.925 65	151	11.074 35	9.998 46	11	9	22.8	22.5	22.2	21.9
		150		151						
50	8.925 61		8.927 16		11.072 84	9.998 45	10	10	25.3	25.0	24.7	24.3
51	8.927 10	149	8.928 66	150	11.071 34	9.998 44	9	20	50.7	50.0	49.3	48.7
52	8.928 59	149	8.930 16	150	11.069 84	9.998 43	8	30	76.0	75.0	74.0	73.0
53	8.930 07	148	8.931 65	149	11.068 35	9.998 42	7	40	101.3	100.0	98.7	97.3
54	8.931 54	147	8.933 13	148	11.066 87	9.998 41	6	50	126.7	125.0	123.3	121.7
		147		149						
55	8.933 01		8.934 62		11.065 38	9.998 40	5			
56	8.934 48	147	8.936 09	147	11.063 91	9.998 39	4			
57	8.935 94	146	8.937 56	147	11.062 44	9.998 38	3			
58	8.937 40	146	8.939 03	147	11.060 97	9.998 37	2			
59	8.938 85	145	8.940 49	146	11.059 51	9.998 36	1			
		145		146						
60	8.940 30		8.941 95		11.058 05	9.998 34	0			
′	L Cos	d	L Cot	cd	L Tan	L Sin	′		Prop. Pts.	

′	L Sin	d	L Tan	cd	L Cot	L Cos	′		Prop. Pts.		
0	**8.940 30**		**8.941 95**		**11.058 05**	**9.998 34**	**60**	″	**146**	**144**	**142**	**140**
1	8.941 74	144	8.943 40	145	11.056 60	9.998 33	59	1	2.4	2.4	2.4	2.3
2	8.943 17	143	8.944 85	145	11.055 15	9.998 32	58	2	4.9	4.8	4.7	4.7
3	8.944 61	144	8.946 30	145	11.053 70	9.998 31	57	3	7.3	7.2	7.1	7.0
4	8.946 03	142	8.947 73	143	11.052 27	9.998 30	56	4	9.7	9.6	9.5	9.3
		143		144								
5	**8.947 46**		**8.949 17**		**11.050 83**	**9.998 29**	**55**	5	12.2	12.0	11.8	11.7
6	8.948 87	141	8.950 60	143	11.049 40	9.998 28	54	6	14.6	14.4	14.2	14.0
7	8.950 29	142	8.952 02	142	11.047 98	9.998 27	53	7	17.0	16.8	16.6	16.3
8	8.951 70	141	8.953 44	142	11.046 56	9.998 25	52	8	19.5	19.2	18.9	18.7
9	8.953 10	140	8.954 86	142	11.045 14	9.998 24	51	9	21.9	21.6	21.3	21.0
		140		141								
10	**8.954 50**		**8.956 27**		**11.043 73**	**9.998 23**	**50**	10	24.3	24.0	23.7	23.3
11	8.955 89	139	8.957 67	140	11.042 33	9.998 22	49	20	48.7	48.0	47.3	46.7
12	8.957 28	139	8.959 08	141	11.040 92	9.998 21	48	30	73.0	72.0	71.0	70.0
13	8.958 67	139	8.960 47	139	11.039 53	9.998 20	47	40	97.3	96.0	94.7	93.3
14	8.960 05	138	8.961 87	140	11.038 13	9.998 19	46	50	121.7	120.0	118.3	116.7
		138		138								
15	**8.961 43**		**8.963 25**		**11.036 75**	**9.998 17**	**45**	″	**138**	**136**		
16	8.962 80	137	8.964 64	139	11.035 36	9.998 16	44	1	2.3	2.3		
17	8.964 17	137	8.966 02	138	11.033 98	9.998 15	43	2	4.6	4.5		
18	8.965 53	136	8.967 39	137	11.032 61	9.998 14	42	3	6.9	6.8		
19	8.966 89	136	8.968 77	138	11.031 23	9.998 13	41	4	9.2	9.1		
		136		136								
20	**8.968 25**		**8.970 13**		**11.029 87**	**9.998 12**	**40**	5	11.5	11.3		
21	8.969 60	135	8.971 50	137	11.028 50	9.998 10	39	6	13.8	13.6		
22	8.970 95	135	8.972 85	135	11.027 15	9.998 09	38	7	16.1	15.9		
23	8.972 29	134	8.974 21	136	11.025 79	9.998 08	37	8	18.4	18.1		
24	8.973 63	134	8.975 56	135	11.024 44	9.998 07	36	9	20.7	20.4		
		133		133								
25	**8.974 96**		**8.976 91**		**11.023 09**	**9.998 06**	**35**	10	23.0	22.7		
26	8.976 29	133	8.978 25	134	11.021 75	9.998 04	34	20	46.0	45.3		
27	8.977 62	133	8.979 59	134	11.020 41	9.998 03	33	30	69.0	68.0		
28	8.978 94	132	8.980 92	133	11.019 08	9.998 02	32	40	92.0	90.7		
29	8.980 26	132	8.982 25	133	11.017 75	9.998 01	31	50	115.0	113.3		
		131		133								
30	**8.981 57**		**8.983 58**		**11.016 42**	**9.998 00**	**30**	″	**134**	**132**	**130**	**128**
31	8.982 88	131	8.984 90	132	11.015 10	9.997 98	29	1	2.2	2.2	2.2	2.1
32	8.984 19	131	8.986 22	132	11.013 78	9.997 97	28	2	4.5	4.4	4.3	4.3
33	8.985 49	130	8.987 53	131	11.012 47	9.997 96	27	3	6.7	6.6	6.5	6.4
34	8.986 79	130	8.988 84	131	11.011 16	9.997 95	26	4	8.9	8.8	8.7	8.5
		129		131								
35	**8.988 08**		**8.990 15**		**11.009 85**	**9.997 93**	**25**	5	11.2	11.0	10.8	10.7
36	8.989 37	129	8.991 45	130	11.008 55	9.997 92	24	6	13.4	13.2	13.0	12.8
37	8.990 66	129	8.992 75	130	11.007 25	9.997 91	23	7	15.6	15.4	15.2	14.9
38	8.991 94	128	8.994 05	130	11.005 95	9.997 90	22	8	17.9	17.6	17.3	17.1
39	8.993 22	128	8.995 34	129	11.004 66	9.997 88	21	9	20.1	19.8	19.5	19.2
		128		128								
40	**8.994 50**		**8.996 62**		**11.003 38**	**9.997 87**	**20**	10	22.3	22.0	21.7	21.3
41	8.995 77	127	8.997 91	129	11.002 09	9.997 86	19	20	44.7	44.0	43.3	42.7
42	8.997 04	127	8.999 19	128	11.000 81	9.997 85	18	30	67.0	66.0	65.0	64.0
43	8.998 30	126	9.000 46	127	10.999 54	9.997 83	17	40	89.3	88.0	86.7	85.3
44	8.999 56	126	9.001 74	128	10.998 26	9.997 82	16	50	111.7	110.0	108.3	106.7
		126		127								
45	**9.000 82**		**9.003 01**		**10.996 99**	**9.997 81**	**15**	″	**126**	**124**	**122**	**120**
46	9.002 07	125	9.004 27	126	10.995 73	9.997 80	14	1	2.1	2.1	2.0	2.0
47	9.003 32	125	9.005 53	126	10.994 47	9.997 78	13	2	4.2	4.1	4.1	4.0
48	9.004 56	124	9.006 79	126	10.993 21	9.997 77	12	3	6.3	6.2	6.1	6.0
49	9.005 81	125	9.008 05	126	10.991 95	9.997 76	11	4	8.4	8.3	8.1	8.0
		123		125								
50	**9.007 04**		**9.009 30**		**10.990 70**	**9.997 75**	**10**	5	10.5	10.3	10.2	10.0
51	9.008 28	124	9.010 55	125	10.989 45	9.997 73	9	6	12.6	12.4	12.2	12.0
52	9.009 51	123	9.011 79	124	10.988 21	9.997 72	8	7	14.7	14.5	14.2	14.0
53	9.010 74	123	9.013 03	124	10.986 97	9.997 71	7	8	16.8	16.5	16.3	16.0
54	9.011 96	122	9.014 27	123	10.985 73	9.997 69	6	9	18.9	18.6	18.3	18.0
		122		123								
55	**9.013 18**		**9.015 50**		**10.984 50**	**9.997 68**	**5**	10	21.0	20.7	20.3	20.0
56	9.014 40	122	9.016 73	123	10.983 27	9.997 67	4	20	42.0	41.3	40.7	40.0
57	9.015 61	121	9.017 96	122	10.982 04	9.997 65	3	30	63.0	62.0	61.0	60.0
58	9.016 82	121	9.019 18	122	10.980 82	9.997 64	2	40	84.0	82.7	81.3	80.0
59	9.018 03	121	9.020 40	122	10.979 60	9.997 63	1	50	105.0	103.3	101.7	100.0
		120		122								
60	**9.019 23**		**9.021 62**		**10.978 38**	**9.997 61**	**0**					
′	L Cos	d	L Cot	cd	L Tan	L Sin	′		Prop. Pts.		

Table 4 / Logarithms of trigonometric functions   □   **675**

′	L Sin	d	L Tan	cd	L Cot	L Cos	′		″	121	120	119	118
0	9.019 23	120	9.021 62	121	10.978 38	9.997 61	60		1	2.0	2.0	2.0	2.0
1	9.020 43	120	9.022 83	121	10.977 17	9.997 60	59		2	4.0	4.0	4.0	3.9
2	9.021 63	120	9.024 04	121	10.975 96	9.997 59	58		3	6.0	6.0	6.0	5.9
3	9.022 83	119	9.025 25	120	10.974 75	9.997 57	57		4	8.1	8.0	7.9	7.9
4	9.024 02	118	9.026 45	121	10.973 55	9.997 56	56						
5	9.025 20	119	9.027 66	119	10.972 34	9.997 55	55		5	10.1	10.0	9.9	9.8
6	9.026 39	118	9.028 85	120	10.971 15	9.997 53	54		6	12.1	12.0	11.9	11.8
7	9.027 57	117	9.030 05	119	10.969 95	9.997 52	53		7	14.1	14.0	13.9	13.8
8	9.028 74	118	9.031 24	118	10.968 76	9.997 51	52		8	16.1	16.0	15.9	15.7
9	9.029 92	117	9.032 42	119	10.967 58	9.997 49	51		9	18.2	18.0	17.8	17.7
10	9.031 09	117	9.033 61	118	10.966 39	9.997 48	50		10	20.2	20.0	19.8	19.7
11	9.032 26	116	9.034 79	118	10.965 21	9.997 47	49		20	40.3	40.0	39.7	39.3
12	9.033 42	116	9.035 97	117	10.964 03	9.997 45	48		30	60.5	60.0	59.5	59.0
13	9.034 58	116	9.037 14	118	10.962 86	9.997 44	47		40	80.7	80.0	79.3	78.7
14	9.035 74	116	9.038 32	116	10.961 68	9.997 42	46		50	100.8	100.0	99.2	98.3
15	9.036 90	115	9.039 48	117	10.960 52	9.997 41	45		″	117	116	115	114
16	9.038 05	115	9.040 65	116	10.959 35	9.997 40	44		1	2.0	1.9	1.9	1.9
17	9.039 20	114	9.041 81	116	10.958 19	9.997 38	43		2	3.9	3.9	3.8	3.8
18	9.040 34	115	9.042 97	116	10.957 03	9.997 37	42		3	5.8	5.8	5.8	5.7
19	9.041 49	113	9.044 13	115	10.955 87	9.997 36	41		4	7.8	7.7	7.7	7.6
20	9.042 62	114	9.045 28	115	10.954 72	9.997 34	40		5	9.8	9.7	9.6	9.5
21	9.043 76	114	9.046 43	115	10.953 57	9.997 33	39		6	11.7	11.5	11.5	11.4
22	9.044 90	113	9.047 58	115	10.952 42	9.997 31	38		7	13.6	13.5	13.4	13.3
23	9.046 03	112	9.048 73	114	10.951 27	9.997 30	37		8	15.6	15.5	15.3	15.2
24	9.047 15	113	9.049 87	114	10.950 13	9.997 28	36		9	17.6	17.4	17.2	17.1
25	9.048 28	112	9.051 01	113	10.948 99	9.997 27	35		10	19.5	19.3	19.2	19.0
26	9.049 40	112	9.052 14	114	10.947 86	9.997 26	34		20	39.0	38.7	38.3	38.0
27	9.050 52	112	9.053 28	113	10.946 72	9.997 24	33		30	58.5	58.0	57.5	57.0
28	9.051 64	111	9.054 41	112	10.945 59	9.997 23	32		40	78.0	77.3	76.7	76.0
29	9.052 75	111	9.055 53	113	10.944 47	9.997 21	31		50	97.5	96.7	95.8	95.0
30	9.053 86	111	9.056 66	112	10.943 34	9.997 20	30		″	113	112	111	110
31	9.054 97	110	9.057 78	112	10.942 22	9.997 18	29		1	1.9	1.9	1.8	1.8
32	9.056 07	110	9.058 90	112	10.941 10	9.997 17	28		2	3.8	3.7	3.7	3.7
33	9.057 17	110	9.060 02	111	10.939 98	9.997 16	27		3	5.6	5.6	5.6	5.5
34	9.058 27	110	9.061 13	111	10.938 87	9.997 14	26		4	7.5	7.5	7.4	7.3
35	9.059 37	109	9.062 24	111	10.937 76	9.997 13	25		5	9.4	9.3	9.2	9.2
36	9.060 46	109	9.063 35	110	10.936 65	9.997 11	24		6	11.3	11.2	11.1	11.0
37	9.061 55	109	9.064 45	111	10.935 55	9.997 10	23		7	13.2	13.1	13.0	12.8
38	9.062 64	108	9.065 56	110	10.934 44	9.997 08	22		8	15.1	14.9	14.8	14.7
39	9.063 72	109	9.066 66	109	10.933 34	9.997 07	21		9	17.0	16.8	16.6	16.5
40	9.064 81	108	9.067 75	110	10.932 25	9.997 05	20		10	18.8	18.7	18.5	18.3
41	9.065 89	107	9.068 85	109	10.931 15	9.997 04	19		20	37.7	37.3	37.0	36.7
42	9.066 96	108	9.069 94	109	10.930 06	9.997 02	18		30	56.5	56.0	55.5	55.0
43	9.068 04	107	9.071 03	108	10.928 97	9.997 01	17		40	75.3	74.7	74.0	73.3
44	9.069 11	107	9.072 11	109	10.927 89	9.996 99	16		50	94.2	93.3	92.5	91.7
45	9.070 18	106	9.073 20	108	10.926 80	9.996 98	15		″	109	108	107	106
46	9.071 24	107	9.074 28	108	10.925 72	9.996 96	14		1	1.8	1.8	1.8	1.8
47	9.072 31	106	9.075 36	107	10.924 64	9.996 95	13		2	3.6	3.6	3.6	3.5
48	9.073 37	105	9.076 43	108	10.923 57	9.996 93	12		3	5.4	5.4	5.4	5.3
49	9.074 42	106	9.077 51	107	10.922 49	9.996 92	11		4	7.3	7.2	7.1	7.1
50	9.075 48	105	9.078 58	106	10.921 42	9.996 90	10		5	9.1	9.0	8.9	8.8
51	9.076 53	105	9.079 64	107	10.920 36	9.996 89	9		6	10.9	10.8	10.7	10.6
52	9.077 58	105	9.080 71	106	10.919 29	9.996 87	8		7	12.7	12.6	12.5	12.4
53	9.078 63	105	9.081 77	106	10.918 23	9.996 86	7		8	14.5	14.4	14.3	14.1
54	9.079 68	104	9.082 83	106	10.917 17	9.996 84	6		9	16.4	16.2	16.0	15.9
55	9.080 72	104	9.083 89	106	10.916 11	9.996 83	5		10	18.2	18.0	17.8	17.7
56	9.081 76	104	9.084 95	105	10.915 05	9.996 81	4		20	36.3	36.0	35.7	35.3
57	9.082 80	103	9.086 00	105	10.914 00	9.996 80	3		30	54.5	54.0	53.5	53.0
58	9.083 83	103	9.087 05	105	10.912 95	9.996 78	2		40	72.7	72.0	71.3	70.7
59	9.084 86	103	9.088 10	104	10.911 90	9.996 77	1		50	90.8	90.0	89.2	88.3
60	9.085 89		9.089 14		10.910 86	9.996 75	0						

| ′ | L Cos | d | L Cot | cd | L Tan | L Sin | ′ | | | Prop. Pts. | | | |

'	L Sin	d	L Tan	cd	L Cot	L Cos	'
0	**9.085 89**		**9.089 14**		**10.910 86**	**9.996 75**	**60**
1	9.086 92	103	9.090 19	105	10.909 81	9.996 74	59
2	9.087 95	103	9.091 23	104	10.908 77	9.996 72	58
3	9.088 97	102	9.092 27	104	10.907 73	9.996 70	57
4	9.089 99	102	9.093 30	103	10.906 70	9.996 69	56
		102		104			
5	**9.091 01**		**9.094 34**		**10.905 66**	**9.996 67**	**55**
6	9.092 02	101	9.095 37	103	10.904 63	9.996 66	54
7	9.093 04	102	9.096 40	103	10.903 60	9.996 64	53
8	9.094 05	101	9.097 42	102	10.902 58	9.996 63	52
9	9.095 06	101	9.098 45	103	10.901 55	9.996 61	51
		100		102			
10	**9.096 06**		**9.099 47**		**10.900 53**	**9.996 59**	**50**
11	9.097 07	101	9.100 49	102	10.899 51	9.996 58	49
12	9.098 07	100	9.101 50	101	10.898 50	9.996 56	48
13	9.099 07	100	9.102 52	102	10.897 48	9.996 55	47
14	9.100 06	100	9.103 53	101	10.896 47	9.996 53	46
		99		101			
15	**9.101 06**		**9.104 54**		**10.895 46**	**9.996 51**	**45**
16	9.102 05	99	9.105 55	101	10.894 45	9.996 50	44
17	9.103 04	99	9.106 56	101	10.893 44	9.996 48	43
18	9.104 02	98	9.107 56	100	10.892 44	9.996 47	42
19	9.105 01	99	9.108 56	100	10.891 44	9.996 45	41
		98		100			
20	**9.105 99**		**9.109 56**		**10.890 44**	**9.996 43**	**40**
21	9.106 97	98	9.110 56	100	10.889 44	9.996 42	39
22	9.107 95	98	9.111 55	99	10.888 45	9.996 40	38
23	9.108 93	98	9.112 54	99	10.887 46	9.996 38	37
24	9.109 90	97	9.113 53	99	10.886 47	9.996 37	36
		97		99			
25	**9.110 87**		**9.114 52**		**10.885 48**	**9.996 35**	**35**
26	9.111 84	97	9.115 51	99	10.884 49	9.996 33	34
27	9.112 81	97	9.116 49	98	10.883 51	9.996 32	33
28	9.113 77	96	9.117 47	98	10.882 53	9.996 30	32
29	9.114 74	97	9.118 45	98	10.881 55	9.996 29	31
		96		98			
30	**9.115 70**		**9.119 43**		**10.880 57**	**9.996 27**	**30**
31	9.116 66	96	9.120 40	97	10.879 60	9.996 25	29
32	9.117 61	95	9.121 38	98	10.878 62	9.996 24	28
33	9.118 57	96	9.122 35	97	10.877 65	9.996 22	27
34	9.119 52	95	9.123 32	97	10.876 68	9.996 20	26
		95		96			
35	**9.120 47**		**9.124 28**		**10.875 72**	**9.996 18**	**25**
36	9.121 42	95	9.125 25	97	10.874 75	9.996 17	24
37	9.122 36	94	9.126 21	96	10.873 79	9.996 15	23
38	9.123 31	95	9.127 17	96	10.872 83	9.996 13	22
39	9.124 25	94	9.128 13	96	10.871 87	9.996 12	21
		94		96			
40	**9.125 19**		**9.129 09**		**10.870 91**	**9.996 10**	**20**
41	9.126 12	93	9.130 04	95	10.869 96	9.996 08	19
42	9.127 06	94	9.130 99	95	10.869 01	9.996 07	18
43	9.127 99	93	9.131 94	95	10.868 06	9.996 05	17
44	9.128 92	93	9.132 89	95	10.867 11	9.996 03	16
		93		95			
45	**9.129 85**		**9.133 84**		**10.866 16**	**9.996 01**	**15**
46	9.130 78	93	9.134 78	94	10.865 22	9.996 00	14
47	9.131 71	93	9.135 73	95	10.864 27	9.995 98	13
48	9.132 63	92	9.136 67	94	10.863 33	9.995 96	12
49	9.133 55	92	9.137 61	94	10.862 39	9.995 95	11
		92		93			
50	**9.134 47**		**9.138 54**		**10.861 46**	**9.995 93**	**10**
51	9.135 39	92	9.139 48	94	10.860 52	9.995 91	9
52	9.136 30	91	9.140 41	93	10.859 59	9.995 89	8
53	9.137 22	92	9.141 34	93	10.858 66	9.995 88	7
54	9.138 13	91	9.142 27	93	10.857 73	9.995 86	6
		91		93			
55	**9.139 04**		**9.143 20**		**10.856 80**	**9.995 84**	**5**
56	9.139 94	90	9.144 12	92	10.855 88	9.995 82	4
57	9.140 85	91	9.145 04	92	10.854 96	9.995 81	3
58	9.141 75	90	9.145 97	93	10.854 03	9.995 79	2
59	9.142 66	91	9.146 88	91	10.853 12	9.995 77	1
		90		92			
60	**9.143 56**		**9.147 80**		**10.852 20**	**9.995 75**	**0**

'	L Cos	d	L Cot	cd	L Tan	L Sin	'

Prop. Pts.

"	105	104	103	102
1	1.8	1.7	1.7	1.7
2	3.5	3.5	3.4	3.4
3	5.2	5.2	5.2	5.1
4	7.0	6.9	6.9	6.8
5	8.8	8.7	8.6	8.5
6	10.5	10.4	10.3	10.2
7	12.2	12.1	12.0	11.9
8	14.0	13.9	13.7	13.6
9	15.8	15.6	15.4	15.3
10	17.5	17.3	17.2	17.0
20	35.0	34.7	34.3	34.0
30	52.5	52.0	51.5	51.0
40	70.0	69.3	68.7	68.0
50	87.5	86.7	85.8	85.0

"	101	100	99	98
1	1.7	1.7	1.6	1.6
2	3.4	3.3	3.3	3.3
3	5.0	5.0	5.0	4.9
4	6.7	6.7	6.6	6.5
5	8.4	8.3	8.2	8.2
6	10.1	10.0	9.9	9.8
7	11.8	11.7	11.6	11.4
8	13.5	13.3	13.2	13.1
9	15.2	15.0	14.8	14.7
10	16.8	16.7	16.5	16.3
20	33.7	33.3	33.0	32.7
30	50.0	50.0	49.5	49.0
40	67.3	66.7	66.0	65.3
50	84.2	83.3	82.5	81.7

"	97	96	95	94
1	1.6	1.6	1.6	1.6
2	3.2	3.2	3.2	3.1
3	4.8	4.8	4.8	4.7
4	6.5	6.4	6.3	6.3
5	8.1	8.0	7.9	7.8
6	9.7	9.6	9.5	9.4
7	11.3	11.2	11.1	11.0
8	12.9	12.8	12.7	12.5
9	14.6	14.4	14.2	14.1
10	16.2	16.0	15.8	15.7
20	32.3	32.0	31.7	31.3
30	48.5	48.0	47.5	47.0
40	64.7	64.0	63.3	62.7
50	80.8	80.0	79.2	78.3

"	93	92	91	90
1	1.6	1.5	1.5	1.5
2	3.1	3.1	3.0	3.0
3	4.6	4.6	4.6	4.5
4	6.2	6.1	6.1	6.0
5	7.8	7.7	7.6	7.5
6	9.3	9.2	9.1	9.0
7	10.8	10.7	10.6	10.5
8	12.4	12.3	12.1	12.0
9	14.0	13.8	13.6	13.5
10	15.5	15.3	15.2	15.0
20	31.0	30.7	30.3	30.0
30	46.5	36.0	45.5	45.0
40	62.0	61.3	60.7	60.0
50	77.5	76.7	75.8	75.0

Prop. Pts.

Table 4 / Logarithms of trigonometric functions   □   **677**

′	L Sin	d	L Tan	cd	L Cot	L Cos	′	″	92	91	90
0	9.143 56	89	9.147 80	92	10.852 20	9.995 75	60		92	91	90
1	9.144 45	90	9.148 72	91	10.851 28	9.995 74	59	1	1.5	1.5	1.5
2	9.145 35	90	9.149 63	91	10.850 37	9.995 72	58	2	3.1	3.0	3.0
3	9.146 24	90	9.150 54	91	10.849 46	9.995 70	57	3	4.6	4.6	4.5
4	9.147 14	89	9.151 45	91	10.848 55	9.995 68	56	4	6.1	6.1	6.0
5	9.148 03	88	9.152 36	91	10.847 64	9.995 66	55	5	7.7	7.6	7.5
6	9.148 91	89	9.153 27	90	10.846 73	9.995 65	54	6	9.2	9.1	9.0
7	9.149 80	89	9.154 17	91	10.845 83	9.995 63	53	7	10.7	10.6	10.5
8	9.150 69	88	9.155 08	90	10.844 92	9.995 61	52	8	12.3	12.1	12.0
9	9.151 57	88	9.155 98	90	10.844 02	9.995 59	51	9	13.8	13.6	13.5
10	9.152 45	88	9.156 88	89	10.843 12	9.995 57	50	10	15.3	15.2	15.0
11	9.153 33	88	9.157 77	90	10.842 23	9.995 56	49	20	30.7	30.3	30.0
12	9.154 21	87	9.158 67	89	10.841 33	9.995 54	48	30	46.0	45.5	45.0
13	9.155 08	88	9.159 56	90	10.840 44	9.995 52	47	40	61.3	60.7	60.0
14	9.155 96	87	9.160 46	89	10.839 54	9.995 50	46	50	76.7	75.8	75.0
15	9.156 83	87	9.161 35	89	10.838 65	9.995 48	45	″	89	88	87
16	9.157 70	87	9.162 24	88	10.837 76	9.995 46	44	1	1.5	1.5	1.4
17	9.158 57	87	9.163 12	89	10.836 88	9.995 45	43	2	3.0	2.9	2.9
18	9.159 44	86	9.164 01	88	10.835 99	9.995 43	42	3	4.4	4.4	4.4
19	9.160 30	86	9.164 89	88	10.835 11	9.995 41	41	4	5.9	5.9	5.8
20	9.161 16	87	9.165 77	88	10.834 23	9.995 39	40	5	7.4	7.3	7.2
21	9.162 03	86	9.166 65	88	10.833 35	9.995 37	39	6	8.9	8.8	8.7
22	9.162 89	85	9.167 53	88	10.832 47	9.995 35	38	7	10.4	10.3	10.2
23	9.163 74	86	9.168 41	87	10.831 59	9.995 33	37	8	11.9	11.7	11.6
24	9.164 60	85	9.169 28	88	10.830 72	9.995 32	36	9	13.4	13.2	13.0
25	9.165 45	86	9.170 16	87	10.829 84	9.995 30	35	10	14.8	14.7	14.5
26	9.166 31	85	9.171 03	87	10.828 97	9.995 28	34	20	29.7	29.3	29.0
27	9.167 16	85	9.171 90	87	10.828 10	9.995 26	33	30	44.5	44.0	43.5
28	9.168 01	85	9.172 77	86	10.827 23	9.995 24	32	40	59.3	58.7	58.0
29	9.168 86	84	9.173 63	87	10.826 37	9.995 22	31	50	74.2	73.3	72.5
30	9.169 70	85	9.174 50	86	10.825 50	9.995 20	30	″	86	85	84
31	9.170 55	84	9.175 36	86	10.824 64	9.995 18	29	1	1.4	1.4	1.4
32	9.171 39	84	9.176 22	86	10.823 78	9.995 17	28	2	2.9	2.8	2.8
33	9.172 23	84	9.177 08	86	10.822 92	9.995 15	27	3	4.3	4.2	4.2
34	9.173 07	84	9.177 94	86	10.822 06	9.995 13	26	4	5.7	5.7	5.6
35	9.173 91	83	9.178 80	85	10.821 20	9.995 11	25	5	7.2	7.1	7.0
36	9.174 74	84	9.179 65	86	10.820 35	9.995 09	24	6	8.6	8.5	8.4
37	9.175 58	83	9.180 51	85	10.819 49	9.995 07	23	7	10.0	9.9	9.8
38	9.176 41	83	9.181 36	85	10.818 64	9.995 05	22	8	11.5	11.3	11.2
39	9.177 24	83	9.182 21	85	10.817 79	9.995 03	21	9	12.9	12.8	12.6
40	9.178 07	83	9.183 06	85	10.816 94	9.995 01	20	10	14.3	14.2	14.0
41	9.178 90	83	9.183 91	84	10.816 09	9.994 99	19	20	28.7	28.3	28.0
42	9.179 73	82	9.184 75	85	10.815 25	9.994 97	18	30	43.0	42.5	42.0
43	9.180 55	82	9.185 60	84	10.814 40	9.994 95	17	40	57.3	56.7	56.0
44	9.181 37	83	9.186 44	84	10.813 56	9.994 94	16	50	71.7	70.8	70.0
45	9.182 20	82	9.187 28	84	10.812 72	9.994 92	15	″	83	82	81
46	9.183 02	81	9.188 12	84	10.818 88	9.994 90	14	1	1.4	1.4	1.4
47	9.183 83	82	9.188 96	83	10.811 04	9.994 88	13	3	2.8	2.7	2.7
48	9.184 65	82	9.189 79	84	10.810 21	9.994 86	12	3	4.2	4.1	4.0
49	9.185 47	81	9.190 63	83	10.809 37	9.994 84	11	4	5.5	5.5	5.4
50	9.186 28	81	9.191 46	83	10.808 54	9.994 82	10	5	6.9	6.8	6.8
51	9.187 09	81	9.192 29	83	10.807 71	9.994 80	9	6	8.3	8.2	8.1
52	9.187 90	81	9.193 12	83	10.806 88	9.994 78	8	7	9.7	9.6	9.4
53	9.188 71	81	9.193 95	83	10.806 05	9.994 76	7	8	11.1	10.9	10.8
54	9.189 52	81	9.194 78	83	10.805 22	9.994 74	6	9	12.4	12.3	12.2
55	9.190 33	80	9.195 61	82	10.804 39	9.994 72	5	10	13.8	13.7	13.5
56	9.191 13	80	9.196 43	82	10.803 57	9.994 70	4	20	27.7	27.3	27.0
57	9.191 93	80	9.197 25	82	10.802 75	9.994 68	3	30	41.5	41.0	40.5
58	9.192 73	80	9.198 07	82	10.801 93	9.994 66	2	40	55.3	54.7	54.0
59	9.193 53	80	9.198 89	82	10.801 11	9.994 64	1	50	69.2	68.3	67.5
60	9.194 33		9.199 71		10.800 29	9.994 62	0				
′	L Cos	d	L Cot	cd	L Tan	L Sin	′		Prop. Pts.		

′	L Sin	d	L Tan	cd	L Cot	L Cos	′
0	**9.194 33**		**9.199 71**		**10.800 29**	**9.994 62**	60
1	9.195 13	80	9.200 53	82	10.799 47	9.994 60	59
2	9.195 92	79	9.201 34	81	10.798 66	9.994 58	58
3	9.196 72	80	9.202 16	82	10.797 84	9.994 56	57
4	9.197 51	79	9.202 97	81	10.797 03	9.994 54	56
5	**9.198 30**	79	**9.203 78**	81	**10.796 22**	**9.994 52**	55
6	9.199 09	79	9.204 59	81	10.795 41	9.994 50	54
7	9.199 88	79	9.205 40	81	10.794 60	9.994 48	53
8	9.200 67	78	9.206 21	80	10.793 79	9.994 46	52
9	9.201 45	78	9.207 01	81	10.792 99	9.994 44	51
10	**9.202 23**	79	**9.207 82**	80	**10.792 18**	**9.994 42**	50
11	9.203 02	78	9.208 62	80	10.791 38	9.994 40	49
12	9.203 80	78	9.209 42	80	10.790 58	9.994 38	48
13	9.204 58	77	9.210 22	80	10.789 78	9.994 36	47
14	9.205 35	78	9.211 02	80	10.788 98	9.994 34	46
15	**9.206 13**	78	**9.211 82**	79	**10.788 18**	**9.994 32**	45
16	9.206 91	77	9.212 61	80	10.787 39	9.994 29	44
17	9.207 68	77	9.213 41	79	10.786 59	9.994 27	43
18	9.208 45	77	9.214 20	79	10.785 80	9.994 25	42
19	9.209 22	77	9.214 99	79	10.785 01	9.994 23	41
20	**9.209 99**	77	**9.215 78**	79	**10.784 22**	**9.994 21**	40
21	9.210 76	77	9.216 57	79	10.783 43	9.994 19	39
22	9.211 53	76	9.217 36	78	10.782 64	9.994 17	38
23	9.212 29	77	9.218 14	79	10.781 86	9.994 15	37
24	9.213 06	76	9.218 93	78	10.781 07	9.994 13	36
25	**9.213 82**	76	**9.219 71**	78	**10.780 29**	**9.994 11**	35
26	9.214 58	76	9.220 49	78	10.779 51	9.994 09	34
27	9.215 34	76	9.221 27	78	10.778 73	9.994 07	33
28	9.216 10	75	9.222 05	78	10.777 95	9.994 04	32
29	9.216 85	76	9.222 83	78	10.777 17	9.994 02	31
30	**9.217 61**	75	**9.223 61**	77	**10.776 39**	**9.994 00**	30
31	9.218 36	76	9.224 38	78	10.775 62	9.993 98	29
32	9.219 12	75	9.225 16	77	10.774 84	9.993 96	28
33	9.219 87	75	9.225 93	77	10.774 07	9.993 94	27
34	9.220 62	75	9.226 70	77	10.773 30	9.993 92	26
35	**9.221 37**	74	**9.227 47**	77	**10.772 53**	**9.993 90**	25
36	9.222 11	75	9.228 24	77	10.771 76	9.993 88	24
37	9.222 86	75	9.229 01	76	10.770 99	9.993 85	23
38	9.223 61	74	9.229 77	77	10.770 23	9.993 83	22
39	9.224 35	74	9.230 54	76	10.769 46	9.993 81	21
40	**9.225 09**	74	**9.231 30**	76	**10.768 70**	**9.993 79**	20
41	9.225 83	74	9.232 06	77	10.767 94	9.993 77	19
42	9.226 57	74	9.232 83	76	10.767 17	9.993 75	18
43	9.227 31	74	9.233 59	76	10.766 41	9.993 72	17
44	9.228 05	73	9.234 35	75	10.765 65	9.993 70	16
45	**9.228 78**	74	**9.235 10**	76	**10.764 90**	**9.993 68**	15
46	9.229 52	73	9.235 86	75	10.764 14	9.993 66	14
47	9.230 25	73	9.236 61	76	10.763 39	9.993 64	13
48	9.230 98	73	9.237 37	75	10.762 63	9.993 62	12
49	9.231 71	73	9.238 12	75	10.761 88	9.993 59	11
50	**9.232 44**	73	**9.238 87**	75	**10.761 13**	**9.993 57**	10
51	9.233 17	73	9.239 62	75	10.760 38	9.993 55	9
52	9.233 90	72	9.240 37	75	10.759 63	9.993 53	8
53	9.234 62	73	9.241 12	74	10.758 88	9.993 51	7
54	9.235 35	72	9.241 86	75	10.758 14	9.993 48	6
55	**9.236 07**	72	**9.242 61**	74	**10.757 39**	**9.993 46**	5
56	9.236 79	73	9.243 35	75	10.756 65	9.993 44	4
57	9.237 52	71	9.244 10	74	10.755 90	9.993 42	3
58	9.238 23	72	9.244 84	74	10.755 16	9.993 40	2
59	9.238 95	72	9.245 58	74	10.754 42	9.993 37	1
60	**9.239 67**		**9.246 32**		**10.753 68**	**9.993 35**	0
′	L Cos	d	L Cot	cd	L Tan	L Sin	′

Prop. Pts.

″	80	79	78	77
1	1.3	1.3	1.3	1.3
2	2.7	2.6	2.6	2.6
3	4.0	4.0	3.9	3.8
4	5.3	5.3	5.2	5.1
5	6.7	6.6	6.5	6.4
6	8.0	7.9	7.8	7.7
7	9.3	9.2	9.1	9.0
8	10.7	10.5	10.4	10.3
9	12.0	11.8	11.7	11.6
10	13.3	13.2	13.0	12.8
20	26.7	26.3	26.0	25.7
30	40.0	39.5	39.0	38.5
40	53.3	52.7	52.0	51.3
50	66.7	65.8	65.0	64.2

″	76	75	74	73
1	1.3	1.2	1.2	1.2
2	2.5	2.5	2.5	2.4
3	3.8	3.8	3.7	3.6
4	5.1	5.0	4.9	4.9
5	6.3	6.2	6.2	6.1
6	7.6	7.5	7.4	7.3
7	8.9	8.8	8.6	8.5
8	10.1	10.0	9.9	9.7
9	11.4	11.2	11.1	11.0
10	12.7	12.5	12.3	12.2
20	25.3	25.0	24.7	24.3
30	38.0	37.5	37.0	36.5
40	50.7	50.0	49.3	48.7
50	63.3	62.5	61.7	60.8

″	72	71	3	2
1	1.2	1.2	0.0	0.0
2	2.4	2.4	0.1	0.1
3	3.6	3.6	0.2	0.1
4	4.8	4.7	0.2	0.1
5	6.0	5.9	0.2	0.2
6	7.2	7.1	0.3	0.2
7	8.4	8.3	0.4	0.2
8	9.6	9.5	0.4	0.3
9	10.8	10.6	0.4	0.3
10	12.0	11.8	0.5	0.3
20	24.0	23.7	1.0	0.7
30	36.0	35.5	1.5	1.0
40	48.0	47.3	2.0	1.3
50	60.0	59.2	2.5	1.7

Prop. Pts.

Table 4 / Logarithms of trigonometric functions □ **679**

′	L Sin	d	L Tan	cd	L Cot	L Cos	d	′		Prop. Pts.		
0	9.239 67	72	9.246 32	74	10.753 68	9.993 35	2	60				
1	9.240 39	71	9.247 06	73	10.752 94	9.993 33	2	59				
2	9.241 10	71	9.247 79	74	10.752 21	9.993 31	2	58				
3	9.241 81	72	9.248 53	73	10.751 47	9.993 28	3	57				
4	9.242 53	71	9.249 26	74	10.750 74	9.993 26	2	56				
5	9.243 24	71	9.250 00	73	10.750 00	9.993 24	2	55				
6	9.243 95	71	9.250 73	73	10.749 27	9.993 22	3	54				
7	9.244 66	70	9.251 46	73	10.748 54	9.993 19	2	53				
8	9.245 36	71	9.252 19	73	10.747 81	9.993 17	2	52		″	74	73	72
9	9.246 07	70	9.252 92	73	10.747 08	9.993 15	2	51		1	1.2	1.2	1.2
10	9.246 77	71	9.253 65	72	10.746 35	9.993 13	3	50		2	2.5	2.4	2.4
11	9.247 48	70	9.254 37	73	10.745 63	9.993 10	2	49		3	3.7	3.6	3.6
12	9.248 18	70	9.255 10	72	10.744 90	9.993 08	2	48		4	4.9	4.9	4.8
13	9.248 88	70	9.255 82	73	10.744 18	9.993 06	2	47		5	6.2	6.1	6.0
14	9.249 58	70	9.256 55	72	10.743 45	9.993 04	3	46		6	7.4	7.3	7.2
15	9.250 28	70	9.257 27	72	10.742 73	9.993 01	2	45		7	8.6	8.5	8.4
16	9.250 98	70	9.257 99	72	10.742 01	9.992 99	2	44		8	9.9	9.7	9.6
17	9.251 68	69	9.258 71	72	10.741 29	9.992 97	3	43		9	11.1	11.0	10.8
18	9.252 37	70	9.259 43	72	10.740 57	9.992 94	2	42		10	12.3	12.2	12.0
19	9.253 07	69	9.260 15	71	10.739 85	9.992 92	2	41		20	24.7	24.3	24.0
20	9.253 76	69	9.260 86	72	10.739 14	9.992 90	2	40		30	37.0	36.5	36.0
21	9.254 45	69	9.261 58	71	10.738 42	9.992 88	3	39		40	49.3	48.7	48.0
22	9.255 14	69	9.262 29	72	10.737 71	9.992 85	2	38		50	61.7	60.8	60.0
23	9.255 83	69	9.263 01	71	10.736 99	9.992 83	2	37		″	71	70	69
24	9.256 52	69	9.263 72	71	10.736 28	9.992 81	3	36		1	1.2	1.2	1.2
25	9.257 21	69	9.264 43	71	10.735 57	9.992 78	2	35		2	2.4	2.3	2.3
26	9.257 90	68	9.265 14	71	10.734 86	9.992 76	2	34		3	3.6	3.5	3.4
27	9.258 58	69	9.265 85	70	10.734 15	9.992 74	3	33		4	4.7	4.7	4.6
28	9.259 27	68	9.266 55	71	10.733 45	9.992 71	2	32		5	5.9	5.8	5.8
29	9.259 95	68	9.267 26	71	10.732 74	9.992 69	2	31		6	7.1	7.0	6.9
30	9.260 63	68	9.267 97	70	10.732 03	9.992 67	3	30		7	8.3	8.2	8.0
31	9.261 31	68	9.268 67	70	10.731 33	9.992 64	2	29		8	9.5	9.3	9.2
32	9.261 99	68	9.269 37	71	10.730 63	9.992 62	2	28		9	10.6	10.5	10.4
33	9.262 67	68	9.270 08	70	10.729 92	9.992 60	3	27		10	11.8	11.7	11.5
34	9.263 35	68	9.270 78	70	10.729 22	9.992 57	2	26		20	23.7	23.3	23.0
35	9.264 03	67	9.271 48	70	10.728 52	9.992 55	3	25		30	35.5	35.0	34.5
36	9.264 70	68	9.272 18	70	10.727 82	9.992 52	2	24		40	47.3	46.7	46.0
37	9.265 38	67	9.272 88	69	10.727 12	9.992 50	2	23		50	59.2	58.3	57.5
38	9.266 05	67	9.273 57	70	10.726 43	9.992 48	3	22		″	68	67	66
39	9.266 72	67	9.274 27	69	10.725 73	9.992 45	2	21		1	1.1	1.1	1.1
40	9.267 39	67	9.274 96	70	10.725 04	9.992 43	2	20		2	2.3	2.2	2.2
41	9.268 06	67	9.275 66	69	10.724 34	9.992 41	3	19		3	3.4	3.4	3.3
42	9.268 73	67	9.276 35	69	10.723 65	9.992 38	2	18		4	4.5	4.5	4.4
43	9.269 40	67	9.277 04	69	10.722 96	9.992 36	3	17		5	5.7	5.6	5.5
44	9.270 07	66	9.277 73	69	10.722 27	9.992 33	2	16		6	6.8	6.7	6.6
45	9.270 73	67	9.278 42	69	10.721 58	9.992 31	2	15		7	7.9	7.8	7.7
46	9.271 40	66	9.279 11	69	10.720 89	9.992 29	3	14		8	9.1	8.9	8.8
47	9.272 06	67	9.279 80	69	10.720 20	9.992 26	2	13		9	10.2	10.0	9.9
48	9.272 73	66	9.280 49	68	10.719 51	9.992 24	3	12		10	11.3	11.2	11.0
49	9.273 39	66	9.281 17	69	10.718 83	9.992 21	2	11		20	22.7	22.3	22.0
50	9.274 05	66	9.281 86	68	10.718 14	9.992 19	2	10		30	34.0	33.5	33.0
51	9.274 71	66	9.282 54	69	10.717 46	9.992 17	3	9		40	45.3	44.7	44.0
52	9.275 37	65	9.283 23	68	10.716 77	9.992 14	2	8		50	56.7	55.8	55.0
53	9.276 02	66	9.283 91	68	10.716 09	9.992 12	3	7					
54	9.276 68	66	9.284 59	68	10.715 41	9.992 09	2	6					
55	9.277 34	65	9.285 27	68	10.714 73	9.992 07	3	5					
56	9.277 99	65	9.285 95	67	10.714 05	9.992 04	2	4					
57	9.278 64	66	9.286 62	68	10.713 38	9.992 02	2	3					
58	9.279 30	65	9.287 30	68	10.712 70	9.992 00	3	2					
59	9.279 95	65	9.287 98	67	10.712 02	9.991 97	2	1					
60	9.280 60		9.288 65		10.711 35	9.991 95		0					
′	L Cos	d	L Cot	cd	L Tan	L Sin	d	′		Prop. Pts.		

′	L Sin	d	L Tan	cd	L Cot	L Cos	d	′	Prop. Pts.
0	**9.280 60**		**9.288 65**		**10.711 35**	**9.991 95**		60	
1	9.281 25	65	9.289 33	68	10.710 67	9.991 92	3	59	
2	9.281 90	65	9.290 00	67	10.710 00	9.991 90	2	58	
3	9.282 54	64	9.290 67	67	10.709 33	9.991 87	3	57	
4	9.283 19	65	9.291 34	67	10.708 66	9.991 85	2	56	
		65		67			3		
5	**9.283 84**		**9.292 01**		**10.707 99**	**9.991 82**		55	
6	9.284 48	64	9.292 68	67	10.707 32	9.991 80	2	54	
7	9.285 12	64	9.293 35	67	10.706 65	9.991 77	3	53	″ **65** **64** **63**
8	9.285 77	65	9.294 02	67	10.705 98	9.991 75	2	52	1 1.1 1.1 1.0
9	9.286 41	64	9.294 68	66	10.705 32	9.991 72	3	51	2 2.2 2.1 2.1
		64		67			2		3 3.2 3.2 3.2
10	**9.287 05**		**9.295 35**		**10.704 65**	**9.991 70**		50	4 4.2 4.3 4.2
11	9.287 69	64	9.296 01	66	10.703 99	9.991 67	3	49	
12	9.288 33	64	9.296 68	67	10.703 32	9.991 65	2	48	5 5.4 5.3 5.2
13	9.288 96	63	9.297 34	66	10.702 66	9.991 62	3	47	6 6.5 6.4 6.3
14	9.289 60	64	9.298 00	66	10.702 00	9.991 60	2	46	7 7.6 7.5 7.4
		64		66			3		8 8.7 8.5 8.4
15	**9.290 24**		**9.298 66**		**10.701 34**	**9.991 57**		45	9 9.8 9.6 9.4
16	9.290 87	63	9.299 32	66	10.700 68	9.991 55	2	44	
17	9.291 50	63	9.299 98	66	10.700 02	9.991 52	3	43	10 10.8 10.7 10.5
18	9.292 14	64	9.300 64	66	10.699 36	9.991 50	2	42	20 21.7 21.3 21.0
19	9.292 77	63	9.301 30	66	10.698 70	9.991 47	3	41	30 32.5 32.0 31.5
		63		65			2		40 43.3 42.7 42.0
20	**9.293 40**		**9.301 95**		**10.698 05**	**9.991 45**		40	50 54.2 53.3 52.5
21	9.294 03	63	9.302 61	66	10.697 39	9.991 42	3	39	
22	9.294 66	63	9.303 26	65	10.696 74	9.991 40	2	38	″ **62** **61** **60**
23	9.295 29	63	9.303 91	65	10.696 09	9.991 37	3	37	1 1.0 1.0 1.0
24	9.295 91	62	9.304 57	66	10.695 43	9.991 35	2	36	2 2.1 2.0 2.0
		63		65			3		3 3.1 3.0 3.0
25	**9.296 54**		**9.305 22**		**10.694 78**	**9.991 32**		35	4 4.1 4.1 4.0
26	9.297 16	62	9.305 87	65	10.694 13	9.991 30	2	34	
27	9.297 79	63	9.306 52	65	10.693 48	9.991 27	3	33	5 5.2 5.1 5.0
28	9.298 41	62	9.307 17	65	10.692 83	9.991 24	3	32	6 6.2 6.1 6.0
29	9.299 03	62	9.307 82	65	10.692 18	9.991 22	2	31	7 7.2 7.1 7.0
		63		64			3		8 8.3 8.1 8.0
30	**9.299 66**		**9.308 46**		**10.691 54**	**9.991 19**		30	9 9.3 9.2 9.0
31	9.300 28	62	9.309 11	65	10.690 89	9.991 17	2	29	
32	9.300 90	62	9.309 75	64	10.690 25	9.991 14	3	28	10 10.3 10.2 10.0
33	9.301 51	61	9.310 40	65	10.689 60	9.991 12	3	27	20 20.7 20.3 20.0
34	9.302 13	62	9.311 04	64	10.688 96	9.991 09	3	26	30 31.0 30.5 30.0
		62		64			3		40 41.3 40.7 40.0
35	**9.302 75**		**9.311 68**		**10.688 32**	**9.991 06**		25	50 51.7 50.8 50.0
36	9.303 36	61	9.312 33	65	10.687 67	9.991 04	2	24	
37	9.303 98	62	9.312 97	64	10.687 03	9.991 01	3	23	″ **59** **3** **2**
38	9.304 59	61	9.313 61	64	10.686 39	9.990 99	2	22	1 1.0 0.0 0.0
39	9.305 21	62	9.314 25	64	10.685 75	9.990 96	3	21	2 2.0 0.1 0.1
		61		64			3		3 3.0 0.2 0.1
40	**9.305 82**		**9.314 89**		**10.685 11**	**9.990 93**		20	4 3.9 0.2 0.1
41	9.306 43	61	9.315 52	63	10.684 48	9.990 91	2	19	
42	9.307 04	61	9.316 16	64	10.683 84	9.990 88	3	18	5 4.9 0.2 0.2
43	9.307 65	61	9.316 79	63	10.683 21	9.990 86	2	17	6 5.9 0.3 0.2
44	9.308 26	61	9.317 43	64	10.682 57	9.990 83	3	16	7 6.9 0.4 0.2
		61		63			3		8 7.9 0.4 0.3
45	**9.308 87**		**9.318 06**		**10.681 94**	**9.990 80**		15	9 8.8 0.4 0.3
46	9.309 47	60	9.318 70	64	10.681 30	9.990 78	2	14	
47	9.310 08	61	9.319 33	63	10.680 67	9.990 75	3	13	10 9.8 0.5 0.3
48	9.310 68	60	9.319 96	63	10.680 04	9.990 72	3	12	20 19.7 1.0 0.7
49	9.311 29	61	9.320 59	63	10.679 41	9.990 70	2	11	30 29.5 1.5 1.0
		60		63			3		40 39.3 2.0 1.3
50	**9.311 89**		**9.321 22**		**10.678 78**	**9.990 67**		10	50 49.2 2.5 1.7
51	9.312 50	61	9.321 85	63	10.678 15	9.990 64	3	9	
52	9.313 10	60	9.322 48	63	10.677 52	9.990 62	2	8	
53	9.313 70	60	9.323 11	63	10.676 89	9.990 59	3	7	
54	9.314 30	60	9.323 73	62	10.676 27	9.990 56	3	6	
		60		63			2		
55	**9.314 90**		**9.324 36**		**10.675 64**	**9.990 54**		5	
56	9.315 49	59	9.324 98	62	10.675 02	9.990 51	3	4	
57	9.316 09	60	9.324 61	63	10.674 39	9.990 48	3	3	
58	9.316 69	60	9.326 23	62	10.673 77	9.990 46	2	2	
59	9.317 28	59	9.326 85	62	10.673 15	9.990 43	3	1	
		60		62			3		
60	**9.317 88**		**9.327 47**		**10.672 53**	**9.990 40**		0	
′	L Cos	d	L Cot	cd	L Tan	L Sin	d	′	Prop. Pts.

Table 4 / Logarithms of trigonometric functions   □   **681**

′	L Sin	d	L Tan	cd	L Cot	L Cos	d	′	Prop. Pts.
0	9.317 88		9.327 47		10.672 53	9.990 40		60	
1	9.318 47	59	9.328 10	63	10.671 90	9.990 38	2	59	
2	9.319 07	60	9.328 72	62	10.671 28	9.990 35	3	58	
3	9.319 66	59	9.329 33	61	10.670 67	9.990 32	3	57	
4	9.320 25	59	9.329 95	62	10.670 05	9.990 30	3	56	
		59		62			3		
5	9.320 84		9.330 57		10.669 43	9.990 27		55	
6	9.321 43	59	9.331 19	62	10.668 81	9.990 24	3	54	
7	9.322 02	59	9.331 80	61	10.668 20	9.990 22	2	53	
8	9.322 61	59	9.332 42	62	10.667 58	9.990 19	3	52	
9	9.323 19	58	9.333 03	61	10.666 97	9.990 16	3	51	
		59		62			3		
10	9.323 78		9.333 65		10.666 35	9.990 13		50	
11	9.324 37	59	9.334 26	61	10.665 74	9.990 11	2	49	
12	9.324 95	58	9.334 87	61	10.665 13	9.990 08	3	48	
13	9.325 53	58	9.335 48	61	10.664 52	9.990 05	3	47	
14	9.326 12	59	9.336 09	61	10.663 91	9.990 02	3	46	
		58		61			2		
15	9.326 70		9.336 70		10.663 30	9.990 00		45	
16	9.327 28	58	9.337 31	61	10.662 69	9.989 97	3	44	
17	9.327 86	58	9.337 92	61	10.662 08	9.989 94	3	43	
18	9.328 44	58	9.338 53	61	10.661 47	9.989 91	3	42	
19	9.329 02	58	9.339 13	60	10.660 87	9.989 89	2	41	
		58		61			3		
20	9.329 60		9.339 74		10.660 26	9.989 86		40	
21	9.330 18	58	9.340 34	60	10.659 66	9.989 83	3	39	
22	9.330 75	57	9.340 95	61	10.659 05	9.989 80	3	38	
23	9.331 33	58	9.341 55	60	10.658 45	9.989 78	2	37	
24	9.331 90	57	9.342 15	60	10.657 85	9.989 75	3	36	
		58		61			3		
25	9.332 48		9.342 76		10.657 24	9.989 72		35	
26	9.333 05	57	9.343 36	60	10.656 64	9.989 69	3	34	
27	9.333 62	57	9.343 96	60	10.656 04	9.989 67	2	33	
28	9.334 20	58	9.344 56	60	10.655 44	9.989 64	3	32	
29	9.334 77	57	9.345 16	60	10.654 84	9.989 61	3	31	
		57		60			3		
30	9.335 34		9.345 76		10.654 24	9.989 58		30	
31	9.335 91	57	9.346 35	59	10.653 65	9.989 55	3	29	
32	9.336 47	56	9.346 95	60	10.653 05	9.989 53	2	28	
33	9.337 04	57	9.347 55	60	10.652 45	9.989 50	3	27	
34	9.337 61	57	9.348 14	59	10.651 86	9.989 47	3	26	
		57		60			3		
35	9.338 18		9.348 74		10.651 26	9.989 44		25	
36	9.338 74	56	9.349 33	59	10.650 67	9.989 41	3	24	
37	9.339 31	57	9.349 92	59	10.650 08	9.989 38	3	23	
38	9.339 87	56	9.350 51	59	10.649 49	9.989 36	2	22	
39	9.340 43	56	9.351 11	60	10.648 89	9.989 33	3	21	
		57		59			3		
40	9.341 00		9.351 70		10.648 30	9.989 30		20	
41	9.341 56	56	9.352 29	59	10.647 71	9.989 27	3	19	
42	9.342 12	56	9.352 88	59	10.647 12	9.989 24	3	18	
43	9.342 68	56	9.353 47	59	10.646 53	9.989 21	2	17	
44	9.343 24	56	9.354 05	58	10.645 95	9.989 19	3	16	
		56		59			3		
45	9.343 80		9.354 64		10.645 36	9.989 16		15	
46	9.344 36	56	9.355 23	59	10.644 77	9.989 13	3	14	
47	9.344 91	56	9.355 81	58	10.644 19	9.989 10	3	13	
48	9.345 47	56	9.356 40	59	10.643 60	9.989 07	3	12	
49	9.346 02	55	9.356 98	58	10.643 02	9.989 04	3	11	
		56		59			3		
50	9.346 58		9.357 57		10.642 43	9.989 01		10	
51	9.347 13	55	9.358 15	58	10.641 85	9.988 98	3	9	
52	9.347 69	56	9.358 73	58	10.641 27	9.988 96	2	8	
53	9.348 24	55	9.359 31	58	10.640 69	9.988 93	3	7	
54	9.348 79	55	9.359 89	58	10.640 11	9.988 90	3	6	
		55		58			3		
55	9.349 34		9.360 47		10.639 53	9.988 87		5	
56	9.349 89	55	9.361 05	58	10.638 95	9.988 84	3	4	
57	9.350 44	55	9.361 63	58	10.638 37	9.988 81	3	3	
58	9.350 99	55	9.362 21	58	10.637 79	9.988 78	3	2	
59	9.351 54	55	9.362 79	57	10.637 21	9.988 75	3	1	
		55					3		
60	9.352 09		9.363 36		10.636 64	9.988 72		0	
′	L Cos	d	L Cot	cd	L Tan	L Sin	d	′	Prop. Pts.

Prop. Pts.

″	63	62	61
1	1.0	1.0	1.0
2	2.1	2.1	2.0
3	3.2	3.1	3.0
4	4.2	4.1	4.1
5	5.2	5.2	5.1
6	6.3	6.2	6.1
7	7.4	7.2	7.1
8	8.4	8.3	8.1
9	9.4	9.3	9.2
10	10.5	10.3	10.2
20	21.0	20.7	20.3
30	31.5	31.0	30.5
40	42.0	41.3	40.7
50	52.5	51.7	50.8

″	60	59	58
1	1.0	1.0	1.0
2	2.0	2.0	1.9
3	3.0	3.0	2.9
4	4.0	3.9	3.9
5	5.0	4.9	4.8
6	6.0	5.9	5.8
7	7.0	6.9	6.8
8	8.0	7.9	7.7
9	9.0	8.8	8.7
10	10.0	9.8	9.7
20	20.0	19.7	19.3
30	30.0	29.5	29.0
40	40.0	39.3	38.7
50	50.0	49.2	48.3

″	57	56	55
1	1.0	0.9	0.9
2	1.9	1.9	1.8
3	2.8	2.8	2.8
4	3.8	3.7	3.7
5	4.8	4.7	4.6
6	5.7	5.6	5.5
7	6.6	6.5	6.4
8	7.6	7.5	7.3
9	8.6	8.4	8.2
10	9.5	9.3	9.2
20	19.0	18.7	18.3
30	28.5	28.0	27.5
40	38.0	37.3	36.7
50	47.5	46.7	45.8

′	L Sin	d	L Tan	cd	L Cot	L Cos	d	′
0	**9.352 09**		**9.363 36**		**10.636 64**	**9.988 72**		**60**
1	9.352 63	54	9.363 94	58	10.636 06	9.988 69	3	59
2	9.353 18	55	9.364 52	58	10.635 48	9.988 67	2	58
3	9.353 73	55	9.365 09	57	10.634 91	9.988 64	3	57
4	9.354 27	54	9.365 66	57	10.634 34	9.988 61	3	56
		54		58			3	
5	**9.354 81**		**9.366 24**		**10.633 76**	**9.988 58**		**55**
6	9.355 36	55	9.366 81	57	10.633 19	9.988 55	3	54
7	9.355 90	54	9.367 38	57	10.632 62	9.988 52	3	53
8	9.356 44	54	9.367 95	57	10.632 05	9.988 49	3	52
9	9.356 98	54	9.368 52	57	10.631 48	9.988 46	3	51
		54		57			3	
10	**9.357 52**		**9.369 09**		**10.630 91**	**9.988 43**		**50**
11	9.358 06	54	9.369 66	57	10.630 34	9.988 40	3	49
12	9.358 60	54	9.370 23	57	10.629 77	9.988 37	3	48
13	9.359 14	54	9.370 80	57	10.629 20	9.988 34	3	47
14	9.359 68	54	9.371 37	57	10.628 63	9.988 31	3	46
		54		56			3	
15	**9.360 22**		**9.371 93**		**10.628 07**	**9.988 28**		**45**
16	9.360 75	53	9.372 50	57	10.627 50	9.988 25	3	44
17	9.361 29	54	9.373 05	56	10.626 94	9.988 22	3	43
18	9.361 82	53	9.373 63	56	10.626 37	9.988 19	3	42
19	9.362 36	54	9.374 19	57	10.625 81	9.988 16	3	41
		53		56			3	
20	**9.362 89**		**9.374 76**		**10.625 24**	**9.988 13**		**40**
21	9.363 42	53	9.375 32	56	10.624 68	9.988 10	3	39
22	9.363 95	53	9.375 88	56	10.624 12	9.988 07	3	38
23	9.364 49	54	9.376 44	56	10.623 56	9.988 04	3	37
24	9.365 02	53	9.377 00	56	10.623 00	9.988 01	3	36
		53		56			3	
25	**9.365 55**		**9.377 56**		**10.622 44**	**9.987 98**		**35**
26	9.366 08	53	9.378 12	56	10.621 88	9.987 95	3	34
27	9.366 60	52	9.378 68	56	10.621 32	9.987 92	3	33
28	9.367 13	53	9.379 24	56	10.620 76	9.987 89	3	32
29	9.367 66	53	9.379 80	55	10.620 20	9.987 86	3	31
		53		55			3	
30	**9.368 19**		**9.380 35**		**10.619 65**	**9.987 83**		**30**
31	9.368 71	52	9.380 91	56	10.619 09	9.987 80	3	29
32	9.369 24	53	9.381 47	56	10.618 53	9.987 77	3	28
33	9.369 76	52	9.382 02	55	10.617 98	9.987 74	3	27
34	9.370 28	52	9.382 57	55	10.617 43	9.987 71	3	26
		53		56			3	
35	**9.370 81**		**9.383 13**		**10.616 87**	**9.987 68**		**25**
36	9.371 33	52	9.383 68	55	10.616 32	9.987 65	3	24
37	9.371 85	52	9.384 23	55	10.615 77	9.987 62	3	23
38	9.372 37	52	9.384 79	56	10.615 21	9.987 59	3	22
39	9.372 89	52	9.385 34	55	10.614 66	9.987 56	3	21
		52		55			3	
40	**9.373 41**		**9.385 89**		**10.614 11**	**9.987 53**		**20**
41	9.373 93	52	9.386 44	55	10.613 56	9.987 50	3	19
42	9.374 45	52	9.386 99	55	10.613 01	9.987 46	4	18
43	9.374 97	52	9.387 54	55	10.612 46	9.987 43	3	17
44	9.375 49	52	9.388 08	54	10.611 92	9.987 40	3	16
		51		55			3	
45	**9.376 00**		**9.388 63**		**10.611 37**	**9.987 37**		**15**
46	9.376 52	52	9.389 18	55	10.610 82	9.987 34	3	14
47	9.377 03	51	9.389 72	54	10.610 28	9.987 31	3	13
48	9.377 55	52	9.390 27	55	10.609 73	9.987 28	3	12
49	9.378 06	51	9.390 82	55	10.609 18	9.987 25	3	11
		52		54			3	
50	**9.378 58**		**9.391 36**		**10.608 64**	**9.987 22**		**10**
51	9.379 09	51	9.391 90	54	10.608 10	9.987 19	3	9
52	9.379 60	51	9.392 45	55	10.607 55	9.987 15	4	8
53	9.380 11	51	9.392 99	54	10.607 01	9.987 12	3	7
54	9.380 62	51	9.393 53	54	10.606 47	9.987 09	3	6
		51		54			3	
55	**9.381 13**		**9.394 07**		**10.605 93**	**9.987 06**		**5**
56	9.381 64	51	9.394 61	54	10.605 39	9.987 03	3	4
57	9.382 15	51	9.395 15	54	10.604 85	9.987 00	3	3
58	9.382 66	51	9.395 69	54	10.604 31	9.986 97	3	2
59	9.383 17	51	9.396 23	54	10.603 77	9.986 94	3	1
		51		54			4	
60	**9.383 68**		**9.396 77**		**10.603 23**	**9.986 90**		**0**
′	L Cos	d	L Cot	cd	L Tan	L Sin	d	′

Prop. Pts.

″	57	56	55
1	1.0	0.9	0.9
2	1.9	1.9	1.8
3	2.8	2.8	2.8
4	3.8	3.7	3.7
5	4.8	4.7	4.6
6	5.7	5.6	5.5
7	6.6	6.5	6.4
8	7.6	7.5	7.3
9	8.6	8.4	8.2
10	9.5	9.3	9.2
20	19.0	18.7	18.3
30	28.5	28.0	27.5
40	38.0	37.3	36.7
50	47.5	46.7	45.8

″	54	53	52
1	0.9	0.9	0.9
2	1.8	1.8	1.7
3	2.7	2.6	2.6
4	3.6	3.5	3.5
5	4.5	4.4	4.3
6	5.4	5.3	5.2
7	6.3	6.2	6.1
8	7.2	7.1	6.9
9	8.1	8.0	7.8
10	9.0	8.8	8.7
20	18.0	17.7	17.3
30	27.0	26.5	26.0
40	36.0	35.3	34.7
50	45.0	44.2	43.3

″	51	4	3	2
1	0.8	0.1	0.0	0.0
2	1.7	0.1	0.1	0.1
3	2.6	0.2	0.2	0.1
4	3.4	0.3	0.2	0.1
5	4.2	0.3	0.2	0.2
6	5.1	0.4	0.3	0.2
7	6.0	0.5	0.4	0.2
8	6.8	0.5	0.4	0.3
9	7.6	0.6	0.4	0.3
10	8.5	0.7	0.5	0.3
20	17.0	1.3	1.0	0.7
30	25.5	2.0	1.5	1.0
40	34.0	2.7	2.0	1.3
50	42.5	3.3	2.5	1.7

Prop. Pts.

Table 4 / Logarithms of trigonometric functions □ **683**

′	L Sin	d	L Tan	cd	L Cot	L Cos	d	′		Prop. Pts.		
0	**9.383 68**	50	**9.396 77**	54	**10.603 23**	**9.986 90**	3	60				
1	9.384 18	50	9.397 31	54	10.602 69	9.986 87	3	59				
2	9.384 69	51	9.397 85	54	10.602 15	9.986 84	3	58				
3	9.385 19	50	9.398 38	53	10.601 62	9.986 81	3	57				
4	9.385 70	51	9.398 92	54	10.601 08	9.986 78	3	56				
		50		53			3					
5	**9.386 20**	50	**9.399 45**	54	**10.600 55**	**9.986 75**	4	55				
6	9.386 70	50	9.399 99	53	10.600 01	9.986 71	3	54		″	**54**	**53**	**52**
7	9.387 21	51	9.400 52	54	10.599 48	9.986 68	3	53		1	0.9	0.9	0.9
8	9.387 71	50	9.401 06	53	10.598 94	9.986 65	3	52		2	1.8	1.8	1.7
9	9.388 21	50	9.401 59	53	10.598 41	9.986 62	3	51		3	2.7	2.6	2.6
		50		53			3			4	3.6	3.5	3.5
10	**9.388 71**	50	**9.402 12**	54	**10.597 88**	**9.986 59**	3	50		5	4.5	4.4	4.3
11	9.389 21	50	9.402 66	53	10.597 34	9.986 56	4	49		6	5.4	5.3	5.2
12	9.389 71	50	9.403 19	53	10.596 81	9.986 52	3	48		7	6.3	6.2	6.1
13	9.390 21	50	9.403 72	53	10.596 28	9.986 49	3	47		8	7.2	7.1	6.9
14	9.390 71	50	9.404 25	53	10.595 75	9.986 46	3	46		9	8.1	8.0	7.8
15	**9.391 21**	49	**9.404 78**	53	**10.595 22**	**9.986 43**	3	45		10	9.0	8.8	8.7
16	9.391 70	50	9.405 31	53	10.594 69	9.986 40	4	44		20	18.0	17.7	17.3
17	9.392 20	50	9.405 84	52	10.594 16	9.986 36	3	43		30	27.0	26.5	26.0
18	9.392 70	49	9.406 36	53	10.593 64	9.986 33	3	42		40	36.0	35.3	34.7
19	9.393 19	50	9.406 89	53	10.593 11	9.986 30	3	41		50	45.0	44.2	43.3
20	**9.393 69**	49	**9.407 42**	53	**10.592 58**	**9.986 27**	4	40		″	**51**	**50**	**49**
21	9.394 18	49	9.407 95	52	10.592 05	9.986 23	3	39		1	0.8	0.8	0.8
22	9.394 67	50	9.408 47	53	10.591 53	9.986 20	3	38		2	1.7	1.7	1.6
23	9.395 17	49	9.409 00	52	10.591 00	9.986 17	3	37		3	2.6	2.5	2.4
24	9.395 66	49	9.409 52	53	10.590 48	9.986 14	4	36		4	3.4	3.3	3.3
25	**9.396 15**	49	**9.410 05**	52	**10.589 95**	**9.986 10**	3	35		5	4.2	4.2	4.1
26	9.396 64	49	9.410 57	52	10.589 43	9.986 07	3	34		6	5.1	5.0	4.9
27	9.397 13	49	9.411 09	52	10.588 91	9.986 04	3	33		7	6.0	5.8	5.7
28	9.397 62	49	9.411 61	53	10.588 39	9.986 01	4	32		8	6.8	6.7	6.5
29	9.398 11	49	9.412 14	52	10.587 86	9.985 97	3	31		9	7.6	7.5	7.4
30	**9.398 60**	49	**9.412 66**	52	**10.587 34**	**9.985 94**	3	30		10	8.5	8.3	8.2
31	9.399 09	49	9.413 18	52	10.586 82	9.985 91	3	29		20	17.0	16.7	16.3
32	9.399 58	49	9.413 70	52	10.586 30	9.985 88	4	28		30	25.5	25.0	24.5
33	9.400 06	49	9.414 22	52	10.585 78	9.985 84	3	27		40	34.0	33.3	32.7
34	9.400 55	48	9.414 74	52	10.585 26	9.985 81	3	26		50	42.5	41.7	40.8
35	**9.401 03**	49	**9.415 26**	52	**10.584 74**	**9.985 78**	4	25		″	**48**	**47**	**4**	**3**
36	9.401 52	48	9.415 78	51	10.584 22	9.985 74	3	24		1	0.8	0.8	0.1	0.0
37	9.402 00	49	9.416 29	52	10.583 71	9.985 71	3	23		2	1.6	1.6	0.1	0.1
38	9.402 49	48	9.416 81	52	10.583 19	9.985 68	3	22		3	2.4	2.4	0.2	0.2
39	9.402 97	49	9.417 33	51	10.582 67	9.985 65	4	21		4	3.2	3.1	0.3	0.2
40	**9.403 46**	48	**9.417 84**	52	**10.582 16**	**9.985 61**	3	20		5	4.0	3.9	0.3	0.2
41	9.403 94	48	9.418 36	51	10.581 64	9.985 58	3	19		6	4.8	4.7	0.4	0.3
42	9.404 42	48	9.418 87	52	10.581 13	9.985 55	4	18		7	5.6	5.5	0.5	0.4
43	9.404 90	48	9.419 39	51	10.580 61	9.985 51	3	17		8	6.4	6.3	0.5	0.4
44	9.405 38	48	9.419 90	51	10.580 10	9.985 48	3	16		9	7.2	7.6	0.6	0.4
45	**9.405 86**	48	**9.420 41**	52	**10.579 59**	**9.985 45**	4	15		10	8.0	7.8	0.7	0.5
46	9.406 34	48	9.420 93	51	10.579 07	9.985 41	3	14		20	16.0	15.7	1.3	1.0
47	9.406 82	48	9.421 44	51	10.578 56	9.985 38	3	13		30	24.0	23.5	2.0	1.5
48	9.407 30	48	9.421 95	51	10.578 05	9.985 35	4	12		40	32.0	31.3	2.7	2.0
49	9.407 78	47	9.422 46	51	10.577 54	9.985 31	3	11		50	40.0	39.2	3.3	2.5
50	**9.408 25**	48	**9.422 97**	51	**10.577 03**	**9.985 28**	3	10					
51	9.408 73	48	9.423 48	51	10.576 52	9.985 25	4	9					
52	9.409 21	47	9.423 99	51	10.576 01	9.985 21	3	8					
53	9.409 68	48	9.424 50	51	10.575 50	9.985 18	3	7					
54	9.410 16	47	9.425 01	51	10.574 99	9.985 15	4	6					
55	**9.410 63**	48	**9.425 52**	51	**10.574 48**	**9.985 11**	3	5					
56	9.411 11	47	9.426 03	50	10.573 97	9.985 08	3	4					
57	9.411 58	47	9.426 53	51	10.573 47	9.985 05	3	3					
58	9.412 05	47	9.427 04	51	10.572 96	9.985 01	4	2					
59	9.412 52	48	9.427 55	50	10.572 45	9.984 98	3	1					
60	**9.413 00**		**9.428 05**		**10.571 95**	**9.984 94**	4	0					

′	L Cos	d	L Cot	cd	L Tan	L Sin	d	′		Prop. Pts.

'	L Sin	d	L Tan	cd	L Cot	L Cos	d	'	Prop. Pts.
0	**9.413 00**		**9.428 05**		**10.571 95**	**9.984 94**		60	
1	9.413 47	47	9.428 56	51	10.571 44	9.984 91	3	59	
2	9.413 94	47	9.429 06	50	10.570 94	9.984 88	3	58	
3	9.414 41	47	9.429 57	51	10.570 43	9.984 84	4	57	
4	9.414 88	47	9.430 07	50	10.569 93	9.984 81	3	56	
		47		50			4		
5	**9.415 35**		**9.430 57**		**10.569 43**	**9.984 77**		55	
6	9.415 82	47	9.431 08	51	10.568 92	9.984 74	3	54	
7	9.416 28	46	9.431 58	50	10.568 42	9.984 71	3	53	" 51 50 49
8	9.416 75	47	9.432 08	50	10.567 92	9.984 67	4	52	1 0.8 0.8 0.8
9	9.417 22	47	9.432 58	50	10.567 42	9.984 64	3	51	2 1.7 1.7 1.6
		46		50			4		3 2.6 2.5 2.4
10	**9.417 68**		**9.433 08**		**10.566 92**	**9.984 60**		50	4 3.4 3.3 3.3
11	9.418 15	47	9.433 58	50	10.566 42	9.984 57	3	49	
12	9.418 61	46	9.434 08	50	10.565 92	9.984 53	4	48	5 4.2 4.2 4.1
13	9.419 08	47	9.434 58	50	10.565 42	9.984 50	3	47	6 5.1 5.0 4.9
14	9.419 54	46	9.435 08	50	10.564 92	9.984 47	3	46	7 6.0 5.8 5.7
		47		50			4		8 6.8 6.7 6.5
15	**9.420 01**		**9.435 58**		**10.564 42**	**9.984 43**		45	9 7.6 7.5 7.4
16	9.420 47	46	9.436 07	49	10.563 93	9.984 40	3	44	
17	9.420 93	46	9.436 57	50	10.563 43	9.984 36	4	43	10 8.5 8.3 8.2
18	9.421 40	47	9.437 07	50	10.562 93	9.984 33	3	42	20 17.0 16.7 16.3
19	9.421 86	46	9.437 56	49	10.562 44	9.984 29	4	41	30 25.5 25.0 24.5
		46		50			3		40 34.0 33.3 32.7
20	**9.422 32**		**9.438 06**		**10.561 94**	**9.984 26**		40	50 42.5 41.7 40.8
21	9.422 78	46	9.438 55	49	10.561 45	9.984 22	4	39	
22	9.423 24	46	9.439 05	50	10.560 95	9.984 19	3	38	" 48 47 46
23	9.423 70	46	9.439 54	49	10.560 46	9.984 15	4	37	1 0.8 0.8 0.8
24	9.424 16	46	9.440 04	50	10.559 96	9.984 12	3	36	2 1.6 1.6 1.5
		45		49			3		3 2.4 2.4 2.3
25	**9.424 61**		**9.440 53**		**10.559 47**	**9.984 09**		35	4 3.2 3.1 3.1
26	9.425 07	46	9.441 02	49	10.558 98	9.984 05	4	34	
27	9.425 53	46	9.441 51	49	10.558 49	9.984 02	3	33	5 4.0 3.9 3.8
28	9.425 99	46	9.442 01	50	10.557 99	9.983 98	4	32	6 4.8 4.7 4.6
29	9.426 44	45	9.442 50	49	10.557 50	9.983 95	3	31	7 5.6 5.5 5.4
		46		49			4		8 6.4 6.3 6.1
30	**9.426 90**		**9.442 99**		**10.557 01**	**9.983 91**		30	9 7.2 7.0 6.9
31	9.427 35	45	9.443 48	49	10.556 52	9.983 88	3	29	
32	9.427 81	46	9.443 97	49	10.556 03	9.983 84	4	28	10 8.0 7.8 7.7
33	9.428 26	45	9.444 46	49	10.555 54	9.983 81	3	27	20 16.0 15.7 15.3
34	9.428 72	46	9.444 95	49	10.555 05	9.983 77	4	26	30 24.0 23.5 23.0
		45		49			4		40 32.0 31.3 30.7
35	**9.429 17**		**9.445 44**		**10.554 56**	**9.983 73**		25	50 40.0 39.2 38.3
36	9.429 62	45	9.445 92	48	10.554 08	9.983 70	3	24	
37	9.430 08	46	9.446 41	49	10.553 59	9.983 66	4	23	" 45 44 4 3
38	9.430 53	45	9.446 90	49	10.553 10	9.983 63	3	22	1 0.8 0.7 0.1 0.0
39	9.430 98	45	9.447 88	48	10.552 62	9.983 59	4	21	2 1.5 1.5 0.1 0.1
		45		49			3		3 2.2 2.2 0.2 0.2
40	**9.431 43**		**9.447 87**		**10.552 13**	**9.983 56**		20	4 3.0 2.9 0.3 0.2
41	9.431 88	45	9.448 36	49	10.551 64	9.983 52	4	19	
42	9.432 33	45	9.448 84	48	10.551 16	9.983 49	3	18	5 3.8 3.7 0.3 0.2
43	9.432 78	45	9.449 33	49	10.550 67	9.993 45	4	17	6 4.5 4.4 0.4 0.3
44	9.433 23	45	9.449 81	48	10.550 19	9.983 42	3	16	7 5.2 5.1 0.5 0.4
		44		48			4		8 6.0 5.9 0.5 0.4
45	**9.433 67**		**9.450 29**		**10.549 71**	**9.983 38**		15	9 6.8 6.6 0.6 0.4
46	9.434 12	45	9.450 78	49	10.549 22	9.983 34	4	14	
47	9.434 57	45	9.451 26	48	10.548 74	9.983 31	3	13	10 7.5 7.3 0.7 0.5
48	9.435 02	45	9.451 74	48	10.548 26	9.983 27	4	12	20 15.0 14.7 1.3 1.0
49	9.435 46	44	9.452 22	48	10.547 78	9.983 24	3	11	30 22.5 22.0 2.0 1.5
		45		49			4		40 30.0 29.3 2.7 2.0
50	**9.435 91**		**9.452 71**		**10.547 29**	**9.983 20**		10	50 37.5 36.7 3.3 2.5
51	9.436 35	44	9.453 19	48	10.546 81	9.983 17	3	9	
52	9.436 80	45	9.453 67	48	10.546 33	9.983 13	4	8	
53	9.437 24	44	9.454 15	48	10.545 85	9.983 09	4	7	
54	9.437 69	45	9.454 63	48	10.545 37	9.983 06	3	6	
		44		48			4		
55	**9.438 13**		**9.455 11**		**10.544 89**	**9.983 02**		5	
56	9.438 57	44	9.455 59	48	10.544 41	9.982 99	3	4	
57	9.439 01	44	9.456 06	47	10.543 94	9.982 95	4	3	
58	9.439 46	45	9.456 54	48	10.543 46	9.982 91	4	2	
59	9.439 90	44	9.457 02	48	10.542 98	9.982 88	3	1	
		44		48			4		
60	**9.440 34**		**9.457 50**		**10.542 50**	**9.982 84**		0	

'	L Cos	d	L Cot	cd	L Tan	L Sin	d	'	Prop. Pts.

     (254°) **74°**

Table 4 / Logarithms of trigonometric functions □ **685**

′	L Sin	d	L Tan	cd	L Cot	L Cos	d	′	Prop. Pts.
0	9.440 34	44	9.457 50	47	10.542 50	9.982 84	3	60	
1	9.440 78	44	9.457 97	48	10.542 03	9.982 81	4	59	
2	9.441 22	44	9.458 45	47	10.541 55	9.982 77	4	58	
3	9.441 66	44	9.458 92	48	10.541 08	9.982 73	3	57	
4	9.442 10	43	9.459 40	47	10.540 60	9.982 70	4	56	
5	9.442 53	44	9.459 87	48	10.540 13	9.982 66	4	55	
6	9.442 97	44	9.460 35	47	10.539 65	9.982 62	3	54	
7	9.443 41	44	9.460 82	48	10.539 18	9.982 59	4	53	
8	9.443 85	43	9.461 30	47	10.538 70	9.982 55	4	52	
9	9.444 28	44	9.461 77	47	10.538 23	9.982 51	3	51	
10	9.444 72	44	9.462 24	47	10.537 76	9.982 48	4	50	
11	9.445 16	43	9.462 71	48	10.537 29	9.982 44	4	49	
12	9.445 59	43	9.463 19	47	10.536 81	9.982 40	3	48	
13	9.446 02	44	9.463 66	47	10.536 34	9.982 37	4	47	
14	9.446 46	43	9.464 13	47	10.535 87	9.982 33	4	46	
15	9.446 89	44	9.464 60	47	10.535 40	9.982 29	3	45	
16	9.447 33	43	9.465 07	47	10.534 93	9.982 26	4	44	
17	9.447 76	43	9.465 54	47	10.534 46	9.982 22	4	43	
18	9.448 19	43	9.466 01	47	10.533 99	9.982 18	3	42	
19	9.448 62	43	9.466 48	46	10.533 52	9.982 15	4	41	
20	9.449 05	43	9.466 94	47	10.533 06	9.982 11	4	40	
21	9.449 48	44	9.467 41	47	10.532 59	9.982 07	3	39	
22	9.449 92	43	9.467 88	47	10.532 12	9.982 04	4	38	
23	9.450 35	42	9.468 35	46	10.531 65	9.982 00	4	37	
24	9.450 77	43	9.468 81	47	10.531 19	9.981 96	4	36	
25	9.451 20	43	9.469 28	47	10.530 72	9.981 92	3	35	
26	9.451 63	43	9.469 75	46	10.530 25	9.981 89	4	34	
27	9.452 06	43	9.470 21	47	10.529 79	9.981 85	4	33	
28	9.452 49	43	9.470 68	46	10.529 32	9.981 81	4	32	
29	9.452 92	42	9.471 14	46	10.528 86	9.981 77	3	31	
30	9.453 34	43	9.471 60	47	10.528 40	9.981 74	4	30	
31	9.453 77	42	9.472 07	46	10.527 93	9.981 70	4	29	
32	9.454 19	43	9.472 53	46	10.527 47	9.981 66	4	28	
33	9.454 62	42	9.472 99	47	10.527 01	9.981 62	3	27	
34	9.455 04	43	9.473 46	46	10.526 54	9.981 59	4	26	
35	9.455 47	42	9.473 92	46	10.526 08	9.981 55	4	25	
36	9.455 89	43	9.474 38	46	10.525 62	9.981 51	4	24	
37	9.456 32	42	9.474 84	46	10.525 16	9.981 47	3	23	
38	9.456 74	42	9.475 30	46	10.524 70	9.981 44	4	22	
39	9.457 16	42	9.475 76	46	10.524 24	9.981 40	4	21	
40	9.457 58	43	9.476 22	46	10.523 78	9.981 36	4	20	
41	9.458 01	42	9.476 68	46	10.523 32	9.981 32	3	19	
42	9.458 43	42	9.477 14	46	10.522 86	9.981 29	4	18	
43	9.458 85	42	9.477 60	46	10.522 40	9.981 25	4	17	
44	9.459 27	42	9.478 06	46	10.521 94	9.981 21	4	16	
45	9.459 69	42	9.478 52	45	10.521 48	9.981 17	4	15	
46	9.460 11	42	9.478 97	46	10.521 03	9.981 13	3	14	
47	9.460 53	42	9.479 43	46	10.520 57	9.981 10	4	13	
48	9.460 95	41	9.479 89	46	10.520 11	9.981 06	4	12	
49	9.461 36	42	9.480 35	45	10.519 65	9.981 02	4	11	
50	9.461 78	42	9.480 80	46	10.519 20	9.980 98	4	10	
51	9.462 20	42	9.481 26	45	10.518 74	9.980 94	4	9	
52	9.462 62	41	9.481 71	46	10.518 29	9.980 90	3	8	
53	9.463 03	42	9.482 17	45	10.517 83	9.980 87	4	7	
54	9.463 45	41	9.482 62	45	10.517 38	9.980 83	4	6	
55	9.463 86	42	9.483 07	46	10.516 93	9.980 79	4	5	
56	9.464 28	41	9.483 53	45	10.516 47	9.980 75	4	4	
57	9.464 69	42	9.483 98	45	10.516 02	9.980 71	4	3	
58	9.465 11	41	9.484 43	46	10.515 57	9.980 67	4	2	
59	9.465 52	42	9.484 88	45	10.515 11	9.980 63	3	1	
60	9.465 94		9.485 34		10.514 66	9.980 60		0	

′	L Cos	d	L Cot	cd	L Tan	L Sin	d	′	Prop. Pts.

Prop. Pts.

″	48	47	46
1	0.8	0.8	0.8
2	1.6	1.6	1.5
3	2.4	2.4	2.3
4	3.2	3.1	3.1
5	4.0	3.9	3.8
6	4.8	4.7	4.6
7	5.6	5.5	5.4
8	6.4	6.3	6.1
9	7.2	7.0	6.9
10	8.0	7.8	7.7
20	16.0	15.7	15.3
30	24.0	23.5	23.0
40	32.0	31.3	30.7
50	40.0	39.2	38.3

″	45	44	43
1	0.8	0.7	0.7
2	1.5	1.5	1.4
3	2.2	2.2	2.2
4	3.0	2.9	2.9
5	3.8	3.7	3.6
6	4.5	4.4	4.3
7	5.2	5.1	5.0
8	6.0	5.9	5.7
9	6.8	6.6	6.4
10	7.5	7.3	7.2
20	15.0	14.7	14.3
30	22.5	22.0	21.5
40	30.0	29.3	28.7
50	37.5	26.7	35.8

″	42	41	4	3
1	0.7	0.7	0.1	0.0
2	1.4	1.4	0.1	0.1
3	2.1	2.0	0.2	0.2
4	2.8	2.7	0.3	0.2
5	3.5	3.4	0.3	0.2
6	4.2	4.1	0.4	0.3
7	4.9	4.8	0.5	0.4
8	5.6	5.5	0.5	0.4
9	6.3	6.2	0.6	0.4
10	7.0	6.8	0.7	0.5
20	14.0	13.7	1.3	1.0
30	21.0	20.5	2.0	1.5
40	28.0	27.3	2.7	2.0
50	35.0	34.2	3.3	2.5

′	L Sin	d	L Tan	cd	L Cot	L Cos	d	′		Prop. Pts.		
0	9.465 94	41	9.485 84	45	10.514 66	9.980 60	4	60				
1	9.466 35	41	9.485 79	45	10.514 21	9.980 56	4	59				
2	9.466 76	41	9.486 24	45	10.513 76	9.980 52	4	58				
3	9.467 17	41	9.486 69	45	10.513 31	9.980 48	4	57				
4	9.467 58	42	9.487 14	45	10.512 86	9.980 44	4	56				
5	9.468 00	41	9.487 59	45	10.512 41	9.980 40	4	55				
6	9.468 41	41	9.488 04	45	10.511 96	9.980 36	4	54				
7	9.468 82	41	9.488 49	45	10.511 51	9.980 32	4	53				
8	9.469 23	41	9.488 94	45	10.511 06	9.980 29	3	52				
9	9.469 64	41	9.489 39	45	10.510 61	9.980 25	4	51	″	45	44	43
10	9.470 05	40	9.489 84	45	10.510 16	9.980 21	4	50	1	0.8	0.7	0.7
11	9.470 45	41	9.490 29	44	10.509 71	9.980 17	4	49	2	1.5	1.5	1.4
12	9.470 86	41	9.490 73	45	10.509 27	9.980 13	4	48	3	2.2	2.2	2.2
13	9.471 27	41	9.491 18	45	10.508 82	9.980 09	4	47	4	3.0	2.9	2.9
14	9.471 68	41	9.491 63	44	10.508 37	9.980 05	4	46	5	3.8	3.7	3.6
15	9.472 09	40	9.492 07	45	10.507 93	9.980 01	4	45	6	4.5	4.4	4.3
16	9.472 49	41	9.492 52	44	10.507 48	9.979 97	4	44	7	5.2	5.1	5.0
17	9.472 90	40	9.492 96	45	10.507 04	9.979 93	4	43	8	6.0	5.9	5.7
18	9.473 30	41	9.493 41	44	10.506 59	9.979 89	3	42	9	6.8	6.6	6.4
19	9.473 71	40	9.493 85	45	10.506 15	9.979 86	4	41	10	7.5	7.3	7.2
20	9.474 11	41	9.494 30	44	10.505 70	9.979 82	4	40	20	15.0	14.7	14.3
21	9.474 52	40	9.494 74	45	10.505 26	9.979 78	4	39	30	22.5	22.0	21.5
22	9.474 92	41	9.495 19	44	10.504 81	9.979 74	4	38	40	30.0	29.2	28.7
23	9.475 33	40	9.495 63	44	10.504 37	9.979 70	4	37	50	37.5	36.7	35.8
24	9.475 73	40	9.496 07	45	10.503 93	9.979 66	4	36	″	42	41	40
25	9.476 13	41	9.496 52	44	10.503 48	9.979 62	4	35	1	0.7	0.7	0.7
26	9.476 54	40	9.496 96	44	10.503 04	9.979 58	4	34	2	1.4	1.4	1.3
27	9.476 94	40	9.497 40	44	10.502 60	9.979 54	4	33	3	2.1	2.0	2.0
28	9.477 34	40	9.497 84	44	10.502 16	9.979 50	4	32	4	2.8	2.7	2.7
29	9.477 74	40	9.498 28	44	10.501 72	9.979 46	4	31	5	3.5	3.4	3.3
30	9.478 14	40	9.498 72	44	10.501 28	9.979 42	4	30	6	4.2	4.1	4.0
31	9.478 54	40	9.499 16	44	10.500 84	9.979 38	4	29	7	4.9	4.8	4.7
32	9.478 94	40	9.499 60	44	10.500 40	9.979 34	4	28	8	5.6	5.5	5.3
33	9.479 34	40	9.500 04	44	10.499 96	9.979 30	4	27	9	6.3	6.2	6.0
34	9.479 74	40	9.500 48	44	10.499 52	9.979 26	4	26	10	7.0	6.8	6.7
35	9.480 14	40	9.500 92	44	10.499 08	9.979 22	4	25	20	14.0	13.7	13.3
36	9.480 54	40	9.501 36	44	10.498 64	9.979 18	4	24	30	21.0	20.5	20.0
37	9.480 94	39	9.501 80	43	10.498 20	9.979 14	4	23	40	28.0	27.3	26.7
38	9.481 33	40	9.502 23	44	10.497 77	9.979 10	4	22	50	35.0	34.2	33.3
39	9.481 73	40	9.502 67	44	10.497 33	9.979 06	4	21	″	39	5	4	3
40	9.482 13	39	9.503 11	44	10.496 89	9.979 02	4	20	1	0.6	0.1	0.1	0.0
41	9.482 52	40	9.503 55	43	10.496 45	9.978 98	4	19	2	1.3	0.2	0.1	0.1
42	9.482 92	40	9.503 98	44	10.496 02	9.978 94	4	18	3	2.0	0.2	0.2	0.2
43	9.483 32	39	9.504 42	43	10.495 58	9.978 90	4	17	4	2.6	0.3	0.3	0.2
44	9.483 71	40	9.504 85	44	10.495 15	9.978 86	4	16	5	3.2	0.4	0.3	0.2
45	9.484 11	39	9.505 29	43	10.494 71	9.978 82	4	15	6	3.9	0.5	0.4	0.3
46	9.484 50	40	9.505 72	44	10.494 28	9.978 78	4	14	7	4.6	0.6	0.5	0.4
47	9.484 90	39	9.506 16	43	10.493 84	9.978 74	4	13	8	5.2	0.7	0.5	0.5
48	9.485 29	39	9.506 59	44	10.493 41	9.978 70	4	12	9	5.8	0.8	0.6	0.4
49	9.485 68	39	9.507 03	43	10.492 97	9.978 66	5	11	10	6.5	0.8	0.7	0.5
50	9.486 07	40	9.507 46	43	10.492 54	9.978 61	4	10	20	13.0	1.7	1.3	1.0
51	9.486 47	39	9.507 89	44	10.492 11	9.978 57	4	9	30	19.5	2.5	2.0	1.5
52	9.486 86	39	9.508 33	43	10.491 67	9.978 53	4	8	40	26.0	3.3	2.7	2.0
53	9.487 25	39	9.508 76	43	10.491 24	9.978 49	4	7	50	32.5	4.2	3.3	2.5
54	9.487 64	39	9.509 19	43	10.490 81	9.978 45	4	6					
55	9.488 03	39	9.509 62	43	10.490 38	9.978 41	4	5					
56	9.488 42	39	9.510 05	43	10 489 95	9.978 37	4	4					
57	9.488 81	39	9.510 48	44	10.489 52	9.978 33	4	3					
58	9.489 20	39	9.510 92	43	10.489 08	9.978 29	4	2					
59	9.489 59	39	9.511 35	43	10.488 65	9.978 25	4	1					
60	9.489 98		9.511 78		10.488 22	9.978 21		0					
′	L Cos	d	L Cot	cd	L Tan	L Sin	d	′		Prop. Pts.		

Table 4 / Logarithms of trigonometric functions   □   **687**

′	L Sin	d	L Tan	cd	L Cot	L Cos	d	′			Prop. Pts.	
0	**9.489 98**		**9.511 78**		**10.488 22**	**9.978 21**		60				
1	9.490 37	39	9.512 21	43	10.487 79	9.978 17	5	59				
2	9.490 76	39	9.512 64	43	10.487 36	9.978 12	4	58				
3	9.491 15	39	9.513 06	42	10.486 94	9.978 08	4	57				
4	9.491 53	38	9.513 49	43	10.486 51	9.978 04	4	56				
		39		43			4					
5	**9.491 92**		**9.513 92**		**10.486 08**	**9.978 00**		55				
6	9.492 31	39	9.514 35	43	10.485 65	9.977 96	4	54				
7	9.492 69	38	9.514 78	43	10.485 22	9.977 92	4	53		**43**	**42**	**41**
8	9.493 08	39	9.515 20	42	10.484 80	9.977 88	4	52	1	0.7	0.7	0.7
9	9.493 47	39	9.515 63	43	10.484 37	9.977 84	4	51	2	1.4	1.4	1.4
		38		43			5		3	2.2	2.1	2.0
10	**9.493 85**		**9.516 06**		**10.483 94**	**9.977 79**		50	4	2.9	2.8	2.7
11	9.494 24	39	9.516 48	42	10.483 52	9.977 75	4	49				
12	9.494 62	38	9.516 91	43	10.483 09	9.977 71	4	48	5	3.6	3.5	3.4
13	9.495 00	38	9.517 34	43	10.482 66	9.977 67	4	47	6	4.3	4.2	4.1
14	9.495 39	39	9.517 76	42	10.482 24	9.977 63	4	46	7	5.0	4.9	4.8
		38		43			4		8	5.7	5.6	5.5
15	**9.495 77**		**9.518 19**		**10.481 81**	**9.977 59**		45	9	6.4	6.3	6.2
16	9.496 15	38	9.518 61	42	10.481 39	9.977 54	5	44				
17	9.496 54	39	9.519 03	42	10.480 97	9.977 50	4	43	10	7.2	7.0	6.8
18	9.496 92	38	9.519 46	43	10.480 54	9.977 46	4	42	20	14.3	14.0	13.7
19	9.497 30	38	9.519 88	42	10.480 12	9.977 42	4	41	30	21.5	21.0	20.5
		38		43			4		40	28.7	28.0	27.3
20	**9.497 68**		**9.520 31**		**10.479 69**	**9.977 38**		40	50	35.8	35.0	34.2
21	9.498 06	38	9.520 73	42	10.479 27	9.977 34	5	39				
22	9.498 44	38	9.521 15	42	10.478 85	9.977 29	4	38	″	**39**	**38**	**37**
23	9.498 82	38	9.521 57	42	10.478 43	9.977 25	4	37	1	0.6	0.6	0.6
24	9.499 20	38	9.522 00	43	10.478 00	9.977 21	4	36	2	1.3	1.3	1.2
		38		42			4		3	2.0	1.9	1.8
25	**9.499 55**		**9.522 42**		**10.477 58**	**9.977 17**		35	4	2.6	2.5	2.5
26	9.499 96	38	9.522 84	42	10.477 16	9.977 13	5	34				
27	9.500 34	38	9.523 26	42	10.476 74	9.977 08	4	33	5	3.2	3.2	3.1
28	9.500 72	38	9.523 68	42	10.476 32	9.977 04	4	32	6	3.9	3.8	3.7
29	9.501 10	38	9.524 10	42	10.475 90	9.977 00	4	31	7	4.6	4.4	4.3
		38		42			5		8	5.2	5.1	4.9
30	**9.501 48**		**9.524 52**		**10.475 48**	**9.976 96**		30	9	5.8	5.7	5.6
31	9.501 85	37	9.524 94	42	10.475 06	9.976 91	4	29				
32	9.502 23	38	9.525 36	42	10.474 64	9.976 87	4	28	10	6.5	6.3	6.2
33	9.502 61	38	9.525 78	42	10.474 22	9.976 83	4	27	20	13.0	12.7	12.3
34	9.502 98	37	9.526 20	42	10.473 80	9.976 79	5	26	30	19.5	19.0	18.5
		38		41			5		40	26.0	25.3	24.7
35	**9.503 36**		**9.526 61**		**10.473 39**	**9.976 74**		25	50	32.5	31.7	30.8
36	9.503 74	38	9.527 03	42	10.472 97	9.976 70	4	24				
37	9.504 11	37	9.527 45	42	10.472 55	9.976 66	4	23	″	**36**	**5**	**4**
38	9.504 49	38	9.527 87	42	10.472 13	9.976 62	4	22	1	0.6	0.1	0.1
39	9.504 86	37	9.528 29	42	10.471 71	9.976 57	5	21	2	1.2	0.2	0.2
		37		41			4		3	1.8	0.2	0.2
40	**9.505 23**		**9.528 70**		**10.471 30**	**9.976 53**		20	4	2.4	0.3	0.3
41	9.505 61	38	9.529 12	42	10.470 88	9.976 49	4	19				
42	9.505 98	37	9.529 53	41	10.470 47	9.976 45	4	18	5	3.0	0.4	0.3
43	9.506 35	37	9.529 95	42	10.470 05	9.976 40	5	17	6	3.6	0.5	0.4
44	9.506 73	38	9.530 37	42	10.469 63	9.976 36	4	16	7	4.2	0.6	0.5
		37		41			4		8	4.8	0.7	0.5
45	**9.507 10**		**9.530 78**		**10.469 22**	**9.976 32**		15	9	5.4	0.8	0.6
46	9.507 47	37	9.531 20	42	10.468 80	9.976 28	4	14				
47	9.507 84	37	9.531 61	41	10.468 39	9.976 23	5	13	10	6.0	0.8	0.7
48	9.508 21	37	9.532 02	41	10.467 98	9.976 19	4	12	20	12.0	1.7	1.3
49	9.508 58	37	9.532 40	41	10.467 56	9.976 15	4	11	30	18.0	2.5	2.0
		38		42			5		40	24.0	3.3	2.7
50	**9.508 96**		**9.532 85**		**10.467 15**	**9.976 10**		10	50	30.0	4.2	3.3
51	9.509 33	37	9.533 27	42	10.466 73	9.976 06	4	9				
52	9.509 70	37	9.533 68	41	10.466 32	9.976 02	4	8				
53	9.510 07	37	9.534 09	41	10.465 91	9.975 97	5	7				
54	9.510 43	36	9.534 50	41	10.465 50	9.975 93	4	6				
		37		42			4					
55	**9.510 80**		**9.534 92**		**10.465 08**	**9.975 89**		5				
56	9.511 17	37	9.535 33	41	10.464 67	9.975 84	5	4				
57	9.511 54	37	9.535 74	41	10.464 26	9.975 80	4	3				
58	9.511 91	37	9.536 15	41	10.463 85	9.975 76	4	2				
59	9.512 27	36	9.536 56	41	10.463 44	9.975 71	5	1				
		37		41			4					
60	**9.512 64**		**9.536 97**		**10.463 03**	**9.975 67**		0				
′	L Cos	d	L Cot	cd	L Tan	L Sin	d	′			Prop. Pts.	

′	L Sin	d	L Tan	cd	L Cot	L Cos	d	′	Prop. Pts.
0	**9.512 64**	37	**9.536 97**	41	**10.463 03**	**9.975 67**	4	60	
1	9.513 01	37	9.537 38	41	10.462 62	9.975 63	5	59	
2	9.513 38	36	9.537 79	41	10.462 21	9.975 58	4	58	
3	9.513 74	37	9.538 20	41	10.461 80	9.975 54	4	57	
4	9.514 11	36	9.538 61	41	10.461 39	9.975 50	5	56	
5	**9.514 47**	37	**9.539 02**	41	**10.460 98**	**9.975 45**	4	55	
6	9.514 84	36	9.539 43	41	10.460 57	9.975 41	5	54	
7	9.515 20	37	9.539 84	41	10.460 16	9.975 36	4	53	
8	9.515 57	36	9.540 25	40	10.459 75	9.975 32	4	52	
9	9.515 93	36	9.540 65	41	10.459 35	9.975 28	5	51	
10	**9.516 29**	37	**9.541 06**	41	**10.458 94**	**9.975 23**	4	50	
11	9.516 66	36	9.541 47	40	10.458 53	9.975 19	4	49	
12	9.517 02	36	9.541 87	41	10.458 13	9.975 15	4	48	
13	9.517 38	36	9.542 28	41	10.457 72	9.975 10	4	47	
14	9.517 74	37	9.542 69	40	10.457 31	9.975 06	5	46	
15	**9.518 11**	36	**9.543 09**	41	**10.456 91**	**9.975 01**	4	45	
16	9.518 47	36	9.543 50	40	10.456 50	9.974 97	4	44	
17	9.518 83	36	9.543 90	41	10.456 10	9.974 92	4	43	
18	9.519 19	36	9.544 31	40	10.455 69	9.974 88	4	42	
19	9.519 55	36	9.544 71	41	10.455 29	9.974 84	5	41	
20	**9.519 91**	36	**9.545 12**	40	**10.454 88**	**9.974 79**	4	40	
21	9.520 27	36	9.545 52	41	10.454 48	9.974 75	5	39	
22	9.520 63	36	9.545 93	40	10.454 07	9.974 70	4	38	
23	9.520 99	36	9.546 33	40	10.453 67	9.974 66	5	37	
24	9.521 35	36	9.546 73	41	10.453 27	9.974 61	4	36	
25	**9.521 71**	36	**9.547 14**	40	**10.452 86**	**9.974 57**	4	35	
26	9.522 07	35	9.547 54	40	10.452 46	9.974 53	5	34	
27	9.522 42	36	9.547 94	41	10.452 06	9.974 48	4	33	
28	9.522 78	36	9.548 35	40	10.451 65	9.974 44	5	32	
29	9.523 14	36	9.548 75	40	10.451 25	9.974 39	4	31	
30	**9.523 50**	35	**9.549 15**	40	**10.450 85**	**9.974 35**	5	30	
31	9.523 85	36	9.549 55	40	10.450 45	9.974 30	4	29	
32	9.524 21	35	9.549 95	40	10.450 05	9.974 26	5	28	
33	9.524 56	36	9.550 35	40	10.449 65	9.974 21	4	27	
34	9.524 92	35	9.550 75	40	10.449 25	9.974 17	5	26	
35	**9.525 27**	36	**9.551 15**	40	**10.448 85**	**9.974 12**	4	25	
36	9.525 63	35	9.551 55	40	10.448 45	9.974 08	5	24	
37	9.525 98	36	9.551 95	40	10.448 05	9.974 03	4	23	
38	9.526 34	35	9.552 35	40	10.447 65	9.973 99	5	22	
39	9.526 69	36	9.552 75	40	10.447 25	9.973 94	4	21	
40	**9.527 05**	35	**9.553 15**	40	**10.446 85**	**9.973 90**	5	20	
41	9.527 40	35	9.553 55	40	10.446 45	9.973 85	4	19	
42	9.527 75	36	9.553 95	39	10.446 05	9.973 81	5	18	
43	9.528 11	35	9.554 34	40	10.445 66	9.973 76	4	17	
44	9.528 46	35	9.554 74	40	10.445 26	9.973 72	5	16	
45	**9.528 81**	35	**9.555 14**	40	**10.444 86**	**9.973 67**	4	15	
46	9.529 16	35	9.555 54	39	10.444 46	9.973 63	5	14	
47	9.529 51	35	9.555 93	40	10.444 07	9.973 58	5	13	
48	9.529 86	35	9.556 33	40	10.443 67	9.973 53	4	12	
49	9.530 21	35	9.556 73	39	10.443 27	9.973 49	5	11	
50	**9.530 56**	36	**9.557 12**	40	**10.442 88**	**9.973 44**	4	10	
51	9.530 92	34	9.557 52	39	10.442 48	9.973 40	5	9	
52	9.531 26	35	9.557 91	40	10.442 09	9.973 35	4	8	
53	9.531 61	35	9.558 31	39	10.441 69	9.973 31	5	7	
54	9.531 96	35	9.558 70	40	10.441 30	9.973 26	4	6	
55	**9.532 31**	35	**9.559 10**	39	**10.440 90**	**9.973 22**	5	5	
56	9.532 66	35	9.559 49	40	10.440 51	9.973 17	5	4	
57	9.533 01	35	9.559 89	39	10.440 11	9.973 12	4	3	
58	9.533 36	34	9.560 28	39	10.439 72	9.973 08	5	2	
59	9.533 70	35	9.560 67	40	10.439 33	9.973 03	4	1	
60	**9.534 05**		**9.561 07**		**10.438 93**	**9.972 99**		0	
′	L Cos	d	L Cot	cd	L Tan	L Sin	d	′	Prop. Pts.

Prop. Pts. table:

″	41	40	39
1	0.7	0.7	0.6
2	1.4	1.3	1.3
3	2.0	2.0	2.0
4	2.7	2.7	2.6
5	3.4	3.3	3.2
6	4.1	4.0	3.9
7	4.8	4.7	4.6
8	5.5	5.3	5.2
9	6.2	6.0	5.8
10	6.8	6.7	6.5
20	13.7	13.3	13.0
30	20.5	20.0	19.5
40	27.3	26.7	26.0
50	34.2	33.3	32.5

″		37	36	35
1		0.6	0.6	0.6
2		1.2	1.2	1.2
3		1.8	1.8	1.8
4		2.5	2.4	2.3
5		3.1	3.0	2.9
6		3.7	3.6	3.5
7		4.3	4.2	4.1
8		4.9	4.8	4.7
9		5.6	5.4	5.2
10		6.2	6.0	5.8
20		12.3	12.0	11.7
30		18.5	18.0	17.5
40		24.7	24.0	23.3
50		30.8	30.0	29.2

″		34	5	4
1		0.6	0.1	0.1
2		1.1	0.2	0.1
3		1.7	0.2	0.2
4		2.3	0.3	0.3
5		2.8	0.4	0.3
6		3.4	0.5	0.4
7		4.0	0.6	0.5
8		4.5	0.7	0.5
9		5.1	0.8	0.6
10		5.7	0.8	0.7
20		11.3	1.7	1.3
30		17.0	2.5	2.0
40		22.7	3.3	2.7
50		28.3	4.2	3.3

′	L Sin	d	L Tan	cd	L Cot	L Cos	d	′
0	9.534 05	35	9.561 07	39	10.438 93	9.972 99	5	60
1	9.534 40	35	9.561 46	39	10.438 54	9.972 94	5	59
2	9.534 75	34	9.561 85	39	10.438 15	9.972 89	5	58
3	9.535 09	35	9.562 24	40	10.437 76	9.972 85	4	57
4	9.535 44	34	9.562 64	39	10.437 36	9.972 80	4	56
5	9.535 78	35	9.563 03	39	10.436 97	9.972 76	5	55
6	9.536 13	34	9.563 42	39	10.436 58	9.972 71	5	54
7	9.536 47	35	9.563 81	39	10.436 19	9.972 66	4	53
8	9.536 82	34	9.564 20	39	10.435 80	9.972 62	5	52
9	9.537 16	35	9.564 59	39	10 .435 41	9.972 57	5	51
10	9.537 51	34	9.564 98	39	10.435 02	9.972 52	4	50
11	9.537 85	34	9.565 37	39	10.434 63	9.972 48	5	49
12	9.538 19	35	9.565 76	39	10.434 24	9.972 43	5	48
13	9.538 54	34	9.566 15	39	10.433 85	9.972 38	4	47
14	9.538 88	34	9.566 54	39	10.433 46	9.972 34	5	46
15	9.539 22	35	9.566 93	39	10.433 07	9.972 29	5	45
16	9.539 57	34	9.567 32	39	10.432 68	9.972 24	4	44
17	9.539 91	34	9.567 71	39	10.432 29	9.972 20	5	43
18	9.540 25	34	9.568 10	39	10.431 90	9.972 15	5	42
19	9.540 59	34	9.568 49	38	10.431 51	9.972 10	4	41
20	9.540 93	34	9.568 87	39	10.431 13	9.972 06	5	40
21	9.541 27	34	9.569 26	39	10.430 74	9.972 01	5	39
22	9.541 61	34	9.569 65	39	10.430 35	9.971 96	4	38
23	9.541 95	34	9.570 04	38	10.429 96	9.971 92	5	37
24	9.542 29	34	9.570 42	39	10.429 58	9.971 87	5	36
25	9.542 63	34	9.570 81	39	10.429 19	9.971 82	4	35
26	9.542 97	34	9.571 20	38	10.428 80	9.971 78	5	34
27	9.543 31	34	9.571 58	39	10.428 42	9.971 73	5	33
28	9.543 65	34	9.571 97	38	10.428 03	9.971 68	5	32
29	9.543 99	34	9.572 35	39	10.427 65	9.971 63	4	31
30	9.544 33	33	9.572 74	38	10.427 26	9.971 59	5	30
31	9.544 66	34	9.573 12	39	10.426 88	9.971 54	5	29
32	9.545 00	34	9.573 51	38	10.426 49	9.971 49	4	28
33	9.545 34	33	9.573 89	39	10.426 11	9.971 45	5	27
34	9.545 67	34	9.574 28	38	10.425 72	9.971 40	5	26
35	9.546 01	34	9.574 66	38	10.425 34	9.971 35	5	25
36	9.546 35	33	9.575 04	39	10.424 96	9.971 30	5	24
37	9.546 68	34	9.575 43	38	10.424 57	9.971 26	5	23
38	9.547 02	33	9.575 81	38	10.424 19	9.971 21	5	22
39	9.547 35	34	9.576 19	39	10.423 81	9.971 16	5	21
40	9.547 69	33	9.576 58	38	10.423 42	9.971 11	4	20
41	9.548 02	34	9.576 96	38	10.423 04	9.971 07	5	19
42	9.548 36	33	9.577 34	38	10.422 66	9.971 02	5	18
43	9.548 69	34	9.577 72	38	10.422 28	9.970 97	5	17
44	9.549 03	33	9.578 10	39	10.421 90	9.970 92	5	16
45	9.549 36	33	9.578 49	38	10.421 51	9.970 87	4	15
46	9.549 69	34	9.578 87	38	10.421 13	9.970 83	5	14
47	9.550 03	33	9.579 25	38	10.420 75	9.970 78	5	13
48	9.550 36	33	9.579 63	38	10.420 37	9.970 73	5	12
49	9.550 69	33	9.580 01	38	10.419 99	9.970 68	5	11
50	9.551 02	34	9.580 39	38	10.419 61	9.970 63	4	10
51	9.551 36	33	9.580 77	38	10.419 23	9.970 59	5	9
52	9.551 69	33	9.581 15	38	10.418 85	9.970 54	5	8
53	9.552 02	33	9.581 53	38	10.418 47	9.970 49	5	7
54	9.552 35	33	9.581 91	38	10.418 09	9.970 44	5	6
55	9.552 68	33	9.582 29	38	10.417 71	9.970 39	4	5
56	9.553 01	33	9.582 67	37	10.417 33	9.970 35	5	4
57	9.553 34	33	9.583 04	38	10.416 96	9.970 30	5	3
58	9.553 67	33	9.583 42	38	10.416 58	9.970 25	5	2
59	9.554 00	33	9.583 80	38	10.416 20	9.970 20	5	1
60	9.554 33		9.584 18		10.415 82	9.970 15		0
′	L Cos	d	L Cot	cd	L Tan	L Sin	d	′

Prop. Pts.

″	40	39	38
1	0.7	0.6	0.6
2	1.3	1.3	1.3
3	2.0	2.0	1.9
4	2.7	2.6	2.5
5	3.3	3.2	3.2
6	4.0	3.9	3.8
7	4.7	4.6	4.4
8	5.3	5.2	5.1
9	6.0	5.8	5.7
10	6.7	6.5	6.3
20	13.3	13.0	12.7
30	20.0	19.5	19.0
40	26.7	26.0	25.3
50	33.3	32.5	31.7

″	37	35	34
1	0.6	0.6	0.6
2	1.2	1.2	1.1
3	1.8	1.8	1.7
4	2.5	2.3	2.3
5	3.1	2.9	2.8
6	3.7	3.5	3.4
7	4.3	4.1	4.0
8	4.9	4.7	4.5
9	5.6	5.2	5.1
10	6.2	5.8	5.7
20	12.3	11.7	11.3
30	18.5	17.5	17.0
40	24.7	23.3	22.7
50	30.8	29.2	28.3

″	33	5	4
1	0.6	0.1	0.1
2	1.1	0.2	0.1
3	1.6	0.2	0.2
4	2.2	0.3	0.3
5	2.8	0.4	0.3
6	3.3	0.5	0.4
7	3.8	0.6	0.5
8	4.4	0.7	0.5
9	5.0	0.8	0.6
10	5.5	0.8	0.7
20	11.0	1.7	1.3
30	16.5	2.5	2.0
40	22.0	3.3	2.7
50	27.5	4.2	3.3

Prop. Pts.

21° (201°)   (338°) **158°**

′	L Sin	d	L Tan	cd	L Cot	L Cos	d	′
0	9.554 33	33	9.584 18	37	10.415 82	9.970 15	5	60
1	9.554 66	33	9.584 55	38	10.415 45	9.970 10	5	59
2	9.554 99	33	9.584 93	38	10.415 07	9.970 05	4	58
3	9.555 32	32	9.585 31	38	10.414 69	9.970 01	5	57
4	9.555 64	33	9.585 69	38	10.414 31	9.969 96	5	56
5	9.555 97	33	9.586 06	38	10.413 94	9.969 91	5	55
6	9.556 30	33	9.586 44	37	10.413 56	9.969 86	5	54
7	9.556 63	32	9.586 81	38	10.413 19	9.969 81	5	53
8	9.556 95	33	9.587 19	38	10.412 81	9.969 76	5	52
9	9.557 28	33	9.587 57	37	10.412 43	9.969 71	5	51
10	9.557 61	32	9.587 94	38	10.412 06	9.969 66	4	50
11	9.557 93	33	9.588 32	37	10.411 68	9.969 62	5	49
12	9.558 26	32	9.588 69	38	10.411 31	9.969 57	5	48
13	9.558 58	33	9.589 07	37	10.410 93	9.969 52	5	47
14	9.558 91	32	9.589 44	37	10.410 56	9.969 47	5	46
15	9.559 23	33	9.589 81	38	10.410 19	9.969 42	5	45
16	9.559 56	32	9.590 19	37	10.409 81	9.969 37	5	44
17	9.559 88	33	9.590 56	38	10.409 44	9.969 32	5	43
18	9.560 21	32	9.590 94	37	10.409 06	9.969 27	5	42
19	9.560 53	32	9.591 31	37	10.408 69	9.969 22	5	41
20	9.560 85	33	9.591 68	37	10.408 32	9.969 17	5	40
21	9.561 18	32	9.592 05	38	10.407 95	9.969 12	5	39
22	9.561 50	32	9.592 43	37	10.407 57	9.969 07	4	38
23	9.561 82	33	9.592 80	37	10.407 20	9.969 03	5	37
24	9.562 15	32	9.593 17	37	10.406 83	9.968 98	5	36
25	9.562 47	32	9.593 54	37	10.406 46	9.968 93	5	35
26	9.562 79	32	9.593 91	38	10.406 09	9.968 88	5	34
27	9.563 11	32	9.594 29	37	10.405 71	9.968 83	5	33
28	9.563 43	32	9.594 66	37	10.405 34	9.968 78	5	32
29	9.563 75	33	9.595 03	37	10.404 97	9.968 73	5	31
30	9.564 08	32	9.595 40	37	10.404 60	9.968 68	5	30
31	9.564 40	32	9.595 77	37	10.404 23	9.968 63	5	29
32	9.564 72	32	9.596 14	37	10.403 86	9.968 58	5	28
33	9.565 04	32	9.596 51	37	10.403 49	9.968 53	5	27
34	9.565 36	32	9.596 88	37	10.403 12	9.968 48	5	26
35	9.565 68	31	9.597 25	37	10.402 75	9.968 43	5	25
36	9.565 99	32	9.597 62	37	10.402 38	9.968 38	5	24
37	9.566 31	32	9.597 99	36	10.402 01	9.968 33	5	23
38	9.566 63	32	9.598 35	37	10.401 65	9.968 28	5	22
39	9.566 95	32	9.598 72	37	10.401 28	9.968 23	5	21
40	9.567 27	32	9.599 09	37	10.400 91	9.968 18	5	20
41	9.567 59	31	9.599 46	37	10.400 54	9.968 13	5	19
42	9.567 90	32	9.599 83	36	10.400 17	9.968 08	5	18
43	9.568 22	32	9.600 19	37	10.399 81	9.968 03	5	17
44	9.568 54	32	9.600 56	37	10.399 44	9.967 98	5	16
45	9.568 86	31	9.600 93	37	10.399 07	9.967 93	5	15
46	9.569 17	32	9.601 30	36	10.398 70	9.967 88	5	14
47	9.569 49	31	9.601 66	37	10.398 34	9.967 83	5	13
48	9.569 80	32	9.602 03	37	10.397 97	9.967 78	6	12
49	9.570 12	32	9.602 40	36	10.397 60	9.967 72	5	11
50	9.570 44	31	9.602 76	37	10.397 24	9.967 67	5	10
51	9.570 75	32	9.603 13	36	10.396 87	9.967 62	5	9
52	9.571 07	31	9.603 49	37	10.396 51	9.967 57	5	8
53	9.571 38	31	9.603 86	36	10.396 14	9.967 52	5	7
54	9.571 69	32	9.604 22	37	10.395 78	9.967 47	5	6
55	9.572 01	31	9.604 59	36	10.395 41	9.967 42	5	5
56	9.572 32	32	9.604 95	37	10.395 05	9.967 37	5	4
57	9.572 64	31	9.605 32	36	10.394 68	9.967 32	5	3
58	9.572 95	31	9.605 68	37	10.394 32	9.967 27	5	2
59	9.573 26	32	9.606 05	36	10.393 95	9.967 22	5	1
60	9.573 58		9.606 41		10.393 59	9.967 17		0

′	L Cos	d	L Cot	cd	L Tan	L Sin	d	′

111° (291°)   (248°) **68°**

Prop. Pts.

″	38	37	36
1	0.6	0.6	0.6
2	1.3	1.2	1.2
3	1.9	1.8	1.8
4	2.5	2.5	2.4
5	3.2	3.1	3.0
6	3.8	3.7	3.6
7	4.4	4.3	4.2
8	5.1	4.9	4.8
9	5.7	5.6	5.4
10	6.3	6.2	6.0
20	12.7	12.3	12.0
30	19.0	18.5	18.0
40	25.3	24.7	24.0
50	31.7	30.8	30.0

″	33	32	31
1	0.6	0.5	0.5
2	1.1	1.1	1.0
3	1.6	1.6	1.6
4	2.2	2.1	2.1
5	2.8	2.7	2.6
6	3.3	3.2	3.1
7	3.8	3.7	3.6
8	4.4	4.3	4.1
9	5.0	4.8	4.6
10	5.5	5.3	5.2
20	11.0	10.7	10.3
30	16.5	16.0	15.5
40	22.0	21.3	20.7
50	27.5	26.7	25.8

″	6	5	4
1	0.1	0.1	0.1
2	0.2	0.2	0.1
3	0.3	0.2	0.2
4	0.4	0.3	0.3
5	0.5	0.4	0.3
6	0.6	0.5	0.4
7	0.7	0.6	0.5
8	0.8	0.7	0.5
9	0.9	0.8	0.6
10	1.0	0.8	0.7
20	2.0	1.7	1.3
30	3.0	2.5	2.0
40	4.0	3.3	2.7
50	5.0	4.2	3.3

Table 4 / Logarithms of trigonometric functions □ **691**

′	L Sin	d	L Tan	cd	L Cot	L Cos	d	′
0	**9.573 58**	31	**9.606 41**	36	**10.393 59**	**9.967 17**	6	60
1	9.573 89	31	9.606 77	37	10.393 23	9.967 11	5	59
2	9.574 20	31	9.607 14	36	10.392 86	9.967 06	5	58
3	9.574 51	31	9.607 50	36	10.392 50	9.967 01	5	57
4	9.574 82	32	9.607 86	37	10.392 14	9.966 96	5	56
5	**9.575 14**	31	**9.608 23**	36	**10.391 77**	**9.966 91**	5	55
6	9.575 45	31	9.608 59	36	10.391 41	9.966 86	5	54
7	9.575 76	31	9.608 95	36	10.391 05	9.966 81	5	53
8	9.576 07	31	9.609 31	36	10.390 69	9.966 76	6	52
9	9.576 38	31	9.609 67	37	10.390 33	9.966 70	5	51
10	**9.576 69**	31	**9.610 04**	36	**10.389 96**	**9.966 65**	5	50
11	9.577 00	31	9.610 40	36	10.389 60	9.966 60	5	49
12	9.577 31	31	9.610 76	36	10.389 24	9.966 55	5	48
13	9.577 62	31	9.611 12	36	10.388 88	9.966 50	5	47
14	9.577 93	31	9.611 48	36	10.388 52	9.966 45	5	46
15	**9.578 24**	31	**9.611 84**	36	**10.388 16**	**9.966 40**	6	45
16	9.578 55	30	9.612 20	36	10.387 80	9.966 34	5	44
17	9.578 85	31	9.612 56	36	10.387 44	9.966 29	5	43
18	9.579 16	31	9.612 92	36	10.387 08	9.966 24	5	42
19	9.579 47	31	9.613 28	36	10.386 72	9.966 19	5	41
20	**9.579 78**	30	**9.613 64**	36	**10.386 36**	**9.966 14**	6	40
21	9.580 08	31	9.614 00	36	10.386 00	9.966 08	5	39
22	9.580 39	31	9.614 36	36	10.385 64	9.966 03	5	38
23	9.580 70	31	9.614 72	36	10.385 28	9.965 98	5	37
24	9.581 01	30	9.615 08	36	10.384 92	9.965 93	5	36
25	**9.581 31**	31	**9.615 44**	35	**10.384 56**	**9.965 88**	6	35
26	9.581 62	30	9.615 79	36	10.384 21	9.965 82	5	34
27	9.581 92	31	9.616 15	36	10.383 85	9.965 77	5	33
28	9.582 23	30	9.616 51	36	10.383 49	9.965 72	5	32
29	9.582 53	31	9.616 87	35	10.383 13	9.965 67	5	31
30	**9.582 84**	30	**9.617 22**	36	**10.382 78**	**9.965 62**	6	30
31	9.583 14	31	9.617 58	36	10.382 42	9.965 56	5	29
32	9.583 45	30	9.617 94	36	10.382 06	9.965 51	5	28
33	9.583 75	31	9.618 30	35	10.381 70	9.965 46	5	27
34	9.584 06	30	9.618 65	36	10.381 35	9.965 41	6	26
35	**9.584 36**	31	**9.619 01**	35	**10.380 99**	**9.965 35**	5	25
36	9.584 67	30	9.619 36	36	10.380 64	9.965 30	5	24
37	9.584 97	30	9.619 72	36	10.380 28	9.965 25	5	23
38	9.585 27	30	9.620 08	35	10.379 92	9.965 20	6	22
39	9.585 57	31	9.620 43	36	10.379 57	9.965 14	5	21
40	**9.585 88**	30	**9.620 79**	35	**10.379 21**	**9.965 09**	5	20
41	9.586 18	30	9.621 14	36	10.378 86	9.965 04	6	19
42	9.586 48	30	9.621 50	35	10.378 50	9.964 98	5	18
43	9.586 78	31	9.621 85	36	10.378 15	9.964 93	5	17
44	9.587 09	30	9.622 21	35	10.377 79	9.964 88	5	16
45	**9.587 39**	30	**9.622 56**	36	**10.377 44**	**9.964 83**	6	15
46	9.587 69	30	9.622 92	35	10.377 08	9.964 77	5	14
47	9.587 99	30	9.623 27	35	10.376 73	9.964 72	5	13
48	9.588 29	30	9.623 62	36	10.376 38	9.964 67	6	12
49	9.588 59	30	9.623 98	35	10.376 02	9.964 61	5	11
50	**9.588 89**	30	**9.624 33**	35	**10.375 67**	**9.964 56**	5	10
51	9.589 19	30	9.624 68	36	10.375 32	9.964 51	6	9
52	9.589 49	30	9.625 04	35	10.374 96	9.964 45	5	8
53	9.589 79	30	9.625 39	35	10.374 61	9.964 40	5	7
54	9.590 09	30	9.625 74	35	10.374 26	9.964 35	6	6
55	**9.590 39**	30	**9.626 09**	36	**10.373 91**	**9.964 29**	5	5
56	9.590 69	29	9.626 45	35	10.373 55	9.964 24	5	4
57	9.590 98	30	9.626 80	35	10.373 20	9.964 19	6	3
58	9.591 28	30	9.627 15	35	10.372 85	9.964 13	5	2
59	9.591 58	30	9.627 50	35	10.372 50	9.964 08	5	1
60	**9.591 88**		**9.627 85**		**10.372 15**	**9.964 03**		0
′	L Cos	d	L Cot	cd	L Tan	L Sin	d	′

Prop. Pts.

″	37	36	35
1	0.6	0.6	0.6
2	1.2	1.2	1.2
3	1.8	1.8	1.8
4	2.5	2.4	2.3
5	3.1	3.0	2.9
6	3.7	3.6	3.5
7	4.3	4.2	4.1
8	4.9	4.8	4.7
9	5.6	5.4	5.2
10	6.2	6.0	5.8
20	12.3	12.0	11.7
30	18.5	18.0	17.5
40	24.7	24.0	23.3
50	30.8	30.0	29.2

″	32	31	30
1	0.5	0.5	0.5
2	1.1	1.0	1.0
3	1.6	1.6	1.5
4	2.1	2.1	2.0
5	2.7	2.6	2.5
6	3.2	3.1	3.0
7	3.7	3.6	3.5
8	4.3	4.1	4.0
9	4.8	4.6	4.5
10	5.3	5.2	5.0
20	10.7	10.3	10.0
30	16.0	15.5	15.0
40	21.3	20.7	20.0
50	26.7	25.8	25.0

″	29	6	5
1	0.5	0.1	0.1
2	1.0	0.2	0.2
3	1.4	0.3	0.2
4	1.9	0.4	0.3
5	2.4	0.5	0.4
6	2.9	0.6	0.5
7	3.4	0.7	0.6
8	3.9	0.8	0.7
9	4.4	0.9	0.8
10	4.8	1.0	0.8
20	9.7	2.0	1.7
30	14.5	3.0	2.5
40	19.3	4.0	3.3
50	24.2	5.0	4.2

Prop. Pts.

′	L Sin	d	L Tan	cd	L Cot	L Cos	d	′
0	9.591 88		9.627 85		10.372 15	9.964 03		60
1	9.592 18	30	9.628 20	35	10.371 80	9.963 97	6	59
2	9.592 47	29	9.628 55	35	10.371 45	9.963 92	5	58
3	9.592 77	30	9.628 90	35	10.371 10	9.963 87	5	57
4	9.593 07	30	9.629 26	36	10.370 74	9.963 81	6	56
5	9.593 36	29	9.629 61	35	10.370 39	9.963 76	5	55
6	9.593 66	30	9.629 96	35	10.370 04	9.963 70	6	54
7	9.593 96	30	9.630 31	35	10.369 69	9.963 65	5	53
8	9.594 25	29	9.630 66	35	10.369 34	9.963 60	5	52
9	9.594 55	30	9.631 01	35	10.368 99	9.963 54	6	51
10	9.594 84	29	9.631 35	34	10.368 65	9.963 49	5	50
11	9.595 14	30	9.631 70	35	10.368 30	9.963 43	6	49
12	9.595 43	29	9.632 05	35	10.367 95	9.963 38	5	48
13	9.595 73	30	9.632 40	35	10.367 60	9.963 33	5	47
14	9.596 02	29	9.632 75	35	10.367 25	9.963 27	6	46
15	9.596 32	30	9.633 10	35	10.366 90	9.963 22	5	45
16	9.596 61	29	9.633 45	35	10.366 55	9.963 16	6	44
17	9.596 90	29	9.633 79	34	10.366 21	9.963 11	5	43
18	9.597 20	30	9.634 14	35	10.365 86	9.963 05	6	42
19	9.597 49	29	9.634 49	35	10.365 51	9.963 00	5	41
20	9.597 78	29	9.634 84	35	10.365 16	9.962 94	6	40
21	9.598 08	30	9.635 19	35	10.364 81	9.962 89	5	39
22	9.598 37	29	9.635 53	34	10.364 47	9.962 84	5	38
23	9.598 66	29	9.635 88	35	10.364 12	9.962 78	6	37
24	9.598 95	29	9.636 23	35	10.363 77	9.962 73	5	36
25	9.599 24	29	9.636 57	34	10.363 43	9.962 67	6	35
26	9.599 54	30	9.636 92	35	10.363 08	9.962 62	5	34
27	9.599 83	29	9.637 26	34	10.362 74	9.962 56	6	33
28	9.600 12	29	9.637 61	35	10.362 39	9.962 51	5	32
29	9.600 41	29	9.637 96	35	10.362 04	9.962 45	6	31
30	9.600 70	29	9.638 30	34	10.361 70	9.962 40	5	30
31	9.600 99	29	9.638 65	35	10.361 35	9.962 34	6	29
32	9.601 28	29	9.638 99	34	10.361 01	9.962 29	5	28
33	9.601 57	29	9.639 34	35	10.360 66	9.962 23	6	27
34	9.601 86	29	9.639 68	34	10.360 32	9.962 18	5	26
35	9.602 15	29	9.640 03	35	10.359 97	9.962 12	6	25
36	9.602 44	29	9.640 37	34	10.359 63	9.962 07	5	24
37	9.602 73	29	9.640 72	35	10.359 28	9.962 01	6	23
38	9.603 02	29	9.641 06	34	10.358 94	9.961 96	5	22
39	9.603 31	29	9.641 40	34	10.358 60	9.961 90	6	21
40	9.603 59	28	9.641 75	35	10.358 25	9.961 85	5	20
41	9.603 88	29	9.642 09	34	10.357 91	9.961 79	6	19
42	9.604 17	29	9.642 43	34	10.357 57	9.961 74	5	18
43	9.604 46	29	9.642 78	35	10.357 22	9.961 68	6	17
44	9.604 74	28	9.643 12	34	10.356 88	9.961 62	6	16
45	9.605 03	29	9.643 46	34	10.356 54	9.961 57	5	15
46	9.605 32	29	9.643 81	35	10.356 19	9.961 51	6	14
47	9.605 61	29	9.644 15	34	10.355 85	9.961 46	5	13
48	9.605 89	28	9.644 49	34	10.355 51	9.961 40	6	12
49	9.606 18	29	9.644 83	34	10.355 17	9.961 35	5	11
50	9.606 46	28	9.645 17	34	10.354 83	9.961 29	6	10
51	9.606 75	29	9.645 52	35	10.354 48	9.961 23	6	9
52	9.607 04	29	9.645 86	34	10.354 14	9.961 18	5	8
53	9.607 32	28	9.646 20	34	10.353 80	9.961 12	6	7
54	9.607 61	29	9.646 54	34	10.353 46	9.961 07	5	6
55	9.607 89	28	9.646 88	34	10.353 12	9.961 01	6	5
56	9.608 18	29	9.647 22	34	10.352 78	9.960 95	6	4
57	9.608 46	28	9.647 56	34	10.352 44	9.960 90	5	3
58	9.608 75	29	9.647 90	34	10.352 10	9.960 84	6	2
59	9.609 03	28	9.648 24	34	10.351 76	9.960 79	5	1
60	9.609 31	28	9.648 58	34	10.351 42	9.960 73	6	0
′	L Cos	d	L Cot	cd	L Tan	L Sin	d	′

Prop. Pts.

″	36	35	34
1	0.6	0.6	0.6
2	1.2	1.2	1.1
3	1.8	1.8	1.7
4	2.4	2.3	2.3
5	3.0	2.9	2.8
6	3.6	3.5	3.4
7	4.2	4.1	4.0
8	4.8	4.7	4.5
9	5.4	5.2	5.1
10	6.0	5.8	5.7
20	12.0	11.7	11.3
30	18.0	17.5	17.0
40	24.0	23.3	22.7
50	30.0	29.2	28.3

″	30	29	28
1	0.5	0.5	0.5
2	1.0	1.0	0.9
3	1.5	1.4	1.4
4	2.0	1.9	1.9
5	2.5	2.4	2.3
6	3.0	2.9	2.8
7	3.5	3.4	3.3
8	4.0	3.9	3.7
9	4.5	4.4	4.2
10	5.0	4.8	4.7
20	10.0	9.7	9.3
30	15.0	14.5	14.0
40	20.0	19.3	18.7
50	25.0	24.2	23.3

″	6	5
1	0.1	0.1
2	0.2	0.2
3	0.3	0.2
4	0.4	0.3
5	0.5	0.4
6	0.6	0.5
7	0.7	0.6
8	0.8	0.7
9	0.9	0.8
10	1.0	0.8
20	2.0	1.7
30	3.0	2.5
40	4.0	3.3
50	5.0	4.2

Table 4 / *Logarithms of trigonometric functions* □ 693

′	L Sin	d	L Tan	cd	L Cot	L Cos	d	′	Prop. Pts.
0	**9.609 31**	29	**9.648 58**	34	**10.351 42**	**9.960 73**	6	60	
1	9.609 60	28	9.648 92	34	10.351 08	9.960 67	5	59	
2	9.609 88	28	9.649 26	34	10.350 74	9.960 62	6	58	
3	9.610 16	29	9.649 60	34	10.350 40	9.960 56	6	57	
4	9.610 45	28	9.649 94	34	10.350 06	9.960 50	5	56	
5	**9.610 73**	28	**9.650 28**	34	**10.349 72**	**9.960 45**	6	55	
6	9.611 01	28	9.650 62	34	10.349 38	9.960 39	5	54	
7	9.611 29	29	9.650 96	34	10.349 04	9.960 34	6	53	″ 34 33
8	9.611 58	28	9.651 30	34	10.348 70	9.960 28	6	52	1 0.6 0.6
9	9.611 86	28	9.651 64	33	10.348 36	9.960 22	5	51	2 1.1 1.1
10	**9.612 14**	28	**9.651 97**	34	**10.348 03**	**9.960 17**	6	50	3 1.7 1.6
11	9.612 42	28	9.652 31	34	10.347 69	9.960 11	6	49	4 2.3 2.2
12	9.612 70	28	9.652 65	34	10.347 35	9.960 05	5	48	5 2.8 2.8
13	9.612 98	28	9.652 99	34	10.347 01	9.960 00	6	47	6 3.4 3.3
14	9.613 26	28	9.653 33	33	10.346 67	9.959 94	6	46	7 4.0 3.8
15	**9.613 54**	28	**9.653 66**	34	**10.346 34**	**9.959 88**	6	45	8 4.5 4.4
16	9.613 82	29	9.654 00	34	10.346 00	9.959 82	5	44	9 5.1 5.0
17	9.614 11	27	9.654 34	33	10.345 66	9.959 77	6	43	10 5.7 5.5
18	9.614 88	28	9.654 67	34	10.345 33	9.959 71	6	42	20 11.3 11.0
19	9.614 66	28	9.655 01	34	10.344 99	9.959 65	5	41	30 17.0 16.5
20	**9.614 94**	28	**9.655 35**	33	**10.344 65**	**9.959 60**	6	40	40 22.7 22.0
21	9.615 22	28	9.655 68	34	10.344 32	9.959 54	6	39	50 28.3 27.5
22	9.615 50	28	9.656 02	34	10.343 98	9.959 48	6	38	″ 29 28 27
23	9.615 78	28	9.656 36	33	10.343 64	9.959 42	5	37	1 0.5 0.5 0.4
24	9.616 06	28	9.656 69	34	10.343 31	9.959 37	6	36	2 1.0 0.9 0.9
25	**9.616 34**	28	**9.657 03**	33	**10.342 97**	**9.959 31**	6	35	3 1.4 1.4 1.4
26	9.616 62	27	9.657 36	34	10.342 64	9.959 25	5	34	4 1.9 1.9 1.8
27	9.616 89	28	9.657 70	33	10.342 30	9.959 20	6	33	5 2.4 2.3 2.2
28	9.617 17	28	9.658 03	34	10.341 97	9.959 14	6	32	6 2.9 2.8 2.7
29	9.617 45	28	9.658 37	33	10.341 63	9.959 08	6	31	7 3.4 3.3 3.2
30	**9.617 73**	27	**9.658 70**	34	**10.341 30**	**9.959 02**	5	30	8 3.9 3.7 3.6
31	9.618 00	28	9.659 04	33	10.340 96	9.958 97	6	29	9 4.4 4.2 4.0
32	9.618 28	28	9.659 37	34	10.340 63	9.958 91	6	28	10 4.8 4.7 4.5
33	9.618 56	27	9.659 71	33	10.340 29	9.958 85	6	27	20 9.7 9.3 9.0
34	9.618 83	28	9.660 04	34	10.339 96	9.958 79	6	26	30 14.5 14.0 13.5
35	**9.619 11**	28	**9.660 38**	33	**10.339 62**	**9.958 73**	5	25	40 19.3 18.7 18.0
36	9.619 39	27	9.660 71	33	10.339 29	9.958 68	6	24	50 24.2 23.3 22.5
37	9.619 66	28	9.661 04	34	10.338 96	9.958 62	6	23	″ 6 5
38	9.619 94	27	9.661 38	33	10.338 62	9.958 56	6	22	1 0.1 0.1
39	9.620 21	28	9.661 71	33	10.338 29	9.958 50	6	21	2 0.2 0.2
40	**9.620 49**	27	**9.662 04**	34	**10.337 96**	**9.958 44**	5	20	3 0.3 0.2
41	9.620 76	28	9.662 38	33	10.337 62	9.958 39	6	19	4 0.4 0.3
42	9.621 04	27	9.662 71	33	10.337 29	9.958 33	6	18	5 0.5 0.4
43	9.621 31	28	9.663 04	33	10.336 96	9.958 27	6	17	6 0.6 0.5
44	9.621 59	27	9.663 37	34	10.336 63	9.958 21	6	16	7 0.7 0.6
45	**9.621 86**	28	**9.663 71**	33	**10.336 29**	**9.958 15**	5	15	8 0.8 0.7
46	9.622 14	27	9.664 04	33	10.335 96	9.958 10	6	14	9 0.9 0.8
47	9.622 41	27	9.664 37	33	10.335 63	9.958 04	6	13	10 1.0 0.8
48	9.622 68	28	9.664 70	33	10.335 30	9.957 98	6	12	20 2.0 1.7
49	9.622 96	27	9.665 03	34	10.334 97	9.957 92	6	11	30 3.0 2.5
50	**9.623 23**	27	**9.665 37**	33	**10.334 63**	**9.957 86**	6	10	40 4.0 3.3
51	9.623 50	27	9.665 70	33	10.334 30	9.957 80	5	9	50 5.0 4.2
52	9.623 77	28	9.666 03	33	10.333 97	9.957 75	6	8	
53	9.624 05	27	9.666 36	33	10.333 64	9.957 69	6	7	
54	9.624 32	27	9.666 69	33	10.333 31	9.957 63	6	6	
55	**9.624 59**	27	**9.667 02**	33	**10.332 98**	**9.957 57**	6	5	
56	9.624 86	27	9.667 35	33	10.332 65	9.957 51	6	4	
57	9.625 13	28	9.667 68	33	10.332 32	9.957 45	6	3	
58	9.625 41	27	9.668 01	33	10.331 99	9.957 39	6	2	
59	9.625 68	27	9.668 34	33	10.331 66	9.957 33	5	1	
60	**9.625 95**		**9.668 67**		**10.331 33**	**9.957 28**		0	
′	L Cos	d	L Cot	cd	L Tan	L Sin	d	′	Prop. Pts.

′	L Sin	d	L Tan	cd	L Cot	L Cos	d	′
0	**9.625 95**	27	**9.668 67**	33	**10.331 33**	**9.957 28**	6	60
1	9.626 22	27	9.669 00	33	10.331 00	9.957 22	6	59
2	9.626 49	27	9.669 33	33	10.330 67	9.957 16	6	58
3	9.626 76	27	9.669 66	33	10.330 34	9.957 10	6	57
4	9.627 03	27	9.669 99	33	10.330 01	9.957 04	6	56
5	**9.627 30**	27	**9.670 32**	33	**10.329 68**	**9.956 98**	6	55
6	9.627 57	27	9.670 65	33	10.329 35	9.956 92	6	54
7	9.627 84	27	9.670 98	33	10.329 02	9.956 86	6	53
8	9.628 11	27	9.671 31	32	10.328 69	9.956 80	6	52
9	9.628 38	27	9.671 63	33	10.328 37	9.956 74	6	51
10	**9.628 65**	27	**9.671 96**	33	**10.328 04**	**9.956 68**	5	50
11	9.628 92	26	9.672 29	33	10.327 71	9.956 63	6	49
12	9.629 18	27	9.672 62	33	10.327 38	9.956 57	6	48
13	9.629 45	27	9.672 95	32	10.327 05	9.956 51	6	47
14	9.629 72	27	9.673 27	33	10.326 73	9.956 45	6	46
15	**9.629 99**	27	**9.673 60**	33	**10.326 40**	**9.956 39**	6	45
16	9.630 26	26	9.673 93	33	10.326 07	9.956 33	6	44
17	9.630 52	27	9.674 26	32	10.325 74	9.956 27	6	43
18	9.630 79	27	9.674 58	33	10.325 42	9.956 21	6	42
19	9.631 06	27	9.674 91	33	10.325 09	9.956 15	6	41
20	**9.631 33**	26	**9.675 24**	32	**10.324 76**	**9.956 09**	6	40
21	9.631 59	27	9.675 56	33	10.324 44	9.956 03	6	39
22	9.631 86	26	9.675 89	33	10.324 11	9.955 97	6	38
23	9.632 12	27	9.676 22	32	10.323 78	9.955 91	6	37
24	9.632 39	27	9.676 54	33	10.323 46	9.955 85	6	36
25	**9.632 66**	26	**9.676 87**	32	**10.323 13**	**9.955 79**	6	35
26	9.632 92	27	9.677 19	33	10.322 81	9.955 73	6	34
27	9.633 19	26	9.677 52	33	10.322 48	9.955 67	6	33
28	9.633 45	27	9.677 85	32	10.322 15	9.955 61	6	32
29	9.633 72	26	9.678 17	33	10.321 83	9.955 55	6	31
30	**9.633 98**	27	**9.678 50**	32	**10.321 50**	**9.955 49**	6	30
31	9.634 25	26	9.678 82	33	10.321 18	9.955 43	7	29
32	9.634 51	27	9.679 15	32	10.320 85	9.955 36	6	28
33	9.634 78	26	9.679 47	33	10.320 53	9.955 30	5	27
34	9.635 04	27	9.679 80	32	10.320 20	9.955 25	6	26
35	**9.635 31**	26	**9.680 12**	32	**10.319 88**	**9.955 19**	6	25
36	9.635 57	26	9.680 44	33	10.319 56	9.955 13	6	24
37	9.635 83	27	9.680 77	32	10.319 23	9.955 07	7	23
38	9.636 10	26	9.681 09	33	10.318 91	9.955 00	6	22
39	9.636 36	26	9.681 42	32	10.318 58	9.954 94	6	21
40	**9.636 62**	27	**9.681 74**	32	**10.318 26**	**9.954 88**	6	20
41	9.636 89	26	9.682 06	33	10.317 94	9.954 82	6	19
42	9.637 15	26	9.682 39	32	10.317 61	9.954 76	6	18
43	9.637 41	26	9.682 71	32	10.317 29	9.954 70	6	17
44	9.637 67	27	9.683 03	33	10.316 97	9.954 64	6	16
45	**9.637 94**	26	**9.683 36**	32	**10.316 64**	**9.954 58**	6	15
46	9.638 20	26	9.683 68	32	10.316 32	9.954 52	6	14
47	9.638 46	26	9.684 00	32	10.316 00	9.954 46	6	13
48	9.638 72	26	9.684 32	33	10.315 68	9.954 40	6	12
49	9.638 98	26	9.684 65	32	10.315 35	9.954 34	7	11
50	**9.639 24**	26	**9.684 97**	32	**10.315 03**	**9.954 27**	6	10
51	9.639 50	26	9.685 29	32	10.314 71	9.954 21	6	9
52	9.639 76	26	9.685 61	32	10.314 39	9.954 15	6	8
53	9.640 02	26	9.685 93	33	10.314 07	9.954 09	6	7
54	9.640 28	26	9.686 26	32	10.313 74	9.954 03	6	6
55	**9.640 54**	26	**9.686 58**	32	**10.313 42**	**9.953 97**	6	5
56	9.640 80	26	9.686 90	32	10.313 10	9.953 91	7	4
57	9.641 06	26	9.687 22	32	10.312 78	9.953 84	6	3
58	9.641 32	26	9.687 54	32	10.312 46	9.953 78	6	2
59	9.641 58	26	9.687 86	32	10.312 14	9.953 72	6	1
60	**9.641 84**		**9.688 18**		**10.311 82**	**9.953 66**		0

| ′ | L Cos | d | L Cot | cd | L Tan | L Sin | d | ′ |

Prop. Pts.

″	33	32
1	0.6	0.5
2	1.1	1.1
3	1.6	1.6
4	2.2	2.1
5	2.8	2.7
6	3.3	3.2
7	3.8	3.7
8	4.4	4.3
9	5.0	4.8
10	5.5	5.3
20	11.0	10.7
30	16.5	16.0
40	22.0	21.3
50	27.5	26.7

″	27	26
1	0.4	0.4
2	0.9	0.9
3	1.4	1.3
4	1.8	1.7
5	2.2	2.2
6	2.7	2.6
7	3.2	3.0
8	3.6	3.5
9	4.0	3.9
10	4.5	4.3
20	9.0	8.7
30	13.5	13.0
40	18.0	17.3
50	22.5	21.7

″	7	6	5
1	0.1	0.1	0.1
2	0.2	0.2	0.2
3	0.4	0.3	0.2
4	0.5	0.4	0.3
5	0.6	0.5	0.4
6	0.7	0.6	0.5
7	0.8	0.7	0.6
8	0.9	0.8	0.7
9	1.0	0.9	0.8
10	1.2	1.0	0.8
20	2.3	2.0	1.7
30	3.5	3.0	2.5
40	4.7	4.0	3.3
50	5.8	5.0	4.2

Table 4 / *Logarithms of trigonometric functions* □ 695

′	L Sin	d	L Tan	cd	L Cot	L Cos	d	′	Prop. Pts.
0	**9.641 84**	26	**9.688 18**	32	**10.311 82**	**9.953 66**	6	60	
1	9.642 10	26	9.688 50	32	10.311 50	9.953 60	6	59	
2	9.642 36	26	9.688 82	32	10.311 18	9.953 54	6	58	
3	9.642 62	26	9.689 14	32	10.310 86	9.953 48	7	57	
4	9.642 88	25	9.689 46	32	10.310 54	9.953 41	6	56	
5	**9.643 13**	26	**9.689 78**	32	**10.310 22**	**9.953 35**	6	55	
6	9.643 39	26	9.690 10	32	10.309 90	9.953 29	6	54	
7	9.643 65	26	9.690 42	32	10.309 58	9.953 23	6	53	
8	9.643 91	26	9.690 74	32	10.309 26	9.953 17	7	52	
9	9.644 17	25	9.691 06	32	10.308 94	9.953 10	6	51	
10	**9.644 42**	26	**9.691 38**	32	**10.308 62**	**9.953 04**	6	50	
11	9.644 68	26	9.691 70	32	10.308 30	9.952 98	6	49	
12	9.644 94	25	9.692 02	32	10.307 98	9.952 92	6	48	
13	9.645 19	26	9.692 34	32	10.307 66	9.952 86	7	47	
14	9.645 45	26	9.692 66	32	10.307 34	9.952 79	6	46	
15	**9.645 71**	25	**9.692 98**	31	**10.307 02**	**9.952 73**	6	45	
16	9.645 96	26	9.693 29	32	10.306 71	9.952 67	6	44	
17	9.646 22	25	9.693 61	32	10.306 39	9.952 61	7	43	
18	9.646 47	26	9.693 93	32	10.306 07	9.952 54	6	42	
19	9.646 73	25	9.694 25	32	10.305 75	9.952 48	6	41	
20	**9.646 98**	26	**9.694 57**	31	**10.305 43**	**9.952 42**	6	40	
21	9.647 24	25	9.694 88	32	10.305 12	9.952 36	7	39	
22	9.647 49	26	9.695 20	32	10.304 80	9.952 29	6	38	
23	9.647 75	25	9.695 52	32	10.304 48	9.952 23	6	37	
24	9.648 00	26	9.695 84	31	10.304 16	9.952 17	6	36	
25	**9.648 26**	25	**9.696 15**	32	**10.303 85**	**9.952 11**	7	35	
26	9.648 51	26	9.696 47	32	10.303 53	9.952 04	6	34	
27	9.648 77	25	9.696 79	31	10.303 21	9.951 98	6	33	
28	9.649 02	25	9.697 10	32	10.302 90	9.951 92	7	32	
29	9.649 27	26	9.697 42	32	10.302 58	9.951 85	6	31	
30	**9.649 53**	25	**9.697 74**	31	**10.302 26**	**9.951 79**	6	30	
31	9.649 78	25	9.698 05	32	10.301 95	9.951 73	6	29	
32	9.650 03	26	9.698 37	31	10.301 63	9.951 67	7	28	
33	9.650 29	25	9.698 68	32	10.301 32	9.951 60	6	27	
34	9.650 54	25	9.699 00	32	10.301 00	9.951 54	6	26	
35	**9.650 79**	25	**9.699 32**	31	**10.300 68**	**9.951 48**	7	25	
36	9.651 04	26	9.699 63	32	10.300 37	9.951 41	6	24	
37	9.651 30	25	9.699 95	31	10.300 05	9.951 35	6	23	
38	9.651 55	25	9.700 26	32	10.299 74	9.951 29	7	22	
39	9.651 80	25	9.700 58	31	10.299 42	9.951 22	6	21	
40	**9.652 05**	25	**9.700 89**	32	**10.299 11**	**9.951 16**	6	20	
41	9.652 30	25	9.701 21	31	10.298 79	9.951 10	7	19	
42	9.652 55	26	9.701 52	32	10.298 48	9.951 03	6	18	
43	9.652 81	25	9.701 84	31	10.298 16	9.950 97	7	17	
44	9.653 06	25	9.702 15	32	10.297 85	9.950 90	6	16	
45	**9.653 31**	25	**9.702 47**	31	**10.297 53**	**9.950 84**	6	15	
46	9.653 56	25	9.702 78	31	10.297 22	9.950 78	7	14	
47	9.653 81	25	9.703 09	32	10.296 91	9.950 71	6	13	
48	9.654 06	25	9.703 41	31	10.296 59	9.950 65	6	12	
49	9.654 31	25	9.703 72	32	10.296 28	9.950 59	7	11	
50	**9.654 56**	25	**9.704 04**	31	**10.295 96**	**9.950 52**	6	10	
51	9.654 81	25	9.704 35	31	10.295 65	9.950 46	7	9	
52	9.655 06	25	9.704 66	32	10.295 34	9.950 39	6	8	
53	9.655 31	25	9.704 98	31	10.295 02	9.950 33	6	7	
54	9.655 56	24	9.705 29	31	10.294 71	9.950 27	7	6	
55	**9.655 80**	25	**9.705 60**	32	**10.294 40**	**9.950 20**	6	5	
56	9.656 05	25	9.705 92	31	10.294 08	9.950 14	7	4	
57	9.656 30	25	9.706 23	31	10.293 77	9.950 07	6	3	
58	9.656 55	25	9.706 54	31	10.293 46	9.950 01	6	2	
59	9.656 80	25	9.706 85	32	10.293 15	9.949 95	7	1	
60	**9.657 05**		**9.707 17**		**10.292 83**	**9.949 88**		0	

′	L Cos	d	L Cot	cd	L Tan	L Sin	d	′	Prop. Pts.

Prop. Pts.

″	32	31	
1	0.5	0.5	
2	1.1	1.0	
3	1.6	1.6	
4	2.1	2.1	
5	2.7	2.6	
6	3.2	3.1	
7	3.7	3.6	
8	4.3	4.1	
9	4.8	4.6	
10	5.3	5.2	
20	10.7	10.3	
30	16.0	15.5	
40	21.3	20.7	
50	26.7	25.8	
″	26	25	24
1	0.4	0.4	0.4
2	0.9	0.8	0.8
3	1.3	1.2	1.2
4	1.7	1.7	1.6
5	2.2	2.1	2.0
6	2.6	2.5	2.4
7	3.0	2.9	2.8
8	3.5	3.3	3.2
9	3.9	3.8	3.6
10	4.3	4.2	4.0
20	8.7	8.3	8.0
30	13.0	12.5	12.0
40	17.3	16.7	16.0
50	21.7	20.8	20.0
″	7	6	
1	0.1	0.1	
2	0.2	0.2	
3	0.4	0.3	
4	0.5	0.4	
5	0.6	0.5	
6	0.7	0.6	
7	0.8	0.7	
8	0.9	0.8	
9	1.0	0.9	
10	1.2	1.0	
20	2.3	2.0	
30	3.5	3.0	
40	4.7	4.0	
50	5.8	5.0	

′	L Sin	d	L Tan	cd	L Cot	L Cos	d	′	Prop. Pts.
0	**9.657 05**	24	**9.707 17**	31	**10.292 83**	**9.949 88**	6	60	
1	9.657 29	25	9.707 48	31	10.292 52	9.949 82	7	59	
2	9.657 54	25	9.707 79	31	10.292 21	9.949 75	6	58	
3	9.657 79	25	9.708 10	31	10.291 90	9.949 69	7	57	
4	9.658 04	24	9.708 41	32	10.291 59	9.949 62	6	56	
5	**9.658 28**	25	**9.708 73**	31	**10.291 27**	**9.949 56**	7	55	
6	9.658 53	25	9.709 04	31	10.290 96	9.949 49	6	54	
7	9.658 78	24	9.709 35	31	10.290 65	9.949 43	7	53	
8	9.659 02	25	9.709 66	31	10.290 34	9.949 36	6	52	
9	9.659 27	25	9.709 97	31	10.290 03	9.949 30	7	51	
10	**9.659 52**	24	**9.710 28**	31	**10.289 72**	**9.949 23**	6	50	
11	9.659 76	25	9.710 59	31	10.289 41	9.949 17	6	49	
12	9.660 01	24	9.710 90	31	10.289 10	9.949 11	7	48	
13	9.660 25	25	9.711 21	32	10.288 79	9.949 04	6	47	
14	9.660 50	25	9.711 53	31	10.288 47	9.948 98	7	46	
15	**9.660 75**	24	**9.711 84**	31	**10.288 16**	**9.948 91**	6	45	
16	9.660 99	25	9.712 15	31	10.287 85	9.948 85	7	44	
17	9.661 24	24	9.712 46	31	10.287 54	9.948 78	7	43	
18	9.661 48	25	9.712 77	31	10.287 23	9.948 71	6	42	
19	9.661 73	24	9.713 08	31	10.286 92	9.948 65	7	41	
20	**9.661 97**	24	**9.713 39**	31	**10.286 61**	**9.948 58**	6	40	
21	9.662 21	25	9.713 70	31	10.286 30	9.948 52	7	39	
22	9.662 46	24	9.714 01	30	10.285 99	9.948 45	6	38	
23	9.662 70	25	9.714 31	31	10.285 69	9.948 39	7	37	
24	9.662 95	24	9.714 62	31	10.285 38	9.948 32	6	36	
25	**9.663 19**	24	**9.714 93**	31	**10.285 07**	**9.948 26**	7	35	
26	9.663 43	25	9.715 24	31	10.284 76	9.948 19	6	34	
27	9.663 68	24	9.715 55	31	10.284 45	9.948 13	7	33	
28	9.663 92	24	9.715 86	31	10.284 14	9.948 06	7	32	
29	9.664 16	24	9.716 17	31	10.283 83	9.947 99	6	31	
30	**9.664 41**	24	**9.716 48**	31	**10.283 52**	**9.947 93**	7	30	
31	9.664 65	24	9.716 79	30	10.283 21	9.947 86	7	29	
32	9.664 89	24	9.717 09	31	10.282 91	9.947 89	7	28	
33	9.665 13	24	9.717 40	31	10.282 60	9.947 73	6	27	
34	9.665 37	25	9.717 71	31	10.282 29	9.947 67	7	26	
35	**9.665 62**	24	**9.718 02**	31	**10.281 98**	**9.947 60**	7	25	
36	9.665 86	24	9.718 33	30	10.281 67	9.947 53	6	24	
37	9.666 10	24	9.718 63	31	10.281 37	9.947 47	7	23	
38	9.666 34	24	9.718 94	31	10.281 06	9.947 40	6	22	
39	9.666 58	24	9.719 25	30	10.280 75	9.947 34	7	21	
40	**9.666 82**	24	**9.719 55**	31	**10.280 45**	**9.947 27**	7	20	
41	9.667 06	25	9.719 86	31	10.280 14	9.947 20	6	19	
42	9.667 31	24	9.720 17	31	10.279 83	9.947 14	7	18	
43	9.667 55	24	9.720 48	30	10.279 52	9.947 07	7	17	
44	9.667 79	24	9.720 78	31	10.279 22	9.947 00	6	16	
45	**9.668 03**	24	**9.721 09**	31	**10.278 91**	**9.946 94**	7	15	
46	9.668 27	24	9.721 40	30	10.278 60	9.946 87	7	14	
47	9.668 51	24	9.721 70	31	10.278 30	9.946 80	6	13	
48	9.668 75	24	9.722 01	30	10.277 99	9.946 74	7	12	
49	9.668 99	23	9.722 31	31	10.277 69	9.946 67	7	11	
50	**9.669 22**	24	**9.722 62**	31	**10.277 38**	**9.946 60**	6	10	
51	9.669 46	24	9.722 93	30	10.277 07	9.946 54	7	9	
52	9.669 70	24	9.723 23	31	10.276 77	9.946 47	7	8	
53	9.669 94	24	9.723 54	30	10.276 46	9.946 40	6	7	
54	9.670 18	24	9.723 84	31	10.276 16	9.946 34	7	6	
55	**9.670 42**	24	**9.724 15**	30	**10.275 85**	**9.946 27**	7	5	
56	9.670 66	24	9.724 45	31	10.275 55	9.946 20	6	4	
57	9.670 90	23	9.724 76	30	10.275 24	9.946 14	7	3	
58	9.671 13	24	9.725 06	31	10.274 94	9.946 07	7	2	
59	9.671 37	24	9.725 37	30	10.274 63	9.946 00	7	1	
60	**9.671 61**		**9.725 67**		**10.274 33**	**9.945 93**		0	
′	L Cos	d	L Cot	cd	L Tan	L Sin	d	′	Prop. Pts.

Prop. Pts. table:

″	32	31	30
1	0.5	0.5	0.5
2	1.1	1.0	1.0
3	1.6	1.6	1.5
4	2.1	2.1	2.0
5	2.7	2.6	2.5
6	3.2	3.1	3.0
7	3.7	3.6	3.5
8	4.3	4.1	4.0
9	4.8	4.6	4.5
10	5.3	5.2	5.0
20	10.7	10.3	10.0
30	16.0	15.5	15.0
40	21.3	20.7	20.0
50	26.7	25.8	25.0

″	25	24	23
1	0.4	0.4	0.4
2	0.8	0.8	0.8
3	1.2	1.2	1.2
4	1.7	1.6	1.5
5	2.1	2.0	1.9
6	2.5	2.4	2.3
7	2.9	2.8	2.7
8	3.3	3.2	3.1
9	3.8	3.6	3.4
10	4.2	4.0	3.8
20	8.3	8.0	7.7
20	12.5	12.0	11.5
40	16.7	16.0	15.3
50	20.8	20.0	19.2

″	7	6
1	0.1	0.1
2	0.2	0.2
3	0.4	0.3
4	0.5	0.4
5	0.6	0.5
6	0.7	0.6
7	0.8	0.7
8	0.9	0.8
9	1.0	0.9
10	1.2	1.0
20	2.3	2.0
30	3.5	3.0
40	4.7	4.0
50	5.8	5.0

Table 4 / Logarithms of trigonometric functions   □   **697**

′	L Sin	d	L Tan	cd	L Cot	L Cos	d	′		Prop. Pts.		
0	**9.671 61**	24	**9.725 67**	31	**10.274 33**	**9.945 93**	6	60				
1	9.671 85	23	9.725 98	30	10.274 02	9.945 87	7	59				
2	9.672 08	24	9.726 28	31	10.273 72	9.945 80	7	58				
3	9.672 32	24	9.726 59	30	10.273 41	9.945 73	7	57				
4	9.672 56	24	9.726 89	31	10.273 11	9.945 67	7	56				
5	**9.672 80**	23	**9.727 20**	30	**10.272 80**	**9.945 60**	7	55				
6	9.673 03	24	9.727 50	30	10.272 50	9.945 53	7	54				
7	9.673 27	23	9.727 80	31	10.272 20	9.945 46	6	53				
8	9.673 50	24	9.728 11	30	10.271 89	9.945 40	7	52	″	**31**	**30**	**29**
9	9.673 74	24	9.728 41	31	10.271 59	9.945 33	7	51	1	0.5	0.5	0.5
10	**9.673 98**	23	**9.728 72**	30	**10.271 28**	**9.945 26**	7	50	2	1.0	1.0	1 0
11	9.674 21	24	9.729 02	30	10.270 98	9.945 19	6	49	3	1.6	1.5	1.4
12	9.674 45	23	9.729 32	31	10.270 68	9.945 13	7	48	4	2.1	2.0	1.9
13	9.674 68	24	9.729 63	30	10.270 37	9.945 06	7	47				
14	9.674 92	23	9.729 93	30	10.270 07	9.944 99	7	46	5	2.6	2.5	2.4
15	**9.675 15**	24	**9.730 23**	31	**10.269 77**	**9.944 92**	7	45	6	3.1	3.0	2.9
16	9.675 39	23	9.730 54	30	10.269 46	9.944 85	6	44	7	3.6	3.5	3.4
17	9.675 62	24	9.730 84	30	10.269 16	9.944 79	7	43	8	4.1	4.0	3.9
18	9.675 86	23	9.731 14	30	10.268 86	9.944 72	7	42	9	4.6	4.5	4.4
19	9.676 09	24	9.731 44	31	10.268 56	9.944 65	7	41	10	5.2	5.0	4.8
20	**9.676 33**	23	**9.731 75**	30	**10.268 25**	**9.944 58**	7	40	20	10.3	10.0	9.7
21	9.676 56	24	9.732 05	30	10.267 95	9.944 51	6	39	30	15.5	15.0	14.5
22	9.676 80	23	9.732 35	30	10.267 65	9.944 45	7	38	40	20.7	20.0	19.3
23	9.677 03	23	9.732 65	30	10.267 35	9.944 38	7	37	50	25.8	25.0	24.2
24	9.677 26	24	9.732 95	31	10.267 05	9.944 31	7	36	″	**24**	**23**	**22**
25	**9.677 50**	23	**9.733 26**	30	**10.266 74**	**9.944 24**	7	35	1	0.4	0.4	0.4
26	9.677 73	23	9.733 56	30	10.266 44	9.944 17	7	34	2	0.8	0.8	0.7
27	9.677 96	24	9.733 86	30	10.266 14	9.944 10	7	33	3	1.2	1.2	1.1
28	9.678 20	23	9.734 16	30	10.265 84	9.944 04	7	32	4	1.6	1.5	1.5
29	9.678 43	23	9.734 46	30	10.265 54	9.943 97	7	31	5	2.0	1.9	1.8
30	**9.678 66**	24	**9.734 76**	31	**10.265 24**	**9.943 90**	7	30	6	2.4	2.3	2.2
31	9.678 90	23	9.735 07	30	10.264 93	9.943 83	7	29	7	2.8	2.7	2.6
32	9.679 13	23	9.735 37	30	10.264 63	9.943 76	7	28	8	3.2	3.1	2.9
33	9.679 36	23	9.735 67	30	10.264 33	9.943 69	7	27	9	3.6	3.4	3.3
34	9.679 59	23	9.735 97	30	10.264 03	9.943 62	7	26	10	4.0	3.8	3.7
35	**9.679 82**	24	**9.736 27**	30	**10.263 73**	**9.943 55**	6	25	20	8.0	7.7	7.3
36	9.680 06	23	9.736 57	30	10.263 43	9.943 49	7	24	30	12.0	11.5	11.0
37	9.680 29	23	9.736 87	30	10.263 13	9.943 42	7	23	40	16.0	15.3	14.7
38	9.680 52	23	9.737 17	30	10.262 83	9.943 35	7	22	50	20.0	19.2	18.3
39	9.680 75	23	9.737 47	30	10.262 53	9.943 28	7	21	″	**7**	**6**	
40	**9.680 98**	23	**9.737 77**	30	**10.262 23**	**9.943 21**	7	20	1	0.1	0.1	
41	9.681 21	23	9.738 07	30	10.261 93	9.943 14	7	19	2	0.2	0.2	
42	9.681 44	23	9.738 37	30	10.261 63	9.943 07	7	18	3	0.4	0.3	
43	9.681 67	23	9.738 67	30	10.261 33	9.943 00	7	17	4	0.5	0.4	
44	9.681 90	23	9.738 97	30	10.261 03	9.942 93	7	16	5	0.6	0.5	
45	**9.682 13**	24	**9.739 27**	30	**10.260 73**	**9.942 86**	7	15	6	0.7	0.6	
46	9.682 37	23	9.739 57	30	10.260 43	9.942 79	6	14	7	0.8	0.7	
47	9.682 60	23	9.739 86	30	10.260 13	9.942 73	7	13	8	0.9	0.8	
48	9.682 83	22	9.740 17	30	10.259 83	9.942 66	7	12	9	1.0	0.9	
49	9.683 05	23	9.740 47	30	10.259 53	9.942 59	7	11	10	1.2	1.0	
50	**9.683 28**	23	**9.740 77**	30	**10.259 23**	**9.942 52**	7	10	20	2.3	2.0	
51	9.683 51	23	9.741 07	30	10.258 93	9.942 45	7	9	30	3.5	3.0	
52	9.683 74	23	9.741 37	29	10.258 63	9.942 38	7	8	40	4.7	4.0	
53	9.683 97	23	9.741 66	30	10.258 34	9.942 31	7	7	50	5.8	5.0	
54	9.684 20	23	9.741 96	30	10.258 04	9.942 24	7	6				
55	**9.684 43**	23	**9.742 26**	30	**10.257 74**	**9.942 17**	7	5				
56	9.684 66	23	9.742 56	30	10.257 44	9.942 10	7	4				
57	9.684 89	23	9.742 86	30	10.257 14	9.942 03	7	3				
58	9.685 12	22	9.743 16	29	10.256 84	9.941 96	7	2				
59	9.685 34	23	9.743 45	30	10.256 55	9.941 89	7	1				
60	**9.685 57**		**9.743 75**		**10.256 25**	**9.941 82**		0				
′	L Cos	d	L Cot	cd	L Tan	L Sin	d	′		Prop. Pts.		

′	L Sin	d	L Tan	cd	L Cot	L Cos	d	′
0	**9.685 57**	23	**9.743 75**	30	**10.256 25**	**9.941 82**	7	60
1	9.685 80	23	9.744 05	30	10.255 95	9.941 75	7	59
2	9.686 03	22	9.744 35	30	10.255 65	9.941 68	7	58
3	9.686 25	23	9.744 65	29	10.255 35	9.941 61	7	57
4	9.686 48	23	9.744 94	30	10.255 06	9.941 54	7	56
5	**9.686 71**	23	**9.745 24**	30	**10.254 76**	**9.941 47**	7	55
6	9.686 94	22	9.745 54	29	10.254 46	9.941 40	7	54
7	9.687 16	23	9.745 83	30	10.254 17	9.941 33	7	53
8	9.687 39	23	9.746 13	30	10.253 87	9.941 26	7	52
9	9.687 62	22	9.746 43	30	10.253 57	9.941 19	7	51
10	**9.687 84**	23	**9.746 73**	29	**10.253 27**	**9.941 12**	7	50
11	9.688 07	22	9.747 02	30	10.252 98	9.941 05	7	49
12	9.688 29	23	9.747 32	30	10.252 68	9.940 98	8	48
13	9.688 52	23	9.747 62	29	10.252 38	9.940 90	7	47
14	9.688 75	22	9.747 91	30	10.252 09	9.940 83	7	46
15	**9.688 97**	23	**9.748 21**	30	**10.251 79**	**9.940 76**	7	45
16	9.689 20	22	9.748 51	29	10.251 49	9.940 69	7	44
17	9.689 42	23	9.748 80	30	10.251 20	9.940 62	7	43
18	9.689 65	22	9.749 10	29	10.250 90	9.940 55	7	42
19	9.689 87	23	9.749 39	30	10.250 61	9.940 48	7	41
20	**9.690 10**	22	**9.749 69**	29	**10.250 31**	**9.940 41**	7	40
21	9.690 32	23	9.749 98	30	10.250 02	9.940 34	7	39
22	9.690 55	22	9.750 28	30	10.249 72	9.940 27	7	38
23	9.690 77	23	9.750 58	29	10.249 42	9.940 20	8	37
24	9.691 00	22	9.750 87	30	10.249 13	9.940 12	7	36
25	**9.691 22**	22	**9.751 16**	29	**10.248 83**	**9.940 05**	7	35
26	9.691 44	23	9.751 46	30	10.248 54	9.939 98	7	34
27	9.691 67	22	9.751 76	29	10.248 24	9.939 91	7	33
28	9.691 89	23	9.752 05	30	10.247 95	9.939 84	7	32
29	9.692 12	22	9.752 35	29	10.247 65	9.939 77	7	31
30	**9.692 34**	22	**9.752 64**	30	**10.247 36**	**9.939 70**	7	30
31	9.692 56	23	9.752 94	29	10.247 06	9.939 63	8	29
32	9.692 79	22	9.753 23	30	10.246 77	9.939 55	7	28
33	9.693 01	22	9.753 53	29	10.246 47	9.939 48	7	27
34	9.693 23	22	9.753 82	29	10.246 18	9.939 41	7	26
35	**9.693 45**	23	**9.754 11**	30	**10.245 89**	**9.939 34**	7	25
36	9.693 68	22	9.754 41	29	10.245 59	9.939 27	7	24
37	9.693 90	22	9.754 70	30	10.245 30	9.939 20	8	23
38	9.694 12	22	9.755 00	29	10.245 00	9.939 12	7	22
39	9.694 34	22	9.755 29	29	10.244 71	9.939 05	7	21
40	**9.694 56**	23	**9.755 58**	30	**10 244 42**	**9.938 98**	7	20
41	9.694 79	22	9.755 88	29	10.244 12	9.938 91	7	19
42	9.695 01	22	9.756 17	30	10.243 83	9.938 84	8	18
43	9.695 23	22	9.756 47	30	10.243 53	9.938 76	7	17
44	9.695 45	22	9.756 76	29	10.243 24	9.938 69	7	16
45	**9.695 67**	22	**9.757 05**	30	**10.242 95**	**9.938 62**	7	15
46	9.695 89	22	9.757 35	29	10.242 65	9.938 55	8	14
47	9.696 11	22	9.757 64	29	10.242 36	9.938 47	7	13
48	9.696 33	22	9.757 93	29	10.242 07	9.938 40	7	12
49	9.696 55	22	9.758 22	30	10.241 78	9.938 33	7	11
50	**9.696 77**	22	**9.758 52**	29	**10.241 48**	**9.938 26**	7	10
51	9.696 99	22	9.758 81	29	10.241 19	9.938 19	8	9
52	9.697 21	22	9.759 10	29	10.240 90	9.938 11	7	8
53	9.697 43	22	9.759 39	29	10.240 61	9.938 04	7	7
54	9.697 65	22	9.759 69	30	10.240 31	9.937 97	8	6
55	**9.697 87**	22	**9.759 98**	29	**10.240 02**	**9.937 89**	7	5
56	9.698 09	22	9.760 27	29	10.239 73	9.937 82	7	4
57	9.698 31	22	9.760 56	30	10.239 44	9.937 75	7	3
58	9.698 53	22	9.760 86	29	10.239 14	9.937 68	8	2
59	9.698 75	22	9.761 15	29	10.238 85	9.937 60	7	1
60	**9.698 97**		**9.761 44**		**10.238 56**	**9.937 53**		0

′	L Cos	d	L Cot	cd	L Tan	L Sin	d	′

Prop. Pts.

″	30	29	23
1	0.5	0.5	0.4
2	1.0	1.0	0.8
3	1.5	1.4	1.2
4	2.0	1.9	1.5
5	2.5	2.4	1.9
6	3.0	2.9	2.3
7	3.5	3.4	2.7
8	4.0	3.9	3.1
9	4.5	4.4	3.4
10	5.0	4.8	3.8
20	10.0	9.7	7.7
30	15.0	14.5	11.5
40	20.0	19.3	15.3
50	25.0	24.2	19.2

″	22	8	7
1	0.4	0.1	0.1
2	0.7	0.3	0.2
3	1.1	0.4	0.4
4	1.5	0.5	0.5
5	1.8	0.7	0.6
6	2.2	0.8	0.7
7	2.6	0.9	0.8
8	2.9	1.1	0.9
9	3.3	1.2	1.0
10	3.7	1.3	1.2
20	7.3	2.7	2.3
30	11.0	4.0	3.5
40	14.7	5.3	4.7
50	18.3	6.7	5.8

Table 4 / Logarithms of trigonometric functions   □   **699**

′	L Sin	d	L Tan	cd	L Cot	L Cos	d	′
0	**9.698 97**	22	**9.761 44**	29	**10.238 56**	**9.937 53**	7	**60**
1	9.699 19	22	9.761 73	29	10.238 27	9.937 46	8	59
2	9.699 41	22	9.762 02	29	10.237 98	9.937 38	7	58
3	9.699 63	22	9.762 31	30	10.237 69	9.937 31	7	57
4	9.699 84	22	9.762 61	29	10.237 39	9.937 24	7	56
5	**9.700 06**	22	**9.762 90**	29	**10.237 10**	**9.937 17**	8	**55**
6	9.700 28	22	9.763 19	29	10.236 81	9.937 09	7	54
7	9.700 50	22	9.763 48	29	10.236 52	9.937 02	7	53
8	9.700 72	21	9.763 77	29	10.236 23	9.936 95	8	52
9	9.700 93	22	9.764 06	29	10.235 94	9.936 87	7	51
10	**9.701 15**	22	**9.764 35**	29	**10.235 65**	**9.936 80**	7	**50**
11	9.701 37	22	9.764 64	29	10.235 36	9.936 73	8	49
12	9.701 59	21	9.764 93	29	10.235 07	9.936 65	7	48
13	9.701 80	22	9.765 22	29	10.234 78	9.936 58	8	47
14	9.702 02	22	9.765 51	29	10.234 49	9.936 50	7	46
15	**9.702 24**	21	**9.765 80**	29	**10.234 20**	**9.936 43**	7	**45**
16	9.702 45	22	9.766 09	30	10.233 91	9.936 36	8	44
17	9.702 67	21	9.766 39	29	10.233 61	9.936 28	7	43
18	9.702 88	22	9.766 68	29	10.233 32	9.936 21	7	42
19	9.703 10	22	9.766 97	29	10.233 03	9.936 14	8	41
20	**9.703 32**	21	**9.767 25**	29	**10.232 75**	**9.936 06**	7	**40**
21	9.703 53	22	9.767 54	29	10.232 46	9.935 99	8	39
22	9.703 75	21	9.767 83	29	10.232 17	9.935 91	7	38
23	9.703 96	22	9.768 12	29	10.231 88	9.935 84	7	37
24	9.704 18	21	9.768 41	29	10.231 59	9.935 77	8	36
25	**9.704 39**	22	**9.768 70**	29	**10.231 30**	**9.935 69**	7	**35**
26	9.704 61	21	9.768 99	29	10.231 01	9.935 62	8	34
27	9.704 82	22	9.769 28	29	10.230 72	9.935 54	7	33
28	9.705 04	21	9.769 57	29	10.230 43	9.935 47	8	32
29	9.705 25	22	9.769 86	29	10.230 14	9.935 39	7	31
30	**9.705 47**	21	**9.770 15**	29	**10.229 85**	**9.935 32**	7	**30**
31	9.705 68	22	9.770 44	29	10.229 56	9.935 25	8	29
32	9.705 90	21	9.770 73	28	10.229 27	9.935 17	7	28
33	9.706 11	22	9.771 01	29	10.228 99	9.935 10	8	27
34	9.706 33	21	9.771 30	29	10.228 70	9.935 02	7	26
35	**9.706 54**	21	**9.771 59**	29	**10.228 41**	**9.934 95**	8	**25**
36	9.706 75	22	9.771 88	29	10.228 12	9.934 87	7	24
37	9.706 97	21	9.772 17	29	10.227 83	9.934 80	8	23
38	9.707 18	21	9.772 46	28	10.227 54	9.934 72	7	22
39	9.707 39	22	9.772 74	29	10.227 26	9.934 65	8	21
40	**9.707 61**	21	**9.773 03**	29	**10.226 97**	**9.934 57**	7	**20**
41	9.707 82	21	9.773 32	29	10.226 68	9.934 50	8	19
42	9.708 03	21	9.773 61	29	10.226 39	9.934 42	7	18
43	9.708 24	22	9.773 90	28	10.226 10	9.934 35	8	17
44	9.708 46	21	9.774 18	29	10.225 82	9.934 27	7	16
45	**9.708 67**	21	**9.774 47**	29	**10.225 53**	**9.934 20**	8	**15**
46	9.708 88	21	9.774 76	29	10.225 24	9.934 12	7	14
47	9.709 09	22	9.775 05	28	10.224 95	9.934 05	8	13
48	9.709 31	21	9.775 33	29	10.224 67	9.933 97	7	12
49	9.709 52	21	9.775 62	29	10.224 38	9.933 90	8	11
50	**9.709 73**	21	**9.775 91**	28	**10.224 09**	**9.933 82**	7	**10**
51	9.709 94	21	9.776 19	29	10.223 81	9.933 75	8	9
52	9.710 15	21	9.776 48	29	10.223 52	9.933 67	7	8
53	9.710 36	22	9.776 77	29	10.223 23	9.933 60	7	7
54	9.710 58	21	9.777 06	28	10.222 94	9.933 52	6	6
55	**9.710 79**	21	**9.777 34**	29	**10.222 66**	**9.933 44**	7	**5**
56	9.711 00	21	9.777 63	28	10.222 37	9.933 37	8	4
57	9.711 21	21	9.777 91	29	10.222 09	9.933 29	8	3
58	9.711 42	21	9.778 20	29	10.221 80	9.933 22	8	2
59	9.711 63	21	9.778 49	28	10.221 51	9.933 14	7	1
60	**9.711 84**		**9.778 77**		**10.221 23**	**9.933 07**		**0**
′	L Cos	d	L Cot	cd	L Tan	L Sin	d	′

Prop. Pts.

″	30	29	28
1	0.5	0.5	0.5
2	1.0	1.0	0.9
3	1.5	1.4	1.4
4	2.0	1.9	1.9
5	2.5	2.4	2.3
6	3.0	2.9	2.8
7	3.5	3.4	3.3
8	4.0	3.9	3.7
9	4.5	4.4	4.2
10	5.0	4.8	4.7
20	10.0	9.7	9.3
30	15.0	14.5	14.0
40	20.0	19.3	18.7
50	25.0	24.2	23.3

″	22	21
1	0.4	0.4
2	0.7	0.7
3	1.1	1.0
4	1.5	1.4
5	1.8	1.8
6	2.2	2.1
7	2.6	2.4
8	2.9	2.8
9	3.3	3.2
10	3.7	3.5
20	7.3	7.0
30	11.0	10.5
40	14.7	14.0
50	18.3	17.5

″	8	7
1	0.1	0.1
2	0.3	0.2
3	0.4	0.4
4	0.5	0.5
5	0.7	0.6
6	0.8	0.7
7	0.9	0.8
8	1.1	0.9
9	1.2	1.0
10	1.3	1.2
20	2.7	2.3
30	4.0	3.5
40	5.3	4.7
50	6.7	5.8

Prop. Pts.

′	L Sin	d	L Tan	cd	L Cot	L Cos	d	′	Prop. Pts.
0	**9.711 84**	21	**9.778 77**	29	**10.221 23**	**9.933 07**	8	60	
1	9.712 05	21	9.779 06	29	10.220 94	9.932 99	8	59	
2	9.712 26	21	9.779 35	28	10.220 65	9.932 91	7	58	
3	9.712 47	21	9.779 63	29	10.220 37	9.932 84	8	57	
4	9.712 68	21	9.779 92	28	10.220 08	9.932 76	7	56	
5	**9.712 89**	21	**9.780 20**	29	**10.219 80**	**9.932 69**	8	55	
6	9.713 10	21	9.780 49	28	10.219 51	9.932 61	8	54	
7	9.713 31	21	9.780 77	29	10.219 23	9.932 53	7	53	
8	9.713 52	21	9.781 06	29	10.218 94	9.932 46	8	52	″ 29 28
9	9.713 73	20	9.781 35	28	10.218 65	9.932 38	8	51	1 0.5 0.5
10	**9.713 93**	21	**9.781 63**	29	**10.218 37**	**9.932 30**	7	50	2 1.0 0.9
11	9.714 14	21	9.781 92	28	10.218 08	9.932 23	8	49	3 1.4 1.4
12	9.714 35	21	9.782 20	29	10.217 80	9.932 1⁙	8	48	4 1.9 1.9
13	9.714 56	21	9.782 49	28	10.217 51	9.932 07	7	47	5 2.4 2.3
14	9.714 77	21	9.782 77	29	10.217 23	9.932 00	8	46	6 2.9 2.8
15	**9.714 98**	21	**9.783 06**	28	**10.216 94**	**9.931 92**	8	45	7 3.4 3.3
16	9.715 19	20	9.783 34	29	10.216 66	9.931 84	7	44	8 3.9 3.7
17	9.715 39	21	9.783 63	28	10.216 37	9.931 77	8	43	9 4.4 4.2
18	9.715 60	21	9.783 91	28	10.216 09	9.931 69	8	42	10 4.8 4.7
19	9.715 81	21	9.784 19	29	10.215 81	9.931 61	7	41	20 9.7 9.3
20	**9.716 02**	20	**9.784 48**	28	**10.215 52**	**9.931 54**	8	40	30 14.5 14.0
21	9.716 22	21	9.784 76	29	10.215 24	9.931 46	8	39	40 19.3 18.7
22	9.716 43	21	9.785 05	28	10.214 95	9.931 38	7	38	50 24.2 23.3
23	9.716 64	21	9.785 33	29	10.214 67	9.931 31	8	37	″ 21 20
24	9.716 85	20	9.785 62	28	10.214 38	9.931 23	8	36	1 0.4 0.3
25	**9.717 05**	21	**9.785 90**	28	**10.214 10**	**9.931 15**	7	35	2 0.7 0.7
26	9.717 26	21	9.786 18	29	10.213 82	9.931 08	8	34	3 1.0 1.0
27	9.717 47	20	9.786 47	28	10.213 53	9.931 00	8	33	4 1.4 1.3
28	9.717 67	21	9.786 75	29	10.213 25	9.930 92	8	32	5 1.8 1.7
29	9.717 88	21	9.787 04	28	10.212 96	9.930 84	7	31	6 2.1 2.0
30	**9.718 09**	20	**9.787 32**	28	**10.212 68**	**9.930 77**	8	30	7 2.4 2.3
31	9.718 29	21	9.787 60	29	10.212 40	9.930 69	8	29	8 2.8 2.7
32	9.718 50	20	9.787 89	28	10.212 11	9.930 61	8	28	9 3.2 3.0
33	9.718 70	21	9.788 17	28	10.211 83	9.930 53	7	27	10 3.5 3.3
34	9.718 91	20	9.788 45	29	10.211 55	9.930 46	8	26	20 7.0 6.7
35	**9.719 11**	21	**9.788 74**	28	**10.211 26**	**9.930 38**	8	25	30 10.5 10.0
36	9.719 32	20	9.789 02	28	10.210 98	9.930 30	8	24	40 14.0 13.3
37	9.719 52	21	9.789 30	29	10.210 70	9.930 22	8	23	50 17.5 16.7
38	9.719 73	21	9.789 59	28	10.210 41	9.930 14	7	22	″ 8 7
39	9.719 94	20	9.789 87	28	10.210 13	9.930 07	8	21	1 0.1 0.1
40	**9.720 14**	20	**9.790 15**	28	**10.209 85**	**9.929 99**	8	20	2 0.3 0.2
41	9.720 34	21	9.790 43	29	10.209 57	9.929 91	8	19	3 0.4 0.4
42	9.720 55	20	9.790 72	28	10.209 28	9.929 83	7	18	4 0.5 0.5
43	9.720 75	21	9.791 00	28	10.209 00	9.929 76	8	17	5 0.7 0.6
44	9.720 96	20	9.791 28	28	10.208 72	9.929 68	8	16	6 0.8 0.7
45	**9.721 16**	21	**9.791 56**	29	**10.208 44**	**9.929 60**	8	15	7 0.9 0.8
46	9.721 37	20	9.791 85	28	10.208 15	9.929 52	8	14	8 1.1 0.9
47	9.721 57	20	9.792 13	28	10.207 87	9.929 44	8	13	9 1.2 1.0
48	9.721 77	21	9.792 41	28	10.207 59	9.929 36	7	12	10 1.3 1.2
49	9.721 98	20	9.792 69	28	10.207 31	9.929 29	8	11	20 2.7 2.3
50	**9.722 18**	20	**9.792 97**	29	**10.207 03**	**9.929 21**	8	10	30 4.0 3.5
51	9.722 38	21	9.793 26	28	10.206 74	9.929 13	8	9	40 5.3 4.7
52	9.722 59	20	9.793 54	28	10.206 46	9.929 05	8	8	50 6.7 5.8
53	9.722 79	20	9.793 82	28	10.206 18	9.928 97	8	7	
54	9.722 99	21	9.794 10	28	10.205 90	9.928 89	8	6	
55	**9.723 20**	20	**9.794 38**	28	**10.205 62**	**9.928 81**	7	5	
56	9.723 40	20	9.794 66	29	10.205 34	9.928 74	8	4	
57	9.723 60	21	9.794 95	28	10.205 05	9.928 66	8	3	
58	9.723 81	20	9.795 23	28	10.204 77	9.928 58	8	2	
59	9.724 01	20	9.795 51	28	10.204 49	9.928 50	8	1	
60	**9.724 21**		**9.795 79**		**10.204 21**	**9.928 42**		0	
′	L Cos	d	L Cot	cd	L Tan	L Sin	d	′	Prop. Pts.

Table 4 / Logarithms of trigonometric functions ☐ **701**

′	L Sin	d	L Tan	cd	L Cot	L Cos	d	′
0	**9.724 21**	20	**9.795 79**	28	**10.204 21**	**9.928 42**	8	60
1	9.724 41	20	9.796 07	28	10.203 93	9.928 34	8	59
2	9.724 61	21	9.796 35	28	10.203 65	9.928 26	8	58
3	9.724 82	20	9.796 63	28	10.203 37	9.928 18	8	57
4	9.725 02	20	9.796 91	28	10.203 09	9.928 10	7	56
5	**9.725 22**	20	**9.797 19**	28	**10.202 81**	**9.928 03**	8	55
6	9.725 42	20	9.797 47	29	10.202 53	9.927 95	8	54
7	9.725 62	20	9.797 76	28	10.202 24	9.927 87	8	53
8	9.725 82	20	9.798 04	28	10.201 96	9.927 79	8	52
9	9.726 02	20	9.798 32	28	10.201 68	9.927 71	8	51
10	**9.726 22**	21	**9.798 60**	28	**10.201 40**	**9.927 63**	8	50
11	9.726 43	20	9.798 88	28	10.201 12	9.927 55	8	49
12	9.726 63	20	9.799 16	28	10.200 84	9.927 47	8	48
13	9.726 83	20	9.799 44	28	10.200 56	9.927 39	8	47
14	9.727 03	20	9.799 72	28	10.200 28	9.927 31	8	46
15	**9.727 23**	20	**9.800 00**	28	**10.200 00**	**9.927 23**	8	45
16	9.727 43	20	9.800 28	28	10.199 72	9.927 15	8	44
17	9.727 63	20	9.800 56	28	10.199 44	9.927 07	8	43
18	9.727 83	20	9.800 84	28	10.199 16	9.926 99	8	42
19	9.728 03	20	9.801 12	28	10.198 88	9.926 91	8	41
20	**9.728 23**	20	**9.801 40**	28	**10.198 60**	**9.926 83**	8	40
21	9.728 43	20	9.801 68	27	10.198 32	9.926 75	8	39
22	9.728 63	20	9.801 95	28	10.198 05	9.926 67	8	38
23	9.728 83	19	9.802 23	28	10.197 77	9.926 59	8	37
24	9.729 02	20	9.802 51	28	10.197 49	9.926 51	8	36
25	**9.729 22**	20	**9.802 79**	28	**10.197 21**	**9.926 43**	8	35
26	9.729 42	20	9.803 07	28	10.196 93	9.926 35	8	34
27	9.729 62	20	9.803 35	28	10.196 65	9.926 27	8	33
28	9.729 82	20	9.803 63	28	10.196 37	9.926 19	8	32
29	9.730 02	20	9.803 91	28	10.196 09	9.926 11	8	31
30	**9.730 22**	19	**9.804 19**	28	**10.195 81**	**9.926 03**	8	30
31	9.730 41	20	9.804 47	27	10.195 53	9.925 95	8	29
32	9.730 61	20	9.804 74	28	10.195 26	9.925 87	8	28
33	9.730 81	20	9.805 02	28	10.194 98	9.925 79	8	27
34	9.731 01	20	9.805 30	28	10.194 70	9.925 71	8	26
35	**9.731 21**	19	**9.805 58**	28	**10.194 42**	**9.925 63**	8	25
36	9.731 40	20	9.805 86	28	10.194 14	9.925 55	9	24
37	9.731 60	20	9.806 14	28	10.193 86	9.925 46	8	23
38	9.731 80	20	9.806 42	27	10.193 58	9.925 38	8	22
39	9.732 00	19	9.806 69	28	10.193 31	9.925 30	8	21
40	**9.732 19**	20	**9.806 97**	28	**10.193 03**	**9.925 22**	8	20
41	9.732 39	20	9.807 25	28	10.192 75	9.925 14	8	19
42	9.732 59	19	9.807 53	28	10.192 47	9.925 06	8	18
43	9.732 78	20	9.807 81	27	10.192 19	9.924 98	8	17
44	9.732 98	20	9.808 08	28	10.191 92	9.924 90	8	16
45	**9.733 18**	19	**9.808 36**	28	**10.191 64**	**9.924 82**	9	15
46	9.733 37	20	9.808 64	28	10.191 36	9.924 73	8	14
47	9.733 57	20	9.808 92	27	10.191 08	9.924 65	8	13
48	9.733 77	19	9.809 19	28	10.190 81	9.924 57	8	12
49	9.733 96	20	9.809 47	28	10.190 53	9.924 49	8	11
50	**9.734 16**	19	**9.809 75**	28	**10.190 25**	**9.924 41**	8	10
51	9.734 35	20	9.810 03	27	10.189 97	9.924 33	8	9
52	9.734 55	19	9.810 30	28	10.189 70	9.924 25	8	8
53	9.734 74	20	9.810 58	28	10.189 42	9.924 16	8	7
54	9.734 94	19	9.810 86	27	10.189 14	9.924 08	8	6
55	**9.735 13**	20	**9.811 13**	28	**10.188 87**	**9.924 00**	8	5
56	9.735 33	19	9.811 41	28	10.188 59	9.923 92	8	4
57	9.735 52	20	9.811 69	27	10.188 31	9.923 84	9	3
58	9.735 72	19	9.811 96	28	10.188 04	9.923 76	9	2
59	9.735 91	20	9.812 24	28	10.187 76	9.923 67	8	1
60	**9.736 11**		**9.812 52**		**10.187 48**	**9.923 59**		0
′	L Cos	d	L Cot	cd	L Tan	L Sin	d	′

Prop. Pts.

″	29	28	27
1	0.5	0.5	0.4
2	1.0	0.9	0.9
3	1.4	1.4	1.4
4	1.9	1.9	1.8
5	2.4	2.3	2.2
6	2.9	2.8	2.7
7	3.4	3.3	3.2
8	3.9	3.7	3.6
9	4.4	4.2	4.0
10	4.8	4.7	4.5
20	9.7	9.3	9.0
30	14.5	14.0	13.5
40	19.3	18.7	18.0
50	24.2	23.3	22.5

″	21	20	19
1	0.4	0.3	0.3
2	0.7	0.7	0.6
3	1.0	1.0	1.0
4	1.4	1.3	1.3
5	1.8	1.7	1.6
6	2.1	2.0	1.9
7	2.4	2.3	2.2
8	2.8	2.7	2.5
9	3.2	3.0	2.8
10	3.5	3.3	3.2
20	7.0	6.7	6.3
30	10.5	10.0	9.5
40	14.0	13.3	12.7
50	17.5	16.7	15.8

″	9	8	7
1	0.2	0.1	0.1
2	0.3	0.3	0.2
3	0.4	0.4	0.4
4	0.6	0.5	0.5
5	0.8	0.7	0.6
6	0.9	0.8	0.7
7	1.0	0.9	0.8
8	1.2	1.1	0.9
9	1.4	1.2	1.0
10	1.5	1.3	1.2
20	3.0	2.7	2.3
30	4.5	4.0	3.5
40	6.0	5.3	4.7
50	7.5	6.7	5.8

Prop. Pts.

′	L Sin	d	L Tan	cd	L Cot	L Cos	d	′
0	9.736 11	19	9.812 52	27	10.187 48	9.923 59	8	60
1	9.736 30	20	9.812 79	28	10.187 21	9.923 51	8	59
2	9.736 50	19	9.813 07	28	10.186 93	9.923 43	8	58
3	9.736 69	20	9.813 35	27	10.186 65	9.923 35	8	57
4	9.736 89	19	9.813 62	28	10.186 38	9.923 26	9	56
5	9.737 08	19	9.813 90	28	10.186 10	9.923 18	8	55
6	9.737 27	20	9.814 18	27	10.185 82	9.923 10	8	54
7	9.737 47	19	9.814 45	28	10.185 55	9.923 02	9	53
8	9.737 66	19	9.814 73	27	10.185 27	9.922 93	8	52
9	9.737 85	20	9.815 00	28	10.185 00	9.922 85	8	51
10	9.738 05	19	9.815 28	28	10.184 72	9.922 77	8	50
11	9.738 24	19	9.815 56	27	10.184 44	9.922 69	9	49
12	9.738 43	20	9.815 83	28	10.184 17	9.922 60	8	48
13	9.738 63	19	9.816 11	27	10.183 89	9.922 52	8	47
14	9.738 82	19	9.816 38	28	10.183 62	9.922 44	9	46
15	9.739 01	20	9.816 66	27	10.183 34	9.922 35	8	45
16	9.739 21	19	9.816 93	28	10.183 07	9.922 27	8	44
17	9.739 40	19	9.817 21	27	10.182 79	9.922 19	8	43
18	9.739 59	19	9.817 48	28	10.182 52	9.922 11	9	42
19	9.739 78	19	9.817 76	27	10.182 24	9.922 02	8	41
20	9.739 97	20	9.818 03	28	10.181 97	9.921 94	8	40
21	9.740 17	19	9.818 31	27	10.181 69	9.921 86	9	39
22	9.740 36	19	9.818 58	28	10.181 42	9.921 77	8	38
23	9.740 55	19	9.818 86	27	10.181 14	9.921 69	8	37
24	9.740 74	19	9.819 13	28	10.180 87	9.921 61	9	36
25	9.740 93	20	9.819 41	27	10.180 59	9.921 52	8	35
26	9.741 13	19	9.819 68	28	10.180 32	9.921 44	8	34
27	9.741 32	19	9.819 96	27	10.180 04	9.921 36	9	33
28	9.741 51	19	9.820 23	28	10.179 77	9.921 27	8	32
29	9.741 70	19	9.820 51	27	10.179 49	9.921 19	8	31
30	9.741 89	19	9.820 78	28	10.179 22	9.921 11	9	30
31	9.742 08	19	9.821 06	27	10.178 94	9.921 02	8	29
32	9.742 27	19	9.821 33	28	10.178 67	9.920 94	8	28
33	9.742 46	19	9.821 61	27	10.178 39	9.920 86	9	27
34	9.742 65	19	9.821 88	27	10.178 12	9.920 77	8	26
35	9.742 84	19	9.822 15	28	10.177 85	9.920 69	9	25
36	9.743 03	19	9.822 43	27	10.177 57	9.920 60	8	24
37	9.743 22	19	9.822 70	28	10.177 30	9.920 52	8	23
38	9.743 41	19	9.822 98	27	10.177 02	9.920 44	9	22
39	9.743 60	19	9.823 25	27	10.176 75	9.920 35	8	21
40	9.743 79	19	9.823 52	28	10.176 48	9.920 27	9	20
41	9.743 98	19	9.823 80	27	10.176 20	9.920 18	8	19
42	9.744 17	19	9.824 07	28	10.175 93	9.920 10	8	18
43	9.744 36	19	9.824 35	27	10.175 65	9.920 02	9	17
44	9.744 55	19	9.824 62	27	10.175 38	9.919 93	8	16
45	9.744 74	19	9.824 89	28	10.175 11	9.919 85	9	15
46	9.744 93	19	9.825 17	27	10.174 83	9.919 76	8	14
47	9.745 12	19	9.825 44	27	10.174 56	9.919 68	9	13
48	9.745 31	18	9.825 71	28	10.174 29	9.919 59	8	12
49	9.745 49	19	9.825 99	27	10.174 01	9.919 51	9	11
50	9.745 68	19	9.826 26	27	10.173 74	9.919 42	8	10
51	9.745 87	19	9.826 53	28	10.173 47	9.919 34	9	9
52	9.746 06	19	9.826 81	27	10.173 19	9.919 25	8	8
53	9.746 25	19	9.827 08	27	10.172 92	9.919 17	9	7
54	9.746 44	18	9.827 35	27	10.172 65	9.919 08	8	6
55	9.746 62	19	9.827 62	28	10.172 38	9.919 00	9	5
56	9.746 81	19	9.827 90	27	10.172 10	9.918 91	8	4
57	9.747 00	19	9.828 17	27	10.171 83	9.918 83	9	3
58	9.747 19	18	9.828 44	27	10.171 56	9.918 74	9	2
59	9.747 37	19	9.828 71	28	10.171 29	9.918 66	9	1
60	9.747 56		9.828 99		10.171 01	9.918 57		0
′	L Cos	d	L Cot	cd	L Tan	L Sin	d	′

Prop. Pts.

″	28	27
1	0.5	0.4
2	0.9	0.9
3	1.4	1.4
4	1.9	1.8
5	2.3	2.2
6	2.8	2.7
7	3.3	3.2
8	3.7	3.6
9	4.2	4.0
10	4.7	4.5
20	9.3	9.0
30	14.0	13.5
40	18.7	18.0
50	23.3	22.5

″	20	19	18
1	0.3	0.3	0.3
2	0.7	0.6	0.6
3	1.0	1.0	0.9
4	1.3	1.3	1.2
5	1.7	1.6	1.5
6	2.0	1.9	1.8
7	2.3	2.2	2.1
8	2.7	2.5	2.4
9	3.0	2.8	2.7
10	3.3	3.2	3.0
20	6.7	6.3	6.0
30	10.0	9.5	9.0
40	13.3	12.7	12.0
50	16.7	15.8	15.0

″	9	8
1	0.2	0.1
2	0.3	0.3
3	0.4	0.4
4	0.6	0.5
5	0.8	0.7
6	0.9	0.8
7	1.0	0.9
8	1.2	1.1
9	1.4	1.2
10	1.5	1.3
20	3.0	2.7
30	4.5	4.0
40	6.0	5.3
50	7.5	6.7

Prop. Pts.

Table 4 / Logarithms of trigonometric functions   □   **703**

′	L Sin	d	L Tan	cd	L Cot	L Cos	d	′	Prop. Pts.
0	9.747 56	19	9.828 99	27	10.171 01	9.918 57	8	60	
1	9.747 75	19	9.829 26	27	10.170 74	9.918 49	9	59	
2	9.747 94	18	9.829 53	27	10.170 47	9.918 40	8	58	
3	9.748 12	19	9.829 80	28	10.170 20	9.918 32	9	57	
4	9.748 31	19	9.830 08	27	10.169 92	9.918 23	8	56	
5	9.748 50	19	9.830 35	27	10.169 65	9.918 15	9	55	
6	9.748 68	19	9.830 62	27	10.169 38	9.918 06	8	54	
7	9.748 87	19	9.830 89	28	10.169 11	9.917 98	9	53	
8	9.749 06	18	9.831 17	27	10.168 83	9.917 89	8	52	
9	9.749 24	19	9.831 44	27	10.168 56	9.917 81	9	51	
10	9.749 43	18	9.831 71	27	10.168 29	9.917 72	9	50	
11	9.749 61	19	9.831 98	27	10.168 02	9.917 63	8	49	
12	9.749 80	19	9.832 25	27	10.167 75	9.917 55	9	48	
13	9.749 99	18	9.832 52	28	10.167 48	9.917 46	8	47	
14	9.750 17	19	9.832 80	27	10.167 20	9.917 38	9	46	
15	9.750 36	18	9.833 07	27	10.166 93	9.917 29	9	45	
16	9.750 54	19	9.833 34	27	10.166 66	9.917 20	8	44	
17	9.750 73	18	9.833 61	27	10.166 39	9.917 12	9	43	
18	9.750 91	19	9.833 88	27	10.166 12	9.917 03	8	42	
19	9.751 10	18	9.834 15	27	10.165 85	9.916 95	9	41	
20	9.751 28	19	9.834 42	28	10.165 58	9.916 86	9	40	
21	9.751 47	18	9.834 70	27	10.165 30	9.916 77	8	39	
22	9.751 65	19	9.834 97	27	10.165 03	9.916 69	9	38	
23	9.751 84	18	9.835 24	27	10.164 76	9.916 60	9	37	
24	9.752 02	19	9.835 51	27	10.164 49	9.916 51	8	36	
25	9.752 21	18	9.835 78	27	10.164 22	9.916 43	9	35	
26	9.752 39	19	9.836 05	27	10.163 95	9.916 34	9	34	
27	9.752 58	18	9.836 32	27	10.163 68	9.916 25	8	33	
28	9.752 76	18	9.836 59	27	10.163 41	9.916 17	9	32	
29	9.752 94	19	9.836 86	27	10.163 14	9.916 08	9	31	
30	9.753 13	18	9.837 13	27	10.162 87	9.915 99	8	30	
31	9.753 31	19	9.837 40	28	10.162 60	9.915 91	9	29	
32	9.753 50	18	9.837 68	27	10.162 32	9.915 82	9	28	
33	9.753 68	18	9.837 95	27	10.162 05	9.915 73	8	27	
34	9.753 86	19	9.838 22	27	10.161 78	9.915 65	9	26	
35	9.754 05	18	9.838 49	27	10.161 51	9.915 56	9	25	
36	9.754 23	18	9.838 76	27	10.161 24	9.915 47	9	24	
37	9.754 41	18	9.839 03	27	10.160 97	9.915 38	8	23	
38	9.754 59	19	9.839 30	27	10.160 70	9.915 30	9	22	
39	9.754 78	18	9.839 57	27	10.160 43	9.915 21	9	21	
40	9.754 96	18	9.839 84	27	10.160 16	9.915 12	8	20	
41	9.755 14	19	9.840 11	27	10.159 89	9.915 04	9	19	
42	9.755 33	18	9.840 38	27	10.159 62	9 914 95	9	18	
43	9.755 51	18	9.840 65	27	10.159 35	9.914 86	9	17	
44	9.755 69	18	9.840 92	27	10.159 08	9.914 77	8	16	
45	9.755 87	18	9.841 19	27	10.158 81	9.914 69	9	15	
46	9.756 05	19	9.841 46	27	10.158 54	9.914 60	9	14	
47	9.756 24	18	9.841 73	27	10.158 27	9.914 51	9	13	
48	9.756 42	18	9.842 00	27	10.158 00	9.914 42	9	12	
49	9.756 60	18	9.842 27	27	10.157 73	9.914 33	8	11	
50	9.756 78	18	9.842 54	26	10.157 46	9.914 25	9	10	
51	9.756 96	18	9.842 80	27	10.157 20	9.914 16	9	9	
52	9.757 14	19	9.843 07	27	10.156 93	9.914 07	9	8	
53	9.757 33	18	9.843 34	27	10.156 66	9.913 98	9	7	
54	9.757 51	18	9.843 61	27	10.156 39	9.913 89	8	6	
55	9.757 69	18	9.843 88	27	10.156 12	9.913 81	9	5	
56	9.757 87	18	9.844 15	27	10.155 85	9.913 72	9	4	
57	9.758 05	18	9.844 42	27	10.155 58	9.913 63	9	3	
58	9.758 23	18	9.844 69	27	10.155 31	9.913 54	9	2	
59	9.758 41	18	9.844 96	27	10.155 04	9.913 45	9	1	
60	9.758 59		9.845 23		10.154 77	9.913 36		0	
′	L Cos	d	L Cot	cd	L Tan	L Sin	d	′	Prop. Pts.

Prop. Pts.

″	28	27	26
1	0.5	0.4	0.4
2	0.9	0.9	0.9
3	1.4	1.4	1.3
4	1.9	1.8	1.7
5	2.3	2.2	2.2
6	2.8	2.7	2.6
7	3.3	3.2	3.0
8	3.7	3.6	3.5
9	4.2	4.0	3.9
10	4.7	4.5	4.3
20	9.3	9.0	8.7
30	14.0	13.5	13.0
40	18.7	18.0	17.3
50	23.3	22.5	21.7

″	19	18
1	0.3	0.3
2	0.6	0.6
3	1.0	0.9
4	1.3	1.2
5	1.6	1.5
6	1.9	1.8
7	2.2	2.1
8	2.5	2.4
9	2.8	2.7
10	3.2	3.0
20	6.3	6.0
30	9.5	9.0
40	12.7	12.0
50	15.8	15.0

″	9	8
1	0.2	0.1
2	0.3	0.3
3	0.4	0.4
4	0.6	0.5
5	0.8	0.7
6	0.9	0.8
7	1.0	0.9
8	1.2	1.1
9	1.4	1.2
10	1.5	1.3
20	3.0	2.7
30	4.5	4.0
40	6.0	5.3
50	7.5	6.7

′	L Sin	d	L Tan	cd	L Cot	L Cos	d	′	Prop. Pts.
0	9.758 59	18	9.845 23	27	10.154 77	9.913 36	8	60	
1	9.758 77	18	9.845 50	26	10.154 50	9.913 28	9	59	
2	9.758 95	18	9.845 76	27	10.154 24	9.913 19	9	58	
3	9.759 13	18	9.846 03	27	10.153 97	9.913 10	9	57	
4	9.759 31	18	9.846 30	27	10.153 70	9.913 01	9	56	
5	9.759 49	18	9.846 57	27	10.153 43	9.912 92	9	55	
6	9.759 67	18	9.846 84	27	10.153 16	9.912 83	9	54	
7	9.759 85	18	9.847 11	27	10.152 89	9.912 74	8	53	
8	9.760 03	18	9.847 38	26	10.152 62	9.912 66	9	52	
9	9.760 21	18	9.847 64	27	10.152 36	9.912 57	9	51	

									″	27	26	18
									1	0.4	0.4	0.3
									2	0.9	0.9	0.6
									3	1.4	1.3	0.9
									4	1.8	1.7	1.2

′	L Sin	d	L Tan	cd	L Cot	L Cos	d	′
10	9.760 39	18	9.847 91	27	10.152 09	9.912 48	9	50
11	9.760 57	18	9.848 18	27	10.151 82	9.912 39	9	49
12	9.760 75	18	9.848 45	27	10.151 55	9.912 30	9	48
13	9.760 93	18	9.848 72	27	10.151 28	9.912 21	9	47
14	9.761 11	18	9.848 99	26	10.151 01	9.912 12	9	46

Prop. Pts.:
5 → 2.2 / 2.2 / 1.5
6 → 2.7 / 2.6 / 1.8
7 → 3.2 / 3.0 / 2.1
8 → 3.6 / 3.5 / 2.4
9 → 4.0 / 3.9 / 2.7

′	L Sin	d	L Tan	cd	L Cot	L Cos	d	′
15	9.761 29	17	9.849 25	27	10.150 75	9.912 03	9	45
16	9.761 46	18	9.849 52	27	10.150 48	9.911 94	9	44
17	9.761 64	18	9.849 79	27	10.150 21	9.911 85	9	43
18	9.761 82	18	9.850 06	27	10.149 94	9.911 76	9	42
19	9.762 00	18	9.850 33	27	10.149 67	9.911 67	9	41

Prop. Pts.:
10 → 4.5 / 4.3 / 3.0
20 → 9.0 / 8.7 / 6.0
30 → 13.5 / 13.0 / 9.0
40 → 18.0 / 17.3 / 12.0
50 → 22.5 / 21.7 / 15.0

′	L Sin	d	L Tan	cd	L Cot	L Cos	d	′
20	9.762 18	18	9.850 59	27	10.149 41	9.911 58	8	40
21	9.762 36	17	9.850 86	27	10.149 14	9.911 49	9	39
22	9.762 53	18	9.851 13	27	10.148 87	9.911 41	9	38
23	9.762 71	18	9.851 40	26	10.148 60	9.911 32	9	37
24	9.762 89	18	9.851 66	27	10.148 34	9.911 23	9	36

	″	17	10
	1	0.3	0.2
	2	0.6	0.3
	3	0.8	0.5
	4	1.1	0.7

′	L Sin	d	L Tan	cd	L Cot	L Cos	d	′
25	9.763 07	17	9.851 93	27	10.148 07	9.911 14	9	35
26	9.763 24	18	9.852 20	27	10.147 80	9.911 05	9	34
27	9.763 42	18	9.852 47	26	10.147 53	9.910 96	9	33
28	9.763 60	18	9.852 73	27	10.147 27	9.910 87	9	32
29	9.763 78	17	9.853 00	27	10.147 00	9.910 78	9	31

Prop. Pts.:
5 → 1.4 / 0.8
6 → 1.7 / 1.0
7 → 2.0 / 1.2
8 → 2.3 / 1.3
9 → 2.6 / 1.5

′	L Sin	d	L Tan	cd	L Cot	L Cos	d	′
30	9.763 95	18	9.853 27	27	10.146 73	9.910 69	9	30
31	9.764 13	18	9.853 54	26	10.146 46	9.910 60	9	29
32	9.764 31	17	9.853 80	27	10.146 20	9.910 51	9	28
33	9.764 48	18	9.854 07	27	10.145 93	9.910 42	9	27
34	9.764 66	18	9.854 34	26	10.145 66	9.910 33	10	26

Prop. Pts.:
10 → 2.8 / 1.7
20 → 5.7 / 3.3
30 → 8.5 / 5.0
40 → 11.3 / 6.7
50 → 14.2 / 8.3

′	L Sin	d	L Tan	cd	L Cot	L Cos	d	′
35	9.764 84	17	9.854 60	27	10.145 40	9.910 23	9	25
36	9.765 01	18	9.854 87	27	10.145 13	9.910 14	9	24
37	9.765 19	18	9.855 14	26	10.144 86	9.910 05	9	23
38	9.765 37	17	9.855 40	27	10.144 60	9.909 96	9	22
39	9.765 54	18	9.855 67	27	10.144 33	9.909 87	9	21

	″	9	8
	1	0.2	0.1
	2	0.3	0.3
	3	0.4	0.4
	4	0.6	0.5

′	L Sin	d	L Tan	cd	L Cot	L Cos	d	′
40	9.765 72	18	9.855 94	26	10.144 06	9.909 78	9	20
41	9.765 90	17	9.856 20	27	10.143 80	9.909 69	9	19
42	9.766 07	18	9.856 47	27	10.143 53	9.909 60	9	18
43	9.766 25	17	9.856 74	26	10.143 26	9.909 51	9	17
44	9.766 42	18	9.857 00	27	10.143 00	9.909 42	9	16

Prop. Pts.:
5 → 0.8 / 0.7
6 → 0.9 / 0.8
7 → 1.0 / 0.9
8 → 1.2 / 1.1
9 → 1.4 / 1.2

′	L Sin	d	L Tan	cd	L Cot	L Cos	d	′
45	9.766 60	17	9.857 27	27	10.142 73	9.909 33	9	15
46	9.766 77	18	9.857 54	26	10.142 46	9.909 24	9	14
47	9.766 95	17	9.857 80	27	10.142 20	9.909 15	9	13
48	9.767 12	18	9.858 07	27	10.141 93	9.909 06	10	12
49	9.767 30	17	9.858 34	26	10.141 66	9.908 96	9	11

Prop. Pts.:
10 → 1.5 / 1.3
20 → 3.0 / 2.7
30 → 4.5 / 4.0
40 → 6.0 / 5.3
50 → 7.5 / 6.7

′	L Sin	d	L Tan	cd	L Cot	L Cos	d	′
50	9.767 47	18	9.858 60	27	10.141 40	9.908 87	9	10
51	9.767 65	17	9.858 87	26	10.141 13	9.908 78	9	9
52	9.767 82	18	9.859 13	27	10.140 87	9.908 69	9	8
53	9.768 00	17	9.859 40	27	10.140 60	9.908 60	9	7
54	9.768 17	18	9.859 67	26	10.140 33	9.908 51	9	6
55	9.768 35	17	9.859 93	27	10.140 07	9.908 42	10	5
56	9.768 52	18	9.860 20	26	10.139 80	9.908 32	9	4
57	9.768 70	17	9.860 46	27	10.139 54	9.908 23	9	3
58	9.768 87	17	9.860 73	27	10.139 27	9.908 14	9	2
59	9.769 04	18	9.861 00	26	10.139 00	9.908 05	9	1
60	9.769 22		9.861 26		10.138 74	9.907 96		0

′	L Cos	d	L Cot	cd	L Tan	L Sin	d	′	Prop. Pts.

Table 4 / Logarithms of trigonometric functions □ 705

′	L Sin	d	L Tan	cd	L Cot	L Cos	d	′	Prop. Pts.
0	9.769 22	17	9.861 26	27	10.138 74	9.907 96	9	60	
1	9.769 39	18	9.861 53	26	10.138 47	9.907 87	10	59	
2	9.769 57	17	9.861 79	27	10.138 21	9.907 77	9	58	
3	9.769 74	17	9.862 06	26	10.137 94	9.907 68	9	57	
4	9.769 91	18	9.862 32	27	10.137 68	9.907 59	9	56	
5	9.770 09	17	9.862 59	26	10.137 41	9.907 50	9	55	
6	9.770 26	17	9.862 85	27	10.137 15	9.907 41	10	54	
7	9.770 43	18	9.863 12	26	10.136 88	9.907 31	9	53	
8	9.770 61	17	9.863 38	27	10.136 62	9.907 22	9	52	
9	9.770 78	17	9.863 65	27	10.136 35	9.907 13	9	51	
10	9.770 95	17	9.863 92	26	10.136 08	9.907 04	10	50	
11	9.771 12	18	9.864 18	27	10.135 82	9.906 94	9	49	
12	9.771 30	17	9.864 45	26	10.135 55	9.906 85	9	48	
13	9.771 47	17	9.864 71	27	10.135 29	9.906 76	9	47	
14	9.771 64	17	9.864 98	26	10.135 02	9.906 67	10	46	
15	9.771 81	18	9.865 24	27	10.134 76	9.906 57	9	45	
16	9.771 99	17	9.865 51	26	10.134 49	9.906 48	9	44	
17	9.772 16	17	9.865 77	26	10.134 23	9.906 39	9	43	
18	9.772 33	17	9.866 03	27	10.133 97	9.906 30	10	42	
19	9.772 50	18	9.866 30	26	10.133 70	9.906 20	9	41	
20	9.772 68	17	9.866 56	27	10.133 44	9.906 11	9	40	
21	9.772 85	17	9.866 83	26	10.133 17	9.906 02	10	39	
22	9.773 02	17	9.867 09	27	10.132 91	9.905 92	9	38	
23	9.773 19	17	9.867 36	26	10.132 64	9.905 83	9	37	
24	9.773 36	17	9.867 62	27	10.132 38	9.905 74	9	36	
25	9.773 53	17	9.867 89	26	10.132 11	9.905 65	10	35	
26	9.773 70	17	9.868 15	27	10.131 85	9.905 55	9	34	
27	9.773 87	18	9.868 42	26	10.131 58	9.905 46	9	33	
28	9.774 05	17	9.868 68	26	10.131 32	9.905 37	10	32	
29	9.774 22	17	9.868 94	27	10.131 06	9.905 27	9	31	
30	9.774 39	17	9.869 21	26	10.130 79	9.905 18	9	30	
31	9.774 56	17	9.869 47	27	10.130 53	9.905 09	10	29	
32	9.774 73	17	9.869 74	26	10.130 26	9.904 99	9	28	
33	9.774 90	17	9.870 00	27	10.130 00	9.904 90	10	27	
34	9.775 07	17	9.870 27	26	10.129 73	9.904 80	9	26	
35	9.775 24	17	9.870 53	26	10.129 47	9.904 71	9	25	
36	9.775 41	17	9.870 79	27	10.129 21	9.904 62	10	24	
37	9.775 58	17	9.871 06	26	10.128 94	9.904 52	9	23	
38	9.775 75	17	9.871 32	26	10.128 68	9.904 43	9	22	
39	9.775 92	17	9.871 58	27	10.128 42	9.904 34	10	21	
40	9.776 09	17	9.871 85	26	10.128 15	9.904 24	9	20	
41	9.776 26	17	9.872 11	27	10.127 89	9.904 15	10	19	
42	9.776 43	17	9.872 38	26	10.127 62	9.904 05	9	18	
43	9.776 60	17	9.872 64	26	10.127 36	9.903 96	10	17	
44	9.776 77	17	9.872 90	27	10 127 10	9.903 86	9	16	
45	9.776 94	17	9.873 17	26	10.126 83	9.903 77	9	15	
46	9.777 11	17	9.873 43	26	10.126 57	9.903 68	10	14	
47	9.777 28	16	9.873 69	27	10.126 31	9.903 58	9	13	
48	9.777 44	17	9.873 96	26	10.126 04	9.903 49	10	12	
49	9.777 61	17	9.874 22	26	10.125 78	9.903 39	9	11	
50	9.777 78	17	9.874 48	27	10.125 52	9.903 30	10	10	
51	9.777 95	17	9.874 75	26	10.125 25	9.903 20	9	9	
52	9.778 12	17	9.875 01	26	10.124 99	9.903 11	10	8	
53	9.778 29	17	9.875 27	27	10.124 73	9.903 01	9	7	
54	9.778 46	16	9.875 54	26	10.124 46	9.902 92	10	6	
55	9.778 62	17	9.875 80	26	10.124 20	9.902 82	9	5	
56	9.778 79	17	9.876 06	27	10.123 94	9.902 73	10	4	
57	9.778 96	17	9.876 33	26	10.123 67	9.902 63	9	3	
58	9.779 13	17	9.876 59	26	10.123 41	9.902 54	10	2	
59	9.779 30	16	9.876 85	26	10.123 15	9.902 44	9	1	
60	9.779 46		9.877 11		10.122 89	9.902 35		0	

′	L Cos	d	L Cot	cd	L Tan	L Sin	d	′	Prop. Pts.

Prop. Pts.

″	27	26	
1	0.4	0.4	
2	0.9	0.9	
3	1.4	1.3	
4	1.8	1.7	
5	2.2	2.2	
6	2.7	2.6	
7	3.2	3.0	
8	3.6	3.5	
9	4.0	3.9	
10	4.5	4.3	
20	9.0	8.7	
30	13.5	13.0	
40	18.0	17.3	
50	22.5	21.7	

″	18	17	16
1	0.3	0.3	0.3
2	0.6	0.6	0.5
3	0.9	0.8	0.8
4	1.2	1.1	1.1
5	1.5	1.4	1.3
6	1.8	1.7	1.6
7	2.1	2.0	1.9
8	2.4	2.3	2.1
9	2.7	2.6	2.4
10	3.0	2.8	2.7
20	6.0	5.7	5.3
30	9.0	8.5	8.0
40	12.0	11.3	10.7
50	15.0	14.2	13.3

″	10	9	
1	0.2	0.2	
2	0.3	0.3	
3	0.5	0.4	
4	0.7	0.6	
5	0.8	0.8	
6	1.0	0.9	
7	1.2	1.0	
8	1.3	1.2	
9	1.5	1.4	
10	1.7	1.5	
20	3.3	3.0	
30	5.0	4.5	
40	6.7	6.0	
50	8.3	7.5	

′	L Sin	d	L Tan	cd	L Cot	L Cos	d	′		Prop. Pts.	
0	9.779 46	17	9.877 11	27	10.122 89	9.902 35	10	60			
1	9.779 63	17	9.877 38	26	10.122 62	9.902 25	9	59			
2	9.779 80	17	9.877 64	26	10.122 36	9.902 16	10	58			
3	9.779 97	16	9.877 90	27	10.122 10	9.902 06	9	57			
4	9.780 13	17	9.878 17	26	10.121 83	9.901 97	10	56			
5	9.780 30	17	9.878 43	26	10.121 87	9.901 87	9	55			
6	9.780 47	16	9.878 69	26	10.121 31	9.901 78	10	54			
7	9.780 63	17	9.878 95	27	10.121 05	9.901 68	9	53		″	27	26
8	9.780 80	17	9.879 22	26	10.120 78	9.901 59	10	52		1	0.4	0.4
9	9.780 97	16	9.879 48	26	10.120 52	9.901 49	10	51		2	0.9	0.9
10	9.781 13	17	9.879 74	26	10.120 26	9.901 39	9	50		3	1.4	1.3
11	9.781 30	17	9.880 00	27	10.120 00	9.901 30	10	49		4	1.8	1.7
12	9.781 47	16	9.880 27	26	10.119 73	9.901 20	9	48				
13	9.781 63	17	9.880 53	26	10.119 47	9.901 11	10	47		5	2.2	2.2
14	9.781 80	17	9.880 79	26	10.119 21	9.901 01	10	46		6	2.7	2.6
										7	3.2	3.0
15	9.781 97	16	9.881 05	26	10.118 95	9.900 91	9	45		8	3.6	3.5
16	9.782 13	17	9.881 31	27	10.118 69	9.900 82	10	44		9	4.0	3.9
17	9.782 30	16	9.881 58	26	10.118 42	9.900 72	9	43				
18	9.782 46	17	9.881 84	26	10.118 16	9.900 63	10	42		10	4.5	4.3
19	9.782 63	17	9.882 10	26	10.117 90	9.900 53	10	41		20	9.0	8.7
										30	13.5	13.0
20	9.782 80	16	9.882 36	26	10.117 64	9.900 43	9	40		40	18.0	17.3
21	9.782 96	17	9.882 62	27	10.117 38	9.900 34	10	39		50	22.5	21.7
22	9.783 13	16	9.882 89	26	10.117 11	9.900 24	10	38				
23	9.783 29	17	9.883 15	26	10.116 85	9.900 14	9	37		″	17	16
24	9.783 46	16	9.883 41	26	10.116 59	9.900 05	10	36		1	0.3	0.3
25	9.783 62	17	9.883 67	26	10.116 33	9.899 95	10	35		2	0.6	0.5
26	9.783 79	16	9.883 93	27	10.116 07	9.899 85	9	34		3	0.8	0.8
27	9.783 95	17	9.884 20	26	10.115 80	9.899 76	10	33		4	1.1	1.1
28	9.784 12	16	9.884 46	26	10.115 54	9.899 66	10	32				
29	9.784 28	17	9.884 72	26	10.115 28	9.899 56	10	31		5	1.4	1.3
										6	1.7	1.6
30	9.784 45	16	9.884 98	26	10.115 02	9.899 47	10	30		7	2.0	1.9
31	9.784 61	17	9.885 24	26	10.114 76	9.899 37	10	29		8	2.3	2.1
32	9.784 78	16	9.885 50	27	10.114 50	9.899 27	9	28		9	2.6	2.4
33	9.784 94	16	9.885 77	26	10.114 23	9.899 18	10	27				
34	9.785 10	17	9.886 03	26	10.113 97	9.899 08	10	26		10	2.8	2.7
										20	5.7	5.3
35	9.785 27	16	9.886 29	26	10.113 71	9.898 98	10	25		30	8.5	8.0
36	9.785 43	17	9.886 55	26	10.113 45	9.898 88	9	24		40	11.3	10.7
37	9.785 60	16	9.886 81	26	10.113 19	9.898 79	10	23		50	14.2	13.3
38	9.785 76	16	9.887 07	26	10.112 93	9.898 69	10	22				
39	9.785 92	17	9.887 33	26	10.112 67	9.898 59	10	21		″	10	9
40	9.786 09	16	9.887 59	27	10.112 41	9.898 49	9	20		1	0.2	0.2
41	9.786 25	17	9.887 86	26	10.112 14	9.898 40	10	19		2	0.3	0.3
42	9.786 42	16	9.888 12	26	10.111 88	9.898 30	10	18		3	0.5	0.4
43	9.786 58	16	9.888 38	26	10.111 62	9.898 20	10	17		4	0.7	0.6
44	9.786 74	17	9.888 64	26	10.111 36	9.898 10	9	16				
										5	0.8	0.8
45	9.786 91	16	9.888 90	26	10.111 10	9.898 01	10	15		6	1.0	0.9
46	9.787 07	16	9.889 16	26	10.110 84	9.897 91	10	14		7	1.2	1.0
47	9.787 23	16	9.889 42	26	10.110 58	9.897 81	10	13		8	1.3	1.2
48	9.787 39	17	9.889 68	26	10.110 32	9.897 71	10	12		9	1.5	1.4
49	9.787 56	16	9.889 94	26	10.110 06	9.897 61	9	11				
										10	1.7	1.5
50	9.787 72	16	9.890 20	26	10.109 80	9.897 52	10	10		20	3.3	3.0
51	9.787 88	17	9.890 46	27	10.109 54	9.897 42	10	9		30	5.0	4.5
52	9.788 05	16	9.890 73	26	10.109 27	9.897 32	10	8		40	6.7	6.0
53	9.788 21	16	9.890 99	26	10.109 01	9.897 22	10	7		50	8.3	7.5
54	9.788 37	16	9.891 25	26	10.108 75	9.897 12	10	6				
55	9.788 53	16	9.891 51	26	10.108 49	9.897 02	9	5				
56	9.788 69	17	9.891 77	26	10.108 23	9.896 93	10	4				
57	9.788 86	16	9.892 03	26	10.107 97	9.896 83	10	3				
58	9.789 02	16	9.892 29	26	10.107 71	9.896 73	10	2				
59	9.789 18	16	9.892 55	26	10.107 45	9.896 63	10	1				
60	9.789 34		9.892 81		10.107 19	9.896 53		0				

′	L Cos	d	L Cot	cd	L Tan	L Sin	d	′		Prop. Pts.

Table 4 / Logarithms of trigonometric functions □ **707**

′	L Sin	d	L Tan	cd	L Cot	L Cos	d	′	Prop. Pts.
0	9.789 34	16	9.892 81	26	10.107 19	9.896 53	10	60	
1	9.789 50	17	9.893 07	26	10.106 93	9.896 43	10	59	
2	9.789 67	16	9.893 33	26	10.106 67	9.896 33	9	58	
3	9.789 83	16	9.893 59	26	10.106 41	9.896 24	10	57	
4	9.789 99	16	9.893 85	26	10.106 15	9.896 14	10	56	
5	9.790 15	16	9.894 11	26	10.105 89	9.896 04	10	55	
6	9.790 31	16	9.894 37	26	10.105 63	9.895 94	10	54	
7	9.790 47	16	9.894 63	26	10.105 37	9.895 84	10	53	″ 26 25
8	9.790 63	16	9.894 89	26	10.105 11	9.895 74	10	52	1 0.4 0.4
9	9.790 79	16	9.895 15	26	10.104 85	9.895 64	10	51	2 0.9 0.8
10	9.790 95	16	9.895 41	26	10.104 59	9.895 54	10	50	3 1.3 1.2
11	9.791 11	17	9.895 67	26	10.104 33	9.895 44	10	49	4 1.7 1.7
12	9.791 28	16	9.895 93	26	10.104 07	9.895 34	10	48	
13	9.791 44	16	9.896 19	26	10.103 81	9.895 24	10	47	5 2.2 2.1
14	9.791 60	16	9.896 45	26	10.103 55	9.895 14	10	46	6 2.6 2.5
									7 3.0 2.9
15	9.791 76	16	9.896 71	26	10.103 29	9.895 04	9	45	8 3.5 3.3
16	9.791 92	16	9.896 97	26	10.103 03	9.894 95	10	44	9 3.9 3.8
17	9.792 08	16	9.897 23	26	10.102 77	9.894 85	10	43	
18	9.792 24	16	9.897 49	26	10.102 51	9.894 75	10	42	10 4.3 4.2
19	9.792 40	16	9.897 75	26	10.102 25	9.894 65	10	41	20 8.7 8.3
									30 13.0 12.5
20	9.792 56	16	9.898 01	26	10.101 99	9.894 55	10	40	40 17.3 16.7
21	9.792 72	16	9.898 27	26	10.101 73	9.894 45	10	39	50 21.7 20.8
22	9.792 88	16	9.898 53	26	10.101 47	9.894 35	10	38	
23	9.793 04	15	9.898 79	26	10.101 21	9.894 25	10	37	″ 17 16 15
24	9.793 19	16	9.899 05	26	10.100 95	9.894 15	10	36	1 0.3 0.3 0.2
									2 0.6 0.5 0.5
25	9.793 35	16	9.899 31	26	10.100 69	9.894 05	10	35	3 0.8 0.8 0.8
26	9.793 51	16	9.899 57	26	10.100 43	9.893 95	10	34	4 1.1 1.1 1.0
27	9.793 67	16	9.899 83	26	10.100 17	9.893 85	10	33	
28	9.793 83	16	9.900 09	26	10.099 91	9.893 75	11	32	5 1.4 1.3 1.2
29	9.793 99	16	9.900 35	26	10.099 65	9.893 64	10	31	6 1.7 1.6 1.5
									7 2.0 1.9 1.8
30	9.794 15	16	9.900 61	25	10.099 39	9.893 54	10	30	8 2.3 2.1 2.0
31	9.794 31	16	9.900 86	26	10.099 14	9.893 44	10	29	9 2.6 2.4 2.2
32	9.794 47	16	9.901 12	26	10.098 88	9.893 34	10	28	
33	9.794 63	15	9.901 38	26	10.098 62	9.893 24	10	27	10 2.8 2.7 2.5
34	9.794 78	16	9.901 64	26	10.098 36	9.893 14	10	26	20 5.7 5.3 5.0
									30 8.5 8.0 7.5
35	9.794 94	16	9.901 90	26	10.098 10	9.893 04	10	25	40 11.3 10.7 10.0
36	9.795 10	16	9.902 16	26	10.097 84	9.892 94	10	24	50 14.2 13.3 12.5
37	9.795 26	16	9.902 42	26	10.097 58	9.892 84	10	23	
38	9.795 42	16	9.902 68	26	10.097 32	9.892 74	10	22	″ 11 10 9
39	9.795 58	15	9.902 94	26	10.097 06	9.892 64	10	21	1 0.2 0.2 0.2
									2 0.4 0.3 0.3
40	9.795 73	16	9.903 20	26	10.096 80	9.892 54	10	20	3 0.6 0.5 0.4
41	9.795 89	16	9.903 46	25	10.096 54	9.892 44	11	19	4 0.7 0.7 0.6
42	9.796 05	16	9.903 71	26	10.096 29	9.892 33	10	18	
43	9.796 21	15	9.903 97	26	10.096 03	9.892 23	10	17	5 0.9 0.8 0.8
44	9.796 36	16	9.904 23	26	10.095 77	9.892 13	10	16	6 1.1 1.0 0.9
									7 1.3 1.2 1.0
45	9.796 52	16	9.904 49	26	10.095 51	9.892 03	10	15	8 1.5 1.3 1.2
46	9.796 68	16	9.904 75	26	10.095 25	9.891 93	10	14	9 1.6 1.5 1.4
47	9.796 84	15	9.905 01	26	10.094 99	9.891 83	10	13	
48	9.796 99	16	9.905 27	26	10.094 73	9.891 73	11	12	10 1.8 1.7 1.5
49	9.797 15	16	9.905 53	25	10.094 47	9.891 62	10	11	20 3.7 3.3 3.0
									30 5.5 5.0 4.5
50	9.797 31	15	9.905 78	26	10.094 22	9.891 52	10	10	40 7.3 6.7 6.0
51	9.797 46	16	9.906 04	26	10.093 96	9.891 42	10	9	50 9.2 8.3 7.5
52	9.797 62	16	9.906 30	26	10.093 70	9.891 32	10	8	
53	9.797 78	15	9.906 56	26	10.093 44	9.891 22	10	7	
54	9.797 93	16	9.906 82	26	10.093 18	9.891 12	11	6	
55	9.798 09	16	9.907 08	26	10.092 92	9.891 01	10	5	
56	9.798 25	15	9.907 34	25	10.092 66	9.890 91	10	4	
57	9.798 40	16	9.907 59	26	10.092 41	9.890 81	10	3	
58	9.798 56	16	9.907 85	26	10.092 15	9.890 71	11	2	
59	9.798 72	15	9.908 11	26	10.091 89	9.890 60	10	1	
60	9.798 87		9.908 37		10.091 63	9.890 50		0	
′	L Cos	d	L Cot	cd	L Tan	L Sin	d	′	Prop. Pts.

′	L Sin	d	L Tan	cd	L Cot	L Cos	d	′		Prop. Pts.	
0	9.798 87	16	9.908 37	26	10.091 63	9.890 50	10	60			
1	9.799 03	15	9.908 63	26	10.091 37	9.890 40	10	59			
2	9.799 18	16	9.908 89	25	10.091 11	9.890 30	10	58			
3	9.799 34	16	9.909 14	26	10.090 86	9.890 20	11	57			
4	9.799 50	15	9.909 40	26	10.090 60	9.890 09	10	56			
5	9.799 65	16	9.909 66	26	10.090 34	9.889 99	10	55			
6	9.799 81	15	9.909 92	26	10.090 08	9.889 89	11	54			
7	9.799 96	16	9.910 18	25	10.089 82	9.889 78	10	53		**26**	**25**
8	9.800 12	15	9.910 43	26	10.089 57	9.889 68	10	52	1	0.4	0.4
9	9.800 27	16	9.910 69	26	10.089 31	9.889 58	10	51	2	0.9	0.8
10	9.800 43	15	9.910 95	26	10.089 05	9.889 48	11	50	3	1.3	1.2
11	9.800 58	16	9.911 21	26	10.088 79	9.889 37	10	49	4	1.7	1.7
12	9.800 74	15	9.911 47	25	10.088 53	9.889 27	10	48			
13	9.800 89	16	9.911 72	26	10.088 28	9.889 17	11	47	5	2.2	2.1
14	9.801 05	15	9.911 98	26	10.088 02	9.889 06	10	46	6	2.6	2.5
									7	3.0	2.9
15	9.801 20	16	9.912 24	26	10.087 76	9.888 96	10	45	8	3.5	3.3
16	9.801 36	15	9.912 50	26	10.087 50	9.888 86	11	44	9	3.9	3.8
17	9.801 51	15	9.912 76	25	10.087 24	9.888 75	10	43			
18	9.801 66	16	9.913 01	26	10.086 99	9.888 65	10	42	10	4.3	4.2
19	9.801 82	15	9.913 27	26	10.086 73	9.888 55	11	41	20	8.7	8.3
									30	13.0	12.5
20	9.801 97	16	9.913 53	26	10.086 47	9.888 44	10	40	40	17.3	16.7
21	9.802 13	15	9.913 79	25	10.086 21	9.888 34	10	39	50	21.7	20.8
22	9.802 28	16	9.914 04	26	10.085 96	9.888 24	11	38			
23	9.802 44	15	9.914 30	26	10.085 70	9.888 13	10	37	″	**16**	**15**
24	9.802 59	15	9.914 56	26	10.085 44	9.888 03	10	36	1	0.3	0.2
25	9.802 74	16	9.914 82	25	10.085 18	9.887 93	11	35	2	0.5	0.5
26	9.802 90	15	9.915 07	26	10.084 93	9.887 82	10	34	3	0.8	0.8
27	9.803 05	15	9.915 33	26	10.084 67	9.887 72	11	33	4	1.1	1.0
28	9.803 20	16	9.915 59	26	10.084 41	9.887 61	10	32			
29	9.803 36	15	9.915 85	25	10.084 15	9.887 51	10	31	5	1.3	1.2
									6	1.6	1.5
30	9.803 51	15	9.916 10	26	10.083 90	9.887 41	11	30	7	1.9	1.8
31	9.803 66	16	9.916 36	26	10.083 64	9.887 30	10	29	8	2.1	2.0
32	9.803 82	15	9.916 62	26	10.083 38	9.887 20	11	28	9	2.4	2.2
33	9.803 97	15	9.916 88	25	10.083 12	9.887 09	10	27			
34	9.804 12	16	9.917 13	26	10.082 87	9.886 99	11	26	10	2.7	2.5
									20	5.3	5.0
35	9.804 28	15	9.917 39	26	10.082 61	9.886 88	10	25	30	8.0	7.5
36	9.804 43	15	9.917 65	26	10.082 35	9.886 78	10	24	40	10.7	10.0
37	9.804 58	15	9.917 91	25	10.082 09	9.886 68	10	23	50	13.3	12.5
38	9.804 73	16	9.918 16	26	10.081 84	9.886 57	10	22			
39	9.804 89	15	9.918 42	26	10.081 58	9.886 47	11	21	″	**11**	**10**
40	9.805 04	15	9.918 68	25	10.081 32	9.886 36	10	20	1	0.2	0.2
41	9.805 19	15	9.918 93	26	10.081 07	9.886 26	10	19	2	0.4	0.3
42	9.805 34	16	9.919 19	26	10.080 81	9.886 15	10	18	3	0.6	0.5
43	9.805 50	15	9.919 45	26	10.080 55	9.886 05	11	17	4	0.7	0.7
44	9.805 65	15	9.919 71	25	10.080 29	9.885 94	10	16			
45	9.805 80	15	9.919 96	26	10.080 04	9.885 84	11	15	5	0.9	0.8
46	9.805 95	15	9.920 22	26	10.079 78	9.885 73	10	14	6	1.1	1.0
47	9.806 10	15	9.920 48	25	10.079 52	9.885 63	11	13	7	1.3	1.2
48	9.806 25	16	9.920 73	26	10.079 27	9.885 52	10	12	8	1.5	1.3
49	9.806 41	15	9.920 99	26	10.079 01	9.885 42	11	11	9	1.6	1.5
									10	1.8	1.7
50	9.806 56	15	9.921 25	25	10.078 75	9.885 31	10	10	20	3.7	3.3
51	9.806 71	15	9.921 50	26	10.078 50	9.885 21	11	9	30	5.5	5.0
52	9.806 86	15	9.921 76	26	10.078 24	9.885 10	11	8	40	7.3	6.7
53	9.807 01	15	9.922 02	25	10.077 98	9.884 99	10	7	50	9.2	8.3
54	9.807 16	15	9.922 27	26	10.077 73	9.884 89	11	6			
55	9.807 31	15	9.922 53	26	10.077 47	9.884 78	10	5			
56	9.807 46	16	9.922 79	25	10.077 21	9.884 68	11	4			
57	9.807 62	15	9.923 04	26	10.076 96	9.884 57	10	3			
58	9.807 77	15	9.923 30	26	10.076 70	9.884 47	11	2			
59	9.807 92	15	9.923 56	25	10.076 44	9.884 36	11	1			
60	9.808 07		9.923 81		10.076 19	9.884 25		0			
′	L Cos	d	L Cot	cd	L Tan	L Sin	d	′		Prop. Pts.	

Table 4 / Logarithms of trigonometric functions □ **709**

′	L Sin	d	L Tan	cd	L Cot	L Cos	d	′
0	9.808 07		9.923 81		10.076 19	9.884 25		60
1	9.808 22	15	9.924 07	26	10.075 93	9.884 15	10	59
2	9.808 37	15	9.924 33	26	10.075 67	9.884 04	11	58
3	9.808 52	15	9.924 58	25	10.075 42	9.883 94	10	57
4	9.808 67	15	9.924 84	26	10.075 16	9.883 83	11	56
5	9.808 82	15	9.925 10	26	10.074 90	9.883 72	11	55
6	9.808 97	15	9.925 35	25	10.074 65	9.883 62	10	54
7	9.809 12	15	9.925 61	26	10.074 39	9.883 51	11	53
8	9.809 27	15	9.925 87	26	10.074 13	9.883 40	11	52
9	9.809 42	15	9.926 12	25	10.073 88	9.883 30	10	51
10	9.809 57	15	9.926 38	26	10.073 62	9.883 19	11	50
11	9.809 72	15	9.926 63	25	10.073 37	9.883 08	11	49
12	9.809 87	15	9.926 89	26	10.073 11	9.882 98	10	48
13	9.810 02	15	9.927 15	26	10.072 85	9.882 87	11	47
14	9.810 17	15	9.927 40	25	10.072 60	9.882 76	11	46
15	9.810 32	15	9.927 66	26	10.072 34	9.882 66	10	45
16	9.810 47	14	9.927 92	26	10.072 08	9.882 55	11	44
17	9.810 61	15	9.928 17	25	10.071 83	9.882 44	11	43
18	9.810 76	15	9.928 43	26	10.071 57	9.882 34	10	42
19	9.810 91	15	9.928 68	25	10.071 32	9.882 23	11	41
20	9.811 06	15	9.928 94	26	10.071 06	9.882 12	11	40
21	9.811 21	15	9.929 20	25	10.070 80	9.882 01	11	39
22	9.811 36	15	9.929 45	26	10.070 55	9.881 91	10	38
23	9.811 51	15	9.929 71	25	10.070 29	9.881 80	11	37
24	9.811 66	14	9.929 96	26	10.070 04	9.881 69	11	36
25	9.811 80	15	9.930 22	26	10.069 78	9.881 58	11	35
26	9.811 95	15	9.930 48	25	10.069 52	9.881 48	10	34
27	9.812 10	15	9.930 73	26	10.069 27	9.881 37	11	33
28	9.812 25	15	9.930 99	25	10.069 01	9.881 26	11	32
29	9.812 40	14	9.931 24	26	10.068 76	9.881 15	10	31
30	9.812 54	15	9.931 50	25	10.068 50	9.881 05	11	30
31	9.812 69	15	9.931 75	26	10.068 25	9.880 94	11	29
32	9.812 84	15	9.932 01	26	10.067 99	9.880 83	11	28
33	9.812 99	15	9.932 27	25	10.067 73	9.880 72	11	27
34	9.813 14	14	9.932 52	26	10.067 48	9.880 61	10	26
35	9.813 28	15	9.932 78	25	10.067 22	9.880 51	11	25
36	9.813 43	15	9.933 03	26	10.066 97	9.880 40	11	24
37	9.813 58	14	9.933 29	25	10.066 71	9.880 29	11	23
38	9.813 72	15	9.933 54	26	10.066 46	9.880 18	11	22
39	9.813 87	15	9.933 80	26	10.066 20	9.880 07	11	21
40	9.814 02	15	9.934 06	25	10.065 94	9.879 96	11	20
41	9.814 17	14	9.934 31	26	10.065 69	9.879 85	10	19
42	9.814 31	15	9.934 57	25	10.065 43	9.879 75	11	18
43	9.814 46	15	9.934 82	26	10.065 18	9.879 64	11	17
44	9.814 61	14	9.935 08	25	10.064 92	9.879 53	11	16
45	9.814 75	15	9.935 33	26	10.064 67	9.879 42	11	15
46	9.814 90	15	9.935 59	25	10.064 41	9.879 31	11	14
47	9.815 05	14	9.935 84	26	10.064 16	9.879 20	11	13
48	9.815 19	15	9.936 10	26	10.063 90	9.879 09	11	12
49	9.815 34	15	9.936 36	25	10.063 64	9.878 98	11	11
50	9.815 49	14	9.936 61	26	10.063 39	9.878 87	10	10
51	9.815 63	15	9.936 87	25	10.063 13	9.878 77	11	9
52	9.815 78	14	9.937 12	26	10.062 88	9.878 66	11	8
53	9.815 92	15	9.937 38	25	10.062 62	9.878 55	11	7
54	9.816 07	15	9.937 63	26	10.062 37	9.878 44	11	6
55	9.816 22	14	9.937 89	25	10.062 11	9.878 33	11	5
56	9.816 36	15	9.938 14	26	10.061 86	9.878 22	11	4
57	9.816 51	14	9.938 40	25	10.061 60	9.878 11	11	3
58	9.816 65	15	9.938 65	26	10.061 35	9.878 00	11	2
59	9.816 80	14	9.938 91	25	10.061 09	9.877 89	11	1
60	9.816 94		9.939 16		10.060 84	9.877 78		0

′	L Cos	d	L Cot	cd	L Tan	L Sin	d	′

Prop. Pts.

″	26	25
1	0.4	0.4
2	0.9	0.8
3	1.3	1.2
4	1.7	1.7
5	2.2	2.1
6	2.6	2.5
7	3.0	2.9
8	3.5	3.3
9	3.9	3.8
10	4.3	4.2
20	8.7	8.3
30	13.0	12.5
40	17.3	16.7
50	21.7	20.8

″	15	14
1	0.2	0.2
2	0.5	0.5
3	0.8	0.7
4	1.0	0.9
5	1.2	1.2
6	1.5	1.5
7	1.8	1.6
8	2.0	1.9
9	2.2	2.1
10	2.5	2.3
20	5.0	4.7
30	7.5	7.0
40	10.0	9.3
50	12.5	11.7

″	11	10
1	0.2	0.2
2	0.4	0.3
3	0.6	0.5
4	0.7	0.7
5	0.9	0.8
6	1.1	1.0
7	1.3	1.2
8	1.5	1.3
9	1.6	1.5
10	1.8	1.7
20	3.7	3.3
30	5.5	5.0
40	7.3	6.7
50	9.2	8.3

′	L Sin	d	L Tan	cd	L Cot	L Cos	d	′		Prop. Pts.	
0	**9.816 94**	15	**9.939 16**	26	**10.060 84**	**9.877 78**	11	60			
1	9.817 09	14	9.939 42	25	10.060 58	9.877 67	11	59			
2	9.817 23	15	9.939 67	26	10.060 33	9.877 56	11	58			
3	9.817 38	14	9.939 93	25	10.060 07	9.877 45	11	57			
4	9.817 52	15	9.940 18	26	10.059 82	9.877 34	11	56			
5	**9.817 67**	14	**9.940 44**	25	**10.059 56**	**9.877 23**	11	55			
6	9.817 81	15	9.940 69	26	10.059 31	9.877 12	11	54			
7	9.817 96	14	9.940 95	25	10.059 05	9.877 01	11	53			
8	9.818 10	15	9.941 20	26	10.058 80	9.876 90	11	52	″	**26**	**25**
9	9.818 25	14	9.941 46	25	10.058 54	9.876 79	11	51	1	0.4	0.4
10	**9.818 39**	15	**9.941 71**	26	**10.058 29**	**9.876 68**	11	50	2	0.9	0.8
11	9.818 54	14	9.941 97	25	10.058 03	9.876 57	11	49	3	1.3	1.2
12	9.818 68	14	9.942 22	26	10.057 78	9.876 46	11	48	4	1.7	1.7
13	9.818 82	15	9.942 48	25	10.057 52	9.876 35	11	47			
14	9.818 97	14	9.942 73	26	10.057 27	9.876 24	11	46	5	2.2	2.1
									6	2.6	2.5
15	**9.819 11**	15	**9.942 99**	25	**10.057 01**	**9.876 13**	12	45	7	3.0	2.9
16	9.819 26	14	9.943 24	26	10.056 76	9.876 01	11	44	8	3.5	3.3
17	9.819 40	15	9.943 50	25	10.056 50	9.875 90	11	43	9	3.9	3.8
18	9.819 55	14	9.943 75	26	10.056 25	9.875 79	11	42			
19	9.819 69	14	9.944 01	25	10.055 99	9.875 68	11	41	10	4.3	4.2
									20	8.7	8.3
20	**9.819 83**	15	**9.944 26**	26	**10.055 74**	**9.875 57**	11	40	30	13.0	12.5
21	9.819 98	14	9.944 52	25	10.055 48	9.875 46	11	39	40	17.3	16.7
22	9.820 12	14	9.944 77	26	10.055 23	9.875 35	11	38	50	21.7	20.8
23	9.820 26	15	9.945 03	25	10.054 97	9.875 24	11	37			
24	9.820 41	14	9.945 28	26	10.054 72	9.875 13	12	36	″	**15**	**14**
25	**9.820 55**	14	**9.945 54**	25	**10.054 46**	**9.875 01**	11	35	1	0.2	0.2
26	9.820 69	15	9.945 79	26	10.054 21	9.874 90	11	34	2	0.5	0.5
27	9.820 84	14	9.946 04	26	10.053 96	9.874 79	11	33	3	0.8	0.7
28	9.820 98	14	9.946 30	25	10.053 70	9.874 68	11	32	4	1.0	0.9
29	9.821 12	14	9.946 55	26	10.053 45	9.874 57	11	31			
30	**9.821 26**	15	**9.946 81**	25	**10.053 19**	**9.874 46**	12	30	5	1.2	1.2
31	9.821 41	14	9.947 06	26	10.052 94	9.874 34	11	29	6	1.5	1.4
32	9.821 55	14	9.947 32	25	10.052 68	9.874 23	11	28	7	1.8	1.6
33	9.821 69	15	9.947 57	26	10.052 43	9.874 12	11	27	8	2.0	1.9
34	9.821 84	14	9.947 83	25	10.052 17	9.874 01	11	26	9	2.2	2.1
35	**9.821 98**	14	**9.948 08**	26	**10.051 92**	**9.873 90**	12	25	10	2.5	2.3
36	9.822 12	14	9.948 34	25	10.051 66	9.873 78	11	24	20	5.0	4.7
37	9.822 26	14	9.948 59	25	10.051 41	9.873 67	11	23	30	7.5	7.0
38	9.822 40	15	9.948 84	26	10.051 16	9.873 56	11	22	40	10.0	9.3
39	9.822 55	14	9.949 10	25	10.050 90	9.873 45	11	21	50	12.5	11.7
40	**9.822 69**	14	**9.949 35**	26	**10.050 65**	**9.873 34**	12	20			
41	9.822 83	14	9.949 61	25	10.050 39	9.873 22	11	19	″	**12**	**11**
42	9.822 97	14	9.949 86	26	10.050 14	9.873 11	11	18	1	0.2	0.2
43	9.823 11	15	9.950 12	25	10.049 88	9.873 00	12	17	2	0.4	0.4
44	9.823 26	14	9.950 37	25	10.049 63	9.872 88	11	16	3	0.6	0.6
									4	0.8	0.7
45	**9.823 40**	14	**9.950 62**	26	**10.049 38**	**9.872 77**	11	15	5	1.0	0.9
46	9.823 54	14	9.950 88	25	10.049 12	9.872 66	11	14	6	1.2	1.1
47	9.823 68	14	9.951 13	26	10.048 87	9.872 55	12	13	7	1.4	1.3
48	9.823 82	14	9.951 39	25	10.048 61	9.872 43	11	12	8	1.6	1.5
49	9.823 96	14	9.951 64	26	10.048 36	9.872 32	11	11	9	1.8	1.6
50	**9.824 10**	14	**9.951 90**	25	**10.048 10**	**9.872 21**	12	10	10	2.0	1.8
51	9.824 24	15	9.952 15	25	10.047 85	9.872 09	11	9	20	4.0	3.7
52	9.824 39	14	9.952 40	26	10.047 60	9.871 98	11	8	30	6.0	5.5
53	9.824 53	14	9.952 66	25	10.047 34	9.871 87	12	7	40	8.0	7.3
54	9.824 67	14	9.952 91	26	10.047 09	9.871 75	11	6	50	10.0	9.2
55	**9.824 81**	14	**9.953 17**	25	**10.046 83**	**9.871 64**	11	5			
56	9.824 95	14	9.953 42	26	10.046 58	9.871 53	12	4			
57	9.825 09	14	9.953 68	25	10.046 32	9.871 41	11	3			
58	9.825 23	14	9.953 93	25	10.046 07	9.871 30	11	2			
59	9.825 37	14	9.954 18	26	10.045 82	9.871 19	12	1			
60	**9.825 51**		**9.954 44**		**10.045 56**	**9.871 07**		0			

| ′ | L Cos | d | L Cot | cd | L Tan | L Sin | d | ′ | | Prop. Pts. | |

Table 4 / Logarithms of trigonometric functions   □   **711**

′	L Sin	d	L Tan	cd	L Cot	L Cos	d	′		Prop. Pts.	
0	9.825 51	14	9.954 44	25	10.045 56	9.871 07	11	60			
1	9.825 65	14	9.954 69	26	10.045 31	9.870 96	11	59			
2	9.825 79	14	9.954 95	25	10.045 05	9.870 85	12	58			
3	9.825 93	14	9.955 20	25	10.044 80	9.870 73	11	57			
4	9.826 07	14	9.955 45	26	10.044 55	9.870 62	12	56			
5	9.826 21	14	9.955 71	25	10.044 29	9.870 50	11	55			
6	9.826 35	14	9.955 96	26	10.044 04	9.870 39	11	54			
7	9.826 49	14	9.956 22	25	10.043 78	9.870 28	12	53	″	26	25
8	9.826 63	14	9.956 47	25	10.043 53	9.870 16	11	52	1	0.4	0.4
9	9.826 77	14	9.956 72	26	10.043 28	9.870 05	12	51	2	0.9	0.8
									3	1.3	1.2
10	9.826 91	14	9.956 98	25	10.043 02	9.869 93	11	50	4	1.7	1.7
11	9.827 05	14	9.957 23	25	10.042 77	9.869 82	12	49			
12	9.827 19	14	9.957 48	26	10.042 52	9.869 70	11	48	5	2.2	2.1
13	9.827 33	14	9.957 74	25	10.042 26	9.869 59	12	47	6	2.6	2.5
14	9.827 47	14	9.957 99	26	10.042 01	9.869 47	11	46	7	3.0	2.9
									8	3.5	3.3
15	9.827 61	14	9.958 25	25	10.041 75	9.869 36	12	45	9	3.9	3.8
16	9.827 75	13	9.958 50	25	10.041 50	9.869 24	11	44			
17	9.827 88	14	9.958 75	26	10.041 25	9.869 13	11	43			
18	9.828 02	14	9.959 01	25	10.040 99	9.869 02	12	42	10	4.3	4.2
19	9.828 16	14	9.959 26	26	10.040 74	9.868 90	11	41	20	8.7	8.3
									30	13.0	12.5
20	9.828 30	14	9.959 52	25	10.040 48	9.868 79	12	40	40	17.3	16.7
21	9.828 44	14	9.959 77	25	10.040 23	9.868 67	12	39	50	21.7	20.8
22	9.828 58	14	9.960 02	26	10.039 98	9.868 55	11	38			
23	9.828 72	13	9.960 28	25	10.039 72	9.868 44	12	37	″	14	13
24	9.828 85	14	9.960 53	25	10.039 47	9.868 32	11	36	1	0.2	0.2
									2	0.5	0.4
25	9.828 99	14	9.960 78	26	10.039 22	9.868 21	12	35	3	0.7	0.6
26	9.829 13	14	9.961 04	25	10.038 96	9.868 09	11	34	4	0.9	0.9
27	9.829 27	14	9.961 29	26	10.038 71	9.867 98	12	33			
28	9.829 41	14	9.961 55	25	10.038 45	9.867 86	11	32	5	1.2	1.1
29	9.829 55	13	9.961 80	25	10.038 20	9.867 75	12	31	6	1.4	1.3
									7	1.6	1.5
30	9.829 68	14	9.962 05	26	10.037 95	9.867 63	11	30	8	1.9	1.7
31	9.829 82	14	9.962 31	25	10.037 69	9.867 52	12	29	9	2.1	2.0
32	9.829 96	14	9.962 56	25	10.037 44	9.867 40	12	28			
33	9.830 10	13	9.962 81	26	10.037 19	9.867 28	11	27	10	2.3	2.2
34	9.830 23	14	9.963 07	25	10.036 93	9.867 17	12	26	20	4.7	4.3
									30	7.0	6.5
35	9.830 37	14	9.963 32	25	10.036 68	9.867 05	11	25	40	9.3	8.7
36	9.830 51	14	9.963 57	26	10.036 43	9.866 94	12	24	50	11.7	10.8
37	9.830 65	13	9.963 83	25	10.036 17	9.866 82	12	23			
38	9.830 78	14	9.964 08	25	10.035 92	9.866 70	11	22	″	12	11
39	9.830 92	14	9.964 33	26	10.035 67	9.866 59	12	21	1	0.2	0.2
									2	0.4	0.4
40	9.831 06	14	9.964 59	25	10.035 41	9.866 47	12	20	3	0.6	0.6
41	9.831 20	13	9.964 84	26	10.035 16	9.866 35	11	19	4	0.8	0.7
42	9.831 33	14	9.965 10	25	10.034 90	9.866 24	12	18			
43	9.831 47	14	9.965 35	25	10.034 65	9.866 12	12	17	5	1.0	0.9
44	9.831 61	13	9.965 60	26	10.034 40	9.866 00	11	16	6	1.2	1.1
									7	1.4	1.3
45	9.831 74	14	9.965 86	25	10.034 14	9.865 89	12	15	8	1.6	1.5
46	9.831 88	14	9.966 11	25	10.033 89	9.865 77	12	14	9	1.8	1.6
47	9.832 02	13	9.966 36	26	10.033 64	9.865 65	11	13			
48	9.832 15	14	9.966 62	25	10.033 38	9.865 54	12	12	10	2.0	1.8
49	9.832 29	13	9.966 87	25	10.033 13	9.865 42	12	11	20	4.0	3.7
									30	6.0	5.5
50	9.832 42	14	9.967 12	26	10.032 88	9.865 30	12	10	40	8.0	7.3
51	9.832 56	14	9.967 38	25	10.032 62	9.865 18	11	9	50	10.0	9.2
52	9.832 70	13	9.967 63	25	10.032 37	9.865 07	12	8			
53	9.832 83	14	9.967 88	26	10.032 12	9.864 95	12	7			
54	9.832 97	13	9.968 14	25	10.031 86	9.864 83	11	6			
55	9.833 10	14	9.968 39	25	10.031 61	9.864 72	12	5			
56	9.833 24	14	9.968 64	26	10.031 36	9.864 60	12	4			
57	9.833 38	13	9.968 90	25	10.031 10	9.864 48	12	3			
58	9.833 51	14	9.969 15	25	10.030 85	9.864 36	11	2			
59	9.833 65	13	9.969 40	26	10.030 60	9.864 25	12	1			
60	9.833 78		9.969 66		10.030 34	9.864 13		0			
′	L Cos	d	L Cot	cd	L Tan	L Sin	d	′		Prop. Pts.	

′	L Sin	d	L Tan	cd	L Cot	L Cos	d	′		Prop. Pts.	
0	**9.833 78**	14	**9.969 66**	25	**10.030 34**	**9.864 13**	12	60			
1	9.833 92	13	9.969 91	25	10.030 09	9.864 01	12	59			
2	9.834 05	14	9.970 16	26	10.029 84	9.863 89	12	58			
3	9.834 19	13	9.970 42	25	10.029 58	9.863 77	11	57			
4	9.834 32	14	9.970 67	25	10.029 33	9.863 66	12	56			
5	**9.834 46**	13	**9.970 92**	26	**10.029 08**	**9.863 54**	12	55			
6	9.834 59	14	9.971 18	25	10.028 82	9.863 42	12	54			
7	9.834 73	13	9.971 43	25	10.028 57	9.863 30	12	53	″	26	25
8	9.834 86	14	9.971 68	25	10.028 32	9.863 18	12	52	1	0.4	0.4
9	9.835 00	13	9.971 93	26	10.028 07	9.863 06	11	51	2	0.9	0.8
10	**9.835 13**	14	**9.972 19**	25	**10.027 81**	**9.862 95**	12	50	3	1.3	1.2
11	9.835 27	13	9.972 44	25	10.027 56	9.862 83	12	49	4	1.7	1.7
12	9.835 40	14	9.972 69	26	10.027 31	9.862 71	12	48			
13	9.835 54	13	9.972 95	25	10.027 05	9.862 59	12	47	5	2.2	2.1
14	9.835 67	14	9.973 20	25	10.026 80	9.862 47	12	46	6	2.6	2.5
									7	3.0	2.9
15	**9.835 81**	13	**9.973 45**	26	**10.026 55**	**9.862 35**	12	45	8	3.5	3.3
16	9.835 94	14	9.973 71	25	10.026 29	9.862 23	12	44	9	3.9	3.8
17	9.836 08	13	9.973 96	25	10.026 04	9.862 11	11	43			
18	9.836 21	13	9.974 21	26	10.025 79	9.862 00	12	42	10	4.3	4.2
19	9.836 34	14	9.974 47	25	10.025 53	9.861 88	12	41	20	8.7	8.3
									30	13.0	12.5
20	**9.836 48**	13	**9.974 72**	25	**10.025 28**	**9.861 76**	12	40	40	17.3	16.7
21	9.836 61	13	9.974 97	26	10.025 03	9.861 64	12	39	50	21.7	20.8
22	9.836 74	14	9.975 23	25	10.024 77	9.861 52	12	38			
23	9.836 88	13	9.975 48	25	10.024 52	9.861 40	12	37	″	14	13
24	9.837 01	14	9.975 73	25	10.024 27	9.861 28	12	36	1	0.2	0.2
									2	0.5	0.4
25	**9.837 15**	13	**9.975 98**	26	**10.024 02**	**9.861 16**	12	35	3	0.7	0.6
26	9.837 28	13	9.976 24	25	10.023 76	9.861 04	12	34	4	0.9	0.9
27	9.837 41	14	9.976 49	25	10.023 51	9.860 92	12	33			
28	9.837 55	13	9.976 74	26	10.023 26	9.860 80	12	32	5	1.2	1.1
29	9.837 68	13	9.977 00	25	10.023 00	9.860 68	12	31	6	1.4	1.3
									7	1.6	1.5
30	**9.837 81**	14	**9.977 25**	25	**10.022 75**	**9.860 56**	12	30	8	1.9	1.7
31	9.837 95	13	9.977 50	26	10.022 50	9.860 44	12	29	9	2.1	2.0
32	9.838 08	13	9.977 76	25	10.022 24	9.860 32	12	28			
33	9.838 21	13	9.978 01	25	10.021 99	9.860 20	12	27	10	2.3	2.2
34	9.838 34	14	9.978 26	25	10.021 74	9.860 08	12	26	20	4.7	4.3
									30	7.0	6.5
35	**9.838 48**	13	**9.978 51**	26	**10.021 49**	**9.859 96**	12	25	40	9.3	8.7
36	9.838 61	13	9.978 77	25	10.021 23	9.859 84	12	24	50	11.7	10.8
37	9.838 74	13	9.979 02	25	10.020 98	9.859 72	12	23			
38	9.838 87	14	9.979 27	26	10.020 73	9.859 60	12	22	″	12	11
39	9.839 01	13	9.979 53	25	10.020 47	9.859 48	12	21	1	0.2	0.2
40	**9.839 14**	13	**9.979 78**	25	**10.020 22**	**9.859 36**	12	20	2	0.4	0.4
41	9.839 27	13	9.980 03	26	10.019 97	9.859 24	12	19	3	0.6	0.6
42	9.839 40	14	9.980 29	25	10.019 71	9.859 12	12	18	4	0.8	0.7
43	9.839 54	13	9.980 54	25	10.019 46	9.859 00	12	17			
44	9.839 67	13	9.980 79	25	10.019 21	9.858 88	12	16	5	1.0	0.9
									6	1.2	1.1
45	**9.839 80**	13	**9.981 04**	26	**10.018 96**	**9.858 76**	12	15	7	1.4	1.3
46	9.839 93	13	9.981 30	25	10.018 70	9.858 64	12	14	8	1.6	1.5
47	9.840 06	14	9.981 55	25	10.018 45	9.858 51	13	13	9	1.8	1.6
48	9.840 20	13	9.981 80	26	10.018 20	9.858 39	12	12			
49	9.840 33	13	9.982 06	25	10.017 94	9.858 27	12	11	10	2.0	1.8
									20	4.0	3.7
50	**9.840 46**	13	**9.982 31**	25	**10.017 69**	**9.858 15**	12	10	30	6.0	5.5
51	9.840 59	13	9.982 56	25	10.017 44	9.858 03	12	9	40	8.0	7.3
52	9.840 72	13	9.982 81	26	10.017 19	9.857 91	12	8	50	10.0	9.2
53	9.840 85	13	9.983 07	25	10.016 93	9.857 79	13	7			
54	9.840 98	14	9.983 32	25	10.016 68	9.857 66	12	6			
55	**9.841 12**	13	**9.983 57**	26	**10.016 43**	**9.857 54**	12	5			
56	9.841 25	13	9.983 83	25	10.016 17	9.857 42	12	4			
57	9.841 38	13	9.984 08	25	10.015 92	9.857 30	12	3			
58	9.841 51	13	9.984 33	25	10.015 67	9.857 18	12	2			
59	9.841 64	13	9.984 58	26	10.015 42	9.857 06	13	1			
60	**9.841 77**		**9.984 84**		**10.015 16**	**9.856 93**		0			

′	L Cos	d	L Cot	cd	L Tan	L Sin	d	′	Prop. Pts.

Table 4 / *Logarithms of trigonometric functions*   □   **713**

'	L Sin	d	L Tan	cd	L Cot	L Cos	d	'	Prop. Pts.
0	**9.841 77**	13	**9.984 84**	25	**10.015 16**	**9.856 93**	12	60	
1	9.841 90	13	9.985 09	25	10.014 91	9.856 81	12	59	
2	9.842 03	13	9.985 34	26	10.014 66	9.856 69	12	58	
3	9.842 16	13	9.985 60	25	10.014 40	9.856 57	12	57	
4	9.842 29	13	9.985 85	25	10.014 15	9.856 45	13	56	
5	**9.842 42**	13	**9.986 10**	25	**10.013 90**	**9.856 32**	12	55	
6	9.842 55	14	9.986 35	26	10.013 65	9.856 20	12	54	
7	9.842 69	13	9.986 61	25	10.013 39	9.856 08	13	53	
8	9.842 82	13	9.986 86	25	10.013 14	9.855 96	13	52	
9	9.842 95	14	9.987 11	26	10.012 89	9.855 83	12	51	
10	**9.843 08**	13	**9.987 37**	25	**10.012 63**	**9.855 71**	12	50	
11	9.843 21	13	9.987 62	25	10.012 38	9.855 59	12	49	
12	9.843 34	13	9.987 87	25	10.012 13	9.855 47	13	48	
13	9.843 47	13	9.988 12	26	10.011 88	9.855 34	12	47	
14	9.843 60	13	9.988 38	25	10.011 62	9.855 22	12	46	
15	**9.843 73**	12	**9.988 63**	25	**10.011 37**	**9.855 10**	13	45	" 26 25
16	9.843 85	13	9.988 88	25	10.011 12	9.854 97	12	44	1 0.4 0.4
17	9.843 98	13	9.989 13	26	10.010 87	9.854 85	12	43	2 0.9 0.8
18	9.844 11	13	9.989 39	25	10.010 61	9.854 73	13	42	3 1.3 1.2
19	9.844 24	13	9.989 64	25	10.010 36	9.854 60	12	41	4 1.7 1.7
20	**9.844 37**	13	**9.989 89**	26	**10.010 11**	**9.854 48**	12	40	5 2.2 2.1
21	9.844 50	13	9.990 15	25	10.009 85	9.854 36	13	39	6 2.6 2.5
22	9.844 63	13	9.990 40	25	10.009 60	9.854 23	12	38	7 3.0 2.9
23	9.844 76	13	9.990 65	25	10.009 35	9.854 11	12	37	8 3.5 3.3
24	9.844 89	13	9.990 90	26	10.009 10	9.853 99	13	36	9 3.9 3.8
25	**9.845 02**	13	**9.991 16**	25	**10.008 84**	**9.853 86**	12	35	10 4.3 4.2
26	9.845 15	13	9.991 41	25	10.008 59	9.853 74	13	34	20 8.7 8.3
27	9.845 28	12	9.991 66	25	10.008 34	9.853 61	13	33	30 13.0 12.5
28	9.845 40	13	9.991 91	26	10.008 09	9.853 49	12	32	40 17.3 16.7
29	9.845 43	13	9.992 17	25	10.007 83	9.853 37	13	31	50 21.7 20.8
30	**9.845 66**	13	**9.992 42**	25	**10.007 58**	**9.853 24**	12	30	" 14 13 12
31	9.845 79	13	9.992 67	26	10.007 33	9.853 12	13	29	1 0.2 0.2 0.2
32	9.845 92	13	9.992 93	25	10.007 07	9.852 99	13	28	2 0.5 0.4 0.4
33	9.846 05	13	9.993 18	25	10.006 82	9.852 87	13	27	3 0.7 0.6 0.6
34	9.846 18	12	9.993 43	25	10.006 57	9.852 74	12	26	4 0.9 0.9 0.8
35	**9.846 30**	13	**9.993 68**	26	**10.006 32**	**9.852 62**	12	25	5 1.2 1.1 1.0
36	9.846 43	13	9.993 94	25	10.006 06	9.852 50	13	24	6 1.4 1.3 1.2
37	9.846 56	13	9.994 19	25	10.005 81	9.852 37	12	23	7 1.6 1.5 1.4
38	9.846 69	13	9.994 44	25	10.005 56	9.852 25	13	22	8 1.9 1.7 1.6
39	9.846 82	12	9.994 69	26	10.005 31	9.852 12	12	21	9 2.1 2.0 1.8
40	**9.846 94**	13	**9.994 95**	25	**10.005 05**	**9.852 00**	13	20	10 2.3 2.2 2.0
41	9.847 07	13	9.995 20	25	10.004 80	9.851 87	12	19	20 4.7 4.3 4.0
42	9.847 20	13	9.995 45	25	10.004 55	9.851 75	13	18	30 7.0 6.5 6.0
43	9.847 33	12	9.995 70	26	10.004 30	9.851 62	12	17	40 9.3 8.7 8.0
44	9.847 45	13	9.995 96	25	10.004 04	9.851 50	13	16	50 11.7 10.8 10.0
45	**9.847 58**	13	**9.996 21**	25	**10.003 79**	**9.851 37**	12	15	
46	9.847 71	13	9.996 46	26	10.003 54	9.851 25	13	14	
47	9.847 84	12	9.996 72	25	10.003 28	9.851 12	12	13	
48	9.847 96	13	9.996 97	25	10.003 03	9.851 00	13	12	
49	9.848 09	13	9.997 22	25	10.002 78	9.850 87	13	11	
50	**9.848 22**	13	**9.997 47**	26	**10.002 53**	**9.850 74**	12	10	
51	9.848 35	12	9.997 73	25	10.002 27	9.850 62	13	9	
52	9.848 47	13	9.997 98	25	10.002 02	9.850 49	12	8	
53	9.848 60	13	9.998 23	25	10.001 77	9.850 37	13	7	
54	9.848 73	12	9.998 48	26	10.001 52	9.850 24	12	6	
55	**9.848 85**	13	**9.998 74**	25	**10.001 26**	**9.850 12**	13	5	
56	9.848 98	13	9.998 99	25	10.001 01	9.849 99	13	4	
57	9.849 11	12	9.999 24	25	10.000 76	9.849 86	12	3	
58	9.849 23	13	9.999 49	26	10.000 51	9.849 74	13	2	
59	9.849 36	13	9.999 75	25	10.000 25	9.849 61	12	1	
60	**9.849 49**		**10.000 00**		**10.000 00**	**9.849 49**		0	
'	L Cos	d	L Cot	cd	L Tan	L Sin	d	'	Prop. Pts.

TABLE 5
Five-Place Natural Trigonometric Functions; Angles in Degrees and Decimals
(Five-place decitrig functions)

θ°	Sin	Tan	Cot	Cos		θ°	Sin	Tan	Cot	Cos	
0.0	0.000 00	0.000 00	—	1.000 00	90.0	6.0	0.104 53	0.105 10	9.514 4	0.994 52	84.0
0.1	0.001 75	0.001 75	572.96	1.000 00	89.9	6.1	0.106 26	0.106 87	9.357 2	0.994 34	83.9
0.2	0.003 49	0.003 49	286.48	0.999 99	89.8	6.2	0.108 00	0.108 63	9.205 2	0.994 15	83.8
0.3	0.005 24	0.005 24	190.98	0.999 99	89.7	6.3	0.109 73	0.110 40	9.057 9	0.993 96	83.7
0.4	0.006 98	0.006 98	143.24	0.999 98	89.6	6.4	0.111 47	0.112 17	8.915 2	0.993 77	83.6
0.5	0.008 73	0.008 73	114.59	0.999 96	89.5	6.5	0.113 20	0.113 94	8.776 9	0.993 57	83.5
0.6	0.010 47	0.010 47	95.489	0.999 95	89.4	6.6	0.114 94	0.115 70	8.642 7	0.993 37	83.4
0.7	0.012 22	0.012 22	81.847	0.999 93	89.3	6.7	0.116 67	0.117 47	8.512 6	0.993 17	83.3
0.8	0.013 96	0.013 96	71.615	0.999 90	89.2	6.8	0.118 40	0.119 24	8.386 3	0.992 97	83.2
0.9	0.015 71	0.015 71	63.657	0.999 88	89.1	6.9	0.120 14	0.121 01	8.263 6	0.992 76	83.1
1.0	0.017 45	0.017 46	57.290	0.999 85	89.0	7.0	0.121 87	0.122 78	8.144 3	0.992 55	83.0
1.1	0.019 20	0.019 20	52.081	0.999 82	88.9	7.1	0.123 60	0.124 56	8.028 5	0.992 33	82.9
1.2	0.020 94	0.020 95	47.740	0.999 78	88.8	7.2	0.125 33	0.126 33	7.915 8	0.992 11	82.8
1.3	0.022 69	0.022 69	44.066	0.999 74	88.7	7.3	0.127 06	0.128 10	7.806 2	0.991 89	82.7
1.4	0.024 43	0.024 44	40.917	0.999 70	88.6	7.4	0.128 80	0.129 88	7.699 6	0.991 67	82.6
1.5	0.026 18	0.026 19	38.188	0.999 66	88.5	7.5	0.130 53	0.131 65	7.595 8	0.991 44	82.5
1.6	0.027 92	0.027 93	35.801	0.999 61	88.4	7.6	0.132 26	0.133 43	7.494 7	0.991 22	82.4
1.7	0.029 67	0.029 68	33.694	0.999 56	88.3	7.7	0.133 99	0.135 21	7.396 2	0.990 98	82.3
1.8	0.031 41	0.031 43	31.821	0.999 51	88.2	7.8	0.135 72	0.136 98	7.300 2	0.990 75	82.2
1.9	0.033 16	0.033 17	30.145	0.999 45	88.1	7.9	0.137 44	0.138 76	7.206 6	0.990 51	82.1
2.0	0.034 90	0.034 92	28.636	0.999 39	88.0	8.0	0.139 17	0.140 54	7.115 4	0.990 27	82.0
2.1	0.036 64	0.036 67	27.271	0.999 33	87.9	8.1	0.140 90	0.142 32	7.026 4	0.990 02	81.9
2.2	0.038 39	0.038 42	26.031	0.999 26	87.8	8.2	0.142 63	0.144 10	6.939 5	0.989 78	81.8
2.3	0.040 13	0.040 16	24.898	0.999 19	87.7	8.3	0.144 36	0.145 88	6.854 8	0.989 53	81.7
2.4	0.041 88	0.041 91	23.859	0.999 12	87.6	8.4	0.146 08	0.147 67	6.772 0	0.989 27	81.6
2.5	0.043 62	0.043 66	22.904	0.999 05	87.5	8.5	0.147 81	0.149 45	6.691 2	0.989 02	81.5
2.6	0.045 36	0.045 41	22.022	0.998 97	87.4	8.6	0.149 54	0.151 24	6.612 2	0.988 76	81.4
2.7	0.047 11	0.047 16	21.205	0.998 89	87.3	8.7	0.151 26	0.153 02	6.535 0	0.988 49	81.3
2.8	0.048 85	0.048 91	20.446	0.998 81	87.2	8.8	0.152 99	0.154 81	6.459 6	0.988 23	81.2
2.9	0.050 59	0.050 66	19.740	0.998 72	87.1	8.9	0.154 71	0.156 60	6.385 9	0.987 96	81.1
3.0	0.052 34	0.052 41	19.081	0.998 63	87.0	9.0	0.156 43	0.158 38	6.313 8	0.987 69	81.0
3.1	0.054 08	0.054 16	18.464	0.998 54	86.9	9.1	0.158 16	0.160 17	6.243 2	0.987 41	80.9
3.2	0.055 82	0.055 91	17.886	0.998 44	86.8	9.2	0.159 88	0.161 96	6.174 2	0.987 14	80.8
3.3	0.057 56	0.057 66	17.343	0.998 34	86.7	9.3	0.161 60	0.163 76	6.106 6	0.986 86	80.7
3.4	0.059 31	0.059 41	16.832	0.998 24	86.6	9.4	0.163 33	0.165 55	6.040 5	0.986 57	80.6
3.5	0.061 05	0.061 16	16.350	0.998 13	86.5	9.5	0.165 05	0.167 34	5.975 8	0.986 29	80.5
3.6	0.062 79	0.062 91	15.895	0.998 03	86.4	9.6	0.166 77	0.169 14	5.912 4	0.986 00	80.4
3.7	0.064 53	0.064 67	15.464	0.997 92	86.3	9.7	0.168 49	0.170 93	5.850 2	0.985 70	80.3
3.8	0.066 27	0.066 42	15.056	0.997 80	86.2	9.8	0.170 21	0.172 73	5.789 4	0.985 41	80.2
3.9	0.068 02	0.068 17	14.669	0.997 68	86.1	9.9	0.171 93	0.174 53	5.729 7	0.985 11	80.1
4.0	0.069 76	0.069 93	14.301	0.997 56	86.0	10.0	0.173 65	0.176 33	5.671 3	0.984 81	80.0
4.1	0.071 50	0.071 68	13.951	0.997 44	85.9	10.1	0.175 37	0.178 13	5.614 0	0.984 50	79.9
4.2	0.073 24	0.073 44	13.617	0.997 31	85.8	10.2	0.177 08	0.179 93	5.557 8	0.984 20	79.8
4.3	0.074 98	0.075 19	13.300	0.997 19	85.7	10.3	0.178 80	0.181 73	5.502 6	0.983 89	79.7
4.4	0.076 72	0.076 95	12.996	0.997 05	85.6	10.4	0.180 52	0.183 53	5.448 6	0.983 57	79.6
4.5	0.078 46	0.078 70	12.706	0.996 92	85.5	10.5	0.182 24	0.185 34	5.395 5	0.983 25	79.5
4.6	0.080 20	0.080 46	12.429	0.996 78	85.4	10.6	0.183 95	0.187 14	5.343 5	0.982 94	79.4
4.7	0.081 94	0.082 21	12.163	0.996 64	85.3	10.7	0.185 67	0.188 95	5.292 4	0.982 61	79.3
4.8	0.083 68	0.083 97	11.909	0.996 49	85.2	10.8	0.187 38	0.190 76	5.242 2	0.982 29	79.2
4.9	0.085 42	0.085 73	11.664	0.996 35	85.1	10.9	0.189 10	0.192 57	5.192 9	0.981 96	79.1
5.0	0.087 16	0.087 49	11.430	0.996 19	85.0	11.0	0.190 81	0.194 38	5.144 6	0.981 63	79.0
5.1	0.088 89	0.089 25	11.205	0.996 04	84.9	11.1	0.192 52	0.196 19	5.097 0	0.981 29	78.9
5.2	0.090 63	0.091 01	10.988	0.995 88	84.8	11.2	0.194 23	0.198 01	5.050 4	0.980 96	78.8
5.3	0.092 37	0.092 77	10.780	0.995 72	84.7	11.3	0.195 95	0.199 82	5.004 5	0.980 61	78.7
5.4	0.094 11	0.094 53	10.579	0.995 56	84.6	11.4	0.197 66	0.201 64	4.959 4	0.980 27	78.6
5.5	0.095 85	0.096 29	10.385	0.995 40	84.5	11.5	0.199 37	0.203 45	4.915 2	0.979 92	78.5
5.6	0.097 58	0.098 05	10.199	0.995 23	84.4	11.6	0.201 08	0.205 27	4.871 6	0.979 58	78.4
5.7	0.099 32	0.099 81	10.019	0.995 06	84.3	11.7	0.202 79	0.207 09	4.828 8	0.979 22	78.3
5.8	0.101 06	0.101 58	9.844 8	0.994 88	84.2	11.8	0.204 50	0.208 91	4.786 7	0.978 87	78.2
5.9	0.102 79	0.103 34	9.676 8	0.994 70	84.1	11.9	0.206 20	0.210 73	4.745 3	0.978 51	78.1
6.0	0.104 53	0.105 10	9.514 4	0.994 52	84.0	12.0	0.207 91	0.212 56	4.704 6	0.978 15	78.0
	Cos	Cot	Tan	Sin	θ°		Cos	Cot	Tan	Sin	θ°

715

$\theta°$	Sin	Tan	Cot	Cos		$\theta°$	Sin	Tan	Cot	Cos	
12.0	**0.207 91**	**0.212 56**	**4.704 6**	**0.978 15**	**78.0**	**18.0**	**0.309 02**	**0.324 92**	**3.077 7**	**0.951 06**	**72.0**
12.1	0.209 62	0.214 38	4.664 6	0.977 78	77.9	18.1	0.310 68	0.326 85	3.059 5	0.950 52	71.9
12.2	0.211 32	0.216 21	4.625 2	0.977 42	77.8	18.2	0.312 33	0.328 78	3.041 5	0.949 97	71.8
12.3	0.213 03	0.218 04	4.586 4	0.977 05	77.7	18.3	0.313 99	0.330 72	3.023 7	0.949 43	71.7
12.4	0.214 74	0.219 86	4.548 3	0.976 67	77.6	18.4	0.315 65	0.332 66	3.006 1	0.948 88	71.6
12.5	**0.216 44**	**0.221 69**	**4.510 7**	**0.976 30**	**77.5**	**18.5**	**0.317 30**	**0.334 60**	**2.988 7**	**0.948 32**	**71.5**
12.6	0.218 14	0.223 53	4.473 7	0.975 92	77.4	18.6	0.318 96	0.336 54	2.971 4	0.947 77	71.4
12.7	0.219 85	0.225 36	4.437 3	0.975 53	77.3	18.7	0.320 61	0.338 48	2.954 4	0.947 21	71.3
12.8	0.221 55	0.227 19	4.401 5	0.975 15	77.2	18.8	0.322 27	0.340 43	2.937 5	0.946 65	71.2
12.9	0.223 25	0.229 03	4.366 2	0.974 76	77.1	18.9	0.323 92	0.342 38	2.920 8	0.946 09	71.1
13.0	**0.224 95**	**0.230 87**	**4.331 5**	**0.974 37**	**77.0**	**19.0**	**0.325 57**	**0.344 33**	**2.904 2**	**0.945 52**	**71.0**
13.1	0.226 65	0.232 71	4.297 2	0.973 98	76.9	19.1	0.327 22	0.346 28	2.887 8	0.944 95	70.9
13.2	0.228 35	0.234 55	4.263 5	0.973 58	76.8	19.2	0.328 87	0.348 24	2.871 6	0.944 38	70.8
13.3	0.230 05	0.236 39	4.230 3	0.973 18	76.7	19.3	0.330 51	0.350 20	2.855 6	0.943 80	70.7
13.4	0.231 75	0.238 23	4.197 6	0.972 78	76.6	19.4	0.332 16	0.352 16	2.839 7	0.943 22	70.6
13.5	**0.233 45**	**0.240 08**	**4.165 3**	**0.972 37**	**76.5**	**19.5**	**0.333 81**	**0.354 12**	**2.823 9**	**0.942 64**	**70.5**
13.6	0.235 14	0.241 93	4.133 5	0.971 96	76.4	19.6	0.335 45	0.356 08	2.808 3	0.942 06	70.4
13.7	0.236 84	0.243 77	4.102 2	0.971 55	76.3	19.7	0.337 10	0.358 05	2.792 9	0.941 47	70.3
13.8	0.238 53	0.245 62	4.071 3	0.971 13	76.2	19.8	0.338 74	0.360 02	2.777 6	0.940 88	70.2
13.9	0.240 23	0.247 47	4.040 8	0.970 72	76.1	19.9	0.340 38	0.361 99	2.762 5	0.940 29	70.1
14.0	**0.241 92**	**0.249 33**	**4.010 8**	**0.970 30**	**76.0**	**20.0**	**0.342 02**	**0.363 97**	**2.747 5**	**0.939 69**	**70.0**
14.1	0.243 62	0.251 18	3.981 2	0.969 87	75.9	20.1	0.343 66	0.365 95	2.732 6	0.939 09	69.9
14.2	0.245 31	0.253 04	3.952 0	0.969 45	75.8	20.2	0.345 30	0.367 93	2.717 9	0.938 49	69.8
14.3	0.247 00	0.254 90	3.923 2	0.969 02	75.7	20.3	0.346 94	0.369 91	2.703 4	0.937 89	69.7
14.4	0.248 69	0.256 76	3.894 7	0.968 58	75.6	20.4	0.348 57	0.371 90	2.688 9	0.937 28	69.6
14.5	**0.250 38**	**0.258 62**	**3.866 7**	**0.968 15**	**75.5**	**20.5**	**0.350 21**	**0.373 88**	**2.674 6**	**0.936 67**	**69.5**
14.6	0.252 07	0.260 48	3.839 1	0.967 71	75.4	20.6	0.351 84	0.375 88	2.660 5	0.936 06	69.4
14.7	0.253 76	0.262 35	3.811 8	0.967 27	75.3	20.7	0.353 47	0.377 87	2.646 4	0.935 44	69.3
14.8	0.255 45	0.264 21	3.784 8	0.966 82	75.2	20.8	0.355 11	0.379 86	2.632 5	0.934 83	69.2
14.9	0.257 13	0.266 08	3.758 3	0.966 38	75.1	20.9	0.356 74	0.381 86	2.618 7	0.934 20	69.1
15.0	**0.258 82**	**0.267 95**	**3.732 1**	**0.965 93**	**75.0**	**21.0**	**0.358 37**	**0.383 86**	**2.605 1**	**0.933 58**	**69.0**
15.1	0.260 50	0.269 82	3.706 2	0.965 47	74.9	21.1	0.360 00	0.385 87	2.591 6	0.932 95	68.9
15.2	0.262 19	0.271 69	3.680 6	0.965 02	74.8	21.2	0.361 62	0.387 87	2.578 2	0.932 32	68.8
15.3	0.263 87	0.273 57	3.655 4	0.964 56	74.7	21.3	0.363 25	0.389 88	2.564 9	0.931 69	68.7
15.4	0.265 56	0.275 45	3.630 5	0.964 10	74.6	21.4	0.364 88	0.391 90	2.551 7	0.931 06	68.6
15.5	**0.267 24**	**0.277 32**	**3.605 9**	**0.963 63**	**74.5**	**21.5**	**0.366 50**	**0.393 91**	**2.538 6**	**0.930 42**	**68.5**
15.6	0.268 92	0.279 21	3.581 6	0.963 16	74.4	21.6	0.368 12	0.395 93	2.525 7	0.929 78	68.4
15.7	0.270 60	0.281 09	3.557 6	0.962 69	74.3	21.7	0.369 75	0.397 95	2.512 9	0.929 13	68.3
15.8	0.272 28	0.282 97	3.533 9	0.962 22	74.2	21.8	0.371 37	0.399 97	2.500 2	0.928 49	68.2
15.9	0.273 96	0.284 86	3.510 5	0.961 74	74.1	21.9	0.372 99	0.402 00	2.487 6	0.927 84	68.1
16.0	**0.275 64**	**0.286 75**	**3.487 4**	**0.961 26**	**74.0**	**22.0**	**0.374 61**	**0.404 03**	**2.475 1**	**0.927 18**	**68.0**
16.1	0.277 31	0.288 64	3.464 6	0.960 78	73.9	22.1	0.376 22	0.406 06	2.462 7	0.926 53	67.9
16.2	0.278 99	0.290 53	3.442 0	0.960 29	73.8	22.2	0.377 84	0.408 09	2.450 4	0.925 87	67.8
16.3	0.280 67	0.292 42	3.419 7	0.959 81	73.7	22.3	0.379 46	0.410 13	2.438 3	0.925 21	67.7
16.4	0.282 34	0.294 32	3.397 7	0.959 31	73.6	22.4	0.381 07	0.412 17	2.426 2	0.924 55	67.6
16.5	**0.284 02**	**0.296 21**	**3.375 9**	**0.958 82**	**73.5**	**22.5**	**0.382 68**	**0.414 21**	**2.414 2**	**0.923 88**	**67.5**
16.6	0.285 69	0.298 11	3.354 4	0.958 32	73.4	22.6	0.384 30	0.416 26	2.402 3	0.923 21	67.4
16.7	0.287 36	0.300 01	3.333 2	0.957 82	73.3	22.7	0.385 91	0.418 31	2.390 6	0.922 54	67.3
16.8	0.289 03	0.301 92	3.312 2	0.957 32	73.2	22.8	0.387 52	0.420 36	2.378 9	0.921 86	67.2
16.9	0.290 70	0.303 82	3.291 4	0.956 81	73.1	22.9	0.389 12	0.422 42	2.367 3	0.921 19	67.1
17.0	**0.292 37**	**0.305 73**	**3.270 9**	**0.956 30**	**73.0**	**23.0**	**0.390 73**	**0.424 47**	**2.355 9**	**0.920 50**	**67.0**
17.1	0.294 04	0.307 64	3.250 6	0.955 79	72.9	23.1	0.392 34	0.426 54	2.344 5	0.919 82	66.9
17.2	0.295 71	0.309 55	3.230 5	0.955 28	72.8	23.2	0.393 94	0.428 60	2.333 2	0.919 14	66.8
17.3	0.297 37	0.311 47	3.210 6	0.954 76	72.7	23.3	0.395 55	0.430 67	2.322 0	0.918 45	66.7
17.4	0.299 04	0.313 38	3.191 0	0.954 24	72.6	23.4	0.397 15	0.432 74	2.310 9	0.917 75	66.6
17.5	**0.300 71**	**0.315 30**	**3.171 6**	**0.953 72**	**72.5**	**23.5**	**0.398 75**	**0.434 81**	**2.299 8**	**0.917 06**	**66.5**
17.6	0.302 37	0.317 22	3.152 4	0.953 19	72.4	23.6	0.400 35	0.436 89	2.288 9	0.916 36	66.4
17.7	0.304 03	0.319 14	3.133 4	0.952 66	72.3	23.7	0.401 95	0.438 97	2.278 1	0.915 66	66.3
17.8	0.305 70	0.321 06	3.114 6	0.952 13	72.2	23.8	0.403 55	0.441 05	2.267 3	0.914 96	66.2
17.9	0.307 36	0.322 99	3.096 1	0.951 59	72.1	23.9	0.405 14	0.443 14	2.256 6	0.914 25	66.1
18.0	**0.309 02**	**0.324 92**	**3.077 7**	**0.951 06**	**72.0**	**24.0**	**0.406 74**	**0.445 23**	**2.246 0**	**0.913 55**	**66.0**
	Cos	Cot	Tan	Sin	$\theta°$		Cos	Cot	Tan	Sin	$\theta°$

θ°	Sin	Tan	Cot	Cos		θ°	Sin	Tan	Cot	Cos	
24.0	**0.406 74**	**0.445 23**	**2.246 0**	**0.913 55**	**66.0**	**30.0**	**0.500 00**	**0.577 35**	**1.732 1**	**0.866 03**	**60.0**
24.1	0.408 33	0.447 32	2.235 5	0.912 83	65.9	30.1	0.501 51	0.579 68	1.725 1	0.865 15	59.9
24.2	0.409 92	0.449 42	2.225 1	0.912 12	65.8	30.2	0.503 02	0.582 01	1.718 2	0.864 27	59.8
24.3	0.411 51	0.451 52	2.214 8	0.911 40	65.7	30.3	0.504 53	0.584 35	1.711 3	0.863 40	59.7
24.4	0.413 10	0.453 62	2.204 5	0.910 68	65.6	30.4	0.506 03	0.586 70	1.704 5	0.862 51	59.6
24.5	**0.414 69**	**0.455 73**	**2.194 3**	**0.909 96**	**65.5**	**30.5**	**0.507 54**	**0.589 05**	**1.697 7**	**0.861 63**	**59.5**
24.6	0.416 28	0.457 84	2.184 2	0.909 24	65.4	30.6	0.509 04	0.591 40	1.690 9	0.860 74	59.4
24.7	0.417 87	0.459 95	2.174 2	0.908 51	65.3	30.7	0.510 54	0.593 76	1.684 2	0.859 85	59.3
24.8	0.419 45	0.462 06	2.164 2	0.907 78	65.2	30.8	0.512 04	0.596 12	1.677 5	0.858 96	59.2
24.9	0.421 04	0.464 18	2.154 3	0.907 04	65.1	30.9	0.513 54	0.598 49	1.670 9	0.858 06	59.1
25.0	**0.422 62**	**0.466 31**	**2.144 5**	**0.906 31**	**65.0**	**31.0**	**0.515 04**	**0.600 86**	**1.664 3**	**0.857 17**	**59.0**
25.1	0.424 20	0.468 43	2.134 8	0.905 57	64.9	31.1	0.516 53	0.603 24	1.657 7	0.856 27	58.9
25.2	0.425 78	0.470 56	2.125 1	0.904 83	64.8	31.2	0.518 03	0.605 62	1.651 2	0.855 36	58.8
25.3	0.427 36	0.472 70	2.115 5	0.904 08	64.7	31.3	0.519 52	0.608 01	1.644 7	0.854 46	58.7
25.4	0.428 94	0.474 83	2.106 0	0.903 34	64.6	31.4	0.521 01	0.610 40	1.638 3	0.853 55	58.6
25.5	**0.430 51**	**0.476 98**	**2.096 5**	**0.902 59**	**64.5**	**31.5**	**0.522 50**	**0.612 80**	**1.631 9**	**0.852 64**	**58.5**
25.6	0.432 09	0.479 12	2.087 2	0.901 83	64.4	31.6	0.523 99	0.615 20	1.625 5	0.851 73	58.4
25.7	0.433 66	0.481 27	2.077 8	0.901 08	64.3	31.7	0.525 47	0.617 61	1.619 1	0.850 81	58.3
25.8	0.435 23	0.483 42	2.068 6	0.900 32	64.2	31.8	0.526 96	0.620 03	1.612 8	0.849 89	58.2
25.9	0.436 80	0.485 57	2.059 4	0.899 56	64.1	31.9	0.528 44	0.622 45	1.606 6	0.848 97	58.1
26.0	**0.438 37**	**0.487 73**	**2.050 3**	**0.898 79**	**64.0**	**32.0**	**0.529 92**	**0.624 87**	**1.600 3**	**0.848 05**	**58.0**
26.1	0.439 94	0.489 89	2.041 3	0.898 03	63.9	32.1	0.531 40	0.627 30	1.594 1	0.847 12	57.9
26.2	0.441 51	0.492 06	2.032 3	0.897 26	63.8	32.2	0.532 88	0.629 73	1.588 0	0.846 19	57.8
26.3	0.443 07	0.494 23	2.023 3	0.896 49	63.7	32.3	0.534 35	0.632 17	1.581 8	0.845 26	57.7
26.4	0.444 64	0.496 40	2.014 5	0.895 71	63.6	32.4	0.535 83	0.634 62	1.575 7	0.844 33	57.6
26.5	**0.446 20**	**0.498 58**	**2.005 7**	**0.894 93**	**63.5**	**32.5**	**0.537 30**	**0.637 07**	**1.569 7**	**0.843 39**	**57.5**
26.6	0.447 76	0.500 76	1.997 0	0.894 15	63.4	32.6	0.538 77	0.639 53	1.563 7	0.842 45	57.4
26.7	0.449 32	0.502 95	1.988 3	0.893 37	63.3	32.7	0.540 24	0.641 99	1.557 7	0.841 51	57.3
26.8	0.450 88	0.505 14	1.979 7	0.892 59	63.2	32.8	0.541 71	0.644 46	1.551 7	0.840 57	57.2
26.9	0.452 43	0.507 33	1.971 1	0.891 80	63.1	32.9	0.543 17	0.646 93	1.545 8	0.839 62	57.1
27.0	**0.453 99**	**0.509 53**	**1.962 6**	**0.891 01**	**63.0**	**33.0**	**0.544 64**	**0.649 41**	**1.539 9**	**0.838 67**	**57.0**
27.1	0.455 54	0.511 73	1.954 2	0.890 21	62.9	33.1	0.546 10	0.651 89	1.534 0	0.837 72	56.9
27.2	0.457 10	0.513 93	1.945 8	0.889 42	62.8	33.2	0.547 56	0.654 38	1.528 2	0.836 76	56.8
27.3	0.458 65	0.516 14	1.937 5	0.888 62	62.7	33.3	0.549 02	0.656 88	1.522 4	0.835 81	56.7
27.4	0.460 20	0.518 35	1.929 2	0.887 82	62.6	33.4	0.550 48	0.659 38	1.516 6	0.834 85	56.6
27.5	**0.461 75**	**0.520 57**	**1.921 0**	**0.887 01**	**62.5**	**33.5**	**0.551 94**	**0.661 89**	**1.510 8**	**0.833 89**	**56.5**
27.6	0.463 30	0.522 79	1.912 8	0.886 20	62.4	33.6	0.553 39	0.664 40	1.505 1	0.832 92	56.4
27.7	0.464 84	0.525 01	1.904 7	0.885 39	62.3	33.7	0.554 84	0.666 92	1.499 4	0.831 95	56.3
27.8	0.466 39	0.527 24	1.896 7	0.884 58	62.2	33.8	0.556 30	0.669 44	1.493 8	0.830 98	56.2
27.9	0.467 93	0.529 47	1.888 7	0.883 77	62.1	33.9	0.557 75	0.671 97	1.488 2	0.830 01	56.1
28.0	**0.469 47**	**0.531 71**	**1.880 7**	**0.882 95**	**62.0**	**34.0**	**0.559 19**	**0.674 51**	**1.482 6**	**0.829 04**	**56.0**
28.1	0.471 01	0.533 95	1.872 8	0.882 13	61.9	34.1	0.560 64	0.677 05	1.477 0	0.828 06	55.9
28.2	0.472 55	0.536 20	1.865 0	0.881 30	61.8	34.2	0.562 08	0.679 60	1.471 5	0.827 08	55.8
28.3	0.474 09	0.538 44	1.857 2	0.880 48	61.7	34.3	0.563 53	0.682 15	1.465 9	0.826 10	55.7
28.4	0.475 62	0.540 70	1.849 5	0.879 65	61.6	34.4	0.564 97	0.684 71	1.460 5	0.825 11	55.6
28.5	**0.477 16**	**0.542 96**	**1.841 8**	**0.878 82**	**61.5**	**34.5**	**0.566 41**	**0.687 28**	**1.455 0**	**0.824 13**	**55.5**
28.6	0.478 69	0.545 22	1.834 1	0.877 98	61.4	34.6	0.567 84	0.689 85	1.449 6	0.823 14	55.4
28.7	0.480 22	0.547 48	1.826 5	0.877 15	61.3	34.7	0.569 28	0.692 43	1.444 2	0.822 14	55.3
28.8	0.481 75	0.549 75	1.819 0	0.876 31	61.2	34.8	0.570 71	0.695 02	1.438 8	0.821 15	55.2
28.9	0.483 28	0.552 03	1.811 5	0.875 46	61.1	34.9	0.572 15	0.697 61	1.433 5	0.820 15	55.1
29.0	**0.484 81**	**0.554 31**	**1.804 0**	**0.874 62**	**61.0**	**35.0**	**0.573 58**	**0.700 21**	**1.428 1**	**0.819 15**	**55.0**
29.1	0.486 34	0.556 59	1.796 6	0.873 77	60.9	35.1	0.575 01	0.702 81	1.422 9	0.818 15	54.9
29.2	0.487 86	0.558 88	1.789 3	0.872 92	60.8	35.2	0.576 43	0.705 42	1.417 6	0.817 14	54.8
29.3	0.489 38	0.561 17	1.782 0	0.872 07	60.7	35.3	0.577 86	0.708 04	1.412 4	0.816 14	54.7
29.4	0.490 90	0.563 47	1.774 7	0.871 21	60.6	35.4	0.579 28	0.710 66	1.407 1	0.815 13	54.6
29.5	**0.492 42**	**0.565 77**	**1.767 5**	**0.870 36**	**60.5**	**35.5**	**0.580 70**	**0.713 29**	**1.401 9**	**0.814 12**	**54.5**
29.6	0.493 94	0.568 08	1.760 3	0.869 49	60.4	35.6	0.582 12	0.715 93	1.396 8	0.813 10	54.4
29.7	0.495 46	0.570 39	1.753 2	0.868 63	60.3	35.7	0.583 54	0.718 57	1.391 6	0.812 08	54.3
29.8	0.496 97	0.572 71	1.746 1	0.867 77	60.2	35.8	0.584 96	0.721 22	1.386 5	0.811 06	54.2
29.9	0.498 49	0.575 03	1.739 1	0.866 90	60.1	35.9	0.586 37	0.723 88	1.381 4	0.810 04	54.1
30.0	**0.500 00**	**0.577 35**	**1.732 1**	**0.866 03**	**60.0**	**36.0**	**0.587 79**	**0.726 54**	**1.376 4**	**0.809 02**	**54.0**
	Cos	Cot	Tan	Sin	θ°		Cos	Cot	Tan	Sin	θ°

Table 5 / Five-place decitrig functions □ **717**

θ°	Sin	Tan	Cot	Cos		θ°	Sin	Tan	Cot	Cos	
36.0	0.587 79	0.726 54	1.376 4	0.809 02	54.0	40.5	0.649 45	0.854 08	1.170 8	0.760 41	49.5
36.1	0.589 20	0.729 21	1.371 3	0.807 99	53.9	40.6	0.650 77	0.857 10	1.166 7	0.759 27	49.4
36.2	0.590 61	0.731 89	1.366 3	0.806 96	53.8	40.7	0.652 10	0.860 14	1.162 6	0.758 13	49.3
36.3	0.592 01	0.734 57	1.361 3	0.805 93	53.7	40.8	0.653 42	0.863 18	1.158 5	0.757 00	49.2
36.4	0.593.42	0.737 26	1.356 4	0.804 89	53.6	40.9	0.654 74	0.866 23	1.154 4	0.755 85	49.1
36.5	0.594 82	0.739 96	1.351 4	0.803 86	53.5	41.0	0.656 06	0.869 29	1.150 4	0.754 71	49.0
36.6	0.596 22	0.742 67	1.346 5	0.802 82	53.4	41.1	0.657 38	0.872 36	1.146 3	0.753 56	48.9
36.7	0.597 63	0.745 38	1.341 6	0.801 78	53.3	41.2	0.658 69	0.875 43	1.142 3	0.752 41	48.8
36.8	0.599 02	0.748 10	1.336 7	0.800 73	53.2	41.3	0.660 00	0.878 52	1.138 3	0.751 26	48.7
36.9	0.600 42	0.750 82	1.331 9	0.799 68	53.1	41.4	0.661 31	0.881 62	1.134 3	0.750 11	48.6
37.0	0.601 82	0.753 55	1.327 0	0.798 64	53.0	41.5	0.662 62	0.884 73	1.130 3	0.748 96	48.5
37.1	0.603 21	0.756 29	1.322 2	0.797 58	52.9	41.6	0.663 93	0.887 84	1.126 3	0.747 80	48.4
37.2	0.604 60	0.759 04	1.317 5	0.796 53	52.8	41.7	0.665 23	0.890 97	1.122 4	0.746 64	48.3
37.3	0.605 99	0.761 80	1.312 7	0.795 47	52.7	41.8	0.666 53	0.897 10	1.118 4	0.745 48	48.2
37.4	0.607 38	0.764 56	1.307 9	0.794 41	52.6	41.9	0.667 83	0.897 25	1.114 5	0.744 31	48.1
37.5	0.608 76	0.767 33	1.303 2	0.793 35	52.5	42.0	0.669 13	0.900 40	1.110 6	0.743 14	48.0
37.6	0.610 15	0.770 10	1.298 5	0.792 29	52.4	42.1	0.670 43	0.903 57	1.106 7	0.741 98	47.9
37.7	0.611 53	0.772 89	1.293 8	0.791 22	52.3	42.2	0.671 72	0.906 74	1.102 8	0.740 80	47.8
37.8	0.612 91	0.775 68	1.289 2	0.790 16	52.2	42.3	0.673 01	0.909 93	1.099 0	0.739 63	47.7
37.9	0.614 29	0.778 48	1.284 6	0.789 08	52.1	42.4	0.674 30	0.913 13	1.095 1	0.738 46	47.6
38.0	0.615 66	0.781 29	1.279 9	0.788 01	52.0	42.5	0.675 59	0.916 33	1.091 3	0.737 28	47.5
38.1	0.617 04	0.784 10	1.275 3	0.786 94	51.9	42.6	0.676 88	0.919 55	1.087 5	0.736 10	47.4
38.2	0.618 41	0.786 92	1.270 8	0.785 86	51.8	42.7	0.678 16	0.922 77	1.083 7	0.734 91	47.3
38.3	0.619 78	0.789 75	1.266 2	0.784 78	51.7	42.8	0.679 44	0.926 01	1.079 9	0.733 73	47.2
38.4	0.621 15	0.792 59	1.261 7	0.783 69	51.6	42.9	0.680 72	0.929 26	1.076 1	0.732 54	47.1
38.5	0.622 51	0.795 44	1.257 2	0.782 61	51.5	43.0	0.682 00	0.932 52	1.072 4	0.731 35	47.0
38.6	0.623 88	0.798 29	1.252 7	0.781 52	51.4	43.1	0.683 27	0.935 78	1.068 6	0.730 16	46.9
38.7	0.625 24	0.811 15	1.248 2	0.780 43	51.3	43.2	0.684 55	0.939 06	1.064 9	0.728 97	46.8
38.8	0.626 60	0.804 02	1.243 7	0.779 34	51.2	43.3	0.685 82	0.942 35	1.061 2	0.727 77	46.7
38.9	0.627 96	0.806 90	1.239 3	0.778 24	51.1	43.4	0.687 09	0.945 65	1.057 5	0.726 57	46.6
39.0	0.629 32	0.809 78	1.234 9	0.777 15	51.0	43.5	0.688 35	0.948 96	1.053 8	0.725 37	46.5
39.1	0.630 68	0.81,2 68	1.230 5	0.776 05	50.9	43.6	0.689 62	0.952 29	1.050 1	0.724 17	46.4
39.2	0.632 03	0.815 58	1.226 1	0.774 94	50.8	43.7	0.690 88	0.955 62	1.046 4	0.722 97	46.3
39.3	0.633 38	0.818 49	1.221 8	0.773 84	50.7	43.8	0.692 14	0.958 97	1.042 8	0.721 76	46.2
39.4	0.634 73	0.821 41	1.217 4	0.772 73	50.6	43.9	0.693 40	0.962 32	1.039 2	0.720 55	46.1
39.5	0.636 08	0.824 34	1.213 1	0.771 62	50.5	44.0	0.694 66	0.965 69	1.035 5	0.719 34	46.0
39.6	0.637 42	0.827 27	1.208 8	0.770 51	50.4	44.1	0.695 91	0.969 07	1.031 9	0.718 13	45.9
39.7	0.638 77	0.830 22	1.204 5	0.769 40	50.3	44.2	0.697 17	0.972 46	1.028 3	0.716 91	45.8
39.8	0.640 11	0.833 17	1.200 2	0.768 28	50.2	44.3	0.698 42	0.975 86	1.024 7	0.715 69	45.7
39.9	0.641 45	0.836 13	1.196 0	0.767 17	50.1	44.4	0.699 66	0.979 27	1.021 2	0.714 47	45.6
40.0	0.642 79	0.839 10	1.191 8	0.766 04	50.0	44.5	0.700 91	0.982 70	1.017 6	0.713 25	45.5
40.1	0.644 12	0.842 08	1.187 5	0.764 92	49.9	44.6	0.702 15	0.986 13	1.014 1	0.712 03	45.4
40.2	0.645 46	0.845 07	1.183 3	0.763 80	49.8	44.7	0.703 39	0.989 58	1.010 5	0.710 80	45.3
40.3	0.646 79	0.848 06	1.179 2	0.762 67	49.7	44.8	0.704 63	0.993 04	1.007 0	0.709 57	45.2
40.4	0.648 12	0.851 07	1.175 0	0.761 54	49.6	44.9	0.705 87	0.996 52	1.003 5	0.708 34	45.1
40.5	0.069 45	0.854 08	1.170 8	0.760 41	49.5	45.0	0.707 11	1.000 00	1.000 0	0.707 11	45.0
	Cos	Cot	Tan	Sin	θ°		Cos	Cot	Tan	Sin	θ°

TABLE 6
Five-Place Common Logarithms of Natural Trigonometric Functions; Angles in Degrees and Decimals (Five-place decitrig logarithms)

Subtract 10 from each entry in the columns headed with ▼. Avoid interpolation for the logarithms of sines, tangents, and cotangents of angles smaller than 3° and for the logarithms of cosines, tangents, and cotangents of angles larger than 87°. Convert angle to minutes and seconds and refer to Table 4.

θ°	▼ L Sin	▼ L Tan	L Cot	▼ L Cos	θ°	θ°	▼ L Sin	▼ L Tan	L Cot	▼ L Cos	θ°
0.0	—	—		0.000 00	90.0	6.0	9.019 23	9.021 62	0.978 38	9.997 61	84.0
0.1	7.241 88	7.241 88	2.758 12	0.000 00	89.9	6.1	9.026 39	9.028 85	0.971 15	9.997 53	83.9
0.2	7.542 91	7.542 91	2.457 09	0.000 00	89.8	6.2	9.033 42	9.035 97	0.964 03	9.997 45	83.8
0.3	7.719 00	7.719 00	2.281 00	9.999 99	89.7	6.3	9.040 34	9.042 97	0.957 03	9.997 37	83.7
0.4	7.843 93	7.843 94	2.156 06	9.999 99	89.6	6.4	9.047 15	9.049 87	0.950 13	9.997 28	83.6
0.5	7.940 84	7.940 86	2.059 14	9.999 98	89.5	6.5	9.053 86	9.056 66	0.943 34	9.997 20	83.5
0.6	8.020 02	8.020 04	1.979 96	9.999 98	89.4	6.6	9.060 46	9.063 35	0.936 65	9.997 11	83.4
0.7	8.086 96	8.087 00	1.913 00	9.999 97	89.3	6.7	9.066 96	9.069 94	0.930 06	9.997 02	83.3
0.8	8.144 95	8.145 00	1.855 00	9.999 96	89.2	6.8	9.073 37	9.076 43	0.923 57	9.996 93	83.2
0.9	8.196 10	8.196 16	1.803 84	9.999 95	89.1	6.9	9.079 68	9.082 83	0.917 17	9.996 84	83.1
1.0	8.241 86	8.241 92	1.758 08	9.999 93	89.0	7.0	9.085 89	9.089 14	0.910 86	9.996 75	83.0
1.1	8.283 24	8.283 32	1.716 68	9.999 92	88.9	7.1	9.092 02	9.095 37	0.904 63	9.996 66	82.9
1.2	8.321 03	8.321 12	1.678 88	9.999 90	88.8	7.2	9.098 07	9.101 50	0.898 50	9.996 56	82.8
1.3	8.355 78	8.355 90	1.644 10	9.999 89	88.7	7.3	9.104 02	9.107 56	0.892 44	9.996 47	82.7
1.4	8.387 96	8.388 09	1.611 91	9.999 87	88.6	7.4	9.109 90	9.113 53	0.886 47	9.996 37	82.6
1.5	8.417 92	8.418 07	1.581 93	9.999 85	88.5	7.5	9.115 70	9.119 43	0.880 57	9.996 27	82.5
1.6	8.445 94	8.446 11	1.553 89	9.999 83	88.4	7.6	9.121 42	9.125 25	0.874 75	9.996 17	82.4
1.7	8.472 26	8.472 45	1.527 55	9.999 81	88.3	7.7	9.127 06	9.130 99	0.869 01	9.996 07	82.3
1.8	8.497 08	8.497 29	1.502 71	9.999 79	88.2	7.8	9.132 63	9.136 67	0.863 33	9.995 96	82.2
1.9	8.520 55	8.520 79	1.479 21	9.999 76	88.1	7.9	9.138 13	9.142 27	0.857 73	9.995 86	82.1
2.0	8.542 82	8.543 08	1.456 92	9.999 74	88.0	8.0	9.143 56	9.147 80	0.852 20	9.995 75	82.0
2.1	8.564 00	8.564 29	1.435 71	9.999 71	87.9	8.1	9.148 91	9.153 27	0.846 73	9.995 65	81.9
2.2	8.584 19	8.584 51	1.415 49	9.999 68	87.8	8.2	9.154 21	9.158 67	0.841 33	9.995 54	81.8
2.3	8.603 49	8.603 84	1.396 16	9.999 65	87.7	8.3	9.159 44	9.164 01	0.835 99	9.995 43	81.7
2.4	8.621 96	8.622 34	1.377 66	9.999 62	87.6	8.4	9.164 60	9.169 28	0.830 72	9.995 32	81.6
2.5	8.639 68	8.640 09	1.359 91	9.999 59	87.5	8.5	9.169 70	9.174 50	0.825 50	9.995 20	81.5
2.6	8.656 70	8.657 15	1.342 85	9.999 55	87.4	8.6	9.174 74	9.179 65	0.820 35	9.995 09	81.4
2.7	8.673 08	8.673 56	1.326 44	9.999 52	87.3	8.7	9.179 73	9.184 75	0.815 25	9.994 97	81.3
2.8	8.688 86	8.689 38	1.310 62	9.999 48	87.2	8.8	9.184 65	9.189 79	0.810 21	9.994 86	81.2
2.9	8.704 09	8.704 65	1.295 35	9.999 44	87.1	8.9	9.189 52	9.194 78	0.805 22	9.994 74	81.1
3.0	8.718 80	8.719 40	1.280 60	9.999 40	87.0	9.0	9.194 33	9.199 71	0.800 29	9.994 62	81.0
3.1	8.733 03	8.733 66	1.266 34	9.999 36	86.9	9.1	9.199 09	9.204 59	0.795 41	9.994 50	80.9
3.2	8.746 80	8.747 48	1.252 52	9.999 32	86.8	9.2	9.203 80	9.209 42	0.790 58	9.994 38	80.8
3.3	8.760 15	8.760 87	1.239 13	9.999 28	86.7	9.3	9.208 45	9.214 20	0.785 80	9.994 25	80.7
3.4	8.773 10	8.773 87	1.226 13	9.999 23	86.6	9.4	9.213 06	9.218 93	0.781 07	9.994 13	80.6
3.5	8.785 68	8.786 49	1.213 51	9.999 19	86.5	9.5	9.217 61	9.223 61	0.776 39	9.994 00	80.5
3.6	8.797 89	8.798 75	1.201 25	9.999 14	86.4	9.6	9.222 11	9.228 24	0.771 76	9.993 88	80.4
3.7	8.809 78	8.810 68	1.189 32	9.999 09	86.3	9.7	9.226 57	9.232 83	0.767 17	9.993 75	80.3
3.8	8.821 34	8.822 30	1.177 70	9.999 04	86.2	9.8	9.230 98	9.237 37	0.762 63	9.993 62	80.2
3.9	8.832 61	8.833 61	1.166 39	9.998 99	86.1	9.9	9.235 35	9.241 86	0.758 14	9.993 48	80.1
4.0	8.843 58	8.844 64	1.155 36	9.998 94	86.0	10.0	9.239 67	9.246 32	0.753 68	9.993 35	80.0
4.1	8.854 29	8.855 40	1.144 60	9.998 89	85.9	10.1	9.243 95	9.250 73	0.749 27	9.993 22	79.9
4.2	8.864 74	8.865 91	1.134 09	9.998 83	85.8	10.2	9.248 18	9.255 10	0.744 90	9.993 08	79.8
4.3	8.874 94	8.876 16	1.123 84	9.998 78	85.7	10.3	9.252 37	9.259 43	0.740 57	9.992 94	79.7
4.4	8.884 90	8.886 18	1.113 82	9.998 72	85.6	10.4	9.256 52	9.263 72	0.736 28	9.992 81	79.6
4.5	8.894 64	8.895 98	1.104 02	9.998 66	85.5	10.5	9.260 63	9.267 97	0.732 03	9.992 67	79.5
4.6	8.904 17	8.905 57	1.094 43	9.998 60	85.4	10.6	9.264 70	9.272 18	0.727 82	9.992 52	79.4
4.7	8.913 49	8.914 95	1.085 05	9.998 54	85.3	10.7	9.268 73	9.276 35	0.723 65	9.992 38	79.3
4.8	8.922 61	8.924 14	1.075 86	9.998 47	85.2	10.8	9.272 73	9.280 49	0.719 51	9.992 24	79.2
4.9	8.931 54	8.933 13	1.066 87	9.998 41	85.1	10.9	9.276 68	9.284 59	0.715 41	9.992 09	79.1
5.0	8.940 30	8.941 95	1.058 05	9.998 34	85.0	11.0	9.280 60	9.288 65	0.711 35	9.991 95	79.0
5.1	8.948 87	8.950 60	1.049 40	9.998 28	84.9	11.1	9.284 48	9.292 68	0.707 32	9.991 80	78.9
5.2	8.957 28	8.959 08	1.040 92	9.998 21	84.8	11.2	9.288 33	9.296 68	0.703 32	9.991 65	78.8
5.3	8.965 53	8.967 39	1.032 61	9.998 14	84.7	11.3	9.292 14	9.300 64	0.699 36	9.991 50	78.7
5.4	8.973 63	8.975 56	1.024 44	9.998 07	84.6	11.4	9.295 91	9.304 57	0.695 43	9.991 35	78.6
5.5	8.981 57	8.983 58	1.016 42	9.998 00	84.5	11.5	9.299 66	9.308 46	0.691 54	9.991 19	78.5
5.6	8.989 37	8.991 45	1.008 55	9.997 92	84.4	11.6	9.303 36	9.312 33	0.687 67	9.991 04	78.4
5.7	8.997 04	8.999 19	1.000 81	9.997 85	84.3	11.7	9.307 04	9.316 16	0.683 84	9.990 88	78.3
5.8	9.004 56	9.006 79	0.993 21	9.997 77	84.2	11.8	9.310 68	9.319 96	0.680 04	9.990 72	78.2
5.9	9.011 96	9.014 27	0.985 73	9.997 69	84.1	11.9	9.314 30	9.323 73	0.676 27	9.990 56	78.1
6.0	9.019 23	9.021 62	0.978 38	9.997 61	84.0	12.0	9.317 88	9.327 47	0.672 53	9.990 40	78.0
θ°	L Cos	L Cot	L Tan	L Sin	θ°	θ°	L Cos	L Cot	L Tan	L Sin	θ°

θ°	▼ L Sin	▼ L Tan	L Cot	▼ L Cos	θ°	θ°	▼ L Sin	▼ L Tan	L Cot	▼ L Cos	θ°
12.0	**9.317 88**	**9.327 47**	**0.672 53**	**9.990 40**	**78.0**	**18.0**	**9.489 98**	**9.511 78**	**0.488 22**	**9.978 21**	**72.0**
12.1	9.321 43	9.331 19	0.668 81	9.990 24	77.9	18.1	9.492 31	9.514 35	0.485 65	9.977 95	71.9
12.2	9.324 95	9.334 87	0.665 13	9.990 08	77.8	18.2	9.494 62	9.516 91	0.483 09	9.977 71	71.8
12.3	9.328 44	9.338 53	0.661 47	9.989 91	77.7	18.3	9.496 92	9.519 46	0.480 54	9.977 46	71.7
12.4	9.331 90	9.342 15	0.657 85	9.989 75	77.6	18.4	9.499 20	9.522 00	0.478 01	9.977 21	71.6
12.5	**9.335 34**	**9.345 76**	**0.654 24**	**9.989 58**	**77.5**	**18.5**	**9.501 48**	**9.524 52**	**0.475 48**	**9.976 96**	**71.5**
12.6	9.338 74	9.349 33	0.650 67	9.989 41	77.4	18.6	9.503 74	9.527 03	0.472 97	9.976 70	71.4
12.7	9.342 12	9.352 88	0.647 12	9.989 24	77.3	18.7	9.505 98	9.529 53	0.470 47	9.976 45	71.3
12.8	9.345 47	9.356 40	0.643 60	9.989 07	77.2	18.8	9.508 21	9.532 02	0.467 98	9.976 19	71.2
12.9	9.348 79	9.359 89	0.640 11	9.988 90	77.1	18.9	9.510 43	9.534 50	0.465 50	9.975 93	71.1
13.0	**9.352 09**	**9.363 36**	**0.636 64**	**9.988 72**	**77.0**	**19.0**	**9.512 64**	**9.536 97**	**0.463 03**	**9.975 67**	**71.0**
13.1	9.355 36	9.366 81	0.633 19	9.988 55	76.9	19.1	9.514 84	9.539 43	0.460 57	9.975 41	70.9
13.2	9.358 60	9.370 23	0.629 77	9.988 37	76.8	19.2	9.517 02	9.541 87	0.458 13	9.975 15	70.8
13.3	9.361 82	9.373 63	0.626 37	9.988 19	76.7	19.3	9.519 19	9.544 31	0.455 69	9.974 88	70.7
13.4	9.365 02	9.377 00	0.623 00	9.988 01	76.6	19.4	9.521 35	9.546 73	0.453 27	9.974 61	70.6
13.5	**9.368 19**	**9.380 35**	**0.619 65**	**9.987 83**	**76.5**	**19.5**	**9.523 50**	**9.549 15**	**0.450 85**	**9.974 35**	**70.5**
13.6	9.371 33	9.383 68	0.616 32	9.987 65	76.4	19.6	9.525 63	9.551 55	0.448 45	9.974 08	70.4
13.7	9.374 45	9.386 99	0.613 01	9.987 46	76.3	19.7	9.527 75	9.553 95	0.446 05	9.973 81	70.3
13.8	9.377 55	9.390 27	0.609 73	9.987 28	76.2	19.8	9.529 86	9.556 33	0.443 67	9.973 53	70.2
13.9	9.380 62	9.393 53	0.606 47	9.987 09	76.1	19.9	9.531 96	9.558 70	0.441 30	9.973 26	70.1
14.0	**9.383 68**	**9.396 77**	**0.603 23**	**9.986 90**	**76.0**	**20.0**	**9.534 05**	**9.561 07**	**0.438 93**	**9.972 99**	**70.0**
14.1	9.386 70	9.399 99	0.600 01	9.986 71	75.9	20.1	9.536 13	9.563 42	0.436 58	9.972 71	69.9
14.2	9.389 71	9.403 19	0.596 81	9.986 52	75.8	20.2	9.538 19	9.565 76	0.434 24	9.972 43	69.8
14.3	9.392 70	9.406 36	0.593 64	9.986 33	75.7	20.3	9.540 25	9.568 10	0.431 90	9.972 15	69.7
14.4	9.395 66	9.409 52	0.590 48	9.986 14	75.6	20.4	9.542 29	9.570 42	0.429 58	9.971 87	69.6
14.5	**9.398 60**	**9.412 66**	**0.587 34**	**9.985 94**	**75.5**	**20.5**	**9.544 33**	**9.572 74**	**0.427 26**	**9.971 59**	**69.5**
14.6	9.401 52	9.415 78	0.584 22	9.985 74	75.4	20.6	9.546 35	9.575 04	0.424 96	9.971 30	69.4
14.7	9.404 42	9.418 87	0.581 13	9.985 55	75.3	20.7	9.548 36	9.577 34	0.422 66	9.971 02	69.3
14.8	9.407 30	9.421 95	0.578 05	9.985 35	75.2	20.8	9.550 36	9.579 63	0.420 37	9.970 73	69.2
14.9	9.410 16	9.425 01	0.574 99	9.985 15	75.1	20.9	9.552 35	9.581 91	0.418 09	9.970 44	69.1
15.0	**9.413 00**	**9.428 05**	**0.571 95**	**9.984 94**	**75.0**	**21.0**	**9.554 33**	**9.584 18**	**0.415 82**	**9.970 15**	**69.0**
15.1	9.415 82	9.431 08	0.568 92	9.984 74	74.9	21.1	9.556 30	9.586 44	0.413 56	9.969 86	68.9
15.2	9.418 61	9.434 08	0.565 92	9.984 53	74.8	21.2	9.558 26	9.588 69	0.411 31	9.969 57	68.8
15.3	9.421 40	9.437 07	0.562 93	9.984 33	74.7	21.3	9.560 21	9.590 94	0.409 06	9.969 27	68.7
15.4	9.424 16	9.440 04	0.559 96	9.984 12	74.6	21.4	9.562 15	9.593 17	0.406 83	9.968 98	68.6
15.5	**9.426 90**	**9.442 99**	**0.557 01**	**9.983 91**	**74.5**	**21.5**	**9.564 07**	**9.595 40**	**0.404 60**	**9.968 68**	**68.5**
15.6	9.429 62	9.445 92	0.554 08	9.983 70	74.4	21.6	9.565 99	9.597 62	0.402 38	9.968 38	68.4
15.7	9.432 33	9.448 84	0.551 16	9.983 49	74.3	21.7	9.567 90	9.599 83	0.400 17	9.968 08	68.3
15.8	9.435 02	9.451 74	0.548 26	9.983 27	74.2	21.8	9.569 80	9.602 03	0.397 97	9.967 78	68.2
15.9	9.437 69	9.454 63	0.545 37	9.983 06	74.1	21.9	9.571 69	9.604 22	0.395 78	9.967 47	68.1
16.0	**9.440 34**	**9.457 50**	**0.542 50**	**9.982 84**	**74.0**	**22.0**	**9.573 58**	**9.606 41**	**0.393 59**	**9.967 17**	**68.0**
16.1	9.442 97	9.460 35	0.539 65	9.982 62	73.9	22.1	9.575 45	9.608 59	0.391 41	9.966 86	67.9
16.2	9.445 59	9.463 19	0.536 81	9.982 40	73.8	22.2	9.577 31	9.610 76	0.389 24	9.966 55	67.8
16.3	9.448 19	9.466 01	0.533 99	9.982 18	73.7	22.3	9.579 16	9.612 92	0.387 08	9.966 24	67.7
16.4	9.450 77	9.468 81	0.531 19	9.981 96	73.6	22.4	9.581 01	9.615 08	0.384 92	9.965 93	67.6
16.5	**9.453 34**	**9.471 60**	**0.528 40**	**9.981 74**	**73.5**	**22.5**	**9.582 84**	**9.617 22**	**0.382 78**	**9.965 62**	**67.5**
16.6	9.455 89	9.474 38	0.525 62	9.981 51	73.4	22.6	9.584 67	9.619 36	0.380 64	9.965 30	67.4
16.7	9.458 43	9.477 14	0.522 86	9.981 29	73.3	22.7	9.586 48	9.621 50	0.378 50	9.964 98	67.3
16.8	9.460 95	9.479 89	0.520 11	9.981 06	73.2	22.8	9.588 29	9.623 62	0.376 38	9.964 67	67.2
16.9	9.463 45	9.482 62	0.517 38	9.980 83	73.1	22.9	9.590 09	9.625 74	0.374 26	9.964 35	67.1
17.0	**9.465 94**	**9.485 34**	**0.514 66**	**9.980 60**	**73.0**	**23.0**	**9.591 88**	**9.627 85**	**0.372 15**	**9.964 03**	**67.0**
17.1	9.468 41	9.488 04	0.511 96	9.980 36	72.9	23.1	9.593 66	9.629 96	0.370 04	9.963 70	66.9
17.2	9.470 86	9.490 73	0.509 27	9.980 13	72.8	23.2	9.595 43	9.632 05	0.367 94	9.963 38	66.8
17.3	9.473 30	9.493 41	0.506 59	9.979 89	72.7	23.3	9.597 20	9.634 14	0.365 86	9.963 05	66.7
17.4	9.475 73	9.496 07	0.503 93	9.979 66	72.6	23.4	9.598 95	9.636 23	0.363 77	9.962 73	66.6
17.5	**9.478 14**	**9.498 72**	**0.501 28**	**9.979 42**	**72.5**	**23.5**	**9.600 70**	**9.638 30**	**0.361 70**	**9.962 40**	**66.5**
17.6	9.480 54	9.501 36	0.498 64	9.979 18	72.4	23.6	9.602 44	9.640 37	0.359 63	9.962 07	66.4
17.7	9.482 92	9.503 98	0.496 02	9.978 94	72.3	23.7	9.604 17	9.642 43	0.357 57	9.961 74	66.3
17.8	9.485 29	9.506 59	0.493 41	9.978 70	72.2	23.8	9.605 89	9.644 49	0.355 51	9.961 40	66.2
17.9	9.487 64	9.509 19	0.490 81	9.978 45	72.1	23.9	9.607 61	9.646 54	0.353 46	9.961 07	66.1
18.0	**9.489 98**	**9.511 78**	**0.488 22**	**9.978 21**	**72.0**	**24.0**	**9.609 31**	**9.648 58**	**0.351 42**	**9.960 73**	**66.0**
θ°	L Cos	L Cot	L Tan	L Sin	θ°	θ°	L Cos	L Cot	L Tan	L Sin	θ°

θ°	▼ L Sin	▼ L Tan	L Cot	▼ L Cos	θ°
24.0	9.609 31	9.648 58	0.351 42	9.960 73	66.0
24.1	9.611 01	9.650 62	0.349 38	9.960 39	65.9
24.2	9.612 70	9.652 65	0.347 35	9.960 05	65.8
24.3	9.614 38	9.654 67	0.345 33	9.959 71	65.7
24.4	9.616 06	9.656 69	0.343 31	9.959 37	65.6
24.5	9.617 73	9.658 70	0.341 30	9.959 02	65.5
24.6	9.619 39	9.660 71	0.339 29	9.958 68	65.4
24.7	9.621 04	9.662 71	0.337 29	9.958 33	65.3
24.8	9.622 68	9.664 70	0.335 30	9.957 98	65.2
24.9	9.624 32	9.666 69	0.333 31	9.957 63	65.1
25.0	9.625 95	9.668 67	0.331 33	9.957 28	65.0
25.1	9.627 57	9.670 65	0.329 35	9.956 92	64.9
25.2	9.629 18	9.672 62	0.327 38	9.956 57	64.8
25.3	9.630 79	9.674 58	0.325 42	9.956 21	64.7
25.4	9.632 39	9.676 54	0.323 46	9.955 85	64.6
25.5	9.633 98	9.678 50	0.321 50	9.955 49	64.5
25.6	9.635 57	9.680 44	0.319 56	9.955 13	64.4
25.7	9.637 15	9.682 39	0.317 61	9.954 76	64.3
25.8	9.638 72	9.684 32	0.315 68	9.954 40	64.2
25.9	9.640 28	9.686 26	0.313 74	9.954 03	64.1
26.0	9.641 84	9.688 18	0.311 82	9.953 66	64.0
26.1	9.643 39	9.690 10	0.309 90	9.953 29	63.9
26.2	9.644 94	9.692 02	0.307 98	9.952 92	63.8
26.3	9.646 47	9.693 92	0.306 07	9.952 54	63.7
26.4	9.648 00	9.695 84	0.304 16	9.952 17	63.6
26.5	9.649 53	9.697 74	0.302 26	9.951 79	63.5
26.6	9.651 04	9.699 63	0.300 37	9.951 41	63.4
26.7	9.652 55	9.701 52	0.298 48	9.951 03	63.3
26.8	9.654 06	9.703 41	0.296 59	9.950 65	63.2
26.9	9.655 56	9.705 29	0.294 71	9.950 27	63.1
27.0	9.657 05	9.707 17	0.292 83	9.949 88	63.0
27.1	9.658 53	9.709 04	0.290 96	9.949 49	62.9
27.2	9.660 01	9.710 90	0.289 10	9.949 11	62.8
27.3	9.661 48	9.712 77	0.287 23	9.948 71	62.7
27.4	9.662 95	9.714 62	0.285 38	9.948 32	62.6
27.5	9.664 41	9.716 48	0.283 52	9.947 93	62.5
27.6	9.665 86	9.718 33	0.281 67	9.947 53	62.4
27.7	9.667 31	9.720 17	0.279 83	9.947 14	62.3
27.8	9.668 75	9.722 01	0.277 99	9.946 74	62.2
27.9	9.670 18	9.723 84	0.276 16	9.946 34	62.1
28.0	9.671 61	9.725 67	0.274 33,	9.945 93	62.0
28.1	9.673 03	9.727 50	0.272 50	9.945 53	61.9
28.2	9.674 45	9.729 32	0.270 68	9.945 13	61.8
28.3	9.675 86	9.731 14	0.268 86	9.944 72	61.7
28.4	9.677 26	9.732 95	0.267 05	9.944 31	61.6
28.5	9.678 66	9.734 76	0.265 24	9.943 90	61.5
28.6	9.680 06	9.736 57	0.263 43	9.943 49	61.4
28.7	9.681 44	9.738 37	0.261 63	9.943 07	61.3
28.8	9.682 83	9.740 17	0.259 83	9.942 66	61.2
28.9	9.684 20	9.741 96	0.258 04	9.942 24	61.1
29.0	9.685 57	9.743 75	0.256 25	9.941 82	61.0
29.1	9.686 94	9.745 54	0.254 46	9.941 40	60.9
29.2	9.688 29	9.747 32	0.252 68	9.940 98	60.8
29.3	9.689 65	9.749 10	0.250 90	9.940 55	60.7
29.4	9.691 00	9.750 87	0.249 13	9.940 12	60.6
29.5	9.692 34	9.752 64	0.247 36	9.939 70	60.5
29.6	9.693 68	9.754 41	0.245 59	9.939 27	60.4
29.7	9.695 01	9.756 17	0.243 83	9.938 84	60.3
29.8	9.696 33	9.757 93	0.242 07	9.938 40	60.2
29.9	9.697 65	9.759 69	0.240 31	9.937 97	60.1
30.0	9.698 97	9.761 44	0.238 56	9.937 53	60.0
θ°	L Cos	L Cot	L Tan	L Sin	θ°

θ°	▼ L Sin	▼ L Tan	L Cot	▼ L Cos	θ°
30.0	9.698 97	9.761 44	0.238 56	9.937 53	60.0
30.1	9.700 28	9.763 19	0.236 81	9.937 09	59.9
30.2	9.701 59	9.764 93	0.235 07	9.936 65	59.8
30.3	9.702 88	9.766 68	0.233 32	9.936 21	59.7
30.4	9.704 18	9.768 41	0.231 59	9.935 77	59.6
30.5	9.705 47	9.770 15	0.229 85	9.935 32	59.5
30.6	9.706 75	9.771 88	0.228 12	9.934 87	59.4
30.7	9.708 03	9.773 61	0.226 39	9.934 42	59.3
30.8	9.709 31	9.775 33	0.224 67	9.933 97	59.2
30.9	9.710 57	9.777 06	0.222 94	9.933 52	59.1
31.0	9.711 84	9.778 77	0.221 23	9.933 07	59.0
31.1	9.713 10	9.780 49	0.219 51	9.932 61	58.9
31.2	9.714 35	9.782 20	0.217 80	9.932 15	58.8
31.3	9.715 60	9.783 91	0.216 09	9.931 69	58.7
31.4	9.716 85	9.785 62	0.214 38	9.931 23	58.6
31.5	9.718 09	9.787 32	0.212 68	9.930 77	58.5
31.6	9.719 32	9.789 02	0.210 98	9.930 30	58.4
31.7	9.720 55	9.790 72	0.209 28	9.929 83	58.3
31.8	9.721 77	9.792 41	0.207 59	9.929 36	58.2
31.9	9.722 99	9.794 10	0.205 90	9.928 89	58.1
32.0	9.724 21	9.795 79	0.204 21	9.928 42	58.0
32.1	9.725 42	9.797 47	0.202 53	9.927 95	57.9
32.2	9.726 63	9.799 16	0.200 84	9.927 47	57.8
32.3	9.727 83	9.800 84	0.199 16	9.926 99	57.7
32.4	9.729 02	9.802 51	0.197 49	9.926 51	57.6
32.5	9.730 22	9.804 19	0.195 81	9.926 03	57.5
32.6	9.731 40	9.805 86	0.194 14	9.925 55	57.4
32.7	9.732 59	9.807 53	0.192 47	9.925 06	57.3
32.8	9.733 76	9.809 19	0.190 81	9.924 57	57.2
32.9	9.734 94	9.810 86	0.189 14	9.924 08	57.1
33.0	9.736 11	9.812 52	0.187 48	9.923 59	57.0
33.1	9.737 27	9.814 18	0.185 82	9.923 10	56.9
33.2	9.738 43	9.815 83	0.184 17	9.922 60	56.8
33.3	9.739 59	9.817 48	0.182 52	9.922 11	56.7
33.4	9.740 74	9.819 13	0.180 87	9.921 61	56.6
33.5	9.741 89	9.820 78	0.179 22	9.921 11	56.5
33.6	9.743 03	9.822 43	0.177 57	9.920 60	56.4
33.7	9.744 17	9.824 07	0.175 93	9.920 10	56.3
33.8	9.745 31	9.825 71	0.174 29	9.919 59	56.2
33.9	9.746 44	9.827 35	0.172 65	9.919 08	56.1
34.0	9.747 56	9.828 99	0.171 01	9.918 57	56.0
34.1	9.748 68	9.830 62	0.169 38	9.918 06	55.9
34.2	9.749 80	9.832 25	0.167 75	9.917 55	55.8
34.3	9.750 91	9.833 88	0.166 12	9.917 03	55.7
34.4	9.752 02	9.835 51	0.164 49	9.916 51	55.6
34.5	9.753 13	9.837 13	0.162 87	9.915 99	55.5
34.6	9.754 23	9.838 76	0.161 24	9.915 47	55.4
34.7	9.755 33	9.840 38	0.159 62	9.914 95	55.3
34.8	9.756 42	9.842 00	0.158 00	9.914 42	55.2
34.9	9.757 51	9.843 61	0.156 39	9.913 89	55.1
35.0	9.758 59	9.845 23	0.154 77	9.913 36	55.0
35.1	9.759 67	9.846 84	0.153 16	9.912 83	54.9
35.2	9.760 75	9.848 45	0.151 55	9.912 30	54.8
35.3	9.761 82	9.850 06	0.149 94	9.911 76	54.7
35.4	9.762 89	9.851 66	0.148 34	9.911 23	54.6
35.5	9.763 95	9.853 27	0.146 73	9.910 69	54.5
35.6	9.765 01	9.854 87	0.145 13	9.910 14	54.4
35.7	9.766 07	9.856 47	0.143 53	9.909 60	54.3
35.8	9.767 12	9.858 07	0.141 93	9.909 06	54.2
35.9	9.768 17	9.859 67	0.140 33	9.908 51	54.1
36.0	9.769 22	9.861 26	0.138 74	9.907 96	54.0
θ°	L Cos	L Cot	L Tan	L Sin	θ°

Table 6 / Five-place decitrig logarithms □ 721

θ°	L Sin	L Tan	L Cot	L Cos	θ°
36.0	9.769 22	9.861 26	0.138 74	9.907 96	54.0
36.1	9.770 26	9.862 85	0.137 15	9.907 41	53.9
36.2	9.771 30	9.864 45	0.135 55	9.906 85	53.8
36.3	9.772 33	9.866 03	0.133 97	9.906 30	53.7
36.4	9.773 36	9.867 62	0.132 38	9.905 74	53.6
36.5	9.774 39	9.869 21	0.130 79	9.905 18	53.5
36.6	9.775 41	9.870 79	0.129 21	9.904 62	53.4
36.7	9.776 43	9.872 38	0.127 62	9.904 05	53.3
36.8	9.777 44	9.873 96	0.126 04	9.903 49	53.2
36.9	9.778 46	9.875 54	0.124 46	9.902 92	53.1
37.0	9.779 46	9.877 11	0.122 89	9.902 35	53.0
37.1	9.780 47	9.878 69	0.121 31	9.901 78	52.9
37.2	9.781 47	9.880 27	0.119 73	9.901 20	52.8
37.3	9.782 46	9.881 84	0.118 16	9.900 63	52.7
37.4	9.783 46	9.883 41	0.116 59	9.900 05	52.6
37.5	9.784 45	9.884 98	0.115 02	9.899 47	52.5
37.6	9.785 43	9.886 55	0.113 45	9.898 88	52.4
37.7	9.786 42	9.888 12	0.111 88	9.898 30	52.3
37.8	9.787 39	9.889 68	0.110 32	9.897 71	52.2
37.9	9.788 37	9.891 25	0.108 75	9.897 12	52.1
38.0	9.789 34	9.892 81	0.107 19	9.896 53	52.0
38.1	9.790 31	9.894 37	0.105 63	9.895 94	51.9
38.2	9.791 28	9.895 93	0.104 07	9.895 34	51.8
38.3	9.792 24	9.897 49	0.102 51	9.894 75	51.7
38.4	9.793 19	9.899 05	0.100 95	9.894 15	51.6
38.5	9.794 15	9.900 61	0.099 39	9.893 54	51.5
38.6	9.795 10	9.902 16	0.097 84	9.892 94	51.4
38.7	9.796 05	9.903 71	0.096 29	9.892 33	51.3
38.8	9.796 99	9.905 27	0.094 73	9.891 73	51.2
38.9	9.797 93	9.906 82	0.093 18,	9.891 12	51.1
39.0	9.798 87	9.908 37	0.091 63	9.890 50	51.0
39.1	9.799 81	9.909 92	0.090 08	9.889 89	50.9
39.2	9.800 74	9.911 47	0.088 53	9.889 27	50.8
39.3	9.801 66	9.913 01	0.086 99	9.888 65	50.7
39.4	9.802 59	9.914 56	0.085 44	9.888 03	50.6
39.5	9.803 51	9.916 10	0.083 90	9.887 41	50.5
39.6	9.804 43	9.917 65	0.082 35	9.886 78	50.4
39.7	9.805 34	9.919 19	0.080 81	9.886 15	50.3
39.8	9.806 25	9.920 73	0.079 27	9.885 52	50.2
39.9	9.807 16	9.922 27	0.077 73	9.884 89	50.1
40.0	9.808 07	9.923 81	0.076 19	9.884 25	50.0
40.1	9.808 97	9.925 35	0.074 65	9.883 62	49.9
40.2	9.809 87	9.926 89	0.073 11	9.882 98	49.8
40.3	9.810 76	9.928 43	0.071 57	9.882 34	49.7
40.4	9.811 66	9.929 96	0.070 04	9.881 69	49.6
40.5	9.812 54	9.931 50	0.068 50	9.881 05	49.5
40.6	9.813 43	9.933 03	0.066 97	9.880 40	49.4
40.7	9.814 31	9.934 57	0.065 43	9.879 75	49.3
40.8	9.815 19	9.936 10	0.063 90	9.879 09	49.2
40.9	9.816 07	9.937 63	0.062 37	9.878 44	49.1
41.0	9.816 94	9.939 16	0.060 84	9.877 78	49.0
θ°	L Cos	L Cot	L Tan	L Sin	θ°

θ°	L Sin	L Tan	L Cot	L Cos	θ°
41.0	9.816 94	9.939 16	0.060 84	9.877 78	49.0
41.1	9.817 81	9.940 69	0.059 31	9.877 12	48.9
41.2	9.818 68	9.942 22	0.057 78	9.876 46	48.8
41.3	9.819 55	9.943 75	0.056 25	9.875 79	48.7
41.4	9.820 41	9.945 28	0.054 72	9.875 13	48.6
41.5	9.821 26	9.946 81	0.053 19	9.874 46	48.5
41.6	9.822 12	9.948 34	0.051 66	9.873 78	48.4
41.7	9.822 97	9.949 86	0.050 14	9.873 11	48.3
41.8	9.823 82	9.951 39	0.048 61	9.872 43	48.2
41.9	9.824 67	9.952 91	0.047 09	9.871 75	48.1
42.0	9.825 51	9.954 44	0.045 56	9.871 07	48.0
42.1	9.826 35	9.955 96	0.044 04	9.870 39	47.9
42.2	9.827 19	9.957 48	0.042 52	9.869 70	47.8
42.3	9.828 02	9.959 01	0.040 99	9.869 02	47.7
42.4	9.828 85	9.960 53	0.039 47	9.868 32	47.6
42.5	9.829 68	9.962 05	0.037 95	9.867 63	47.5
42.6	9.830 51	9.963 57	0.036 43	9.866 94	47.4
42.7	9.831 33	9.965 10	0.034 90	9.866 24	47.3
42.8	9.832 15	9.966 62	0.033 38	9.865 54	47.2
42.9	9.832 97	9.968 14	0.031 86	9.864 83	47.1
43.0	9.833 78	9.969 66	0.030 34	9.864 13	47.0
43.1	9.834 59	9.971 18	0.028 82	9.863 42	46.9
43.2	9.835 40	9.972 69	0.027 31	9.862 71	46.8
43.3	9.836 21	9.974 21	0.025 79	9.862 00	46.7
43.4	9.837 01	9.975 73	0.024 27	9.861 28	46.6
43.5	9.837 81	9.977 25	0.022 75	9.860 56	46.5
43.6	9.838 61	9.978 77	0.021 23	9.859 84	46.4
43.7	9.839 40	9.980 29	0.019 71	9.859 12	46.3
43.8	9.840 20	9.981 80	0.018 20	9.858 39	46.2
43.9	9.840 98	9.983 32	0.016 68	9.857 66	46.1
44.0	9.841 77	9.984 84	0.015 16	9.856 93	46.0
44.1	9.842 55	9.986 35	0.013 65	9.856 20	45.9
44.2	9.843 34	9.987 87	0.012 13	9.855 47	45.8
44.3	9.844 11	9.989 39	0.010 61	9.854 73	45.7
44.4	9.844 89	9.990 90	0.009 10	9.853 99	45.6
44.5	9.845 66	9.992 42	0.007 58	9.853 24	45.5
44.6	9.846 43	9.993 94	0.006 06	9.852 50	45.4
45.7	9.847 20	9.995 45	0.004 55	9.851 75	45.3
44.8	9.847 96	9.996 97	0.003 03	9.851 00	45.2
44.9	9.848 73	9.998 48	0.001 52	9.850 24	45.1
45.0	9.849 49	0.000 00	0.000 00	9.849 49	45.0
θ°	L Cos	L Cot	L Tan	L Sin	θ°

TABLE 7
Five-Place Mantissas for Common Logarithms†

N	0	1	2	3	4	5	6	7	8	9
100	00 000	043	087	130	173	217	260	303	346	389
101	00 432	475	518	561	604	647	689	732	775	817
102	00 860	903	945	988	*030	*072	*115	*157	*199	*242
103	01 284	326	368	410	452	494	536	578	620	662
104	01 703	745	787	828	870	912	953	995	*036	*078
105	02 119	160	202	243	284	325	366	407	449	490
106	02 531	572	612	653	694	735	776	816	857	898
107	02 938	979	*019	*060	*100	*141	*181	*222	*262	*302
108	03 342	383	423	463	503	543	583	623	663	703
109	03 743	782	822	862	902	941	981	*021	*060	*100
110	04 139	179	218	258	297	336	376	415	454	493
111	04 532	571	610	650	689	727	766	805	844	883
112	04 922	961	999	*038	*077	*115	*154	*192	*231	*269
113	05 308	346	385	423	461	500	538	576	614	652
114	05 690	729	767	805	843	881	918	956	994	*032
115	06 070	108	145	183	221	258	296	333	371	408
116	06 446	483	521	558	595	633	670	707	744	781
117	06 819	856	893	930	967	*004	*041	*078	*115	*151
118	07 188	225	262	298	335	372	408	445	482	518
119	07 555	591	628	664	700	737	773	809	846	882
120	07 918	954	990	*027	*063	*099	*135	*171	*207	*243
121	08 279	314	350	386	422	458	493	529	565	600
122	08 636	672	707	743	778	814	849	884	920	955
123	08 991	*026	*061	*096	*132	*167	*202	*237	*272	*307
124	09 342	377	412	447	482	517	552	587	621	656
125	09 691	726	760	795	830	864	899	934	968	*003
126	10 037	072	106	140	175	209	243	278	312	346
127	10 380	415	449	483	517	551	585	619	653	687
128	10 721	755	789	823	857	890	924	958	992	*025
129	11 059	093	126	160	193	227	261	294	327	361
130	11 394	428	461	494	528	561	594	628	661	694
131	11 727	760	793	826	860	893	926	959	992	*024
132	12 057	090	123	156	189	222	254	287	320	352
133	12 385	418	450	483	516	548	581	613	646	678
134	12 710	743	775	808	840	872	905	937	969	*001
135	13 033	066	098	130	162	194	226	258	290	322
136	13 354	386	418	450	481	513	545	577	609	640
137	13 672	704	735	767	799	830	862	893	925	956
138	13 988	*019	*051	*082	*114	*145	*176	*208	*239	*270
139	14 301	333	364	395	426	457	489	520	551	582
140	14 613	644	675	706	737	768	799	829	860	891
141	14 922	953	983	*014	*045	*076	*106	*137	*168	*198
142	15 229	259	290	320	351	381	412	442	473	503
143	15 534	564	594	625	655	685	715	746	776	806
144	15 836	866	897	927	957	987	*017	*047	*077	*107
145	16 137	167	197	227	256	286	316	346	376	406
146	16 435	465	495	524	554	584	613	643	673	702
147	16 732	761	791	820	850	879	909	938	967	997
148	17 026	056	085	114	143	173	202	231	260	289
149	17 319	348	377	406	435	464	493	522	551	580
150	17 609	638	667	696	725	754	782	811	840	869
N	0	1	2	3	4	5	6	7	8	9

Prop. Pts.

	44	43	42
1	4.4	4.3	4.2
2	8.8	8.6	8.4
3	13.2	12.9	12.6
4	17.6	17.2	16.8
5	22.0	21.5	21.0
6	26.4	25.8	25.2
7	30.8	30.1	29.4
8	35.2	34.4	33.6
9	39.6	38.7	37.8

	41	40	39
1	4.1	4.0	3.9
2	8.2	8.0	7.8
3	12.3	12.0	11.7
4	16.4	16.0	15.6
5	20.5	20.0	19.5
6	24.6	24.0	23.4
7	28.7	28.0	27.3
8	32.8	32.0	31.2
9	36.9	36.0	35.1

	38	37	36
1	3.8	3.7	3.6
2	7.6	7.4	7.2
3	11.4	11.1	10.8
4	15.2	14.8	14.4
5	19.0	18.5	18.0
6	22.8	22.2	21.6
7	26.6	25.9	25.2
8	30.4	29.6	28.8
9	34.2	33.3	32.4

	35	34	33
1	3.5	3.4	3.3
2	7.0	6.8	6.6
3	10.5	10.2	9.9
4	14.0	13.6	13.2
5	17.5	17.0	16.5
6	21.0	20.4	19.8
7	24.5	23.8	23.1
8	28.0	27.2	26.4
9	31.5	30.6	29.7

	32	31	30
1	3.2	3.1	3.0
2	6.4	6.2	6.0
3	9.6	9.3	9.0
4	12.8	12.4	12.0
5	16.0	15.5	15.0
6	19.2	18.6	18.0
7	22.4	21.7	21.0
8	25.6	24.8	24.0
9	28.8	27.9	27.0

† From P. R. Rider. *Plane and Spherical Trigonometry*. New York: The Macmillan Company, 1965.

N	0	1	2	3	4	5	6	7	8	9
150	**17 609**	**638**	**667**	**696**	**725**	**754**	**782**	**811**	**840**	**869**
151	17 898	926	955	984	*013	*041	*070	*099	*127	*156
152	18 184	213	241	270	298	327	355	384	412	441
153	18 469	498	526	554	583	611	639	667	696	724
154	18 752	780	808	837	865	893	921	949	977	*005
155	**19 033**	**061**	**089**	**117**	**145**	**173**	**201**	**229**	**257**	**285**
156	19 312	340	368	396	424	451	479	507	535	562
157	19 590	618	645	673	700	728	756	783	811	838
158	19 866	893	921	948	976	*003	*030	*058	*085	*112
159	20 140	167	194	222	249	276	303	330	358	385
160	**20 412**	**439**	**466**	**493**	**520**	**548**	**575**	**602**	**629**	**656**
161	20 683	710	737	763	790	817	844	871	898	925
162	20 952	978	*005	*032	*059	*085	*112	*139	*165	*192
163	21 219	245	272	299	325	352	378	405	431	458
164	21 484	511	537	564	590	617	643	669	696	722
165	**21 748**	**775**	**801**	**827**	**854**	**880**	**906**	**932**	**958**	**985**
166	22 011	037	063	089	115	141	167	194	220	246
167	22 272	298	324	350	376	401	427	453	479	505
168	22 531	557	583	608	634	660	686	712	737	763
169	22 789	814	840	866	891	917	943	968	994	*019
170	**23 045**	**070**	**096**	**121**	**147**	**172**	**198**	**223**	**249**	**274**
171	23 300	325	350	376	401	426	452	477	502	528
172	23 553	578	603	629	654	679	704	729	754	779
173	23 805	830	855	880	905	930	955	980	*005	*030
174	24 055	080	105	130	155	180	204	229	254	279
175	**24 304**	**329**	**353**	**378**	**403**	**428**	**452**	**477**	**502**	**527**
176	24 551	576	601	625	650	674	699	724	748	773
177	24 797	822	846	871	895	920	944	969	993	*018
178	25 042	066	091	115	139	164	188	212	237	261
179	25 285	310	334	358	382	406	431	455	479	503
180	**25 527**	**551**	**575**	**600**	**624**	**648**	**672**	**696**	**720**	**744**
181	25 768	792	816	840	864	888	912	935	959	983
182	26 007	031	055	079	102	126	150	174	198	221
183	26 245	269	293	316	340	364	387	411	435	458
184	26 482	505	529	553	576	600	623	647	670	694
185	**26 717**	**741**	**764**	**788**	**811**	**834**	**858**	**881**	**905**	**928**
186	26 951	975	998	*021	*045	*068	*091	*114	*138	*161
187	27 184	207	231	254	277	300	323	346	370	393
188	27 416	439	462	485	508	531	554	577	600	623
189	27 646	669	692	715	738	761	784	807	830	852
190	**27 875**	**898**	**921**	**944**	**967**	**989**	***012**	***035**	***058**	***081**
191	28 103	126	149	171	194	217	240	262	285	307
192	28 330	353	375	398	421	443	466	488	511	533
193	28 556	578	601	623	646	668	691	713	735	758
194	28 780	803	825	847	870	892	914	937	959	981
195	**29 003**	**026**	**048**	**070**	**092**	**115**	**137**	**159**	**181**	**203**
196	29 226	248	270	292	314	336	358	380	403	425
197	29 447	469	491	513	535	557	579	601	623	645
198	29 667	688	710	732	754	776	798	820	842	863
199	29 885	907	929	951	973	994	*016	*038	*060	*081
200	**30 103**	**125**	**146**	**168**	**190**	**211**	**233**	**255**	**276**	**298**
N	0	1	2	3	4	5	6	7	8	9

Prop. Pts.

	29	28
1	2.9	2.8
2	5.8	5.6
3	8.7	8.4
4	11.6	11.2
5	14.5	14.0
6	17.4	16.8
7	20.3	19.6
8	23.2	22.4
9	26.1	25.2

	27	26
1	2.7	2.6
2	5.4	5.2
3	8.1	7.8
4	10.8	10.4
5	13.5	13.0
6	16.2	15.6
7	18.9	18.2
8	21.6	20.8
9	24.3	23.4

	25	24
1	2.5	2.4
2	5.0	4.8
3	7.5	7.2
4	10.0	9.6
5	12.5	12.0
6	15.0	14.4
7	17.5	16.8
8	20.0	19.2
9	22.5	21.6

	23	22
1	2.3	2.2
2	4.6	4.4
3	6.9	6.6
4	9.2	8.8
5	11.5	11.0
6	13.8	13.2
7	16.1	15.4
8	18.4	17.6
9	20.7	19.8

	21
1	2.1
2	4.2
3	6.3
4	8.4
5	10.5
6	12.6
7	14.7
8	16.8
9	18.9

Prop. Pts.

N	0	1	2	3	4	5	6	7	8	9		Prop. Pts.	
200	**30 103**	**125**	**146**	**168**	**190**	**211**	**233**	**255**	**276**	**298**		**22**	**21**
201	30 320	341	363	384	406	428	449	471	492	514	1	2.2	2.1
202	30 535	557	578	600	621	643	664	685	707	728	2	4.4	4.2
203	30 750	771	792	814	835	856	878	899	920	942	3	6.6	6.3
204	30 963	984	*006	*027	*048	*069	*091	*112	*133	*154	4	8.8	8.4
205	**31 175**	**197**	**218**	**239**	**260**	**281**	**302**	**323**	**345**	**366**	5	11.0	10.5
206	31 387	408	429	450	471	492	513	534	555	576	6	13.2	12.6
207	31 597	618	639	660	681	702	723	744	765	785	7	15.4	14.7
208	31 806	827	848	869	890	911	931	952	973	994	8	17.6	16.8
209	32 015	035	056	077	098	118	139	160	181	201	9	19.8	18.9
210	**32 222**	**243**	**263**	**284**	**305**	**325**	**346**	**366**	**387**	**408**		**20**	
211	32 428	449	469	490	510	531	552	572	593	613	1	2	
212	32 634	654	675	695	715	736	756	777	797	818	2	4	
213	32 838	858	879	899	919	940	960	980	*001	*021	3	6	
214	33 041	062	082	102	122	143	163	183	203	224	4	8	
215	**33 244**	**264**	**284**	**304**	**325**	**345**	**365**	**385**	**405**	**425**	5	10	
216	33 445	465	486	506	526	546	566	586	606	626	6	12	
217	33 646	666	686	706	726	746	766	786	806	826	7	14	
218	33 846	866	885	905	925	945	965	985	*005	*025	8	16	
219	34 044	064	084	104	124	143	163	183	203	223	9	18	
220	**34 242**	**262**	**282**	**301**	**321**	**341**	**361**	**380**	**400**	**420**		**19**	
221	34 439	459	479	498	518	537	557	577	596	616	1	1.9	
222	34 635	655	674	694	713	733	753	772	792	811	2	3.8	
223	34 830	850	869	889	908	928	947	967	986	*005	3	5.7	
224	35 025	044	064	083	102	122	141	160	180	199	4	7.6	
225	**35 218**	**238**	**257**	**276**	**295**	**315**	**334**	**353**	**372**	**392**	5	9.5	
226	35 411	430	449	468	488	507	526	545	564	583	6	11.4	
227	35 603	622	641	660	679	698	717	736	755	774	7	13.3	
228	35 793	813	832	851	870	889	908	927	946	965	8	15.2	
229	35 984	*003	*021	*040	*059	*078	*097	*116	*135	*154	9	17.1	
230	**36 173**	**192**	**211**	**229**	**248**	**267**	**286**	**305**	**324**	**342**		**18**	
231	36 361	380	399	418	436	455	474	493	511	530	1	1.8	
232	36 549	568	586	605	624	642	661	680	698	717	2	3.6	
233	36 736	754	773	791	810	829	847	866	884	903	3	5.4	
234	36 922	940	959	977	996	*014	*033	*051	*070	*088	4	7.2	
235	**37 107**	**125**	**144**	**162**	**181**	**199**	**218**	**236**	**254**	**273**	5	9.0	
236	37 291	310	328	346	365	383	401	420	438	457	6	10.8	
237	37 475	493	511	530	548	566	585	603	621	639	7	12.6	
238	37 658	676	694	712	731	749	767	785	803	822	8	14.4	
239	37 840	858	876	894	912	931	949	967	985	*003	9	16.2	
240	**38 021**	**039**	**057**	**075**	**093**	**112**	**130**	**148**	**166**	**184**		**17**	
241	38 202	220	238	256	274	292	310	328	346	364	1	1.7	
242	38 382	399	417	435	453	471	489	507	525	543	2	3.4	
243	38 561	578	596	614	632	650	668	686	703	721	3	5.1	
244	38 739	757	775	792	810	828	846	863	881	899	4	6.8	
245	**38 917**	**934**	**952**	**970**	**987**	***005**	***023**	***041**	***058**	***076**	5	8.5	
246	39 094	111	129	146	164	182	199	217	235	252	6	10.2	
247	39 270	287	305	322	340	358	375	393	410	428	7	11.9	
248	39 445	463	480	498	515	533	550	568	585	602	8	13.6	
249	39 620	637	655	672	690	707	724	742	759	777	9	15.3	
250	**39 794**	**811**	**829**	**846**	**863**	**881**	**898**	**915**	**933**	**950**			
N	0	1	2	3	4	5	6	7	8	9		Prop. Pts.	

Table 7 / Mantissas of logarithms ☐ **725**

N	0	1	2	3	4	5	6	7	8	9
250	39 794	811	829	846	863	881	898	915	933	950
251	39 967	985	*002	*019	*037	*054	*071	*088	*106	*123
252	40 140	157	175	192	209	226	243	261	278	295
253	40 312	329	346	364	381	398	415	432	449	466
254	40 483	500	518	535	552	569	586	603	620	637
255	40 654	671	688	705	722	739	756	773	790	807
256	40 824	841	858	875	892	909	926	943	960	976
257	40 993	*010	*027	*044	*061	*078	*095	*111	*128	*145
258	41 162	179	196	212	229	246	263	280	296	313
259	41 330	347	363	380	397	414	430	447	464	481
260	41 497	514	531	547	564	581	597	614	631	647
261	41 664	681	697	714	731	747	764	780	797	814
262	41 830	847	863	880	896	913	929	946	963	979
263	41 996	*012	*029	*045	*062	*078	*095	*111	*127	*144
264	42 160	177	193	210	226	243	259	275	292	308
265	42 325	341	357	374	390	406	423	439	455	472
266	42 488	504	521	537	553	570	586	602	619	635
267	42 651	667	684	700	716	732	749	765	781	797
268	42 813	830	846	862	878	894	911	927	943	959
269	42 975	991	*008	*024	*040	*056	*072	*088	*104	*120
270	43 136	152	169	185	201	217	233	249	265	281
271	43 297	313	329	345	361	377	393	409	425	441
272	43 457	473	489	505	521	537	553	569	584	600
273	43 616	632	648	664	680	696	712	727	743	759
274	43 775	791	807	823	838	854	870	886	902	917
275	43 933	949	965	981	996	*012	*028	*044	*059	*075
276	44 091	107	122	138	154	170	185	201	217	232
277	44 248	264	279	295	311	326	342	358	373	389
278	44 404	420	436	451	467	483	498	514	529	545
279	44 560	576	592	607	623	638	654	669	685	700
280	44 716	731	747	762	778	793	809	824	840	855
281	44 871	886	902	917	932	948	963	979	994	*010
282	45 025	040	056	071	086	102	117	133	148	163
283	45 179	194	209	225	240	255	271	286	301	317
284	45 332	347	362	378	393	408	423	439	454	469
285	45 484	500	515	530	545	561	576	591	606	621
286	45 637	652	667	682	697	712	728	743	758	773
287	45 788	803	818	834	849	864	879	894	909	924
288	45 939	954	969	984	*000	*015	*030	*045	*060	*075
289	46 090	105	120	135	150	165	180	195	210	225
290	46 240	255	270	285	300	315	330	345	359	374
291	46 389	404	419	434	449	464	479	494	509	523
292	46 538	553	568	583	598	613	627	642	657	672
293	46 687	702	716	731	746	761	776	790	805	820
294	46 835	850	864	879	894	909	923	938	953	967
295	46 982	997	*012	*026	*041	*056	*070	*085	*100	*114
296	47 129	144	159	173	188	202	217	232	246	261
297	47 276	290	305	319	334	349	363	378	392	407
298	47 422	436	451	465	480	494	509	524	538	553
299	47 567	582	596	611	625	640	654	669	683	698
300	47 712	727	741	756	770	784	799	813	828	842
N	0	1	2	3	4	5	6	7	8	9

Prop. Pts.

	18	17
1	1.8	1.7
2	3.6	3.4
3	5.4	5.1
4	7.2	6.8
5	9.0	8.5
6	10.8	10.2
7	12.6	11.9
8	14.4	13.6
9	16.2	15.3

M

$= \log_{10} e$

$= \log_{10} 2.718 \cdots$

$= 0.434\ 294\ 481\ 9$

	16	15
1	1.6	1.5
2	3.2	3.0
3	4.8	4.5
4	6.4	6.0
5	8.0	7.5
6	9.6	9.0
7	11.2	10.5
8	12.8	12.0
9	14.4	13.5

	14
1	1.4
2	2.8
3	4.2
4	5.6
5	7.0
6	8.4
7	9.8
8	11.2
9	12.6

Prop. Pts.

N	0	1	2	3	4	5	6	7	8	9
300	47 712	727	741	756	770	784	799	813	828	842
301	47 857	871	885	900	914	929	943	958	972	986
302	48 001	015	029	044	058	073	087	101	116	130
303	48 144	159	173	187	202	216	230	244	259	273
304	48 287	302	316	330	344	359	373	387	401	416
305	48 430	444	458	473	487	501	515	530	544	558
306	48 572	586	601	615	629	643	657	671	686	700
307	48 714	728	742	756	770	785	799	813	827	841
308	48 855	869	883	897	911	926	940	954	968	982
309	48 996	*010	*024	*038	*052	*066	*080	*094	*108	*122
310	49 136	150	164	178	192	206	220	234	248	262
311	49 276	290	304	318	332	346	360	374	388	402
312	49 415	429	443	457	471	485	499	513	527	541
313	49 554	568	582	596	610	624	638	651	665	679
314	49 693	707	721	734	748	762	776	790	803	817
315	49 831	845	859	872	886	900	914	927	941	955
316	49 969	982	996	*010	*024	*037	*051	*065	*079	*092
317	50 106	120	133	147	161	174	188	202	215	229
318	50 243	256	270	284	297	311	325	338	352	365
319	50 379	393	406	420	433	447	461	474	488	501
320	50 515	529	542	556	569	583	596	610	623	637
321	50 651	664	678	691	705	718	732	745	759	772
322	50 786	799	813	826	840	853	866	880	893	907
323	50 920	933	947	961	974	987	*001	*014	*028	*041
324	51 055	068	081	095	108	121	135	148	162	175
325	51 188	202	215	228	242	255	268	282	295	308
326	51 322	335	348	362	375	388	402	415	428	441
327	51 455	468	481	495	508	521	534	548	561	574
328	51 587	601	614	627	640	654	667	680	693	706
329	51 720	733	746	759	772	786	799	812	825	838
330	51 851	865	878	891	904	917	930	943	957	970
331	51 983	996	*009	*022	*035	*048	*061	*075	*088	*101
332	52 114	127	140	153	166	179	192	205	218	231
333	52 244	257	270	284	297	310	323	336	349	362
334	52 375	388	401	414	427	440	453	466	479	492
335	52 504	517	530	543	556	569	582	595	608	621
336	52 634	647	660	673	686	699	711	724	737	750
337	52 763	776	789	802	815	827	840	853	866	879
338	52 892	905	917	930	943	956	969	982	994	*007
339	53 020	033	046	058	071	084	097	110	122	135
340	53 148	161	173	186	199	212	224	237	250	263
341	53 275	288	301	314	326	339	352	364	377	390
342	53 403	415	428	441	453	466	479	491	504	517
343	53 529	542	555	567	580	593	605	618	631	643
344	53 656	668	681	694	706	719	732	744	757	769
345	53 782	794	807	820	832	845	857	870	882	895
346	53 908	920	933	945	958	970	983	995	*008	*020
347	54 033	045	058	070	083	095	108	120	133	145
348	54 158	170	183	195	208	220	233	245	258	270
349	54 283	295	307	320	332	345	357	370	382	394
350	54 407	419	432	444	456	469	481	494	506	518
N	0	1	2	3	4	5	6	7	8	9

Prop. Pts.

	15		14		13		12
1	1.5	1	1.4	1	1.3	1	1.2
2	3.0	2	2.8	2	2.6	2	2.4
3	4.5	3	4.2	3	3.9	3	3.6
4	6.0	4	5.6	4	5.2	4	4.8
5	7.5	5	7.0	5	6.5	5	6.0
6	9.0	6	8.4	6	7.8	6	7.2
7	10.5	7	9.8	7	9.1	7	8.4
8	12.0	8	11.2	8	10.4	8	9.6
9	13.5	9	12.6	9	11.7	9	10.8

Table 7 / Mantissas of logarithms □ 727

N	0	1	2	3	4	5	6	7	8	9
350	**54 407**	**419**	**432**	**444**	**456**	**469**	**481**	**494**	**506**	**518**
351	54 531	543	555	568	580	593	605	617	630	642
352	54 654	667	679	691	704	716	728	741	753	765
353	54 777	790	802	814	827	839	851	864	876	888
354	54 900	913	925	937	949	962	974	986	998	*011
355	**55 023**	**035**	**047**	**060**	**072**	**084**	**096**	**108**	**121**	**133**
356	55 145	157	169	182	194	206	218	230	242	255
357	55 267	279	291	303	315	328	340	352	364	376
358	55 388	400	413	425	437	449	461	473	485	497
359	55 509	522	534	546	558	570	582	594	606	618
360	**55 630**	**642**	**654**	**666**	**678**	**691**	**703**	**715**	**727**	**739**
361	55 751	763	775	787	799	811	823	835	847	859
362	55 871	883	895	907	919	931	943	955	967	979
363	55 991	*003	*015	*027	*038	*050	*062	*074	*086	*098
364	56 110	122	134	146	158	170	182	194	205	217
365	**56 229**	**241**	**253**	**265**	**277**	**289**	**301**	**312**	**324**	**336**
366	56 348	360	372	384	396	407	419	431	443	455
367	56 467	478	490	502	514	526	538	549	561	573
368	56 585	597	608	620	632	644	656	667	679	691
369	56 703	714	726	738	750	761	773	785	797	808
370	**56 820**	**832**	**844**	**855**	**867**	**879**	**891**	**902**	**914**	**926**
371	56 937	949	961	972	984	996	*008	*019	*031	*043
372	57 054	066	078	089	101	113	124	136	148	159
373	57 171	183	194	206	217	229	241	252	264	276
374	57 287	299	310	322	334	345	357	368	380	392
375	**57 403**	**415**	**426**	**438**	**449**	**461**	**473**	**484**	**496**	**507**
376	57 519	530	542	553	565	576	588	600	611	623
377	57 634	646	657	669	680	692	703	715	726	738
378	57 749	761	772	784	795	807	818	830	841	852
379	57 864	875	887	898	910	921	933	944	955	967
380	**57 978**	**990**	***100**	***013**	***024**	***035**	***047**	***058**	***070**	***081**
381	58 092	104	115	127	138	149	161	172	184	195
382	58 206	218	229	240	252	263	274	286	297	309
383	58 320	331	343	354	365	377	388	399	410	422
384	58 433	444	456	467	478	490	501	512	524	535
385	**58 546**	**557**	**569**	**580**	**591**	**602**	**614**	**625**	**636**	**647**
386	58 659	670	681	692	704	715	726	737	749	760
387	58 771	782	794	805	816	827	838	850	861	872
388	58 883	894	906	917	928	939	950	961	973	984
389	58 995	*006	*017	*028	*040	*051	*062	*073	*084	*095
390	**59 106**	**118**	**129**	**140**	**151**	**162**	**173**	**184**	**195**	**207**
391	59 218	229	240	251	262	273	284	295	306	318
392	59 329	340	351	362	373	384	395	406	417	428
393	59 439	450	461	472	483	494	506	517	528	539
394	59 550	561	572	583	594	605	616	627	638	649
395	**59 660**	**671**	**682**	**693**	**704**	**715**	**726**	**737**	**748**	**759**
396	59 770	780	791	802	813	824	835	846	857	868
397	59 879	890	901	912	923	934	945	956	966	977
398	59 988	999	*010	*021	*032	*043	*054	*065	*076	*086
399	60 097	108	119	130	141	152	163	173	184	195
400	**60 206**	**217**	**228**	**239**	**249**	**260**	**271**	**282**	**293**	**304**
N	0	1	2	3	4	5	6	7	8	9

Prop. Pts.

	13	12
1	1.3	1.2
2	2.6	2.4
3	3.9	3.6
4	5.2	4.8
5	6.5	6.0
6	7.8	7.2
7	9.1	8.4
8	10.4	9.6
9	11.7	10.8

	11	10
1	1.1	1.0
2	2.2	2.0
3	3.3	3.0
4	4.4	4.0
5	5.5	5.0
6	6.6	6.0
7	7.7	7.0
8	8.8	8.0
9	9.9	9.0

N	0	1	2	3	4	5	6	7	8	9	Prop. Pts.
400	60 206	217	228	239	249	260	271	282	293	304	
401	60 314	325	336	347	358	369	379	390	401	412	
402	60 423	433	444	455	466	477	487	498	509	520	
403	60 531	541	552	563	574	584	595	606	617	627	
404	60 638	649	660	670	681	692	703	713	724	735	
405	60 746	756	767	778	788	799	810	821	831	842	
406	60 853	863	874	885	895	906	917	927	938	949	
407	60 959	970	981	991	*002	*013	*023	*034	*045	*055	
408	61 066	077	087	098	109	119	130	140	151	162	
409	61 172	183	194	204	215	225	236	247	257	268	
410	61 278	289	300	310	321	331	342	352	363	374	
411	61 384	395	405	416	426	437	448	458	469	479	
412	61 490	500	511	521	532	542	553	563	574	584	
413	61 595	606	616	627	637	648	658	669	679	690	
414	61 700	711	721	731	742	752	763	773	784	794	
415	61 805	815	826	836	847	857	868	878	888	899	
416	61 909	920	930	941	951	962	972	982	993	*003	
417	62 014	024	034	045	055	066	076	086	097	107	
418	62 118	128	138	149	159	170	180	190	201	211	
419	62 221	232	242	252	263	273	284	294	304	315	
420	62 325	335	346	356	366	377	387	397	408	418	
421	62 428	439	449	459	469	480	490	500	511	521	
422	62 531	542	552	562	572	583	593	603	613	624	
423	62 634	644	655	665	675	685	696	706	716	726	
424	62 737	747	757	767	778	788	798	808	818	829	
425	62 839	849	859	870	880	890	900	910	921	931	
426	62 941	951	961	972	982	992	*002	*012	*022	*033	
427	63 043	053	063	073	083	094	104	114	124	134	
428	63 144	155	165	175	185	195	205	215	225	236	
429	63 246	256	266	276	286	296	306	317	327	337	
430	63 347	357	367	377	387	397	407	417	428	438	
431	63 448	458	468	478	488	498	508	518	528	538	
432	63 548	558	568	579	589	599	609	619	629	639	
433	63 649	659	669	679	689	699	709	719	729	739	
434	63 749	759	769	779	789	799	809	819	829	839	
435	63 849	859	869	879	889	899	909	919	929	939	
436	63 949	959	969	979	988	998	*008	*018	*028	*038	
437	64 048	058	068	078	088	098	108	118	128	137	
438	64 147	157	167	177	187	197	207	217	227	237	
439	64 246	256	266	276	286	296	306	316	326	335	
440	64 345	355	365	375	385	395	404	414	424	434	
441	64 444	454	464	473	483	493	503	513	523	532	
442	64 542	552	562	572	582	591	601	611	631	631	
443	64 640	650	660	670	680	689	699	709	719	729	
444	64 738	748	758	768	777	787	797	807	816	826	
445	64 836	846	856	865	875	885	895	904	914	924	
446	64 933	943	953	963	972	982	992	*002	*011	*021	
447	65 031	040	050	060	070	079	089	099	108	118	
448	65 128	137	147	157	167	176	186	196	205	215	
449	65 225	234	244	254	263	273	283	292	302	312	
450	65 321	331	341	350	360	369	379	389	398	408	
N	0	1	2	3	4	5	6	7	8	9	Prop. Pts.

Prop. Pts.

11
1 1.1
2 2.2
3 3.3
4 4.4
5 5.5
6 6.6
7 7.7
8 8.8
9 9.9

10
1 1.0
2 2.0
3 3.0
4 4.0
5 5.0
6 6.0
7 7.0
8 8.0
9 9.0

9
1 0.9
2 1.8
3 2.7
4 3.6
5 4.5
6 5.4
7 6.3
8 7.2
9 8.1

Table 7 / Mantissas of logarithms □ 729

N	0	1	2	3	4	5	6	7	8	9
450	**65 321**	**331**	**341**	**350**	**360**	**369**	**379**	**389**	**398**	**408**
451	65 418	427	437	447	456	466	475	485	495	504
452	65 514	523	533	543	552	562	571	581	591	600
453	65 610	619	629	639	648	658	667	677	686	696
454	65 706	715	725	734	744	753	763	772	782	792
455	**65 801**	**811**	**820**	**830**	**839**	**849**	**858**	**868**	**877**	**887**
456	65 896	906	916	925	935	944	954	963	973	982
457	65 992	*001	*011	*020	*030	*039	*049	*058	*068	*077
458	66 087	096	106	115	124	134	143	153	162	172
459	66 181	191	200	210	219	229	238	247	257	266
460	**66 276**	**285**	**295**	**304**	**314**	**323**	**332**	**342**	**351**	**361**
461	66 370	380	389	398	408	417	427	436	445	455
462	66 464	474	483	492	502	511	521	530	539	549
463	66 558	567	577	586	596	605	614	624	633	642
464	66 652	661	671	680	689	699	708	717	727	736
465	**66 745**	**755**	**764**	**773**	**783**	**792**	**801**	**811**	**820**	**829**
466	66 839	848	857	867	876	885	894	904	913	922
467	66 932	941	950	960	969	978	987	997	*006	*015
468	67 025	034	043	052	062	071	080	089	099	108
469	67 117	127	136	145	154	164	173	182	191	201
470	**67 210**	**219**	**228**	**237**	**247**	**256**	**265**	**274**	**284**	**293**
471	67 302	311	321	330	339	348	357	367	376	385
472	67 394	403	413	422	431	440	449	459	468	477
473	67 486	495	504	514	523	532	541	550	560	569
474	67 578	587	596	605	614	624	633	642	651	660
475	**67 669**	**679**	**688**	**697**	**706**	**715**	**724**	**733**	**742**	**752**
476	67 761	770	779	788	797	806	815	825	834	843
477	67 852	861	870	879	888	897	906	916	925	934
478	67 943	952	961	970	979	988	997	*006	*015	*024
479	68 034	043	052	061	070	079	088	097	106	115
480	**68 124**	**133**	**142**	**151**	**160**	**169**	**178**	**187**	**196**	**205**
481	68 215	224	233	242	251	260	269	278	287	296
482	68 305	314	323	332	341	350	359	368	377	386
483	68 395	404	413	422	431	440	449	458	467	476
484	68 485	494	502	511	520	529	538	547	556	565
485	**68 574**	**583**	**592**	**601**	**610**	**619**	**628**	**637**	**646**	**655**
486	68 664	673	681	690	699	708	717	726	735	744
487	68 753	762	771	780	789	797	806	815	824	833
488	68 842	851	860	869	878	886	895	904	913	922
489	68 931	940	949	958	966	975	984	993	*002	*011
490	**69 020**	**028**	**037**	**046**	**055**	**064**	**073**	**082**	**090**	**099**
491	69 108	117	126	135	144	152	161	170	179	188
492	69 197	205	214	223	232	241	249	258	267	276
493	69 285	294	302	311	320	329	338	346	355	364
494	69 373	381	390	399	408	417	425	434	443	452
495	**69 461**	**469**	**478**	**487**	**496**	**504**	**513**	**522**	**531**	**539**
496	69 548	557	566	574	583	592	601	609	618	627
497	69 636	644	653	662	671	679	688	697	705	714
498	69 723	732	740	749	758	767	775	784	793	801
499	69 810	819	827	836	845	854	862	871	880	888
500	**69 897**	**906**	**914**	**923**	**932**	**940**	**949**	**958**	**966**	**975**
N	0	1	2	3	4	5	6	7	8	9

Prop. Pts.

	10	9
1	1.0	0.9
2	2.0	1.8
3	3.0	2.7
4	4.0	3.6
5	5.0	4.5
6	6.0	5.4
7	7.0	6.3
8	8.0	7.2
9	9.0	8.1

	8
1	0.8
2	1.6
3	2.4
4	3.2
5	4.0
6	4.8
7	5.6
8	6.4
9	7.2

N	0	1	2	3	4	5	6	7	8	9
500	69 897	906	914	923	932	940	949	958	966	975
501	69 984	992	*001	*010	*018	*027	*036	*044	*053	*062
502	70 070	079	088	096	105	114	122	131	140	148
503	70 157	165	174	183	191	200	209	217	226	234
504	70 243	252	260	269	278	286	295	303	312	321
505	70 329	338	346	355	364	372	381	389	398	406
506	70 415	424	432	441	449	458	467	475	484	492
507	70 501	509	518	526	535	544	552	561	569	578
508	70 586	595	603	612	621	629	638	646	655	663
509	70 672	680	689	697	706	714	723	731	740	749
510	70 757	766	774	783	791	800	808	817	825	834
511	70 842	851	859	868	876	885	893	902	910	919
512	70 927	935	944	952	961	969	978	896	995	*003
513	71 012	020	029	037	046	054	063	071	079	088
514	71 096	105	113	122	130	139	147	155	164	172
515	71 181	189	198	206	214	223	231	240	248	257
516	71 265	273	282	290	299	307	315	324	332	341
517	71 349	357	366	374	383	391	399	408	416	425
518	71 433	441	450	458	466	475	483	492	500	508
519	71 517	525	533	542	550	559	567	575	584	592
520	71 600	609	617	625	634	642	650	659	667	675
521	71 684	692	700	709	717	725	734	742	750	759
522	71 767	775	784	792	800	809	817	825	834	842
523	71 850	858	867	875	883	892	900	908	917	925
524	71 933	941	950	958	966	975	983	991	999	*008
525	72 016	024	032	041	049	057	066	074	082	090
526	72 099	107	115	123	132	140	148	156	165	173
527	72 181	189	198	206	214	222	230	239	247	255
528	72 263	272	280	288	296	304	313	321	329	337
529	72 346	354	362	370	378	387	395	403	411	419
530	72 428	436	444	452	460	469	477	485	493	501
531	72 509	518	526	534	542	550	558	567	575	583
532	72 591	599	607	616	624	632	640	648	656	665
533	72 673	681	689	697	705	713	722	730	738	746
534	72 754	762	770	779	787	795	803	811	819	827
535	72 835	843	852	860	868	876	884	892	900	908
536	72 916	925	933	941	949	957	965	973	981	989
537	72 997	*006	*014	*022	*030	*038	*046 *	054	*062	*070
538	73 078	086	094	102	111	119	127	135	143	151
539	73 159	167	175	183	191	199	207	215	223	231
540	73 239	247	255	263	272	280	288	296	304	312
541	73 320	328	336	344	352	360	368	376	384	392
542	73 400	408	416	424	432	440	448	456	464	472
543	73 480	488	496	504	512	520	528	536	544	552
544	73 560	568	576	584	592	600	608	616	624	632
545	73 640	648	656	664	672	679	687	695	703	711
546	73 719	727	735	743	751	759	767	775	783	791
547	73 799	807	815	823	830	838	846	854	862	870
548	73 878	886	894	902	910	918	926	933	941	949
549	73 957	965	973	981	989	997	*005	*013	*020	*028
550	74 036	044	052	060	068	076	084	092	099	107
N	0	1	2	3	4	5	6	7	8	9

Prop Pts.

9
1	0.9
2	1.8
3	2.7
4	3.6
5	4.5
6	5.4
7	6.3
8	7.2
9	8.1

8
1	0.8
2	1.6
3	2.4
4	3.2
5	4.0
6	4.8
7	5.6
8	6.4
9	7.2

7
1	0.7
2	1.4
3	2.1
4	2.8
5	3.5
6	4.2
7	4.9
8	5.6
9	6.3

Table 7 / Mantissas of logarithms □ **731**

N	0	1	2	3	4	5	6	7	8	9
550	**74 036**	**044**	**052**	**060**	**068**	**076**	**084**	**092**	**099**	**107**
551	74 115	123	131	139	147	155	162	170	178	186
552	74 194	202	210	218	225	233	241	249	257	265
553	74 273	280	288	296	304	312	320	327	335	343
554	74 351	359	367	374	382	390	398	406	414	421
555	**74 429**	**437**	**445**	**453**	**461**	**468**	**476**	**484**	**492**	**500**
556	74 507	515	523	531	539	547	554	562	570	578
557	74 586	593	601	609	617	624	632	640	648	656
558	74 663	671	679	687	695	702	710	718	726	733
559	74 741	749	757	764	772	780	788	796	803	811
560	**74 819**	**827**	**834**	**842**	**850**	**858**	**865**	**873**	**881**	**889**
561	74 896	904	912	920	927	935	943	950	958	966
562	74 974	981	989	997	*005	*012	*020	*028	*035	*043
563	75 051	059	066	074	082	089	097	105	113	120
564	75 128	136	143	151	159	166	174	182	189	197
565	**75 205**	**213**	**220**	**228**	**236**	**243**	**251**	**259**	**266**	**274**
566	75 282	289	297	305	312	320	328	335	343	351
567	75 358	366	374	381	389	397	404	412	420	427
568	75 435	442	450	458	465	473	481	488	496	504
569	75 511	519	526	534	542	549	557	565	572	580
570	**75 587**	**595**	**603**	**610**	**618**	**626**	**633**	**641**	**648**	**656**
571	75 664	671	679	686	694	702	709	717	724	732
572	75 740	747	755	762	770	778	785	793	800	808
573	75 815	823	831	838	846	853	861	868	876	884
574	75 891	899	906	914	921	929	937	944	952	959
575	**75 967**	**974**	**982**	**989**	**997**	***005**	***012**	***020**	***027**	***035**
576	76 042	050	057	065	072	080	087	095	103	110
577	76 118	125	133	140	148	155	163	170	178	185
578	76 193	200	208	215	223	230	238	245	253	260
579	76 268	275	283	290	298	305	313	320	328	335
580	**76 343**	**350**	**358**	**365**	**373**	**380**	**388**	**395**	**403**	**410**
581	76 418	425	433	440	448	455	462	470	477	485
582	76 492	500	507	515	522	530	537	545	552	559
583	76 567	574	582	589	597	604	612	619	626	634
584	76 641	649	656	664	671	678	686	693	701	708
585	**76 716**	**723**	**730**	**738**	**745**	**753**	**760**	**768**	**775**	**782**
586	76 790	797	805	812	819	827	834	842	849	856
587	76 864	871	879	886	893	901	908	916	923	930
588	76 938	945	953	960	967	975	982	989	997	*004
589	77 012	019	026	034	041	048	056	063	070	078
590	**77 085**	**093**	**100**	**107**	**115**	**122**	**129**	**137**	**144**	**151**
591	77 159	166	173	181	188	195	203	210	217	225
592	77 232	240	247	254	262	269	276	283	291	298
593	77 305	313	320	327	335	342	349	357	364	371
594	77 379	386	393	401	408	415	422	430	437	444
595	**77 452**	**459**	**466**	**474**	**481**	**488**	**495**	**503**	**510**	**517**
596	77 525	532	539	546	554	561	568	576	583	590
597	77 597	605	612	619	627	634	641	648	656	663
598	77 670	677	685	692	699	706	714	721	728	735
599	77 743	750	757	764	772	779	786	793	801	808
600	**77 815**	**822**	**830**	**837**	**844**	**851**	**859**	**866**	**873**	**880**
N	0	1	2	3	4	5	6	7	8	9

Prop. Pts.

	8	7
1	0.8	0.7
2	1.6	1.4
3	2.4	2.1
4	3.2	2.8
5	4.0	3.5
6	4.8	4.2
7	5.6	4.9
8	6.4	5.6
9	7.2	6.3

Prop. Pts.

Table 7 / Mantissas of logarithms □ 733

N	0	1	2	3	4	5	6	7	8	9
600	77 815	822	830	837	844	851	859	866	873	880
601	77 887	895	902	909	916	924	931	938	945	952
602	77 960	967	974	981	988	996	*003	*010	*017	*025
603	78 032	039	046	053	061	068	075	082	089	097
604	78 104	111	118	125	132	140	147	154	161	168
605	78 176	183	190	197	204	211	219	226	233	240
606	78 247	254	262	269	276	283	290	297	305	312
607	78 319	326	333	340	347	355	362	369	376	383
608	78 390	398	405	412	419	426	433	440	447	455
609	78 462	469	476	483	490	497	504	512	519	526
610	78 533	540	547	554	561	569	576	583	590	597
611	78 604	611	618	625	633	640	647	654	661	668
612	78 675	682	689	696	704	711	718	725	732	739
613	78 746	753	760	767	774	781	789	796	803	810
614	78 817	824	831	838	845	852	859	866	873	880
615	78 888	895	902	909	916	923	930	937	944	951
616	78 958	965	972	979	986	993	*000	*007	*014	*021
617	79 029	036	043	050	057	064	071	078	085	092
618	79 099	106	113	120	127	134	141	148	155	162
619	79 169	176	183	190	197	204	211	218	225	232
620	79 239	246	253	260	267	274	281	288	295	302
621	79 309	316	323	330	337	344	351	358	365	372
622	79 379	386	393	400	407	414	421	428	435	442
623	79 449	456	463	470	477	484	491	498	505	511
624	79 518	525	532	539	546	553	560	567	574	581
625	79 588	595	602	609	616	623	630	637	644	650
626	79 657	664	671	678	685	692	699	706	713	720
627	79 727	734	741	748	754	761	768	775	782	789
628	79 796	803	810	817	824	831	837	844	851	858
629	79 865	872	879	886	893	900	906	913	920	927
630	79 934	941	948	955	962	969	975	982	989	996
631	80 003	010	017	024	030	037	044	051	058	065
632	80 072	079	085	092	099	106	113	120	127	134
633	80 140	147	154	161	168	175	182	188	195	202
634	80 209	216	223	229	236	243	250	257	264	271
635	80 277	284	291	298	305	312	318	325	332	339
636	80 346	353	359	366	373	380	387	393	400	407
637	80 414	421	428	434	441	448	455	462	468	475
638	80 482	489	496	502	509	516	523	530	536	543
639	80 550	557	564	570	577	584	591	598	604	611
640	80 618	625	632	638	645	652	659	665	672	679
641	80 686	693	699	706	713	720	726	733	740	747
642	80 754	760	767	774	781	787	794	801	808	814
643	80 821	828	835	841	848	855	862	868	875	882
644	80 889	895	902	909	916	922	929	936	943	949
645	80 956	963	969	976	983	990	996	*003	*010	*017
646	81 023	030	037	043	050	057	064	070	077	084
647	81 090	097	104	111	117	124	131	137	144	151
648	81 158	164	171	178	184	191	198	204	211	218
649	81 224	231	238	245	251	258	265	271	278	285
650	81 291	298	305	311	318	325	331	338	345	351
N	0	1	2	3	4	5	6	7	8	9

Prop. Pts.

8

1	0.8
2	1.6
3	2.4
4	3.2
5	4.0
6	4.8
7	5.6
8	6.4
9	7.2

7

1	0.7
2	1.4
3	2.1
4	2.8
5	3.5
6	4.2
7	4.9
8	5.6
9	6.3

6

1	0.6
2	1.2
3	1.8
4	2.4
5	3.0
6	3.6
7	4.2
8	4.8
9	5.4

N	0	1	2	3	4	5	6	7	8	9
650	**81 291**	**298**	**305**	**311**	**318**	**325**	**331**	**338**	**345**	**351**
651	81 358	365	371	378	385	391	398	405	411	418
652	81 425	431	438	445	451	458	465	471	478	485
653	81 491	498	505	511	518	525	531	538	544	551
654	81 558	564	571	578	584	591	598	604	611	617
655	**81 624**	**631**	**637**	**644**	**651**	**657**	**664**	**671**	**677**	**684**
656	81 690	697	704	710	717	723	730	737	743	750
657	81 757	763	770	776	783	790	796	803	809	816
658	81 823	829	836	842	849	856	862	869	875	882
659	81 889	895	902	908	915	921	928	935	941	948
660	**81 954**	**961**	**968**	**974**	**981**	**987**	**994**	*000	*007	*014
661	82 020	027	033	040	046	053	060	066	073	079
662	82 086	092	099	105	112	119	125	132	138	145
663	82 151	158	164	171	178	184	191	197	204	210
664	82 217	223	230	236	243	249	256	263	269	276
665	**82 282**	**289**	**295**	**302**	**308**	**315**	**321**	**328**	**334**	**341**
666	82 347	354	360	367	373	380	387	393	400	406
667	82 413	419	426	432	439	445	452	458	465	471
668	82 478	484	491	497	504	510	517	523	530	536
669	82 543	549	556	562	569	575	582	588	595	601
670	**82 607**	**614**	**620**	**627**	**633**	**640**	**646**	**653**	**659**	**666**
671	82 672	679	685	692	698	705	711	718	724	730
672	82 737	743	750	756	763	769	776	782	789	795
673	82 802	808	814	821	827	834	840	847	853	860
674	82 866	872	879	885	892	898	905	911	918	924
675	**82 930**	**937**	**943**	**950**	**956**	**963**	**969**	**975**	**982**	**988**
676	82 995	*001	*008	*014	*020	*027	*033	*040	*046	*052
677	83 059	065	072	078	085	091	097	104	110	117
678	83 123	129	136	142	149	155	161	168	174	181
679	83 187	193	200	206	213	219	225	232	238	245
680	**83 251**	**257**	**264**	**270**	**276**	**283**	**289**	**296**	**302**	**308**
681	83 315	321	327	334	340	347	353	359	366	372
682	83 378	385	391	398	404	410	417	423	429	436
683	83 442	448	455	461	467	474	480	487	493	499
684	83 506	512	518	525	531	537	544	550	556	563
685	**83 569**	**575**	**582**	**588**	**594**	**601**	**607**	**613**	**620**	**626**
686	83 632	639	645	651	658	664	670	677	683	689
687	83 696	702	708	715	721	727	734	740	746	753
688	83 759	765	771	778	784	790	797	803	809	816
689	83 822	828	835	841	847	853	860	866	872	879
690	**83 885**	**891**	**897**	**904**	**910**	**916**	**923**	**929**	**935**	**942**
691	83 948	954	960	967	973	979	985	992	998	*004
692	84 011	017	023	029	036	042	048	055	061	067
693	84 073	080	086	092	098	105	111	117	123	130
694	84 136	142	148	155	161	167	173	180	186	192
695	**84 198**	**205**	**211**	**217**	**223**	**230**	**236**	**242**	**248**	**255**
696	84 261	267	273	280	286	292	298	305	311	317
697	84 323	330	336	342	348	354	361	367	373	379
698	84 386	392	398	404	410	417	423	429	435	442
699	84 448	454	460	466	473	479	485	491	497	504
700	**84 510**	**516**	**522**	**528**	**535**	**541**	**547**	**553**	**559**	**566**
N	0	1	2	3	4	5	6	7	8	9

Prop. Pts.

	7	6
1	0.7	0.6
2	1.4	1.2
3	2.1	1.8
4	2.8	2.4
5	3.5	3.0
6	4.2	3.6
7	4.9	4.2
8	5.6	4.8
9	6.3	5.4

N	0	1	2	3	4	5	6	7	8	9	Prop. Pts.
700	**84 510**	**516**	**522**	**528**	**535**	**541**	**547**	**553**	**559**	**566**	
701	84 572	578	584	590	597	603	609	615	621	628	
702	84 634	640	646	652	658	665	671	677	683	689	
703	84 696	702	708	714	720	726	733	739	745	751	
704	84 757	763	770	776	782	788	794	800	807	813	
705	**84 819**	**825**	**831**	**837**	**844**	**850**	**856**	**862**	**868**	**874**	
706	84 880	887	893	899	905	911	917	924	930	936	
707	84 942	948	954	960	967	973	979	985	991	997	
708	85 003	009	016	022	028	034	040	046	052	058	
709	85 065	071	077	083	089	095	101	107	114	120	
710	**85 126**	**132**	**138**	**144**	**150**	**156**	**163**	**169**	**175**	**181**	
711	85 187	193	199	205	211	217	224	230	236	242	
712	85 248	254	260	266	272	278	285	291	297	303	
713	85 309	315	321	327	333	339	345	352	358	364	
714	85 370	376	382	388	394	400	406	412	418	425	
715	**85 431**	**437**	**443**	**449**	**455**	**461**	**467**	**473**	**479**	**485**	
716	85 491	497	503	509	516	522	528	534	540	546	
717	85 552	558	564	570	576	582	588	594	600	606	
718	85 612	618	625	631	637	643	649	655	661	667	
719	85 673	679	685	691	697	703	709	715	721	727	
720	**85 733**	**739**	**745**	**751**	**757**	**763**	**769**	**775**	**781**	**788**	
721	85 794	800	806	812	818	824	830	836	842	848	
722	85 854	860	866	872	878	884	890	896	902	908	
723	85 914	920	926	932	938	944	950	956	962	968	
724	85 974	980	986	992	998	*004	*010	*016	*022	*028	
725	**86 034**	**040**	**046**	**052**	**058**	**064**	**070**	**076**	**082**	**088**	
726	86 094	100	106	112	118	124	130	136	141	147	
727	86 153	159	165	171	177	183	189	195	201	207	
728	86 213	219	225	231	237	243	249	255	261	267	
729	86 273	279	285	291	297	303	308	314	320	326	
730	**86 332**	**338**	**344**	**350**	**356**	**362**	**368**	**374**	**380**	**386**	
731	86 392	398	404	410	415	421	427	433	439	445	
732	86 451	457	463	469	475	481	487	493	499	504	
733	86 510	516	522	528	534	540	546	552	558	564	
734	86 570	576	581	587	593	599	605	611	617	623	
735	**86 629**	**635**	**641**	**646**	**652**	**658**	**664**	**670**	**676**	**682**	
736	86 688	694	700	705	711	717	723	729	735	741	
737	86 747	753	759	764	770	776	782	788	794	800	
738	86 806	812	817	823	829	835	841	847	853	859	
739	86 864	870	876	882	888	894	900	906	911	917	
740	**86 923**	**929**	**935**	**941**	**947**	**953**	**958**	**964**	**970**	**976**	
741	86 982	988	994	999	*005	*011	*017	*023	*029	*035	
742	87 040	046	052	058	064	070	075	081	087	093	
743	87 099	105	111	116	122	128	134	140	146	151	
744	87 157	163	169	175	181	186	192	198	204	210	
745	**87 216**	**221**	**227**	**233**	**239**	**245**	**251**	**256**	**262**	**268**	
746	87 274	280	286	291	297	303	309	315	320	326	
747	87 332	338	344	349	355	361	367	373	379	384	
748	87 390	396	402	408	413	419	425	431	437	442	
749	87 448	454	460	466	471	477	483	489	495	500	
750	**87 506**	**512**	**518**	**523**	**529**	**535**	**541**	**547**	**552**	**558**	
N	0	1	2	3	4	5	6	7	8	9	Prop. Pts.

Prop. Pts.

7
1 0.7
2 1.4
3 2.1
4 2.8
5 3.5
6 4.2
7 4.9
8 5.6
9 6.3

6
1 0.6
2 1.2
3 1.8
4 2.4
5 3.0
6 3.6
7 4.2
8 4.8
9 5.4

5
1 0.5
2 1.0
3 1.5
4 2.0
5 2.5
6 3.0
7 3.5
8 4.0
9 4.5

Table 7 / Mantissas of logarithms □ **735**

N	0	1	2	3	4	5	6	7	8	9
750	**87 506**	**512**	**518**	**523**	**529**	**535**	**541**	**547**	**552**	**558**
751	87 564	570	576	581	587	593	599	604	610	616
752	87 622	628	633	639	645	651	656	662	668	674
753	87 679	685	691	697	703	708	714	720	726	731
754	87 737	743	749	754	760	766	772	777	783	789
755	**87 795**	**800**	**806**	**812**	**818**	**823**	**829**	**835**	**841**	**846**
756	87 852	858	864	869	875	881	887	892	898	904
757	87 910	915	921	927	933	938	944	950	955	961
758	87 967	973	978	984	990	996	*001	*007	*013	*018
759	88 024	030	036	041	047	053	058	064	070	076
760	**88 081**	**087**	**093**	**098**	**104**	**110**	**116**	**121**	**127**	**133**
761	88 138	144	150	156	161	167	173	178	184	190
762	88 195	201	207	213	218	224	230	235	241	247
763	88 252	258	264	270	275	281	287	292	298	304
764	88 309	315	321	326	332	338	343	349	355	360
765	**88 366**	**372**	**377**	**383**	**389**	**395**	**400**	**406**	**412**	**417**
766	88 423	429	434	440	446	451	457	463	468	474
767	88 480	485	491	497	502	508	513	519	525	530
768	88 536	542	547	553	559	564	570	576	581	587
769	88 593	598	604	610	615	621	627	632	638	643
770	**88 649**	**655**	**660**	**666**	**672**	**677**	**683**	**689**	**694**	**700**
771	88 705	711	717	722	728	734	739	745	750	756
772	88 762	767	773	779	784	790	795	801	807	812
773	88 818	824	829	835	840	846	852	857	863	868
774	88 874	880	885	891	897	902	908	913	919	925
775	**88 930**	**936**	**941**	**947**	**953**	**958**	**964**	**969**	**975**	**981**
776	88 986	992	997	*003	*009	*014	*020	*025	*031	*037
777	89 042	048	053	059	064	070	076	081	087	092
778	89 098	104	109	115	120	126	131	137	143	148
779	89 154	159	165	170	176	182	187	193	198	204
780	**89 209**	**215**	**221**	**226**	**232**	**237**	**243**	**248**	**254**	**260**
781	89 265	271	276	282	287	293	298	304	310	315
782	89 321	326	332	337	343	348	354	360	365	371
783	89 376	382	387	393	398	404	409	415	421	426
784	89 432	437	443	448	454	459	465	470	476	481
785	**89 487**	**492**	**498**	**504**	**509**	**515**	**520**	**526**	**531**	**537**
786	89 542	548	553	559	564	570	575	581	586	592
787	89 597	603	609	614	620	625	631	636	642	647
788	89 653	658	664	669	675	680	686	691	697	702
789	89 708	713	719	724	730	735	741	746	752	757
790	**89 763**	**768**	**774**	**779**	**785**	**790**	**796**	**801**	**807**	**812**
791	89 818	823	829	834	840	845	851	856	862	867
792	89 873	878	883	889	894	900	905	911	916	922
793	89 927	933	938	944	949	955	960	966	971	977
794	89 982	988	993	998	*004	*009	*015	*020	*026	*031
795	**90 037**	**042**	**048**	**053**	**059**	**064**	**069**	**075**	**080**	**086**
796	90 091	097	102	108	113	119	124	129	135	140
797	90 146	151	157	162	168	173	179	184	189	195
798	90 200	206	211	217	222	227	233	238	244	249
799	90 255	260	266	271	276	282	287	293	298	304
800	**90 309**	**314**	**320**	**325**	**331**	**336**	**342**	**347**	**352**	**358**
N	0	1	2	3	4	5	6	7	8	9

Prop. Pts.

	6	5
1	0.6	0.5
2	1.2	1.0
3	1.8	1.5
4	2.4	2.0
5	3.0	2.5
6	3.6	3.0
7	4.2	3.5
8	4.8	4.0
9	5.4	4.5

N	0	1	2	3	4	5	6	7	8	9	Prop. Pts.
800	**90 309**	**314**	**320**	**325**	**331**	**336**	**342**	**347**	**352**	**358**	
801	90 363	369	374	380	385	390	396	401	407	412	
802	90 417	423	428	434	439	445	450	455	461	466	
803	90 472	477	482	488	493	499	504	509	515	520	
804	90 526	531	536	542	547	553	558	563	569	574	
805	**90 580**	**585**	**590**	**596**	**601**	**607**	**612**	**617**	**623**	**628**	
806	90 634	639	644	650	655	660	666	671	677	682	
807	90 687	693	698	703	709	714	720	725	730	736	
808	90 741	747	752	757	763	768	773	779	784	789	
809	90 795	800	806	811	816	822	827	832	838	843	
810	**90 849**	**854**	**859**	**865**	**870**	**875**	**881**	**886**	**891**	**897**	
811	90 902	907	913	918	924	929	934	940	945	950	
812	90 956	961	966	972	977	982	988	993	998	*004	
813	91 009	014	020	025	030	036	041	046	052	057	
814	91 062	068	073	078	084	089	094	100	105	110	
815	**91 116**	**121**	**126**	**132**	**137**	**142**	**148**	**153**	**158**	**164**	
816	91 169	174	180	185	190	196	201	206	212	217	
817	91 222	228	233	238	243	249	254	259	265	270	
818	91 275	281	286	291	297	302	307	312	318	323	
819	91 328	334	339	344	350	355	360	365	371	376	
820	**91 381**	**387**	**392**	**397**	**403**	**408**	**413**	**418**	**424**	**429**	
821	91 434	440	445	450	455	461	466	471	477	482	
822	91 487	492	498	503	508	514	519	524	529	535	
823	91 540	545	551	556	561	566	572	577	582	587	
824	91 593	598	603	609	614	619	624	630	635	640	
825	**91 645**	**651**	**656**	**661**	**666**	**672**	**677**	**682**	**687**	**693**	
826	91 698	703	709	714	719	724	730	735	740	745	
827	91 751	756	761	766	772	777	782	787	793	798	
828	91 803	808	814	819	824	829	834	840	845	850	
829	91 855	861	866	871	876	882	887	892	897	903	
830	**91 908**	**913**	**918**	**924**	**929**	**934**	**939**	**944**	**950**	**955**	
831	91 960	965	971	976	981	986	991	997	*002	*007	
832	92 012	018	023	028	033	038	044	049	054	059	
833	92 065	070	075	080	085	091	096	101	106	111	
834	92 117	122	127	132	137	143	148	153	158	163	
835	**92 169**	**174**	**179**	**184**	**189**	**195**	**200**	**205**	**210**	**215**	
836	92 221	226	231	236	241	247	252	257	262	267	
837	92 273	278	283	288	293	298	304	309	314	319	
838	92 324	330	335	340	345	350	355	361	366	371	
839	92 376	381	387	392	397	402	407	412	418	423	
840	**92 428**	**433**	**438**	**443**	**449**	**454**	**459**	**464**	**469**	**474**	
841	92 480	485	490	495	500	505	511	516	521	526	
842	92 531	536	542	547	552	557	562	567	572	578	
843	92 583	588	593	598	603	609	614	619	624	629	
844	92 634	639	645	650	655	660	665	670	675	681	
845	**92 686**	**691**	**696**	**701**	**706**	**711**	**716**	**722**	**727**	**732**	
846	92 737	742	747	752	758	763	768	773	778	783	
847	92 788	793	799	804	809	814	819	824	829	834	
848	92 840	845	850	855	860	865	870	875	881	886	
849	92 891	896	901	906	911	916	921	927	932	937	
850	**92 942**	**947**	**952**	**957**	**962**	**967**	**973**	**978**	**983**	**988**	
N	0	1	2	3	4	5	6	7	8	9	Prop. Pts.

6
1	0.6
2	1.2
3	1.8
4	2.4
5	3.0
6	3.6
7	4.2
8	4.8
9	5.4

5
1	0.5
2	1.0
3	1.5
4	2.0
5	2.5
6	3.0
7	3.5
8	4.0
9	4.5

Table 7 / Mantissas of logarithms □ 737

N	0	1	2	3	4	5	6	7	8	9	Prop. Pts.
850	**92 942**	**947**	**952**	**957**	**962**	**967**	**973**	**978**	**983**	**988**	
851	92 993	998	*003	*008	*013	*018	*024	*029	*034	*039	
852	93 044	049	054	059	064	069	075	080	085	090	
853	93 095	100	105	110	115	120	125	131	136	141	
854	93 146	151	156	161	166	171	176	181	186	192	
855	**93 197**	**202**	**207**	**212**	**217**	**222**	**227**	**232**	**237**	**242**	
856	93 247	252	258	263	268	273	278	283	288	293	
857	93 298	303	308	313	318	323	328	334	339	344	
858	93 349	354	359	364	369	374	379	384	389	394	
859	93 399	404	409	414	420	425	430	435	440	445	
860	**93 450**	**455**	**460**	**465**	**470**	**475**	**480**	**485**	**490**	**495**	
861	93 500	505	510	515	520	526	531	536	541	546	
862	93 551	556	561	566	571	576	581	586	591	596	
863	93 601	606	611	616	621	626	631	636	641	646	
864	93 651	656	661	666	671	676	682	687	692	697	
865	**93 702**	**707**	**712**	**717**	**722**	**727**	**732**	**737**	**742**	**747**	
866	93 752	757	762	767	772	777	782	787	792	797	
867	93 802	807	812	817	822	827	832	837	842	847	
868	93 852	857	862	867	872	877	882	887	892	897	
869	93 902	907	912	917	922	927	932	937	942	947	
870	**93 952**	**957**	**962**	**967**	**972**	**977**	**982**	**987**	**992**	**997**	
871	94 002	007	012	017	022	027	032	037	042	047	
872	94 052	057	062	067	072	077	082	086	091	096	
873	94 101	106	111	116	121	126	131	136	141	146	
874	94 151	156	161	166	171	176	181	186	191	196	
875	**94 201**	**206**	**211**	**216**	**221**	**226**	**231**	**236**	**240**	**245**	
876	94 250	255	260	265	270	275	280	285	290	295	
877	94 300	305	310	315	320	325	330	335	340	345	
878	94 349	354	359	364	369	374	379	384	389	394	
879	94 399	404	409	414	419	424	429	433	438	443	
880	**94 448**	**453**	**458**	**463**	**468**	**473**	**478**	**483**	**488**	**493**	
881	94 498	503	507	512	517	522	527	532	537	542	
882	94 547	552	557	562	567	571	576	581	586	591	
883	94 596	601	606	611	616	621	626	630	635	640	
884	94 645	650	655	660	665	670	675	680	685	689	
885	**94 694**	**699**	**704**	**709**	**714**	**719**	**724**	**729**	**734**	**738**	
886	94 743	748	753	758	763	768	773	778	783	787	
887	94 792	797	802	807	812	817	822	827	832	836	
888	94 841	846	851	856	861	866	871	876	880	885	
889	94 890	895	900	905	910	915	919	924	929	934	
890	**94 939**	**944**	**949**	**954**	**959**	**963**	**968**	**973**	**978**	**983**	
891	94 988	993	998	*002	*007	*012	*017	*022	*027	*032	
892	95 036	041	046	051	056	061	066	071	075	080	
893	95 085	090	095	100	105	109	114	119	124	129	
894	95 134	139	143	148	153	158	163	168	173	177	
895	**95 182**	**187**	**192**	**197**	**202**	**207**	**211**	**216**	**221**	**226**	
896	95 231	236	240	245	250	255	260	265	270	274	
897	95 279	284	289	294,	299	303	308	313	318	323	
898	95 328	332	337	342	347	352	357	361	366	371	
899	95 376	381	386	390	395	400	405	410	415	419	
900	**95 424**	**429**	**434**	**439**	**444**	**448**	**453**	**458**	**463**	**468**	
N	0	1	2	3	4	5	6	7	8	9	Prop. Pts.

Prop. Pts.

	6	5
1	0.6	0.5
2	1.2	1.0
3	1.8	1.5
4	2.4	2.0
5	3.0	2.5
6	3.6	3.0
7	4.2	3.5
8	4.8	4.0
9	5.4	4.5

	4
1	0.4
2	0.8
3	1.2
4	1.6
5	2.0
6	2.4
7	2.8
8	3.2
9	3.6

N	0	1	2	3	4	5	6	7	8	9	Prop. Pts.
900	95 424	429	434	439	444	448	453	458	463	468	
901	95 472	477	482	487	492	497	501	506	511	516	
902	95 521	525	530	535	540	545	550	554	559	564	
903	95 569	574	578	583	588	593	598	602	607	612	
904	95 617	622	626	631	636	641	646	650	655	660	
905	95 665	670	674	679	684	689	694	698	703	708	
906	95 713	718	722	727	732	737	742	746	751	756	
907	95 761	766	770	775	780	785	789	794	799	804	
908	95 809	813	818	823	828	832	837	842	847	852	
909	95 856	861	866	871	875	880	885	890	895	899	
910	95 904	909	914	918	923	928	933	938	942	947	
911	95 952	957	961	966	971	976	980	985	990	995	
912	95 999	*004	*009	*014	*019	*023	*028	*033	*038	*042	
913	96 047	052	057	061	066	071	076	080	085	090	
914	96 095	099	104	109	114	118	123	128	133	137	

			5
1	0.5
2	1.0
3	1.5
4	2.0
5	2.5
6	3.0
7	3.5
8	4.0
9	4.5

N	0	1	2	3	4	5	6	7	8	9
915	96 142	147	152	156	161	166	171	175	180	185
916	96 190	194	199	204	209	213	218	223	227	232
917	96 237	242	246	251	256	261	265	270	275	280
918	96 284	289	294	298	303	308	313	317	322	327
919	96 332	336	341	346	350	355	360	365	369	374
920	96 379	384	388	393	398	402	407	412	417	421
921	96 426	431	435	440	445	450	454	459	464	468
922	96 473	478	483	487	492	497	501	506	511	515
923	96 520	525	530	534	539	544	548	553	558	562
924	96 567	572	577	581	586	591	595	600	605	609
925	96 614	619	624	628	633	638	642	647	652	656
926	96 661	666	670	675	680	685	689	694	699	703
927	96 708	713	717	722	727	731	736	741	745	750
928	96 755	759	764	769	774	778	783	788	792	797
929	96 802	806	811	816	820	825	830	834	839	844

			4
1	0.4
2	0.8
3	1.2
4	1.6
5	2.0
6	2.4
7	2.8
8	3.2
9	3.6

N	0	1	2	3	4	5	6	7	8	9
930	96 848	853	858	862	867	872	876	881	886	890
931	96 895	900	904	909	914	918	923	928	932	937
932	96 942	946	951	956	960	965	970	974	979	984
933	96 988	993	997	*002	*007	*011	*016	*021	*025	*030
934	97 035	039	044	049	053	058	063	067	072	077
935	97 081	086	090	095	100	104	109	114	118	123
936	97 128	132	137	142	146	151	155	160	165	169
937	97 174	179	183	188	192	197	202	206	211	216
938	97 220	225	230	234	239	243	248	253	257	262
939	97 267	271	276	280	285	290	294	299	304	308
940	97 313	317	322	327	331	336	340	345	350	354
941	97 359	364	368	373	377	382	387	391	396	400
942	97 405	410	414	419	424	428	433	437	442	447
943	97 451	456	460	465	470	474	479	483	488	493
944	97 497	502	506	511	516	520	525	529	534	539
945	97 543	548	552	557	562	566	571	575	580	585
946	97 589	594	598	603	607	612	617	621	626	630
947	97 635	640	644	649	653	658	663	667	672	676
948	97 681	685	690	695	699	704	708	713	717	722
949	97 727	731	736	740	745	749	754	759	763	768
950	97 772	777	782	786	791	795	800	804	809	813
N	0	1	2	3	4	5	6	7	8	9	Prop. Pts.

Table 7 / *Mantissas of logarithms* □ **739**

N	0	1	2	3	4	5	6	7	8	9
950	97 772	777	782	786	791	795	800	804	809	813
951	97 818	823	827	832	836	841	845	850	855	859
952	97 864	868	873	877	882	886	891	896	900	905
953	97 909	914	918	923	928	932	937	941	946	950
954	97 955	959	964	968	973	978	982	987	991	996
955	98 000	005	009	014	019	023	028	032	037	041
956	98 046	050	055	059	064	068	073	078	082	087
957	98 091	096	100	105	109	114	118	123	127	132
958	98 137	141	146	150	155	159	164	168	173	177
959	98 182	186	191	195	200	204	209	214	218	223
960	98 227	232	236	241	245	250	254	259	263	268
961	98 272	277	281	286	290	295	299	304	308	313
962	98 318	322	327	331	336	340	345	349	354	358
963	98 363	367	372	376	381	385	390	394	399	403
964	98 408	412	417	421	426	430	435	439	444	448
965	98 453	457	462	466	471	475	480	484	489	493
966	98 498	502	507	511	516	520	525	529	534	538
967	98 543	547	552	556	561	565	570	574	579	583
968	98 588	592	597	601	605	610	614	619	623	628
969	98 632	637	641	646	650	655	659	664	668	673
970	98 677	682	686	691	695	700	704	709	713	717
971	98 722	726	731	735	740	744	749	753	758	762
972	98 767	771	776	780	784	789	793	798	802	807
973	98 811	816	820	825	829	834	838	843	847	851
974	98 856	860	865	869	874	878	883	887	892	896
975	98 900	905	909	914	918	923	927	932	936	941
976	98 945	949	954	958	963	967	972	976	981	985
977	98 989	994	998	*003	*007	*012	*016	*021	*025	*029
978	99 034	038	043	047	052	056	061	065	069	074
979	99 078	083	087	092	096	100	105	109	114	118
980	99 123	127	131	136	140	145	149	154	158	162
981	99 167	171	176	180	185	189	193	198	202	207
982	99 211	216	220	224	229	233	238	242	247	251
983	99 255	260	264	269	273	277	282	286	291	295
984	99 300	304	308	313	317	322	326	330	335	339
985	99 344	348	352	357	361	366	370	374	379	383
986	99 388	392	396	401	405	410	414	419	423	427
987	99 432	436	441	445	449	454	458	463	467	471
988	99 476	480	484	489	493	498	502	506	511	515
989	99 520	524	528	533	537	542	546	550	555	559
990	99 564	568	572	577	581	585	590	594	599	603
991	99 607	612	616	621	625	629	634	638	642	647
992	99 651	656	660	664	669	673	677	682	686	691
993	99 695	699	704	708	712	717	721	726	730	734
994	99 739	743	747	752	756	760	765	769	774	778
995	99 782	787	791	795	800	804	808	813	817	822
996	99 826	830	835	839	843	848	852	856	861	865
997	99 870	874	878	883	887	891	896	900	904	909
998	99 913	917	922	926	930	935	939	944	948	952
999	99 957	961	965	970	974	978	983	987	991	996
1000	00 000	004	009	013	017	022	026	030	035	039

Prop. Pts.

	5	4
1	0.5	0.4
2	1.0	0.8
3	1.5	1.2
4	2.0	1.6
5	2.5	2.0
6	3.0	2.4
7	3.5	2.8
8	4.0	3.2
9	4.5	3.6

TABLE 8
Selected Constants and Their Common Logarithms

Constant	Value	Logarithm
π	3.141 59	0.497 150
$\dfrac{\pi}{2}$	1.570 80	0.196 120
$\dfrac{\pi}{3}$	1.047 20	0.020 029
$\dfrac{\pi}{4}$	0.785 40	9.895 090 $-$ 10
$\dfrac{\pi}{5}$	0.628 32	9.798 181 $-$ 10
$\dfrac{\pi}{6}$	0.523 60	9.718 999 $-$ 10
$\dfrac{\pi}{7}$	0.448 80	9.652 053 $-$ 10
$\dfrac{\pi}{8}$	0.392 70	9.594 060 $-$ 10
$\dfrac{\pi}{180}$	0.017 453	8.241 877 $-$ 10
π^2	9.869 60	0.994 300
$\sqrt{\pi}$	1.772 45	0.248 575
π^3	31.006 28	1.491 450
$\sqrt[3]{\pi}$	1.464 59	0.165 717
$\dfrac{1}{\pi}$	0.318 31	9.502 850 $-$ 10
e	2.718 28	0.434 294
$\dfrac{1}{e}$	0.367 88	9.565 706 $-$ 10
$\dfrac{1}{\log e}$	2.302 585	0.362 216
Standard g	980.665 cm/sec^2 32.1740 ft/sec^2	2.991 521 1.507 505
1 atmosphere	14.696 psi	1.167 20

TABLE 9

Symbols and the Modern Units: Recommended Unit Prefixes (as adopted by International Committee on Weights and Measures, 1963)

Multiples and submultiples	Prefixes	Symbols	Pronunciation
10^{12}	tera	T	ter′ ä
10^9	giga	G	ji′ gä
10^6	mega	M	meg′ ä
10^3	kilo	k	kil′ ō
10^2	hecto	h	hek′ tō
10	deka	da	dek′ ä
10^{-1}	deci	d	des′ i
10^{-2}	centi	c	sen′ ti
10^{-3}	milli	m	mil′ i
10^{-6}	micro	μ	mī′krō
10^{-9}	nano	n	nan′ō
10^{-12}	pico	p	pē′kō
10^{-15}	femto	f	fem′tō
10^{-18}	atto	a	at′tō

The Greek Alphabet

Capital	Lowercase	Handwritten	Greek name	Capital	Lowercase	Handwritten	Greek name
A	α	$\propto$	Alpha	N	ν	∂	Nu
B	β	β	Beta	Ξ	ξ	ξ	Xi (zī)
Γ	γ	γ	Gamma	O	o	(*)	Omicron
Δ	δ	δ	Delta	Π	π	π	Pi
E	ε	ϵ	Epsilon	P	ρ	ρ	Rho
Z	ζ	ζ	Zeta	Σ	σ	σ	Sigma
H	η	η	Eta	T	τ	τ	Tau (töw)
Θ	θ	θ	Theta	Υ	υ	(*)	Upsilon
I	ι	(*)	Iota	Φ	ϕ	ϕ	Phi (fee)
K	κ	(*)	Kappa	X	χ	χ	Chi (kī)
Λ	λ	λ	Lambda	Ψ	ψ	ψ	Psi
M	μ	μ	Mu	Ω	ω	ω	Omega

(*) Indicates that the letter should be avoided, as it resembles the English.

742

International System Units (SI)

Basic measurement	S.I. unit	Derived units	Basic U.S. unit and approximate relationship	Derived U.S. unit and approximate relationship
Length	Meter	*Area* Square meter Hectare *Volume* Cubic meter Liter	Foot: 1 ft $\approx$ 0.3 meter	Mile: 1 mile $\approx$ 1.6 kilometers *Area* Square feet (sq ft) $\approx$ 0.09 square meter Acre $\approx$ 0.4 hectare *Volume* Cubic feet (cu ft) $\approx$ 0.03 cubic meter Gallon (gal) $\approx$ 3.8 liters
Time	Second	*Speed* Meters/second Kilometers/hour *Acceleration* Meters/sec^2 *Frequency* Hertz = cycles/second	Same	*Speed* Feet/second $\approx$ 0.3 meters/second Miles/hour $\approx$ 1.6 kilometers/hour *Acceleration* Feet/sec^2 $\approx$ 0.3 meters/sec^2
Mass	Kilogram	*Force* Newton = $\dfrac{1(\text{kilogram})(\text{meter})}{(\text{seconds})^2}$ *Work and Energy* Joule = 1 (newton)(meter) *Power* Watt = $\dfrac{1 \text{ Joule}}{1 \text{ second}}$	Pound (mass) = slug = poundal $\approx$ 0.014 kilo- gram	*Force* Pound $\approx$ 0.5 kilogram *Work and Energy* Foot-pound $\approx$ 1.3 Joule *Power* Horsepower $\approx$ 750 watts
Temperature	°Kelvin	°Celsius $= T°K - 273.15$	°Fahrenheit $= \frac{8}{5}T°C + 32$	°Absolute $T°A = T°F + 459.67$
Electric current	Ampere	*Voltage* Volt = $\dfrac{1 \text{ watt}}{1 \text{ ampere}}$ *Resistance* Ohm = $\dfrac{1 \text{ volt}}{1 \text{ ampere}}$	Identical	Identical
Luminous intensity	Candella	*Light Flux* Lumen: 1 candella intensity radiated in all directions produces a flux of 4π lumen *Illumination* Lux = $\dfrac{1 \text{ lumen}}{1 \text{ square meter}}$	Candle (identical to 1 candela in intensity)	*Light Flux* Lumen: 1 candle intensity producing 4π lumen *Illumination* Foot candle = $\dfrac{1 \text{ lumen}}{1 \text{ square foot}}$ $\approx$ 0.09 lux

TABLE 10
Conversion Equivalents

Units of length

One	*Is equal to*
Angstrom unit	10^{-10} meter
Centimeter	0.032 808 4 foot = 0.393 701 inch
Fathom	6 feet
Foot	0.3048 meter
Furlong	$\frac{1}{8}$ mile (40 rods or 1000 chains)*
Inch	2.54 centimeters (by law)
Kilometer	0.621 371 miles = 3280.84 feet
Meter	3.280 84 feet = 1.093 61 yards
Micron	0.001 millimeter = 10,000 angstrom units
Mil	0.001 inch = 25.4 microns
Millimeter	0.039 370 1 inch
Mile	1.609 34 kilometers = 0.868 98 nautical mile
Nautical mile	1.150 78 statute miles = 6076.115 5 feet
Rod	16.5 feet ($\frac{1}{4}$ of a Gunter's chain or 25 links)*
Yard	0.9144 meter

* Units in parentheses are obsolete but appear in old deeds.

Units of area

One	*Is equal to*
Acre	43,560 sq ft.= 4046.85 sq m = 0.001 562 sq mile
Circular mil	(Defined: area of a circle with a diameter of 1 mil) = 0.7854 sq mil = 5.0671×10^{-6} sq cm
Hectare	10,000 sq m = 2.471 05 acres = 107,637 sq ft
Square centimeter	0.155 00 sq in. = 0.001 076 sq ft.= 197,350 circular mils
Square foot	0.092 903 00 sq m = 2.296×10^{-5} acre = 929.0 sq cm = 3.587×10^{-8} sq mile
Square inch	6.4516 sq cm = 1.273×10^{6} circular mils = 7.716×10^{-4} sq yd
Square kilometer	0.3861 sq mile = 1.076×10^{7} sq ft = 247,104 acres
Square meter	10.7639 sq ft = 1.195 99 sq yd
Square mile	2.788×10^{7} sq ft.= 2.590 sq km.= 640 acres
Squard yard	0.836 127 sq m
Square (architects')	100 sq ft

Units of volume

One	*Is equal to*
Acre-foot	43,560 cu ft = 325,851 gal
Board-foot	144 cu in.
Bushel (dry)	1.2445 cu ft = 0.035 24 cu m
Cubic centimeter	0.061 023 7 cu in. = 0.033 814 oz
Cubic foot	0.028 316 8 cu m = 7.481 gal = 0.037 04 cu yd
Cubic inch	16.3871 cc = 0.004 329 gal = 0.554 oz
Cubic meter	35.3147 cu ft = 1.307 95 cu yd = 264.2 gal

Cubic yard	0.764 555 cu m = 46,656 cu in. = 202.0 gal
Gallon	0.003 785 41 cu m = 231 cu in. = 0.1337 cu ft = 8.3452 lb water
Liter	0.2642 gal = 61.02 cu in. = 0.035 31 cu ft
Ounce, fluid	1.805 cu in. = 29.58 cc = 0.007 812 5 gal
Pint, liquid	0.125 gal = 0.473 176 liter
Quart, liquid	0.946 353 liter = 57.75 cu in. = 0.033 42 cu ft
Stere	1 cu m
Barrel, cement	376 lb
Barrel, oil	42 gal

Units of mass and weight*

One	Is equal to
Grain	0.064 81 g = 0.002 286 oz
Gram	0.035 274 oz = 15.43 grains = 980.665 dynes
Kilogram	2.204 62 lb = 35.2739 oz
Ounce (avoirdupois)	437.5 grains = 28.3495 g
Pound (avoirdupois)	0.453 592 kg = 0.031 081 slug = 7000 grains
Slug	32.174 lb
Ton	0.9072 metric ton
Ton (metric)	1.102 31 tons = 2204.62 lb

* *Notes:* Troy weight is used by jewelers for gold and silver; apothecaries' weight by druggists. These two systems are alike at 1 grain and at 1 ounce but have different subdivisions.

1 pound (Troy) = 12 ounces = 5760 grains = 0.822 86 pound avoirdupois
1 pound (avoirdupois) = 1.2153 pounds (Troy or apothecaries')

The British system (being phased out) uses:

1 stone = 14 pounds
1 hundredweight = 112 pounds
1 long ton = 20 hundredweight = 2240 pounds

An object marked 1-6-3-11 would weigh 2240 + 6(112) + 3(14) + 11, or 2965 lb

Units of density

One	Is equal to
Gram/cc	62.43 pcf = 0.036 13 pci
Pound/cu ft	0.016 02 g/cc = 5.787×10^{-4} pci
Pound/cu in.	27.68 g/cc = 1728 pcf

Units of force

One	Is equal to
Dyne	1.0197×10^{-6} kg = 2.2481×10^{-6} lb = 7.233×10^{-5} poundal
Kilogram	980,665 dynes = 70.93 poundals
Kip	1000 lb
Newton	100,000 dynes = 7.233 poundals
Pound	32.174 poundals = 4.448 newtons
Poundal	13,825 dynes = 0.031 081 lb

Units of pressure

One	Is equal to
Atmosphere, standard	1.0133 bars = 76.00 cm Hg = 29.92 in. mercury = 406.79 in. water = 2116.35 psf = 14.70 psi = 10,329 kg/sq m
Bar (megabarye)	0.9869 atm = 10,197 kg/sq m = 2089 psf = 14.50 psi
Centimeter of mercury, 0°C	0.013 158 atm = 5.354 in. water = 136.0 kg/sq m = 27.85 psf = 0.193 37 psi
Inch of mercury, 0°C	0.033 42 atm = 13.60 in. water = 345.3 kg/sq m = 70.73 psf = 0.4912 psi
Inch of water, 39°F	0.002 458 atm = 0.1868 cm mercury = 0.073 55 in. mercury = 25.38 kg/sq m = 5.2022 psf = 0.036 125 psi
Kilogram/square meter	9.807 Pa = 0.2048 psf = 0.001 422 psi
Pascal	1 Newton/sq m = 7.501×10^{-4} cm mercury = 0.1020 kg/sq m = 1.450×10^{-4} psi
Pound/square foot	4.725×10^{-4} atm = 0.035 91 cm mercury = 0.014 14 in. mercury
Pound/square inch	0.068 04 atm = 5.171 cm mercury = 2.036 in. mercury = 27.68 in. water = 703.1 kg/sq m

Units of moment or torque

One	Is equal to
Dyne-centimeter (erg)	7.3756×10^{-8} lb-ft = 1.020 kg-m
Kilogram-meter	9.807×10^{7} dyne-cm = 7.233 lb-ft = 9.807 N-m
Pound-feet	1.356 dyne-cm = 0.1383 kg-m

Units of linear velocity

One	Is equal to
Centimeter/second	1.939 fpm = 0.032 81 fps = 0.036 km/hr = 0.019 43 knot = 0.6 m/min = 0.022 37 mph = 3.728 miles/min
Foot/minute	0.5080 cm/sec = 0.018 29 km/hr = 0.009 868 knot = 0.3048 m/min = 0.011 36 mph = 1.892×10^{-4} mile/min
Foot/second	30.48 cm/sec = 1.097 km/hr = 0.5921 knot = 18.29 m/min = 0.6818 mph = 0.011 36 mile/min
Kilometer/hour	27.78 cm/sec = 54.68 fpm = 0.9113 fps = 0.539 96 knot = 16.67 m/min = 0.6214 mph = 0.010 36 mile/min
Knot	5144 cm/sec = 101.3 fpm = 1.688 fps = 1.852 km/hr = 30.87 m/min = 1.150 78 mph = 0.019 19 mile/min
Meter/minute	1.667 cm/sec = 3.281 fpm = 0.054 68 fps = 0.032 38 knot = 0.037 28 mph = 6.214×10^{-4} mile/min
Mile/hour	44.70 cm/sec = 88 fpm = 1.467 fps = 1.609 km/hr = 0.868 98 knot = 26.82 m/min = 0.016 67 mile/min
Mile/minute	2682 cm/sec = 88 fps = 96.54 km/hr = 52.10 knots = 1609 m/min = 60 mph

Units of linear acceleration

One	Is equal to
Centimeter/second^2	$0.032\,81$ ft/sec^2 = 0.036 km/hr/sec = $0.022\,37$ mph/sec
Foot/second^2	30.48 cm/sec^2 = 1.097 km/hr/sec = 0.6818 mph/sec
kilometer/hour/second	27.78 cm/sec^2 = 0.9113 ft/sec^2 = 0.6214 mph/sec
Mile/hour/second	44.70 cm/sec^2 = 1.467 ft/sec^2 = 1.609 km/hr/sec

Units of angular velocity

One	Is equal to
Degree/second	$0.017\,45$ rad/sec = 0.1667 rpm = $0.002\,778$ rps
Radian/second	57.296 °/sec = 9.549 rpm = 0.1592 rps
Revolution/minute	6 °/sec = 0.1047 rad/sec = $0.016\,67$ rps
Revolution/second	360°/sec = 6.283 rad/sec

Units of angular acceleration

One	Is equal to
Radian/second^2	573 rpm/min = 9.549 rpm/sec = 0.1592 rps/sec
Rpm/minute	$0.001\,745$ rad/sec^2 = 2.778×10^{-4} rps/sec
Rpm/second	0.1047 rad/sec^2
Rps/second	6.283 rad/sec^2 = 3600 rpm/min

Units of discharge or flow

One	Is equal to
Acre-foot/hour	726 cfm = 12.10 cfs = 5432 gpm = $45{,}320$ lb/min = 342.7 liters/sec
Cubic foot/minute	7.481 gpm = 62.43 lb/min = 0.6667 miner's inch = 0.4720 liter/sec = $0.028\,32$ cu m/min
Cubic foot/second	448.8 gpm = 3746 lb/min = 40 miner's inches = 28.32 liter/sec = 1.6992 cu m/min = 1.9834 acre-ft/day = $0.646\,35$ mgd
Cubic meter/minute	35.32 cfm = 0.5886 cfs = 264.2 gpm
Gallon/minute	0.1337 cfm = $0.002\,228$ cfs = 8.345 lb/min = $0.089\,13$ miner's inch = $0.063\,09$ liter/sec = $0.001\,44$ mgd = $0.004\,419$ acre-ft/day
Liter/second	2.119 cfm = $0.035\,31$ cfs = 1585 gpm = $132\,3$ lb/min = 0.06 cu m/min
Millions of gallons/day	694.444 gpm = 92.847 cfm = 1.547 cfs = 43.806 liter/sec = 5795 lb/min
Miner's inch*	1.5 cfm = 0.0250 cfs = 11.22 gpm = 93.65 lb/min = 0.7080 liter/sec
Pounds of water/minute	$0.010\,68$ cfm = 2.670×10^{-4} cfs = 0.1198 gpm = $0.010\,68$ miner's inch = $0.007\,56$ liter/sec

* A miner's inch varies with state law. This table is based upon 1 miner's inch to 1.5 cfm, which is the law of Arizona, California, Montana, and Oregon. Other states vary from 1.2 to 1.562 cfm.

Units of energy, work, and heat

One	Is equal to
British thermal unit	1.076 cm-g = 778.104 ft-lb = 3.929×10^{-4} hp-hr = 1054.8 J = 0.2520 kg-cal = 2.930×10^{-4} kwh
Centimeter-gram	9.297×10^{-8} Btu = 7.233×10^{-5} ft-lb = 3.654×10^{-11} hp-hr = 9.807×10^{-5} J = 2.343×10^{-8} kg-cal = 2.724×10^{-11} kwh
Foot-pound	0.001 285 Btu = 1.383×10^4 cm-g = 5.050×10^{-7} hp-hr = 1.356 J = 3.239×10^{-4} kg-cal = 3.766×10^{-7} kwh
Horsepower-hour	2545 Btu = 2.737×10^{10} cm-g = 1.98×10^6 ft-lb = $2,684 \times 10^6$ J = 641.3 kg-cal = 0.7457 kwh
Joule (watt-sec)	10^7 ergs $\times$ 9.480 = 10^{-4} Btu = 1.020×10^4 cm-g = 0.7376 ft.lb = 3.722×10^{-7} hp-hr = 2.389×10^{-4} kg-cal = 2.778×10^{-7} kwh
Kilogram-calorie	3.9698 Btu = 4.269×10^7 cm-g = 3087 ft-lb = 0.001 559 hp-hr = 4186 J = 0.001 163 kwh
Kilowatt-hour	3414 Btu = 3.671×10^{10} cm-g = 2.655 10 $\times 10^6$ ft-lb = 1.341 hp-hr = 3.6×10^6 J = 860 kg-cal

Units of power*

One	Is equal to
Btu/minute	1.758×10^8 ergs/sec = 778.0 ft-lb/min = 0.023 57 hp = 0.2530 kg-cal/min = 0.017 58 kw = 0.023 90 metric hp
Erg/second	5.689×10^9 Btu/min = 4.426×10^{-6} ft-lb/min = 1.341 $\times 10^{-10}$ hp = 1.433×10^{-9} kg-cal/min = 10^{-10} kw = 1.360 metric hp
Foot-pound/minute	0.001 285 Btu/min = 2.259×10^5 ergs/sec = 3.030 $\times 10^{-5}$ hp = 3.239×10^{-4} kg-cal/min = 2.260 kw = 3.072×10^{-5} metric hp
Horsepower	42.418 Btu/min = 7.457×10^9 ergs/sec = 3.3×10^4 ft-lb/min = 10.69 kg-cal/min = 0.745 700 kw = 1.014 metric hp
Kilogram-calorie/minute	3.969 Btu/min = 6.977×10^8 ergs/sec = 3087 ft-lb/min = 0.093 55 hp = 0.069 77 kw = 0.094 85 metric hp
Kilogram-meter/second	0.5577 Btu/min = 7.355×10^{-9} erg/sec = 433.98 ft-lb/min = 0.013 15 hp = 0.140 52 kg-cal/min = 0.009 807 kw = 0.013 33 metric hp
Kilowatt	56.89 Btu/min = 44,254 ft-lb/min = 737.6 ft-lb/sec = 1.341 02 hp = 14.33 kg-cal/min = 1.360 metric hp
Metric horsepower	41.83 Btu/min = 3.255×10^4 ft-lb/min = 524.5 ft-lb/sec = 0.9863 hp = 10.54 kg-cal/min = 0.7355 kw

Notes: A U.S. horsepower is by definition 550 ft-lb/sec. A metric horsepower (Cheval-vapeur) is, by definition, 75 kg-m/sec. A Poncelet is a special metric unit equal to 100 kg-m/sec.

Note

The ASTM Metric Practice Guide was prepared by a committee of the American Society for Testing and Materials and published in 1967 by the Department of Commerce as *National Bureau of Standards Handbook 102*. It can be purchased from the Manager, Public Documents Distribution Center, 5801 Tabor Ave, Philadelphia, Pa. 19120. It contains guidance on the use of metric styles and their applications and an excellent table of conversion factors. Factors are given to seven significant figures, but instead of the scientific notation used in this book and other published tables, the computer form of indicating the power of 10 is used. 10^7 would be written E + 07, and 10^{-11} would become E − 11. (NBS Special Publication 300, printed Jan. 1971, contains the new SI units.)

TABLE 11
Decimal Equivalents of Inches and Feet

Fractions of Inch	Decimal (Inch or Foot)	Inch Equiv. to Foot Fractions	Fractions of Inch	Decimal (Inch or Foot)	Inch Equiv. to Foot Fractions	Fractions of Inch	Decimal (Inch or Foot)	Inch Equiv. to Foot Fractions	Fractions of Inch	Decimal (Inch or Foot)	Inch Equiv. to Foot Fractions
	0.005 2	1/16		0.255 2	3 1/16		0.505 2	6 1/16		0.755 2	9 1/16
	0.010 4	1/8		0.260 4	3 1/8		0.510 4	6 1/8		0.760 4	9 1/8
1/64	0.015 625	3/16	17/64	0.265 625	3 3/16	33/64	0.515 625	6 3/16	49/64	0.765 625	9 3/16
	0.020 8	1/4		0.270 8	3 1/4		0.520 8	6 1/4		0.770 8	9 1/4
	0.026 0	5/16		0.276 0	3 5/16		0.526 0	6 5/16		4.776 0	9 5/16
1/32	0.031 25	3/8	9/32	0.281 25	3 3/8	17/32	0.531 25	6 3/8	25/32	0.781 25	9 3/8
	0.036 5	7/16		0.286 5	3 7/16		0.536 5	6 7/16		0.786 5	9 7/16
	0.041 7	1/2		0.291 7	3 1/2		0.541 7	6 1/2		0.791 7	9 1/2
3/64	0.046 875	9/16	19/64	0.296 875	3 9/16	35/64	0.546 875	6 9/16	51/64	0.796 875	9 9/16
	0.052 1	5/8		0.302 1	3 5/8		0.552 1	6 5/8		0.802 1	9 5/8
	0.057 3	11/16		0.307 3	3 11/16		0.557 3	6 11/16		0.807 3	9 11/16
1/16	0.062 5	3/4	5/16	0.312 5	3 3/4	9/16	0.562 5	6 3/4	13/16	0.812 5	9 3/4
	0.067 7	13/16		0.317 7	3 13/16		0.567 7	6 13/16		0.817 7	9 13/16
	0.072 9	7/8		0.322 9	3 7/8		0.572 9	6 7/8		0.822 9	9 7/8
5/64	0.078 125	15/16	21/64	0.328 125	3 15/16	37/64	0.578 125	6 15/16	53/64	0.828 125	9 15/16
	0.083 3	1		0.333 3	4		0.583 3	7		0.833 3	10
	0.088 5	1 1/16		0.338 5	4 1/16		0.588 5	7 1/16		0.838 5	10 1/16
3/32	0.093 75	1 1/8	11/32	0.343 75	4 1/8	19/32	0.593 75	7 1/8	27/32	0.843 75	10 1/8
	0.099 0	1 3/16		0.349 0	4 3/16		0.599 0	7 3/16		0.849 0	10 3/16
	0.104 2	1 1/4		0.354 2	4 1/4		0.604 2	7 1/4		0.854 2	10 1/4
7/64	0.109 375	1 5/16	23/64	0.359 375	4 5/16	39/64	0.609 375	7 5/16	55/64	0.859 375	10 5/16
	0.114 6	1 3/8		0.364 6	4 3/8		0.614 6	7 3/8		0.864 6	10 3/8
	0.119 8	1 7/16		0.369 8	4 7/16		0.619 8	7 7/16		0.869 3	10 7/16
1/8	0.125 0	1 1/2	3/8	0.375 0	4 1/2	5/8	0.625 0	7 1/2	7/8	0.875 0	10 1/2
	0.130 2	1 9/16		0.380 2	4 9/16		0.630 2	7 9/16		0.880 2	10 9/16
	0.135 4	1 5/8		0.385 4	4 5/8		0.635 4	7 5/8		0.885 4	10 5/8
9/64	0.140 625	1 11/16	25/64	0.390 625	4 11/16	41/64	0.640 625	7 11/16	57/64	0.890 625	10 11/16
	0.145 8	1 3/4		0.395 8	4 3/4		0.645 8	7 3/4		0.895 8	10 3/4
	0.151 0	1 13/16		0.401 0	4 13/16		0.651 0	7 13/16		0.901 0	10 13/16
5/32	0.156 25	1 7/8	13/32	0.406 25	4 7/8	21/32	0.656 25	7 7/8	29/32	0.906 25	10 7/8
	0.161 5	1 15/16		0.411 5	4 15/16		0.661 5	7 15/16		0.911 5	10 15/16
	0.166 7	2		0.416 7	5		0.666 7	8		0.916 7	11
11/64	0.171 875	2 1/16	27/64	0.421 875	5 1/16	43/64	0.671 875	8 1/16	59/64	0.921 875	11 1/16
	0.177 1	2 1/8		0.427 1	5 1/8		0.677 1	8 1/8		0.927 1	11 1/8
	0.182 3	2 3/16		0.432 3	5 3/16		0.682 3	8 3/16		0.932 3	11 3/16
3/16	0.187 5	2 1/4	7/16	0.437 5	5 1/4	11/16	0.687 5	8 1/4	15/16	0.937 5	11 1/4
	0.192 7	2 5/16		0.442 7	5 5/16		0.692 7	8 5/16		0.942 7	11 5/16
	0.197 9	2 3/8		0.447 9	5 3/8		0.697 9	8 3/8		0.947 9	11 3/8
13/64	0.203 125	2 7/16	29/64	0.453 125	5 7/16	45/64	0.703 125	8 7/16	61/64	0.953 125	11 7/16
	0.208 3	2 1/2		0.458 3	5 1/2		0.708 3	8 1/2		0.958 3	11 1/2
	0.213 5	2 9/16		0.463 5	5 9/16		0.713 5	8 9/16		0.963 5	11 9/16
7/32	0.218 75	2 5/8	15/32	0.468 75	5 5/8	23/32	0.718 75	8 5/8	31/32	0.968 75	11 5/8
	0.224 0	2 11/16		0.474 0	5 11/16		0.724 0	8 11/16		0.974 0	11 11/16
	0.229 2	2 3/4		0.479 2	5 3/4		0.729 2	8 3/4		0.979 2	11 3/4
15/64	0.234 375	2 13/16	31/64	0.484 375	5 13/16	47/64	0.734 375	8 13/16	63/64	0.984 375	11 13/16
	0.239 6	2 7/8		0.489 6	5 7/8		0.739 6	8 7/8		0.989 6	11 7/8
	0.244 8	2 15/16		0.494 8	5 15/16		0.744 8	8 15/16		0.994 8	11 15/16
1/4	0.250 0	3	1/2	0.500 0	6	3/4	0.750 0	9	1	1.000 0	12

Chapter 1

Problem Set 1.1, pages 6–7

1. {Jan, Mar, May, July, Aug, Oct, Dec}   **3.** {Feb}   **5.** {1960, 1964, 1968, 1972, 1976, 1980}   **7.** {0, 1, 2, 3, 4}   **9.** {0, 1, 2, 3, 4, 5, 6, 7}   **11.** {6}   **13.** {0, 2, 4, 6, 8}   **15.** {5}   **17.** {1, 2, 3, 4}   **19.** {1, 2, 3, ..., 12}   **21.** {3}   **23.** {2, 4, 6, 8, 10, 12}   **25.** $S = \{x \mid x \in U$ and $x = $ a multiple of 10$\}$ **27.** $S = \{x^3 \mid x \in U$ and $1 \le x \le 4\}$ **29.** $\{x \mid x \in U$ and $95 \le x \le 100\}$

Problem Set 1.2, pages 10–11

1. {2, 3, 5, 7, 11, 13, 17, 19, 23, 29}   **3.** {101, 103, 107, 109, 113}
5. 9 units

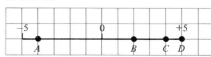

7. 13 units

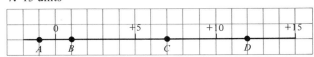

9. 20 units

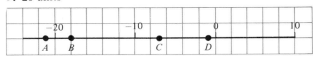

11. 25 units

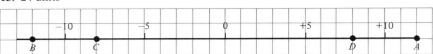

13. 24 units

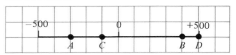

15. 800 units

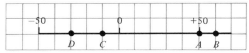

1 sq. = 100 units

17. $AB = 10, AC = 60, AD = 80$

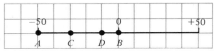

1 sq. = 10 units

19. $AB = 50, AC = 20, AD = 40$

1 sq. = 10 units

21. 373°C   **23.** 19,776 ft

Problem Set 1.3, pages 13–15

1. $\{-\sqrt{3}, -1, 0, \sqrt{3}, 2, 5\}$ **3.** $\{-2, -\frac{7}{4}, -\frac{5}{3}, \sqrt{4}, |-3|\}$

5.

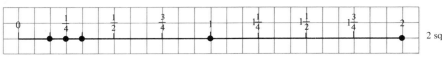

2 sq. = 1 unit

7.

2 sq. = 1 unit

9.

12 sq. = 1 unit

11. 0.375   **13.** 0.888...   **15.** 3.41666...   **17.** $\frac{2}{3}$ **19.** $\frac{12}{1}$ **21.** irrational
23. irrational   **25.** $\frac{1}{8}$ **27.** $\frac{1}{7}$ **29.** $\frac{1}{22}$ **31.** (a) all reals; (b) −410, 410 ft
below sea level; (c) sea level   **33.** (a) all integers except 0; (b) −1980, 1980 B.C.;
(c) no meaning (zero had not been invented at this time)   **35.** (a) positive reals;

(b) no meaning; (c) no meaning   **37.** (a) all reals; (b) $-\frac{7}{8}$, a decrease; (c) no change in price   **39.** (a) nonnegative integers; (b) no meaning; (c) no score made

Problem Set 1.4, pages 16–17

1. N/A, integers, N/A   **3.** N/A, complex numbers, N/A   **5.** $\frac{9}{10}$, rationals, N/A
7. N/A, integers, even and factorable   **9.** 3, digits, odd and prime   **11.** N/A,
complex numbers, N/A   **13.** $\frac{1}{2}$, rationals, N/A   **15.** $\frac{3}{4}$, rationals, N/A   **17.** 4,
digits, even and factorable   **19.** ≈ 1.73, reals, N/A

Problem Set 1.5, pages 21–22

1. true   **3.** false   **5.** true   **7.** true   **9.** true   **11.** false   **13.** true
15. false   **17.** false   **19.** true   **21.** $40 + 30 = 70$ **23.** $9 + 7 = 16$
25. $1200 + 80 + 6 = 1286$ **27.** $7(4 + 5)$ **29.** $11(7 + 2 + 11)$ **31.** $(45 + 55)$
$+ 79 = 179$ **33.** $(4 \cdot 25)786 = 78,600$ **35.** $\frac{1}{6}(18) + \frac{1}{6}(24) = 7$ **37.** $\frac{4}{9}(35 + 55)$
$= 40$ **39.** $\frac{1}{5}(20 + \frac{4}{5}) = 4\frac{4}{25}$ **41.** $2\frac{3}{4} + 9 = 11\frac{3}{4}$ $11\frac{3}{4} = 11\frac{3}{4}$ **43.** $2 + 1$
$= 4 - 1$ $3 = 3$ **45.** $1 + \frac{1}{2} = 3 - \frac{3}{2}$ $1\frac{1}{2} = 1\frac{1}{2}$ **47.** $10 + 3 = 17 - 4$
$13 = 13$ **49.** $25 - 5 = 15 + 5$ $20 = 20$

Problem Set 1.6, pages 29–32

1. 0.005 ft, 1 : 3500, 0.029%   **3.** 0.000 05 in., 1 : 24, 4.17%   **5.** $\frac{1}{8}$ in., 1 : 46, 2.17%
7. $\frac{1}{2}$ in., 1 : 146, 0.68%   **9.** 0.5 in., 1 : 36,000, 0.0028%   **11.** 145.02   **13.** 0.0029
15. 10   **7.** 2.71   **19.** 17   **21.** 376   **23.** 36   **25.** 70,693 screws
27. 1.31 in.   **29.** 0.065 in.   **31.** A 16 cm; B 17 cm; C 9.08 cm; D 6.11 cm; E 12.02
cm; F 19.10 cm

Problem Set 1.7, pages 37–40

1. 2.240×10^3 lb   **3.** 1.256×10^8 cu yd   **5.** 1.000×10^{-7} m   **7.** 3.937×10^{-2}
in.   **9.** 6.076×10^3 ft   **11.** 9.844×10^{-1} **13.** 2.817×10^9 miles   **15.** 5.540
$\times 10^6$ votes, 5.444×10^6 votes   **17.** 4.803×10^{-10} esu   **19.** 1.672×10^{-24} g
21. 14,200,000 people   **23.** 0.000 000 015 cm   **25.** 0.000 000 000 000 038 3 cal
27. 104,500,000 Hz   **29.** $-460°$F   **31.** 29.9 giga cm/sec   **33.** 141 megamiles
35. 26.13 tera Mev   **37.** 4.9918 femto erg-sec   **39.** 548.75 micro amu   **41.** 81
43. 15,625   **45.** 5   **47.** 8   **49.** 2   **51.** 10   **53.** 10^6 **55.** 10^2 **57.** 10^6
59. 10^7 **61.** 10^3 **63.** 10^8 **65.** 10^{-10} **67.** 10^{12} **69.** 10^{-9}

Problem Set 1.8, pages 46–47

1. 1.54×10^6 **3.** 96.4   **5.** 72,500   **7.** 0.992   **9.** 1.04×10^{-13} **11.** 303
13. 958   **15.** 0.958   **17.** 0.441   **19.** 2.18   **21.** 105,000   **23.** 5.29
25. 9.60×10^{-8} **27.** 4.97   **29.** 3.00   **31.** 0.967   **33.** 0.454   **35.** 29.2
37. 0.0638   **39.** 0.112

Problem Set 1.9, pages 50–51

1. 6.091×10^6 sq m   **3.** 0.005 561 sq in.   **5.** 3.320×10^{10} cu m   **7.** 0.000 963 4
cu ft   **9.** 111.4 cm   **11.** 0.1114 ft   **13.** 14.94 m   **15.** 32.18 in.   **17.** 0.4147
19. 0.089 34   **21.** 0.019 25   **23.** 0.4600   **25.** 8.032   **27.** $C = 40.46$ in.,
$A = 130.3$ sq in.   **29.** $C = 0.093\ 87$ m, $A = 0.000\ 701\ 2$ sq m

Chapter 2

Problem Set 2.1, pages 69–71

A	C	CI	K	L
1. 1.22	1.10	9.05	1.35	0.0430
3. 31.0	5.57	1.80	173	0.746
5. 36.0	6.00	1.67	216	0.778
7. 21.6	4.65	2.15	101	0.667

9. $K = 91.1$, $A = 20.2$, $B = 9.00$, $CI = 3.33$, $D = 4.50$ **11.** 408   **13.** 915
15. 9.19×10^7 **17.** 0.008 42   **19.** 0.000 674   **21.** 4.99   **23.** 2.91   **25.** 59.1
27. 1042   **29.** 0.805   **31.** 928   **33.** 60.9   **35.** 295   **37.** 16.82   **39.** 12.09

Problem Set 2.2, pages 75–76

1. 0.980   **3.** 0.000 191   **5.** 74,400   **7.** 1.75×10^{-7} **9.** 11,340   **11.** 10.57
13. 14.53   **15.** 5.02   **17.** 3.30   **19.** 5.84   **21.** lead 33.1 %; copper 24.4 %;
tin 19.5 %; vanadium 14.0 %; antimony 5.4 %; bismuth 3.6 %

Problem Set 2.3, page 79

1. 554   **3.** 0.296   **5.** 1.147×10^{11} **7.** 8860   **9.** 9.42×10^{-11} **11.** 1.000
13. 3.00×10^8 **15.** 5.01×10^{-11} **17.** 148.8   **19.** 1.200×10^{13}

Problem Set 2.4, pages 82–83

1. 530   **3.** 61.0   **5.** 0.001 592   **7.** 0.001 342   **9.** 0.1104   **11.** 5.07×10^6
13. 3.09×10^{-9} **15.** 1.620

Problem Set 2.5, page 86

1. 24.0   **3.** 148.8   **5.** 0.002 72   **7.** 17.78   **9.** 3.64×10^{-7} **11.** 1.295 sq in.
13. 3160 sq in.   **15.** 32,400 sq in.   **17.** 0.422   **19.** 49.8

Problem Set 2.6, pages 90–91

1. 93.0   **3.** 6.88   **5.** 0.0824   **7.** 5.10   **9.** 0.379   **11.** 24.9   **13.** 0.0326
15. 1.031   **17.** 32.6   **19.** 4.88   **21.** 28.0 fps   **23.** 8.45 mps

Problem Set 2.7, pages 94–95

1. 234 cu ft sand, 390 cu ft rock

3. mph	0	10	20	30	40	50	60
fps	0	14.7	29.3	44	58.7	73.3	88

5. 0.434 cu ft   **7.** 2.17 cu ft   **9.** 104.8   **11.** 3.22×10^{-12} **13.** 1.086×10^{16}
15. 3.41   **17.** 0.002 18   **19.** 88.3

Chapter 3

Problem Set 3.1, pages 110–113

1. (a) polynomial; (b) 8   **3.** (a) polynomial; (b) $12\frac{3}{4}$ **5.** (a) not a polynomial; division by a variable; (b) 17   **7.** (a) not a polynomial; radicand contains a variable; (b) 0   **9.** (a) polynomial; (b) 19   **11.** (a) binomial; (b) $2y$; (c) 2   **13.** (a) trinomial; (b) $-4y^2$; (c) -1 **15.** monomial; (b) $0.5y^2z$; (c) 0.5   **17.** (a) binomial; (b) $\frac{1}{2}$; (c) $\frac{1}{2}$ **19.** (a) none of these; (b) $-2y^3$; (c) 4   **21.** 5   **23.** 1   **25.** $9y$ **27.** a **29.** $4x^3y^3$ **31.** $20 - (10 - 5)$ **33.** $2 \cdot 3^2$ **35.** $5 \cdot (6 + 4)$ **37.** $7 - 2 \cdot (4 - 1)$ **39.** $(9 - 3)^2$ **41.** 13   **43.** 6   **45.** 0   **47.** 11   **49.** 80   **51.** 3   **53.** -3 **55.** -13 **57.** -3 **59.** 1   **61.** 4   **63.** -11 **65.** -1 **67.** -10 **69.** 2   **71.** $-2\frac{1}{8}$ **73.** $-11\frac{11}{16}$ **75.** -28.37 **77.** -3.019 **79.** $-0.000\,38$ **81.** $9\frac{3}{8}$ **83.** $-2\frac{11}{16}$ **85.** 218.87   **87.** 1.011   **89.** $-0.001\,46$ **91.** $+278.55$ **93.** \$100.75   **95.** (a) $18°$; (b) $29°$; (c) $13°$ **97.** 55 mm west of 0

Problem Set 3.2, pages 118–120

1. -20 **3.** $+54$ **5.** $+\frac{15}{64}$ **7.** $-\frac{3}{7}$ **9.** -1 **11.** $+10.5$ **13.** -8 **15.** $+\frac{4}{15}$ **17.** 0   **19.** $+\frac{1}{5}$ **21.** -8 **23.** $+13$ **25.** $-1/20{,}000$ **27.** $+\frac{5}{6}$ **29.** -2.0202 **31.** $+\frac{25}{3}$ **33.** -158.4 **35.** $+5600$ **37.** $-560{,}000$ **39.** 0   **41.** 3   **43.** undefined   **45.** undefined   **47.** -5.05 **49.** undefined   **51.** 1250 miles south   **53.** 1250 miles south   **55.** 750 miles north   **57.** 1050 miles south   **59.** 420 miles north   **61.** 150 ft lb counterclockwise torque   **63.** 150 ft lb clockwise torque   **65.** 100 ft lb counterclockwise torque   **67.** 100 ft lb clockwise torque

Problem Set 3.3, page 124

1. $x + y$; $(1 - 1 + 3 = 3)$ **3.** $\frac{4}{3}x^2 + \frac{5}{6}x - \frac{3}{2}$; $(14 + 36\frac{1}{4} + 1\frac{1}{4} = 51\frac{1}{2})$ **5.** $3b^2$ **7.** $3x^3 + x^2y - 4xy^2 - y^3$ **9.** $6.02x^2 + 2.46x - 1.24$ **11.** $2x^3 - 3x^2 - 8x + 7$ **13.** $a - c$ **15.** $-9x + 9$ **17.** $x^3 + 6x^2 + x - 6$ **19.** $-3x - 1$

Problem Set 3.4, pages 127–128

1. $5^4x^2y^3$ **3.** $5^2a^3x^3y^4$ **5.** $7^3r^3s^6$ **7.** $(-2x)^4$ **9.** $\left(-\dfrac{5r}{2}\right)^3$ **11.** $30x^3y^4$ **13.** $32x^{10}$ **15.** $-400x^6$ **17.** $-x^3y^{12}$ **19.** $-243a^{10}/32$ **21.** $-24a^6b^4c^5$ **23.** $x^{12}y^8z^4/256$ **25.** $-243x^{10}y^{20}$ **27.** $1.50x^5y - 0.75x^2y^4$ **29.** $-0.60a^3b^3c^3 - 1.80a^4b^4c^4$ **31.** $-0.0025t^8 + 0.0075t^7 - 0.0005t^5$ **33.** $14x^4 + 35x^3 - 14x^2$ **35.** $a^2bcd + ab^2cd - abc^2d - abcd^2$ **37.** $8x^3 + 27y^3$ **39.** $x^5 - 1$ **41.** $2x^{ab}$ **43.** $3a^4 - 2a^2b^2 + 4b^4$ **45.** $3x^2 - 12xy + 2y^2$ **47.** $z^{n+1} - z$ **49.** 3^{4x} **51.** $6x^2 - 26x$ **53.** $-8x^2$ **55.** $x^3 + 8$ **57.** $2xy + 2xz$ **59.** $4xy$

Problem Set 3.5, page 130

1. $x^2 + x - 6$ **3.** $x^2 + 7x + 10$ **5.** $x^2 - 11x + 30$ **7.** $x^2 - 9$ **9.** $4x^2 - 25y^2$ **11.** $25x^2 + 30x + 9$ **13.** $36x^2 - 60xy + 25y^2$ **15.** $6x^2 + 5x - 4$ **17.** $42y^2 - 85y + 42$ **19.** $100x^2 + 133xy + 10y^2$ **21.** $x^3 - 8$ **23.** $y^3 + 125$ **25.** $a^2 - b^2 - 2bc - c^2$ **27.** $x^4 - 10x^2 + 9$ **29.** $xy + 2x - 3y - 6$ **31.** $x^3 - 7x^2 + x - 7$ **33.** $y^5 - 9y^3 - y^2 + 9$ **35.** $8x^2y - 4x^2 - 18y + 9$ **37.** $x^4 - y^4$ **39.** $x^4 + 8x^3 + 24x^2 + 32x + 16$

Problem Set 3.6, pages 132–133

1. $4x^3y$ **3.** $-4a^3b^4c^4$ **5.** $27P^3Q$ **7.** $-6r^8s^6$ **9.** $-\frac{1}{2}xy^3$ **11.** $x - 9$
13. $-5xy + 6$ **15.** $-7x^2 + 5x - 4$ **17.** $7x^2 - 6x + 4$ **19.** $-160a^2b$
$- 80ac^2 + 40b^2 + 20$

Problem Set 3.7, pages 135–136

1. $9x^2 - 16y^2$ **3.** $25x^2y^2 - 1$ **5.** $81a^2b^2 - 18ab + 1$ **7.** $4x^2 + 12xy + 9y^2$
9. $x^2 + 29.6x - 12$ **11.** $y^2 - 0.34y + 0.012$ **13.** $10x^2 + 19x + 6$ **15.** $5y^2$
$+ 28y - 12$ **17.** $0.06xy - 0.10x + 0.09y - 0.15$ **19.** $1.1 - 0.44x - 3.0y +$
$1.2xy$ **21.** $x^3 + 125$ **23.** $27x^3 - 1$ **25.** $x^3 - 4x^2 + 4x - 16$ **27.** $xy +$
$6x + 6y + 36$ **29.** $81x^6 - y^4$ **31.** $0.0169a^4b^6 - 0.208a^2b^3c^4 + 0.64c^8$ **33.**
$x^{12} - 512$ **35.** $0.001r^{18} + 0.064$ **37.** $x^2 + 2xy + y^2 - 1$ **39.** $x^4 - 81y^4$

Problem Set 3.8, pages 140–141

1. $5(x - 4y)$ **3.** $4x^2(7x + 2y - 1)$ **5.** $26x^4y^3(x^2 + 4y^2)$ **7.** $abc(4a - 8b + c)$
9. $r(1 + st)$ **11.** $(x + 3)(x - 3)$ **13.** $(5x + 2y)(5x - 2y)$ **15.** $(9a + 1) \times$
$(9a - 1)$ **17.** no solution   **19.** $(4r^2 + t)(4r^2 - t)$ **21.** $(x^3 + 20y^4z^2)(x^3 -$
$20y^4z^2)$ **23.** no solution   **25.** $(x - 7)^2$ **27.** $(3a + 1)^2$ **29.** $(5r - 2s)^2$
31. no solution   **33.** $(9x^2 + 1)^2$ **35.** $(a^5 - 13)^2$ **37.** no solution   **39.**
$(x - 2)(x - 3)$ **41.** $(x^2 + 7y)(x^2 - 3y)$ **43.** no solution   **45.** $(t - 12)(t + 5)$
47. $(b - 40c^3)(b - 30c^3)$ **49.** $(3x - 1)(x + 2)$ **51.** $(3y - 1)(2y - 1)$ **53.**
$(8a - 3b)(a + b)$ **55.** no solution   **57.** $(3c^2 - 4)(c^2 + 1)$ **59.** $(3x^4 - 2) \times$
$(2x^4 - 3)$ **61.** $(4x - 9y)(3x + 5y)$ **63.** $(x + 3)(y + 2)$ **65.** $(x^2 + 1)(5xy + 1)$
67. $(a + 2)(2a^3 - 1)$ **69.** $(x + 3)(y - 4)$ **71.** $(x + y)(y + 3)$ **73.** $(x - 1) \times$
$(x^2 + 1)$ **75.** $(a - 2)(3a^2 - 1)$ **77.** $(x^2 + y^2)(x^4y^4 - 5)$ **79.** $(x + 2) \times$
$(x^2 - 2x + 4)$ **81.** $(7y - 1)(49y^2 + 7y + 1)$ **83.** $(5x - 4y)(25x^2 + 20xy + 16y^2)$
85. $(3y^2 + 4z^3)(9y^4 - 12y^2z^3 + 16z^6)$ **87.** no solution   **89.** $2a(a^2 + 3b^2)$

Problem Set 3.9, page 144

1. $6(x + 2)(x - 2)$ **3.** $x(x + 8)(x - 8)$ **5.** $2x(x + 3)(x - 3)(x^2 + 9)$ **7.**
$2x(x^2 + 4)(x^4 - 4x^2 + 16)$ **9.** no solution   **11.** $(x + 2)(x - 2)(x^2 + 9)$
13. $7(x + 1)(x^3 - 2)(x^2 - x + 1)$ **15.** $4y^2(x + y)(x - y)(x + 5y)(x - 5y)$ **17.**
$5y(y + 1)(y + 2)(y - 2)$ **19.** $8(3x + y)(x + 3y)$ **21.** $-16(x^2 + 2x + 5)(x^2 -$
$2x + 5)$ **23.** $(x + y - 7)(x - y - 7)$ **25.** $16(x^2 + 2x + 2)(x^2 - 2x + 2)$
27. no solution   **29.** $(x + y - 2)(x - y - 14)$ **31.** $12xy^2z(x^2 - y)(x^2 + y) \times$
$(x^4 + y^2)$ **33.** no solution   **35.** $(x + 2)(x^2 - 5)(x^2 + 5)(x^2 - 2x + 4)$
37. $(x + 2)(x - 2)(x - 5)(x^2 + 5x + 25)$ **39.** $(2x + 3y - 2)(2x - 3y - 4)$ **41.**
$(x + 2y)(x - 2y - 4)$ **43.** $(x + 2)^3$ **45.** $(x^2 + y^2)(x^2 + x + 1)$ **47.** $5(2a +$
$b)(2a - b)(x + 2)(3x - 5)$

Problem Set 3.10, page 146

1. $(x + \frac{1}{2})(x + \frac{1}{4})$ **3.** $(y - \frac{1}{2})(y - \frac{1}{3})$ **5.** $(x + 0.1)^2$ **7.** $0.3(2t + 1)(5t + 1)$
9. $0.01(5x - 3)(10x + 1)$ **11.** $(\frac{1}{3}x - 1)^2$ **13.** $0.04(x + 5)^2$ **15.** $0.01(z - 1) \times$
$(3z + 2)$ **17.** $0.001(23x + 5)(17x - 5)$ **19.** $0.001(13y - 8)(7y + 9)$ **21.**
$0.01(24t - 19)^2$ **23.** $0.005(3x + 2y)(3x - 2y)(9x^2 + 4y^2)$ **25.** $\frac{1}{12}(x + 2)(y + 3)$

Chapter 4

1. $\overrightarrow{AB}, \overrightarrow{AC}, \overrightarrow{BC}, \overrightarrow{CD}, \overrightarrow{AD}$ **3.** $\overrightarrow{CB}$ and $\overrightarrow{CD}$ **5.** $\overline{AE} = \overline{EB} = 2$ in., $\angle AEC = \angle CEB$ = 90°, CD is the perpendicular bisector of AB **7.** (a) $\angle ADF = \angle DEG = 60°$; (b) parallel lines; (c) corresponding angles of parallel lines; (d) $\overline{FG} = \overline{DH} = 3.46$ in.; (e) parallel lines are a constant distance apart   **9.** $\angle AOB$ or $\angle AOC$ **11.** $\angle AOD$
13. $\angle AOB$ **15.** $\angle AOC$ **17.** $\angle BOF$ **19.** $\angle EOF$ **21.** 25°   **23.** 154°
25. 45°   **27.** $\angle BCE$ **29.** $\angle FGC$ **31.** $\angle ABF$ **33.** $\angle FGC$ **35.**
$\angle EAD = 75°$, $\angle DAC = 29°$, $\angle BAC = 76°$

1. no   **3.** yes   **5.** yes   **7.** yes   **9.** no   **11.** 400   **13.** 1.58   **15.** 2.90
17. not a triangle   **19.** 31.2   **21.** 56.2

	a	b	c	A	B	C
23.	6	8	11	32°	45°	103°
25.	(infinitely many triangles)			20°	60°	100°
27.	6.7	4.3	9	45°	27°	108°
29.	7	11	13.5	31°	54°	95°
31.	7.8	7.8	12	40°	40°	100°
33.	8	10	19	(no triangle, 8 + 10 = 18 < 19)		
35.	7.5	10.0	12.5	37°	53°	90°

37. 0.64 in.   **39.** $129.38   **41.** 0.574 acre   **43.** 1.15 in.   **45.** 2.16 in.
47.

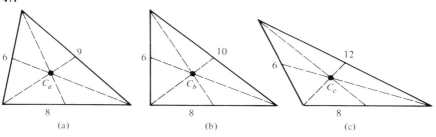

49. (a) acute; (b) right; (c) obtuse
51.

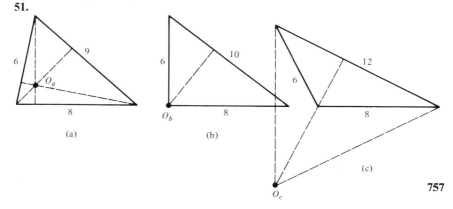

53. 10   **55.** 70°   **57.** $A = 0.84$, $p = 5.6$ **59.** (a) right angle, $12^2 + 16^2 = 20^2$; (b) right angle, $6^2 + 8^2 = 10^2$; (c) $\angle FHE = \angle HBA$, corresponding angles of parallel lines are equal; (d) 116 ft   **61.** (a) congruent, ASA; (b) 87 ft 9 in.   **63.** 2284 lb   **65.** $r = 330$ ft, 200 ft east and 262 ft south of A **67.** $21\frac{3}{4}$ in. diameter

Problem Set 4.3, pages 181–188
1. 70°   **3.** 110°   **5.** 33.5 acres   **7.** 5.61 sq in.   **9.** 184 ft   **11.** 19 quarter acres, \$114   **13.** 7.93 oz   **15.** both volumes $= 880{,}000$ cu ft   **17.** (a) 20.78 sq in.; (b) 16.97 sq in.   **19.** (a) \$48; (b) 2546 ft   **21.** \$35   **23.** (a) 3.50 sq in.; (b) 6.66 sq in.; (c) 2.48 sq in.

Problem Set 4.4, pages 196–199
1. 1.73 in.   **3.** 1.41 in.   **5.** 180°, $\frac{1}{2}$ sum of intercepted arcs $= \frac{1}{2}(360°) = 180°$ **7.** 1.20 in.   **9.** (a) 108°; (b) 89°, 102°, 91°, 78°; (c) 85°   **11.** (a) 80°, 120°, 160°; (b) 100°, 60°, 20°; (c) 20°, 80°, 80°   **13.** (a) 45°; (b) 90°; (c) 67.5°   **15.** $6\frac{1}{4}$ in.   **17.** (a) 1 in.; (b) 3.16 in.   **19.** 7.5 in.   **21.** 22,100 sq ft   **23.** 36 lb   **25.** 4,105,000 sq ft   **27.** 22.5 tons

Problem Set 4.5, pages 205–206

1.

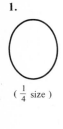

($\frac{1}{4}$ size)

3.

($\frac{1}{4}$ size)

5.

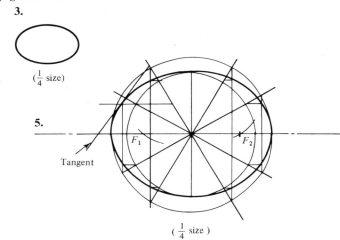

Tangent

($\frac{1}{4}$ size)

7. 248,000 sq ft, area; 1777 ft, perimeter   **9.** 103 ft   **11.** 35 ft
13. 136 ft

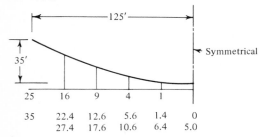

├─────────125'─────────┤

35'

Symmetrical

25	16	9	4	1	
35	22.4	12.6	5.6	1.4	0
	27.4	17.6	10.6	6.4	5.0

15. 44,000 cu ft

Problem Set 4.6, pages 219–225
1. 1.91 tons, 2.45 : 1   **3.** (a) 129.0 sq in.; (b) 119.7 cu in.   **5.** diamond   **7.** 38 in.
9. 82.58 sq in., $16\frac{3}{8}$ by $8\frac{1}{4}$ in.

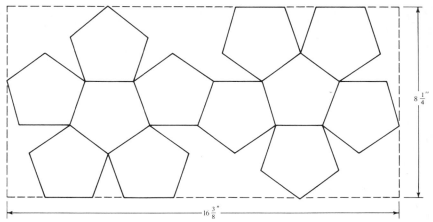

11. 2.21 lb   **13.** 21.7 lb   **15.** 367.5 lb
17. (a) 256 bushels; (b) 1.1 gal   **19.** (a) 2,290,000 blocks; (b) 46,250 blocks   **21.**
1037 tons   **23.** (a) 322 sq ft; (b) 384 cu ft   **25.** (a) 26.9 cu in.; (b) 40.5 sq. in.   **27.**
(a) 846,000 gal; (b) 132,200 gal; (c) 113 gal   **29.** (a) 174.2 sq ft; (b) (1) 261.3 cu ft,
(2) 261.2 cu ft; (c) 7840 cu ft   **31.** 2980 lb   **33.** (a) 40 gal; (b) 17.45 sq ft   **35.**
(a) 49.5 cu ft; (b) 75.4 sq ft   **37.** (a) 560 cu in.; (b) 286.2 sq in.   **39.** 1.93 lb

Chapter 5

Problem Set 5.1, pages 238–241
1. $\frac{2}{3}$ **3.** $\frac{1}{4}$ **5.** $\frac{3}{8}$ **7.** 3   **9.** $\frac{19}{41}$ **11.** 8   **13.** 60   **15.** 30   **17.** 20
19. 3   **21.** $\frac{3}{2}$ **23.** $\frac{4}{7}$ **25.** 7   **27.** 3   **29.** $\frac{4}{7}$ **31.** $\frac{4}{3}$ **33.** $\frac{1}{6}$ **35.** $\frac{10}{21}$
37. $\frac{2}{7}$ **39.** $\frac{32}{105}$ **41.** $\frac{45}{121}$ **43.** $\frac{7}{5}$ **45.** $\frac{4}{5}$ **47.** $\frac{32}{87}$ **49.** $\frac{2}{7}$ **51.** $\frac{19}{12}$
53. $\frac{41}{392}$ **55.** $\frac{1}{20}$ **57.** $\frac{4}{225}$ **59.** $\frac{7}{2664}$ **61.** $\frac{29}{24}$ **63.** $\frac{2}{5}$ **65.** $-\frac{1}{77}$ **67.** $\frac{3}{4}$
69. $\frac{2}{43}$ **71.** $381\frac{6}{7}$ cu in.   **73.** 5 lb   **75.** 4 ft $5\frac{3}{4}$ in.   **77.** \$6.64   **79.** 3 cu yd
81. $17\frac{1}{2}$ turns

Problem Set 5.2, pages 244–245
1. $-x$ **3.** $3y$ **5.** -1 **7.** 9   **9.** $x + 4$ **11.** $y - 6$ **13.** $x + 3$
15. $-(t + 4)^2$ **17.** $b^2 - 16$ **19.** $x + 2$ **21.** $\dfrac{5x}{7y}$ **23.** $\dfrac{-8c^6}{7a^6}$ **25.** $2x^3y^4$
27. $\dfrac{x + 6}{x + 3}$ **29.** $\dfrac{-y}{4}$ **31.** $\dfrac{-x}{x + 7}$ **33.** $\dfrac{x + 2}{x - 2}$ **35.** $\dfrac{2 - x}{2 + x}$ **37.** $\dfrac{-4x}{x^2 + 16}$
39. $\dfrac{4(x + 5y)}{2x + 5y}$ **41.** $\dfrac{x - 2}{x}$ **43.** $\dfrac{5}{2x + 3y}$ **45.** $\dfrac{(x + 1)^2}{x^2 + 1}$ **47.** $\dfrac{2(4v + 5)}{4v - 5}$
49. $\dfrac{\pi h(R^2 + Rr + r^2)}{3}$ **51.** $\dfrac{c_1 F_1{}^2 - c_2 F_2{}^2}{c_1 F_1 - c_2 F_2}$

Problem Set 5.3, pages 248–250

1. $\dfrac{x}{3y}$ **3.** $\dfrac{R_1}{R_2}$ **5.** $\dfrac{9p}{25V^2}$ **7.** 1 **9.** $\dfrac{x+2}{x-2}$ **11.** $\dfrac{F_1{}^2 + F_2{}^2}{F_1{}^2 - F_2{}^2}$ **13.** $\dfrac{x-2}{x+3}$

15. $\dfrac{2x-y}{x+2y}$ **17.** $\dfrac{(R+1)^2}{(T+1)^2}$ **19.** $\dfrac{v}{u^2}$ **21.** $\dfrac{4a}{9c}$ **23.** $\dfrac{1}{2y-x}$ **25.** $\dfrac{v-5}{2(v+5)}$

27. $\dfrac{2x+1}{2x+3}$ **29.** $\dfrac{h_1 h_2}{R_1 R_2}$ **31.** $-(v_1 + v_2)$ **33.** $\dfrac{2ab}{a+b}$ **35.** $\dfrac{x}{x^2 - x + 1}$

37. $\dfrac{r_1{}^2 + r_2{}^2}{r_1{}^3 + r_2{}^3}$ **39.** $\dfrac{5x}{y}$ **41.** $\dfrac{2x+1}{3}$ **43.** $\dfrac{-v}{16}$

Problem Set 5.4, pages 252–254

1. $\dfrac{47b}{90x}$ **3.** $\dfrac{31}{125xy}$ **5.** $\dfrac{2}{x^3}$ **7.** $\dfrac{2 - 6y^2}{9y^3}$ **9.** $\dfrac{x^2 + y^2}{kxy}$ **11.** 0

13. $\dfrac{7}{10(x-3)}$ **15.** $\dfrac{6-4y}{9y(y+2)}$ **17.** $\dfrac{1}{x-y}$ **19.** $\dfrac{a^2 + b^2}{a^2 - b^2}$ **21.** $\dfrac{1}{x}$

23. $\dfrac{x^2 + 9x + 10}{(x+2)^2}$ **25.** $\dfrac{2y-7}{y-3}$ **27.** $\dfrac{x^2}{x-y}$ **29.** $\dfrac{-1}{x+4}$ **31.** $\dfrac{x^2}{x^2 - 16}$

33. $\dfrac{20x}{x^2 - 16}$ **35.** $\dfrac{-x}{(x+5)(x-2)(x-3)}$ **37.** $\dfrac{1}{r^7}$ **39.** $\dfrac{4a^5 b^5}{a^{10} - b^{10}}$

41. $\dfrac{-2x^2}{(2x-5)(x+4)(x-3)}$ **43.** $\dfrac{2}{r^2 - 1}$ **45.** 0 **47.** $\dfrac{2(R+L)}{(R-K)(K-L)}$

49. $\dfrac{3x^2 - 2x - 3}{x^2 - 1}$ **51.** $\dfrac{0.2}{y(2y-1)}$ **53.** $-(a+b)$ **55.** $\dfrac{(3t-1)^2}{6t}$

57. $\dfrac{1}{y^4(x^4 - y^4)}$

Problem Set 5.5, pages 257–259

1. $\frac{5}{14}$ **3.** $\frac{2}{3}$ **5.** $\dfrac{a^4}{b^2}$ **7.** 1 **9.** $\dfrac{-b}{a}$ **11.** $\frac{1}{2}$ **13.** $\dfrac{1}{x}$ **15.** $\dfrac{t}{3t+1}$

17. $\dfrac{R_1(R_2 - R_1)}{R_2}$ **19.** $\dfrac{r_n}{r_n{}^2 + 1}$ **21.** $\dfrac{2r_1 r_2}{r_1 + r_2}$ **23.** $\dfrac{x-2}{x^2 - 2x + 4}$ **25.** $\dfrac{x+5}{x-7}$

27. $\dfrac{3x + 2y}{4y(2x+y)}$ **29.** $\dfrac{1}{a}$ **31.** $\dfrac{k^2}{R^2}$ **33.** $\dfrac{x-3}{x-5}$ **35.** $\dfrac{-(x^2 + 1)}{2x}$ **37.** $\frac{5}{8}$

39. $1 - x$ **41.** $\dfrac{-x}{y}$

Chapter 6

Problem Set 6.1, page 265

1. I **3.** F **5.** T **7.** C **9.** C **11.** yes **13.** no **15.** no **17.** yes
19. no **21.** 4 **23.** 3, -2 **25.** none **27.** 0, 1, -1 **29.** all

Problem Set 6.2, pages 269–270

1. $\{3\}$ **3.** $\{-12\}$ **5.** $\{-4\}$ **7.** $\{7\}$ **9.** $\{6\}$ **11.** $\{4\}$ **13.** $\{8.64\}$
15. $\{6.51\}$ **17.** $x \neq -2; \varnothing$ **19.** $x \neq 5; \{\frac{3}{2}\}$

Problem Set 6.3, pages 272–273

1. $n \neq 0; \{4\}$ **3.** $p \neq -5; R - \{-5\}$ **5.** $r \neq -4; \varnothing$ **7.** $s \neq -3, 2; \{7\}$
9. $s \neq \frac{3}{2}, \frac{2}{3}; \{-5\}$ **11.** $u \neq 0; \{2.5\}$ **13.** $v \neq 1, 4; \{\frac{2}{3}\}$ **15.** $w \neq -1, -\frac{1}{2}; \{\frac{1}{2}\}$
17. $x \neq \pm 5; \{0\}$ **19.** $t \neq \pm 0.80; \{1\}$

Problem Set 6.4, pages 274–278

1. $n = \dfrac{D}{A} + 1$ **3.** $T_1 = T_2 - \dfrac{V_i - V_o}{\beta V_o}$ **5.** $m_1 = \dfrac{m_2 P_1 V_1 t_2}{P_2 V_2 t_1}$ **7.** $t_1 = t_f - \dfrac{Q}{mc}$

9. $v_0 = \dfrac{v_s f'}{f' - f}$ **11.** $M = \dfrac{0.3125}{p - E_1}$ **13.** $D_N = \dfrac{D_R S}{R}$ **15.** $K_{ts} = 1 + \dfrac{K - 1}{q}$

17. $u = \dfrac{Q_M}{K_M rml}$ **19.** $W = \dfrac{3413 P_g}{h_1 - h_2}$ **21.** $t_1 = 1 + t_2 - \dfrac{R'}{R}$ **23.** $r_v = \dfrac{R x_1}{x_2 T - x_1}$

25. $r_0 = \dfrac{r_1 R_1 - r_x R_x}{R_1 - R_x}$ **27.** $b = \dfrac{4a}{4 - a^2}$ **29.** $b = \dfrac{a(y + L)}{x + r}$ **31.** $p = p_0 + \dfrac{AEc_p}{L}$

33. $c = 2d' - a + b - d$ **35.** $s = \dfrac{D - (f + c)}{k}$ **37.** $A_m = \dfrac{1}{4}\left(\dfrac{6V}{L} - A_1 - A_2\right)$

39. $g_1 = g_2 - rL$ **41.** $n_a = \dfrac{n_s(p - p_s)}{p_s}$ **43.** $h_3 = \dfrac{G_1 h_1 + G_2 h_2}{G_1 + G_2}$

45. $p_1 = \dfrac{2p_2}{2 - kM^2}$ **47.** $r_0 = \dfrac{r_1}{1 - 4\pi k r_1 R}$ **49.** $P_a = \dfrac{E P_0 P_f}{V_t(P_0 - P_f)}$

Problem Set 6.5, pages 284–294

1. 10 **3.** 6 **5.** 38 **7.** $\frac{4}{7}$ **9.** 52, 54 **11.** 64 by 16 ft **13.** 0.318 ft
15. 48°, 12°, 120° **17.** 10.5 in., 7.5 in. **19.** 4 in. **21.** (a) $2\frac{1}{2}$ hr; (b) $6\frac{1}{2}$ hr;
(c) 1625 miles **23.** 350 mph **25.** 10:20 A.M. **27.** $1\frac{1}{2}$ mph **29.** 4788 ft
31. 1A, 28 lb; 5A, 40 lb **33.** 200 lb **35.** 1.21 qt **37.** \$20 **39.** A, 8 units;
B, 4 units; C, 3 units **41.** 2 hr **43.** 9 hr, 12 hr **45.** 1 hr 15 min **47.** $4\frac{1}{2}$ hr
49. 18 hr 45 min **51.** 40 years **53.** 22 of $\frac{3}{16}$ in., 22 of $\frac{1}{4}$ in., 56 of $\frac{5}{16}$ in. **55.**
28 Ω, 56 Ω, 14 Ω **57.** 4.8 ft **59.** \$400/acre, 1600 acres

Problem Set 6.6, pages 303–304

1. $x > 4$

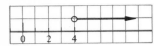

3. $x \le \frac{1}{2}$

5. $\frac{1}{2} < x < \frac{7}{2}$

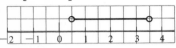

7. $-2 < x \le 2$

9. $x \le \frac{1}{12}, x \ne -\frac{1}{2}$

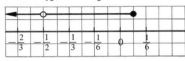

11. $7, -3$

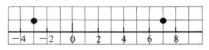

13. $-1, -\frac{7}{3}$

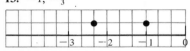

15. $x > 4$ or $x < 0$

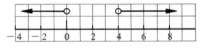

17. $-\frac{1}{2} \le x \le \frac{7}{2}$

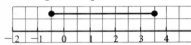

19. $\frac{1}{5} < x < 3$

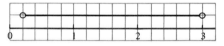

21. $4.3\% < x < 29.3\%$ **23.** (a) $23.3 \le t \le 23.7$; (b) $1.77 \le P \le 1.79$; (c) $8.27 \times 10^{-9} \le q \le 8.37 \times 10^{-9}$; (d) $6.66 \times 10^{12} \le v \le 7.16 \times 10^{12}$ **25.** (a) $65° \le C < 155°$; (b) $0° < C \le 65°$; (c) $0° < C \le 35°$; (d) $65° \le C \le 110°$ **27.** $20 < R_2 < 60$

Chapter 7

Problem Set 7.1, pages 309–310

1. (a) domain = range = R; (b) function; (c) $(-2,-4)$, $(-1,-2)$, $(0,0)$, $(1,2)$, $(2,4)$
3. (a) domain = range = R; (b) not a function; (c) $(-5,0)$, $(-5,1)$, $(-5,2)$, $(-5,3)$, $(-5,4)$, $(0,1)$, $(0,2)$, $(0,3)$, $(0,4)$, $(5,2)$, $(5,3)$, $(5,4)$ **5.** (a) domain = R, range: $y \ge 0$; (b) function; (c) $(-2,4)$, $(-1,1)$, $(0,0)$, $(1,1)$, $(2,4)$ **7.** (a) domain: $x \ge 0$, range = R; (b) not a function; (c) $(0,0)$, $(1,1)$, $(4,2)$, $(9,3)$, $(1,-1)$, $(4,-2)$, $(9,-3)$ **9.** (a) domain = range = R; (b) function; (c) $(-8,-2)$, $(-1,-1)$, $(0,0)$, $(1,1)$, $(8,2)$ **11.** (a) domain: $x \ge 0$, range = R; (b) not a function; (c) $(0,0)$, $(1,1)$, $(1,-1)$, $(2,2)$, $(2,-2)$, $(3,3)$, $(3,-3)$, $(4,4)$, $(4,-4)$ **13.** function   **15.** function   **17.** relation   **19.** relation

Problem Set 7.2, pages 315–318

1.

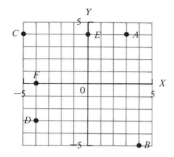

3.

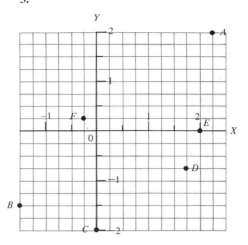

5.

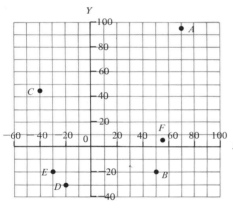

7.

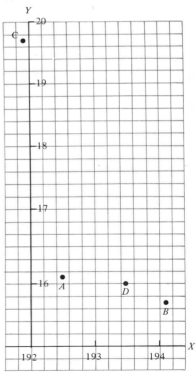

9.

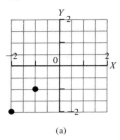

(a)

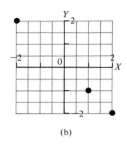

(b)

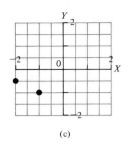

(c)

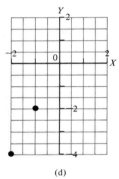

(d)

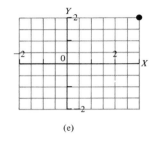

(e)

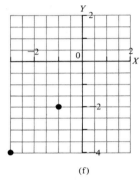

(f)

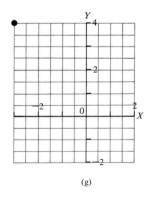

(g)

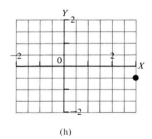

(h)

11.

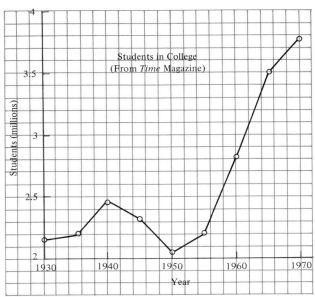

13.

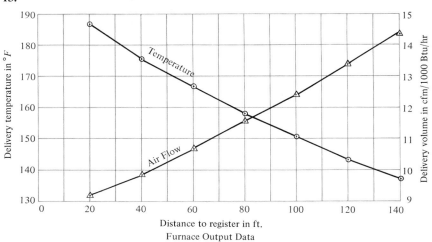

Distance to register in ft.
Furnace Output Data

15.

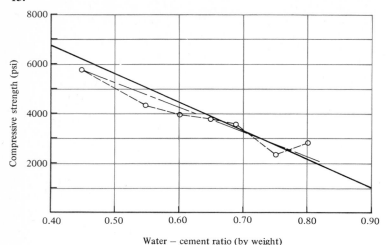

Water — cement ratio (by weight)

Problem Set 7.3, pages 320–322

1. $5, 8, -16$ **3.** $f(2)$ and $f(-2)$ do not exist; $f(0) = -1$ **5.** $g(0) = g(1) = 0$,
$g(2)$ and $g(3)$ do not exist   **7.** $h(0) = 1, h(10) = \frac{79}{24}, h(2)$ does not exist   **9.** $x^2 +$
$\frac{1}{x^2}, \frac{1}{x} + x, \frac{1}{x^2} + x^2$ **11.** $a^2 - a^4, a^2 - p^4, a^2 - (a^2 - p^2)^2$ **13.** $3s^2 + 3sh + h^2$
15. $\pi(2r + 0.001)$ **17.** $(\sqrt{A})^3, \frac{27}{64}$ **19.** (a) $y = 27t^3$; (b) $y = y$ **21.** a, b, d

Problem Set 7.4, pages 325–326

1. $-3, -3, 3, 3$ **3.** $0, -\frac{1}{2}, \frac{3}{2}, 1$ **5.** $\frac{b^2}{a^2}, ab, \frac{a^2}{b^2}$ **7.** $A = f(h, b_1, b_2) = \frac{1}{2}h(b_1 + b_2)$

9. $d = f(p) = \frac{\sqrt{2}}{4}p$ **11.** $A = f(s) = \frac{1}{2}s^2$ **13.** $s = f(r) = \frac{\pi r}{6}$ **15.** $V =$

$f(B,h) = \frac{Bh}{3}; \ h = f^{-1}(V) = \frac{3V}{B}$ **17.** $V = f(a,b,h) = \frac{\pi abh}{3}; \ h = f^{-1}(V) = \frac{3V}{\pi ab}$

19. sphere: $V = f(r) = \frac{4\pi r^3}{3}, r = f^{-1}(V) = \sqrt[3]{\frac{3V}{4\pi}}$; any regular polyhedron: $V =$
$f(L) = kL^3$ with k chosen from Table 4.1, $L = f^{-1}(V) = \sqrt[3]{\frac{V}{k}}$

21. $A_C = f(A_S) = \frac{4}{\pi}A_S$ **23.** $s = f(A) = \sqrt{\frac{A}{1.732\,05}}$

Problem Set 7.5, pages 330–331

1.

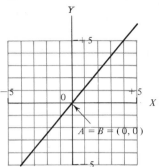

3.

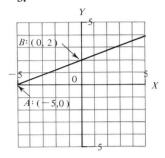

5.

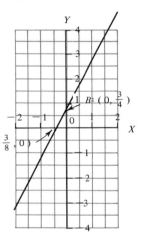

7.

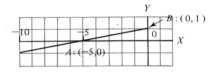

9.

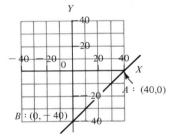

11.

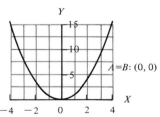

13.

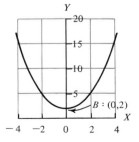

15.

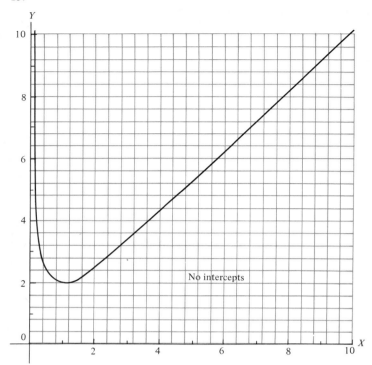

No intercepts

17.

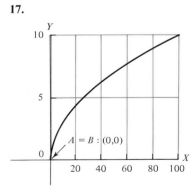

$A = B : (0,0)$

19.

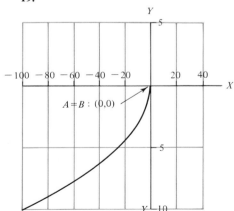

$A = B : (0,0)$

Problem Set 7.6, page 334

1.

3.

5.

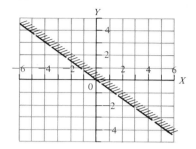

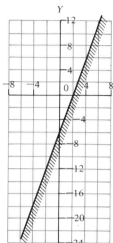

9.

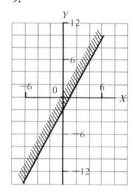

7.

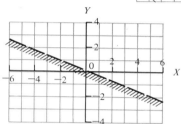

11.

13.

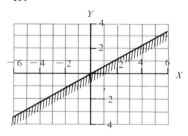

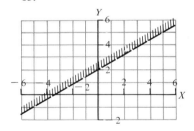

15.

17.

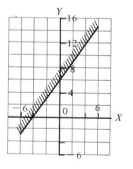

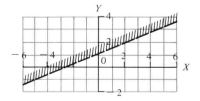

19.

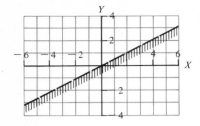

21.

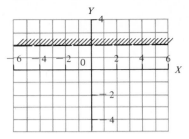

23.

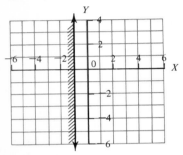

25.

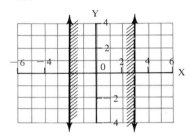

27.

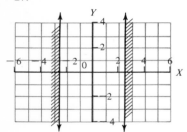

29.

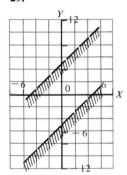

Problem Set 7.7, pages 342–345

1. (a)

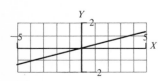

(b) $x - 4y = 0$

3. (a)

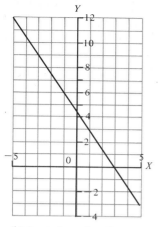

(b) $3x + 2y - 9 = 0$

5. (a)

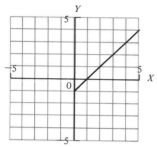

(b) $x + y - 1 = 0$ and $x \geq 0$

7. (a)

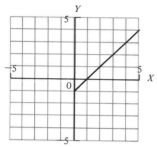

(b) $x - y - 1 = 0$ and $x \geq 0$

9. (a) 106,000 ft; (b) 35,200 yd; (c) 32.2 km; (d) 17.4 nautical mi   **11.** (a) 11.1 sq yd;
(b) 9.29 sq m; (c) 14,400 sq in.   **13.** (a) 32 oz; (b) 0.25 gal; (c) 57.8 cu in.; (d) 946 cc;
(e) 0.946 liter   **15.** (a) 90.7%; (b) 102%   **17** (a) 11,200 kg/m; (b) 0.405 lb/cu in.;
(c) 699 lb/cu ft   **19.** (a) 19.3 cu in./sec; (b) 0.668 cfm; (c) 315 cc/sec; (d) 18.9 liter/min
21. (a) 125% increase; (b) 20.4% decrease; (c) 34.5% increase   **23.** 2.38 in.   **25.** 4.12
27 new rpm $= 50.9\%$ of old rpm   **29.** 16.2:1

Chapter 8

Problem Set 8.1, pages 354–355

1. 5   **3.** 5   **5.** 5   **7.** (a) 2; (b) 4; (c) -2; (d) -4; (e) 6; (f) -6; (g) -1; (h) 8;
(j) -3 **9.** $9.6021 - 10$ **11.** 0.6021   **13.** $7.6021 - 10$ **15.** 9.6021
17. $8.6021 - 10$ **19.** 3.778 15   **21.** $18.778\ 15 - 20$ **23.** $28.778\ 15 - 30$
25. $39.778\ 15 - 40$ **27.** $-0.221\ 85$ **29.** 1.778 15   **31.** $-1.221\ 85$
33. $-3.221\ 85$

Problem Set 8.2, pages 359–360

1. 2.330 41   **3.** 3.812 31   **5.** 6.764 03   **7.** 9.953 76 − 10   **9.** 3.460 00
11. 7.560 50 − 10   **13.** 0.899 82   **15.** 9.000 87 − 10   **17.** 0.336 46 − 10
19. 0.845 59   **21.** 4.763 86   **23.** 0.845 65   **25.** 2.321 66   **27.** 9.266 14 − 10
29. 0.096 88   **31.** 1.160 35   **33.** 2.290 21   **35.** 9.300 03 − 10   **37.** 3.271 66
39. 8.599 92 − 10   **41.** −0.602 06   **43.** −1.055 02   **45.** −2.119 70
47. −3.400 01   **49.** −0.454 06   **51.** 0.2408   **53.** 2.6599   **55.** 9.6676 − 10
57. 6.8400   **59.** 9.6900 − 10   **61.** 4.875   **63.** 9.837 − 10   **65.** 1.577
67. 2.611   **69.** 6.260 − 10

Problem Set 8.3, page 362

1. 2.590   **3.** 100.3   **5.** 0.002 010   **7.** 0.027 81   **9.** 0.0861   **11.** 1.940
13. 0.173 90   **15.** 38.02   **17.** 7.008   **19.** 5,890,000   **21.** 9.7504   **23.** 0.853 18
25. 5500.5   **27.** 5.6247   **29.** 0.462 01   **31.** 3.6308   **33.** 1.7012×10^9 **35.** 148.08
37. 17.948   **39.** 12.915   **41.** 17.162   **43.** 0.752 56   **45.** 5.8268×10^8
47. 4911.3   **49.** 0.173 78   **51.** 0.080 000   **53.** 0.272 90   **55.** 6.3100×10^{-5}
57. 0.002 138 0   **59.** 0.000 110 30

Problem Set 8.4, pages 370–373

1. 2823   **3.** 17.96 in.^{4} **5.** 12.889 in. or $12\frac{57}{64}$ in.   **7.** 3.15 cpm   **9.** 0.000 60
in./boiler hp   **11.** 32.1 psf   **13.** 11.12 in.   **15.** 0.0249 in.   **17.** 567 psi

Problem Set 8.5, pages 378–379

1. 6.86 cfs, 6.78 cfs   **3.** 22.4 cfs   **5.** 8.69 cfs   **7.** 86.9 cfs, 85.2 cfs   **9.** 8.58 cfs,
8.81 cfs   **11.** 16.0 Btuh/sq ft   **13.** 11.7 Btuh/sq ft   **15.** 0.528   **17.** 0.539
19. 1456 psf

Problem Set 8.6, pages 381–385

1. 103 psi   **3.** 0.114 Ω/1000 ft   **5.** 0.0341 henry   **7.** 43,950 psi   **9.** 0.0993 μF

11. 0.059   **13.** 49,600 lb   **15.** 0.001 03   **17.** $0.0038\dfrac{°\text{F-hr}}{\text{Btu}}$

Chapter 9

Problem Set 9.1, page 395

1.
3.

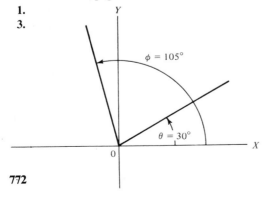

5.
7.

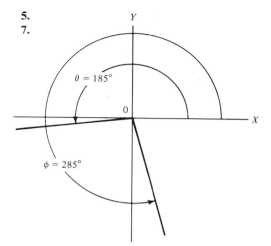

9.
11.

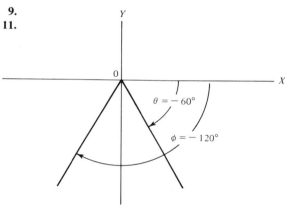

13.

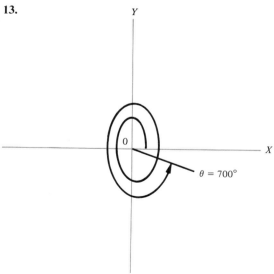

15.

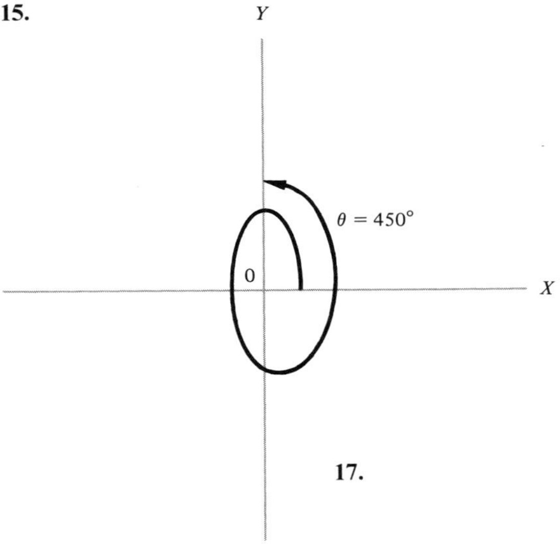

$\theta = 450°$

17.

$\theta = -420°$

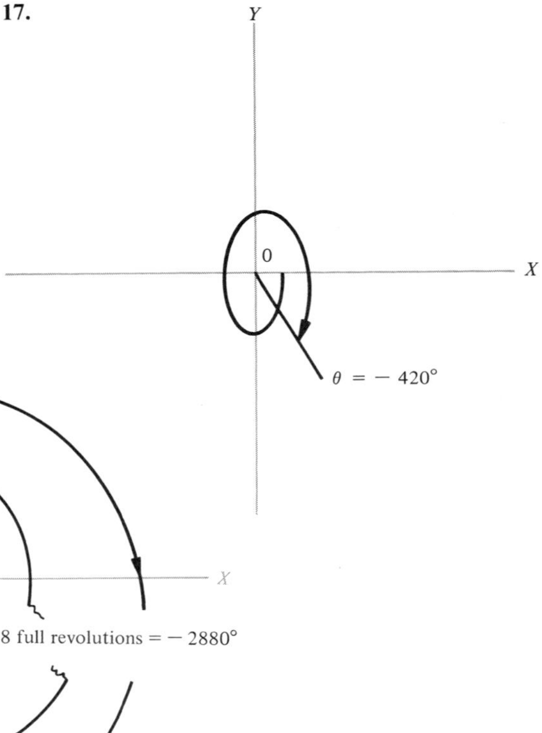

19.

8 full revolutions $= -2880°$

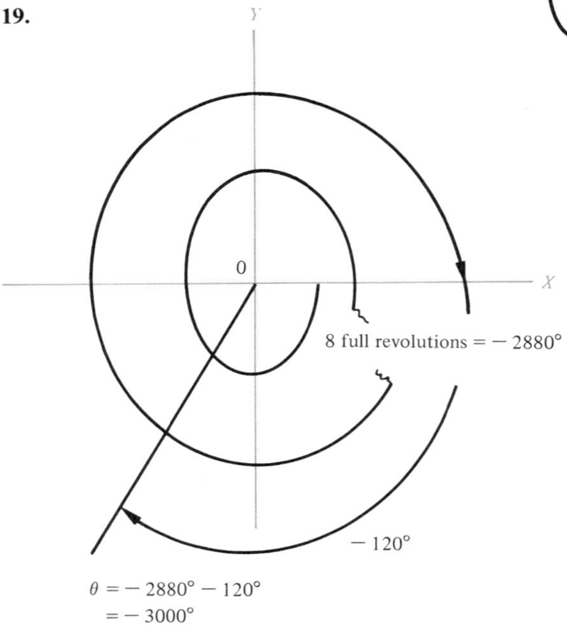

$-120°$

$\theta = -2880° - 120°$
$= -3000°$

21.
23.
25.

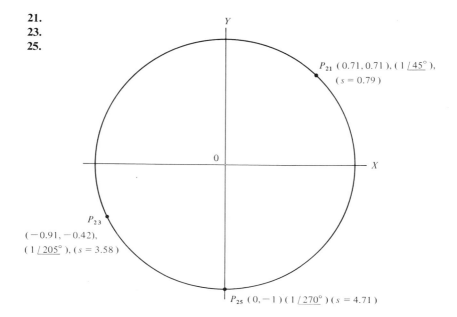

P_{21} (0.71, 0.71), (1 $\underline{/45°}$),
($s = 0.79$)

P_{23}
(−0.91, −0.42),
(1 $\underline{/205°}$), ($s = 3.58$)

P_{25} (0, −1) (1 $\underline{/270°}$) ($s = 4.71$)

27.
29.
31.

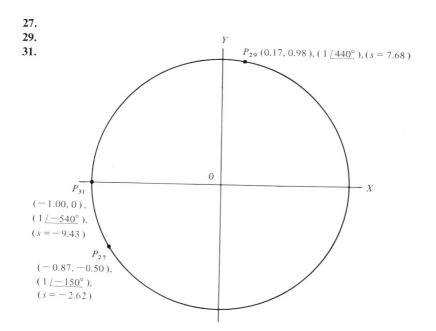

P_{29} (0.17, 0.98), (1 $\underline{/440°}$), ($s = 7.68$)

P_{31}
(−1.00, 0),
(1 $\underline{/−540°}$),
($s = −9.43$)

P_{27}
(−0.87, −0.50),
(1 $\underline{/−150°}$),
($s = −2.62$)

33.
35.

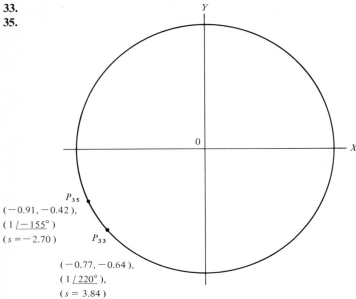

P_{35}
$(-0.91, -0.42)$,
$(1 \underline{/-155°})$
$(s = -2.70)$

P_{33}

$(-0.77, -0.64)$,
$(1 \underline{/220°})$,
$(s = 3.84)$

37.
39.

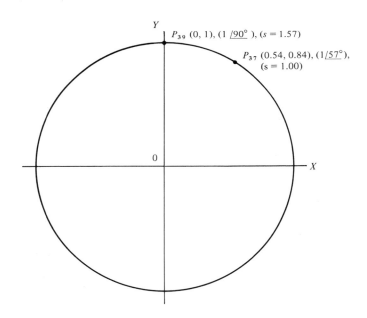

P_{39} $(0, 1)$, $(1 \underline{/90°})$, $(s = 1.57)$

P_{37} $(0.54, 0.84)$, $(1 \underline{/57°})$,
$(s = 1.00)$

Problem Set 9.2, page 399

	Sin	Cos	Tan	Cot	Sec	Csc
1.	0.800	0.600	1.33	0.750	1.67	1.25
3.	0.960	0.280	3.43	0.292	3.57	1.04
5.	0.976	0.220	4.44	0.225	4.56	1.02

7.	0.139	−0.990	−0.141	−7.12	−1.01	7.19
9.	−0.743	−0.669	1.11	0.901	−1.49	−1.35
11.	−0.882	0.470	−1.88	−0.533	2.13	−1.13
13.	0.531	0.847	0.627	1.60	1.18	1.88
15.	−0.829	0.559	−1.48	−0.675	1.79	−1.21
17.	−0.959	−0.283	3.39	0.295	−3.53	−1.04
19.	0.999	−0.0451	−22.2	0.0451	−22.2	1.00

Problem Set 9.3, pages 403–404

1. 32.206 67° **3.** 122.372 78° **5.** 191.786 69° **7.** 271.613 55° **9.** −372.239 44°
11. 37°7′22.8″ **13.** 269°50′13.2″ **15.** 3°10′29.3″ **17.** 364°13′40.4″
19. −72°51′13.3″ **21.** 120°19′16.1″ **23.** 24°24′28.8″ **25.** 30° **27.** 268°5′13.0″
29. −47°14′46.0″ **31.** 120.3212° **33.** 24.4080° **35.** 30.0000°
37. 268.0870° **39.** −47.2461° **41.** 0.649 26 **43.** 5.108 33 **45.** −0.050 81
47. 0.063 08 **49.** 3.102 47 **51.** (a) 0.5236 in.; (b) 2.6180 in. **53.** (a) 10.4720 ft;
(b) 26.1800 ft **55.** (a) 2 m; (b) 0.0349 m **57.** 0.125 rad, 7°10′ **59.** 267.69 ft
61. (a) 65,940 miles; (b) 0.000 716 8 rad

Problem Set 9.4, pages 409–410

1. $\pi/6, \pi/4, \pi/3, \pi/2$ **3.** $7\pi/6, 5\pi/4, 4\pi/3, 3\pi/2$ **5.** $-\pi/4, -\pi/3, -5\pi/6, -\pi$
7. $-\frac{1}{2}\sqrt{3}, -0.866$ **9.** $\frac{1}{2}\sqrt{2}, 0.707$ **11.** 1, 1.00 **13.** 2, 2.00 **15.** undefined
17. $\frac{1}{2}, 0.500$ **19.** $\sqrt{3}, 1.73$ **21.** $-\sqrt{2}, -1.41$

Problem Set 9.5, page 415

	Sin	Cos	Tan	Cot	Sec	Csc
1.	0.518 52	0.855 06	0.606 42	1.6490	1.1695	1.9285
3.	0.793 53	0.608 53	1.3040	0.766 86	1.6433	1.2602
5.	0.999 90	0.013 96	71.615	0.013 96	71.622	1.0001
7.	0.379 24	0.925 30	0.409 86	2.4399	1.0807	2.6368
9.	0.064 71	0.997 91	0.064 85	15.421	1.0021	15.453
11.	0.460 20	0.887 82	0.518 35	1.9292	1.1264	2.1730
13.	0.932 32	0.361 62	2.5782	0.387 87	2.7653	1.0726
15.	0.222 91	0.974 84	0.228 66	4.3733	1.0258	4.4861
17.	0.974 85	0.222 84	4.3746	0.228 57	4.4875	1.0258
19.	0.238 50	0 971 14	0.245 58	4.0719	1.0297	4.1929

Problem Set 9.6, page 419

	Quadrant	Reference Angle	Sin	Tan	Cot	Cos
1.	II		0.867 62	−1.7449	−0.573 09	−0.497 23
3.	III		−0.979 98	4.9225	0.203 15	−0.199 08
5.	IV	68.1°	−0.927 84	−2.4876	−0.402 00	0.372 99
7.	IV	19.3°	−0.330 51	−0.350 20	−2.8556	0.943 80
9.	IV		−0.775 27	−1.2274	−0.814 71	0.631 62
11.	III		−0.492 99	0.566 63	1.7648	−0.870 04
13.	I	41.34°	0.660 52	0.879 76	1.1367	0.750 80

15.	III	61.89°	−0.882 05	1.8720	0.534 16	−0.471 16
17.	IV	21°47′43″	−0.371 29	−0.399 87	−2.5008	0.928 52
19.	I	54°58′47.6″	0.818 95	1.4271	0.700 73	0.573 86
21.	IV		−0.834 69	−1.5156	−0.659 80	0.550 72
23.	III	73.21°	−0.957 37	3.3143	0.301 73	−0.288 86
25.	II		0.174 79	−0.177 53	−5.6329	−0.984 61
27.	I	74.84°	0.965 20	3.6908	0.270 94	0.261 52
29.	IV	40°54′	−0.654 74	−0.866 23	−1.1544	0.755 85

Problem Set 9.7, page 424

1. 85°54′0″ **3.** 84°7′1″ **5.** 41°24′35″ **7.** 25°3′20″ **9.** 6°20′25″
11. 36°52′12″ **13.** −14.300° **15.** 42.895° **17.** 3.627° **19.** −33.689°
21. 0.0993 and 3.0423 ± 2$n\pi$ **23.** 1.7350 ± $n\pi$ **25.** 0.0910

Problem Set 9.8, pages 426–427

	Sin	Cos	Tan	Cot	Sec	Csc
1.	$\frac{2}{3}$	$\frac{1}{3}\sqrt{5}$	$2/\sqrt{5}$	$\frac{1}{2}\sqrt{5}$	$3/\sqrt{5}$	$3/2$
3.	$-7/25$	$24/25$	$-7/24$	$-24/7$	$25/24$	$-25/7$
5.	$-2/\sqrt{5}$	$-1/\sqrt{5}$	2	$1/2$	$-\sqrt{5}$	$-\frac{1}{2}\sqrt{5}$
7.	$13/\sqrt{313}$	$-12/\sqrt{313}$	$-13/12$	$-12/13$	$-\sqrt{313}/12$	$-\sqrt{313}/13$
9.	$3/10$	$-\sqrt{91}/10$	$-3/\sqrt{91}$	$-\frac{1}{3}\sqrt{91}$	$-10/\sqrt{91}$	$10/3$
11.	$-1/\sqrt{65}$	$-8/\sqrt{65}$	$1/8$	8	$-\sqrt{65}/8$	$-\sqrt{65}$
13.	$1/4$	$-\frac{1}{4}\sqrt{15}$	$-1/\sqrt{15}$	$-\sqrt{15}$	$-4/\sqrt{15}$	4
15.	$-2/5$	$-\frac{1}{5}\sqrt{21}$	$2/\sqrt{21}$	$\frac{1}{2}\sqrt{21}$	$-5/\sqrt{21}$	$-5/2$
17.	$1/\sqrt{10}$	$-3/\sqrt{10}$	$-1/3$	-3	$-\frac{1}{3}\sqrt{10}$	$\sqrt{10}$
19.	$5/\sqrt{281}$	$16/\sqrt{281}$	$5/16$	$16/5$	$\sqrt{281}/16$	$\frac{1}{5}\sqrt{281}$

Problem Set 9.9, page 430

1. 0.113 **3.** 0.136 **5.** 0.636 **7.** 0.696 **9.** 4.02 **11.** 4.57 **13.** 0.883
15. 0.934 **17.** 1.47 **19.** 2.09

Problem Set 9.10, page 434

1. 0.000 204 **3.** 0.000 103 **5.** 0.016 634 **7.** 0.002 147 **9.** 0.003 722
11. 0.000 053 3 **13.** 0.003 55 **15.** 0.002 06 **17.** 0.0226 **19.** 0.0693

Chapter 10

Problem Set 10.1, page 453

1. 9.680 91 − 10 **3.** 0.333 75 **5.** 0.608 90 **7.** 9.990 06 − 10
9. 9.500 67 − 10 **11.** 0.070 95 **13.** 9.849 22 − 10 **15.** 7.645 96 − 10
17. 6.639 81 − 10 **19.** 288 **21.** 0.2324 **23.** 890,000 **25.** 1194.5
27. 3283.8

1. (a) 69.6; (b) 305; (c) 9.53; (d) 14.0   **3.** 102.5 sec   **5.** 0.4715 sq in.   **7** (a) 0.4226; (b) 121 Btu/sq ft/hr   **9.** 0.003 165 min   **11.** (a) 0 in., 0 in., 9.51 in.; (b) 10 in., 10 in., 3.09 in.; (c) 1257 in., 125.7 in., 12.57 in.   **13.** (a) 20 cm, 0 cm, −20 cm, 20 cm; (b) 0.0102 sec, 0.0208 sec, 0.0336 sec, 0.0625 sec   **15.** 4.8 sec

17.

θ	L	θ	L
0	68.7033	50	69.1147
10	68.7243	60	66.2297
20	68.7850	70	69.3238
30	68.8781	80	69.3853
40	68.9925	90	69.4068

19. (a) 44.97 days, 45.37 days; (b) 3.25 days, 3.34 days   **21.** 89.0 sq units

1. $a = 23$ $A = 28°10'$
$b = 43$ $B = 61°50'$
$c = 49$ $C = 90°$

3. $a = 317,$ $A = 29°7'$
$b = 569$ $B = 60°53'$
$c = 651$ $C = 90°$

5. $a = 0.22$ $A = 22°10'$
$b = 0.54$ $B = 67°50'$
$c = 0.58$ $C = 90°$

7. $a = 0.0631$ $A = 62°38'$
$b = 0.0327$ $B = 27°22'$
$c = 0.0711$ $C = 90°$

9. $a = 524$ $A = 71.2°$
$b = 178$ $B = 18.8°$
$c = 553$ $C = 90°$

11. $a = 37.0$ $A = 62°38'$
$b = 19.1$ $B = 27°22'$
$c = 41.7$ $C = 90°$

13. $a = 1.473$ $A = 35°0'0''$
$b = 2.104$ $B = 55°0'0''$
$c = 2.568$ $C = 90°$

15. $a = 1.3582$ $A = 54°24'27''$
$b = 1.8976$ $B = 35°35'33''$
$c = 2.3336$ $C = 90°$

17. $a = 4572$ $A = 36°28'49''$
$b = 6183$ $B = 53°31'11''$
$c = 7690$ $C = 90°$

19. $a = 11,510$ $A = 46.3956°$
$b = 10,962$ $B = 43.6044°$
$c = 15,895$ $C = 90°$

1. 58.3 ft   **3.** (a) 7.6536 in.; (b) 3.9018 in.; (c) 1.9604 in.; (d) 0.9814 in.   **5.** 205.4 sq. in.   **7.** 33°36′   **9.** 4.0 cm   **11.** (a) 18.618 ft; (b) $L = 2\sqrt{d^2 - (r_2 - r_1)^2} +$

$\pi(r_2 + r_1) + 2(r_2 - r_1) \operatorname{Sin}^{-1}\dfrac{r_2 - r_1}{d}$, 18.622 ft, 0.0215%   **13.** 9°24′34″   **15.** (a)

S 86°26′23″E, 450.87 mph; (b) N 3°53′25″W, 250.58 mph   **17.** 292.2 lb   **19.** 36°24′

21. 794 mph   **23.** $d = \dfrac{h}{\tan\theta + \tan\phi}$ **25.** 9.38 ft   **27.** (a) 517.82 ft; (b) 6.21 ft

29. 374 ft   **31.** 314.3 ft   **33.** 187.72 ft   **35.** 60.0 nautical miles north, 55.3 nautical miles east   **37.** 17° 27′   **39.** (a) S 30° W; (b) 30 min 51 sec

Problem Set 10.5, pages 489–490

1.

B

A R_1

$R_1 = 6.4$
$\theta = 51°$

3.

$-E$ A

R_3

$R_3 = 6.1$
$\theta = 189 \frac{1}{2}°$

5.

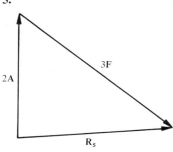

2A   3F

R_5

$R_5 = 12.05$
$\theta = 5°$

7.

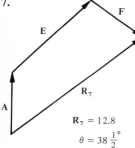

E   F

A

R_7

$R_7 = 12.8$
$\theta = 38 \frac{1}{2}°$

9.

G

$-B$

A R_9

$R_9 = 7.3$
$\theta = 74°$

11.

$-B$

$\frac{1}{4} R_{11}$ A

$R_{11} = 4\,(6.4)$
$= 25.6$
$\theta = 129°$

13.

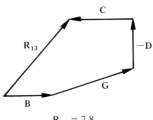

C

R_{13} $-D$

G

B

$R_{13} = 7.8$
$\theta = 50 \frac{1}{2}°$

15.

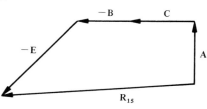

$-B$ C

$-E$ A

R_{15}

$R_{15} = 15$
$\theta = 184°$

17.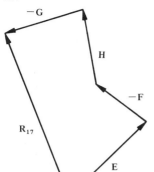

$R_{17} = 13.9$
$\theta = 111°$

19.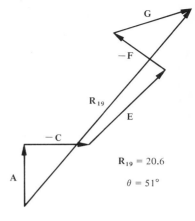

$R_{19} = 20.6$
$\theta = 51°$

21. (75, 225°)

Problem Set 10.6, page 494

1. (a) $4\mathbf{i} + 4\mathbf{j}$; (b) (5.66,45°)   **3.** (a) $5\mathbf{i} - 9\mathbf{j}$; (b) (10.30,299°3′)   **5.** (a) $-7\mathbf{i} - 11\mathbf{j}$;
(b) (13.04,237°32′)   **7.** (a) $-10\mathbf{i} + 24\mathbf{j}$; (b) (26,112°37′)   **9.** $6.40 \angle \theta = 51°20′$
11. $6.71 \searrow \theta = 26°34′$ **13.** (62.4,36.0)   **15.** $(-7.52, -2.74)$ **17.** $(1060, -1060)$
19. $(-0.435, 0.1165)$

Problem Set 10.7, pages 498–500

1. N2°7′E, 13.8 fps   **3.** $B(0.5,4.6)$, $C(2.0,7.2)$, $D(5.0,7.2)$, $E(6.5,4.6)$, $F(5.0,2.0)$ **5.** (44
miles, S2°20′W)   **7.** at R, $(15.6^k, 220°)$, $(11.9^k, 0°)$; at S, $(15.6^k, 40°)$, $(15.6^k, 140°)$,
$(20^k, 270°)$ **9.** (24.8 units, 80°0′)

Chapter 11

Problem Set 11.1, pages 510–512

1. $6\sqrt{6}$ **3.** $15\sqrt[3]{2}$ **5.** $6\sqrt{35}$ **7.** $\sqrt{7} - \sqrt{3}$ **9.** $7\sqrt[3]{2} - \sqrt[3]{3}$ **11.** $6\sqrt{5} - 14$

13. $\frac{7}{4}$ **15.** $\frac{11\sqrt{10}}{45}$ **17.** $-9 - 4\sqrt{5}$ **19.** $8(\sqrt{5} - \sqrt{3})$ **21.** $9\sqrt{2} - 6\sqrt{6}$

23. $-2\sqrt{2}$ **25.** $5 - 2\sqrt{6}$ **27.** $3 - 2\sqrt{2}$ **29.** $17\sqrt{2}\,x$ **31.** $4x\sqrt{13x}$

33. $2x^2(\sqrt{2x} - \sqrt{2})$ **35.** $2y\sqrt[3]{3y} - 1$ **37.** $-(25\tfrac{3}{4} + 8t\sqrt[3]{t^2})$ **39.** $1728w^4$

41. $900\sqrt{3}\,y^6$ **43.** $\frac{11\sqrt{2}\,r}{16}$ **45.** $\frac{14t^2}{15r^2}$ **47.** $\frac{2(x^2 + \sqrt{3}x - 6)}{3(x^2 - 12)}$ **49.** $\frac{x - \sqrt{xy}}{x - y}$

51. 3.146

Problem Set 11.2, pages 513–514

1. $\frac{1}{25}$ **3.** $\frac{27}{125}$ **5.** 8 **7.** -32 **9.** $\frac{1}{4}$ **11.** $\frac{1}{x^5}$ **13.** 1 **15.** $\frac{r^6}{9}$ **17.** $\frac{81}{t^6}$

19. $\frac{25}{z^2}$ **21.** 1 **23.** $\frac{(x-1)^{14}}{x+2}$ **25.** $\frac{1}{2(x+2)}$ **27.** $\frac{v_1^4 v_2^4}{(v_1^2 + v_2^2)^2}$ **29.** $r^2 st$

Problem Set 11.3, pages 517–518

1. 8 **3.** 9 **5.** 4 **7.** not real **9.** $\frac{9}{4}$ **11.** 118.0 **13.** 0.249 **15.** $\frac{5^{1/3}}{5}$

17. $\frac{2^{2/3} x^{1/2}}{2x}$ **19.** $s^{2/3} t^{1/2}$ **21.** $t^{0.35} u^2$ **23.** 1 **25.** $\frac{p^{0.8} r^{0.2} s^{0.8}}{ps^2}$

27. $\frac{s^{0.62} t^{0.53}}{st}$ **29.** $\frac{x^{1/2} y^{1/8}}{xy}$ **31.** $\frac{1}{81}$ **33.** $r^{\pi-2} + 1$ **35.** $\frac{625}{t^4}$

37. $u^{2.475}$ **39.** $w^{0.194}$

Problem Set 11.4, pages 520–521

1. $\log_{10} 1000 = 3$ **3.** $\log_{10} \frac{1}{10} = -1$ **5.** $\log_2 8 = 3$ **7.** $\log_4 2 = \frac{1}{2}$
9. $\log_7 1 = 0$ **11.** $10^{-3} = 0.001$ **13.** $10^4 = 10{,}000$ **15.** $49^{1/2} = 7$
17. $32^{2/5} = 4$ **19.** $e^4 = 54.6$ **21.** 8 **23.** -4 **25.** 0 **27.** -3
29. 0.147

Problem Set 11.5, pages 528–530

5. 288 **7.** 2 **9.** 4.5 **11.** 2197 **13.** 0.493 76 **15.** 1.3752 **17.** 0.998 44
19. 6.6492×10^{16}

Problem Set 11.6, page 531

1. $3^{1/2} x^{1/2}$ **3.** $18^{1/3} x^{2/3}$ **5.** $y(7^{1/4})(x^{3/4})(y^{1/2})$ **7.** $p(p^{1/14})(v^{3/5})$ **9.** $\frac{3^{1/3} x^{2/3} y^{1/3}}{3xy}$ **11.** $\frac{2v^{1/2} x^{2/3} z^{3/4}}{3z}$ **13.** $(r^6 s^4 t^3)^{1/12}$ **15.** $\frac{(v^8 w^9 x^8)^{1/12}}{vw}$

17. $10(t^{15} u^{40} v^{36})^{1/60}$ **19.** 0.908 56 **21.** 3.7991 **23.** 0.004 308 9 **25.** 0.428 00

Problem Set 11.7, page 532

1. $\frac{(1.268x + 7)x^{2/3}}{x}$ **3.** $4.732 x^{3/8}$ **5.** $(5 - 4rs)(rs)^{1/2}$ **7.** $7\, uv^2 (uv)^{1/2}$

9. $\frac{(1 - 3xy)(x^{3/4} y^{1/4})}{xy}$ **11.** $-21.863 x^2$

Problem Set 11.8, pages 536–537

1. $6p - 17p^{1/2} r^{1/3} + 12r^{2/3}$ **3.** $24 x^{13/12}$ **5.** $t - 27$ **7.** $64 + 48x^{2/3} + 12x^{4/3} + x^2$ **9.** $32 - 80z^{4/5} + 80z^{8/5} - 40z^{12/5} + 10z^{16/5} - z^4$ **11.** $4(4^{1/3}) - 32(2^{1/4}) + 48(32^{1/6}) - 64(32^{1/12}) + 32$ **13.** $\frac{3st^{1/2} + 4s^{1/2} t}{9s - 16t}$

15. $\dfrac{4 + 3\sqrt{3} + \sqrt{5} - 2\sqrt{15}}{22}$ **17.** $x^{2/3} - 2x^{1/3} + 4$ **19.** $1 - r^{1/3} + r^{2/3}$

21. $(x - 2y)(9x^{2/3} + 6x^{1/3}y^{1/3} + 4y^{2/3})$

Problem Set 11.9, pages 544–546

1. $j(-4)$ **3.** $j9\sqrt[3]{4}$ **5.** $j\dfrac{\sqrt{6}}{3}$ **7.** 0 **9.** $(3 - \sqrt{6}) + j(\sqrt{6} - 2)$

11. $-3 + j2\sqrt{2}$ **13.** $11 - j\sqrt{5}$ **15.** $\dfrac{6 + \sqrt{6}}{12} + j\dfrac{3\sqrt{2} - 2\sqrt{3}}{12}$ **17.** $-j$

19. $\dfrac{-23}{25} - j\dfrac{4\sqrt{6}}{25}$ **21.** $x = 5, y = 3$ **23.** $x = 25, y = 2$ **25.** $x = \frac{1}{10}, y = -\frac{1}{15}$

27.

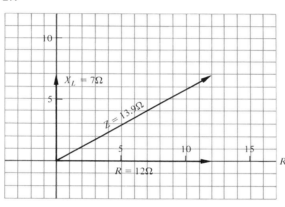

29.

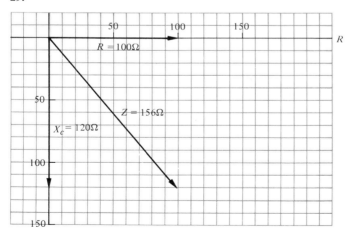

31. (a)

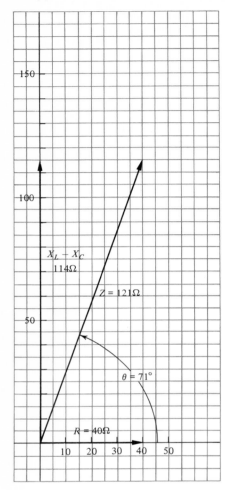

(b) lagging; (c) $Z = 40 + j114$; (d) $71°$; (e) $70.7°$; (f) 18.7%, 12.2%, 33.1%; (g) 132.6 va; (h) 132.6 va

Problem Set 11.10, page 550

1. 10 **3.** $2, 3$ **5.** 4 **7.** $-5, \frac{3}{2}$ **9.** 6 **11.** 2 **13.** 4 **15.** 5 **17.** -2

Problem Set 11.11, pages 555–557

1. $\frac{3}{4}, \frac{4}{3}$ **3.** $-\frac{1}{2}, 3$ **5.** $-\frac{7}{2}, 5$ **7.** $-7, 3$ **9.** $-6, 2$ **11.** 12 in.
13. 46.7 fpm   **15.** $-\frac{2}{3}$ **17.** 0.337 **19.** 12.6 years   **21.** 1.39 **23.** -6
25. $\frac{14}{3}$ **27.** 4 **29.** $\frac{1}{5}$

Chapter 12

1. $-3, 0$ **3.** $0, \frac{4}{5}$ **5.** $0, \frac{7}{2}$ **7.** $\pm\frac{1}{5}$ **9.** $\frac{1}{3}(\pm 2\sqrt{6})$ **11.** $\pm j$ **13.** $\pm\frac{1}{5}(j\sqrt{35})$
15. 0 **17.** $0, 7$ **19.** ± 0.05
21. determines steepness

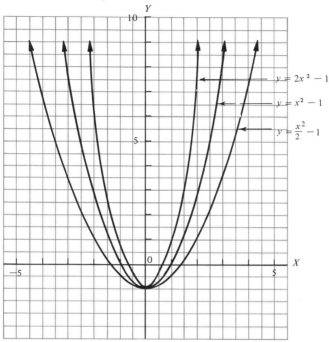

$y = 2x^2 - 1$

$y = x^2 - 1$

$y = \frac{x^2}{2} - 1$

23. shifts graph upward or downward   **25.** (a)

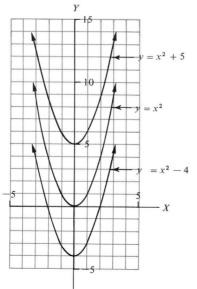

$y = x^2 + 5$

$y = x^2$

$y = x^2 - 4$

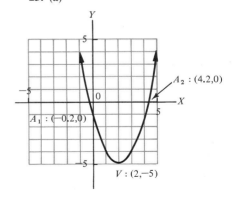

$A_2 : (4.2, 0)$

$A_1 : (-0.2, 0)$

$V : (2, -5)$

27. (a)

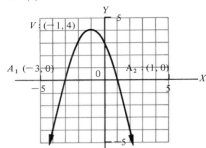

(b) $(-1,4)$; (c) $1, -3$

29. (a)

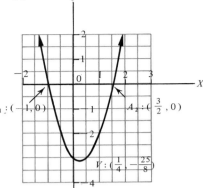

(b) $(\frac{1}{4}, -\frac{25}{8})$; (c) $\frac{3}{2}, -1$

31. (a)

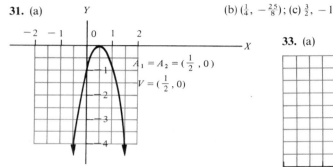

(b) $(\frac{1}{2},0)$; (c) $\frac{1}{2}$

33. (a)

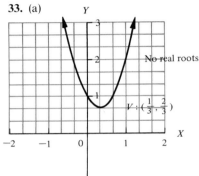

(b) $(\frac{1}{3}, \frac{2}{3})$; (c) none

35. (a)

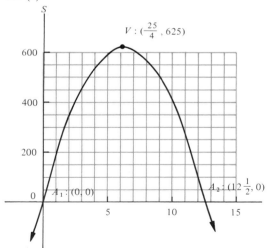

(b) $\frac{25}{4},625)$; (c) $0, \frac{25}{2}$

37. (a)

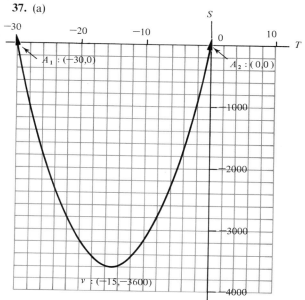

(b) $(-15, -3600)$; (c) $-30, 0$

39. (a)

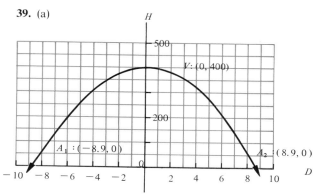

(b) $(0, 400)$; (c) ± 8.9

Problem Set 12.2, page 570

1. ± 4 **3.** $0, \frac{1}{16}$ **5.** $3, 5$ **7.** $-1, 2$ **9.** $-3, 4$ **11.** $-1, 6$ **13.** $-4, 7$

15. $\frac{1}{2}, 2$ **17.** $-4, \frac{3}{5}$ **19.** $-\frac{3}{2}, \frac{7}{2}$ **21.** $\frac{5}{3}, 2$ **23.** $4, 6$ **25.** $\frac{3}{2}, \frac{7}{2}$

27. $-0.025, 0.0075$ **29.** $\frac{5}{16}, \frac{3}{8}$

Problem Set 12.3, page 573

1. $-4 \pm \sqrt{19}$ **3.** $\frac{1}{2}(3 \pm \sqrt{5})$ **5.** $\frac{1}{2}(-2 \pm \sqrt{2})$ **7.** $\frac{1}{2} \pm \frac{1}{10}\sqrt{65}$ **9.** $-3 \pm j$

11. $\frac{1}{3}$ **13.** $-\frac{1}{2}(1 \pm j\sqrt{3})$ **15.** $-1, \frac{1}{2}$ **17.** $\frac{1}{2}, \frac{7}{10}$ **19.** $-400, 2000$

21. $(2, 5)$ **23.** $(-4, 3)$ **25.** $(1, 6)$

Problem Set 12.4, pages 578–579

1. $-2.351, 0.851$ **3.** $-\frac{3}{5}, 1$ **5.** $\frac{1}{12}(-7 \pm j\sqrt{119})$ **7.** $-0.646, 4.646$
9. $\frac{1}{2}(3 \pm j4)$ **11.** $\frac{1}{13}(-6 \pm j\sqrt{133})$ **13.** $-7.702, -1.298$ **15.** $-\frac{4}{5}, 1$
17. $\frac{1}{16}(-3 \pm j\sqrt{23})$ **19.** ± 4.183 **21.** $x^2 - 5x + 6 = 0$; 2, 3   **23.** $4x^2 +$
$12x + 1 = 0$; $-2.914, -0.086$ **25.** $25x^2 + 10x + 1 = 0$; $-\frac{1}{5}$ **27.** $x^2 - 70x +$
$1325 = 0$; $35 \pm j10$ **29.** $3x^2 - 4x - 1 = 0$; $-0.215, 1.549$

Problem Set 12.5, page 580

1. $\pm 2, \pm 5$ **3.** 64   **5.** $\frac{1}{9}, \frac{1}{7}$ **7.** $\pm \frac{1}{2}, \pm 1, \pm \frac{1}{2}j, \pm j$ **9.** 0.0193, 52.0
11. 2.29, 3.71   **13.** $30°, 150°, 270° \pm n360°$ **15.** $30° \pm n180°$ **17.** 0.845
19. $-10.9, -0.0917, 0.146, 6.85$

Problem Set 12.6, pages 582–583

1. $R = \sqrt{\dfrac{GMm}{F}}$ **3.** $v_0 = \sqrt{\dfrac{Rg}{\sin 2\theta}}$ **5.** $r_1 = \sqrt{\dfrac{c_1 r_2^2}{c_2}}$

7. $r = \dfrac{1}{2}\left(-s + \sqrt{s^2 + \dfrac{4T}{\pi}}\right)$ **9.** $x = \dfrac{v_0^2\left(\tan\theta \pm \sqrt{\tan^2\theta - \dfrac{2gy\sec^2\theta}{v_0^2}}\,\right)}{g\sec^2\theta}$

11. $r_1 = \sqrt[4]{r_2^2 - \dfrac{4I}{\pi}}$ **13.** $v_z = \sqrt{v^2 - v_x^2 - v_y^2}$

15. $x = \left(\dfrac{-b + \sqrt{b^2 + 4aP}}{2P}\right)^{1/6}$ **17.** $A_1 = \dfrac{QA_2}{\sqrt{kh + Q^2}}$

19. $T = \dfrac{1}{2B}\left[-A \pm \sqrt{A^2 + 4B\left(\dfrac{R}{R_0} - 1\right)}\right]$ **21.** $i = \dfrac{1}{2R}(E \pm \sqrt{E^2 - 4RW})$

23. $m = \dfrac{k \pm \sqrt{k^2 - 16\pi^2 r^2 f^2}}{8\pi^2 f^2}$ **25.** $a = \sqrt{2b^2(G^2 \pm G\sqrt{G^2 - 1}\,)}$

27. $\dfrac{H}{w} = \frac{1}{2}(-y \pm \sqrt{2s^2 - y^2}\,)$

Problem Set 12.7, pages 586–591

1. 5 in. or $7\frac{1}{2}$ in.   **3.** 2.20 ft   **5.** 1.5 in.   **7.** 8.78 ft   **9.** 0 ft, 7.2 ft, 12.8 ft,
16.8 ft, 19.2 ft, 20 ft   **11.** $15\frac{1}{16}$ in.   **13.** $r_1 = 17.75$ in., $r_2 = 2.25$ in.   **15.** $9.19 \times$
10^{-4} mol/liter   **17.** (a) $3\,\Omega, 6\,\Omega$; (b) $0\,\Omega, 9\,\Omega$ **19.** 60.6 ft   **21.** (a) 8.83 ft,
3.17 ft; (b) 6 ft; (c) at each end   **23.** 2.521 Å   **25.** 3 hr   **27.** (a) $150 or $40;
(b) $9025   **29.** 12.5 cm, 50 cm

Problem Set 12.8, page 595

3. $x \le -1.5$ or $x \ge 1.5$

5. $y < 0$ or $y > \frac{1}{5}$.

7. $r \leq -1$ or $r \geq \frac{3}{2}$

9. $\varnothing$

11. R

13. $\dfrac{1 - \sqrt{6}}{2} \leq x \leq \dfrac{1 + \sqrt{6}}{2}$

15. $\frac{1}{4}(1 - \sqrt{41}) < y < \frac{1}{4}(1 + \sqrt{41})$

17. $R < -877$ or $R > 3560$

19. $20 < t < 25, 24.5 < t < 25$ **21.** 1346 amps $< I < 1434$ amps   **23.** $v_0 \leq 45$ mph

Index

List of mathematical symbols...

Symbol	Meaning	Example
$+$	Positive	$+5$
$+$	Add (plus)	$2 + 3 = 5$
$-$	Negative	-5 or (-5)
$-$	Subtract (minus)	$5 - 2 = 3$
$\times$ or $\cdot$	Multiply	$3 \times 2 = 6,\ 3 \cdot 2 = 6$
$\div$ or $-$	Divide	$6 \div 3 = 2,\ \dfrac{6}{3} = 2$
$(\ \ )$	Parentheses ⎫	⎧ $2(3 + 1) = 8$
$[\ \ ]$	Brackets ⎬ Grouping	⎨ $2[1 + (2 + 1)] = 8$
$\{\ \ \}$	Braces ⎭	⎩ $2\{1 + [1 + (1 + 1)]\} = 8$
$=$	Equals	$6 = 3 + 3$
$\neq$	Does not equal	$5 \neq 3 + 3$
$\equiv$	Is identical to	$2 \equiv 2$
$>$	Is greater than	$3 > 2$
$\geq$	Is greater than or equal to	$x \geq n$
$\ngtr$	Is not greater than	$2 \ngtr 3$
$<$	Is less than	$2 < 3$
$\leq$	Is less than or equal to	$x \leq n$
$\nless$	Is not less than	$3 \nless 2$
$\pm$	Plus or minus	$x = \pm\, 2;\ x = +\, 2$ or $x = -2$
$\mp$	Minus or plus	$3 \mp 2;\ 3 - 2 = 1$ or $3 + 2 = 5$
$:$	A point whose coordinates are	$P : (3, 2)$
$\sqrt{\ \ }$	Positive square root	$\sqrt{9} = 3$
$\sqrt[n]{\ \ }$	Real nth root	$\sqrt[3]{8} = 2$ and $\sqrt[3]{-8} = -2$
$\lvert x \rvert$	Absolute value	$\lvert -2 \rvert$ means without sign, or 2
$\sim$	Varies as	$C \sim r$ (circumference varies as the radius)
$\approx$	Approximately equals	$\sqrt{5} \approx 2.4$
$\rightarrow$	Implies	$7462 \rightarrow 7500$ if rounded off to two significant digits
∞	Infinity, infinite Numerically larger than any fixed value	As x gets close to 0, $\dfrac{1}{x}$ tends to ∞
$1, 2, 3, \ldots$	An infinite set of numbers; the three dots mean "and so on"	
$1, 2, \ldots, 7$	A finite set of numbers 1 through 7	